In memory of Peter

 ADDISON-WESLEY PUBLISHING COMPANY

BIOLOGY

SECOND EDITION

JOHN W. KIMBALL

READING, MASSACHUSETTS • MENLO PARK, CALIFORNIA • LONDON • DON MILLS, ONTARIO

This book is in the
Addison-Wesley Series in Biology
Harper Follansbee, Consulting Editor
Drawings by William A. Davis

Second Printing   December 1969

PREFACE TO
THE FIRST EDITION

This book grew out of an introductory course in biology for students who were fairly mature and showed promise of being well motivated. However, most of the students in the course had had no prior exposure to biology and consequently the book presupposes none. Those occasional students with a taxonomically oriented course in their background have found that the chapters of Part II provide them with a quick refresher and that the remainder of the book duplicates their earlier course little in content, still less in approach. While some participants in the course have gone on to further work in biology, for many it was their only formal exposure to biology and, in a few cases, to science.

The book is organized along *functional* lines; that is, the various aspects of biology are examined from the point of view of the features and problems shared by all living things. These range from their molecular and cellular organization to their features of metabolism, responsiveness, reproduction, evolution, and ecology. It is hoped that this organization will provide a framework upon which the many facts of biology can be placed in a way that makes sense and makes them easier to remember. Perhaps, too, from it will grow a better appreciation of the unity underlying the diversity of life. Such a system seems to have the advantage of interspersing botanical topics among zoological ones, thus reducing the too-common student antipathy to the former.

Just as a scientist builds upon the work of the past, so students can better understand the significance of the recent discoveries in biology if they first learn the classical statements of the problems. Furthermore, the earlier interpretations are more closely related to what the student can see about him with the aid of the relatively simple tools and techniques of the elementary laboratory. Therefore, the older knowledge is examined first in the chapters. Only then are the discoveries of electron microscopy, biochemistry, and modern physiological techniques discussed.

No attempt has been made in this book to single out just a few areas of biology as illustrative of the materials and techniques of the field as a whole. Most beginning students seem to want the opportunity to see the whole panorama of the subject. All of the topics of the Advanced Placement Program Syllabus are included as well as a good many others.

One of the most important aspects to teach of any science is the *process* by which knowledge in the field is gained. The interplay of experimentation and reasoning in the growth of science should be made explicit. Unfortunately, to explain the process by which conclusions are reached is far more time-consuming than to describe the conclusions themselves. I have, however, attempted to do it wherever practical. In particular, the chapters on photosynthesis and the work of Mendel are especially designed to impart some appreciation for the process of scientific investigation.

Problems are included at the end of each chapter. These vary from some requiring simply a one-word answer to some for which a sizable essay will have to be outlined. For the student who is interested in pursuing any subject further, additional readings are listed at the end of each chapter. In many cases, the books are available in relatively inexpensive paperback editions. Most of the *Scientific American* articles referred to can be secured in inexpensive reprints from the W. H. Freeman Company of San Francisco. Generally, the references are listed in the same order as that in which the topics they amplify are developed within the chapter.

A great many people have helped me with the preparation of this book. For two years each of my students returned to me—chapter by chapter—his comments and criticisms on the manuscript. In addition, each of the following read the manuscript, in whole or in part, and gave me the benefit of his professional judgment on ways to improve it:

John E. Dowling, Harvard University; Mrs. Frank Eccles, Andover, Mass.; Harper Follansbee, Phillips Academy; Edward Herbert, University of Oregon; Johns Hopkins, III, Harvard University; Herman W. Lewis, National Science Foundation; Alfred Novak, Stephens College; Joseph D. Novak, Purdue University; George K. Sanborn, Phillips Academy; Vincent Silluzio, Newton South High School, Newton, Mass.; Jonathan J. Westfall, University of Georgia; Edward O. Wilson, Harvard University.

Mr. Follansbee deserves special thanks for his constant encouragement and assistance during the years this book was in preparation.

I also wish to thank the many people who so graciously supplied photographs and electron micrographs for the book. Their names appear by their contributions. (The photographs for which no credit is given are my own.) Thanks are due also to Gerard Piel and the editors of *Scientific American,* not only for their helpfulness with this project but also for having done so much to bring new scientific discoveries out of the laboratories and technical journals to the layman. Their efforts have perhaps done more to bring and keep the teaching of introductory biology up to date than any other single force.

The line drawings are the work of William A. Davis. Tirelessly, he worked to match them to the text and to make them not only effective teaching devices but esthetically pleasing as well.

To the staff of Addison-Wesley go my thanks for their cooperation in all aspects of producing the book. And, to my wife, Margaret, my gratitude for the endless hours she spent typing and proofreading version after version, preparing the index and glossary, and for her unfailing support.

All who have participated in the preparation of this book have worked hard to make it as useful and accurate as possible. We hope that its readers will communicate to us any suggestions they may have for its improvement.

Phillips Academy, Andover, Mass.   J.W.K.
November, 1964

PREFACE TO
THE SECOND EDITION

The rapidity with which knowledge in biology is advancing dooms any book on the subject to early obsolescence. This edition represents an attempt to narrow the gap momentarily. Literally every section of the book has been reworked in an attempt to bring it more nearly up to date. In particular, the material on the genetic code and gene action has been revised to better reflect the rapid strides being made in that area. The discussion of embryonic development has been rewritten in terms of the selective and sequential unlocking of the genetic code. In this section, the Jacob-Monod theory and its implications for the problems of embryonic development are also examined.

Perhaps the most drastic alteration in the book has been the placing of the material on responsiveness *after* the section on reproduction. This has made possible the rewriting of the chapters on hormones—plant as well as animal—in terms of their action on the transcription and translation of the genetic code.

Among the many other alterations are updated discussions of cell structure and function, nerve and muscle physiology, and new material on the mechanism and control of enzyme action, plant growth and growth regulators, and animal behavior. There are 20 new photographs, photomicrographs, and electron micrographs as well as many new drawings and diagrams.

Material has been deleted as well as added. The survey of organisms in Part II has been made somewhat less formidable by the dropping of some minor groups and the substitution of common names for technical ones in many cases. In fact, the number of technical terms in this edition is substantially lower than in the first.

Many people have assisted with the preparation of this edition. My colleagues and students have been most helpful with their suggestions for improvement. Thanks are due also to the many teachers at colleges and junior colleges across the country who have offered their suggestions and whose acceptance of the first edition has justified the publication of a second. I want to thank also the members of the staff at Addison-Wesley who have worked so hard to make this edition attractive in its appearance.

I am especially grateful to Dr. Jonas Salk and his staff, not only for making their splendid facilities at the Salk Institute for Biological Studies available to me during the preparation of this edition, but for giving so generously of their time and knowledge as well. And, as before, my deep appreciation to my wife, Margaret, for her uncounted hours of typing and proofreading and for her moral support throughout.

La Jolla, California   J.W.K.
March, 1968

CONTENTS

Learned Behavior

PART VII   EVOLUTION

31. Evolution: The Evidence

32. Evolution: The Mechanism

The Origin of Species

33. The Origin and Evolution of Life: Protists and Plants

The Evolution of the Protists

The Evolution of the Plants

34. The Evolution of Animals

The Evolution of the Vertebrates

PART I

THE CHARACTERISTICS OF LIFE

WHY STUDY BIOLOGY?

There is just one reason for studying biology: to learn more about ourselves and the world we live in. Man is an animal. In many ways he differs but little from other animals. In a few ways he differs so greatly as to occupy a unique position in the world. Although it is a debatable point whether man has any attributes not shown to some degree by other animals, it is perfectly clear that he displays some to a far greater degree. One of these is curiosity. *Homo sapiens* is "the man who knows." It is man who always wants to know. Thus we study biology for the same reason we study physics, mathematics, history, literature, and art: to gain knowledge about still another aspect of our lives and our world.

We should also note that productive, rewarding careers can be built on a knowledge of biology. University laboratories are always in need of men and women to make the new discoveries that soon will make this book obsolete. Men and women are also needed to apply their knowledge of biology in such practical fields as medicine and agricultural research. Teachers of biology will continue to be needed to pass the knowledge acquired by earlier generations on to the generations to come.

Every citizen will be able to participate more effectively in a democracy if he or she can speak out and vote intelligently on questions that involve both biological principles and human welfare. The use of food additives, drugs, insecticides, radiation, and population control measures are just a few of the many ways in which our lives may be altered by biological knowledge. Whether this knowledge is used in ways that increase the value of our lives or ways that rob our lives of value can best be decided by informed citizens. To be truly informed will require not only a clear understanding of the values worth protecting and developing in our lives but also a knowledge of the physical and biological principles that underlie our lives. Knowledge of the first must come from a study of history, religion, philosophy, literature, and art, in other words, the humanities. Knowledge of the second must come from a study of the sciences. This book is an attempt to aid in the study of one of these: biology, the science of life.

WHAT IS LIFE?

Life is usually easier to recognize than define. We all recognize that a dog is alive, a stone is not. What, then, are the properties of the dog that distinguish it from the stone?

1. The Complex Organization of Life

Some stones may seem to be rather complex with various minerals scattered through them. Their organization is simplicity itself, however, when contrasted with that of a dog. If we examine any part of a dog's body with a microscope, we shall discover that it is made of **cells.** These units, generally too small to be seen with the unaided eye, are organized into **tissues** which, in turn, form **organs** such as the stomach and kidney. Several organs, e.g. the stomach, liver, and intestine, work together as a **system.**

Biologists have studied these levels of the organization of life for many years. More recently they have been able to probe still deeper into the complexity of living things. The electron microscope has revealed a degree of subcellular structure and organization that twenty years ago was hardly suspected. Physical and chemical tools and techniques are now enabling us to dissect these subcellular structures into the molecules and atoms of which they are made.

Rocks are made of atoms, too, but never in such intricate patterns or with such variety. Furthermore, the atoms of a rock are more rigid in their organization. The rock we see today contains the same atoms it contained last year. The dog we see today is largely constructed of atoms acquired since we saw him last year. Those he has lost have returned to the environment. This rapid turnover of material in living things is part of their **metabolism.**

2. Metabolism

A dog continually exchanges material with its surroundings. We see it eat and drink. It defecates and urinates. It breathes. With proper equipment, we can show that the air the dog exhales differs in composition from the air inhaled: oxygen has been removed and carbon dioxide added.

All organisms share this property with the dog. Whether rapidly or slowly, they all take in material from and give material back to the environment. Furthermore, the material given back is not the same as the material taken in. We have seen that exhaled air differs from inhaled air. Many substances found in fecal matter and urine were not present in the food that was eaten. During their relatively brief stay within the dog's body, food materials undergo extensive transformations. As they do so, energy is liberated. Ultimately this energy appears as heat and warms the dog. But before this occurs, the energy may be used for some of the other activities characteristic of life.

3. Reproduction

In its most fundamental aspect, reproduction in a living organism is the self-controlled duplication of the structures characteristic of it. It occurs when the organism takes in more material from its environment than it gives back and organizes these materials into its own structures. We call this kind of reproductive activity **growth.**

To do this, the organism must expend some of the energy released during its metabolism, and it must have a pattern that will guide the building of its structures. If you have studied chemistry, you might argue that the crystals in a rock, once at least, grew in the same way. A crystal placed in a solution of its units does slowly organize these units according to its pattern and thus grows. There is one basic difference, however, between growth of a crystal and growth of a living organism. The crystal grows by accumulating from its surroundings units that are already identical with those in the crystal. The living organism, on the other hand, grows by transforming materials that are not unique to it into those that are. Our dog can thrive on the same diet that we eat. He, however, converts this diet into more "dog"; we convert it into more "human."

Reproduction also involves the production, from time to time, of copies of the organism that can live independently of it. All living things must die sometime and, if their kind is to survive, they must make copies of themselves before they die.

Among plants and the less complex animals, this aspect of reproduction may simply be an extension of the growth process. The growing strawberry plant sends out horizontal stems on which develop "daughter" plants. This kind of reproduction is called **asexual** because only one parent is involved. Generally, the daughter plants are identical with the parent.

Almost all organisms (including dogs) engage in another kind of reproduction. **Sexual** reproduction requires that *two* parents contribute to the formation of the new individual. In this way, new combinations of traits can be produced. This is apt to involve greater complexities than asexual reproduction, as the two parents must locate each other and, in many cases, be equipped to care for their offspring until the offspring can care for themselves.

4. Responsiveness

All living things are capable of responding to certain changes (**stimuli**) in their surroundings. Changes in light, heat, gravity, sound, mechanical contact, and chemicals in the surroundings are common stimuli to which living organisms respond. In order to respond to these stimuli, the organism must have a means of detecting them. The eyes, ears, and nose of the dog are effective stimulus detectors, as anyone who has watched these animals can testify.

In order to be effective, responses to changes in the environment must be coordinated. Even the simplest organisms consist of many parts and each of these must do the right thing at the right time for an appropriate action to be carried out. When our dog is called to supper, some of his muscles must contract, others must relax, his digestive glands must begin to function and so on. Each part must work in harmony with the others. A system of **nerves** and a system of chemical regulators called **hormones** coordinate the actions of the dog and many other animals. Plants rely on hormones for their coordination.

The action carried out by an organism in response to a stimulus is accomplished by its **effectors.** Muscles and glands are the most important ones in animals. Like all other parts of the coordinating system, they consume energy. Energy enables the dog's muscles to contract and his glands to synthesize the enzymes with which he will digest his supper.

Organisms respond to changes in their environment by altering their relationship to it. In running to his supper dish, the dog is changing his position in response to your signal. These responses, which often occur in definite patterns, make up the organism's **behavior.** It is an active, not a passive, thing. A dislodged stone rolling downhill is not behaving; it is simply being carried along passively by the force of gravity. Our hungry dog, on the other hand, is *creating* the change in his relationship to his surroundings.

5. Evolution

When organisms reproduce themselves, their pattern is copied with marvelous accuracy. Dogs have puppies, not kittens. Children sometimes share distinctive traits with their mother or father. The little marine animal *Neopilina,* which was dredged up from the bottom of the Pacific in 1952, looks practically identical with its ancestors preserved as fossils over 500 million years ago (Fig. 1-1).

Neopilina is not, however, identical with its ancestors. Nor are any other organisms found on earth today identical with those that lived in ages past. Over long periods of time, changes have occurred. These changes mark the evolution of the organisms. Evolution has often been adaptive; that is, the changes have enabled the organisms to live in their environment—to metabolize, reproduce, and respond—more efficiently than their ancestors could have in the same environment. The many breeds of dogs testify to the ability of organisms to evolve over time, although many of the changes which man has wrought in dog evolution can hardly be thought of as adaptive.

Evolution involves something else. The number of kinds of organisms that now live on the earth is far greater than the number that were present 500 million years ago. From that time to this, there has been a proliferation of kinds of organisms. This aspect of evolution has occurred as single groups of organisms have given rise to two or more distinct kinds of descendants. All our present dogs, for example, are probably descendants of one ancestral type.

Fig. 1-1

Neopilina. This primitive mollusk was discovered in 1952. It differs little from its closest relative, *Pilina,* which has been extinct for 350 million years. (From the *Galathea Report.*)

6. Ecology

Living organisms are continuously surrounded by and influenced by their environment. This includes its nonliving features (sunlight, temperature, moisture, etc.) as well as the other organisms in it. The study of the interrelationships between organisms and their environment is called **ecology.** Of course nonliving things have an environment, too, but living things are different in being able to do something about their environment. For example, they may hibernate or migrate, thus escaping unfavorable changes in the environment. Furthermore, living organisms can actively alter the environment. Many plants living in a forest today would not be there were it not for the activities of other plants that preceded them. The man-made desert in Tennessee's Copper Basin (Fig. 37-9) has distinctly warmer temperatures and less rainfall than the surrounding areas because of the lack of vegetation which, in turn, was brought about by man's industrial activities.

These then are the major characteristics of living things. Although all share them, how they accomplish or express them differs to some extent from one organism to another. We will examine how representative organisms accomplish each of the major activities of life as we take these up in Parts III through VIII of this book. But first we must become familiar with the great variety of forms in which life appears on our earth, their special characteristics, and how they are classified. This is the object of Part II, a *Who's Who* of the world of living things.

EXERCISES AND PROBLEMS

1 What are the main characteristics that distinguish living from nonliving things?

2 Does a candle flame show any of the characteristics of life? Is it alive?

3 Make a list of the terms printed in boldface in this chapter and check their meanings in the glossary.

4 In what ways are growth and reproduction similar? In what ways are they different?

5 How is metabolism related to growth?

6 How is responsiveness related to metabolism?

7 What are the differences between sexual and asexual reproduction?

8 Can most animals reproduce asexually? Can most plants?

9 What is a stimulus?

10 In what ways have discoveries in biology affected your life?

REFERENCES

Stevens, R. B., *Career Opportunities in Biology,* National Academy of Sciences—National Research Council, 2101 Constitution Avenue, N.W., Washington, D.C. This pamphlet summarizes the various careers in biology and the qualifications needed for each. Included is a list of references from which more detailed information on specific fields can be secured.

PART II

THE VARIETY OF LIFE

Life in the sea. Almost every phylum of protists
and animals is represented in the sea.
(Courtesy Ewing Galloway.)

CHAPTER 2 THE CLASSIFICATION OF LIVING THINGS

IMPORTANCE

Life occurs on our earth in a bewildering number of different forms. At least 1.2 million kinds of living organisms have already been discovered, and the list grows longer every year. In addition, fossil remains tell us of many other kinds of organisms that once inhabited the earth but are now extinct.

Before biology could be placed on any sort of scientific, comprehensible basis, it was necessary to bring some order out of the chaos of such large numbers. This was done by attempting to place the various forms of life in categories, in other words, to classify them. Organisms that were similar to one another were placed in a group together. For example, all green organisms which had no power of locomotion were grouped in the plant kingdom, while nongreen organisms capable of locomotion were placed in the animal kingdom. A few organisms, mushrooms for example, did not quite fit into either category, but these occasional difficulties were solved simply by assigning the perplexing forms to what seemed to be the more appropriate of the two kingdoms.

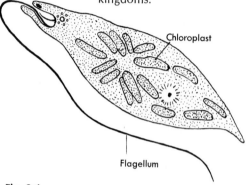

Chloroplast

Flagellum

Fig. 2-1

Euglena, 1400 X. This little creature has characteristics of both plants and animals.

With the discovery in the seventeenth century of the world of microorganisms, the problems of classification became more troublesome. The Dutch lens grinder van Leeuwenhoek and the microscopists who came after him discovered myriads of tiny organisms that possessed characteristics typical of neither kingdom. These, the bacteria for example, were taken rather arbitrarily into the plant kingdom by the botanists (biologists who study plants). They also discovered forms such as the microscopic, green, swimming organism *Euglena* (Fig. 2-1), that had *both* plant and animal features. These became a serious bone of contention between the botanists and the zoologists (animal biologists). Even today, most books on botany claim *Euglena* and similar debatable forms, while the zoology books do, too.

About one hundred years ago, the German biologist Haeckel suggested a way out of this confusing state of affairs. He proposed setting up a third kingdom, the **Protista,** to include those organisms which do not clearly fit into either the plant or the animal kingdoms. His idea has been slow to gain acceptance, but in this book we will follow it.

At this point you may well feel that it is high-handed, to say the least, to create a third kingdom. Many students feel that to do so is also an admission of a failure to resolve our difficulties and to determine once and for all just what—plant or animal —each of these little creatures is. While such a feeling is understandable, it completely misses the point of what a classification system is and does.

THE PRINCIPLES OF CLASSIFICATION

Classification consists of placing together in categories those things that resemble each other. While this sounds simple, in actual practice it may be quite difficult. First of all, we have to decide what kind of similarities are the most important for our purpose. One of the earliest classification schemes placed in one category all those organisms which lived in the same habitat. Thus fishes, whales, and penguins

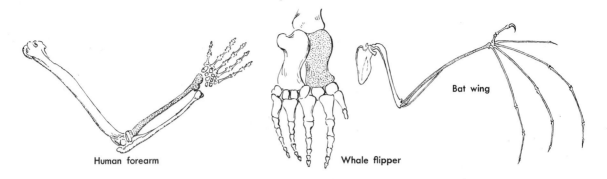

Human forearm   Whale flipper   Bat wing

Three vertebrate forelimbs; a study in homologous organs. In each case the bone that is stippled is the radius. The forelimbs are not drawn to the same scale.

Fig. 2-2

were classified as swimming creatures. This type of classification was often based on the principle that creatures possessing **analogous organs** should be classified together. Analogous organs are organs that have the same function. The fins of fishes and the flippers of whales and penguins are analogous organs because they are all used for swimming. The wings of birds, bats, and insects are analogous organs that make flying possible.

As more knowledge was gained about the anatomy of living things, it became apparent that similarities of habitat and of analogous organs were often rather superficial. The fact that bats have fur and nurse their young, birds have feathers and lay eggs, while insects are cold-blooded and have no internal skeleton suggested that these organisms differ from one another in more important ways than they resemble one another. An appreciation of the truly significant ways in which organisms resemble or differ from one another enabled the Swedish naturalist Carolus Linnaeus to found the modern system of classification. In 1753 he published a classification of the plants which was followed, in 1758, by a classification of the animals. For this work he is often called the father of **taxonomy,** the name given to the study of classification. His system of classification is fundamentally the system we use today. It is based on the principle of **homology.** Homologous organs are organs which show the same basic structure, the same general relationship to other organs, and the same pattern of very early growth. They need not, however, share the same function. An examination of the bones of the whale's flipper, the bat's wing, and man's arm reveals the same basic pattern (Fig. 2-2). Furthermore, all these appendages are found in the same part of the body and develop in similar ways. They are homologous organs, although they are used to carry out quite different functions. Linnaeus felt that the difference in function was trivial, while the homology of the organs provided a sound basis for grouping these animals together.

Why is a classification based upon homology so significant? The answer to this question was not given until 1859 when Charles Darwin published his theory of evolution. According to Darwin, a classification based upon the presence of homologous organs is a classification based upon kinship. He felt that all creatures sharing homologous organs are related to one another, having inherited their homologous organs from a common ancestor. Thus man, the bat, and the whale all had a single ancestor who possessed the basic forelimb structure that these creatures possess—although obviously in a quite modified form—today.

Distribution of Eight Homologous Structures

	SPECIES	A	B	C	D	E	F	G	H	I	J
1. Feathers		+	+	+	+	+	+	+	+	+	+
2. Serrated bill						+					
3. Partial webbing between toes			+								
4. Perching feet		+		+	+		+	+	+	+	+
5. Slender bill					+			+			+
6. Short, stout bill		+		+			+		+	+	
7. Yellow plumage on top of head					+			+			
8. Reddish-brown plumage on back		+								+	

Groupings Made on the Basis of These Structures

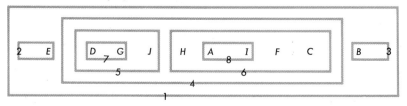

2-3   AN EXAMPLE

The essence of any modern classification scheme, then, is to group all those organisms that are related to one another. However, in the frequent absence of fossil remains of common ancestors, we have to guess the evolutionary relationships by studying the degree of similarity of the organisms we are attempting to classify. Figure 2-3 shows ten organisms. It is perfectly clear that all ten are animals and even that all ten are birds. But how should they be classified with respect to one another? Closer inspection reveals that some of the birds (A and I, for example) are quite similar in appearance. Perhaps, then, these should be placed together in one category. Another category might include D, G, and J, which show similarities of bill shape, size, and general body contour. C, F, and H seem to fall into still a third group, while B and E seem quite different in appearance. In fact, our first three groups seem to have more features in common with each other than they do with either B or E. Perhaps these three subgroups should be placed together in a larger group which excludes B and E.

This, then, is the basic process involved in classification. Of course, we have been somewhat limited in our efforts here by being restricted to a view of the external anatomy. Were a knowledge of all homologous features available to us, we could tabulate the distribution of each of these throughout the entire group (Fig. 2-3). Those birds sharing the largest number of homologous features would be grouped together. This reflects our belief that they are most closely related, in other words, have most recently descended from a common ancestor. These first groups would then be organized into larger groups on the basis of all their members' sharing a smaller number of homologous features. We assume that the members of these larger groups are more distantly related than the members of the smaller groups. The common ancestor from which they are descended existed in a more remote time.

In the case of our birds, each one represents a single kind, or **species,** of bird. This is the fundamental unit of classification. The groups in which we place the various species are called genera (singular, **genus**). The two sparrows, A and I, are classified in the genus *Spizella*. Related genera are, in turn, placed in **families.** Related families make up **orders,** and orders are grouped together in **classes** (in this case, Aves, or birds). Similar classes are placed in a given **phylum** and all related phyla make up a kingdom (Fig. 2-4).

In addition to these major groups, taxonomists often find it convenient to establish others: phyla may be divided into subphyla, and super- as well as subclasses and -families are also formed in some cases. The currently accepted classification of our ten birds is shown in Fig. 2-5.

Fig. 2-5

The actual classification of the ten birds shown in Fig. 2-3 and a deduction as to the evolutionary history of these birds.

The Classification of Man

Kingdom	— Animal
Phylum	— Chordata
Subphylum	— Vertebrata
Class	— Mammalia
Order	— Primates
Family	— Hominidae
Genus	— *Homo*
Species	— *sapiens*

Fig. 2-4

The major taxonomic categories as they are used in the classification of man.

Class Aves—birds
  Subclass Neornithes—modern birds
    Superorder Neognathae—flying birds
      Order Anseriformes—flat-billed swimmers
        Family Anatidae—swans, geese, ducks
          Subfamily Mergansers (E)
      Order Charadriiformes—shore birds
        Family Scolopacidae
          Genus *Ereunetes* (B)—sandpiper
      Order Passeriformes—perching birds
        Family Parulidae—warblers
          Genus *Dendroica* (D and G)
          Genus *Geothlypis* (J)
        Family Fringillidae
          Genus *Spizella* (A and I)—sparrows
          Genus *Pheucticus* (H)—grosbeak
          Genus *Carpodacus* (C)—finch
          Genus *Spinus* (F)—finch

EVOLUTIONARY IMPLICATIONS OF MODERN TAXONOMY

If, as we hope, our classification scheme reflects degree of kinship, then we should be able to set up a family tree showing the evolutionary history of the group (Fig. 2-5). The species are all placed at the tips of the branches, and the common ancestors at the forks. It is important to remember two things when dealing with such a family tree. First, if the genealogy is correct, all the species in any one group, no matter what its rank, have shared a common ancestor among themselves more recently than they have with species in any other group. Second, no living organism is the ancestor of other organisms. This seems obvious, but many biology students persist in thinking that the more primitive organisms living today are the ancestors of the more complex organisms. This is not true, although we may assume that during the course of evolutionary descent from a common ancestor, the more primitive organisms have changed less than the more complex ones. The only direct evidence of common ancestors ("missing links") that we can ever hope to find is their fossilized remains.

This second point is related to a third: the general history of life on earth seems to have been the formation of more and more different kinds of organisms. Each fork in the family tree represents two kinds of organisms *diverging* from one, the common ancestor.

Occasionally, evolution seems to work the other way. Two unrelated lines may come to resemble each other closely. This **convergent evolution** explains the superficial similarity of penguins, whales, and fishes, and of birds, bats, and insects. The need to swim or fly efficiently imposes definite limitations on body form. As unrelated forms have taken to the water or to the air, they have evolved in ways appropriate to the new medium. This has resulted in the development of many similarities of structure and, as we have seen, posed something of a puzzle for the taxonomist. Fortunately for him, careful inspection of the forms usually reveals their true affinities. Even the layman knows that the penguin is a bird, not a fish. The whale seems more puzzling, but its real ancestry is quite clear. Unlike true fishes, it is warm-blooded, possesses fur, bears living young, and nurses them with milk. This makes the whale more closely related to us (mammals) than to the fishes. Furthermore, dissection of the whale (a big job!) reveals the presence of rudimentary bones that are homologous to the hind legs of the four-legged land animals. Despite convergent evolution, the whale has not been able to erase the evidence of its true ancestry.

SCIENTIFIC NAMES

Although Linnaeus did not believe in evolution, his intuitive grasp of the importance of homologies gave us a system of classification that still works today. He also deserves the gratitude of biologists everywhere for providing a system for the naming of species. Every language has its own words for plants and animals. Our *dog* is the German's *Hund* and the Frenchman's *chien*. Knowledge in biology, as in the other sciences, is discovered independently of national boundaries. It is important, therefore, that biologists in each country know just what organism their colleagues in other countries have been working with. The system of scientific names, established by Linnaeus, achieves this goal.

The scientific name of each species consists of two parts. The first is the name of the genus to which the organism belongs, the second the name of the species. Thus the family dog is *Canis familiaris*. Latin names were used by Linnaeus, but so many species have been discovered since then that now taxonomists simply coin new words and cast the genus name in the form of a Latin noun and the species name as a Latin adjective. Both names are printed in italics, the genus name capitalized, but not the species name. Note, too, that our Roman letters are always used for this purpose even by biologists in countries such as Japan, where different characters are used for ordinary purposes (Fig. 2-6).

————旗口水母類　**Semaeostomae**————

3.　**ミズクラゲ　Aurelia aurita** (Linnaeus) [Aureliidae]

　傘は円盤状で，直径10〜17 cm，ときには30 cmを越えるものもある。寒天質は比較的柔軟で，放射管を白く残し，やや青味をおびる程度で，大体無色透明。但し生殖腺は雌では褐色，雄では紫がかった青色を呈する。刺胞毒は認められない。三大洋に広く分布するが，本邦では北海道の西岸忍路及び関東地方以南の暖流区域に多産する。北海道以北の寒流区域には，これに代わって，もっと大形で放射管が網状に連絡しているキタミズクラゲ **A. limbata** Brandt が見られる。

Fig. 2-6

The description, as it appears in a Japanese guide to marine life, of a common jellyfish. (Courtesy Hoikusha Publishing Company, Ltd., Osaka, Japan.)

Frequently, the species name may be derived from the name of the discoverer. Thus Brewer's sparrow is *Spizella breweri*. Sometimes you will see another name or initial, not italicized, written after the scientific name. This is the name or initial of the taxonomist who coined the scientific name. Linnaeus himself proposed the name we use for the dog, so it is often written *Canis familiaris* L. You can well imagine that with the vast number of species to be named, two or more taxonomists may independently propose different names for the same organism. Definite rules, enforced by international commissions, have been set up to resolve such difficulties.

Occasionally a third italicized and Latinized word is included in the scientific name of an organism. This is the subspecies name; it serves to distinguish a particular, often local, form of the species from other forms of that same species. Despite their apparent differences, all breeds of dog belong to one species. Other species are known which contain two or more fairly distinct "breeds." These different breeds

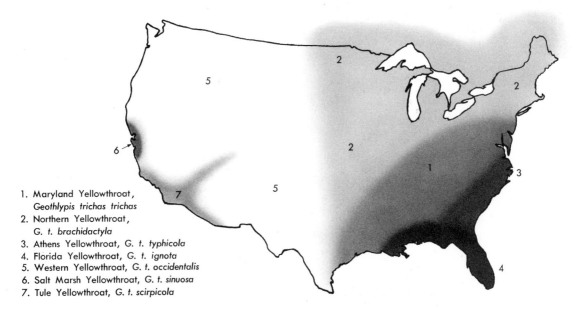

1. Maryland Yellowthroat, *Geothlypis trichas trichas*
2. Northern Yellowthroat, *G. t. brachidactyla*
3. Athens Yellowthroat, *G. t. typhicola*
4. Florida Yellowthroat, *G. t. ignota*
5. Western Yellowthroat, *G. t. occidentalis*
6. Salt Marsh Yellowthroat, *G. t. sinuosa*
7. Tule Yellowthroat, *G. t. scirpicola*

Geographical distribution of the seven subspecies of *Geothlypis trichas*. As a general rule, two subspecies of a single species do not breed in the same territory.

Fig. 2-7

are technically called races, varieties, or subspecies. *Geothlypis trichas,* the yellow-throat, a warbler (species *J* in our classification—see Fig. 2-3), actually occurs as seven rather distinct subspecies (Fig. 2-7). The significance of subspecies in evolution will be considered in Chapter 32.

2-6   HIGHER CATEGORIES

Now that you have seen how the system of classification works, it should be easier to realize just how arbitrary it is. The only taxonomic group which exists outside of our own minds is the species. All members of a given species should be capable of breeding successfully with one another, although definite information on this point is often difficult to secure. For breeding to be considered successful, the offspring should be just as fertile as the parents. Thus the fact that a horse and a donkey can mate does not prevent us from classifying them in separate species, because the mule which they produce is sterile. The species, then, is a unit which exists in nature. All the other taxonomic categories are man-made. The creation of genera, families, orders, etc., is a matter of human judgment.

This would be true even if all taxonomists agreed on the evolutionary relationships of the species they were studying. Refer, for example, to the family tree of our ten bird species (Fig. 2-5): should species *D, G,* and *J* each be placed in a separate genus? Or do *D* and *G* share certain features not possessed by *J,* so that they should be placed together in a single genus? Or should all three perhaps be in one genus?

A similar problem arises with the creation of families. Should all the birds but *B* and *E* be placed in one family or should *D, G,* and *J* be placed in one family and *A, C, F, H,* and *I* in another? Note that either choice would not violate our rule that all the members of any one group must have had a common ancestor more recent than any they have shared with species in other groups. (Placing *D, G, J,* and *E* in one genus would, however, violate this rule.) Thus, even though we think we know the evolutionary history of our species, there is still plenty of room for disagreement as to just how closely the different species should be grouped.

As a matter of practice, it is extremely difficult to establish the evolutionary history of most species. Many species, especially the soft-bodied animals and the microorganisms, have left practically no fossil remains. Consequently, taxonomists must try to reconstruct the evolutionary history of many groups by mixing indirect evidence, chiefly the homologies exhibited by living forms, with liberal doses of shrewd guesswork. Is it any wonder then that there are almost as many classification schemes as there are books on the subject?

Even the plant and animal kingdoms are manmade attempts at classification. Faced with organisms that do not fit well into either, you can now see that it is reasonable to establish a third kingdom, the Protista. In fact, three kingdoms may be too few. The general trend in classification has been to raise the status of the more primitive groups. The blue-green algae, for example (Section 3-3, 6), were once considered an order within the class Algae, which in turn was part of the phylum Thallophyta, of the plant kingdom. Today most taxonomists place the blue-green algae in a phylum of their own and some, at least, place this phylum in the kingdom Protista. All this is really another way of saying that we are gradually realizing that many of the major groups of living things have had a very long and independent evolutionary history. There may be more than three main branches to the family tree of life. In this book, however, we will place all living things in one of three kingdoms: protists, plants, and animals.

EXERCISES AND PROBLEMS

1 List in descending order the major taxonomic categories.

2 Distinguish between homology and analogy.

3 Set up a classification system, as we did for the birds, that includes the horse, cat, donkey, zebra, tiger, and rattlesnake.

4 What evidence did you use in setting up this system?

5 What does your system tell us about the evolution of these animals?

6 Draw a family tree which is consistent with the judgments you make in Question 5.

7 What are the advantages of creating a third kingdom, the Protista?

8 What are the disadvantages?

9 What can you deduce about an animal whose scientific name is *Canis floridanus* Miller?

10 The wildcat of the eastern United States is called *Lynx ruffus ruffus* Güld. What can you deduce about the following:
  Lynx ruffus floridanus Rafinesque?
  Lynx ruffus texensis Allen?
  Lynx ruffus californicus Mearns?

11 Check the plant classification schemes in as many textbooks as you can find. In what ways do they differ? Do you think that any one scheme is right?

REFERENCES

1 Hanson, E. D., *Animal Diversity*, 2nd ed., Foundations Of Modern Biology Series, Prentice-Hall, Inc., 1964. Chapter 2 outlines the principles which guide modern taxonomists in their work. Subsequent chapters show the evolutionary basis of modern taxonomy.

2 Bold, H. C., *The Plant Kingdom*, 2nd ed., Foundations of Modern Biology Series, Prentice-Hall, Inc., 1964. The first chapter compares three widely used but different systems of plant classification.

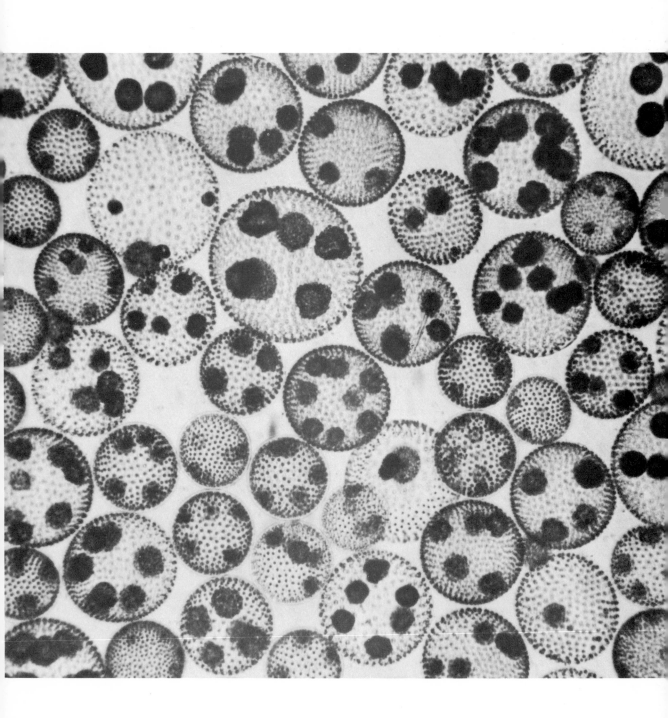

The kingdom Protista was established for those organisms that do not resemble our typical "plants" and "animals" or, in some cases, that have characteristics of both of these kingdoms. With one exception, every phylum that we place in the Protista contains species the members of which are constructed from just a single cell. Several phyla also contain species whose members are made up of many cells, but in none of these is there the development of specialized tissues, organs, etc. that we will find in plants and animals.

The name *Protista* means literally "the very first." Although their evolutionary relationships are quite obscure, it is reasonably certain that most of the phyla that we include in the Protista appeared on earth before either the plants or the animals. One or two may have evolved later, but independently of the plants and animals and without ever achieving the latter's structural complexity and diversity.

Included in this group are some 30,000 tiny, single-celled, nongreen organisms. While generally considered a single phylum, the group is such a diverse one that it may eventually be wise to break it up into two or more separate phyla. For the present, however, its members are assigned to one of four classes on the basis of the method of locomotion they use. This may be a poor basis for claiming kinship, but in the absence of better criteria, it will have to do.

1. The Rhizopods

The members of this class move by the flowing of their cell contents into temporary projections called **pseudopodia.** *Amoeba* (Fig. 3-1) is the classic example of the group and has caused this type of movement to be described as *amoeboid.* The amoeba is about the size of one of the periods printed on this page and lives in fresh water. It is of only scientific interest to us, but one of its relatives is a common intestinal parasite of people in tropical countries. It causes the often serious disease amoebic dysentery.

Two large groups of marine protozoans are also frequently included in this class. The first, the **foraminifera,** are protected by a many-chambered external skeleton made of calcium carbonate. The chalk cliffs of Dover, England, were formed from deep sediments of foraminifera shells. The second, the **radiolaria,** are especially abundant in the Indian and Pacific Oceans. These organisms possess an internal skeleton made of silica which is often of remarkable intricacy and beauty (Fig. 3-1). Although pseudopodia are present in both these groups, these organisms are probably not really closely related to the amoeba or even to each other. Eventually they may well be assigned to different classes.

◀ A cluster of *Volvox.* (60 X, Courtesy General Biological Supply House, Inc.)

Fig. 3-1 Representative Protozoa. (Radiolarian, courtesy American Museum of Natural History. Trypanosomes, courtesy General Biological Supply House, Inc.)

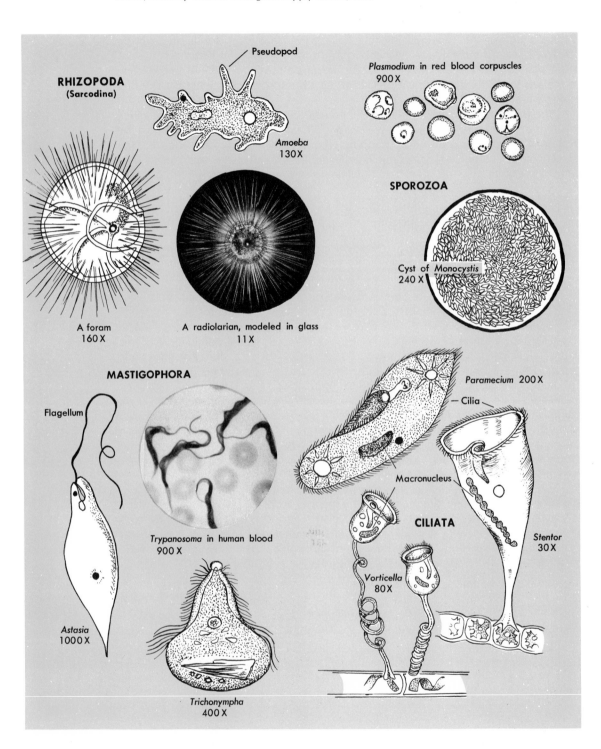

RHIZOPODA
(Sarcodina)

Pseudopod

Amoeba
130X

Plasmodium in red blood corpuscles
900X

SPOROZOA

A foram
160X

A radiolarian, modeled in glass
11X

Cyst of *Monocystis*
240X

MASTIGOPHORA

Flagellum

Paramecium 200X

Cilia

Macronucleus

Trypanosoma in human blood
900X

CILIATA

Vorticella
80X

Stentor
30X

Astasia
1000X

Trichonympha
400X

2. The Flagellates

As the name implies, flagellates (class Mastigophora) move by means of one or more whiplike appendages called **flagella.** *Trypanosoma gambiense,* a member of this group, causes the dread disease African sleeping sickness. *Trichonympha* is a flagellate which lives within the gut of termites and digests the wood particles that they eat. *Astasia* is a colorless replica of *Euglena* (see Section 2-1) and it, too, is included in this phylum.

Some flagellates also move by pseudopodia. This suggests that the rhizopods and flagellates may be rather closely related. In fact, some taxonomists feel that *Amoeba* is more closely related to the flagellates than it is to the radiolarians. If this view turns out to be well founded, it will, of course, cause a revision in the classification of the protozoa.

3. The Ciliates

Ciliates move by rhythmic beating of many short hairlike **cilia.** Although all ciliates are single-celled, some are sufficiently large to be seen with the unaided eye. They are unusual in having at least two controlling centers, called nuclei, in their cells. One of these, the macronucleus, is much larger than the other(s). Its size is probably a reflection of the large size of these single-celled creatures and thus the large amount of complex internal machinery that must be properly controlled.

The slipper-shaped *Paramecium* is the classic example of this group. It is commonly found in fresh water along with other ciliates such as *Stentor* and *Vorticella* (Fig. 3-1).

It is a common error to think of all the protozoa as simple, primitive organisms because they are constructed of only one cell. In the case of the ciliates, nothing could be further from the truth. *Paramecium* and the other members of the phylum are complex, highly specialized creatures. They have special, well-coordinated mechanisms for feeding, swimming, and defense. Their structure and behavior is really quite a bit more complex than that of a few of the multicellular animals we will discuss. In a sense, they represent the limit to which the evolution of a single cell could reach. In fact, many biologists prefer to consider the ciliates and other protozoans as complex organisms that happen not to be constructed of cells. They refer to them as acellular rather than unicellular. Whether this is a sound approach or not, it serves to emphasize the remarkable complexity of structure and function found in these organisms.

4. The Sporozoans

All sporozoans are parasitic in the bodies of other animals and have complex life histories. The most notorious members of this phylum belong to the genus *Plasmodium*. These microorganisms cause malaria, one of the greatest scourges of mankind. In order to complete their life cycle, they must enter the bodies of mosquitoes of the genus *Anopheles*. It is through the latter's bite that the disease passes back and forth between mosquitoes and humans.

If you have the opportunity to study the reproductory structures of a freshly killed earthworm under the microscope, you will undoubtedly see *Monocystis,* another member of the phylum (Fig. 3-1).

Sporozoans lack the power of locomotion during most (in some cases, all) of their life cycle.

Fig. 3-2   Representative green algae (Chlorophyta) and, at upper right, *Euglena*. (Photo courtesy General Biological Supply House, Inc.)

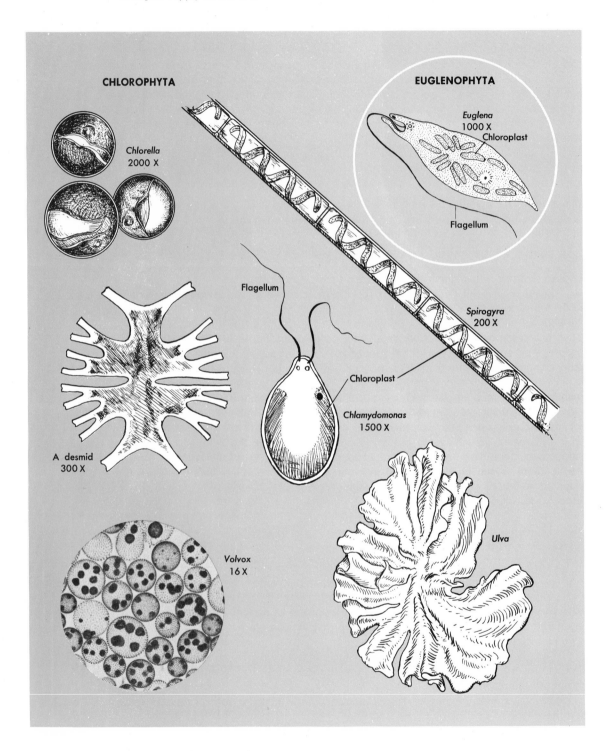

The word **algae** is not a formal taxonomic term but rather a common name for a large number of chlorophyll-containing, photosynthetic, but rather simple organisms. Because they are photosynthetic, most botanists claim them as members of the plant kingdom. Indeed, some are quite plantlike, but others bear only the most superficial resemblances to the organisms we generally know as plants.

Most algae live in the ocean, but fresh-water forms are abundant, too. Six phyla are of particular interest to us.

1.   Phylum Euglenophyta

These organisms are photosynthetic flagellates that are not encased by a rigid cell wall. *Euglena* is a typical member of the phylum. Lacking a cell wall, it can change shape easily. It moves rapidly by means of a long flagellum located at the front end and has a red, light-sensitive pigment spot or "eye." Were it not for the presence of the green pigment chlorophyll, *Euglena* would be practically indistinguishable from *Astasia* (Section 3-2, 2). It seems reasonably certain that we are violating our principles of taxonomy by placing these two organisms in separate phyla when it is only the presence or absence of chlorophyll that distinguishes them.

2.   The Green Algae

The members of this phylum (e.g. the unicellular flagellate *Chlamydomonas,* Fig. 3-2) are no greener than the members of the Euglenophyta. They differ from them, however, in having rigid walls around their cells and thus a fixed shape. In addition to many single-celled members like *Chlamydomonas,* this phylum also contains colonial and multicellular forms. *Spirogyra* grows as a green filament of cells, each of which leads an independent life. This type of organization is called a colony. *Volvox* and *Ulva* (sea lettuce) probably should be considered multicellular forms; that is, the hollow sphere of cells of *Volvox* makes up one individual as does the flat sheet of cells of *Ulva*. The line between colonies of individual cells and a single multicellular organism is not always easy to draw. Even in those members of the phylum that seem to be truly multicellular the constituent cells are not specialized to form specific tissues or organs.

Many of the nonmotile (immobile) members of this phylum are quite plantlike in appearance. Aside from being green, they have cell walls made of cellulose, a characteristic of all plants. This is really not surprising if it is true, as most biologists believe, that the plant kingdom evolved from early members of this phylum.

Green algae are important as a source of food for many protozoans and animals, both in fresh water and the oceans. Today man is experimenting to see if unicellular forms such as *Chlorella* can be grown for human food in areas unsuitable for conventional agriculture (Fig. 3-3).

3.   The Golden Algae

The golden algae (Chrysophyta) get their name from a yellow-brown pigment that is found (in addition to chlorophyll) within their cells. Most of them are unicellular and many are flagellated, although the most important members of the phylum, the **diatoms,** are not. Diatoms have a cell wall or shell that is made up of two overlapping

Fig. 3-3   Pilot plant for growing *Chlorella* in mass culture. (Courtesy Arthur D. Little, Inc., Cambridge, Mass.)

halves. These shells are impregnated with silica and are often beautifully ornamented. In fact, the delicate sculpturing of the shells of some species provides a good test of the quality of microscope lenses (Fig. 3-4).

Diatoms play an important role in the economy of nature. Both in fresh water and in the oceans, they accomplish a major part of all the photosynthesis that occurs. Thus they serve as a vital source of food materials for many colorless protists and small animals. These, in turn, serve as food for still larger animals. As the main food producers in aquatic environments, the diatoms thus sustain a multitude of other, nonphotosynthetic organisms.

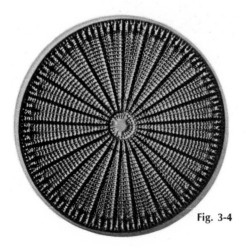

The glassy shells of the diatoms do not decay after death. Consequently they may accumulate in deep layers at the bottom of the ocean in regions where diatoms are especially abundant. In some cases, these deposits have, millions of years later, been lifted above sea level by geological forces. This has occurred in California and the deposits are now mined and sold as "diatomaceous earth." This material is used as a filtering agent for clarifying liquids and is also incorporated in soundproofing materials. The countless numbers of tiny glassy shells make a fine abrasive, and scouring powders, silver polish, etc. often contain diatomaceous earth.

Fig. 3-4   A diatom shell. (200 X, courtesy General Biological Supply House, Inc.)

4.   The Brown Algae

The members of this phylum (Phaeophyta) have a brown pigment which masks the green of the chlorophyll they also possess. They are all multicellular, somewhat plant-like forms found almost exclusively in salt water. The rockweeds, which form a dense mat on rocks exposed to the changing tides (Fig. 3-5), and the kelps are large and widespread members of the phylum. There is some specialization of parts in these organisms, and many have rather complex life cycles. Giant kelps along our Pacific coast grow as long as 100 feet. Despite their great size, the organization of these forms is still quite simple compared with that of true plants.

Brown algae are used for food in some coastal areas of the world and, in this country, as a source of fertilizer and iodine.

5.   The Red Algae

The red algae (Rhodophyta) have chlorophyll but its color is masked by the presence of a red pigment. Some red algae are unicellular but most of them are multicellular forms that live in salt water. They are generally found anchored to rocks, wharves, etc., below the level of the average low tide (Fig. 3-5).

Some red algae are used for food in coastal regions, particularly in the Orient. Agar-agar, which is widely used as a base for culturing bacteria and other organisms, is extracted from a red alga. You will undoubtedly use agar-agar several times in the course of your laboratory work in biology.

Seaweeds exposed at low tide. Two species of brown algae and one red alga (the mossy material at the water line) grow here tightly attached to the rocks.

Fig. 3-5

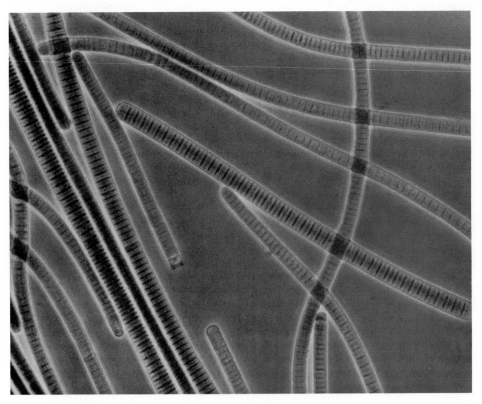

Fig. 3-6   *Oscillatoria*, a filamentous blue-green alga (1000 X). Each of the disks in the chains is one cell.

6. The Blue-Green Algae

The members of this phylum (Cyanophyta) get their common name from the blue pigment that is present in their cells along with chlorophyll. However, some also have substantial quantities of a red pigment, which causes them to appear red or purple and not blue-green at all. These latter forms are still included in the phylum, though, because they share with the others two features that are not possessed by any other algae. First, their chlorophyll and other pigments are not incorporated in discrete packets—the chloroplasts—as they are in the other algae (and in the plants as well). Second, there is no nucleus present in their cells.

Most of the algae in this phylum are unicellular, although filaments are commonly found, too. Some of the filamentous types, e.g. *Oscillatoria* (Fig. 3-6), are capable of a slow, gliding motion, but how they accomplish this is not known. Many of the blue-green algae are coated with a slimy, gelatinous sheath.

The blue-green algae are widely distributed in nature. Fresh water, salt water, and soil all provide habitats for many species. These organisms are extremely hardy. The black band found at the high-tide mark on rocks along the sea coast is formed by blue-green algae. Figure 3-7 shows a mat of blue-green algae growing luxuriantly on the surface of the water of one of the hot springs in Yellowstone National Park. The temperature of the water when the photograph was taken was 161°F, hot enough to cook an egg!

A hot spring in Yellowstone National Park. Floating at the edge of the water is a slimy mat of blue-green algae. The temperature of the water on the day this picture was taken was 161°F, hot enough to cook an egg. (The light areas at the right are caused by steam rising from the water.)

Fig. 3-7

The blue-green algae affect man most directly when they cause "blooms" in his water reservoirs and lakes. Under suitable conditions of temperature and fertility, these organisms may reproduce explosively. This is followed by their widespread death and decomposition. The offensive odors that result make swimming and drinking, of the water unpleasant.

THE BACTERIA   3-4

Bacteria are in many respects similar to blue-green algae. They do not have a nucleus, and in the few cases where photosynthetic pigments are present, these are not confined to plastids. Some members move by gliding in a way similar to that exhibited by *Oscillatoria*. Others are nonmotile or move by means of flagella.

Bacteria are microscopic forms which range from one micron or less to several micra in length.* They have a rigid cell wall and occur in three basic cell shapes: (1) rodlike forms, called **bacilli,** (2) spherical forms, the **cocci,** and (3) curved forms, the **spirilla** (Fig. 3-8). All of them "multiply by dividing," that is, by division of the cell into two. Under suitable conditions, this may occur as often as once every 20 minutes.

---

* A micron (μ) is a unit of length used in the metric system of measurement. It is approximately equal to 4/100,000 of an inch. In dealing with objects this small, the metric system is far more convenient to use than the English system. In fact, the metric system is now used in practically all scientific work. A table explaining the system appears on page 748.

Fig. 3-9

Some Diseases Caused by Bacteria

1. Coccus forms:
   rheumatic fever
   gonorrhea
   scarlet fever
   some kinds of pneumonia
   carbuncles
   some kinds of meningitis

2. Bacillus forms:
   diphtheria
   typhoid fever
   bubonic plague
   tetanus
   tuberculosis
   anthrax
   whooping cough
   botulism (from toxin in spoiled food)
   leprosy
   tularemia
   undulant fever

3. Spirillum forms:
   asiatic cholera

Fig. 3-8

The three shapes of bacteria.

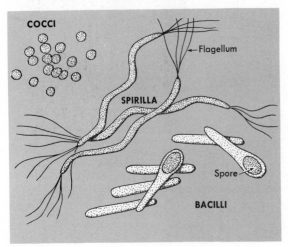

Some bacteria produce resting bodies called **spores** when conditions become unfavorable for further growth. These are extremely resistant to harsh conditions in the environment. Some bacterial spores can survive prolonged exposure to boiling water (212° F) on the one hand or liquid helium (−507° F) on the other.

Bacteria are found literally everywhere. Soil teems with them. They are found in both fresh and salt water, and are present on the surfaces and within the bodies of all animals and plants. Aircraft flying at 45,000 feet have recovered bacterial spores from the air.

Although a few species manufacture food by photosynthesis in somewhat the same way that green plants do, most bacteria secure their food ready-made from their surroundings. There is probably no chemical substance produced by any living organism that cannot serve as food for some species of bacteria.

With over 2000 species already known, it is quite important that the bacteria be further classified. They have been, but their classification differs in two important ways from the classification of other kinds of organisms. First, there has been little or no attempt made to classify the bacteria on the basis of evolutionary relationships. This is unfortunate, but the fact is that no one knows what these relationships are. Consequently, the bacteria are classified on the basis of rather arbitrary criteria. Second, so many different kinds of bacteria look exactly alike that it is impossible to group them solely on the basis of their structure (**morphology**). Information on what the bacteria do—their **physiology**—is also needed to distinguish between the various species. Many details of bacterial biochemistry are studied in order to establish to which group a given bacterium belongs.

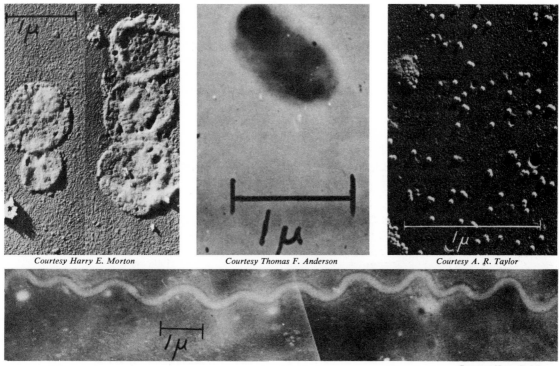

Several disease-producing organisms of uncertain classification. Top left: mycoplasmas. Center: the rickettsia that causes typhus fever. Right: one of the polio viruses. Bottom: the spirochete that causes syphilis. Note the 1-micron scale superimposed on each view.   **Fig. 3-10**

Most people, if given the chance, would choose to have the bacteria disappear from the earth. When one considers the great number of human diseases caused by bacteria (Fig. 3-9), it is easy to sympathize with such a view. As a group, however, the bacteria are essential to man's welfare. Many of them are responsible for the decay of dead plant and animal remains. Not only do they make our surroundings more pleasant by doing this, but in the process they release essential chemical substances for re-use by living organisms. Without the bacteria of decay, the essential materials of life would soon all be locked up in the corpses of the dead.

Bacteria also aid man in other ways. Some species increase the fertility of the soil. Others convert alcohol into vinegar, make sour milk for the production of cheese, and break down human sewage into safe and inoffensive products.

Three other groups of microorganisms are often included with the bacteria because of their similarities in cell structure, size, and ecology (they all include species that cause disease). The spirochetes are long, thin, spiral-shaped microorganisms that range in length from just a few to as many as 500 micra (Fig. 3-10). Unlike the "true" bacteria, they do not have a rigid cell wall and thus are free to bend easily. Although some spirochetes live harmlessly in fresh water, soil, or in the bodies of animals, others are serious parasites. Perhaps the most notorious of these is the spirochete that causes the human venereal disease, syphilis.

In recent years an increasing amount of attention has been given to a small group of microorganisms called mycoplasmas. In many ways they resemble tiny bacteria without cell walls. Some are free-living while others are parasites. One of the latter causes a type of pneumonia, called pleuropneumonia, in man. For this reason, the mycoplasmas are also known as the pleuropneumonia-like organisms or PPLO.

The mycoplasmas have the distinction of including the smallest free-living organisms known (Fig. 3-10). Although many are so small (0.1μ) as to be visible only under the electron microscope, they contain everything needed to carry on all the fundamental activities of life.

Rickettsias, like the mycoplasmas, are so small that they can barely be distinguished in the light microscope. They differ from the mycoplasmas in that all of them are obligate parasites. This means that they can grow and reproduce only so long as they are present within the living cells of a host organism. In some cases they live harmlessly in the cells of their host; in other cases they cause symptoms of disease. Typhus fever is caused by a rickettsia injected into man by the bite of the body louse. Rocky Mountain spotted fever is caused by a rickettsia transmitted to man through the bite of a tick.

3-5   **THE VIRUSES**

Viruses (Fig. 3-10) are too small to be seen under the light microscope. They range in size from 30 mμ (smaller than the smallest mycoplasmas) to 300 mμ (0.3μ), which is larger than some mycoplasmas and almost as large as a rickettsia. Like the rickettsias (but in contrast to the mycoplasmas), the viruses are obligate parasites. They can be grown only within the cells of living hosts.

With the discovery by Stanley in 1935 that the virus causing tobacco mosaic disease can be crystallized, the true nature of viruses became a hotly debated topic. The formation of crystals is a property that we associate with purified chemical substances, not with living things. It hardly seems possible that a living organism could be crystallized and stored indefinitely in a bottle. Nevertheless, if at any time these inert crystals of tobacco mosaic virus (TMV) are dissolved in water and rubbed on tobacco leaves, the symptoms of the disease appear quickly. Something more than a poisoning must be involved because a vastly greater number of TMV particles can be recovered from a sick plant than were originally inoculated into it. The virus seems to have reproduced itself and this, you remember, is one of the characteristic features of life. Furthermore, viruses have been shown to evolve, to change their properties over a series of generations. This, too, is a fundamental feature of life.

Are the viruses alive or not? The answer to this question seems to depend upon one's definition of life. If we use all the criteria discussed in Chapter 1, the viruses cannot be considered to be alive. They have no metabolism of their own nor do they show responsiveness. Reproduction does occur, but only in the living host cell. Actually, it is the host cell that manufactures the new virus particles according to the plan carried by the infecting particle. As for complexity of organization, the fact that some viruses (not all) can be crystallized indicates that rather simple units are involved. All biologists will agree that viruses are in some way related to or derived from living organisms, and, since some viruses are agents of disease, it is useful to treat them as such. However, they cannot be considered to live in the sense in which we used the term in Chapter 1 and in the sense that all the organisms discussed in these chapters live.

Animals as well as plants suffer from virus-caused diseases. Polio, influenza, yellow fever, smallpox, chicken pox, mumps, and the common cold are some of the virus diseases of man. Algae and bacteria are attacked by viruses, which in the latter case are usually referred to as **bacteriophages.**

These protists consist of single cells or, more often, of tubular filaments called **hyphae.** The interwoven mass of hyphae into which most fungi develop is referred to as a **mycelium.**

Fungi do not have chlorophyll and hence cannot carry on photosynthesis. They are thus dependent upon an external supply of food. This may be derived from such sources as rich soil, manufactured food products, and the bodies of plants and animals (both dead and living). Those that live within a living host are parasites and in many cases cause disease.

Fungi disperse themselves to new locations by releasing spores. In some aquatic species, these swim by means of flagella. However, the spores of the many terrestrial fungi are wind-blown. They are so light and are produced in such numbers that they are present almost everywhere. The spores of the wheat rust fungus have been found 14,000 feet in the air and more than 900 miles from the place where they were released.

There are some 30,000 species of fungi known. The phylum, which includes the molds, mushrooms, and yeasts, is usually divided into three classes.

The **phycomycetes** produce their spores in sporangia which develop at the tips of the hyphae. These spores are produced asexually; that is, two parents are not needed for the process. In the case of the water molds, the spores are flagellated and swim to new locations. Terrestrial phycomycetes produce airborne spores.

Some phycomycetes are parasitic on such organisms as fish and plants. Most are simply **saprophytes** living on dead remains of once-living organisms. They perform a valuable service in so doing because they aid the bacteria of decay in disposing of the dead and releasing their materials for re-use. Of course, the decay process can sometimes be a nuisance when valuable food products are involved. The common black bread mold (*Rhizopus nigricans*—Fig. 3-11), for example, grows upon bread or other carbohydrate-rich substrate from which it gets its nourishment.

The fungi of the class **basidiomycetes** are dispersed by spores borne at the tips of club-shaped structures called basidia (Fig. 3-11). This class includes the mushrooms, shelf fungi, puffballs, rusts, and smuts.

The familiar mushroom or toadstool is only a portion of the fungus body. The main part of the mycelium grows beneath the surface of the ground. Only when conditions are suitable does the mycelium send mushrooms up above the surface. These are simply masses of interwoven hyphae. The basidia develop on the under sides and release their spores (four from each basidium) into the air.

The basidiomycetes are of great economic importance to man. Mushrooms are widely used for food and their cultivation is an important business. Many wild mushrooms are edible, too, but unless one takes the trouble to learn to recognize the individual species, it is best to leave them alone. A few species such as *Amanita muscaria* are extremely poisonous.

Although some basidiomycetes are good to eat, they never compensate for the food losses caused by their cousins, the smuts and rusts. The latter, especially, are responsible for serious losses to such crops as wheat, oats, and rye. These cereal

Fig. 3-11   Representative fungi (Eumycophyta.)

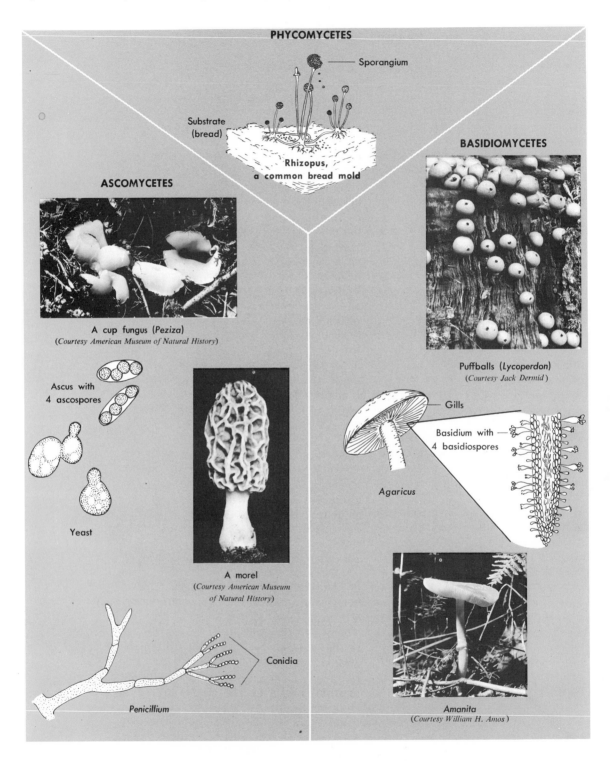

PHYCOMYCETES

Sporangium

Substrate
(bread)

**Rhizopus,
a common bread mold**

ASCOMYCETES

A cup fungus (Peziza)
(Courtesy American Museum of Natural History)

Ascus with
4 ascospores

Yeast

A morel
*(Courtesy American Museum
of Natural History)*

Conidia

Penicillium

BASIDIOMYCETES

Puffballs (Lycoperdon)
(Courtesy Jack Dermid)

Gills

Basidium with
4 basidiospores

Agaricus

Amanita
(Courtesy William H. Amos)

grains are a major source of food for the world's population and the control of rusts is thus of vital importance to mankind. Agricultural scientists throughout the world work unceasingly at research focused on the development of rust-resistant strains of the cereal grains.

Some of the rusts have rather complex life histories. Wheat rust parasitizes not just wheat but also barberries. Where the winters are cold, the rust cannot complete its life cycle unless it invades wheat plants and barberry plants alternately. Four different kinds of spores are produced during the process. The eradication of barberry plants has been attempted in wheat-growing areas in an effort to control this rust. White pine trees are attacked fatally by the white-pine blister rust. This rust, too, requires an alternate host, gooseberry or wild currant bushes, in order to complete its life cycle. In areas where white pines are an important lumber or ornamental tree, it is often against the law to raise gooseberries or wild currants.

Ascomycetes produce two kinds of spores. Those that are formed asexually, called **conidia,** develop in chains at the tips of the hyphae (Fig. 3-11). These spores are equivalent to the spores produced by the sporangium of the phycomycetes. A second kind of spore is produced as a result of sexual reproduction. Four or eight of these spores, the **ascospores,** develop inside a saclike **ascus.** We will examine in detail the life history of a typical ascomycete in Chapter 20.

The ascomycetes play many important roles in our lives. On the deficit side of the ledger, they attack many valuable plants. The powdery mildews, which belong to this class, parasitize a variety of crop and ornamental plants. The chestnut blight is caused by an ascomycete. This organism has literally eliminated from our country what just a few decades ago was one of our major forest trees. The Dutch elm disease, also caused by an ascomycete, shows promise of doing the same to our stately American elms.

On the asset side, the ascomycete *Penicillium* produces the life-saving antibiotic penicillin. Other species in the same genus are used in the production of Camembert and Roquefort cheeses. The tasty morel, which is often thought to be a mushroom, is actually an ascomycete (Fig. 3-11). So, too, is the truffle, considered by some to be one of the world's great delicacies.

Yeast plants are also members of this class. They do not, however, possess hyphae but are unicellular. Brewer's (or baker's) yeast is capable of breaking sugar down into alcohol and the gas carbon dioxide. This process is called fermentation. It is of enormous commercial value not only as a source of alcoholic beverages (beer, wine, etc.) but as a source of alcohol for industrial purposes. The same reaction is exploited in the baking industry, but here the desired product is the gas, not the alcohol. The carbon dioxide makes bread and cakes "rise" and gives them a spongy, palatable texture. The alcohol produced by the yeast evaporates during the baking process. Yeast is also used in the commercial production of vitamins.

The ascomycetes and basidiomycetes are distinguished by the type of sexual spore they produce, ascospores in the first case, basidiospores in the second. However, many of these fungi cannot produce sexual spores unless two different strains are present to serve as the two parents. There are several thousand fungi of which only one strain is known or which for some other reason fail to reproduce sexually. In this situation, there is no way of telling whether the fungus is an ascomycete or a basidiomycete. Consequently, it is placed in a special "dustbin" category, the **fungi imperfecti.** The parasites which cause ringworm and athlete's foot in man are so classified. It is significant, however, that from time to time the sexual stage of one of these "imperfect" fungi is discovered and then it is immediately reclassified, usually to the ascomycetes.

THE LICHENS

The lichens are not single organisms at all but a composite of a fungus mycelium within which algal cells are imbedded (Fig. 3-12). In a few tropical lichens, the fungus is a basidiomycete, but in the majority it is an ascomycete. The alga is either green or blue-green and is unicellular. Although lichens are given scientific names as though they were a single organism, it probably makes more sense to assign separate names to the fungus and alga. Many, if not all, of the algae found in lichens also grow independently in nature. The fungi, however, are normally found only in lichens, although biologists have succeeded in growing them in isolation in the laboratory.

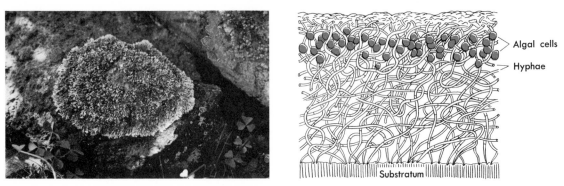

Fig. 3-12   Left: a common rock lichen. Right: its structural organization.

As we have seen, most fungi are found in areas where there is plenty of organic matter to serve as food. The fungi found in lichens are, in contrast, capable of living in the most forbidding environment. Some lichens grow profusely right on the surfaces of rocks. Lichens are a dominant feature of the vegetation in the Arctic and Antarctic. What enables fungi to thrive in such locations? Is it the presence of the algal cells which produce food by photosynthesis and supply not only their own needs but those of the surrounding fungus as well. The fungus thus seems to be just another parasite, in this case deriving its nourishment from an alga. Unlike most parasites, however, the fungus member of the lichens does not harm its internal "host" and actually confers some benefits on it. The tough, gelatinous mycelium of the fungus holds water and protects the alga from drying out. Probably the fungus also protects the alga from mechanical damage and excessive exposure to light. Besides, it produces acids which may decompose the rock substrate and release minerals for the nutrition of the alga. When two different organisms live closely together and both benefit, the relationship is said to be *mutualistic*.

The dispersal of lichens is not yet understood. The fungus member produces wind-blown spores but these are not accompanied by the alga. Perhaps the spores meet the appropriate algae by chance when they land in a new location, but this seems rather unlikely. Probably dispersal in the lichens is accomplished when fragments of the lichen, containing both fungus and alga, become detached from the parent body and are transported to new locations.

Lichens are of interest in the economy of nature because they are among the first organisms to colonize harsh, newly created environments. Rocks exposed by retreating glaciers, land slides, etc. soon develop lichen growth. The acids secreted by the lichens may aid the process of decomposing the rock into soil particles. As portions of the lichen body die and decay, organic matter, or humus, is produced. In time, enough soil may form in the crevices of the rock so that plants such as mosses can become established. Eventually what was once a desolate area may support a luxuriant growth of vegetation.

THE SLIME MOLDS 3-8

The members of this phylum are popularly known as slime molds because at one stage in their life cycle they consist of a spreading slimy mass, the **plasmodium.** The plasmodium, which contains thousands of nuclei, moves slowly over the substrate (e.g. a rotten log) engulfing food and growing as it does so. Eventually, the plasmodium develops elaborate stalks that produce and release spores (Fig. 3-13). If the spores land in a suitable location, they germinate to form single cells which move by both flagella and pseudopodia. These fuse in pairs and start the formation of a new plasmodium.

In other slime molds, the plasmodium is formed by the coming together of thousands of individual, amoebalike cells rather than by the growth of a single pair of cells. Experiments have shown that the individual cells are attracted to each other by a chemical substance that they release. In the course of their life cycle, these curious organisms are unicellular, multicellular, funguslike (spores), and protozoalike (amoeboid). Such a collection of traits makes them of great scientific interest. With the exception of one species that causes powdery scab in potatoes, however, these organisms are of little economic importance to man.

Stemonitis, a common slime mold. Left: the plasmodium stage just prior to the formation of sporangia. (Courtesy Prof. I. K. Ross.) Right: fully developed sporangia. (Courtesy General Biological Supply House, Inc.) **Fig. 3-13**

In this chapter we have examined a diverse group of primitive organisms. They are primitive in the sense that their basic organization dates back to the dawn of life on this earth. They are probably not all so closely related to one another as some of them are to the plants and animals. The kingdom, then, is something of a catchall, and we can look forward to improvements in the classification of these creatures. Grouping them as protists does, however, serve the useful function of emphasizing how different most of them are from the organisms we commonly call plants and animals. It is to these organisms that we now turn our attention.

EXERCISES AND PROBLEMS

1 What materials important to man are derived from ascomycetes?

2 Summarize the animallike and plantlike characteristics of *Euglena*.

3 Distinguish between (a) true bacteria, (b) mycoplasmas, (c) rickettsias, (d) viruses.

4 How many microns (μ) are there in 1 mm?

5 Distinguish between morphology and physiology.

REFERENCES

1 Doyle, W. T., *Nonvascular Plants: Form and Function,* Wadsworth Publishing Co., Inc., Belmont, Calif., 1964. Chapters 2–10 treat all the protists except the protozoa.

2 Echlin, P., "The Blue-Green Algae," *Scientific American,* Reprint No. 1044, June, 1966.

3 Milner, H. W., "Algae as Food," *Scientific American,* October, 1953. Describes experiments in the mass production of *Chlorella* for food.

4 Morowitz, H. J., and M. E. Tourtellotte, "The Smallest Living Cells," *Scientific American,* Reprint No. 1005, March, 1962. The nature of the mycoplasmas, also known as the pleuro-pneumonia-like organisms (PPLO).

5 Burnet, F. M., "Viruses," *Scientific American,* Reprint No. 2, May, 1951.

6 Stanley, W. M., "Isolation of a Crystalline Protein Possessing the Properties of Tobacco-Mosaic Virus," in *Great Experiments in Biology,* ed. by M. L. Gabriel and S. Fogel, Prentice-Hall, Inc., 1955. A brief report of the first experimental evidence that viruses are "infectious molecules."

7 Rose, A. H., "Yeasts," *Scientific American,* February, 1960.

8 Lamb, I. M., "Lichens," *Scientific American,* Reprint No. 111, October, 1959. Includes a discussion of reproductory mechanisms in these curious composite "organisms."

Indian pipe, a flowering plant that lacks chlorophyll. It gets its nourishment from the decaying organic matter in which it grows. (Courtesy J. W. Thompson.)

CHAPTER 4   THE PLANT KINGDOM

We shall include in the plant kingdom all those organisms that (1) contain the green pigment chlorophyll, (2) lack the power of motion or locomotion by means of contracting fibers, (3) have bodies made up of many cells specialized to form tissues and organs, (4) have sex organs composed of many accessory cells, and (5) produce offspring that, as partially developed embryos, are protected and nourished for a time within the body of the parent plant. We shall not be dismayed if, as a result of a secondary loss, an occasional plant lacks chlorophyll. The Indian pipe (chapter opening photo) contains none, but in all other respects is quite plantlike. We are sure that it is descended from green ancestors.

Many, if not most, botanists would also include the algae in the plant kingdom. By including them, however, they have to eliminate requirements (3) through (5). None of the algae meets requirements (4) and (5), and although some are multicellular, there is little specialization. For reasons already mentioned, we have cast our lot with Haeckel and placed the algae in the kingdom Protista. Having done so, we find that the plant kingdom is conveniently divided into two phyla (botanists often call them *divisions* rather than phyla), the *Bryophyta* and the *Tracheophyta*.

4-1   **PHYLUM BRYOPHYTA**

This phylum contains the **mosses** and **liverworts,** of which some 23,000 species are known. These are small, fairly simple plants that are usually found growing in moist places. They have no woody tissues for support and thus never grow very large. They have no vascular system, that is, no system of specialized vessels for the transport of water throughout the plant. They may well be plants that have evolved from aquatic, algal ancestors but have not developed all the structural features necessary for successful dry-land living.

Fig. 4-1   Representative bryophytes. Left: the common haircap moss *Polytrichum commune*. (Courtesy American Museum of Natural History.) Right: a common liverwort *Ricciocarpus natans*. (Courtesy William C. Steere and *AIBS Bulletin*.)

The liverworts have a thin, leathery plant body that grows flat upon the supporting medium: still water or moist soil. Figure 4-1 shows a common liverwort growing on the surface of pond water.

The plant body of mosses is a little more elaborate than that of the liverworts. It consists of an erect shoot bearing tiny leaflets arranged in spirals. The sex organs are formed at the tips of the leafy shoots. Sperm cells released by the male sex organs swim in dew or rain water to the female sex organs, each of which contains an egg. The lack of a specialized system for conducting water throughout the plant and the need of free water for sexual reproduction are two reasons why mosses are restricted to habitats that, periodically at least, have abundant moisture.

The cell produced by union of sperm and egg develops into an embryo plant. This is retained within the female parent and derives nourishment from it. Eventually the embryo forms a stalk that grows up out of the parent plant (Fig. 4-1). Tiny spores, released from the tip of this stalk and blown by the wind, serve to disperse the species to new locations.

Approximately 14,000 species of mosses are known. The haircap moss, *Polytrichum commune*, is a widely distributed and commonly studied form. *Sphagnum* moss grows luxuriantly in bogs and, when partially decomposed, is sold as peat moss to gardeners wishing to improve their soil.

Mosses play an important role in the economy of nature. They are among the first plants to grow in barren areas such as rock ledges exposed by a retreating glacier. They grow rapidly and form a great deal of decomposed plant material, **humus,** which rapidly forms soil suitable for the growth of more complex plants. In established forests, the spongy texture of moss beds absorbs water from rain and melting snow. This reduces the likelihood of floods in the springtime and of dried-up streams in the summer. It also reduces the loss of soil by water erosion.

PHYLUM TRACHEOPHYTA 4-2

The second phylum of plants, the Tracheophyta, includes over 211,000 species. Every one of these is characterized by the presence of specialized water-conducting vessels or tubes in the plant body. These conducting vessels make up the **vascular** system. The various species are grouped into four subphyla on the basis of (1) the anatomical arrangement of the conducting vessels in the vascular system, (2) the methods and structures used in sexual reproduction, and (3) the general pattern of growth in the plant.

A. Subphylum Psilopsida

The members of this subphylum have a vascular system only in the stem. Part of the stem grows underground and helps to anchor the plant. There are no true roots and no leaves.

Although only four species are known to exist on earth today, fossil remains tell us that these plants were once very prevalent. They were among the first plant types to colonize the earth and must have been a conspicuous feature of the landscape at that time (Fig. 4-2).

B. Subphylum Lycopsida

The members of this subphylum are commonly called club mosses. The name is derived from their superficial resemblance to mosses (they commonly grow close to the ground and possess tiny leaves) and from the fact that they bear spores in clublike

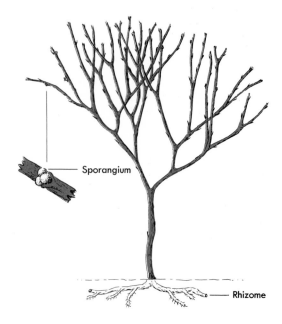

Fig. 4-2

Left: a reconstruction of the Devonian landscape, showing three species of psilopsids in the foreground. (Courtesy Brooklyn Botanic Garden.) Right: *Psilotum nudum,* a psilopsid that still grows in Florida and elsewhere.

Sporangium

Rhizome

Fig. 4-3

Lycopodium growing close to the forest floor. Although commonly called "ground pines," they are actually members of the subphylum Lycopsida, an entirely different group. Note the spore-producing strobili. (Courtesy William H. Amos.)

structures called **strobili** (Fig. 4-3). They are not mosses at all, but vascular plants with conducting vessels in the roots and leaves as well as the stem. The leaves are quite small, with the vessels clustered in a single vein.

About 1000 species are known in this subphylum. The genera *Selaginella* and *Lycopodium* are fairly common in this country. Members of the latter genus are commonly called ground pines and are used for Christmas decorations. In the fall, a hiker passing through a clump of *Lycopodium* may stir up small clouds of spores. These serve to disperse the species to new locations. Although all the members of this subphylum living today are quite small, fossil remains have been found of species that reached heights of 100 feet. These trees were abundant at one time in our earth's history and their remains contributed to the formation of coal deposits.

C. Subphylum Sphenopsida

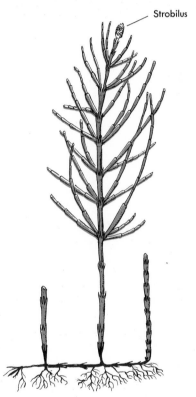

The plants in this subphylum are commonly called horsetails or scouring rushes. The first name is derived from their characteristic method of branching: whorls or rings of branchlets arising from the main branch (Fig. 4-4). The main branches develop each season from an underground stem. The second name is derived from the fact that these plants were once used for cleaning pots and pans. Horsetails often grow in sandy locations and incorporate substantial quantities of the glassy substance *silica* in their stems. The silica makes the stems quite abrasive and hence an effective scouring material. The leaves are very small and are arranged in whorls or rings around the stem.

Only one genus, *Equisetum,* containing about 25 species, exists today. Many other, and larger, species were, however, once dominant features in the landscape and, like the early Lycopsida, contributed to the formation of coal.

Fig. 4-4

Equisetum palustre, a common horsetail. It is a member of the subphylum Sphenopsida.

D. Subphylum Pteropsida

The plants in this subphylum differ from those in the other three in possessing relatively large leaves with many, often branching, veins. The subphylum is subdivided into three classes.

1. Class Filicinae (ferns). Approximately 9500 species of ferns live on the earth today. Most of these are found in the tropics, where some may grow to heights of 40 feet or more. A smaller number are found in temperate regions. These generally grow in

Fig. 4-5

Ferns. Top: tree ferns in Samoa. (Courtesy American Museum of Natural History.) Middle: Ferns of temperate climates have underground stems. Bottom: The sporangia are organs of asexual reproduction and dispersal.

damp, shady locations. Their vascular roots and stem (the **rhizome**) are located beneath the ground. The leaves grow up from the rhizome each spring and manufacture food by photosynthesis. In our largest temperate species they may grow as tall as three or four feet. Although the leaves are generally killed by the first frost, the rhizome and the root system remain alive through the winter. We use the term *perennial* to describe a plant which thus continues to live season after season.

Ferns are dispersed to new locations by means of tiny wind-blown spores. These structures are formed in sporangia which develop on the leaves late in the growing season (Fig. 4-5).

The delicate, elaborate branching patterns of fern leaves make these plants highly prized for ornamental purposes. Earlier in our earth's history, ferns grew in great profusion; their remains also contributed to the formation of coal.

2.   Class Gymnospermae. Gymnosperms are perennials with aerial (above ground) stems that grow thicker and taller each year. As a result, most gymnosperms grow into sizable trees, although a few assume a low, shrubby type of growth. Many gymnosperms are evergreen, retaining their leaves throughout the entire year. The feature that best distinguishes them from the other plants discussed up to now, however, is their method of dispersal. This is accomplished by **seeds,** dormant embryo plants released by the parent.

The gymnosperms include the cycads, the ginkgo, and the conifers. The cycads are tropical plants that bear a superficial resemblance to palms. Only one genus grows wild in this country and that is found only in Florida. The ginkgo (Fig. 4-6) is the last surviving species of a once prominent group of plants. Although the ginkgo may still grow wild in the interior of China, it grows only in cultivation elsewhere.

Fig. 4-6

Representative gymnosperms. Above: the ginkgo and its leaves. Below, left: The majority of today's gymnosperms are cone bearers (conifers) such as the loblolly pine, a branch of which is shown. Below, right: a cycad. (Cycad, courtesy William H. Amos; ginkgo leaves, courtesy Francis R. Cookson; the others, courtesy U.S. Forest Service.)

Fig. 4-7

A common "duckweed," one of the smallest angiosperms.

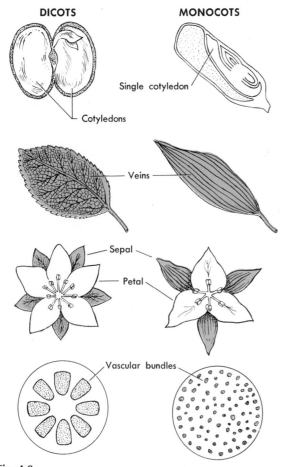

Fig. 4-8

A comparison of the structural patterns found in dicots and monocots.

It is widely cultivated in temperate regions, however, because it grows rapidly and seems especially tolerant of smoke and other conditions of city life. The sexes are separate in the ginkgo, and male trees are generally preferred for shade-tree planting. This is because the seeds, which are produced by the female trees only, give off an unpleasant odor when crushed underfoot.

The most common gymnosperms are the conifers. They are widely distributed especially in the colder regions of the earth. Most of them are evergreen with their leaves modified in shape to form "needles." The seeds are produced in **cones.** The pines, spruces, firs, hemlocks, and cedars are all conifers. This group includes the largest and oldest of all living organisms. One redwood (genus *Sequoia)* growing in California is 367 feet high. Bristlecone pines growing high in the mountains of eastern California have been shown to be over 4000 years old.

The coniferous forests of our country supply us with a large part of all the lumber used for building. The paper industry also depends to a large degree on conifers as a source of paper pulp.

3. **Class Angiospermae.** The angiosperms are the flowering plants. **Flowers** are organs of reproduction and, like cones, produce seeds which are used to disperse the species to new locations. Angiosperm seeds differ from those of the gymnosperms in being protected by a covering of **fruit** that develops from the tissues of the flower.

The angiosperms are the most successful group of plants living on the earth today. About 200,000 different species have been identified, which is far more than in all the other plant groups taken together. Angiosperms flourish in almost every possible habitat. Boggy soil, desert sand, fresh water, and rocky ledges as well as rich soil support their growth. They range in size from majestic trees to the tiny duckweed (Fig. 4-7).

The class is divided into two subclasses, the dicotyledons (**dicots** for short) and the monocotyledons (**monocots**). These names are used because there are two food storage organs, or cotyledons, in the seeds of the first group, while only one is present in the seeds of the second (Fig. 4-8). Dicots and monocots also differ in several other respects. The veins in dicot leaves are arranged in a network pattern while in monocots they lie parallel to one another. The vascular bundles in the dicot stem are arranged in a radial pattern like the spokes of a wheel, while in monocots they are scattered randomly throughout the stem. The various parts which make up the dicot flower (petals, for example) usually occur in fours, fives, or some multiple thereof. Flower parts in monocots occur in threes or some multiple of three.

The dicots are the larger of the two groups, with approximately 150,000 species known. The buttercup, snapdragon, carnation, magnolia, poppy, cabbage, rose, pea, poinsettia, cotton plant, cactus, carrot, blueberry, mint, tomato, sunflower, elm, oak, and maple represent 19 of the 250 families of dicots.

About 50,000 species of monocots are known. These include the lilies, palms, orchids, irises, tulips, sedges (a grasslike plant of marshy locations), onions, asparagus, and the grasses. The grasses include corn, wheat, rice, and all the other cereal grains upon which we depend so heavily for food.

THE STRUCTURE OF ANGIOSPERMS 4-3

The widespread occurrence of angiosperms and their importance to man justifies our using them to illustrate the main features of plant structure. As in most of the tracheophytes, the plant body is made up of three main organs: **roots, stem,** and **leaves.**

Roots anchor the plant to the soil and absorb water and minerals from it. These materials are then transported to stem and leaves by the vascular system. Some angiosperms, the carrot, for example, also use their roots for the storage of food (Fig. 4-9).

The **stem** produces the leaves and supports them so that they are properly exposed to the sun. Under special circumstances, stems also produce flower buds. These develop into flowers and enable the plant to carry on sexual reproduction.

Stems are also important simply as a connecting link between the roots and the leaves. Leaves manufacture food without which the roots would starve. Roots absorb soil water and minerals without which the leaves could not produce food. The vascular system of the stem insures that these essential materials travel rapidly between the roots and the leaves.

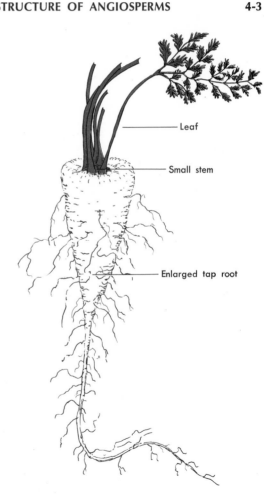

Leaf

Small stem

Enlarged tap root

Fig. 4-9
The carrot, a biennial. The tap root stores food.

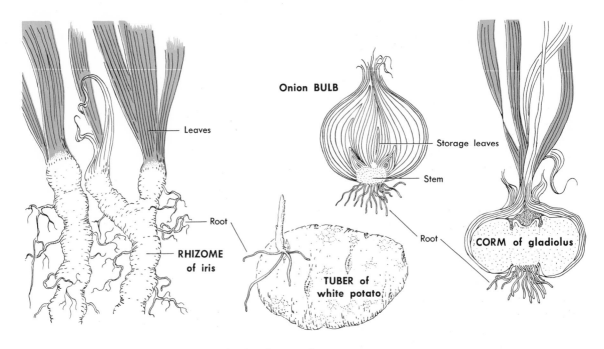

Fig. 4-10   Four kinds of underground stems.

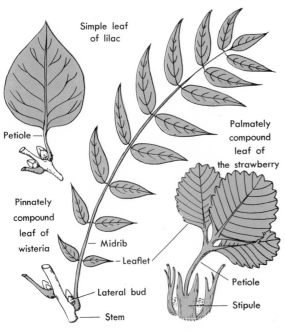

Fig. 4-11   Leaf forms.

Stems are sometimes used for the storage of food. The most striking examples of this are found in the swollen underground stems of such plants as the iris, gladiolus, and white potato (Fig. 4-10).

The main function of **leaves** is the manufacture of food by photosynthesis. This occurs in the thin flat blade of the leaf. In most dicots, the blade is attached to the stem by a petiole. The vascular system of the stem extends into the petiole and, as veins, into the blade itself. The veins not only transport materials to and from the leaf but also provide a skeleton to strengthen the leaf.

Angiosperm leaves may be **simple** or **compound.** In simple leaves the blade consists of only a single part attached to the petiole. Compound leaves are subdivided into leaflets. Palmately compound leaves, as in the strawberry, are made up of leaflets radiating from a single point. In pinnately compound leaves, the leaflets are arranged along either side of the midrib of the leaf (Fig. 4-11).

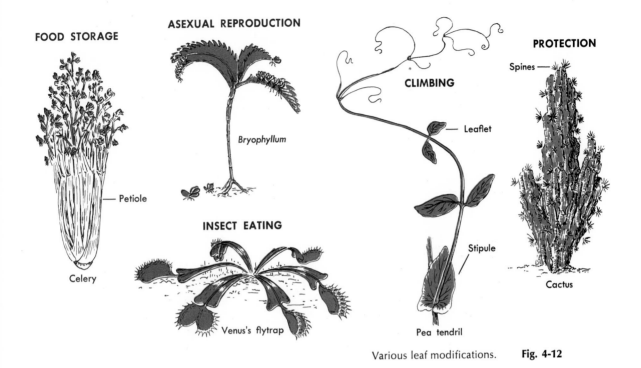

FOOD STORAGE

ASEXUAL REPRODUCTION

Bryophyllum

Petiole

Celery

INSECT EATING

Venus's flytrap

CLIMBING

Leaflet

Stipule

Pea tendril

PROTECTION

Spines

Cactus

Various leaf modifications. **Fig. 4-12**

Many angiosperm leaves are modified for functions other than photosynthesis. The **tendrils** by which the pea vine clings to its support are modified leaves as are the protective **spines** of the cactus. The large petioles of celery and rhubarb leaves serve to store food. So, too, do the fleshy underground leaves of the onion bulb. Insect-eating plants such as the pitcher plant and Venus's flytrap use modified leaves to catch their prey. The leaves of the ornamental plant *Bryophyllum* develop miniature plants along their margins and thus serve to reproduce the species (Fig. 4-12).

Flowers contain the organs of sexual reproduction and thus produce the **seeds.** Flowers also produce the **fruit** which covers the seed and frequently aids in its dispersal. We will examine in detail the structure and function of flowers, seeds, and fruits in Chapter 21.

Patterns of growth vary widely among the angiosperms. Trees, shrubs, and some vines are **perennial.** Their aerial, woody stems grow longer and thicker during each growing season. Many of these are deciduous, i.e., all the leaves are shed in the autumn. Other perennials produce only soft, herbaceous stems. In temperate climates, the portions above ground die in the autumn. The underground portions (roots and often a rhizome) remain alive, however, and send up new shoots (stems and leaves) the following spring. Many of our grasses and wildflowers are herbaceous perennials.

Some angiosperms are **biennials,** completing their life cycle in two years. The carrot, for example, sends leaves above the ground during the first season (Fig. 4-9). These die in the fall, but the roots and short stem remain alive. The following year, the stem sends up a stalk that bears flowers in which the seeds are produced. After the seeds are liberated, the entire plant dies.

The **annual** angiosperms are herbaceous plants that develop from seeds, grow, flower, produce seeds, and die all in one season. Their seeds serve not only to disperse the plant to new locations but also to enable the species to appear again the next season. Many cultivated flowers, weeds, and some grasses, including the cereal grains, are annuals.

It is difficult to overestimate the importance of angiosperms to our existence. They provide us with most of our food, both directly and as the chief food upon which our domestic crop animals (cattle, pigs, sheep, etc.) feed. All plant parts, roots, stems,

Courtesy U.S. Forest Service

leaves, flowers, seeds, and fruits, have been exploited by man for food. Remember, too, that fruits include not only the succulent peaches, pears, apples, etc., that we usually think of but also nuts, some vegetables (e.g. squashes, green beans), and all the cereal grains upon which most of mankind depends for survival. Angiosperms also supply us with many other materials. Cotton and linen fabrics are plant products. We get natural rubber, paper, wood, tobacco, and the raw materials for certain plastics from angiosperms. Many valuable drugs are extracted from angiosperm organs, although the triumphs of synthetic chemistry are supplanting some of these.

As the dominant plants on earth today, angiosperms play an important role in providing a suitable, productive habitat for man as well as all the other terrestrial animals. Their extensive root systems aid in holding the soil against the eroding forces of wind and water. Their decaying bodies enrich the soil. As anyone who has walked from a paved parking lot into a grove of trees can testify, angiosperms (gymnosperms, too) help to moderate the severity of our climate. The canopy of leaves spread by a forest of trees absorbs the sun's rays and releases cooling moisture to the air. A thick carpet of angiosperms reduces the force of falling rain and acts as a sponge to hold water in the soil. This diminishes the chances of floods and water erosion while providing a reservoir of ground water to keep wells, ponds, and streams filled throughout the dry summer months.

Finally, the unceasing efforts of gardeners, florists, and arborists remind us of the beauty of angiosperms. Who can deny that the colors and patterns with which they surround us enrich our lives?

EXERCISES AND PROBLEMS

1 Prepare a list of foods derived from plant stems.

2 Do the same for (a) roots, (b) leaves, (c) flowers.

3 Would you expect a lily flower to have five stamens?

4 In what ways are the members of the plant kingdom different from the green algae?

5 What objects do you see about you that have been derived from members of the plant kingdom?

6 Distinguish between a rhizome and a root.

REFERENCES

1 Bold, H. C., *The Plant Kingdom*, 2nd ed., Foundations Of Modern Biology Series, Prentice-Hall, Inc., 1964. A brief, well-illustrated survey of the plant kingdom. Algae, bacteria, slime molds, and fungi are covered, too.

2 Wilson, C. L., and W. E. Loomis, *Botany*, Holt, Rinehart and Winston, New York, 1962.

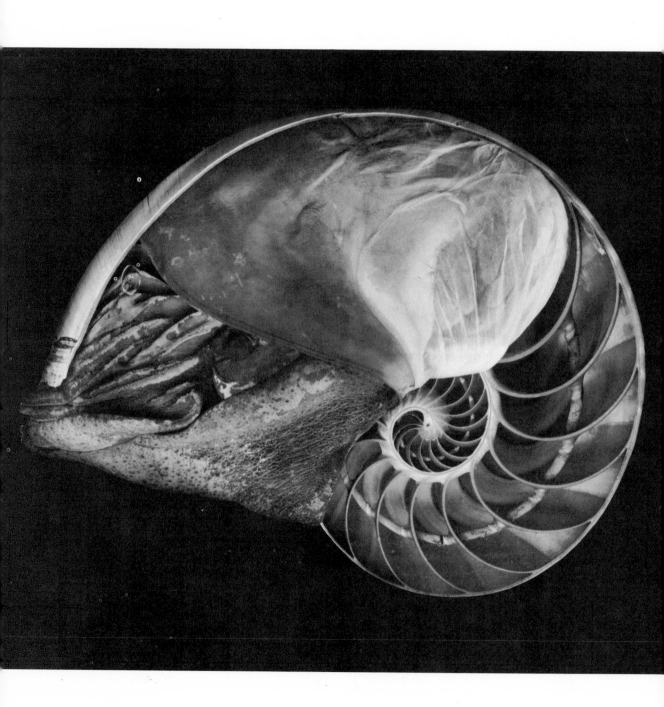

We shall place in the animal kingdom all those organisms that (1) do not possess chlorophyll, (2) are capable of locomotion or body movement by means of contracting fibers, and (3) are made up of many cells. We shall not be disturbed at including a few organisms that fail to meet requirement (2) but that in other respects show close similarities to those that do. Note, also, that requirement (3) forces us to exclude the protozoa, which many biologists include in the animal kingdom. We have placed those forms in the kingdom Protista, and will restrict the animal kingdom to the so-called **metazoa,** or multicellular animals.

The animal kingdom is made up of some 20 to 24 different phyla. (Animal taxonomists have a difficult time agreeing, too!) Of these, 9 contain organisms with which every biology student should be familiar. We shall therefore concentrate our attention on this group. The remaining phyla contain forms seldom seen by anyone but the specialist.

PHYLUM PORIFERA   5-1

In this phylum are placed the sponges. These are simple animals that spend their lives anchored to a rock or other solid surface underneath the water. About 4000 species are known, a few of which live in fresh water, but most in the ocean. The phylum gets its name from the many small openings or pores that perforate the sponge body. The animals feed by drawing water in through these pores and filtering out tiny food particles that may be present (Fig. 5-1).

The sponge body consists of two layers of cells with a layer of jellylike material, the **mesoglea,** between them. The cells of the inner layer have flagella which set up the water currents. These cells also consume the filtered food particles.

The shape of the sponge is maintained by a skeleton of spicules formed by scattered cells in the mesoglea. The spicules are quite hard, being composed of either silica or limestone (calcium carbonate). Some sponges have no spicules but instead are supported by a network of flexible, tough fibers. These sponges, which occur in shallow tropical waters, are harvested by divers and after processing are sold for cleaning purposes.

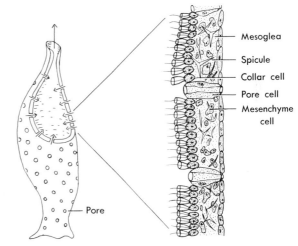

Fig. 5-1

Structure of a simple sponge. Sponges secure food and oxygen from the water which is continuously drawn in through their pores.

As we saw in the last chapter, organisms that are anchored to one spot must have some means of dispersing their offspring to new locations. The sponges accomplish this by producing small, free-swimming young, called **larvae.** These swim away from the parent sponge and after finding a suitable new surface attach themselves to it and develop into adults.

◀ The chambered nautilus. The shell has been cut to reveal its construction. (Courtesy American Museum of Natural History.)

Fig. 5-2 Representative cnidarians. Most of the members of this phylum live in salt water.

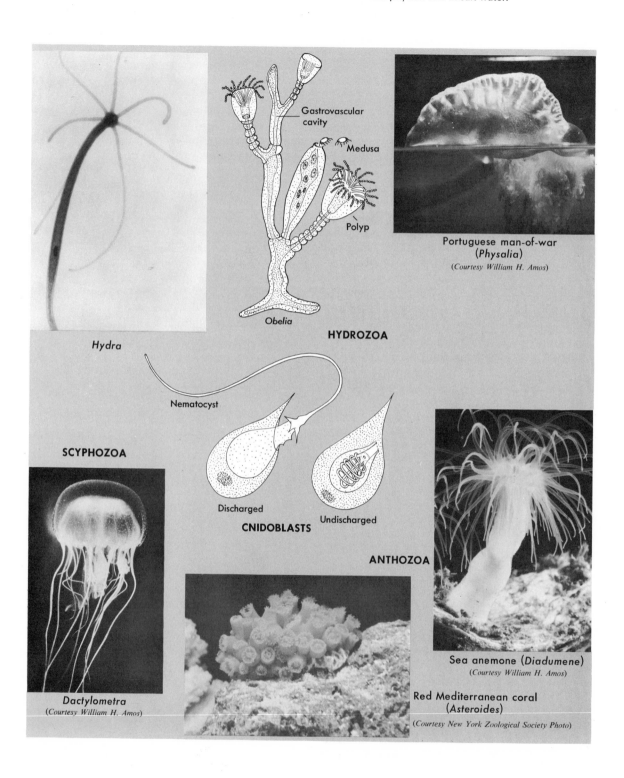

Gastrovascular cavity

Medusa

Polyp

Obelia

HYDROZOA

Portuguese man-of-war
(*Physalia*)
(Courtesy William H. Amos)

Hydra

Nematocyst

SCYPHOZOA

Discharged

Undischarged

CNIDOBLASTS

ANTHOZOA

Dactylometra
(Courtesy William H. Amos)

Sea anemone (*Diadumene*)
(Courtesy William H. Amos)

Red Mediterranean coral
(*Asteroides*)
(Courtesy New York Zoological Society Photo)

Fossil remains indicate that sponges were one of the earliest forms of animal life to appear on earth. There is no evidence, however, that any other animal forms have evolved from sponges since then. The sponges seem to occupy a rather unique place in the animal kingdom and have, in fact, been placed in their own subkingdom, Parazoa, by some taxonomists.

All the members of this phylum possess specialized stinging cells called **cnidoblasts** that have given rise to the phylum name. Each cnidoblast contains a poison-filled, barbed thread, the nematocyst (Fig. 5-2). When the trigger of the cnidoblast is touched, the nematocyst is discharged. It is used for trapping and paralyzing prey as well as for defense against enemies.

The body of all members of this phylum consists of two layers of cells with a jelly-like mesoglea between them. The mesoglea has cells scattered through it, however, and is considered by some biologists to be a third cell layer. The body is organized as a hollow cylinder with a single opening at one end. Food is introduced through this opening, the mouth, and into the inner cavity, called the **gastrovascular cavity.** This cavity is also called a coelenteron and for many years the name of this phylum was Coelenterata. Another group of animals (called comb jellies) were included then as they also have a coelenteron. They have no cnidoblasts, however, and are no longer thought to be closely related to the forms we are discussing.

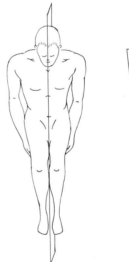 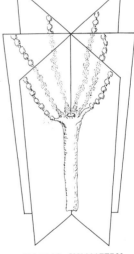

Fig. 5-3

Bilateral symmetry is characteristic of animals that move about actively. They have right and left sides, a front and a back. Animals with radial symmetry spend their lives anchored to one spot or move about quite sluggishly.

BILATERAL SYMMETRY   **RADIAL SYMMETRY**

All the parts, such as tentacles, in the Cnidaria are arranged in a circle around the cylindrical body. This pattern of organization is known as radial symmetry. If we should cut a hydra from the head (anterior) to the base (posterior) in any plane passing through the midline, the organism would be divided into two equal halves. Contrast this with the bilateral symmetry of man. There is only one plane passing through the midline that will divide the human body into two equal halves. This is the plane running from the back (dorsal) surface to the front (ventral) surface (Fig. 5-3). It divides the body into right and left halves. Radially symmetrical animals like the cnidarians have neither dorsal and ventral surfaces nor right and left sides.

About 9600 species of Cnidaria are known. Most of these are found in the oceans, although a few species, such as *Hydra* (Fig. 5-2), occur in fresh water. The phylum is divided into three classes.

The ready availability of the common fresh-water hydra makes it the most common cnidarian studied by biology students. Although it exhibits the major structural features of the phylum, it is really not typical of either its phylum or its class (Hydrozoa). First of all, unlike most of the other members of the phylum it is found in fresh water. Second, it exists as a single individual. Most members of its class are colonial, that is, many individuals live attached to one another. Third, *Hydra* exhibits only one body form, the **polyp** (Fig. 5-4). Most members of the class produce a second body type, the **medusa,** that floats or swims freely in the water and aids in the dispersal of the species. Despite its superficial difference in appearance, the medusa is basically an upside-down polyp. Figure 5-2 shows the two body forms as they occur in *Obelia,* a more nearly typical member of the class. The Portuguese man-of-war *(Physalia),* whose nematocysts may cause serious, even fatal, poisoning in man, is also a member of this class. It consists of a floating, gas-filled bag from which dangle long chains of polyps.

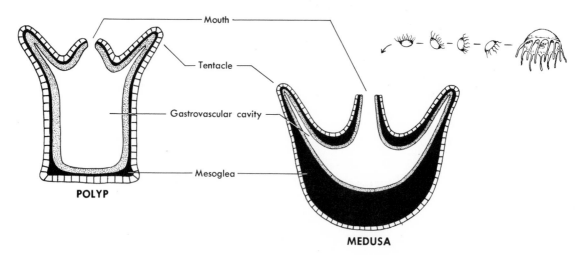

POLYP   MEDUSA

Fig. 5-4   The two body forms found in cnidarians. The medusa has been turned upside down to show its basic similarity to the polyp. The jelly of a jellyfish (medusa) is a greatly enlarged mesoglea.

The main body form of jellyfishes (cnidarians of the class Scyphozoa) is the medusa. Their jelly is simply a greatly enlarged mesoglea. The tentacles of the medusa bear the cnidoblasts, which in some species can cause considerable pain to unwary swimmers. Sea anemones and corals (which belong to the class Anthozoa) consist of a polyp stage only. The corals secrete limestone shelters that are responsible for the development of great reefs and atolls in tropical waters.

5-3   **PHYLUM PLATYHELMINTHES**

This phylum contains some 7000 species of **flatworms** (Fig. 5-5). These organisms are aptly named: many are almost ribbonlike in shape. They are bilaterally symmetrical with right and left sides and a dorsal and ventral surface as well as an anterior and posterior. This type of symmetry seems to be associated with active locomotion.

Many of the common fresh-water flatworms, called **planarians,** can move quite rapidly. When attached to an underwater surface, they secrete a slimy mucus layer underneath them and then propel themselves forward on the mucus by the beating of myriads of cilia on their ventral surface. When suspended freely in the water, planarians swim by undulating body movements. The efficient locomotion of the planarians enables them to seek their food actively, in contrast to the radially symmetrical cnidarians.

Bilateral symmetry is also associated with a concentration of sense organs at the anterior end of the animal. Planarians have light, touch, and vibration receptors at their anterior end, the end that meets changes in the environment first. Such a concentration of sensory equipment in the head is called **cephalization.**

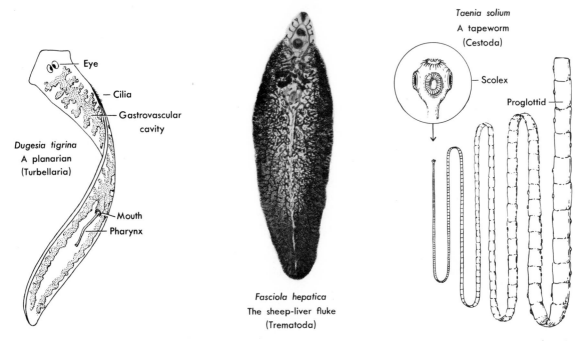

Representative flatworms (Platyhelminthes). The tapeworm has no digestive organs. (Photo courtesy General Biological Supply House, Inc.)

Fig. 5-5

The food of the planarian is taken in through a mouth on the ventral surface and into a gastrovascular cavity. Although this cavity is much more elaborate in shape than that of the hydra, it is built upon the same saclike plan. Undigested material must still leave by the mouth as it does in the hydra.

Many of the free-living flatworms (Class Turbellaria) are not nearly as complex as the common fresh-water planarians that we have been discussing. In fact, some of them are constructed so simply that biologists feel they are the most primitive bilaterally symmetrical animals and perhaps all the other phyla we will discuss evolved from early members of this group. Today these worms can be found in moist soil and salt water as well as in fresh water.

Two classes of flatworms are composed of parasitic forms exclusively, that is, they live on or in the bodies of other animals and get their nourishment from them. Adult **flukes** (Trematoda) remain attached to their host by means of suckers on the ventral surface. Many produce larvae that are also parasitic but in a different host, usually some species of snail. The sheep-liver fluke (Fig. 5-5) is a common and dangerous parasite of sheep and cattle. Blood flukes and lung flukes, as well as liver flukes, are serious parasites of man, particularly in some of the warmer regions of the earth.

Tapeworms, like flukes, are parasitic. The adults live in the intestine of their hosts and absorb nourishment from their surroundings. They form a long, ribbonlike colony of relatively independent proglottids. This may grow to lengths of 30 feet or more.

Most tapeworms need two or more different hosts in order to complete their life cycle. Common tapeworms of man are acquired by eating infected, undercooked fish, beef, and pork. We will consider the detailed life history of the pork tapeworm in Chapter 17.

Tapeworms have no digestive organs and no sense organs. Considering their way of life, such organs would be of little value. Probably these creatures, as well as the flukes, have evolved from free-living flatworms. In the process they have lost those structures no longer appropriate to their parasitic way of life.

5-4   PHYLUM ASCHELMINTHES

The most important members of this phylum are the **roundworms** or nematodes. These are elongated, cylindrical creatures. Unlike flatworms, each roundworm has either male or female sex organs, that is, the sexes are separate. The worms have a one-way digestive tract running from a mouth at the front to an anus at the rear. This one-way digestive system is advantageous as it eliminates the mixing of incoming food with outgoing wastes. After food enters the mouth, it can be processed step-by-step as it passes from one section of the digestive tract to another. Finally, undigested remains are eliminated at the anus.

The majority of nematodes are quite small. A few, such as *Ascaris* (Fig. 5-6), may be almost a foot in length and one, a veritable giant that parasitizes whales, reaches a length of 30 feet! Most nematodes, however, are not much bigger than small bits of thread. They can nevertheless be easily identified by the thrashing, whiplike movements they make. Rich soil literally teems with these little organisms and examination with a lens of a little soil and water is sure to reveal their presence.

About 10,000 species of nematodes have been identified so far, but the list is surely far from complete. Nematodes live practically everywhere. They are found in fresh water and salt water, as well as soil. As parasites, they live in the bodies of plants and other animals. It has been said that if all the matter of our earth disappeared except for roundworms, we would still be able to recognize all the formerly existing features— living as well as nonliving — by the nematodes they had contained.

Most nematodes are free-living. It is the parasitic forms, however, that are of greatest interest to man. One of the most serious of these in this country is the hookworm. This organism lives attached to the wall of man's intestine and sucks blood and tissue fluids from it. A heavy infestation causes great weakness and lethargy. The disease is usually contracted by walking barefoot on soil contaminated by human excrement. At one time the American hookworm infected over two million inhabitants of the southeastern part of our country. Now proper sanitation and the wearing of shoes have done much to reduce the incidence of infection.

The Southeast has no monopoly on nematode infections. According to some estimates, over 27 million people throughout the United States have been more or less heavily infected with the nematode *Trichinella spiralis*. Infection comes from eating raw or undercooked pork that contains the organisms (Fig. 5-6). One is wise to assume that all pork contains them, because the federal government neither inspects for the

Fig. 5-6

Two parasitic nematodes. Top: *Ascaris* in the human intestine. Bottom: larvae of *Trichinella spiralis* encysted in pig muscle (16 X).

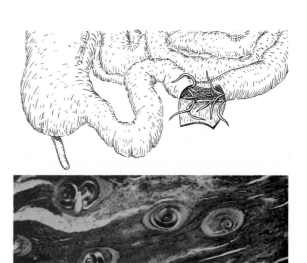

presence of this parasite nor forces pig growers to take the necessary precautions to avoid contamination of their animals. Infection of man by *Trichinella spiralis* is something of a biological mistake. Inasmuch as we do not practice cannibalism or leave the bodies of our dead around carelessly, there is no way for the worms to escape to another host animal. They simply form a resting stage in our muscles and ultimately die. In a heavy infection, however, the worms may cause such serious body disturbances that death of the host from **trichinosis** results.

Humans, especially children, are also frequently infected with other kinds of nematodes, such as *Ascaris,* whipworms, and pinworms. These all live in the intestine and are contracted by careless sanitary habits. Infestation is usually not serious, however, and can be easily cured. The "worms" for which we have the family dog treated periodically are usually also nematodes of the genus *Ascaris.* The filarial worm, which causes the gross deformity of elephantiasis, is one of several parasitic nematodes that afflict humans living in tropical regions (Fig. 14-15).

Our survey of the nematodes would not be complete without mentioning the great damage that they do to crop plants such as oranges, tobacco, and strawberries. These parasites seldom kill their host outright, but they may weaken it so that it succumbs to some other invader. Only in recent years have agricultural scientists come to realize that nematode attack may be the basic cause of a large percentage of our annual crop losses.

Fig. 5-7

Floscularia, a tube-dwelling rotifer. (Courtesy William H. Amos.)

There are several other classes in the phylum Aschelminthes. One of these, the rotifers, is worth mentioning here, however, because it is a rare biology student who will not see these organisms when he examines pond water under the microscope (Fig. 5-7). These little creatures are not much larger than many of the one-celled protists found in fresh water. Nevertheless, they are multicellular. (In fact, the number of cells has been found to be fixed precisely in each species.) They often attach themselves to some underwater object by their "toes" and feed on microorganisms in the water, sweeping it past their mouth by means of a wheel-like ring of cilia.

5-5   PHYLUM ANNELIDA

The worms in this phylum are segmented, that is, their bodies are made up of repeating units. Although some organs, such as the digestive tract, extend the entire length of the worm, others such as the excretory organs are repeated in segment after segment. The segmentation is revealed externally as a series of rings (Fig. 5-8).

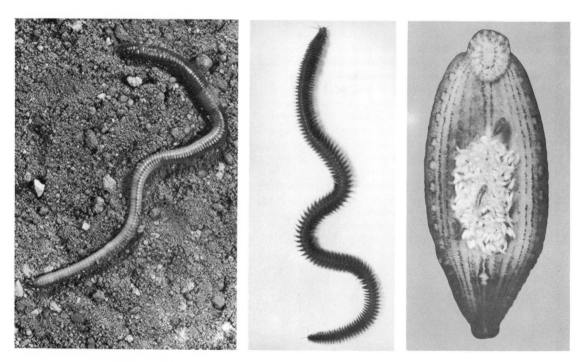

Fig. 5-8   Representative annelids. Left: an earthworm. (Courtesy American Museum of Natural History.) Center: a clam worm. (Courtesy New York Zoological Society.) Right: a leech. (Courtesy William H. Amos.) The leech is carrying its young who are themselves being preyed upon by three small leeches of another species.

Other characteristics of the annelids are bilateral symmetry, a good circulatory system with blood pumped through a closed system of blood vessels, and a fairly elaborate nervous system. The major nerve trunk runs along the ventral side.

About 7000 species of annelids have been discovered living throughout the world in fresh water, salt water, sand flats, and soil. The classic example of an annelid worm is the earthworm (Fig. 5-8). As its name implies, it lives in the soil where it feeds on plant and animal remains. It was the famous nineteenth-century biologist Charles Darwin who first told of the vital role that earthworms play in agriculture. By literally eating their way through the earth, the worms form burrows which make the soil more porous and more easily cultivated. They also mix fallen leaves, etc., with the soil, thus increasing its content of humus. After passing through the worm, the soil is discharged on top of the ground as "castings." This brings about a continual mixing of the soil. It has been estimated that earthworms deposit 18 tons of castings a year over each acre of fertile ground.

Although every biology student studies the earthworm as a typical example of an annelid worm, its habitat is not really characteristic of the group. Most of the annelid worms are marine, living in burrows or under rocks near the coastline (Fig. 5-8). The clamworm (*Nereis*) is a common example.

Another group of all-too-familiar annelids are the leeches or bloodsuckers. They have suckers at either end of the body. The posterior sucker serves to anchor the leech temporarily to its host while the anterior sucker is used to suck blood. Not much more than 100 years ago, many doctors believed that bloodletting was an excellent treatment for a variety of ailments. Literally millions of leeches were raised and sold for this purpose.

PHYLUM MOLLUSCA   5-6

With about 100,000 living species, this phylum must be included among the most important animal phyla on earth today. It consists of soft-bodied unsegmented (with one exception) animals many of whom are protected by one or more shells made of limestone (calcium carbonate). These shells (or valves) are formed by a special fold of the body wall called the **mantle.** The great majority of the mollusks live in salt water, but many are found in fresh water and some occur on land. The phylum is divided into three major and several minor classes.

The clams, oysters, mussels, scallops, etc., are commonly known as **bivalves** because two shells encase the body. The bivalves have bilateral symmetry, but in their case it is not associated with rapid locomotion. Those that move at all do so by extending a thick, muscular foot from between the valves. All members of the class feed by filtering food particles from water which they draw in under the mantle.

Many bivalves are prized by man as food. In addition, pearls are produced by certain species of oysters. On the negative side of the ledger, the "shipworm" does great damage to wooden wharves and boats. This organism is not a worm at all, but a bivalve which uses its two valves to bore tunnels in wood that is submerged in salt water.

A second large class of mollusks includes all the **snails** and their shell-less relatives, the **slugs.** Snails are often referred to as **univalves** because of their single shell. This shell is coiled, as are the internal organs of the animal. There is no plane of symmetry in adult snails although they develop from bilaterally symmetrical larvae. Snails feed by scraping food with a rasping, tonguelike *radula*. They have a distinct head with two eyes which are often located on stalks. The great majority of snail species live in salt water but some are also found in fresh water and even on land. The latter breathe air by means of a lunglike adaptation of the mantle. Their shell-less relatives, the slugs, are found in salt water and on land. Terrestrial ("garden") slugs are rather dark in appearance but marine slugs are often brilliantly colored and decorated (Fig. 5-9).

Fig. 5-9   Representative mollusks.

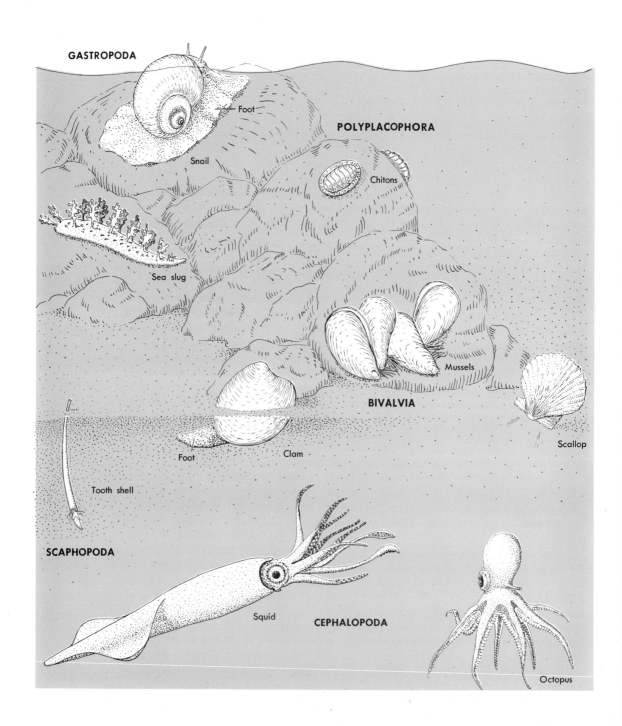

GASTROPODA

Foot

Snail

POLYPLACOPHORA

Chitons

Sea slug

Mussels

BIVALVIA

Scallop

Foot   Clam

Tooth shell

SCAPHOPODA

Squid   CEPHALOPODA

Octopus

Although some species are prized as food, snails cause far more food loss for man than their consumption compensates for. Many marine snails, such as the oyster drill, feed upon commercially valuable bivalves. But far more serious is the destruction brought to crops in some parts of the world by the terrestrial slugs and snails. Some snails, as you have already learned (Section 5-3), also serve as an intermediate host for flukes. Despite the damage caused by some species, the group as a whole should be prized if only for the extraordinary array of beautiful snail shells that are cast up on our beaches, bringing delight to casual and serious shell collectors alike.

The various species of octopus and squid (Fig. 5-9) as well as the chambered nautilus belong to the class Cephalopoda. All of these organisms have a large, well-developed head bearing prominent eyes and surrounded by a ring of arms (eight in the octopus, ten in the squid) which aid in locomotion and the grasping of prey. They are found exclusively in salt water. Although the cephalopod eye looks and functions much like the vertebrate eye (such as ours), these are analogous, not homologous, organs and have arisen as a result of convergent evolution (Section 2-4). Only the chambered nautilus has a large shell. The shell of squids is reduced to a thin plate imbedded in the mantle while octopuses have no shell at all.

The cephalopod mollusks are the most complex members of the phylum. They also include the largest of all the invertebrates. Records exist of a 28-foot octopus and a 50-foot squid. Squids have curious methods of locomotion and defense. They can move very rapidly by forcibly ejecting a stream of water from under the mantle. When in danger, the squid supplements its jet-propelled escape by squirting a black, inky fluid into the water and thus distracting its enemy. Both octopuses and squid form an important item of man's diet in some parts of the world.

Other interesting mollusks are the "tooth shells," a small class of marine mollusks that spend their adult lives almost buried in the sand. They feed by filtering tiny organisms out of the water that is drawn in through the opening in the protruding end of their shell (Fig. 5-9). Chitons are sluggish organisms that live inconspicuously at the seashore (Fig. 5-9). Their shell consists of several (usually eight) separate, overlapping plates. Although this gives them the appearance of being segmented, their internal organs are not.

Until *Neopilina* (Fig. 1-1) was discovered in 1952, the class to which it belongs was thought to have been extinct for millions of years. This mollusk is of great interest because in addition to possessing all the typical molluscan features, it is segmented internally. In this latter respect, it is like the annelids and thus supports the widely held view that the mollusks and the annelids are closely related.

PHYLUM ARTHROPODA   5-7

If number of species is any criterion, this is the major phylum on earth today. Over 765,000 different species of arthropods have been identified. That is more than all the other species of living things—plant, animal, and protist—put together. Each year still more arthropod species are found, living in every conceivable habitat. Fresh water, salt water, soil, and practically the entire surface of the earth abound with them. They are almost the only animals to be found in the interior of Antarctica and on the snow- and rock-strewn slopes of our highest mountains.

All members of this phylum have a segmented body enclosed in a tough, jointed external skeleton made principally of a material called **chitin.** The symmetry is bilateral and is clearly marked by the pairs of jointed appendages arranged along either side of the midventral axis. In all living arthropods, the various appendages in a given species show considerable variety of structure and function. In addition to locomotion, they may aid in food-getting, in sensation, and as offensive and defensive weapons.

Unlike those of annelids, the segments of arthropods show considerable variation in structure from front to back. They are usually combined into three main regions: the **head, thorax,** and **abdomen.** Arthropods have a circulatory system which is considered "open" inasmuch as the blood (in contrast to that of the annelids) is not confined within blood vessels at all times. The main part of the nervous system of arthropods, like that of the annelids, runs along the ventral side of the organism.

There are five major classes of arthropods.

1.   Class Chilopoda

These are the **centipedes** (Fig. 5-10). They are elongated and flattened in appearance. Each segment behind the head bears one pair of legs but, despite their name, the total number is considerably less than one hundred. The centipedes are carnivorous, feeding upon other animals with the aid of strong jaws and a poisonous bite.

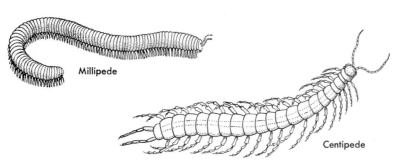

Millipede

Centipede

Fig. 5-10

Millipedes have two pairs of legs on each segment; the centipedes have only one pair per segment.

2.   Class Diplopoda

The members of this class, the **millipedes** (Fig. 5-10), differ from the centipedes in having two pairs of legs in each segment. In this case, too, the total number is far less than the thousand which their name implies. Millipedes are more cylindrical in shape than centipedes and have an herbivorous (vegetarian) diet.

3.   Class Crustacea

The crustaceans differ from other arthropods in having two pairs of sensory "feelers" or antennae. In addition, the head and thorax regions are fused into a single **cephalothorax.** The class includes crayfish, lobsters, barnacles, crabs, and myriads of tiny shrimplike organisms. With the exception of the "pill bug," which lives under logs and stones, the crustaceans are aquatic, being found in both fresh water and salt water. All members of the class breathe by means of gills. They range in size from microscopic forms to lobsters and crabs weighing several pounds (Fig. 5-11).

In certain locations, lobsters, crabs, and shrimp are important items in man's diet. Crustaceans are also the chief source of food for many fish and mammals both in fresh water and the oceans. The great blue whale, whose 100-foot length makes it the largest animal that ever lived, feeds exclusively on tiny marine crustaceans.

Fig. 5-11

Representative crustaceans. This class of arthropods has been most successful in the sea.

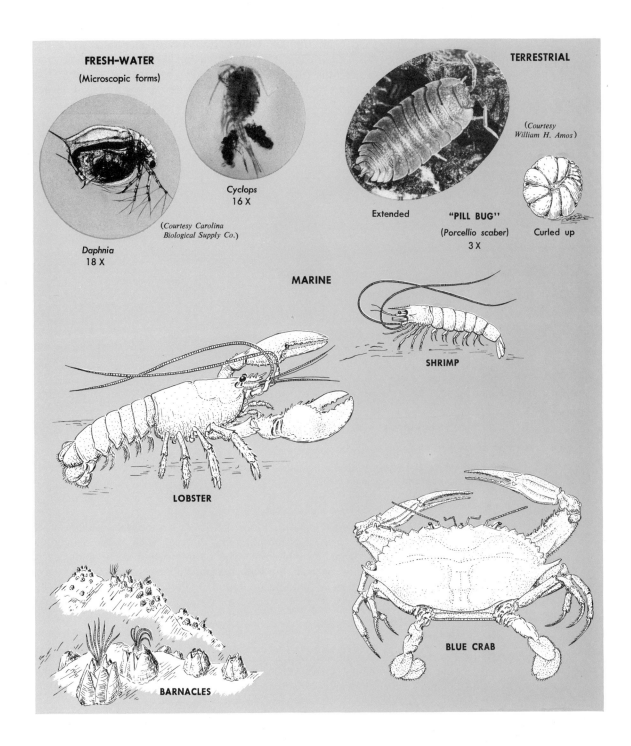

FRESH-WATER
(Microscopic forms)

Cyclops
16 X

(Courtesy Carolina Biological Supply Co.)

Daphnia
18 X

TERRESTRIAL

(Courtesy William H. Amos)

Extended

"PILL BUG"
(Porcellio scaber)
3 X

Curled up

MARINE

SHRIMP

LOBSTER

BARNACLES

BLUE CRAB

4. Class Arachnida

The arachnids, like the crustaceans, have the head and thorax fused into a cephalo-thorax. Unlike the crustaceans, though, almost all the arachnids are terrestrial and breathe air. Locomotion is by four pairs of legs. Antennae are not present. The class includes the spiders, daddy longlegs, ticks, mites, and scorpions. It also includes the marine king or horseshoe crab, *Limulus*, which is found so plentifully along the Atlantic coast (Fig. 5-12). *Limulus* is not a crab at all but an unusual arachnid that seems to have changed but little from the earliest known arthropods. In fact, it is so similar to its fossil ancestors that it, like *Neopilina*, is often referred to as a "living fossil."

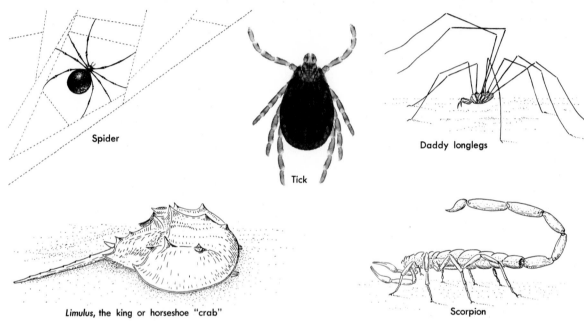

Spider

Tick

Daddy longlegs

Limulus, the king or horseshoe "crab"

Scorpion

Fig. 5-12   Representative arachnids. With the exception of *Limulus*, the members of this class are land-dwellers. They have four pairs of legs.

Mites and ticks are generally parasitic forms that cause a good deal of discomfort to man and other animals. Ticks also transmit some diseases, such as the dangerous Rocky Mountain spotted fever, by their bite. The scorpions and some spiders can inflict painful stings and bites on man, but with the possible exception of that of the black widow spider, the bites of the species found in this country are not usually dangerous to adults.

5. Class Insecta

This is the dominant class of arthropods in every habitat but salt water (where the crustaceans reign supreme). Over 700,000 currently living species of insects have been identified, which is over one-half of all the kinds of living things found upon the earth.

The insect body is divided into three regions: head, thorax, and abdomen. The thorax itself consists of three distinct segments, each of which bears a pair of legs. Thus the insects are the six-legged creatures. Most of them, when adult, also have one or two pairs of wings on the thorax. They have a single pair of antennae mounted on the head.

Insects pass through a series of larval stages as they develop from the egg to the adult. In many insects, these stages have no physical resemblance to the adult stage. Who would guess that the garden caterpillar (a larva) is the same species as a colorful butterfly (the adult)? The transformation of the caterpillar into the butterfly requires extensive rebuilding of the body. This takes place during a dormant stage known as the **pupa.** The transformation process itself is called **metamorphosis.**

With 700,000 species in one class, you can well imagine that a great deal of attention has been paid to the lesser taxonomic categories. About two dozen orders have been established on the basis of differences in metamorphosis, wing structure, and mouth parts. Figure 5-13 illustrates some of the major insect orders.

Our existence is profoundly affected by the insects. Some species, such as lice, bedbugs, fleas, mosquitoes, and certain flies, feed directly on us. Aside from the nuisance and discomfort involved, they may infect us with serious diseases in the process. Malaria, yellow fever, certain types of "sleeping sickness," and the filarial worm that causes elephantiasis (Section 5-4) are all transmitted by the bite of a mosquito. The rickettsia causing typhus fever is transmitted to man through the bite of the body louse or "cootie." Bubonic plague, the black death of the Middle Ages, is often transmitted to man by fleas.

Perhaps even more important than their role as transmitters of disease is the competition that insects give us for food. Every plant crop that man raises for his own use also feeds a multitude of insects. Some insects suck the juices of plants, stunting their

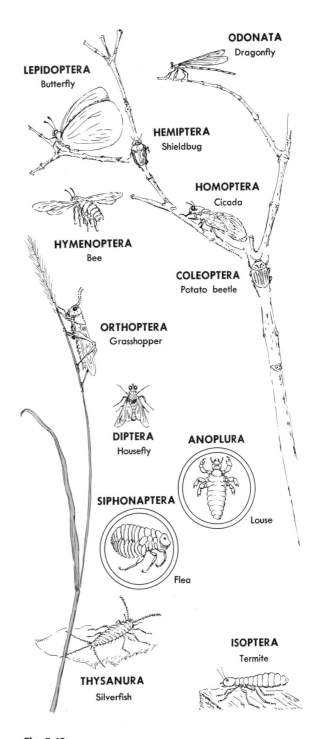

Fig. 5-13

Representatives of the major insect orders. All insects have six legs.

Fig. 5-14

Top: a locust plague. Bottom: a cornfield before and after invasion by grasshoppers.

*Courtesy
Jean Manuel*

*Courtesy
U.S.D.A.*

growth and making them easy prey for disease organisms. Other insects actually chew and devour plant parts. A swarm of grasshoppers can consume every green leaf in a field of corn in a remarkably brief period (Fig. 5-14). The larvae of many moths, butterflies, and beetles are also destructive crop pests. In those parts of the world where the human population barely has enough to eat, competition with the insects often results in serious famine. Even where there is enough food, we must depend on the untiring efforts of agricultural scientists and farmers in their war on insect enemies.

Of all the animals, insects pose the greatest threat to man's welfare. Nevertheless, the many problems that they cause should not obscure the fact that the culprits represent only a small percent (less than 1%) of all the insect species. Most of the insects are of no direct consequence to us and *some* of the insects are decidedly helpful to us. The silkworm (Order Lepidoptera) spins threads of silk, which despite the popularity of synthetic fabrics is still an important textile material. In addition to producing beeswax and honey, the honeybee aids us immeasurably by pollinating many of the angiosperms upon whose seeds and fruits we depend for food. Less conspicuous but of enormous benefit to man are the many insect species, such as the ladybird beetle, that prey upon our insect enemies and thus help us to keep them under control.

PHYLUM ECHINODERMATA 5-8

This phylum consists of about 6000 species, all of which live in salt water. Their most conspicuous characteristics are their spiny skin and their radial symmetry. Perhaps their most interesting feature, though, is their water vascular system (Fig. 5-15). Sea water is taken into a system of canals and is used to extend the many **tube feet.** These latter structures have suckers on their tips and aid the animal in attaching itself to solid surfaces. The phylum is subdivided into five classes, the scientific names of which are given in Fig. 5-15.

As their name suggests, sea lilies are rather plantlike in appearance. Many of them are sessile, that is, they live firmly attached by a stalk to some underwater object. It is this way of life that probably accounts for their radial symmetry, and not any evolutionary relationship to the other radially symmetrical animals, the Cnidaria. Bilateral symmetry is associated with rapid locomotion, as we have seen; radial symmetry is more appropriate for a sessile creature that must concern itself with all directions. However, all the echinoderms do produce free-swimming larvae that are bilaterally symmetrical. This is interpreted to mean that the echinoderms have evolved from bilaterally symmetrical ancestors. The presence of radial symmetry in both the Cnidaria and adult echinoderms is thus an illustration of what type of evolution?

The **starfish** body consists of a central disk containing the mouth and surrounded by five arms. Starfishes are able to move about with the aid of their tube feet but only very slowly. Of all the echinoderms, they are the only ones of much practical importance to man. This stems from their habit of preying on commercially valuable bivalves such as oysters. Brittle stars differ from starfishes in having long, thin arms which are distinct from the central disk and in being able to move about quite rapidly (for an echinoderm!). Photographs taken of the ocean bottom sometimes reveal fantastic numbers of these organisms living side by side.

Sea urchins and sand dollars have a hollow, rigid, boxlike skeleton. Hinged to it are spines, which in some sea urchins are quite long. Rows of openings in the skeleton permit the long, slender tube feet to extend outward. Together, the spines and tube feet enable the sea urchin to move about slowly. Sea urchins are eaten occasionally in some coastal regions of the world.

Fig. 5-15   Representative echinoderms. All members of the phylum live in salt water, have a spiny skin and radial symmetry (as adults), and move slowly with the aid of their tube feet. Extension and retraction of the tube feet is accomplished by the movement of sea water in and out of the water vascular system.

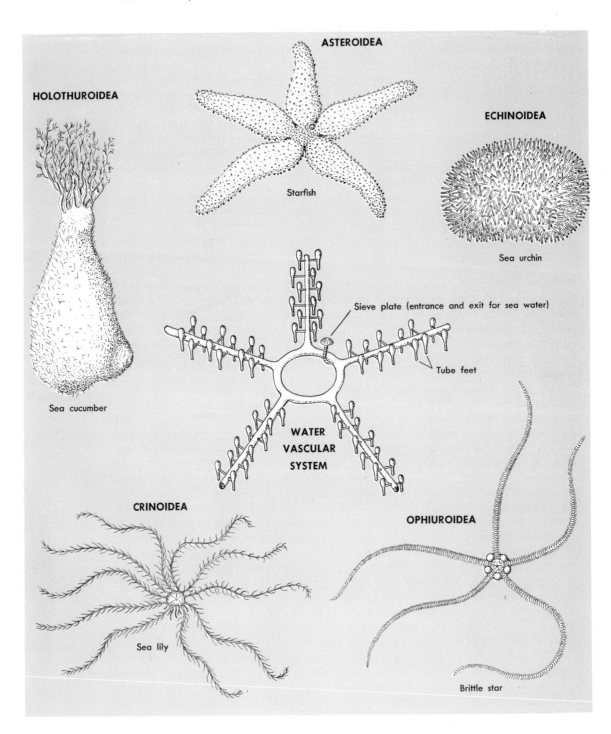

Sea cucumbers have a leathery (rather than spiny) skin, no arms, and virtually no skeleton. Although generally rather unremarkable in appearance and behavior, their response to potential predators is quite startling. When sufficiently disturbed, they contract their muscular body wall until the internal pressure becomes so great that the body wall splits open. With this, their internal organs, along with a good deal of sticky, gelatinous material, spill out into the water. Often, while the potential predator is coping with this, the remains of the sea cucumber crawl away and begin the process of rebuilding its missing organs.

PHYLUM CHORDATA 5-9

Containing over 44,000 species of fishes, amphibians, reptiles, birds, and mammals, this phylum certainly qualifies as one of the three most important animal phyla. (Do you remember the other two?) All of its members have bilateral symmetry, some degree of segmentation, and an internal skeleton. What sets them apart from all the other animals, however, are three unique features (Fig. 5-16). (1) All chordates possess a flexible, rodlike structure, the **notochord,** at some stage of their development. This is located dorsal to the digestive tract and provides internal support for the body. In most chordates, it is replaced by a vertebral column or backbone long before maturity

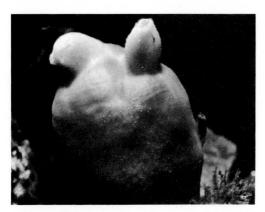

ADULT TUNICATE (*Halocynthia*)
(*Courtesy Ralph Buchsbaum*)

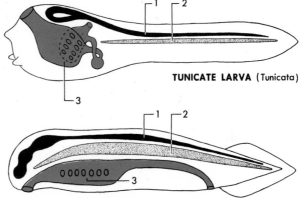

TUNICATE LARVA (Tunicata)

LARVA OF A JAWLESS FISH (Vertebrata)

1. Dorsal nerve cord

2. Notochord

3. Gill slits

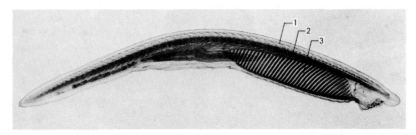

AMPHIOXUS (Cephalochordata)
(*Courtesy General Biological Supply House, Inc.*)

Three chordates. Although the adult forms of these three animals differ strikingly, at some time each shows the three basic chordate characteristics listed.

Fig. 5-16

is reached. (2) At some stage in development, all chordates possess pairs of **gill pouches.** These are lateral outpocketings of the throat. They are matched on the exterior by paired grooves. In aquatic chordates, the gill pouches break through to the exterior grooves, forming **gill slits.** These provide an exit for water that is taken in through the mouth and passed over the gills. In the land chordates, the gill pouches do not break through but become greatly modified during the later course of development. (3) All chordates possess a hollow nerve cord that develops on the dorsal side of the body above the notochord. At its anterior end, it becomes enlarged to form the brain.

The phylum is composed of three subphyla.

1. Subphylum Cephalochordata

The representative member of this tiny subphylum is a small (two-inch), fishlike organism, the **amphioxus.** Throughout its entire life, the amphioxus possesses a notochord, a dorsal tubular nerve cord, and functional gill slits (Fig. 5-16). Although capable of swimming, it spends most of its time partially buried in the sand while it filters microscopic food particles from the water. It is a marine form living close to the shore.

2. Subphylum Tunicata (Urochordata)

The members of this subphylum are also found exclusively in salt water. They are sessile animals that live by straining sea water through their gill slits and ingesting any food particles that are trapped in the process. The phylum gets its name from the tough covering, the tunic, which surrounds the body. Curiously enough, the tunic contains substantial quantities of cellulose, a substance generally confined to the plant kingdom and certain protists. Tunicates are frequently referred to as sea squirts because of the streams of water they expel when the body is contracted suddenly.

Aside from the presence of gill slits, it is hard to see what makes these animals chordates. There is neither notochord nor dorsal tubular nervous system. Like all sessile animals, however, the tunicates produce free-swimming larvae that can disperse the species to new locations, and the structure of these larvae is distinctly chordate. They have both a notochord and a dorsal nervous system (Fig. 5-16). Only when the larva settles on some underwater object and develops into the adult does it lose these features that reveal its true chordate affinities.

Fig. 5-17

An acorn worm (Hemichordata). This marine animal has both echinoderm and chordate features. (Courtesy William H. Amos.)

For many years biologists included still a third group of primitive marine animals as a subphylum of the Chordata. The acorn worms (Fig. 5-17) achieved this status by virtue of possessing gill slits, a dorsal nerve cord (as well as a ventral one) and what was thought to be a rudimentary notochord. There is now, however, so much doubt as to whether the structure is homologous to the notochord of the other chordates that the acorn worms have been placed in a phylum (Hemichordata) of their own. We would all like to know more about their evolutionary history because not only do they show certain chordate characteristics, but they resemble echinoderms in several ways, too.

3. Subphylum Vertebrata

When we say that the phylum Chordata is one of the three major animal phyla on earth today, it is only because it includes the subphylum Vertebrata. In this subphylum are the animals with which we all are most familiar: fishes, frogs, snakes, birds, and mammals of all kinds, including ourselves. In fact, the vertebrates are so important to us that we often talk of the animal kingdom as being made up of vertebrates and "invertebrates," the latter including all the other animal phyla.

All the thousands of vertebrates share two unique features. (1) In every adult, the notochord is either surrounded by or replaced by a column of vertebrae constructed of a flexible material, cartilage, or of bone. This is the spine or "backbone." Running through the vertebral column is the dorsal nerve cord, the spinal cord. (2) The brain at the anterior end of the spinal cord is protected within a boxlike cranium or skull.

The subphylum is often further divided into two superclasses: **Pisces,** which includes all the types of fish, and **Tetrapoda,** which includes all the four-legged vertebrates.

SUPERCLASS PISCES   5-10

Three classes are recognized within the superclass Pisces.

A. Class Agnatha

These are the jawless fishes. Fossil evidence suggests that the earliest vertebrates belonged to this class and that they once formed a sizable group. Today, however, only the lampreys and hagfish remain (Fig. 5-18). These organisms are still the most primitive of the vertebrates. Besides lacking jaws, they have no paired fins. The notochord persists throughout the life of the organism. It is never completely replaced by the skeleton, which is made of cartilage. There are no scales on the body.

Despite its isolated position in the world of the vertebrates, the sea lamprey has proved to be a great nuisance to man. It feeds by attaching itself with its sucking mouth to the bodies of true fishes and sucking their tissue fluids. With the construction of the Welland Canal around Niagara Falls, the sea lamprey has been able to move into the Great Lakes from its former marine habitat. In a remarkably short time, it has virtually wiped out the large lake trout fishing industry that once existed. The recent discovery of a chemical that selectively kills young lampreys while sparing other organisms gives promise that the numbers of this pest may eventually be reduced and the fish population of the Great Lakes restored.

Fig. 5-18   Representative fishes. Top left: The sea lamprey has no paired fins. Note the gill slits. (Courtesy Carolina Biological Supply Co.) Top right: the satinfin shiner, a bony fish. Note the paired fins and the single opening behind the gill chamber. (Courtesy William H. Amos.) Bottom: The sand tiger shark has five pairs of gill slits. The two smaller fishes attached to the underside of the shark are remoras. Their presence does not seem to inconvenience the shark, and they benefit from scraps of food left uneaten by their host. Remoras, like the satinfin shiner, are bony fishes. (Courtesy New York Zoological Society.)

B. Class Chondrichthyes

This class is made up of the sharks, skates, and rays (Fig. 5-18). Almost all of them are marine, although a very few species are found in fresh water. They have strong jaws, paired fins, and a skeleton made of cartilage. Because of this last trait (and perhaps because "chondrichthyes" is such a jawbreaker!) they are frequently referred to as the **cartilaginous fishes.** They may be recognized by the five or more pairs of gill openings out of which water flows after passing over the gills. Sharks are carnivores and are not averse to including man in their diet. Every year there are records of their attacking humans in the water.

C. Class Osteichthyes

All the members of this class have an internal skeleton made of bone. Consequently, the group is often referred to as the **bony fishes.** It includes thousands of species inhabiting both fresh and salt water. Trout, catfish, bass, salmon, perch, herring, mackerel, eels, and all the other game fish and commercial fish are members of this class. Most of them can be easily distinguished from the cartilaginous fishes by the single opening behind each gill chamber and by the fact that the body is covered with overlapping, flat scales. In addition to their paired pectoral and pelvic fins, they have a tail fin, an anal fin, and one or more dorsal fins. Most members of the class have a swim bladder which enables them to alter their buoyancy to suit the depth at which they are swimming.

SUPERCLASS TETRAPODA 5-11

Almost all the members of this class have two pairs of appendages containing the pattern of bones that you studied in Chapter 2 (Fig. 2-2). Those few species that do not, such as the snakes, have lost them during the course of evolution from ancestors that did. Thus the tetrapods are, as their name implies, the four-legged vertebrates. They are divided into four classes.

A. Class Amphibia

As their name suggests, amphibians are partly aquatic and partly terrestrial in their habits. As adults they breathe air and walk on four legs. In these respects, they are adapted to life on land. However, body water is easily lost through their smooth, moist skin and, as a consequence, these animals are restricted to damp locations where there is no danger that the body will dry out. Amphibians require fresh water for reproduction. (None of them are marine.) The eggs are laid and fertilized in the water and develop into gill-breathing larvae. After a period of growth, the larvae develop into adults in the process of metamorphosis.

The class is subdivided into three orders (Fig. 5-19). The **salamanders** and their close relations, the newts, have a tail, and all four of their legs are of approximately the same size. The **frogs** and **toads,** on the other hand, do not have a tail but have large hind legs that enable them to jump and swim efficiently. Members of the third group, the **caecilians,** are legless, wormlike forms found burrowing in the soil of tropical forests.

B. Class Reptilia

The reptiles are fully adapted to life on land. In addition to lungs and legs, they have a dry, scaly, waterproof skin which greatly retards the loss of water from the body. Consequently, the reptiles can thrive in even such hot dry locations as the desert. Unlike the amphibians, they do not need water for reproduction. Most of them lay their eggs in sand or soil. These are encased in a leathery, waterproof shell and thus are protected from drying out. They must be fertilized before the shell is formed, however, so that the sperm can reach the egg cell itself. This is accomplished by internal fertilization with the male introducing sperm directly into the body of the female.

Fig. 5-19   Representative amphibians. Upper left: The tiger salamander is a common inhabitant of moist woods. (Courtesy Carolina Biological Supply Co.) Right: The leopard frog is a favorite laboratory animal. (Courtesy Ward's Natural Science Establishment, Inc.) Lower left: The wormlike caecilians are found in the tropics. (Courtesy New York Zoological Society.)

Fossil remains tell us that reptiles were once far more numerous and diverse than they are today. There were flying reptiles, a great variety of dinosaurs, and other kinds of reptiles in the past. Today, however, only four orders remain.

1) Turtles. The ribs of these animals are greatly enlarged and form bony plates which are fused into a box enclosing most of the body. Turtles are a familiar sight in our fresh-water ponds and streams (Fig. 5-20). Other species are found in damp woods and in the ocean. As a group, the turtles seem to be remarkably long-lived, with some marine species thought to live as long as 150 years.

Southern copperhead

Spotted turtle

American
crocodile

American chameleon

Tuatara (*Sphenodon*)
A "living fossil"

Gila monster

Representative reptiles. Reptiles are air-breathing animals. They are more abundant in warm climates than in cold. Some live in water but must come to the surface from time to time in order to breathe. (Turtle and Gila monster, courtesy American Museum of Natural History. The others, courtesy New York Zoological Society.)

Fig. 5-20

2) **Lizards** and **snakes.** Although these animals are superficially dissimilar, snakes seem to have evolved but little from ancestral legless, burrowing lizards. Both groups are very common in dry regions, although moist woods, fresh water, and salt water are also habitats for many. The American chameleon sold at circuses is a lizard with which most of us are familiar.

Snakes have no limbs, although vestigial remnants of hind legs can be found in the boa constrictor and python. Despite their slim body, snakes devour prey much thicker than themselves. They are aided in the process by a jaw which can be temporarily dislocated to permit extra-large animals to be swallowed.

While most snake species in this country are quite harmless, a few inject poisonous venom in the process of biting their prey. Several species of rattlesnakes, the copperhead, the water moccasin (cottonmouth), and the coral snake are the poisonous snakes found in the United States. Of these, only the rattlesnakes cause much trouble for us. Even their bite is seldom fatal, especially if medical care is secured promptly. Only one poisonous lizard, the Gila monster, is found, and this sluggish creature rarely poses any threat to man (Fig. 5-20).

3) **Crocodiles** and **alligators.** One species of each is found in this country. The crocodile can be distinguished from the alligator by its more pointed snout, protruding teeth, and preference for salt, or at least brackish, water.

Inasmuch as the reptiles were the first vertebrates fully adapted to life on land, it is interesting that so many species (both formerly and at present) have taken to living in an aquatic environment. Nevertheless, they retain the adaptations that enabled their ancestors to colonize the land. They must surface from time to time in order to breathe, and they return to land to lay their eggs.

4) One rare species of reptile, found in the islands off the coast of New Zealand, belongs to a separate order, all of whose other members are now extinct. The so-called **tuatara** resembles closely our conception of what some of the earliest reptiles looked like (Fig. 5-20). This primitive creature will in all probability soon become extinct like the others of its order.

Thanks largely to the aversion many people have to snakes, the reptiles are not very popular. Man does, however, eat some species of both snakes and turtles. Alligators are raised for their skins, out of which shoes and handbags are made. Most important of all, our terrestrial snakes and lizards aid man greatly by consuming large numbers of harmful rodents and insects. Except for poisonous species, snakes around the home and farm should be appreciated for the good they do rather than be hunted and killed.

C. Class Aves (Birds)

Birds share several traits with the reptiles from which they are thought to have evolved. Like the reptiles, they practice internal fertilization followed by the laying of a shelled egg. Their legs are covered with scales, although the rest of the body is covered with **feathers.** Like turtles, they have a horny beak with no teeth.

Birds differ from the reptiles in being able to maintain a constant body temperature. For this reason, birds are often referred to as "warm-blooded," but *homeothermic* is a better term because it is not the warmth of the blood that is so significant but rather the stability of its temperature. In hot locations, a "cold-blooded" reptile may have blood just as warm as that of a bird. However, "cold-blooded" vertebrates, including fishes and amphibians as well as reptiles, cannot maintain the temperature of their blood independent of that of the surroundings. They are said to be *poikilothermic*.

Aside from feathers, the most conspicuous feature of birds is their wings. These are forelimbs that are modified for flight. Some of the other ways in which the bird body is modified for efficient flying will be considered in Chapter 34.

Birds play many important roles in the welfare of man. Chickens, of course, are domesticated birds and are a valuable source of food in many parts of the world. Hawks and owls feed largely upon rodents, including rats and mice. Perhaps the greatest service that birds perform for man is the eating of insects. One of the most dramatic examples of this occurred in 1848 just after the founding of Salt Lake City, when flocks of gulls put a speedy end to a cricket plague that threatened to destroy the first crops of the Mormon settlers. To this day, a visitor to that city can view a tall monument erected in honor of these birds. Less dramatic, but equally important, are the efforts of the hundreds of other species of insect-eating birds that aid man greatly in keeping the population of his insect enemies in check. As many as five hundred mosquitoes have been found within the stomach of a single nighthawk.

D. Class Mammalia

The outstanding feature of this class, the feature from which its name is derived, is the presence of **mammary glands** in the skin. These secrete milk which is used by mothers for feeding their young. In addition, all mammals possess **hair.** For most of them this makes up a coat of fur, but the distribution of hair is more limited in some (such as one species of porpoise which has only six hairs on its body). All the mammals breathe air, and like the birds, are homeothermic. They have teeth which differ from the teeth of other vertebrates in being of three distinct types: incisors for cutting food, canines for tearing it, and molars for grinding. Most mammals are **viviparous,** which means that they give birth to living young. However, a few primitive species, the monotremes, are oviparous, that is, like their reptile ancestors, they lay eggs. These are the duckbill platypus and the spiny anteaters or echidnas (Fig. 5-21). These animals are found only in Australia and New Guinea.

The only egg-laying mammals that survive today. Left: The duckbill platypus raises its young in a nest. Right: The spiny anteater places them in a pouch on the abdomen. (Courtesy New York Zoological Society.)

Fig. 5-21

Fig. 5-22

Representative marsupials. The euro kangaroo (top right) and the koala bear (left) are two of many marsupial species found in Australia. Bottom right: The common opossum is the only marsupial found in North America. These young are sufficiently well developed to leave their mother's pouch and climb on her back. (Koala bear, courtesy American Museum of Natural History. The others, courtesy New York Zoological Society.)

There are approximately 5000 living species of mammals. These vary greatly in size, body shape, and habitat. They range in size from the pigmy shrew, which weighs no more than a dime, to the great blue whale, which may weigh as much as 170 tons. Mammals live successfully in cold climates and hot, and in dry climates as well as wet ones. Some species, such as the whales, live exclusively in the sea; others, the bats, have taken to the air.

The class is divided into two subclasses. One contains only the egg-laying platypus and echidnas mentioned above. The second includes all the viviparous mammals, that is, the marsupials and the placental mammals.

Although marsupials are viviparous, the young are born in such an immature state that they must remain for a long period inside a special pouch on the mother's abdomen. The mammary glands are located within the pouch and supply nourishment to the young. The only marsupial in this country is the opossum, but marsupials such as the koala bear, kangaroos, etc., are the dominant mammalian form in Australia (Fig. 5-22).

All the placental mammals retain the young within the mother's body until they are quite well developed. Up until the time of birth, the young derive nourishment from the mother's bloodstream by means of a **placenta.**

All the mammals with which most of us are familar, including ourselves, are placental mammals. This group is divided into some 16 orders. Figure 5-23 lists 14 of these along with typical examples in each. In Chapter 34, we shall examine our own order, primates, in more detail.

In this chapter we have glanced briefly at the various animal phyla from the simplest to the most complex. It would be a mistake, however, to infer from the order of presentation that each group of animals has evolved from the preceding group. It may well be true that some animals, such as the ancestors of today's flatworms, were also the ancestors of some of the other, more "advanced" animal phyla. However, most of the phyla that we have discussed are the culmination of a long period of independent evolution from an ancestor about whose appearance we can only speculate. A genealogy of the animal phyla would more nearly resemble a branching tree than a ladder (Fig. 5-24). In Chapter 34 we shall attempt to reconstruct as best we can the evolutionary history of these groups.

It is impossible in the space of one chapter to do more than simply introduce the main types of living animals. A detailed study of some of these organisms should be undertaken, however, and can be accomplished in two ways. First, in the laboratory you will want to make careful dissections of typical representatives of each of the major phyla. Second, you will meet most of these organisms again in later chapters and study how they carry out the major functions of life.

This survey of the animal kingdom concludes our brief study of the remarkable variety of forms in which life occurs on the earth. We have laid our emphasis on the ways in which the thousands of different kinds of living things differ from one another. Underlying this diversity, however, is a great unity of structure and function. All these myriads of organisms are alive and, we are beginning to discover, share many fundamental properties. The time has now come to turn our attention to the ways in which living things are similar to one another, to the organization and activities common to all life.

1. Insectivora: shrews, moles
2. Scaly Anteaters
3. Edentata: armadillos
4. Chiroptera: bats
5. Rodentia: squirrels, rats, mice, beaver
6. Lagomorpha: rabbits and hares
7. Carnivora: lion, cats, dogs, skunk, walrus, sea lion
8. Odd-toed Ungulates: zebra, horse, rhinoceros.
9. Even-toed Ungulates: camels, elk, giraffe, bison, sheep, hippopotamus
10. Cetacea: whales, dolphins, porpoises
11. Sirenia: manatee, dugong
12. Proboscidea: elephants
13. Aardvarks
14. Primates: lemurs, New World monkeys, Old World monkeys, great apes, man

Fig. 5-23

Orders of placental mammals and representatives of each.

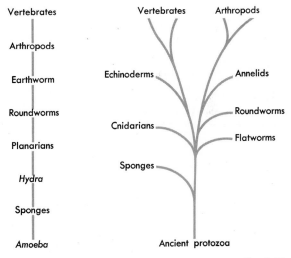

Fig. 5-24

Two views of animal evolution. The view on the right more closely approximates our present understanding of the evolutionary relationships of modern animals.

EXERCISES AND PROBLEMS

1 If you were given a specimen of each of the classes of arthropods, how would you assign each to its proper class?

2 What two features are unique to the mammals?

3 In what ways is *Hydra* not a typical member of its phylum?

4 What trait is unique to the birds?

5 How does a trout differ from a shark?

6 In what ways are they similar?

7 Name a human parasite from each of four phyla of animals.

8 Many farmers try to kill any hawks or snakes they see. Is this a wise practice? Explain.

9 In what ways are reptiles better adapted to life on land than amphibians?

REFERENCES

1 Hanson, E. D., *Animal Diversity,* 2nd ed., Foundations of Modern Biology Series, Prentice-Hall, Inc., 1964. Chapter 7 provides a brief survey of the animals (including the protozoa) and speculates on their evolutionary relationships.

2 Buchsbaum, R., *Animals Without Backbones,* University of Chicago Press, Chicago, Illinois, 1948. A superbly illustrated and complete survey of the invertebrates.

3 Romer, A. S., *The Vertebrate Story,* University of Chicago Press, Chicago, Illinois, 1959. An entertaining survey of the vertebrates and their evolutionary history.

PART III

THE ORGANIZATION OF LIFE

Crystals of a salt adhering to the bottom of a one-liter flask (approximately life-size). The pattern is a reflection of the orderly stacking of positive and negative ions in the crystal lattice (see Section 6-6). (Courtesy Dr. Waldo E. Cohn and Photographic Services Dept. of Oak Ridge National Laboratory.)

Life occurs on our planet in an almost unbelievable array of forms. For many years, biologists were fully occupied with the discovery, the classification, and the anatomical study of the many species of living things. However, as more and more was learned from the study of energy (physics) and the study of matter (chemistry), it became possible to analyze living things in terms of structural units far smaller than even those visible under the microscope. These units are atoms and molecules.

As a result of such studies, two things have become clear.

1) Although living things are diverse in their appearance, habitat, etc., their basic chemical organization is remarkably similar.

2) Although the chemical organization of living matter is very complex, it is based upon the same materials and principles as those found in the world of nonliving things.

These two discoveries have had far-reaching consequences. They have shifted the attention of biologists from the many ways in which living things differ from one another to the many ways in which they are similar. This shift in approach has gone hand in hand with an enlargement of our way of looking at living things. No longer can a biologist be content simply to study **morphology,** that is, the way in which organisms are put together out of cells, tissues, and organs. Now he must ask how these various structural parts of the organism work; that is, he must also examine their **physiology.** To find the answers he must understand the chemical makeup of the living cell and the chemical principles underlying its activity.

6-1 **ELEMENTS**

All the things found on this planet—air, sea water, soil, rocks, etc.—are composed of one or more fundamental building blocks of matter, the elements. Despite the large number of kinds of rocks, minerals, etc., only 90 different elements have been found occurring naturally on earth. Actually, 103 different elements are known, but 13 of these have been man-made in the laboratories of nuclear physics.

We can define an element as a substance that cannot be further decomposed by chemical means. Iron, oxygen, aluminum, and silicon are four common elements found on or near the surface of the earth. To say that everything on this earth is composed of, and is thus reducible to, one or more of 90 different elements does not exclude living things. They, too, are made up of elements. Of the 90 present generally on earth, however, only about one-quarter are found in living organisms. Not only is the number of elements found in living organisms smaller, but the relative prevalence of these elements is different. Figure 6-1 compares the elemental composition of the crust of the earth with that typical of a living organism. Obviously, living organisms are not simply a reflection of the chemical composition of their environment. Some elements found abundantly in the nonliving world (e.g. aluminum) play no role in living things. On the other hand, carbon, hydrogen, and nitrogen are found greatly concentrated in living organisms. In fact, these three elements plus oxygen make up 96% of all living material. It looks as though one feature of life is its ability to accumulate and concentrate elements that are relatively rare in the nonliving environment.

Other elements are essential to life, too. Calcium, phosphorus, sodium, potassium, magnesium, chlorine, sulfur, and iron are always found in living things. Added to the previous four, these account for 99.9% of the weight of living organisms. The remaining one-tenth of one percent is made up of a few other elements such as copper, manganese, zinc, cobalt, iodine, vanadium, fluorine, and (in plants only) boron and molybdenum. Because these latter elements are present in such tiny quantities, they are called trace elements. This does not mean that they do not play an important role in life. It is simply that a little goes a long way.

Fig. 6-1

The distribution of elements in the crust of the earth compared with their distribution in a living organism.

Distribution of elements in the crust of the earth, including land, air, and water	
	% by weight
Oxygen (O)	49.5
Silicon (Si)	25.3
Aluminum (Al)	7.5
Iron (Fe)	5.08
Calcium (Ca)	3.39
Sodium (Na)	2.63
Potassium (K)	2.40
Magnesium (Mg)	1.93
	97.69%
Hydrogen (H)	0.87
Titanium (Ti)	0.63
Chlorine (Cl)	0.19
Phosphorus (P)	0.12
	99.50%
Manganese (Mn)	0.090
Carbon (C)	0.080
Sulfur (S)	0.060
Barium (Ba)	0.040
Chromium (Cr)	0.038
Nitrogen (N)	0.030
Fluorine (F)	0.026
Zirconium (Zr)	0.023
Strontium (Sr)	0.020
Nickel (Ni)	0.018
Zinc (Zn)	0.017
Vanadium (V)	0.018
Copper (Cu)	0.010
Total	99.96%

Distribution of elements in living things	
	% by weight
O	65
C	18
H	10
N	3
Ca	2
P	1
	99%
K, S, Cl, Na, Mg, Fe	0.9%
Mn, Cu, I (iodine), Co (cobalt), Zn; B (boron), Mo (molybdenum)	0.1%
Total	100.0%

ATOMS 6-2

Each of the 103 elements known to man is composed of one particular kind of atom. We can define an atom as the smallest part of an element that can enter into combinations with other elements. (More of this in a moment.) For ease in discussing elements and the atoms of which they are composed, we use symbols, one for each element (Fig. 6-2).

We have said that elements cannot be further decomposed by chemical means. The same is true, of course, of the atoms of which they are composed. Atoms can, however, be decomposed by the use of more violent, physical methods. Years of such work have shown that atoms, too, have a very definite and orderly structure.

The simplest atom, the hydrogen atom, consists of a single positively charged particle, the **proton,** surrounded by a single negatively charged particle, the **electron.** The two charges are equal in magnitude so the atom is electrically neutral. Almost all the weight of the atom is accounted for by the weight of the proton.

The element with the next most complicated atom is the gas helium (He). Its atoms have two protons and also two other particles called **neutrons.** Neutrons are the same weight as protons but do not have any electrical charge. Both the protons and neutrons adhere tightly together to form the dense, positively charged nucleus of the atom. Around this nucleus are two electrons so that, once again, the atom as a whole is neutral.

The structure of all the other atoms follows the same plan. Each of the other 101 kinds, from lithium (No. 3) to lawrencium (No. 103), consists of one more proton

Fig. 6-2
Periodic table of the elements.

KEY

Electrons in 1st shell → 2 Electrons in 2nd shell → 8 Electrons in 3rd shell → 18 Electrons in 4tn shell → 32 Electrons in 5th shell → 18 Electrons in 6th shell → 8 Electrons in 7th shell → 2	Radium 88 Ra (226)	← Name ← Atomic number, Symbol ← Atomic weight

Note:
( ) indicates most stable or best known isotope.

1 Hydrogen 1 H 1.00797																	2 Helium 2 He 4.0026
2 1 Lithium 3 Li 6.939	2 2 Beryllium 4 Be 9.0122											2 3 Boron 5 B 10.811	2 4 Carbon 6 C 12.0111	2 5 Nitrogen 7 N 14.0067	2 6 Oxygen 8 O 15.9994	2 7 Fluorine 9 F 18.9984	2 8 Neon 10 Ne 20.183
2 8 1 Sodium 11 Na 22.9898	2 8 2 Magnesium 12 Mg 24.312											2 8 3 Aluminum 13 Al 26.9815	2 8 4 Silicon 14 Si 28.086	2 8 5 Phosphorus 15 P 30.9738	2 8 6 Sulfur 16 S 32.064	2 8 7 Chlorine 17 Cl 35.453	2 8 8 Argon 18 Ar 39.948
2 8 8 1 Potassium 19 K 39.102	2 8 8 2 Calcium 20 Ca 40.08	2 8 9 2 Scandium 21 Sc 44.956	2 8 10 2 Titanium 22 Ti 47.90	2 8 11 2 Vanadium 23 V 50.942	2 8 13 1 Chromium 24 Cr 51.996	2 8 13 2 Manganese 25 Mn 54.938	2 8 14 2 Iron 26 Fe 55.847	2 8 15 2 Cobalt 27 Co 58.933	2 8 16 2 Nickel 28 Ni 58.71	2 8 18 1 Copper 29 Cu 63.54	2 8 18 2 Zinc 30 Zn 65.37	2 8 18 3 Gallium 31 Ga 69 72	2 8 18 4 Germa-nium 32 Ge 72.59	2 8 18 5 Arsenic 33 As 74.922	2 8 18 6 Selenium 34 Se 78.96	2 8 18 7 Bromine 35 Br 79.909	2 8 18 8 Krypton 36 Kr 83.80
2 8 18 8 1 Rubidium 37 Rb 85.47	2 8 18 8 2 Strontium 38 Sr 87.62	2 8 18 9 2 Yttrium 39 Y 88.905	2 8 18 10 2 Zirconium 40 Zr 91.22	2 8 18 12 1 Niobium 41 Nb 92.906	2 8 18 13 1 Molyb-denum 42 Mo 95.94	2 8 18 13 2 Technetium 43 Tc (99)	2 8 18 15 1 Ruthenium 44 Ru 101.07	2 8 18 16 1 Rhodium 45 Rh 102.905	2 8 18 18 Palladium 46 Pd 106.4	2 8 18 18 1 Silver 47 Ag 107.870	2 8 18 18 2 Cadmium 48 Cd 112.40	2 8 18 18 3 Indium 49 In 114.82	2 8 18 18 4 Tin 50 Sn 118.69	2 8 18 18 5 Antimony 51 Sb 121.75	2 8 18 18 6 Tellurium 52 Te 127.60	2 8 18 18 7 Iodine 53 I 126.904	2 8 18 18 8 Xenon 54 Xe 131.30
2 8 18 18 8 1 Cesium 55 Cs 132.905	2 8 18 18 8 2 Barium 56 Ba 137.34	57-71 See Lanthanide Series	2 8 18 32 10 2 Hafnium 72 Hf 178.49	2 8 18 32 11 2 Tantaium 73 Ta 180.948	2 8 18 32 12 2 Wolfram 74 W 183.85	2 8 18 32 13 2 Rhenium 75 Re 186.2	2 8 18 32 14 2 Osmium 76 Os 190.2	2 8 18 32 15 2 Iridium 77 Ir 192.2	2 8 18 32 17 1 Platinum 78 Pt 195.09	2 8 18 32 18 1 Gold 79 Au 196.967	2 8 18 32 18 2 Mercury 80 Hg 200.59	2 8 18 32 18 3 Thallium 81 Tl 204.37	2 8 18 32 18 4 Lead 82 Pb 207.19	2 8 18 32 18 5 Bismuth 83 Bi 208.980	2 8 18 32 18 6 Polonium 84 Po (210)	2 8 18 32 18 7 Astatine 85 At (210)	2 8 18 32 18 8 Radon 86 Rn (222)
2 8 18 32 18 8 1 Francium 87 Fr (223)	2 8 18 32 18 8 2 Radium 88 Ra (226)	89-103 See Actinide Series															

Lanthanide Series (Rare Earth Elements)	2 8 18 18 9 2 Lanthanum 57 La 138.91	4 8 18 19 9 2 Cerium 58 Ce 140.12	2 8 18 21 8 2 Praseo-dymium 59 Pr 140.907	2 8 18 22 8 2 Neodym-ium 60 Nd 144.24	2 8 18 23 8 2 Prometh-ium 61 Pm (147)	2 8 18 24 8 2 Samarium 62 Sm 150.35	2 8 18 25 9 2 Europium 63 Eu 151.96	2 8 18 25 9 2 Gadolin-ium 64 Gd 157.25	2 8 18 26 9 2 Terbium 65 Tb 158.924	2 8 18 28 8 2 Dyspro-sium 66 Dy 162.50	2 8 18 29 8 2 Holmium 67 Ho 164.930	2 8 18 30 8 2 Erbium 68 Er 167.26	2 8 18 31 8 2 Thulium 69 Tm 168.934	2 8 18 32 8 2 Ytterbium 70 Yb 173.04	2 8 18 32 9 2 Lutetium 71 Lu 174.97
Actinide Series	2 8 18 32 18 9 2 Actinium 89 Ac (227)	2 8 18 32 18 10 2 Thorium 90 Th 232.038	2 8 18 32 20 9 2 Protac-tinium 91 Pa (231)	2 8 18 32 21 9 2 Uranium 92 U 238.04	2 8 18 32 22 9 2 Neptunium 93 Np (237)	2 8 18 32 23 9 2 Plutonium 94 Pu (242)	2 8 18 32 24 9 2 Americium 95 Am (243)	2 8 18 32 25 9 2 Curium 96 Cm (247)	2 8 18 32 26 9 2 Berkelium 97 Bk (247)	2 8 18 32 27 9 2 Califor-nium 98 Cf (251)	2 8 18 32 28 9 2 Einsteinium 99 Es (254)	2 8 18 32 29 9 2 Fermium 100 Fm (253)	2 8 18 32 30 9 2 Mendele-vium 101 Md (256)	Nobelium 102 No (254)	Lawren-cium 103 Lw (257)

and one more electron than the atom just before it in the list (Fig. 6-2). Different atoms of a single element may have a different number of neutrons in the nucleus (these variant atoms are called **isotopes**), but this has little or no effect on the chemical properties of the atom.

The electrons surrounding the nucleus of each atom are restricted to certain definite "shells" or energy levels. These shells can be thought of as existing on the surface of a hollow sphere of a definite radius. Furthermore, there are limits to the number of electrons that can be present at any single energy level. At the innermost energy level only two can be present. Thus this level is filled in the helium atom. The next level can hold a maximum of eight electrons. These are arranged in four pairs. The atom of the gas neon has eight electrons in this second shell (Fig. 6-3). The maximum number of electrons which can exist at any given level (n) can be computed from the expression

$$\text{maximum number} = 2n^2.$$

Thus, the third energy level can hold up to 18 electrons (nine pairs). How many electrons can exist at the fourth level?

There is one other important rule that describes the arrangement of electrons in the electrically neutral atom. This is that no more than eight electrons will be found in any energy level when it is the outermost one. For example, the third energy level can hold up to 18 electrons. It cannot hold more than eight, however, unless there are electrons in the fourth shell.

Fig. 6-3

The atomic structure of helium, neon, and argon. In each case there is a full complement of electrons in the outermost shell. Consequently, these elements do not react readily with other elements. They are called inert gases.

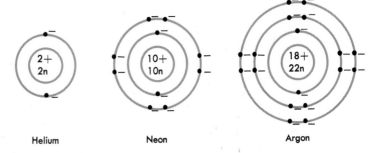

Helium   Neon   Argon

The arrangement of electrons in the atom plays a crucial role in its chemistry. Atoms are most stable when their outer shell contains its full quota of electrons. The so-called inert gases (e.g. neon and argon) have eight electrons in their outer shell.

Other atoms tend to gain or lose electrons until their outer shell also has the stable arrangement of the inert gases. Atoms with one, two, or three electrons in the outer shell usually lose these so that the next inner shell, with a more stable set of electrons, is left exposed. These atoms are called **electropositive.** The elements with atoms of this kind are the metals, such as sodium, magnesium, potassium, and calcium. Atoms with four, five, six, or seven electrons in their outer shell tend to add the necessary number of electrons to complete this shell. These atoms are **electronegative.** The elements with atoms of this kind are the nonmetals, such as carbon, nitrogen, oxygen, phosphorus, sulfur, and chlorine. The tendency for atoms to achieve a stable arrangement of electrons in the outer energy level explains why the various elements combine with one another the way they do. For example, table salt, sodium chloride, is made from equal numbers of sodium and chlorine atoms. The sodium atoms, with one electron in their outer shell, release this electron and thus gain stability. The chlorine atoms, with seven electrons in their outer shell, take on the electron from the sodium atoms and likewise gain stability (Fig. 6-4).

Our emphasis on the stable arrangements of electrons in an atom should not obscure the fact that unstable arrangements can exist. By adding energy to an atom, it is possible to "kick" electrons from a lower to a higher energy level. Such an atom is known as an "excited" atom. It is unstable. If left alone, the electron will soon return to its former energy level. In so doing, it will give back most of the energy that it had absorbed in the first place. When certain minerals are placed under ultraviolet light, they glow in brilliant colors. This is called **fluorescence.** It occurs because the electrons in the atoms of the mineral absorb energy from the ultraviolet light and are raised to a higher energy level. An instant later, however, they return to their former positions, giving up the absorbed energy in the form of visible light. (Fluorescent lamps work on exactly the same principle.) We will see later on that this ability of electrons to store energy is vitally important to the existence of life itself.

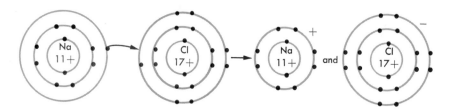

Fig. 6-4   Formation of sodium chloride. In the transfer of an electron from a sodium atom to a chlorine atom, each atom acquires an outer shell of 8 electrons and thus attains stability. Each also acquires an electrical charge. Charged atoms are called ions.

One other property of atoms that we should note is the fact that they have weight. Almost all of this is accounted for by the weight of the protons and neutrons in the nucleus. Hydrogen, with just a single proton in its nucleus, is the lightest atom. Uranium, with 92 protons and 146 neutrons in its nucleus, is the heaviest naturally occurring atom.

The weight of any single atom is, of course, infinitesimal when calculated in common units such as grams or ounces. To make calculations easier, we express the weights of atoms in terms of a special unit, the **atomic weight unit.** This unit is set arbitrarily as one-twelfth of the weight of a single atom of carbon (with six protons and six neutrons). Such a unit is very convenient because it makes the lightest element, hydrogen, have an atomic weight of 1. (Why?) It also makes individual protons and neutrons have a weight of 1. Thus the most common type of oxygen atom, which has eight protons and eight neutrons in its nucleus, has an atomic weight of 16. It is designated as O^{16}. It is only one of 3 so-called **isotopes** of oxygen found in the atmosphere. The others, however, make up less than 1% of the total number of oxygen atoms present. One of these isotopes has 8 protons and 9 neutrons in its nucleus, and thus its atomic weight is 17. Its symbol is O^{17}. The other, O^{18}, has 8 protons and 10 neutrons in its nucleus and thus an atomic weight of 18. Note that all the isotopes of oxygen have just 8 protons in the nucleus.

6-3   CHEMICAL COMPOUNDS

A chemical compound is a substance that can be decomposed into two or more simpler substances. If these simpler substances are also compounds, then they can be further decomposed. Ultimately, compounds can be decomposed into elements.

The amounts of the elements in a given compound are not variable but are always present in definite proportions by weight. This is a reflection of the fact that the atoms of the elements in a compound are attached to one another in a precise way. Water is a compound. It is made up of the elements hydrogen and oxygen. The weight of the hydrogen in the compound is one-eighth the weight of the oxygen. This is understandable if two atoms of hydrogen (Atomic weight = 1) are attached to each oxygen atom (Atomic weight = 16) in the compound.

One of the most important things to remember about compounds is that their properties, such as color, taste, chemical activity, etc., are usually quite different from the properties of the elements of which they are made. The element sodium is poisonous and reacts explosively with water. The element chlorine was used as a poison gas during World War I. The compound sodium chloride, however, is absolutely vital to life activities. Its properties are quite different from those of either sodium or chlorine. Similarly, the properties of water are not the properties of the hydrogen or oxygen of which it is composed.

MOLECULES 6-4

Most of the compounds of special interest to biologists are made up of units called molecules. Each molecule consists of a precise arrangement of the atoms of the elements in the compound. It is this precise arrangement which accounts for the fixed ratio of elements in the compound. Because the constituent atoms have weight, the molecules have weight. The molecular weight (M.W.) is equal to the sum of the atomic weights of the atoms in the molecule. The molecular weight of water is 18. What is the molecular weight of carbon dioxide, CO_2?

It should be noted that many common gaseous *elements*, e.g. hydrogen, oxygen, nitrogen, and chlorine, are also composed of molecules. In these cases, only two atoms are present in the molecule, and the two atoms are alike. We designate these molecules as H_2, O_2, N_2, and Cl_2 respectively. What is the molecular weight of each of these molecules?

As we have seen, water is made up of molecules consisting of one oxygen atom to which are attached two hydrogen atoms. These atoms are held together by their tendency to achieve the most stable arrangement of electrons in their outer shells. Oxygen, with six electrons in its second shell, lacks two electrons to make a stable set of eight. Hydrogen, with one electron, needs a second to reach the stable arrangement of two electrons in its shell. By sharing electrons between them, each atom in a molecule of water gains a stable arrangement. Each hydrogen atom contributes an electron to the oxygen but, at the same time, electrons of the oxygen atom contribute to the formation of a pair for each of the hydrogen atoms. We can illustrate this by representing the nucleus (and all electron shells except the outer one) of the atoms by the symbol of the element and indicating the electrons in the outermost shell by dots or small crosses.

$$\overset{\displaystyle ..}{\underset{\displaystyle \cdot\ \times}{:\text{O}:}\text{H}}$$
$$\text{H}$$

Note that the oxygen atom now is surrounded by eight electrons and each hydrogen atom is surrounded by two. The process of sharing electrons causes the atoms to be linked or bonded together. This kind of bond is known as a **covalent bond.**

The number of electrons that a given atom has available to share in the making of covalent bonds sets a definite limit on its ability to combine with other atoms. Hydrogen, with just one electron to share, can only combine with one other atom. It is said to have a combining power, or **valence,** of one. Oxygen, needing to pair two of its electrons with two from elsewhere in order to achieve a complete set of eight, has a valence of 2. Nitrogen, with five electrons in its outer shell, needs three more electrons to form eight. Hence, it will share three of its electrons with three electrons from elsewhere. It has a valence of 3. The compound of nitrogen and hydrogen consists of one atom of nitrogen and three atoms of hydrogen.

$$H \overset{}{\underset{\bullet\,\times}{\times}} N \overset{\bullet\bullet}{\underset{}{\bullet}} H$$

$$H$$

It is the substance ammonia. Carbon, needing four electrons to share with its own four electrons has a valence of 4. Its compound with hydrogen can be expressed as

$$H$$
$$H \overset{}{\times} C \overset{\times\,\bullet}{\underset{\bullet\,\times}{\times}} H$$
$$H$$

This substance is a gas, methane, frequently produced in marshes.

Carbon atoms with a valence of 4 and oxygen atoms with a valence of 2 can also unite. In this case, two oxygen atoms unite with one carbon atom to form a molecule of the gas carbon dioxide, CO_2. The electron-dot representation of this molecule is interesting because it shows that not one, but two, pairs of electrons are shared between the respective atoms.

$$\overset{\bullet\bullet}{:} O :\overset{\times}{\underset{\times}{:}} C \overset{\times}{\underset{\times}{:}} O \overset{\bullet\bullet}{:}$$

This arrangement is known as a **double** covalent bond. Note that it still provides for a complete set of eight electrons around each atom in the molecule.

6-5

FORMULAS

The electron-dot representations of the structures of molecules are a kind of formula. While they tell us a great deal about the arrangement of atoms in the molecule, they are a little complicated for regular use, particularly in considering large, complex molecules. Consequently, chemists have devised other, shorthand expressions for indicating the makeup of a compound.

One of these is the molecular formula. This formula simply lists all the kinds of atoms found in the molecule and, after each atom, includes a subscript giving the number of times (over one) that the atom appears in the molecule. The molecular formula for water is H_2O. The molecular formula for a molecule of the milk protein beta-lactoglobulin is approximately $C_{1864}H_{3012}O_{576}N_{468}S_{21}$. Note that the molecular formula simply gives the number of each of the various atoms that are found in the molecule. It does not tell us anything about the way in which these atoms are bonded together. In the case of beta-lactoglobulin, in fact, the arrangement of the atoms in the molecule is not yet known.

For many molecules we do know the actual physical arrangements of the atoms in the molecule. This is very important information, too, because the properties of a compound depend greatly on the actual way the atoms are linked together. For example, the common beverage alcohol, ethanol, has the formula C_2H_6O. However, there is another compound, an ether (related to the ether commonly used as an anesthetic), that also has the formula C_2H_6O. The difference in properties of these two compounds can be explained by the difference in the way the atoms are assembled in the molecule. We can show this difference by drawing a **structural formula** of each. In a structural formula we use a dash to represent each of the covalent bonds (which we showed above by pairs of dots and crosses). Using this system, we represent the ethanol molecule thus:

$$
\begin{array}{cc}
\text{H} & \text{H} \\
| & | \\
\text{H}-\text{C}-\text{C}-\text{OH} \\
| & | \\
\text{H} & \text{H}
\end{array}
$$

On the other hand, the atoms of the ether molecule are attached to each other like this:

$$
\begin{array}{cc}
\text{H} & \text{H} \\
| & | \\
\text{H}-\text{C}-\text{O}-\text{C}-\text{H} \\
| & | \\
\text{H} & \text{H}
\end{array}
$$

Note that each molecule has exactly the same number of atoms in it. Note also that in each case all of the valences are satisfied. Each of the two carbon atoms forms four bonds, the oxygen atom has two bonds, and each of the hydrogens forms only one bond. Two molecules, such as these, that have the same molecular formula but different structural formulas are called **isomers.** Isomers are found frequently in compounds containing carbon.

Even structural formulas are a little complex to use all the time. Consequently, chemists have devised condensed versions of them which still impart the essential information. Using condensed structural formulas, we can represent ethanol as CH_3CH_2OH or even C_2H_5OH. The ether is represented as CH_3OCH_3. Note that these condensed structural formulas have the great convenience of being able to be typed or printed in a single line. Note also that the distinguishing feature of each molecule, the "active group," is clearly shown. All alcohols have the $-OH$ group. All ethers have the $-O-$ arrangement.

You may well ask how chemists are able to determine the structural formula of a molecule. The first step is to determine its molecular formula. This is done by carefully decomposing a weighed amount of the compound into its constituent elements (or simple, inorganic molecules of these elements such as CO_2 and H_2O). From the weights of the breakdown products, it is possible to compute the relative numbers of the different atoms in the original molecule. A knowledge of the molecular weight gives the actual numbers and thus the molecular formula. (See question 10.)

There is no single next step in the procedure for determining the structural formula. The process depends upon the vast amount of knowledge about chemical properties of substances and "active groups" that has been accumulated by chemists for well over 100 years. Taking our earlier example, chemists know that the rules of valence will permit two carbon atoms, six hydrogen atoms, and one oxygen atom to be combined in just two ways. Through the years it has been found that alcohols react with other substances in certain ways, ethers, in different ways. By finding out whether the chemical activity of our unknown compound is characteristic of the —OH group or the —O— group, we can hope to establish the true structural formula. The ultimate test comes, however, when we synthesize a compound, using another body of principles and rules, with the structural formula we have tentatively assigned to our "unknown." If the synthesized compound has the same physical and chemical properties as our "unknown," we can be quite confident that we do indeed understand the way the molecule is put together.

<table>
<tr><td>6-6</td><td></td></tr>
</table>

IONIC COMPOUNDS

Not all compounds are made of molecules. When atoms combine to form many compounds, the affinity of one of the atoms for electrons is so powerful that it is able to remove outer electrons completely from the other atom or atoms. Table salt is a good example of this. Chlorine, with its one missing electron, is so electron-attracting (**electronegative**) that it completely pulls away the one outer electron of the sodium atom (Fig. 6-4). Sodium, like all metals, does not have a great affinity for its outer electron (it is **electropositive**) so it gives its electron up readily. Having lost an electron, however, it now possesses a single positive charge (11 protons, but only 10 electrons). Similarly, the chlorine atom now has a single negative charge because of its additional electron (17 protons, 18 electrons). These charged atoms are called **ions.** The mutual attraction of opposite electrical charges holds the ions together by **ionic** bonds. The ions are not held together in pairs but are stacked in three-dimensional arrays (Fig. 6-5). Each sodium ion is held to six chloride ions (above, below, front, back, left, and right) while each chloride ion is, in turn, held by six sodium ions. The result of this stacking of ions is a crystal of table salt. At no place can one single out a pair of ions and refer to it as a molecule.

Since compounds that are ionically bonded contain no molecules, can we write formulas for them? Certainly, but in this case we are restricted to a formula that simply shows the ratios of the various positive and negative ions in the crystal. The formula NaCl shows that these two ions are present in a one-to-one ratio. Magnesium, with a valence of 2, forms crystals with two chloride ions for every one magnesium ion. The formula for this compound is $MgCl_2$. What would be the formula for aluminum chloride?

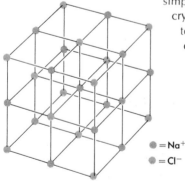

● $= Na^+$
● $= Cl^-$

Fig. 6-5

The lattice structure of a crystal of NaCl. The orderly stacking of Na^+ and Cl^- ions produces a crystal in the shape of a cube.

Because ionic compounds are not made of molecules, we cannot properly speak of molecular weight. We can easily arrive at the equivalent value, however, by adding up the atomic weights of the minimum ratio of ions in the crystal. We call this value the **formula weight.** The formula weight of sodium chloride is 58.5 (Na = 23, Cl = 35.5).

Ionic compounds are widespread in nature. Although we naturally associate them with the nonliving world of rocks and minerals, many ionic compounds are essential to life. Salts of sodium, potassium, calcium, chlorine, and other elements are found dissolved in the water of blood, cell fluid, etc. In this condition, the positive and negative ions become separated or **dissociated** from each other. The essential chemical properties of the substance are not changed in the process, however. Sodium ions (Na^+) and chloride ions (Cl^-) dissolved in water still retain the properties of table salt. They do not regain the poisonous properties of the neutral atoms from which these ions were made.

ACIDS **6-7**

Even the molecules of covalently bonded compounds may dissociate into ions when they dissolve in water. Many covalent compounds containing hydrogen atoms are able to release one or more of them to nearby water molecules. For example, the gas hydrogen chloride is made up of molecules containing the two atoms held together by a shared pair of electrons, a covalent bond:

$$\overset{\bullet\bullet}{\underset{\bullet\bullet}{:}}\text{Cl} \overset{\times}{:} \text{H}$$

When this gas dissolves in water, the nucleus of the hydrogen atom (a proton) is attracted to one of the unshared electron pairs of a nearby water molecule. This leaves a negatively charged chloride ion

$$\overset{\bullet\bullet}{\underset{\bullet\bullet}{:}}\text{Cl} \overset{\times}{:} \quad ^-$$

and produces a positively charged **hydronium** ion, H_3O^+:

$$H^+$$
$$H \overset{\bullet\bullet}{\underset{\times}{:}} O \overset{\bullet\bullet}{\underset{\bullet\times}{:}}$$
$$H$$

The resulting solution is hydrochloric acid. It has a sour taste and other properties associated with acids. Any organic compound that possesses the **carboxyl** group

will also dissociate into ions when placed in water. One of these will be a proton (H^+) which will immediately combine with a water molecule to form the hydronium ion (H_3O^+). Acetic acid has one carboxyl group and ionizes to form an acetate ion (CH_3COO^-) and a proton.

$$CH_3COOH + H_2O \rightarrow CH_3COO^- + H_3O^+$$

Any compound that liberates protons in water solution is an acid.

Chemical changes are changes in which new substances with new properties are formed. When hot sodium is surrounded by chlorine gas, the sodium bursts into flame. Table salt, sodium chloride, results. This is an example of a chemical change. The burning of coal is another example. Can you think of others?

All chemical changes involve a rearrangement of atoms (or ions). We can express these changes by means of an equation. To write a chemical equation we must first write the formulas of all the substances used in the chemical change. These are the **reactants.** Then we draw an arrow and write the formulas of all the substances produced by the chemical change, the **products.** When ethanol (ethyl alcohol) is exposed to air and the action of vinegar bacteria, it is changed chemically into vinegar (acetic acid) and water. We express this change by the equation

$$C_2H_5OH + O_2 \rightarrow CH_3COOH + H_2O$$

Note carefully that every atom present on the left side of the equation is accounted for on the right. If it is not, then the equation does not give a true picture of the chemical change. This is simply another way of saying that matter can neither be created nor destroyed. (We may neglect the special case of nuclear changes that occur in atom bombs, etc.)

In many chemical changes, the substances do not react in simple one-to-one ratios as they do in the production of acetic acid. When magnesium is burned in air, for example, two atoms of magnesium react with just a single molecule of oxygen. Two parts of the white powder magnesium oxide are produced. We express these relationships by placing the prefix 2 before the symbol for magnesium and the formula for magnesium oxide:

$$2Mg + O_2 \rightarrow 2MgO$$

You can easily carry out this chemical change yourself. Grasp a small piece of magnesium ribbon in a spring-type clothespin and hold the tip of the ribbon in a candle or bunsen burner flame. The heat of the flame will first soften the ribbon. Then the ribbon will begin to burn. In so doing, it gives off a good deal of heat and a brilliant light. (Do not stare at the light.) When the burning is completed, a white powder, magnesium oxide, remains.

An equation can tell us even more than what rearrangement of atoms has taken place. It can also tell us what the relative weights of the reactants and products of the chemical change are. From the equation given above, you might think that 1 gram (gm) of ethanol and 1 gm of oxygen would produce 1 gm of acetic acid and 1 gm of water. Such is not the case, however. The equation tells us that one molecule of ethanol reacts with one molecule of oxygen. It implies that likewise a billion molecules of one will react with exactly a billion molecules of the other. Thus, the 1:1 ratio expresses the number of each type of molecule in the reaction. You can quickly see by computing the molecular weights of these two molecules that the ethanol molecule is somewhat heavier (M.W. = 46) than the oxygen molecule (M.W. = 32). If we want a given quantity of ethanol to react completely with oxygen, we must supply one molecule of oxygen for every molecule of ethanol. Counting molecules is not practical. Weighing substances, on the other hand, is a very efficient technique. To make sure that equal numbers of ethanol and oxygen molecules react, we must bring about a reaction between weights of these two substances which are in the ratio of 46:32.

Another example may help make this point clear. As a biology student, you might be interested in comparing the effects of sodium chloride and potassium chloride solutions on the rate of beating of an isolated frog heart. At first you might plan to prepare one-percent solutions (1 gm of the salt in 99 gm of water) of each substance. This would be a poor technique, however. The formula weights of these two salts are 58.5 and 74.5 respectively. A one-percent solution of sodium chloride would thus contain almost half again as many ions as a one-percent solution of the potassium chloride. (Why?) In such a case, you could not properly relate the response of the frog heart to the kind of metal ion applied.

A much better technique is to make up the salt solutions so that equal volumes of each of the two solutions contain equal numbers of the ions. To do this, we simply weigh out 58.5 parts of NaCl to every 74.5 parts of KCl. Then these two quantities must each be added to enough water to make the two resulting solutions of exactly equal volume. Once this is done, you know that, drop for drop, the two solutions have exactly the same concentration in terms of numbers of ions present.

In trying to weigh out two substances in the ratio of 58.5 to 74.5, what could be more simple than to weigh out 58.5 gm of one and 74.5 gm of the other? In so doing, you would have weighed out a quantity of each substance called a **mole.** If you then add enough water to each substance to make exactly one liter of solution, you will have made a 1-molar (1-M) solution of each salt. [A specially graduated flask is a useful device in which to do this. After the substance is added to the flask, enough water is added to bring the volume up to the engraved line on the neck of the flask. The volume of solution is then exactly one liter (Fig. 6-6.)] A 1-M solution of these salts would undoubtedly be too strong for the experiment on the frog heart. It would probably be better to make up a liter of each solution containing 5.85 and 7.45 gm respectively. Such solutions would be designated one-tenth molar (0.1M) solutions. Drop for drop, these two solutions would also contain exactly the same number of ions because they are of the same molarity.

Fig. 6-6

A volumetric flask. When filled to the etched line, it contains exactly one liter. Such a flask is used to prepare solutions of precise molarity.

Looking back at our earlier example, we are now in a position to estimate how much acetic acid and how much water would be produced as a result of reacting one mole of ethanol (46 gm) with one mole of oxygen (32 gm). One mole of each substance would be produced, namely 60 gm of CH_3COOH and 18 gm of water. Note, also, that the total weight of the products (60 gm + 18 gm = 78 gm) is exactly equal to the total weight of the reactants (46 gm + 32 gm = 78 gm). This, once again, illustrates the principle that during chemical changes, matter is neither created nor destroyed. (In practice, when organic compounds react, one seldom gets a mole of each product for each mole of reactant, i.e. 100% efficiency. This is not because any matter is lost. It is simply because other reactions, "side" reactions, go on simultaneously and produce unwanted products.)

TYPES OF CHEMICAL CHANGE 6-9

There are several types of chemical change. Two of these are of special importance to the beginning biology student. These are ion-exchange reactions and oxidation-reduction (REDOX) reactions.

1. Ion-Exchange Reactions

When hydrogen chloride gas (HCl) is dissolved in water, a solution of hydrochloric acid is produced.

$$HCl + H_2O \rightarrow H_3O^+ + Cl^-$$

As explained earlier, this reaction simply involves the transfer of an ion, a proton (H^+), from one molecule to another. There has been no change in the arrangement of the electrons. The HCl molecule donated the proton and, like all proton donors, is called an acid. The water molecule, which accepts the proton, acts as a **base.** It is not a very strong base, though, because it will readily give its proton up to other proton acceptors. One of the most powerful of these is the hydroxyl ion. This ion is produced when substances called hydroxides (e.g. NaOH) are dissolved in water. The OH^- ion has a greater affinity for protons than does the water molecule. Consequently, the proton shifts from the hydronium ion, now the acid, to the hydroxyl ion, the base.

$$H_3O^+ + OH^- \rightarrow 2H_2O$$

If one adds equal volumes of an acid solution and a basic solution (of the same concentration of reacting ions) together, they will react completely in this way. This process is called **neutralization** because the resulting solution has neither the properties of an acid nor the properties of a base. In fact, the solution produced by this particular neutralization is simply salt water.

$$H_3O^+ + Cl^- + Na^+ + OH^- \rightarrow 2H_2O + Na^+ + Cl^-$$

The OH^- ion is a very powerful proton acceptor and thus a very strong base. It is never found in high concentrations in living organisms. Probably the most important base in living tissue is the bicarbonate ion, HCO_3^-. This base readily neutralizes excess acid that may be formed by cell metabolism. Perhaps you know of people who take sodium bicarbonate to neutralize the hydrochloric acid in their stomachs in an attempt to alleviate "acid indigestion."

$$H_3O^+ + Cl^- + Na^+ + HCO_3^- \rightarrow H_2O + H_2CO_3 + Na^+ + Cl^-$$

In summary, when any molecule or ion gives up a proton, it is acting as an acid. When any molecule or ion takes on a proton, it is acting as a base. Any acid and any base will neutralize each other if each solution contains the same number of ions.

2. Oxidation-Reduction Reactions

Oxidation-reduction reactions differ from ion-exchange reactions in that a transfer of electrons is always involved. You remember that when sodium burns in chlorine (Fig. 6-4) each sodium atom loses an electron to a chlorine atom. The atom that loses the electron (sodium) is said to have been **oxidized.** The atom that gains the electron (chlorine) is said to have been **reduced.** The two processes are completely linked. Whenever any substance gives up electrons, it is oxidized. The substance to which it gives its electrons is called the oxidizing agent. Note, however, that any substance, in the process of acting as an oxidizing agent, is itself reduced. Because oxidations always go hand in hand with reductions, we refer to these reactions as REDOX reactions.

The Chemical Basis of Life: Principles / 6-9

You may wonder why the reaction between sodium and chlorine is called an oxidation when oxygen plays no part in it. The answer is simply a matter of history. Oxygen has a great affinity for electrons and is thus one of the best and most common oxidizing agents known. Because of its effectiveness in this role, it has supplied the name for all reactions of this type.

The burning of magnesium is an example of an oxidation that actually does involve oxygen. The outer two electrons on the magnesium atom (an electropositive element—see Section 6-6) are taken on by an atom of oxygen (a strongly electronegative element), thus completing its outer shell of eight electrons. All strongly electronegative elements like oxygen and chlorine are good oxidizing agents. They are very effective at removing electrons from other substances. Conversely, electropositive elements like sodium and magnesium are easily oxidized. They give up their outer electrons easily. They are good reducing agents.

Some biological oxidations involve the addition of oxygen to the molecule being oxidized. In the reaction between ethanol and O_2, one atom of oxygen joins the molecule. Although the added oxygen atom does not remove electrons sufficiently far to form ions (as in the case of NaCl and MgO), it nevertheless does attract two electrons away from the carbon atom and much closer to itself (Fig. 6-7).

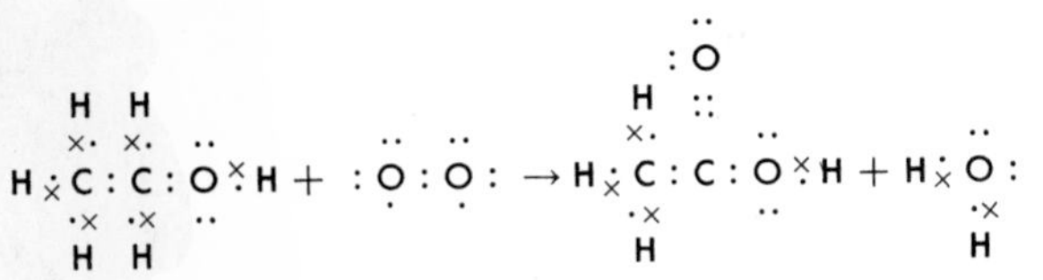

Fig. 6-7

The oxidation of ethanol. Oxidation has occurred both by the addition of an oxygen atom and by the removal of hydrogen atoms. In each case, electrons are moved away from carbon atoms.

The most common kind of biological oxidation is accomplished by the removal of hydrogen atoms from a substance. The oxidation of ethanol also exhibits this kind of oxidation. Two hydrogen atoms, each with its single electron, are removed by the second oxygen atom. These unite to form a molecule of water.

REDOX reactions in which the electrons shift from a less electronegative atom to a more electronegative one proceed spontaneously and liberate energy in the form of heat. The burning of the magnesium strip is an excellent illustration of this. The reason that energy is liberated is that the electrons are moving from a less stable but energy-rich arrangement to a more stable but energy-poor one. The products of the reaction contain less potential ("stored") energy than the reactants. In the process of the reaction, the difference is liberated as heat and light.

We heat our homes and run electric generators and automobile engines with the energy released by the oxidation of fuels (e.g. coal, oil, and gasoline) which all contain substantial quantities of potential energy. The products of their oxidation, CO_2 and H_2O, contain far less potential energy. We run our own life activities on the energy released by oxidizing the foods we eat. This process of biological oxidation is called **respiration.**

REDOX reactions in which the shift of electrons is from a more electronegative to a less electronegative atom require an input of energy. The energy is required to force electrons away from the more electronegative (greater electron affinity) atom to the less electronegative (less electron affinity) atom. The most important reductions in the biological world are those carried out by green plants during the process of photosynthesis. Light supplies the energy for these. Some of the light energy becomes stored as the potential energy of the foods produced. In fact, it is this stored energy that is released again when foods and other fuels are oxidized. The oxidation of a given quantity of food, or any other energy-rich substance, releases just the amount of energy that was consumed during the formation of that substance.

Reductions in living organisms are often accomplished by the addition of hydrogen atoms (each with its electron) to a substance. They may also be accomplished simply by the transfer of electrons alone. Some of the metallic elements found in living things have variable valences and play an important part in this. Iron atoms may be quite easily oxidized by the removal of the two electrons in the outer shell.

$$Fe - 2e^- \rightarrow Fe^{++}$$

A third electron, this one from the shell beneath, can also be removed by oxidation.

$$Fe^{++} - 1e^- \rightarrow Fe^{+++}$$

The Fe^{+++} ion is a fairly good oxidizing agent itself, however. It can remove an electron from some other substance (which is thus oxidized) and become the Fe^{++} ion once again. Then it can turn right around and act as a mild reducing agent, donating its recently acquired electron to still another substance. This ability of iron to pick up and pass on electrons depends upon its variable valence. Iron and certain other metallic elements play a major role in the REDOX reactions carried out in living things.

6-10   **RATE OF CHEMICAL REACTION**

Several factors affect the speed at which chemical changes take place. One of the most important of these is simply the **nature of the reacting materials.** You can well imagine that a vigorous, energy-releasing oxidation, with electrons passing from electropositive to electronegative atoms (as in the burning magnesium ribbon), proceeds much more rapidly than the reverse.

Temperature also affects the rate of chemical reaction. A great deal of the energy liberated by the burning magnesium ribbon is in the form of heat. This heat energizes still-unoxidized magnesium atoms so that they combine even more quickly with oxygen atoms. As a general rule, the speed at which chemical reactions take place doubles with every 10° C rise in temperature. This is true not only for reactions in the test tube but also, within limits, for reactions in living things.

The **concentration** of reacting substances is a third factor in regulating the speed at which chemical changes occur. If the reacting molecules are far apart, their opportunities for colliding and exchanging atoms and electrons are limited. On the other hand, if they are packed closely together, there is a much greater probability of their colliding and of a resulting chemical change.

The reaction $2Mg + O_2 \rightarrow 2MgO$ involves materials that are brought together whenever a piece of magnesium ribbon is exposed to the air. Why doesn't the reaction proceed spontaneously? Why is it necessary to add energy (heat) to the magnesium ribbon when the reaction between magnesium and oxygen yields such abundant amounts of energy? The answer lies in the need to activate the magnesium atoms. Magnesium atoms will not transfer their electrons to oxygen atoms unless they are activated by the input of energy. At ordinary temperatures, very few atoms become sufficiently active to combine with oxygen. Those that do, however, liberate far more energy in the course of reacting than it took to activate them (Fig. 6-8). Nevertheless, because of the small numbers involved, the resulting heat is liberated so slowly that it does not warm up the metal. Consequently the oxidation of magnesium proceeds very slowly. (The slow oxidation of metals is called corrosion or, in the case of iron, rusting.)

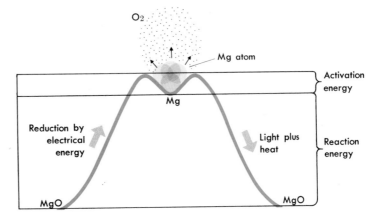

Fig. 6-8

A model showing the energy changes in a REDOX reaction.

At higher temperatures, a sufficiently large number of magnesium atoms become activated and react with oxygen so that the resulting heat raises the temperature of the metal still further. This activates still other atoms and the reaction becomes self-sustaining. Heat is the most common way in which we supply the energy of activation for chemical reactions. The sparkplug on a gasoline motor and the blasting cap in a stick of dynamite are two examples. Can you think of others?

CATALYSIS   6-11

The use of heat to supply activation energy is not too suitable for use by living things. High temperatures are quite destructive to life, as we all know. Fortunately, there is a way around the problem. This is to reduce the energy of activation needed by the use of a suitable **catalyst.** A catalyst is a chemical substance that speeds up the rate at which a given chemical change takes place without becoming permanently altered in the process. Many catalysts accomplish this by temporarily uniting with one of the reacting substances and lowering the amount of activation energy needed. When the reaction is completed, the catalyst is released unchanged and ready for re-use. You can demonstrate catalysis easily with a small quantity of a 3% solution of hydrogen peroxide (H_2O_2)—available in any drug store—and a pinch of the black compound manganese dioxide (MnO_2). At room temperature and atmospheric pressure, and especially when exposed to light, hydrogen peroxide breaks down to form water and oxygen ($2H_2O_2 \rightarrow 2H_2O + O_2$). (This is why the manufacturer puts the solution up in a brown glass bottle and recommends that it be kept in a cool place with the cap screwed on tightly.) When the solution is poured into a glass, a few bubbles of O_2 soon form. Adding a pinch of MnO_2 greatly increases the speed of the reaction, however. A froth of O_2 bubbles forms immediately (Fig. 6-9). Thus catalysis takes its place as one of the factors that speed up the rate of chemical reactions.

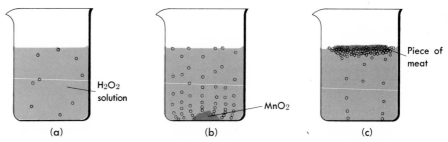

Fig. 6-9

Catalysis. (a) A solution of H_2O_2 spontaneously decomposes, releasing a few bubbles of oxygen. (b) The action is greatly speeded by the addition of the inorganic catalyst manganese dioxide. (c) Cells, in a piece of meat in this case, contain an enzyme, catalase, that likewise hastens the action.

Living cells have catalysts, too, and thus are able to carry out their chemical activities quickly but at safe temperatures. These catalysts are called **enzymes.** It is thought that every chemical reaction occurring in living things (there may be thousands of them) requires the presence of a specific enzyme. Most cells even have an enzyme, called *catalase*, that decomposes H_2O_2 just as MnO_2 does. It is responsible for the frothing which occurs when hydrogen peroxide is poured into an open wound. You can, however, demonstrate the action of the enzyme under more pleasant circumstances by adding a piece of fresh meat to a container of H_2O_2. The meat will quickly float to the top, buoyed up by the bubbles of O_2 that form on its surface.

6-12

REVERSIBLE REACTIONS

In Section 6-9, you learned that the hydronium ion and the bicarbonate ion react to form water and carbonic acid according to the equation:

$$H_3O^+ + HCO_3^- \rightarrow H_2O + H_2CO_3$$

The carbonic acid (H_2CO_3) that is formed is unstable and decomposes into a molecule of carbon dioxide and a molecule of water:

$$H_2CO_3 \rightarrow H_2O + CO_2$$

The complete reaction is thus

$$H_3O^+ + HCO_3^- \rightarrow H_2O + H_2CO_3$$
$$\downarrow$$
$$H_2O + CO_2$$

In a test tube, the carbon dioxide is released into the air, and all the hydronium ions are eventually neutralized. In a closed container, the situation is somewhat different. The carbon dioxide that is produced remains in contact with the water. As the reaction continues, the concentration of CO_2 increases steadily. Soon carbon dioxide molecules are colliding with water molecules and *back-reacting* to form H_2CO_3. Some of this additional H_2CO_3 dissociates in water to form H_3O^+ and HCO_3^-. Reactions in which the products can back-react to form the reactants again are called

reversible. We use double arrows to indicate the reversible nature of the reaction.

$$H_3O^+ + HCO_3^- \rightleftharpoons H_2O + H_2CO_3$$
$$\updownarrow$$
$$H_2O + CO_2$$

In a closed system, the forward and reverse reactions eventually reach **equilibrium.** At this time, the rate of the forward reactions exactly equals the rate of the reverse reactions. This does not necessarily mean that the concentrations of products and reactants are equal. At equilibrium in the second reaction of our example, in fact, the concentration of CO_2 and H_2O may be some 1000 times greater than that of H_2CO_3. For every molecule of CO_2 that reacts with H_2O, however, a molecule of H_2CO_3 decomposes into H_2O and CO_2. Similarly, at equilibrium, for every hydronium ion that reacts with a bicarbonate ion, a molecule of H_2CO_3 dissociates into its ions.

Equilibria can be disturbed in several ways. Changing **temperature** usually favors one reaction over the other, and thus brings about a shift in the equilibrium. **Adding fresh reactants** to the system favors the reaction that consumes the reactants. In our example (see the previous equation) addition of fresh acid displaces the equilibrium to the right, favoring the formation of increased amounts of carbon dioxide. **Removing a product** accomplishes the same thing. As we noted above, in an open test tube the carbon dioxide leaves the reaction mixture and no back reaction is possible. Under these conditions, the forward reaction (neutralization) is said to go to completion.

What about catalysts? Although catalysts have dramatic effects on the rates at which reactions occur, they do not displace reversible reactions in either direction. This is because both the forward and back reactions are speeded up to the same extent. Catalysts thus enable equilibrium to be reached more quickly but do not favor one reaction over its reverse.

The majority of the chemical reactions that occur in living organisms are reversible. Which direction is favored depends upon changes in the factors mentioned above. Proper functioning in the organism depends, in turn, upon the reaction's proceeding in a particular direction at a particular time.

MIXTURES   6-13

A mixture is a material composed of two or more pure substances each of which retains its own characteristic properties. When sand is stirred into water, a mixture results. The properties of the sand and the water are unchanged in the process. (You remember that compounds have properties quite different from the properties of their constituents.) Another way in which mixtures differ from compounds is that their composition can be varied. You can mix varying amounts of sand and water together. Magnesium oxide, on the other hand, always contains magnesium atoms and oxygen atoms in the ratio of 24:16 parts by weight.

A mixture like that of sand and water is called a **suspension.** After a period of time, the sand particles (crystals of SiO_2) settle to the bottom of the container under the influence of gravity. Quite a different sort of mixture is a **solution.** In a solution, individual molecules or ions of a substance (the **solute**) become suspended in a liquid medium (the **solvent**). These molecules or ions are so small (less than 1 mμ) that they never settle out under the influence of gravity. Their own motion counteracts the gravitational force acting on them. When a salt ($NaCl$, KCl, etc.) or sugar is added to water, a solution results. The mixture is homogeneous, that is, even under the microscope it is perfectly uniform in appearance. While it is easy to separate sand and water by filtering through a cone of paper (Fig. 6-10), solutions cannot be separated in this way. The sizes of the solute molecules and ions in a solution are approximately the same as the size of the solvent molecules and pass through the pores of the filter paper just as easily. Although other liquids can act as solvents, water is the major solvent in living things.

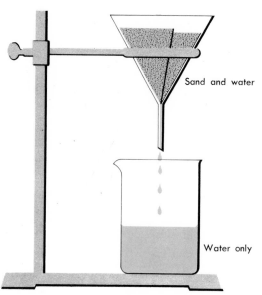

Water only

Sand and water

Fig. 6-10

Filtration. Any particles, such as sand, too large to pass through the pores in the paper can be separated in this way from smaller molecules such as those of water.

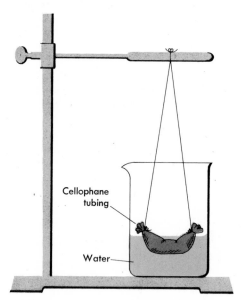

Cellophane tubing

Water

Fig. 6-11

Dialysis. The pores in a piece of cellophane are so small that macromolecules (e.g. starch, egg white) are retained inside while small molecules and ions (e.g. glucose, Na^+, Cl^-) pass out readily into the surrounding water. Dialysis is the separation of macromolecules from small molecules and ions.

The student of biology should also be familiar with a third kind of mixture, the **colloid.** Colloids are suspensions of particles that are larger than those in true solutions but still too small to settle out under the influence of gravity. These particles may consist of single, large molecules (1 — 100 mμ) or solid clumps of smaller molecules. They are large enough to be seen under very high magnifications. They cannot be filtered out by ordinary filter paper because the pores in the paper are too large to stop their passage. Cellophane, however, has pores sufficiently small to separate colloidal particles from smaller molecules (Fig. 6-11). Egg white is a familiar colloid.

The biologist is especially interested in colloids because a large proportion of the molecules found within living cells are **macromolecules,** that is, molecules so large that they form colloids.

We now turn our attention to the general topic of the molecules from which living things are made.

EXERCISES AND PROBLEMS

1 Which of the following substances are composed of molecules: (a) oxygen, (b) water, (c) sodium chloride, (d) glucose, (e) steel?

2 Distinguish between an atom and an ion.

3 What ion is produced by all acids?

4 A mole of methane (CH_4) weighs how many grams?

5 Give an example of a strongly electropositive element.

6 Write electron-dot formulas for the molecules of (a) water, (b) ammonia, (c) methane, (d) ethane (CH_3CH_3).

7 Summarize the differences between mixtures and compounds.

8 Distinguish between organic and inorganic compounds.

9 Which of the following elements would you expect to react with chlorine: (a) hydrogen, (b) neon, (c) sodium, (d) fluorine, (e) calcium, (f) carbon?

10 Chemical analysis shows that the ratio of C atoms to H atoms in a substance is 1 to 3. The molecular weight of the substance is 30. What is the molecular formula?

11 Show by means of electron-dot formulas the combining of a lithium atom (3 electrons) with a fluorine atom (9 electrons).

12 A student needs 200 ml of 0.1 M NaOH solution. What weight of solid is used?

13 What is the molecular weight (MW) of acetic acid (CH_3COOH)?

14 When methane (CH_4) burns in oxygen, carbon dioxide and water are the products. Write a balanced equation to represent this chemical change.

15 What volume of 0.4 M hydrochloric acid will neutralize 200 ml of 0.2 M NaOH solution?

16 What is the most abundant metal in the crust of the earth?

17 Convert 98.6°F into °C.

18 Write a structural formula for butane (C_4H_{10}).

19 Write a different structural formula for butane.

20 What term is used to describe these two compounds?

21 Each member of a class of 24 students takes 10 gm of sodium chloride from a one-pound jar. How many grams are left?

22 Distinguish between electron, proton, and neutron.

23 Write an electron-dot formula for carbon tetrachloride (CCl_4).

24 Distinguish between isomers and isotopes.

REFERENCES

Additional information on the topics discussed in this chapter can be found in any good textbook on introductory chemistry.

A small book that covers topics in chemistry and physics, selected and developed with the needs of biology students in mind, is:

Baker, J. J. W., and G. E. Allen, *Matter, Energy, and Life: An Introduction for Biology Students,* Addison-Wesley, Reading, Massachusetts, 1965.

CHAPTER 7 THE CHEMICAL BASIS OF LIFE: THE MOLECULES OF LIFE

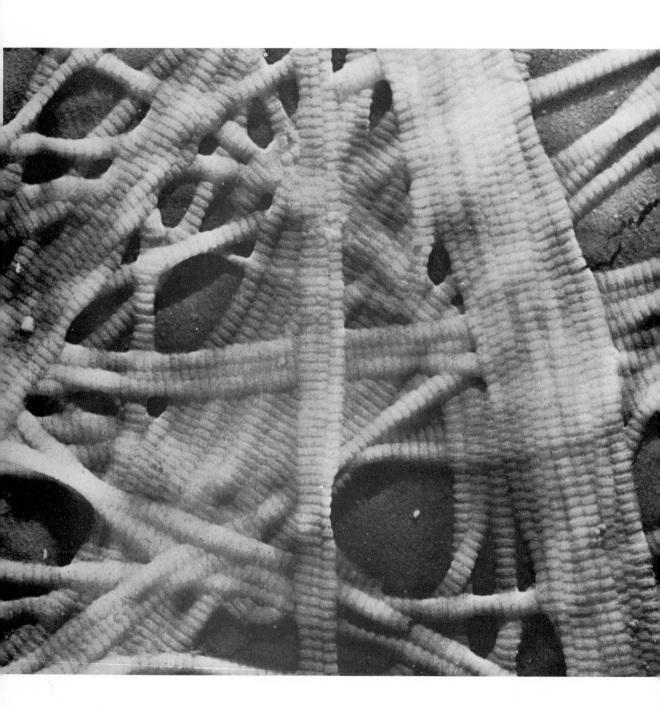

Fig. 7-1

Molecular composition of the human infant	
Water	66%
Proteins + nucleic acids	16%
Fats and lipids	12.5%
Ash (minerals)	5%
Carbohydrates	0.5%
Vitamins	trace

In the human infant, water represents almost two-thirds of its weight.

The same basic chemical principles apply to matter found in living as well as nonliving things. Matter found in living things does, however, have certain distinguishing characteristics. One is that the number of different elements found in living matter is considerably smaller than the number found in nonliving matter. Furthermore, living things are largely composed of carbon, hydrogen, nitrogen, and oxygen. Of these elements, only oxygen is plentiful in the nonliving world.

Perhaps the one element which, more than any other, is characteristic of living matter is carbon. Because of the ability of carbon atoms (1) to unite with one another and thus form long chains and (2) to form double covalent bonds, they participate in the formation of an almost infinite variety of molecules. Such variety is essential for such an incredibly complex organization of matter as a living thing. It is no wonder, then, that molecules containing carbon form the very basis of life itself. In fact, the chemistry of carbon compounds is called **organic chemistry** because these compounds are almost exclusively associated with life processes.

It is fortunate for our understanding of the organization and functioning of living things that the almost unlimited numbers of organic compounds do fall into a reasonable number of distinct categories. As far as quantity is concerned, organisms are composed mainly of water, proteins, fats and other lipids, carbohydrates, nucleic acids, and minerals (Fig. 7-1). Of these, water and minerals are inorganic. The other substances are all organic.

CARBOHYDRATES 7-1

Carbohydrates are essential to life. Almost all organisms use them as a fuel, exploiting their rich supply of potential energy to maintain life. Carbohydrates also serve as an important structural material in some animals (cellulose in sea squirts, chitin in arthropods), all plants (cellulose), and many protists. Carbohydrates are made of molecules containing carbon, hydrogen, and oxygen atoms with the ratio of hydrogen atoms to oxygen atoms always 2:1. In view of this, can you imagine how the word carbohydrate came to be used for these compounds?

Many carbohydrate molecules are extremely large, possessing molecular weights of 500,000 or more. Fortunately, these **macromolecules** are composed of simpler, repeating units, and this makes them relatively easy to study. The repeating units are called sugars.

◀ Filaments of collagen, a protein, 31,000 X. (Courtesy Dr. Jerome Gross.)

1. Sugars

The most important sugar is **glucose.** It has the molecular formula $C_6H_{12}O_6$, but as is so often the case in organic chemistry, the molecular formula is not sufficient to describe the molecule fully. There are other common sugars that have precisely the same molecular formula and thus are **isomers** of glucose. Glucose can, however, be distinguished from these by its structural formula (Fig. 7-2). Five of the six carbon atoms and one of the oxygen atoms form a flat ring. The hydrogen atoms and other groups extend above and below the plane of this ring.

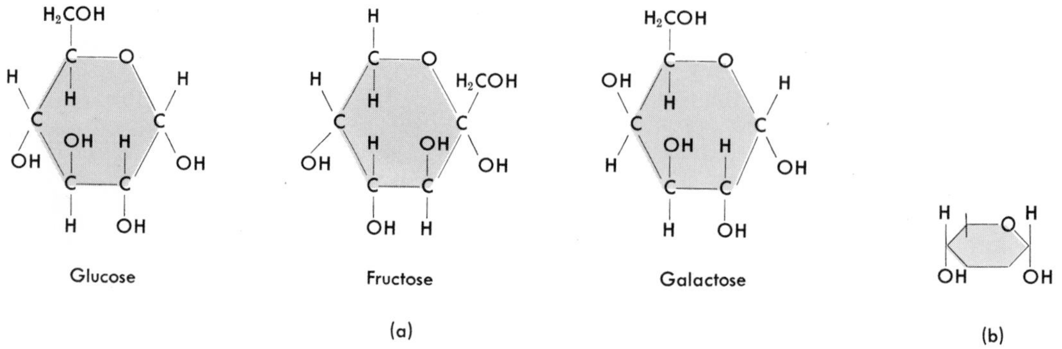

Glucose   Fructose   Galactose

(a)   (b)

Fig. 7-2   (a) Structural formulas of glucose and two of its isomers. (b) Simplified version of the glucose molecule.

The great importance of glucose to life is that it serves as the basic, transportable form of fuel for the organism. It is soluble and thus easily transported by body fluids. In humans, glucose is actually referred to as "blood sugar." Its concentration in the blood must be maintained within narrow limits or serious disturbances will result. Glucose is the starting material for cellular respiration, the process from which most organisms derive the energy they need to run their life activities.

Two glucose units can be linked together by an oxygen bridge between them (Fig. 7–3). This is formed by the removal of a molecule of H_2O. A molecule of **maltose** results. It is a double sugar or **disaccharide,** with the molecular formula

$$C_{12}H_{22}O_{11} \qquad (2C_6H_{12}O_6 - H_2O).$$

Maltose is produced when starch is digested (see below).

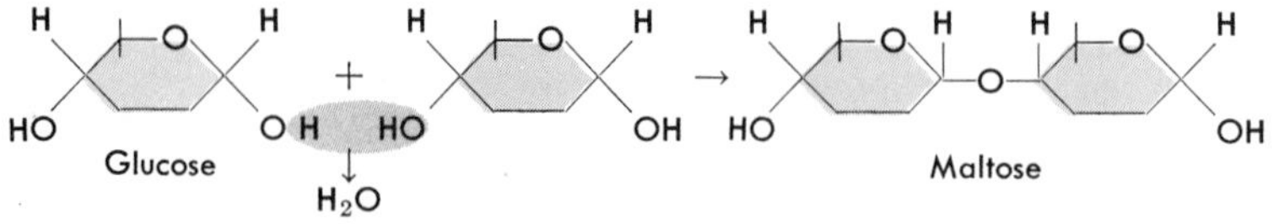

Glucose   Maltose

H_2O

Fig. 7-3   Synthesis of maltose.

The sugar that you put in your coffee or on your breakfast cereal, **sucrose,** is also a disaccharide. It is formed by the linking together of a glucose unit and a unit of its isomer **fructose.** (What, then, is the molecular formula of sucrose?) Our chief source of sucrose is sugar cane and sugar beets. Most higher plants transport carbohydrate as sucrose. It is very soluble in water and can thus be easily transported in sap.

Starches are large carbohydrate molecules made up of chains of glucose units (Fig. 7-4). We use the term **polymer** to describe chainlike molecules of this sort. The "links" in the chain are **monomers.** Most natural starches contain both unbranched chains of several hundred glucose units (amylose) and branched chains totalling more than a thousand glucose units (amylopectin). Because of the many sugar units present in starches, they are called **polysaccharides.**

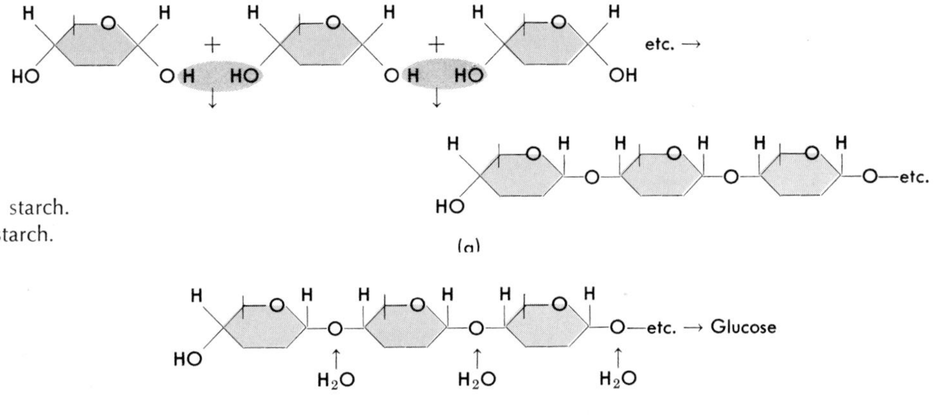

Fig. 7-4

(a) Synthesis of starch.
(b) Hydrolysis of starch.

(a)

(b)

Starches are important because they serve as a storage form of sugar. Surplus sugar can be converted into starch, which is insoluble, and stored. This takes place in both plants and animals. Man's greatest source of carbohydrates is plant starch. Most of the world's population satisfies its energy needs with the starches of rice, wheat, corn and potatoes. Before starches can be absorbed into the body, however, they must be digested. This simply means that the long chains are broken back down into their sugar links. This process requires both water and starch-digesting enzymes called **amylases.** With the aid of amylases, water molecules enter at each oxygen bridge, re-forming free sugar molecules (Fig. 7-4). The process of breaking up a molecule by inserting water is called **hydrolysis.**

Amylases hydrolyze starches into the disaccharide maltose. Another enzyme, maltase, hydrolyzes the maltose molecule into two glucose molecules.

When man takes in more glucose than he needs, he converts some (not all) of the excess to starch. This starch, as well as that produced by other animals, differs somewhat in its properties from plant starch. For this reason it is often given a special name, **glycogen.** The main difference between glycogen and plant starch lies in the pattern of branching. There seem to be no straight chain molecules in glycogen like the amylose chains in plant starches.

Man stores glycogen in his muscles and in his liver. In these locations, it is quickly available for breakdown into glucose and subsequent energy production. Glycogen is not, however, the major storage form of energy in man. We depend on fat deposits for most of our energy reserves. There are some animals, though, that do rely almost entirely on glycogen stores. These are apt to be animals such as mussels (mollusks) that regularly undergo periods of oxygen shortage. The advantages of glycogen as a source of energy when oxygen is lacking will be discussed in Chapter 11.

3. Cellulose

Cellulose is another important polysaccharide. It is universally found in plants and is, in fact, their chief structural material. The rigidity of plants is a consequence of the large quantities of cellulose they produce. Wood is chiefly cellulose. Cotton and the paper upon which this book is printed are almost pure cellulose. The extensive use of cellulose as a structural material in plants makes it without doubt the most prevalent organic molecule on earth.

Although cellulose is rightly associated with plants, it has also been found in some animals. The sea squirts (subphylum Tunicata) are encased in an envelope of cellulose. Small quantities of cellulose have even been found in the skin of aging humans.

Like amylopectin molecules, cellulose molecules consist of long, branched chains of glucose units. A single cellulose molecule may contain over three thousand of these. Cellulose differs from starch, however, in the way the glucose molecules are attached to one another. In starches, the glucose molecules are all oriented in the same fashion. In cellulose the orientation of the glucose units alternates from one glucose molecule to the next (Fig. 7-5).

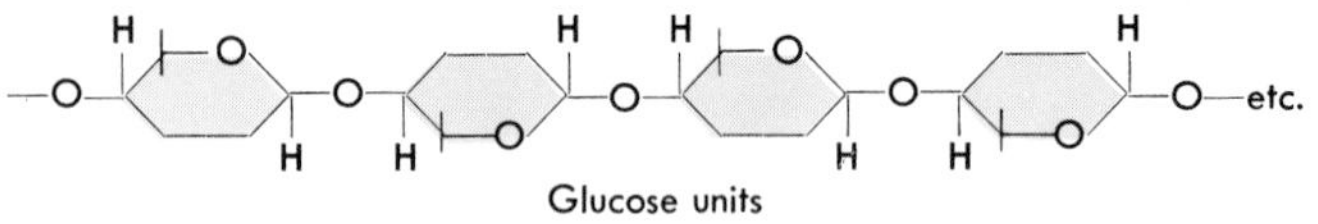

Glucose units

Fig. 7-5   Structure of cellulose. Compare its structure with that of starch (**Fig. 7-4**).

This difference in molecular structure is sufficiently great that amylases are unable to hydrolyze cellulose. Cellulose can be digested by **cellulases,** which are produced by certain bacteria, protozoans, and a few invertebrates such as terrestrial snails and some insects. What of the cows, rabbits, and termites which seem to thrive on cellulose? In each of these cases, the cellulose digestion is accomplished by microorganisms living within the animal's digestive system. The rumen of cows and the caecum of rabbits are large pouches in which food is stored while bacteria digest cellulose with their cellulases. Both the bacteria and their mammalian host then absorb the sugars produced. Termites depend upon the flagellate *Trichonympha* to carry out the same function in their gut.

Although cellulose is not digested by man, it does form a valuable part of his diet by providing bulk and thus giving his digestive tract something to work on. Preparations of purified cellulose are even marketed for use by people who feel that added "roughage" in their diets will stimulate movement of the bowels and cure constipation.

7-2   FATS

Fat molecules are also composed solely of carbon, hydrogen, and oxygen atoms. In contrast to carbohydrates, however, the ratio of hydrogen atoms to oxygen atoms is a great deal higher than 2:1. Tristearin, to take a common example of a fat, has the molecular formula $C_{57}H_{110}O_6$.

The high proportion of hydrogen in a fat molecule is significant in two ways. First, it tells us that the molecule is much less oxidized than a carbohydrate molecule. This means that a given weight of fat stores a good deal more energy than the same weight of carbohydrate. Pound for pound, fats provide the most concentrated energy reserve available to the organism.

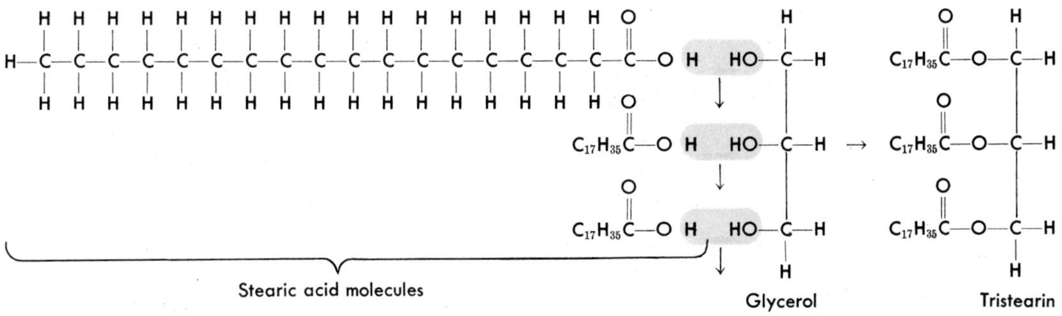

Stearic acid molecules   Glycerol   Tristearin

(a)

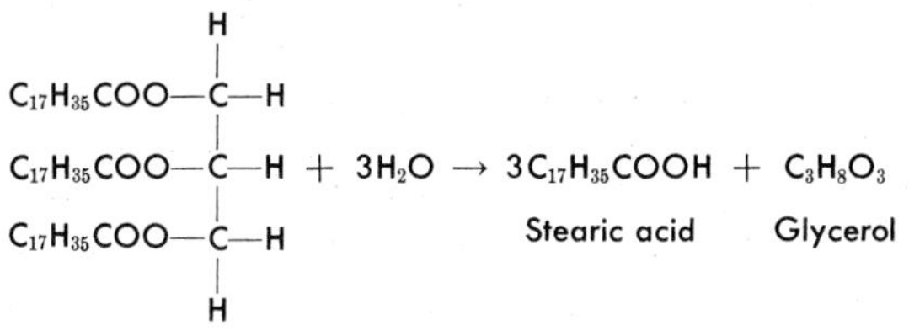

$$C_{17}H_{35}COO-C-H$$
$$C_{17}H_{35}COO-C-H + 3H_2O \rightarrow 3C_{17}H_{35}COOH + C_3H_8O_3$$
$$C_{17}H_{35}COO-C-H$$

Stearic acid   Glycerol

(b)

Fig. 7-6

(a) Synthesis of tristearin, a fat. The three stearic acid molecules are bracketed. (b) Hydrolysis of tristearin.

The energy locked up in fats is released when the molecule is oxidized in the process of respiration. Oxidation of the large amount of hydrogen in the molecule results in the production of a correspondingly large amount of water. Although really a by-product of the process of respiration, this water may be important to an animal living in a very dry environment. The kangaroo rat of our Southwestern deserts, along with many other mammals and birds that live in arid regions, consumes a high proportion of fats in its diet. The water produced during the oxidation of these fats satisfies a substantial part of the water needs of the animal. In fact, kangaroo rats normally do not drink water even when it is available to them. The water needs of the unhatched chick are also met to a large extent by the oxidation of fats.

The fat molecule itself is made up of four parts: a **glycerol** molecule and three molecules of **fatty acids.** Each of the three —OH groups on the glycerol molecule is capable of reacting with the

$$-C-OH$$

group of a fatty acid molecule. A molecule of water is removed in this process, too, and the fatty acid becomes attached to the glycerol molecule (Fig. 7-6). The three fatty acids in a single fat molecule may be all alike or they may be different. They may contain as few as four carbon atoms or as many as 24. Curiously enough, the number of carbon atoms in the fatty acid is almost always an even number. 16-carbon (palmitic acid) and 18-carbon (stearic acid) fatty acid molecules are the most common in fats.

Just as polysaccharides can be hydrolyzed into their constituent sugar units, so fats can be hydrolyzed into glycerol and fatty acids (Fig. 7-6). Water is necessary, of course, as well as an enzyme called a **lipase.** The hydrolysis of fat is an important step in the digestive process.

Some fatty acids have one or more double bonds in the molecule. Fats formed from these molecules are known as unsaturated fats. As they are likely to melt at temperatures below room temperature, we call them oils. Cottonseed oil and olive oil are two examples. These oils should not be confused with oils derived from petroleum. Their chemical nature is quite different.

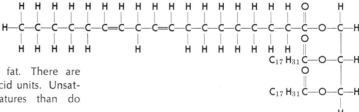

Fig. 7-7

Structure of trilinolein, an unsaturated fat. There are two double bonds in each of the fatty acid units. Unsaturated fats liquefy at lower temperatures than do saturated fats and hence are called oils.

Humans and other animals are able to manufacture fats from carbohydrates. Most "fat" people get so from eating large amounts of carbohydrates rather than fats. This does not mean that we do not need fats in our diet. We do seem to need some natural fats, particularly unsaturated ones like trilinolein (Fig. 7-7). Doctors and laymen alike are anxiously awaiting new information on the relative effects of saturated and unsaturated fats on the development of diseases of the heart and circulatory system.

Fig. 7-8

The nut is supported by three pins.

Plants manufacture some fats. These are stored within cells in the form of clear oil droplets or globules. Fats are insoluble in water and this enables them to be stored easily in this way even though surrounded by watery cell contents. Most plant fats are stored in seeds, although other plant parts such as fruits and bulbs may be used, too. Cottonseeds, peanuts, flax seeds, and soybeans all contain large quantities of oil. Figure 7-8 shows a Brazil nut burning like a candle, thanks to its rich oil stores.

Animals store fat in large clear globules within the cells of fatty, **adipose** tissue. Not only does adipose tissue thus serve as a storage area for fats but it has other useful functions as well. The layer that lies just beneath the skin provides heat insulation for the body. (This layer is thicker in women than in men and accounts for women's greater tolerance to cold. The slower rate at which heat passes from their bodies into the surrounding water enables women to swim happily while their male companions are blue and shivering with cold.) Adipose tissue also surrounds most of our internal organs. Its soft, spongy texture absorbs the shock of sudden blows and thus protects our vital organs from mechanical damage.

It used to be thought that fat deposits were a deep storage form of energy, put down only when surplus food was ingested and used only in times of partial starvation. We now know that this is not true. The fat deposits in the body are constantly being formed and broken down again. There is, of course, a net accumulation of stored fat during times of plenty and a net loss during times of starvation. But even with no net gain or loss, there is a constant exchange of fats between the storage depots and the rest of the body. It has been estimated that an adult mouse replaces up to one-half of all its fat deposits in a week.

How has this discovery been made? By feeding mice "labelled" fats, it is possible to follow what happens to them in the body. The "label" identifies the fat and distinguishes it from the fats that were already present. The labels used are isotopes— atoms of an element that differ in the number of neutrons present in the nucleus. By being synthesized with isotopes not found naturally, the fat becomes "labelled." Remember that the number of electrons is the same in all isotopes of a given element, so that the chemical behavior of isotopically labelled compounds is quite similar to that of the natural compound. The presence of the isotope can, however, be detected by its different weight or, in some cases, by the fact that it is radioactive. The constant deposition and withdrawal of fat from the body's fat storage areas was discovered by using fat labelled with deuterium. Deuterium is an isotope of hydrogen which has a neutron as well as a proton in the nucleus. This makes the weight of the atom twice that of the common isotope of hydrogen (Section 6-2). Its use in studying fat metabolism is described in Reference 1 at the end of the chapter.

Fats are insoluble in water and it seems strange that such a constant exchange takes place between the fat deposits of the body and the watery contents of cells, blood, etc. Probably fats must first be converted into a water-soluble form before they can be mobilized. This water-soluble form is achieved by substituting a phosphorus-containing molecule for one of the three fatty acid molecules. The resulting substance, a **phospholipid,** is then free to be transported in the watery environment of the body.

Phospholipids play other vital roles in the organism. In close association with protein, they participate in forming some of the structural components of living cells. In man, the brain is especially rich in phospholipids.

There is another way in which fats can be converted into a form which will mix with water. This is to emulsify them. **Emulsions** are colloids containing colloidal size droplets of one liquid suspended in another. Homogenized milk is an example of an emulsion of fat (cream) in the watery portion ("skim milk") of the milk. In order to keep the droplets of an emulsion from meeting and combining, it is necessary to coat them with a third substance, an emulsifying agent. Soaps and synthetic detergents are effective emulsifying agents for fats. We use these substances to emulsify fat deposits on our bodies and dishes. In the form of an emulsion, the fat can then be easily rinsed away.

A good deal of the fat we eat is first emulsified in the digestive tract before it is used by the body. The body's emulsifying agent is a fluid called bile which is secreted into the intestine by the liver. The active ingredients in bile are substances called bile salts. They are members of a large group of closely related chemical compounds, the **steroids.** All steroids contain a skeleton of seventeen carbon atoms organized into four rings (Fig. 7-9). Each different steroid has its own side groups attached to several points on the skeleton. The most abundant steroid in the human body is cholesterol (about one-half pound per person). From it are synthesized the bile salts, one of our vitamins, and a number of important hormones. All the sex hormones, of which progesterone is one (Fig. 7-9), are steroids.

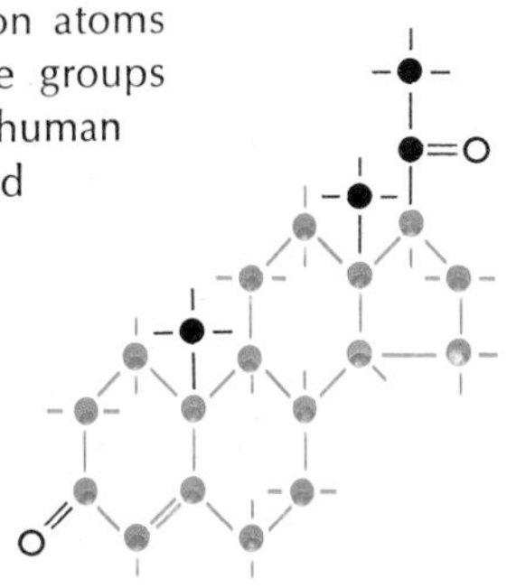

Fig. 7-9

Progesterone, an important sex hormone in women. Like all steroids, it is constructed from a skeleton of 17 carbon atoms (shown in color). Each short dash represents a hydrogen atom.

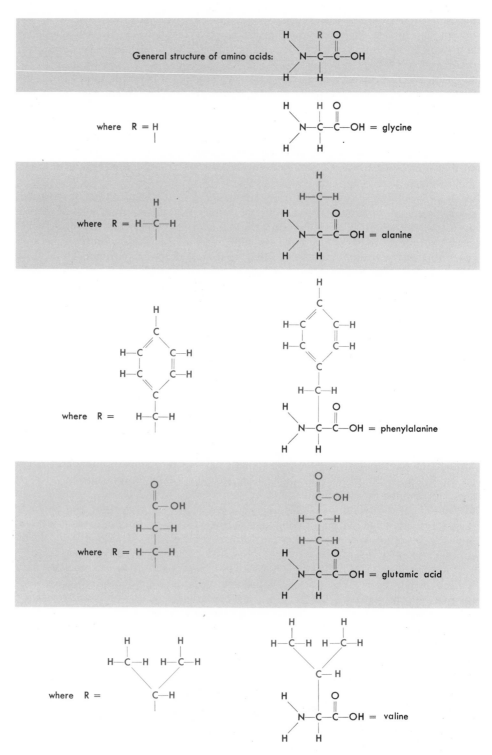

Fig. 7-10   Structures of five common amino acids. There are some 15 others generally found in proteins.

Proteins are among the most complex of all the organic compounds. They are made up of macromolecules which contain carbon, hydrogen, oxygen, and nitrogen atoms. Sulfur atoms are usually present, too. Certain proteins contain phosphorus or some trace metal element, such as iron or copper, in addition to the other elements.

Most protein molecules are so large and complex that it has not yet been possible to learn much about their structure except their size and, in some cases, their molecular formula. Beta-lactoglobulin, a protein with a relatively small molecule, has the molecular formula $C_{1864}H_{3012}O_{576}N_{468}S_{21}$. Its molecular weight is about 42,000. Many proteins are even larger than this. Hemocyanin, an oxygen-carrying pigment found in some crustaceans, has a molecular weight greater than six million.

At first glance, it might seem a hopeless task to learn more about the structure of such enormous molecules. Fortunately, the problem is not quite so insurmountable as it might seem. Despite their great size, protein molecules are built up in an orderly way. They are polymers consisting of long chains of relatively simple monomers called amino acids. There are twenty different kinds of amino acids commonly found in proteins. Each of these is built according to the plan:

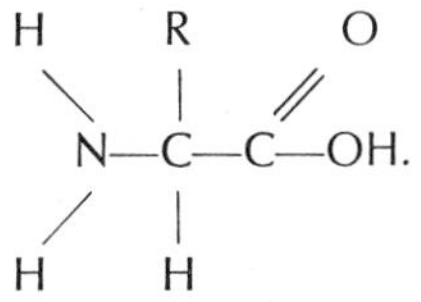

The $-NH_2$ group is called the amino group. The

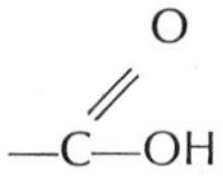

group is the acid group. The chemical nature of R is different for each of the different amino acids. In every case, however, the R group is relatively simple and its structural formula is known (Fig. 7-10).

Amino acids are linked together by the removal of water molecules from between them (Fig. 7-11). Crosslinks between chains are found where sulfur-containing amino

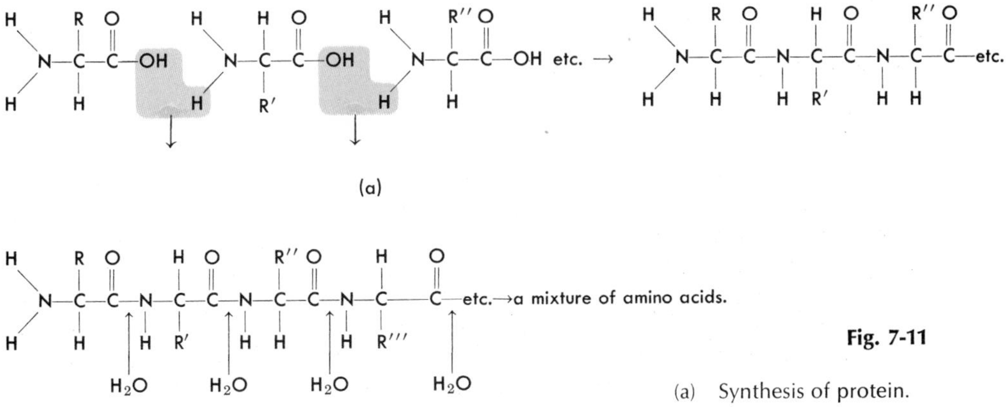

(a)

(b)

Fig. 7-11

(a) Synthesis of protein.
(b) Hydrolysis of protein.

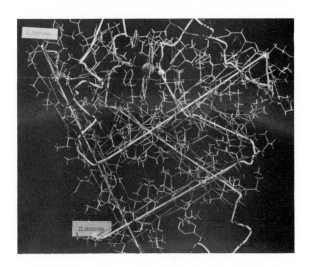

Fig. 7-12

Three-dimensional model of the myoglobin molecule. About 150 amino acids are present in the single, folded chain. The dark sphere represents the iron atom at the center of the prosthetic group, heme. The light sphere represents a molecule of water. (Courtesy of Dr. John C. Kendrew.)

acids are present. The chains are also folded. Figure 7–12 shows a model of the arrangement of the amino acid chain in the myoglobin molecule. This molecule is one-quarter of the size of the hemoglobin molecule, having a molecular weight of 17,000.

Although even the most complex proteins are made up of simple, repeating units of amino acids, we are still a long way from working out detailed structural formulas for them. In fact, it was not until 1954 that the structural formula of the first protein was established. The protein was insulin, one of the most important hormones in our body. Its molecular formula, $C_{254}H_{377}N_{65}O_{75}S_6$, shows that its molecule is small compared with most proteins. Nevertheless, it took Dr. Frederick Sanger and his colleagues at the University of Cambridge in England ten years (1944-1954) to work out the sequence of amino acids and the locations of the crosslinks in this protein. Using clever, but tedious, steps of chemical degradation, they determined the exact sequence of the 51 amino acids present in the molecule (Fig. 7-13). Since their discovery, other workers have applied similar techniques in an effort to work out the structure of still other proteins.

Proteins, like starches and fats, are degraded by hydrolysis. The peptide linkages are opened with the insertion of a molecule of water at that point (Fig. 7-11). This breaks the protein molecule into shorter chains of amino acids called **polypeptides.** Finally the polypeptides are completely hydrolyzed into their constituent amino acids.

Life as we know it could not exist without proteins. They are the chief molecules out of which living cells are made. Some protein molecules are dissolved or suspended in the watery contents of the cell. Others are incorporated into various structures of the cell.

Many cell proteins are found chemically united with other kinds of molecules. These proteins are called **conjugated proteins.** Protein-lipid, protein-nucleic acid and protein-pigment combinations all play important roles in living cells. All enzymes are proteins and many of them are conjugated with smaller molecules (**prosthetic groups**) such as metal-containing pigments and vitamins.

Proteins are also found outside of cells. These extracellular proteins are important supporting and strengthening materials in animals. (Plants differ in this respect from animals. Their cells are supported and strengthened by what extracellular, organic molecules?) Bone, cartilage, tendons, and ligaments are all examples of supporting structures which contain substantial quantities of extracellular proteins, such as collagen. The "cement" which causes animal cells to stick together contains protein, too.

Although we can make statements about the general kinds of proteins found in different organisms, it is important to realize that these proteins may not be exactly alike. Every species manufactures proteins unique to that species. Furthermore, even the individuals within a species may have some protein molecules that are absolutely unique. With the exception of identical twins, we are quite sure that no two human beings, for example, have precisely the same proteins.

At first glance, it seems unbelievable that each individual now living on earth has certain protein molecules unique to him. When you appreciate the great complexity and possibilities for variety in protein molecules, however, this specificity seems more reasonable. Just think for a moment of the large number of words in an English unabridged dictionary. Every one of these is made up from an alphabet of 26 letters. Proteins are made up from an "alphabet" of about twenty amino acids. Then think of the dictionaries in other languages that also use the Roman alphabet. Consider, too, that it is a rare word indeed that contains more than twenty letters. A single protein molecule, on the other hand, may contain thousands of amino acids. These are not arranged in just one dimension, either, as are the letters in a word. Instead, the chains of amino acids are folded into elaborate, three-dimensional shapes. Truly, the number of possible protein molecules is inconceivably large.

The importance of the three-dimensional structure of proteins is nicely illustrated by the phenomenon of **denaturation.** Proteins are quite sensitive to a variety of chemical and physical agents. When exposed to these agents, they may lose their characteristic pattern of folding. This is denaturation. It can occur under conditions that do not affect the actual peptide linkages themselves. Nevertheless, the biochemical properties of the protein may be completely altered. For example, denaturation destroys the activity of enzyme molecules. When the white of an egg cooks, the protein (albumin) is undergoing denaturation.

Proteins can also be used by living organisms as a source of energy. If more protein is consumed in the diet than is needed to satisfy the structural needs of the body (growth and repair), the excess can be used as fuel. After the protein is hydrolyzed into its constituent amino acids, the nitrogen-containing, or amino, portion of these molecules is removed. In man, this process, called **deamination,** occurs chiefly in the liver. The non-nitrogen-containing residue is then oxidized in the same way as carbohydrate and fat materials. This process may even occur with the structural proteins of the body. These thus serve as a third reservoir of energy. In times of starvation, the individual

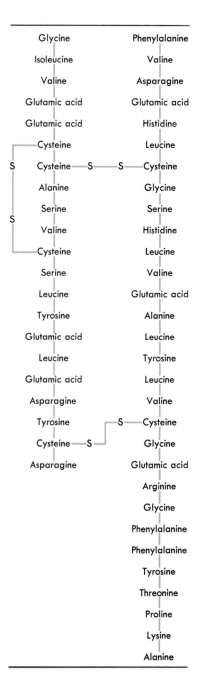

Fig 7-13

Sequence of amino acids in the insulin molecule. The insulin molecule consists of two polypeptide chains held together by sulfur bridges.

first exhausts his stores of glycogen. Next the fat deposits are mobilized and used. If starvation continues, the body proteins are then broken down and used as fuel. This, of course, means a breakdown of the structure of the body itself. The process cannot continue indefinitely. The individual becomes emaciated and death ultimately follows unless he is able to find an outside source of food.

7-4

NUCLEIC ACIDS

Nucleic acid molecules are even larger than protein molecules, with molecular weights that run into the billions. They, too, are polymers. The monomers of nucleic acid molecules are called **nucleotides.** Each consists of three subunits: a sugar, a phosphate, and a nitrogenous base. The sugar and phosphate groups alternate as links in the chain. The nitrogenous bases project out from the axis of the chain, with one base attached to each sugar link (Fig. 7-14).

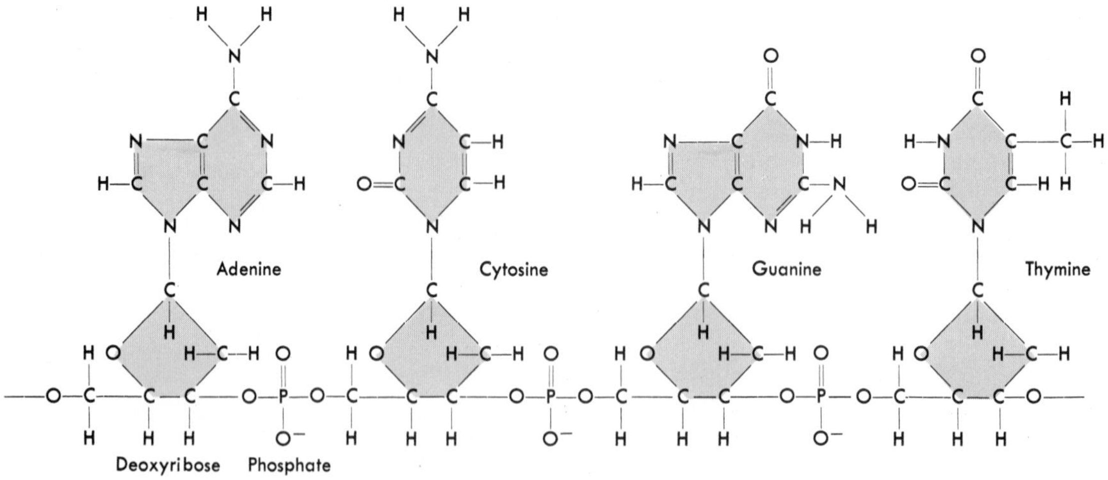

Fig. 7-14   Molecular organization of DNA. In RNA the pyrimidine uracil is found in place of thymine.

There are two distinct kinds of nucleic acid. One is called deoxyribonucleic acid or DNA. The other is ribonucleic acid or RNA. DNA is found localized within the control center of the cell, the nucleus. Some RNA is also found there, but more of it is found in the surrounding cell contents, the cytoplasm.

RNA gets its name from its sugar unit, a five-carbon sugar called ribose. Attached to each ribose unit is one of four possible nitrogenous bases, cytosine, uracil, adenine, and guanine (C, U, A, and G). The first two of these bases are single-ring substances called pyrimidines. The second two are double-ring substances called purines.

The sugar unit in DNA is deoxyribose. As its name suggests, it has one less oxygen atom than ribose. The pyrimidines, cytosine and thymine, and the purines, adenine and guanine (C, T, A, and G), are the bases found in DNA.

Normally, DNA differs from RNA in another important respect. Its molecule is made up of not one, but two chains of alternating sugars and phosphates. These two chains are twisted around each other something like a double spiral staircase (Fig. 7-15). At each sugar, a purine or pyrimidine projects into the "stairwell." Here it joins with the pyrimidine or purine projecting out from the opposite staircase. Weak forces of attraction between these bases are sufficient to hold the two chains together.

The most interesting thing about this structure is that there is not room enough across the "stairwell" for two purines to fit at the same level, and there is too much room for two pyrimidines to meet and bond together. Consequently, a purine on one chain can be paired only with a pyrimidine on the other. Furthermore, the location of the bonds is such that the purine adenine can pair only with thymine. Similarly, guanine always pairs with cytosine. Thus the two interlocking strands of a DNA molecule are complementary to each other. In a real sense, one is the "negative" of the other. If we know the sequence of bases on one strand, we know the sequence of bases on the other.

In recent years many biologists have turned their attention to the nature and role of DNA and the three types of RNA that are found within cells. Their interest stems from an ever-growing conviction that within these molecules resides the information that controls the structure and activities of all organisms and the machinery for translating this information. They see DNA as a master blueprint, written in the code of purine-pyrimidine pairs, for the building and operating of a living organism. They see each of the three major types of RNA as playing an essential role in the execution of the instructions coded within the DNA molecules. (Some of the discoveries that have led to these ideas will be discussed in the next chapter and in Chapter 20.)

Perhaps one day the fundamental nature of life itself can be understood in molecular terms; it begins to look as though the study of the nucleic acids will bring us closer to this goal than ever before.

Fig. 7-15

The Watson-Crick model of DNA structure. The small spheres represent phosphate groups; the open pentagons represent deoxyribose. The solid planar structures represent the purine and pyrimidine bases. (Photo courtesy Dr. Donald M. Reynolds.)

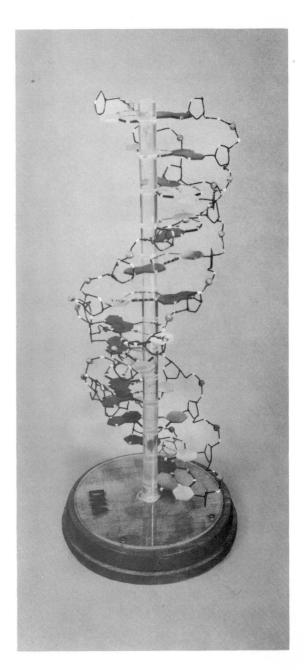

The carbohydrates, fats, proteins, and nucleic acids are the most prevalent organic molecules found in living things. There are others such as organic acids, alcohols, and steroids, that play important roles, too. These are all small molecules, however, and do not contribute to the fixed, structural components of the cell. Furthermore, almost all of them can be synthesized by the organism from one or more of the major kinds of molecules that we have been discussing.

The few organic molecules that an organism cannot manufacture from carbohydrate, fat, protein, or nucleic acid sources are called vitamins. With a few exceptions, green plants have no vitamin requirements as they manufacture every organic molecule they need. Among these, however, are substances that are vitamins for nongreen plants, protists, and animals. It is important to realize that the term vitamin does not refer to a particular chemical group. The only way in which the various vitamins are similar to one another is that (1) they are all organic, (2) they are not used as an energy source or for construction of the cell, and (3) the organism cannot synthesize them from the standard foods in its diet. Note, too, that what may be a vitamin for one organism is not necessarily a vitamin for another.

Vitamins are needed in only very small quantities. Years of research have shown that some of them, at least, are incorporated into enzymes. These vitamins are conjugated as a "prosthetic group" with the protein part of the enzyme. In view of this role, it is not surprising that their presence is vital to the welfare of the organism. If it cannot synthesize them, then it must include them in its diet. If it fails to do so, a **deficiency disease** may result.

Men have suspected for a long time that certain diseases result from special deficiencies in the diet. Years ago on long ocean voyages, when fresh fruits and vegetables might be unavailable for months at a time, sailors became prone to the disease **scurvy.** As early as 1771, Captain Cook made it a practice to carry limes on his voyages. Adding them to the diet of his crew prevented the appearance of scurvy and gave the British sailors a nickname they bear to this day: "limeys."

It was not until this century that scientists began to search for the specific chemical substances that would prevent or cure deficiency diseases. In 1915, the American nutritionists E. V. McCollum and M. J. Davis discovered that both a fat-soluble substance (vitamin A) and a water-soluble substance (vitamin B) were needed for proper growth in laboratory rats.

Since their discovery, other vitamins have been found. Vitamin A has turned out to consist of two different kinds of molecules. Vitamin B has been found to consist of almost a dozen different substances. Today we place these latter in the "B-complex" family of vitamins. They do not, however, have any greater chemical similarities to each other than they do to any of the other vitamins.

Figure 7-16 lists the vitamins that we think are needed by man, the symptoms caused by a deficiency of these vitamins, rich sources of the vitamins, and some supplementary information. In the case of vitamin E (and also some other "vitamins" that are not included in this table), there is some doubt whether the substances are really vitamins for man. Their discovery has come about as a result of diet experiments in laboratory animals like the rat, and it is somewhat risky to apply to man discoveries made in other animals. We know, for example, that the laboratory rat can synthesize its own "vitamin C." (Thus, for the rat, it is not a vitamin.) If we need an external supply of a substance which the rat does not need, is it not possible that the reverse may also be true? In the case of vitamin E, no sound evidence of a deficiency disease in man has been found, although the substance is definitely present in the body (where it seems to participate in the metabolism of unsaturated fatty acids).

VITAMIN	DEFICIENCY DISEASE	SOURCES	OTHER INFORMATION
A	Night blindness	Milk, butter, fish liver oils, carrots, and other vegetables	Precursor in the synthesis of the light-absorbing pigments of the eye Stored in the liver Toxic in large doses
Thiamine (B_1)	Beriberi Damage to nerves and heart	Yeast, meat, unpolished cereal grains	Coenzyme in cellular respiration
Riboflavin (B_2)	Inflammation of the tongue Damage to the eyes General weakness	Liver, eggs, cheese, milk	Prosthetic group of flavoprotein enzymes used in cellular respiration
Nicotinic acid (Niacin)	Pellagra (Damage to skin, lining of intestine and perhaps nerves)	Meat, yeast, milk	Converted into nicotinamide, a precursor of NAD and NADP—two important coenzymes for REDOX reactions in the cell
Folic acid	Anemia	Green leafy vegetables Synthesized by intestinal bacteria	Used in synthesis of coenzymes of nucleic acid metabolism
B_{12}	Pernicious anemia	Liver	Each molecule contains one atom of cobalt.
Ascorbic acid (C)	Scurvy	Citrus fruits, tomatoes, green peppers	May act as a reducing agent in the body
D	Rickets (Abnormal Ca^{++} and $PO_4^{\equiv}$ metabolism resulting in abnormal bone and tooth development)	Fish liver oils, butter, steroid-containing foods irradiated with ultraviolet light	Synthesized in the human skin upon exposure to ultraviolet light Toxic in large doses
E	No deficiency disease known in humans	Egg yolk, salad greens, vegetable oils	–
K	Slow clotting of the blood	Spinach and other green leafy vegetables Synthesized by intestinal bacteria	Necessary for the synthesis of prothrombin, an essential agent in the clotting of blood

Some of the principal vitamins.   **Fig. 7-16**

The problem of determining the vitamin requirements of man is further complicated by the fact that some of them may be stored in the body. Vitamin A, for example, is stored in the liver. Even if vitamin A is excluded from the diet for a period of time, symptoms of deficiency are slow to appear. Another complication is the presence in our large intestine of bacteria which live on organic molecules not absorbed in the small intestine. In the course of their chemical activities, they may produce vitamins which we can then absorb. Vitamin B_{12}, a deficiency of which causes pernicious anemia, is synthesized in this way. Man's need for this vitamin was long obscured by the fact that his intestinal bacteria were relieving him of the necessity of including the vitamin in his diet.

One of the B-complex vitamins of particular interest is **nicotinic acid.** (Food manufacturers who "fortify" their products with this vitamin prefer to use the term *niacin.* They are concerned about the associations that the consumer might make when he sees the words *nicotinic* and *acid* on their packages.) Nicotinic acid is sometimes also called the *pellagra-preventive* factor because it is effective in doing just that. Pellagra is a disease characterized by severe damage to the tongue, skin, and digestive tract, accompanied by diarrhea and even serious mental disturbance. It is a disease of poverty-stricken areas. At one time, it was very common in the rural areas of the South, where the main items of diet were corn bread, molasses, salt pork, and black-eyed peas. Unfortunately, none of these foods contain nicotinic acid or any other B-complex vitamin. In fact, corn may even contain an antivitamin, acetylpyridine. Antivitamins are substances with molecules closely resembling those of vitamins but lacking their activity and interfering with their action. Presumably, when acetylpyridine is present in the body, it competes with any nicotinic acid present for incorporation into an important coenzyme. Unfortunately, the coenzyme formed with acetylpyridine cannot carry out the vital functions that are carried out when nicotinic acid is used. Laboratory animals develop pellagralike symptoms when acetylpyridine is added to their diet. A glance at Fig. 7-17 will show why the body might well confuse one molecule with the other.

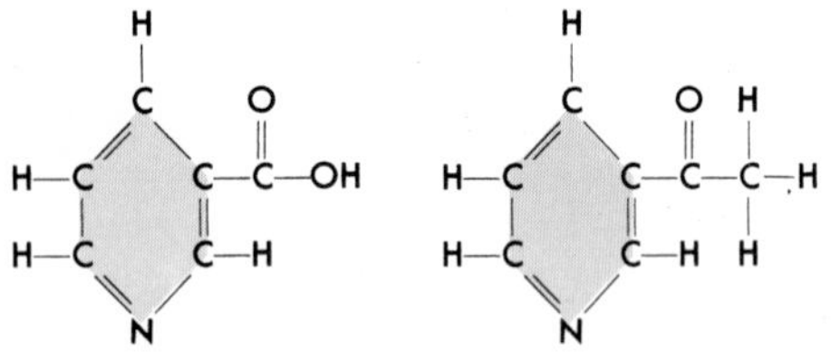

Fig. 7-17

Structure of nicotinic acid and acetylpyridine. Nicotinic acid is one of man's vitamins. Disease symptoms are produced by either a deficiency of this vitamin or administration of the antivitamin, acetylpyridine. The body seems to be misled by the similarity of the two molecules.

Nicotinic acid   Acetylpyridine

Vitamin D is not necessarily a vitamin at all. We can synthesize it if we expose our skin to rays of ultraviolet light. Bright sunlight is rich in these rays, but they are completely filtered out when the light passes through window glass. A deficiency of this vitamin can occur in people who get neither sufficient exposure to the sun nor the vitamin in their diet. (Only fish liver oils, butter, and egg yolks contain appreciable amounts of this vitamin.) The deficiency is characterized by a faulty use of calcium and phosphorus in the body. In children the teeth and bones develop poorly, resulting in the condition known as rickets. Vitamin D is a steroid (Section 7-2). Its synthesis in our skin occurs as a result of the action of ultraviolet rays on a closely related steroid, ergosterol. Although most foods do not contain vitamin D, many of them do contain steroids such as ergosterol. In 1924 Dr. Harry Steenbock and Alfred F. Hess discovered that these foods could be made rich in vitamin D by simply irradiating them with ultraviolet light. Milk, otherwise quite lacking in vitamin D, is often fortified in this manner.

The discovery of the vitamins has created a great interest in the general subject of diet. This has caused deficiency diseases to become far less common than they used to be, at least in areas where the standard of living is reasonably high. Unfortunately, the great interest in vitamins has also had drawbacks. Many people now consume commercial vitamin preparations when there is absolutely no medical reason for doing so. Apparently, they feel that if a little of something is good, more must be better. This is not true of the vitamins. Not only does the annual expenditure in this country of millions of dollars on the purchase of vitamins represent a great waste of money, but it can lead to unpleasant complications. Excess intake of vitamin A or D is quite apt to produce disease symptoms. A glance at the list of vitamin sources in Fig. 7-16 should make it quite clear that a normal, well-balanced diet (including fresh fruits, vegetables, meat, and milk) provides all the vitamins that most of us need. Only in special circumstances do our diets need to be supplemented with vitamin pills or "drops." In these cases, a doctor should be consulted and his advice followed.

MINERALS 7-6

Although living organisms are distinguished by the complex array of organic molecules of which they are made, inorganic substances play an important part, too. Aside from C, H, O, N, and S, most of the elements found in living things are present in the form of ions of salts. These are the inorganic minerals of the body. Some of these minerals are quite insoluble in water and form solid deposits. Many organisms exploit these as supporting and protecting structures. Calcium carbonate ($CaCO_3$) is the principal constituent of the shells of mollusks and the foraminifera (Sections 5-6 and 3-2). The glassy material silica (SiO_2) is used in the shells of diatoms and radiolarians. The bones of vertebrate skeletons contain calcium carbonate, large amounts of calcium phosphate [$Ca_3(PO_4)_2$] and some magnesium and fluoride ions. All these substances provide rigid support and protection for soft tissues of the body. Inorganic ions also carry out other important roles in living things. We will examine some of these in Chapter 9.

WATER 7-7

Water is also an inorganic substance and an indispensable constituent of life. Figure 7-1 shows that 66% of the weight of the human body is water. The water content of most cells is about the same, although some of the jellyfishes (phylum Cnidaria) are more than 90% water.

Water has several important properties that make it an ideal constituent of living things. One of these is that it remains liquid over the range of temperatures generally found on earth. In liquid form it is an excellent solvent for thousands of other substances, both organic and inorganic. Its liquid nature and great solvent power make it unexcelled as a transport medium. Blood, which is 90% water, serves to transport materials throughout our body. The fact that water dissolves so many substances means that these substances can be brought together in the form of individual molecules and ions. In this form, reactions between different substances can occur quickly. Water thus serves as the medium in which almost every chemical reaction in living things takes place. Water is also a reactant and/or product of many chemical reactions in living organisms. (Can you name one?)

Another important property of water is the slowness with which it changes temperature or changes from solid (ice) to liquid, or liquid to gas, as heat is added.

It takes more heat to accomplish these changes with water than with almost any other substance known. (Our unit of heat, the calorie, is, in fact, defined as the quantity of heat needed to raise one gram of water one degree Celsius—see table on page 748.) This property of water is extremely important to life. It means that the temperature of living organisms changes relatively slowly despite sudden temperature changes in the environment. The great amount of heat absorbed when water vaporizes is exploited in sweating. Evaporation of water from the skin absorbs heat from the body, thus cooling it. Not only do the thermal properties of water affect organisms directly, but they also bring about a moderating effect in the environment. Freshwater and marine organisms are subject to a far smaller range of temperatures than land-living animals of the same region. Even land-living animals benefit from the temperature-moderating effect of nearby bodies of water. The ocean's slow absorption of heat in the summer and slow release of heat in the winter tend to reduce violent extremes of temperature in coastal regions. It is no accident that record low temperatures as well as record high temperatures are made in inland areas such as central Siberia, and central North America.

Even when water does get cold enough to freeze, the ice that is formed is less dense than the water, and thus floats on top of the water. This enables aquatic organisms to remain surrounded by water under the ice and also provides for speedy melting of the ice in the spring. The solid form of most substances is more dense than the liquid. It is interesting to speculate on what life in the "temperate" regions of the earth would be like if water were not an unusual substance in this respect.

In this chapter we have examined some of the chemical substances of which living things are composed. In the next chapter, we will try to learn how these chemical substances are organized to make up the various structures of the basic unit of life itself, the cell.

EXERCISES AND PROBLEMS

1 Pound for pound, what food yields the most metabolic water when oxidized?

2 What element is found in all proteins but in no oils?

3 Summarize the importance of water to living things.

4 What is a vitamin?

5 How does RNA differ·from DNA?

6 Write the structural formula for the neutral fat tripalmitin (palmitic acid = $C_{15}H_{31}COOH$).

7 Write the structural formula for the tripeptide containing glycine — alanine — phenylalanine.

8 Show by means of structural formulas the hydrolysis of the tripeptide described in Question 7.

9 Distinguish between saturated and unsaturated fats.

10 Name an isomer of glucose; of sucrose.

11 What is the sequence in which the organic molecules of the body are consumed for energy during periods of starvation?

REFERENCES

1 Schoenheimer, R., and D. Rittenberg, "Deuterium as an Indicator in the Study of Intermediary Metabolism," *Great Experiments in Biology,* ed. by M. L. Gabriel and S. Fogel, Prentice-Hall, Inc., 1955. Explains how deuterium is used to trace the fate of dietary fats in the body.

2 Doty, P., "Proteins," *Scientific American,* Reprint No. 7, September, 1957. Their chemical and physical make-up.

3 Thompson, E. O. P., "The Insulin Molecule," *Scientific American,* Reprint No. 42, May, 1955. Describes the techniques used to determine the *chemical* structure of the insulin molecule.

4 Kendrew, J. C., "The Three-Dimensional Structure of a Protein Molecule," *Scientific American,* Reprint No. 121, December, 1961. Describes the techniques used to determine the *physical* structure of the myoglobin molecule.

5 Crick, F. H. C., "Nucleic Acids," *Scientific American,* Reprint No. 54, September, 1957. The author shared a Nobel prize for his work in deducing the organization of nucleic acid molecules.

CHAPTER 8 THE CELLULAR BASIS OF LIFE

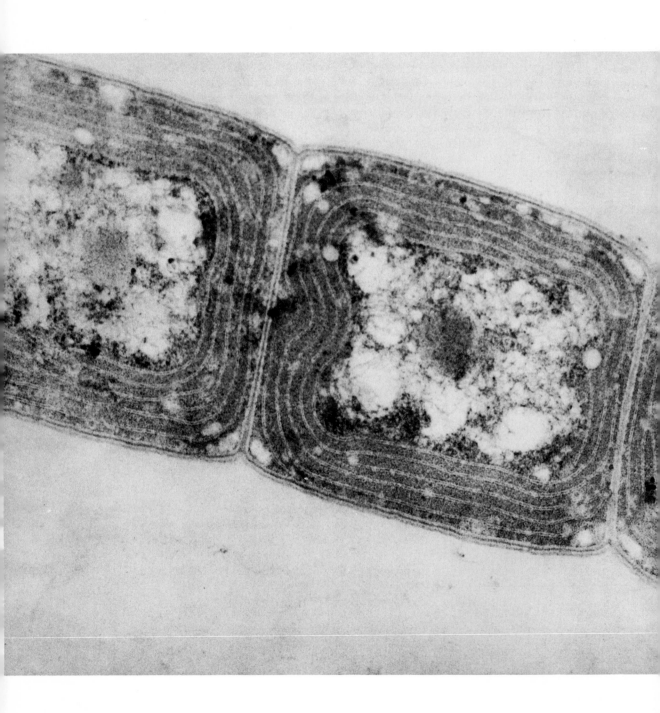

The carbohydrate, lipid, protein, nucleic acid, and other molecules that make up living things are not themselves alive. It is only when these molecules become organized in precise ways that the phenomenon of life appears. The minimum organization of this matter that can live is called the cell.

THE CELL "THEORY" 8-1

We owe the term *cell* to the research of the Englishman, Robert Hooke. In 1665, he told of examining thin slivers of cork under his microscope and finding them to be made up of many neatly arranged little chambers (Fig. 8-1). He called these chambers *cells*. All that Hooke saw, however, were the cellulose walls laid down by once-living material. Today we use the term *cell* to include the active, living contents of such chambers. Sometimes the term *protoplast* is used when one wishes to emphasize that the active materials within any outer covering or wall are being considered.

The term *protoplast* is itself derived from the word *proto-plasm*. Protoplasm is the material that makes up the proto-plast. The term is falling into disuse, however, because no single material *does* make up the protoplast. As we have seen, living material is composed of a large variety of different molecules. There is no single living substance. Actually, the word can still be useful to the biologist, but only as a shorter equivalent of "living material" or "the molecules that make up living things." In this sense, one can speak of growth resulting in an increase in the amount of protoplasm. On the other hand, one should not use the term as though it referred to a single, specific substance. To say that "living things are made of protoplasm" in the sense that one says "sand is made of silica (SiO_2)" is as meaningless as to say that "television sets are made of videoplasm."

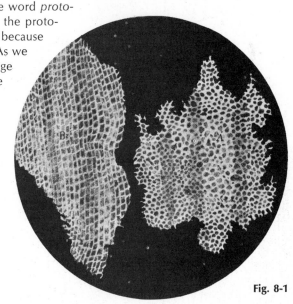

Fig. 8-1

Robert Hooke's drawings of the cellular structure of cork were published in 1665. (Courtesy Bettmann Archive.)

The idea that the cell is the fundamental unit of which all living things are constructed grew out of the work of the German botanist Schleiden and the German zoologist Schwann. Schleiden trained his microscope on a wide variety of plant structures and in every case found that they were made of cells. Schwann made the same discovery in his microscopic examination of animal parts. Their dual discovery, which was set forth in 1839, is called the cell theory. It is not really a theory, though, but an observable fact (with a few exceptions—see Section 8-17) of nature.

◄ Cells of the blue-green alga *Plectonema boryanum*. While the cells of this organism do not have many of the structures described in this chapter, they are nonetheless exceedingly intricate in their organization and capable of carrying out all the functions of life (45,000 X, courtesy Kenneth M. Smith and R. Malcolm Brown, Jr.).

SIZES AND SHAPES

Cells occur in a variety of sizes and shapes. Eggs are single cells and most of them can be seen easily with the unaided eye. This is because of the bulky food reserves that they contain. Some of the larger unicellular protists are just visible to the naked eye. An amoeba cell, some 300μ across, is about the size of the periods printed on this page. Tissue cells are generally microscopic. In man, they may be as small as the red blood corpuscles, which are 7.5μ in diameter, or as large as the cells lining the inner surface of the cheek, which are some ten times that size. The smallest bacteria are just under 1μ in diameter, while some of the smallest mycoplasmas are only a tenth of that. The mycoplasmas probably represent the smallest size a cell can be and still have all the attributes of life (Fig. 8-2).

Cells vary markedly in shape as well as size. The shape of a cell is usually a clear reflection of the function it carries out in the organism. Nerve cells, which must transmit electrical impulses over long distances, have long extensions, in some cases several feet in length. Muscle cells are elongated so that the force of contraction can be exerted efficiently in one direction. Epithelial cells are flattened in the plane of the surface they are covering (Fig. 8-14). The supporting cells of a plant have thick walls. Where masses of cells are simply packed together, they assume the shape of a polyhedron, a solid with many faces. This shape permits close packing of the cells without a large amount of space between them.

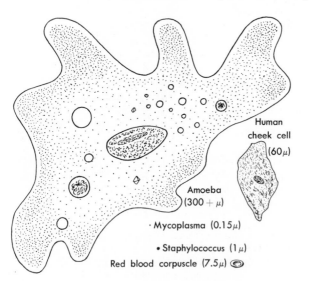

Human cheek cell (60μ)

Amoeba (300 + μ)

· Mycoplasma (0.15μ)

• Staphylococcus (1μ)

Red blood corpuscle (7.5μ) ◎

Fig. 8-2

Comparative sizes of various cells. The amoeba is just visible to the unaided eye. Mycoplasmas can be seen clearly only under the electron microscope.

THE CELL MEMBRANE

The outer surface of all protoplasts is bounded by a very thin, elastic membrane. It is so thin (75–100 A*) that its structure can be observed only under the electron microscope.

The cell membrane provides an important barrier between the interior of the cell and the exterior. Water and many other small molecules pass through it quite easily. On the other hand, many ions such as the sodium ion (Na$^+$) and large molecules such as protein molecules pass through with greater difficulty. A membrane that permits the free passage of some materials and not others is called a semi- or differentially permeable membrane. The permeability of the cell membrane changes with changing conditions and this suggests that it is no passive barrier but exerts a selective action on which materials pass through it.

---

* One angstrom (A) = $10^{-4}μ$ = 0.1 mμ.

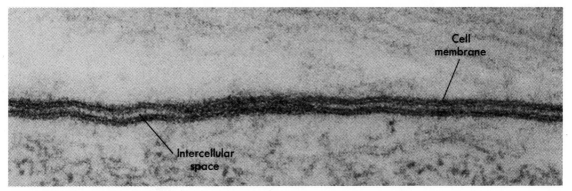

Cell membranes (140,000 X). The membranes of *two* adjoining cells are shown here. The triple-layer construction of each of these "unit" membranes shows clearly. (From Fawcett: *The Cell: Its Organelles and Inclusions,* W.B. Saunders Co., 1966.)

Fig. 8-3

Chemical and physical studies of the cell membrane lead to the conclusion that it is made up of three layers, of roughly equal thickness, sandwiched together. The outer layer seems to be composed chiefly of protein molecules. The middle layer is actually a double layer of phospholipid molecules (see Section 7-2). The inner layer is another protein layer. The protein layers account for the elasticity of the membrane, since the folded protein molecules that make them up can be stretched a moderate amount. The lipid layer accounts for the ease with which many fat-soluble molecules pass through the cell membrane.

The picture of the cell membrane that has been derived from chemical and physical studies has been nicely supported by electron micrographs. Figure 8-3 shows the membranes of two adjacent cells. The sandwich construction of the membranes is clearly visible.

Membranes of this construction bound the cells of all organisms: protists, plants, and animals. Membranes of similar, often identical, construction are also found within the interior of cells. Here they serve to establish a variety of special compartments. In fact, the protein-lipid-protein membrane seems to be such a fundamental structural unit throughout the cell that it has been given a special name: the **unit membrane.**

Except in the bacteria and blue-green algae, there are two major compartments of the cell, the cytoplasm and the nucleus.

THE NUCLEUS   **8-4**

The nucleus is separated from the cytoplasm by a pair of unit membranes. The envelope thus formed is not continuous but, as can be seen in Fig. 8-4, contains pores. These probably permit materials to pass between the nucleus and the cytoplasm.

Within the nuclear membrane there is a semifluid medium in which are suspended the **chromosomes.** Usually these are present as very elongated structures and cannot be easily observed under the light microscope. Sometimes the term *chromatin* is used to describe them when they are in this condition.

When a cell is preparing to divide into two cells, the appearance of the chromosomes changes. The long thin strands coil up into thickened, dense bodies, which (with the help of an appropriate stain) are easily visible in the light microscope (Fig.

Fig. 8-4 The nucleus and surrounding cytoplasm of a cell from the pancreas of a bat (18,000 X). Note the double-layer construction of the nuclear membrane and the pores in it. What other cell structures can you identify? (Electron micrograph courtesy of Dr. Don W. Fawcett.)

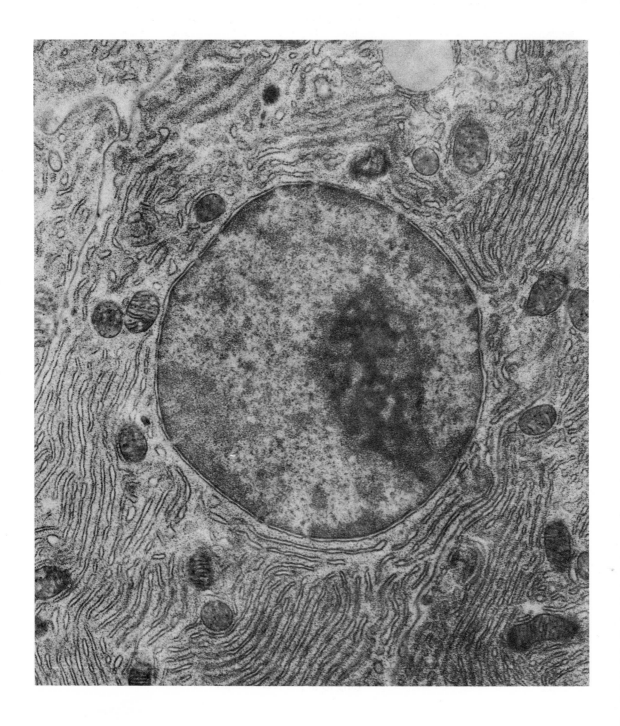

8-13). During the process of cell division, the chromosomes are distributed in precisely equal numbers to the two daughter cells.

Chemically, the chromosomes are made up of DNA and protein. We do not yet know whether a single chromosome contains only a single DNA molecule or many of them. The protein is a special type called *histone*.

During the period between cell divisions, when the chromosomes are in the extended state, one or more of them may have a large, spherical body attached. This body, the **nucleolus,** is easily visible in the light microscope. Here are synthesized several kinds of RNA and protein molecules (including histones). Some of the RNA manufactured here is assembled into **ribosomes.** These tiny bodies are essential for protein synthesis both here and elsewhere in the cell.

The nucleus functions as the control center of the cell. Our appreciation of its role has come from many experiments and observations. In particular, the development of micromanipulators has enabled cytologists to remove or transplant nuclei from single cells and to study the results of these operations. If the nucleus is removed from an amoeba, the organism continues to live for a few days. It cannot reproduce, however, and eventually it dies. That it is the loss of the nucleus which causes this and not just mechanical damage from the operation can be shown by piercing an amoeba with the microtools but not actually removing the nucleus. Such an amoeba recovers fully from this experimental procedure.

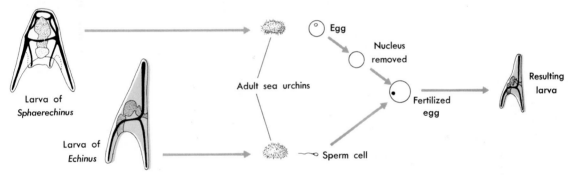

Boveri's experiment, which demonstrated the importance of the nucleus in controlling the cell. An *Echinus* nucleus in *Sphaerechinus* cytoplasm resulted in a larva with *Echinus* characteristics.   **Fig. 8-5**

Even before the invention of micromanipulators, the importance of the nucleus in determining what the cytoplasm does had been demonstrated by the German biologist Theodor Boveri. By vigorous shaking, Boveri was able to remove the nucleus from the eggs of a species of sea urchin of the genus *Sphaerechinus*. He then allowed these "enucleated" eggs to be fertilized by sperm from sea urchins of the genus *Echinus*. Sperm cells are much smaller than egg cells. They consist of little more than a nucleus and a tail to propel it. In the process of fertilization, the nucleus penetrates the egg. Thus fertilization of enucleated *Sphaerechinus* eggs by *Echinus* sperm resulted in the substitution of one kind of nucleus for another. The stimulus of fertilization caused the egg to undergo cell division and it developed into a sea urchin larva. A glance at Fig. 8-5 shows that this larva possessed the traits of the *Echinus* species rather than of the *Sphaerechinus* species. Although *Echinus* contributed little more than a single tiny nucleus to the system, this nucleus caused the great mass of *Sphaerechinus* cytoplasm to develop according to the *Echinus* blueprint.

8-5   THE CYTOPLASM

The term *cytoplasm* suffers from much the same defect as the term *protoplasm*. Cytoplasm is a complex, heterogeneous material. Basically, it consists of a rather watery medium, the "ground substance," in which is suspended a variety of distinct structures. The functions of the cytoplasm are, for all practical purposes, the functions of the structures suspended in it. We will now examine these.

8-6   RIBOSOMES

Among the smallest structures suspended in the cytoplasm are the ribosomes. These roughly-spherical bodies are so small (150 A) that they can be seen only under the electron microscope (Fig. 8-4). They are composed of RNA and protein. All the proteins of the cell, including all enzymes, are synthesized by the ribosomes. As we shall see in Chapter 20, the ribosomes literally carry out the instructions contained within the DNA code of the nucleus.

The ribosomes that are engaged in synthesizing proteins for use within the cell are distributed randomly in the ground substance of the cell. However, many cells, such as those of the liver and pancreas, also synthesize proteins that are secreted *outside* the cell. The ribosomes that synthesize these proteins are found attached to the membranes of the endoplasmic reticulum.

8-7   THE ENDOPLASMIC RETICULUM

The endoplasmic reticulum is an elaborate system of membranes that have the same basic structure as the other membranes we have described. They are organized in pairs and thus form totally enclosed spaces within the ground substance of the cell. If you look closely at Fig. 8-4, you can see rows of ribosomes adhering to the outer surface of the reticular membranes, that is, the surface in contact with the ground substance of the cell. The protein that is produced by these ribosomes is secreted into the cavity of the endoplasmic reticulum for eventual export to the outside.

Not all the membranes of the endoplasmic reticulum have ribosomes adhering to them. Those that do not (the "smooth" endoplasmic reticulum) may be active in the synthesis and/or accumulation of other types of molecules such as polysaccharides and steroids.

Prominent in cells that secrete large quantities of material is the **Golgi complex.** This consists of neat stacks of membranes like those of the endoplasmic reticulum but without any ribosomes attached to them. The spaces within the membranes of the Golgi complex may connect from time to time with the spaces of the endoplasmic reticulum. In this way proteins are transferred to the Golgi complex and assembled in granules prior to being secreted from the cell. Polysaccharides such as cellulose (in plant cells) and mucus may also be present in the Golgi complex before being transported to the outside. There may well be other important functions of this structure that have yet to be discovered.

8-8   THE MITOCHONDRIA

The mitochondria are spherical or rod-shaped bodies that range in size from 0.2μ to 5μ. The number in a cell varies, but active cells (e.g., liver cells) may have over a thousand of them.

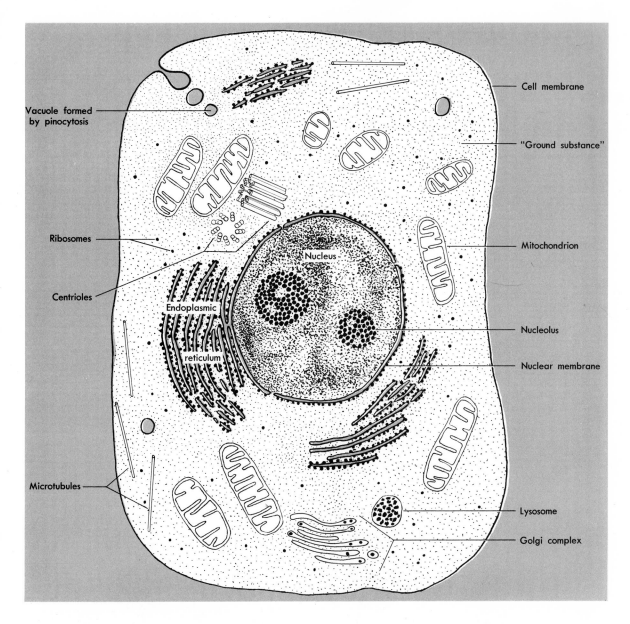

An idealized view of an animal cell as it might be seen under the electron microscope. Although no single electron micrograph has revealed all the structures shown, the drawing represents a composite view of what many electron micrographs suggest is the organization of the parts of the cell.

Fig. 8-6

Although the larger mitochondria can be seen under the light microscope, only the electron microscope can reveal their basic structure. Electron micrographs show that each mitochondrion is bounded by a double membrane. The outer membrane provides a smooth, uninterrupted boundary to the mitochondrion. The inner membrane is repeatedly extended into folds that project into the interior space of the mitochondrion (Fig. 8-6). These shelflike inner folds are called **cristae.** The interior space of the mitochondrion is filled with a fluid rich in enzymes. Other enzymes adhere directly to the membranes themselves.

The membranes of the mitochondria appear to be similar to the cell membrane. Like it, they consist of a double layer of phospholipid molecules sandwiched between layers of protein molecules. Also like cell membranes, they can expand and contract. In fact, mitochondria are frequently observed to enlarge or shrink as the metabolic activity of the cell varies.

The function of the mitochondria is quite clear. They contain the enzymes that carry out the oxidation of food substances. Thus the mitochondria convert the potential energy of different food materials into a form of energy that can be used by the cell to carry out its various activities. In view of this, it is not surprising that mitochondria tend to congregate in the most active regions of a cell. Nerve cells, muscle cells, and secretory cells all contain many mitochondria located in the regions of the cell most actively engaged in transmission of electrical impulses, contraction, and secretion, respectively. The mitochondria have been aptly called the powerhouses of the cell.

8-9   PLASTIDS

Plastids are found only in plant cells and the cells of most photosynthetic protists. Some plastids contain red, yellow, or orange pigments and impart these colors to flowers and ripe fruits. Some plastids are colorless. These are usually found in plant parts that are not exposed to the light and serve as a storage area for starch. The starch accumulates in grains. Figure 8-7 shows starch grains in the cells of the white potato.

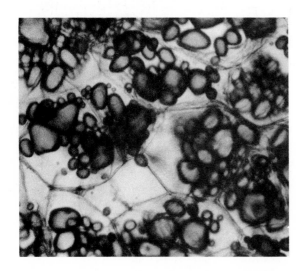

Fig. 8-7

Starch grains in the cells of a white potato. Note the cell walls. The starch grains have been lightly stained with iodine.

By far the most important plastids are the chloroplasts. These contain the green pigment **chlorophyll.** It is chlorophyll which traps the energy of sunlight and enables it to be used for the manufacture of food. Thus the chloroplasts are the site at which photosynthesis takes place.

In plants, the chloroplasts are usually disk-shaped structures, 5–8μ in diameter and 1μ thick. Photosynthesizing cells may contain as many as 50 or more of them. Among the algae, the chloroplasts may assume a wide variety of shapes and only

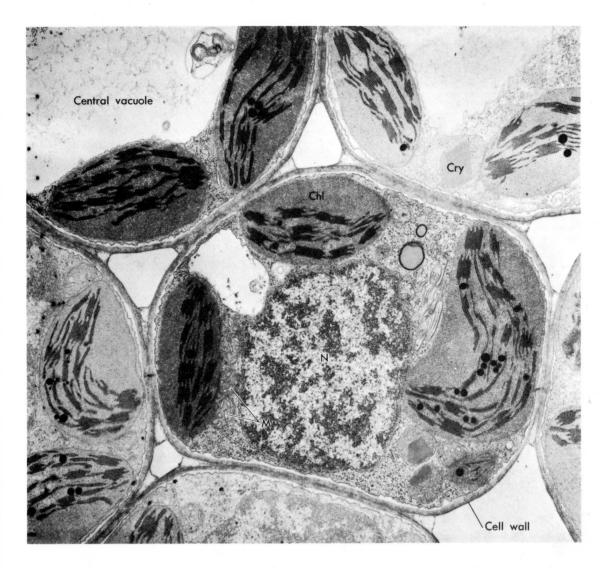

Cells from the leaf of a sunflower. Note the nucleus (N), chloroplasts (Chl), mitochondria (M), crystals (Cry), central vacuole, and primary cell wall in these typical plant cells. (Electron micrograph courtesy of H. J. Arnott and Kenneth M. Smith).

Fig. 8-8

one or a few be present in a cell. Figure 3-2 shows the spiral chloroplast of *Spirogyra* and the cup-shaped chloroplast of *Chlamydomonas*.

Chemical studies show that chloroplasts are rich in structural protein and phospholipids. This suggests that a protein-lipid-protein unit membrane may also be present in chloroplasts, and electron micrographs have indeed revealed its presence. Under the electron microscope, the chloroplast is seen to be bounded by a unit membrane and also to contain interconnecting stacks of membranes in its interior (Fig. 8-8). These, in turn, appear to be made up of layers of chlorophyll and lipid molecules sandwiched between the layers of protein. This arrangement spreads the chlorophyll molecules over a large area and seems to provide for maximum efficiency of light absorption and photosynthesis.

VACUOLES

Vacuoles are fluid-filled "bubbles" in the cytoplasm. They are bordered by a unit membrane that is probably identical to the cell membrane. In fact, vacuoles are often formed by an infolding and pinching-off of a portion of the cell membrane (Fig. 8-6). Food materials or wastes may be found inside vacuoles.

A young plant cell contains many small vacuoles, but as the cell matures, these unite to form a large **central vacuole** (Fig. 8-8). Dissolved food molecules, waste materials, and pigments may be found in it.

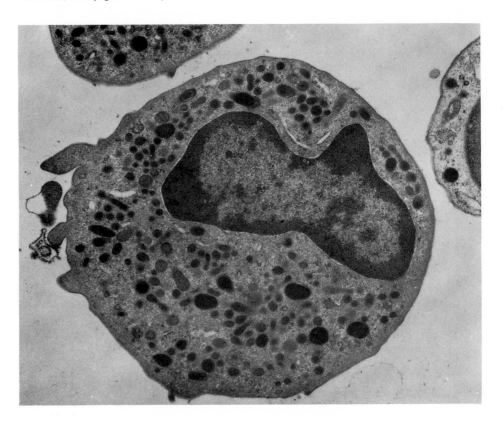

Fig. 8-9   White blood corpuscle from a guinea pig. The small dark bodies in the cytoplasm are lysosomes. (9,500 X, from Fawcett: *The Cell: Its Organelles and Inclusions,* W. B. Saunders Co., 1966.)

8-11   ## LYSOSOMES

Lysosomes (Fig. 8-9) are cell structures about the size of mitochondria and bounded by a unit membrane. Within them are contained a number of enzymes that catalyze the breakdown of polysaccharide, protein, and nucleic acid molecules. Presumably, these enzymes are kept within the lysosomes to prevent breakdown of the cell itself.

When materials within the cell are to be digested, they are first incorporated into a lysosome. These materials may be other subcellular structures, such as mitochondria, that have ceased to function efficiently. They may be food particles that have been taken into the cell. In the case of the white blood cell shown in Fig. 8-9, they are bacteria or other harmful particles that have been scavenged by the cell.

Lysosomes also play an important role in the death of cells. When a cell is injured or dies, its lysosomes aid in its disintegration. This clears the area so that a healthy cell can replace the damaged one. Cell death is also a normal process in some organisms. For example, as a tadpole changes into a frog, its tail is gradually absorbed. The tail cells, which are richly supplied with lysosomes, die and the products of their disintegration are used in the growth of new cells in the developing frog.

Lysosomes have not been conclusively shown to occur in plant cells.

CRYSTALS AND OIL DROPLETS 8-12

Crystals are deposits of food or waste materials that are surrounded by a unit membrane. As the name implies, the deposits are crystalline, that is, polyhedrons with flat faces and sharp edges. Crystals are most common in plant cells (Fig. 8-8) and are usually deposits of calcium salts. These are presumably waste products of the cell's metabolism. In animal cells, the crystals are generally protein.

Oil droplets are common in both plant and animal cells. They differ from crystals in that there is usually no unit membrane separating the oil from the rest of the cytoplasm. Under the microscope, the droplets generally appear as tiny, glistening spheres. However, in the specialized fat storage cells of some plant and animal tissues, the amount of oil present may be so great as to practically fill the entire cell (Fig. 8-14). Oil droplets serve as a reserve supply of energy-rich fuel for the cell. As mentioned in the last chapter, there is a constant interchange of fatty molecules between the droplets and the rest of the cell.

This fact illustrates a very important principle about subcellular structures, namely, that they all participate in the activities of the cell. Some biologists refer to certain cell parts as being living while they consider others to be nonliving. The cytoplasm is always placed in the former category while crystals and fat droplets are placed in the latter. This distinction is not a good one. While it may be true that mitochondria participate more actively in the metabolism of the cell than do crystals and oil droplets, the latter nonetheless are far from permanent, unchanging structures. They increase and decrease in size in harmony with the needs of the cell. The basic point is this: the cell is the structural unit of life. Therefore, the smallest unit that we can properly consider to be alive is the whole cell, not its parts. The cell can live, of course, only if all its parts are properly organized and properly functioning.

All of the cell structures discussed so far have unit membranes as part of their construction. In general, there seem to be two main functions accomplished by these membranes. One is simply to establish a number of compartments within the cell. The bearers of the hereditary code, the chromosomes, are separated from the rest of the cell by the nuclear membrane. The potentially destructive digestive enzymes in the lysosomes are kept from contact with the ground substance of the cytoplasm by their bounding membrane. The secretory products of the cell are sequestered in the channels of the endoplasmic reticulum and Golgi complex.

The second important role played by the membranes of the cell is to provide for the neat spatial organization of enzymes and pigments. Chlorophyll is incorporated in the internal membranes of the chloroplast. Many of the enzymes which carry out the oxidation of food are neatly arranged on the cristae of the mitochondria. It is quite likely that other important enzymes are present in or on the cell membrane and the membranes of the endoplasmic reticulum.

8-13   MICROTUBULES

Microtubules are straight cylinders of protein that are found in many cells. These cylinders are about 250 A in diameter and quite long (Fig. 8-6). They are also quite stiff and therefore give some rigidity to those parts of the cell in which they are located. They often have a second function as well. In many cells, the cytoplasm (or some parts of it) flows from place to place within the cell. This is especially dramatic in the formation of pseudopodia by an amoeba (see Section 3-2) or a white blood corpuscle but occurs in many other cells as well. Wherever this has been observed, it appears to be associated with the presence of microtubules.

One special case of intracellular movement occurs during the precise distribution of chromosomes to the daughter cells that are formed in cell division. Each chromosome moves to its final destination attached to a long microtubule. The entire array of microtubules participating in the process is called the spindle. It can be seen in several of the photomicrographs of dividing cells that appear in Chapter 17.

8-14   CENTRIOLES

Animal cells and the cells of many protists contain two centrioles located near the exterior surface of the nucleus. Each centriole consists of a cylindrical array of nine microtubules. However, each of the nine microtubules has two partial (as seen in cross section) tubules attached to it (Fig. 8-6). The two centrioles are usually placed at right angles to each other.

Just before a cell divides, its centrioles duplicate and one pair migrates to the opposite side of the nucleus. The spindle (see above) then forms between them.

In some cells, the centrioles duplicate to produce the basal bodies of cilia and flagella.

8-15   CILIA AND FLAGELLA

Many cells have whiplike extensions, either short ones (cilia) or long ones (flagella). Among the protists (e.g. *Paramecium*, *Chlamydomonas*), cilia and flagella are used for locomotion. However, many animals have cells the cilia of which serve simply to move materials past the cell. The cells lining the inner surface of our trachea ("windpipe") are ciliated.

The origin and structure of cilia and flagella seem to be fundamentally the same. In each case they grow out of basal bodies. These have the same structure as centrioles and are formed by them.

The cilium or flagellum itself has not only the outer ring of 9 microtubules (each now with just *one* accessory tubule attached to it) but also two central fibrils that are identical to microtubules in their construction (Fig. 8-10). In both cilia and flagella, the entire assembly is sheathed in a unit membrane which is simply an extension of the cell membrane.

The similarities between the structure of cilia, flagella, basal bodies, and centrioles and the structure of microtubules suggest that the microtubule is another one of the fundamental architectural components of cells. In function, also, it is interesting that in most cases where the microtubular structure appears, it is in some way associated with cell motion.

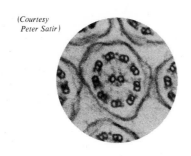

(Courtesy
Peter Satir)

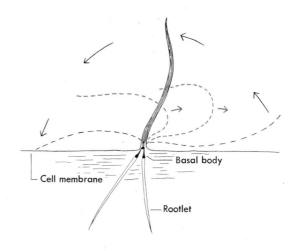

Basal body

Cell membrane

Rootlet

Fig. 8-10

At right, drawing of a single cilium. The power stroke is shown in black; the recovery stroke, in color. Above, an electron micrograph of a single cilium in cross section. Note the characteristic pattern of filaments.

CELL COATINGS   8-16

Only rarely is the cell membrane the outer surface of the cell. Usually some type of exterior coating is present. In animal cells this appears to be constructed from a protein-polysaccharide complex. It is not rigid but does serve to cement adjacent cells together. In Fig. 8-3, it is represented by the thin line between the two unit membranes. In many cases, however, it is much thicker than shown here. Filaments of the protein collagen (see Section 7-3) are often embedded in the thicker coatings.

The outer coating of certain protists such as *Paramecium* and *Euglena* is rather stiff and gives a definite shape to the organism. It can, however, be easily deformed as the organism moves about.

In many algae and in all plants, the exterior coating is made of the polysaccharide cellulose. This forms a rigid, boxlike **cell wall** which is one of the most characteristic features of these cells. The "cells" that Hooke saw (Fig. 8-1) were the walls of once-living cork cells.

In Fig. 8-8, the *primary* cell wall that surrounds each of the sunflower cells is clearly visible. A cementing layer, the *middle lamella,* holds adjacent cells together except at their corners. The cellulose molecules that make up the primary wall are deposited in an orderly pattern or "weave" that increases the mechanical strength of the wall. As the cell grows, the primary wall grows, too, in a few cases as much as a thousandfold.

The cell wall is porous, permitting molecules, both small and large, to pass through it with relative ease. Unlike the cell membrane, it does not exert any control over the kinds of molecules that pass through it.

Some plant cells, after they reach full size, deposit a **secondary cell wall** between the protoplast and the primary wall. This is built up of additional layers of cellulose that are impregnated with a plastic, cementing, material called **lignin.** Thick, lignified cell walls are important in providing strength for the plant (Fig. 8-13). Wood is simply lignified cell walls. Frequently the secondary cell wall is not deposited in a uniform layer. Instead, depressions, called pits, are left as it develops. The pits in the secondary wall of one cell are lined up just opposite the pits in the walls of adjacent cells. Such an arrangement makes up a "pit pair" and presumably allows for easy exchange of materials between adjacent cells.

Rigid cell walls are also characteristic of bacteria, fungi, and diatoms. In each of these groups the main constituent of the wall is a polymer of some sort but in none of these cases is it cellulose. No matter what its composition, however, all cell walls share two features that are not characteristic of the other cell coatings described earlier. The first is their rigidity and the second is the lack of adhesion between the cell membrane and the wall. As we shall see in Chapter 9, by removing water from the cell it is possible to cause the *protoplast* to shrink away from its surrounding walls.

8-17   **EXCEPTIONS TO THE CELL THEORY**

The statement that all living things are made of cells requires some qualification. At one stage in the life of certain slime molds the organism consists of a spreading sheet of cytoplasm containing thousands of nuclei. While this **plasmodium** (Fig. 3-13) is definitely not made up of cells, it is formed as a result of the growth (with repeated division of the nucleus) of a single cell. Such a multinucleate mass developing from a single cell is called a **coenocyte.** Many fungi and a few green algae are also coenocytic. They consist of long tubes of cytoplasm filled with many nuclei. These tubes also develop from a single cell which grows with repeated division of its nucleus.

The muscles with which we carry out all voluntary movements are composed of long fibers each containing many nuclei. These fibers, however, are formed by the fusion of individual cells. This type of construction is called a **syncytium.** It is also found in some flatworms (Section 5-3) and rotifers (Section 5-4).

These exceptions to the cell principle are more apparent than real. Each of them represents a secondary departure from a truly cellular basis. All these organisms or structures begin as typical cells but ultimately modify this structure. Presumably these modifications are adaptations to the peculiar mode of existence of the organisms or structures concerned.

If we consider viruses to be living organisms, then they are also exceptions to the cell theory. As you learned in Section 3-5, viruses are particles, rich in nucleic acids, which show none of the attributes of life unless introduced into the cells of an appropriate host organism. It may well be that we are dealing in this case with a subcellular particle which has, in some way, been derived from a living cell. If that is the case, to call viruses alive would be to make the same mistake that we make when we refer to any cell structure as being alive. The viruses are probably no more (and no less) alive than, say, the chromosomes of a cell. What lives is the complex organization we call the cell, and its invasion by a virus simply causes drastic changes in the cell's pattern of living.

8-18   **THE CELL AS THE UNIT OF STRUCTURE OF LIVING THINGS**

We have seen that living things are made of one or more cells. *Chlamydomonas* is a single-celled organism. Within its single cell, it contains all the equipment needed to carry out the various functions of life. From time to time, *Chlamydomonas* divides and forms two individuals where before there was one. Each daughter cell receives a complete set of the nuclear controls present in the parent cell. Prior to actual division of the cell, each chromosome in the nucleus is duplicated. Then, during the process of cell division itself, these duplicated chromosomes become separated. With remarkable precision, a complete set migrates to each of the two daughter cells (Fig. 8-13). **Mitosis** is the term used to describe this important process. A detailed examination of mitosis will be made in Chapter 17.

Mitosis provides a mechanism for the reproduction of single-celled organisms. It also provides a mechanism for growth in multicellular organisms. In both cases,

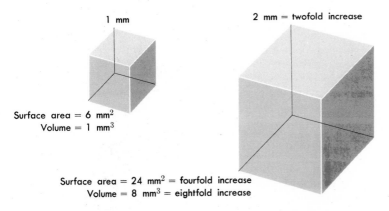

1 mm

2 mm = twofold increase

Surface area = 6 mm^2
Volume = 1 mm^3

Surface area = 24 mm^2 = fourfold increase
Volume = 8 mm^3 = eightfold increase

Fig. 8-11

The ratio of surface area to volume of the cube decreases as its size increases. The same relationship holds for cells and organisms.

it provides an escape from excessive growth or enlargement of single cells. Small cells can usually operate more efficiently than large ones. One reason for this is that small cells have a larger ratio of surface area to volume than big ones (Fig. 8-11). Thus a more rapid exchange of materials can occur between the cytoplasm and the external environment of the cell. Furthermore, excessively large cells contain more cytoplasm than can be efficiently controlled by the nucleus. The large macronuclei of ciliates such as *Paramecium* and *Stentor* (Fig. 3-1) and the coenocytic arrangement of the bread mold hyphae are surely no accident. Each of these seems to be an alternative solution to the problem of nuclear control over unusually large volumes of cytoplasm. Frequent mitosis is, however, the solution employed by most organisms.

Among the flagellated green algae are several interesting colonial forms (Fig. 8-12). These species are called colonial because they are simply made up of clusters of independent cells. If a single cell of *Gonium, Pandorina,* or *Eudorina* is isolated from the rest of the colony, it will swim away looking quite like a *Chlamydomonas* cell. Then, as it undergoes mitosis, it will form a new colony with the characteristic number of cells in that colony. The situation in *Pleodorina* and *Volvox* is somewhat different. In these cases, some of the cells of the colony (most, in *Volvox*) are not able to live independently. If a nonreproductive cell is isolated from a *Volvox* colony, it will fail to reproduce itself by mitosis and eventually it will die. What has happened?

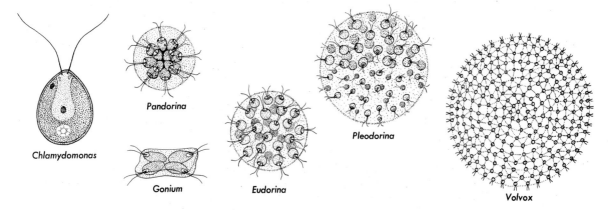

Chlamydomonas

Pandorina

Gonium

Eudorina

Pleodorina

Volvox

A group of flagellated green algae whose constituent cells are strikingly similar and which illustrate the unicellular, colonial, and multicellular levels of organization. The small cells in *Pleodorina* and most of the cells in *Volvox* are incapable of reproduction. The scale of the drawings diminishes from left to right.

Fig. 8-12

In some way, as yet unclear, *Volvox* has crossed the line separating simple colonial organisms from truly multicellular ones. Unlike *Gonium*, *Volvox* cannot be considered simply a colony or cluster of individual cells. It is a single organism whose cells have lost their ability to live independently. If a sufficient number of them become damaged for some reason, the entire sphere of cells will die.

What has *Volvox* gained by this arrangement? In giving up their independence, the cells of *Volvox* have become specialists. No longer does every cell carry out all of life's functions (as in colonial forms); instead, certain cells specialize to carry out certain functions while leaving other functions to other specialists. In *Volvox* this process goes no further than having certain cells specialized for reproduction while others, unable to reproduce themselves, fulfill the needs for photosynthesis and loco-motion. In more complex multicellular organisms, such as man, the degree of special-ization is carried to greater lengths. Each cell has one or two precise functions to carry out. It depends on other cells to carry out all the other functions necessary to maintain the life of the organism and thus its own. This process of specialization and division of labor among cells is called **differentiation.** One of the great problems of biology is how differentiation arises among cells, all of which, having arisen by mitosis, share the same nuclear controls. We will examine some tentative answers to this problem in Chapter 23.

Specialization and division of labor results in increased efficiency in the same way that a modern shoe factory is more efficient than the individual bootmaker of earlier times. A price must be paid, however, for this increased efficiency. If accurate communication and coordination between the various parts of the shoe factory break down, the output of the factory will be adversely affected. In multicellular organisms, too, there must be proper communication and coordination between all parts. We do not know just how this is accomplished in *Volvox*. We do have ideas of how it is accomplished in many of the more elaborate multicellular forms. Part VI of this book will be largely devoted to the topic of how the parts of an organism communi-cate and coordinate their diverse activities.

Our shoe factory analogy can be pushed one step further. If the workers in any one production department go out on strike, the output of shoes from the factory will soon cease. In an analogous way, if one group of specialized cells in a multi-cellular organism ceases to carry out its function, all the other cells of the organism will be affected. If the human heart fails, every other cell in the body will soon die no matter how vigorously and efficiently each had been functioning at the time.

You might well argue that a multicellular organism like man is really no more efficient at carrying out life's activities than a *Chlamydomonas* cell. In the sense that *Chlamydomonas* seems to be in no more (perhaps even less) danger of extinction than man, this is true. However, a comparison of its habitat with that of man may reveal what is really gained by specialization and division of labor. *Chlamydomonas* is almost entirely at the mercy of its environment. About its only means for coping with any adverse change in its environment is to swim away from it or form a resting stage until such time as conditions improve. Many changes in its environmental conditions (e.g., temperature or chemical changes in the water) can cause its death. Thus the habitat of *Chlamydomonas* is a very narrow one and it is at the mercy of it. Man, on the other hand, can live successfully in a great variety of habitats. When conditions change, he is usually able to cope successfully with them. Changes in temperature, diet, etc., have remarkably little effect upon the individual cells of which his body is composed. Some of the mechanisms by which man and other multicellular organisms gain such a mastery over their environment will be considered later, in Part IV.

We cannot be certain that *Gonium, Pandorina, Eudorina,* and *Pleodorina* represent stages in the evolution of multicellular *Volvox* from unicellular *Chlamydomonas.* Whether they do or not, these organisms illustrate one way in which colonial forms may have arisen from unicellular ones and multicellular forms from colonial ones. They also illustrate the subtle shift in cell relationships that occurs as one crosses the uncertain boundary between colonial forms and multicellular, differentiated ones.

PLANT TISSUES 8-19

The cells that make up multicellular organisms become differentiated in a large, but not unlimited, number of ways. If we examine a mature vascular plant, we can identify several distinct cell types. These are grouped together in tissues. Some tissues consist of only one cell type. Some consist of several.

1. Meristematic. The chief function of meristematic cells is mitosis (Fig. 8-13). The cells are small and thin-walled, with no central vacuole and no specialized features. They are located in tissues (the apical meristems) at the growing points of roots and stems. In dicots, a ring of meristematic tissue, the cambium, is also found within the mature stem. Mitosis in the meristems produces new cells for the growth of the plant. The cells produced by the meristems soon become differentiated into one or another of several types.

2. Protective. The cells of protective tissues are found on the surface of roots, stems and leaves. They are flattened cells whose top and bottom surfaces are parallel but whose sides may be arranged quite irregularly (Fig. 8-13). These cells provide protection to the cells lying beneath.

3. Parenchyma. Parenchyma cells are widely distributed throughout plants. They are large, thin-walled cells and usually have a central vacuole. Frequently they become partially separated from one another (the split occurs at the middle lamella) and gas fills the resulting intercellular space. They are liberally supplied with plastids. In areas not exposed to light, leucoplasts predominate and food storage is the main function. The cells of the white potato are parenchyma cells. In areas where light is present, e.g. in the leaf, chloroplasts predominate and photosynthesis is the main function.

4. Collenchyma. Collenchyma cells have thick secondary walls that are especially developed at the corners of the cell (Fig. 8-13). These cells provide mechanical support for the plant. They are most frequently found in regions of the plant that are growing rapidly and need to be strengthened. The petiole ("stalk") of leaves is usually reinforced with collenchyma cells.

5. Sclerenchyma. Sclerenchyma cells are a more common type of supporting cell. The secondary walls of these cells are very thick and are built up in a uniform layer around the entire margin of the cell (Fig. 8-13). Sclerenchyma cells are usually found associated with other cell types and give mechanical support to them. In many cases, the protoplasts of sclerenchyma cells die after the secondary cell wall is fully formed. Sclerenchyma cells are found in stems and are also associated with the veins of leaves. They are the exclusive component of the hard outer covering of seeds and nuts.

6. Xylem. The xylem is a "mixed tissue" composed of several cell types. The most characteristic and important of these are the xylem vessels and xylem tracheids.

Fig. 8-13   Plant tissues. Each of these specialized types develops from the cells produced in meristems. The dark, horseshoe-shaped structures in the meristematic cells are chromosomes. In most cells they can be made visible only at the time of cell division. (Photo courtesy General Biological Supply House, Inc.)

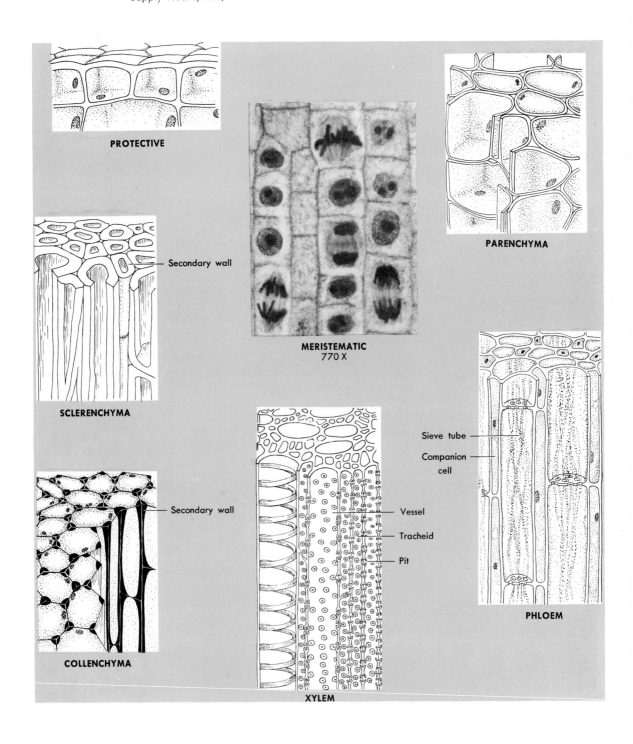

PROTECTIVE

PARENCHYMA

SCLERENCHYMA

– Secondary wall

MERISTEMATIC
770 X

COLLENCHYMA

– Secondary wall

XYLEM

– Vessel

– Tracheid

– Pit

PHLOEM

Sieve tube –

Companion
cell –

(Gymnosperm xylem contains only tracheids.) Xylem vessels have thickened secondary cell walls. The walls are not deposited in a uniform layer but are usually thickened in a pattern of spiral bands (Fig. 8-13). When fully developed, the end walls of xylem vessels dissolve away and the protoplasts die. This produces a long tube. Tracheids differ from vessels in that the cells lack spiral banding and are tapered at the ends. The tapered ends of vertically stacked tracheids overlap and are interconnected by means of many pits. Both tracheids and vessels are used to transport water and minerals from the roots to the leaves. In woody plants, the older xylem ceases to participate in transport and simply serves to give strength to the trunk of the growing plant. Wood is xylem. When one counts the annual rings of a tree, one is counting rings of xylem.

7. **Phloem.** The phloem is also a mixed tissue. The most important cells in it are the sieve tubes. They are so named because their end walls become perforated (Fig. 8-13). This allows cytoplasmic connections to be established between cells. These presumably aid the cells in carrying out their chief function: the transport of food and hormones throughout the plant. At maturity, sieve tubes do not possess a nucleus. Adjacent to them are nucleated "companion cells," however, and these may take over general control of the sieve tube cells. Frequently sclerenchyma cells also occur in phloem tissue and impart strength to it.

The various plant tissues are themselves organized in definite patterns. The groups of organized tissues make up the organs of the plant. Roots, stems, and leaves are the major organs of higher plants. Their proper functioning depends upon the proper arrangement and coordination of the tissues of which they are composed.

ANIMAL TISSUES   8-20

The cells of animals are also differentiated into a wide variety of specialized types. These diverse types are organized into tissues. In man, the following kinds of tissues can be distinguished.

1. **Epithelial.** Epithelial tissues are made up of closely packed cells arranged in flat sheets. These tissues line the various cavities and tubes of the body. They also form the skin which covers the body.

Epithelial tissues carry out a variety of functions. In every case, these functions reflect the fact that epithelia are always found at the boundary between cell masses and a cavity or space. The epithelium of the skin protects underlying tissues from damage by mechanical abrasion, ultraviolet radiation, dehydration, and bacterial invasion. In carrying out these protective functions, the surface layers of epithelium may become damaged and lost. This is especially obvious when the skin "peels" after it becomes sunburned. Fortunately, mitosis in the underlying cells replaces this lost epithelium. In fact, extra thick layers of epithelium (calluses) may form in areas where mechanical abrasion is particularly severe.

Epithelia also function in the transport of materials to and from the tissues and the cavities that they separate. The columnar epithelium of the intestine secretes digestive enzymes into the intestine and also absorbs the end products of food digestion from it. All the digestive glands of the body are lined with epithelium. Epithelium also lines the air tubes and lung cavities. This epithelium secretes mucus to keep from drying out and to trap inhaled dust particles. These cells also possess cilia on the "free" surface which propel the mucus with its load of foreign matter back up to the throat.

Fig. 8-14   Animal tissues.

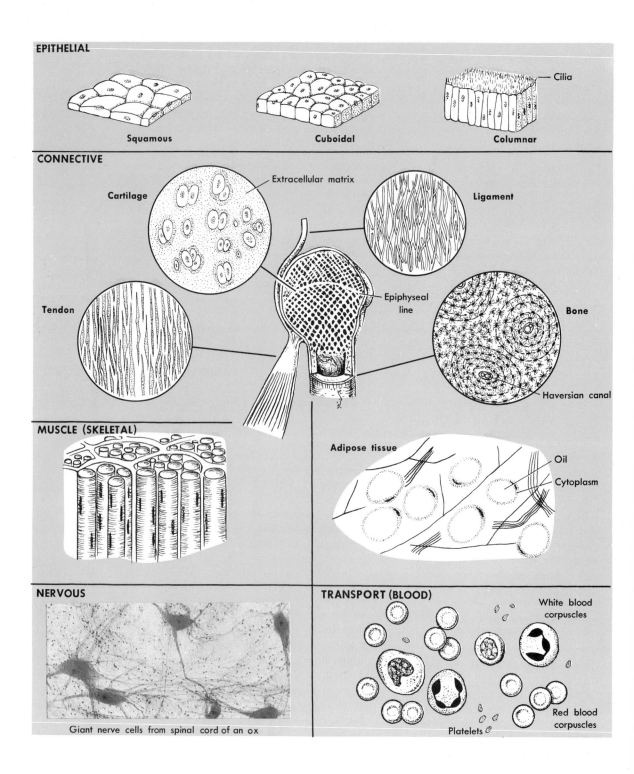

EPITHELIAL

Squamous

Cuboidal

Columnar

Cilia

CONNECTIVE

Cartilage

Extracellular matrix

Ligament

Tendon

Epiphyseal line

Bone

Haversian canal

MUSCLE (SKELETAL)

Adipose tissue

Oil

Cytoplasm

NERVOUS

Giant nerve cells from spinal cord of an ox

TRANSPORT (BLOOD)

White blood corpuscles

Platelets

Red blood corpuscles

The sex cells must be released from the body in order to function in sexual reproduction. Thus we find that they, too, arise from an epithelium, in this case, the germinal epithelium. The countless millions of sperm cells produced by mature human males arise by repeated cell division in this tissue.

2. Connective. Several types of connective tissue are found in the human body. Each of these consists of specialized cells imbedded in a great deal of extracellular material. This **matrix,** as it is called, is secreted by the cells. **Supporting** connective tissue is used to give strength, support, and protection to the soft parts of the body. **Cartilage** and **bone** are the two kinds of supporting connective tissue found in man. The matrix in cartilage is a protein-polysaccharide mixture, called chondrin. Our outer ear gets its shape from its cartilage skeleton.

The extracellular matrix in bone contains both protein fibers of collagen and mineral deposits. The main component of the latter is calcium phosphate, $Ca_3(PO_4)_2$, although magnesium, carbonate, and fluoride ions are also found. The living cells embedded in the bony matrix are connected with one another by cytoplasmic extensions. These cells receive their blood and nerve supply by way of Haversian canals which penetrate throughout the bone. The bone cells and their bony matrix are arranged in concentric rings around these canals (Fig. 8-14).

Binding connective tissue serves, as its name suggests, to bind body parts together. **Tendons** connect muscle to bone. The matrix is principally the protein collagen and the fibers are all oriented parallel to each other. This gives great strength to the tissue. Tendons are not elastic, however.

Ligaments attach one bone to another. In addition to collagen fibers, ligaments contain the protein elastin. This protein permits the ligaments to be stretched. If ligaments become torn or damaged, a dislocation of the joint may result.

Fibrous connective tissue is found distributed throughout the body. It serves as a packing and binding material for most of our organs. It also provides a pathway for blood vessels and nerves to reach them. Collagen and other proteins are found in the matrix. Fascia is fibrous connective tissue which binds muscles together and binds the skin to the underlying structures. Adipose tissue is fibrous connective tissue in which the cells have become almost filled with *oil* (Section 7-2).

3. Muscle. Three kinds of muscle tissue are found in man. **Skeletal** muscle is made up of long fibers whose contraction provides the force for locomotion and other types of voluntary body movements. **Smooth** muscle lines the walls of all the hollow organs of the body such as the intestine and blood vessels. Its contraction, which is involuntary, reduces the size of the body's hollow organs. **Cardiac** muscle is the muscle out of which the heart is made. It is capable of rhythmic contraction without any outside source of stimulation.

4. Nervous. Nervous tissue is composed chiefly of **neurons.** These are cells that are specialized for the conduction of electrochemical nerve impulses. Each neuron consists of a cell body, which contains the nucleus, and one or more hairlike extensions. It is along these extensions, which in a few cases may extend several feet, that the nerve impulse travels. The tips of the extensions either meet other neurons (Fig. 8-14) or some other kind of tissue, e.g. muscle, that is stimulated by the neuron. The structure and organization of the several kinds of neurons found in the human body will be described in Chapter 28.

The human brain and spinal cord consist chiefly of nervous tissue. The cell bodies of virtually all our neurons are found here. Their extensions, bundled together in **nerves,** extend out from the brain and spinal cord to all parts of the body.

5. Transport. Another important tissue of our body is **blood,** a fluid tissue. Aside from its special consistency, blood is just as much a tissue as any other. Suspended in a watery matrix, the plasma, are several types of cells. Most numerous are the red blood corpuscles which are vital to the transport of gases. White blood corpuscles play an important role in protecting the body from disease. Platelets are tiny cell fragments that initiate the process of blood clotting when breaks or leaks occur in the blood vessels. The liquid tissue solidifies and blood loss is stopped.

We have examined the most common tissues of the human body. In every case, these are made up of differentiated cells specialized to carry out one or, at most, a few functions. In some tissues, only one type of cell predominates. Other tissues contain several cell types. Where several types are found, however, they are organized in such a way that the overall function of the tissue can be accomplished efficiently.

8-21 **HIGHER LEVELS OF ORGANIZATION**

The various tissues of the body are not arranged haphazardly either. Different tissues are organized and integrated into **organs.** The stomach, the liver and the heart are just three of many organs in the body. The stomach is an organ made up of epithelial, connective, and muscle tissue. Its proper functioning and coordination also depend upon nervous tissue and blood.

The various organs of the body are, in turn, organized into **systems.** Each system accomplishes a major function for the body. The digestive system functions in the digestion of food. The stomach, the liver, the pancreas, and the small and large intestines are some of the organs that make up this system. The system as a whole works only if its various constituent organs carry out their functions in a well-coordinated way. The respiratory, circulatory, excretory, nervous, skeletal, muscle, endocrine, and reproductive systems are other vital systems in man. We will examine in detail the structure and functioning of these systems in later chapters. Their proper anatomical arrangement and harmonious functioning produce the **organism.**

Although we say that the cell is the basic structural and functional unit of life, the life of an organism as complex as man requires that the cells be organized into intermediate levels of complexity: the tissues, organs, and systems. Many biologists see an even higher level of organization in some living things. When many different organisms function in a coordinated way, a **society** exists. The honeybee provides a good example of this. Solitary honeybees can never survive for long. The life of any individual bee, as well as the life of the society (colony), depends upon the properly coordinated activities of workers, drones, and queen. Human societies also depend, although to a lesser degree, upon specialization and division of labor among the individuals who belong to it. Except for the differences between the sexes, we do not, however, have special body types appropriate to particular functions as do the honeybees. Furthermore, if a society does represent a higher level of biological organization, its components are surely far less rigidly organized than are the cells, tissues, organs, and systems of which individual organisms are composed.

One of the principal features of living things is the complex organization of the matter out of which they are made. In these chapters we have examined the various levels of this organization from the protons, neutrons, and electrons out of which all matter is made to the organ systems without which our most complex animals and plants could not function. Our understanding of the structure and function of any level depends upon our understanding of the structure and properties of earlier levels. Thus we understand the functioning of the organism in terms of its systems which, in turn, are understood through a knowledge of the organs, tissues, cells, and even the molecules, atoms, and subatomic particles of which they are composed.

The organization of life is not a static, unchanging thing. To be alive is to constantly build, tear down, and rebuild the structural materials out of which the organism is composed. This building up and tearing down depends upon the exchange of materials between the organism and its environment. The exchange of materials and the chemical transformations carried out on these materials within the organism constitute its **metabolism.** It is the topic we will study in Part IV.

EXERCISES AND PROBLEMS

1   In what ways do typical plant cells differ from animal cells?

2   What plant tissues are found in the angiosperms but not in the mosses?

3   Summarize the functions of adipose tissue in the human body.

4   List all those structures found in a rat liver cell that seem to be constructed from "unit membranes."

5   What are the advantages of specialization and division of labor among the cells of an organism? What are the disadvantages?

6   Distinguish between organ and organism.

7   Assuming them to be spherical in shape, compare the surface areas of a mycoplasma, staphylococcus and human cheek cell (see Fig. 8-2).

8   How would their *volumes* compare if they were all spherical?

9   What organic molecules are used in the construction of the (a) plant cell wall, (b) chromosome, (c) ribosome, (d) cell membrane, (e) lysosome, (f) oil droplet?

10   Distinguish between coenocyte and syncytium.

REFERENCES

1   Brachet, J., "The Living Cell," *Scientific American,* Reprint No. 90, September, 1961. Presents an excellent summary of cell structure as revealed by the electron microscope.

2   Swanson, C. P., *The Cell,* 2nd ed., Foundations Of Modern Biology Series, Prentice-Hall, Inc., 1964. The first 4 chapters discuss general cytological techniques and what they have revealed about cell structure.

3   Robertson, J. D., "The Membrane of the Living Cell," *Scientific American,* Reprint No. 151, April, 1962. Discusses the structure of the cell membrane and speculates about how other "unit membrane" structures may have developed from it.

4   Dippell, Ruth V., "Ultrastructure and Function," *This Is Life,* ed. by W. H. Johnson and W. C. Steere, Holt, Rinehart and Winston, New York, 1962. Emphasis on the many roles played in the cell by "unit membrane" systems.

5   Preston, R. D., "Cellulose," *Scientific American*, September, 1957. Helps to bridge the gap between our knowledge of the structure of individual molecules and the cell structures made from them. This article not only describes the structure of individual cellulose molecules but also shows how they are organized to form cell walls.

6   de Duve, C., "The Lysosome," *Scientific American*, Reprint No. 156, May, 1963.

7   Jensen, W. A., *The Plant Cell*, Fundamentals of Botany Series, Wadsworth Publishing Company, Inc., Belmont, California, 1964.

8   Hokin, L. E., and Mabel R. Hokin, "The Chemistry of Cell Membranes," *Scientific American*, Reprint No. 1022, October, 1965. Emphasizes the role of phospholipids in the structure and functioning of the cell membrane.

PART IV

METABOLISM

Plasmolyzed cells in the fresh-water plant *Anacharis densa,* which has been placed in sea water. The space between the cell membranes and the cell walls has become filled with sea water.

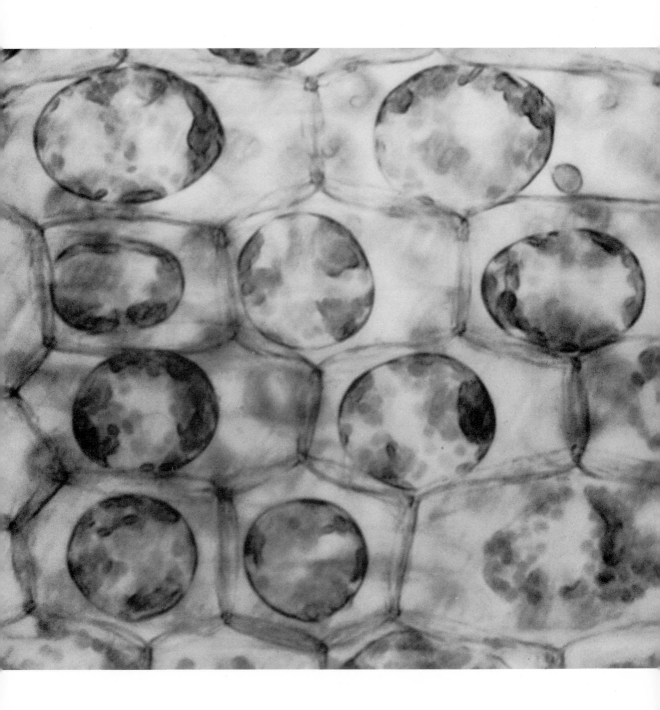

Among the fundamental characteristics of living things discussed in Chapter 1 was metabolism. Metabolism is the *exchange* of matter and energy between the organism and its environment and the *transformation* of matter and energy within the organism.

An understanding of the metabolism of living things depends on an understanding of the metabolism of the individual cells of which they are made. Each cell, to survive, must secure matter and energy from its environment, transform this matter and energy, and release the waste products of these transformations back to the environment.

9-1   ## THE CELLULAR ENVIRONMENT

What is the environment of cells? All living cells are bathed by liquid. This statement may seem perfectly obvious when one considers the protists, plants, and animals that live in fresh or salt water. But what of the many organisms that live in a terrestrial environment—in the earth, on the surface of the earth, or occasionally flying above the earth? A close examination reveals that in all these cases, too, each living cell is continually bathed in liquid. The skin which man and his fellow vertebrates expose to the air consists of layers of dead cells which protect the living cells beneath from the drying effects of the air. Where living cells are exposed to the environment, as in the epithelium that lines our air passages and the transparent cornea at the front of our eyes, secretory cells bathe the exposed surfaces in a continuous supply of moisture. In a similar way, the exoskeleton of insects, the bark of trees, and the waxy cuticle of leaves all consist of dead cells or waterproof secretions of cells which permit the underlying living cells to remain protected by at least a film of moisture.

Within the soil itself, living cells may be directly exposed to the environment, but here again the environment is liquid. Each soil particle is surrounded by a film of moisture. The delicate root hairs of vascular plants, and myriads of protists and tiny invertebrates that live in the soil are in contact with this moisture.

In considering the cellular environment of more complex plants and animals, one must consider also the environment of the cells that are not close to the exterior of the organism. These deep-lying inner cells are also in contact with liquid. Sap in plants, the blood of insects, and lymph in man are examples of fluids that bathe the inner cells of higher organisms. Lymph and the blood plasma from which it is derived make up about 20% of the body weight of man. Because these fluids are outside the cells, we will refer to them as the *extracellular fluid* or **ECF.** For the living cells of our body, the ECF *is* the environment. To distinguish between the external environment of our bodies (air) and the actual environment of our cells, the French physiologist Claude Bernard a century ago referred to the latter as the *internal environment.* He studied its properties carefully and found them to be remarkably stable. This is particularly true of the most complex of the multicellular organisms, the birds and mammals. Whether placed in warm locations or cold, whether recently fed or starved, no matter what kind of food taken in the diet, he found that the composition of the ECF remains relatively unchanged. In a real sense, the most adaptable of our higher animals actually are made of cells whose environment, the ECF, remains unchanged despite wide fluctuations in the external environment. Bernard was able to discover several mechanisms by which the mammalian body is able to maintain this constancy of its internal environment. He was so struck by these findings that he wrote: "The constancy of the internal environment is the condition of a free and independent life."

In the years since Bernard's discoveries, physiologists have studied the internal environment of other kinds of animals and found that they, too, have mechanisms for maintaining a stable ECF. The less complex animals are, however, less capable in this respect, and this may well account for the more restricted lives that they live. In the early twentieth century, the American physiologist Walter Cannon discovered still other mechanisms by which the stability of the internal environment is maintained. He coined the word **homeostasis** to describe this constancy of the ECF. Throughout Part IV, many examples of homeostasis and the mechanisms that maintain it will be described.

1.   Water. The most obvious component of the ECF of any organism—animal, plant, or protist—is water. This substance is uniquely suited for the functions it must carry out as the chief component of the ECF. It is unsurpassed as a solvent. In this role it brings to the cell many of the other molecules and ions that make up the ECF and without which life would be impossible. Not only does water serve as the medium in which substances are carried to and away from cells, but it also enters cells and plays a vital role in the chemical activities within.

2.   Gases. The ECF also contains gases, the most important of which are oxygen and carbon dioxide. Almost all living cells require oxygen and must get rid of their waste carbon dioxide. When chlorophyll-containing cells are exposed to the light, they take carbon dioxide from and release oxygen to the ECF.

Substantial quantities	"Trace" quantities	
Na^+ (except for plants)	Fe^{++}	
K^+	Cu^{++}	
Ca^{++}	Mn^{++}	
Mg^{++}	Zn^{++}	
$PO_4^{\equiv}$	B^{+++}	— required by plants; certain protists
Cl^-	Mo^+	— required by plants; certain protists and animals
$SO_4^=$	V^{++}	— certain protists and animals
HCO_3^-	Co^{++}	— certain animals, protists, and plants
	I^- } $Se^=$ }	— certain animals only

Inorganic ions necessary for most organisms.   **Fig. 9-1**

3.   Minerals. The ECF also contains dissolved minerals, or salts, in the form of positively and negatively charged ions. Figure 9-1 lists most of the ions that are found in the ECF of animals and plants. Some, such as calcium (Ca^{++}), potassium (K^+), sodium (Na^+), chloride (Cl^-), phosphate ($PO_4\equiv$), and bicarbonate (HCO_3^-), are present in relatively large quantities in animals. Calcium ions are an essential constitutent of our bones as well as of the "cement" that holds individual cells together in tissues. A proper balance of potassium and sodium ions within and without the cell is necessary for the responsiveness shown by nerve and muscle cells. Chloride ions play a major role in maintaining the normal physical properties of the ECF. Phosphate ions, as we shall see, are intimately involved in the distribution and use of energy within the cell. Bicarbonate ions function in the transport of carbon dioxide and help keep the ECF from becoming too acid or too alkaline. More will be said about this function later. Plants require substantial quantities of nitrates (NO_3^-) in order to synthesize amino acids and, from them, proteins.

Many other ions are required only in minute quantities. Most of these "trace elements" (e.g., Cu^{++}, Zn^{++}, Mn^{++}, Co^{++}) are either incorporated in enzymes directly or are necessary for the activation of enzymes. Iodine is incorporated in the hormone thyroxin, and small quantities of the fluoride ion (F^-) are important in strengthening the mineral portions of teeth and bone.

Some years ago, sheep growers in parts of Australia were plagued by a mysterious disease which became prevalent in their flocks. Although pastured in lush fields, their animals developed symptoms of extreme starvation and anemia (insufficient hemoglobin in the blood). Death followed frequently. The anemia suggested an iron deficiency and, sure enough, it was found that treatment with crude iron compounds often prevented the appearance of symptoms. It was soon realized, though, that it was not the iron which was preventing the disease, but tiny traces of cobalt present as impurities in the iron salts. Just one ounce of cobalt was found to be enough to maintain 800 sheep in good health for a year. Curiously, injections of cobalt failed to prevent the symptoms of the disease, but tiny traces taken by mouth worked dramatically. The answer to this riddle turned out to be that the cobalt was not being used directly by the sheep at all, but by bacteria living in their digestive systems. These bacteria used the cobalt to synthesize vitamin B_{12}, which in turn was absorbed by the sheep. You will remember that vitamins are organic substances needed by an organism but which it cannot synthesize itself from the products of protein, carbohydrate, or lipid digestion.

Not only must certain ions be present in the ECF, but the relative concentration of the various ions must often be held within rather narrow limits. When physiological experimentation is performed with organs or tissues removed from animal bodies, it is necessary to keep the specimen moistened with a solution which contains the same ratio of the major ions (Ca^{++}, Na^+, K^+) as is found in the ECF of the intact organism. One such solution is called Ringer's solution after the British physiologist, Sidney Ringer, who developed it.

	Na^+	K^+	Ca^{++}	Mg^{++}	$SO_4^=$	Cl^-
Sea water	100	3.6	3.9	12.1	20.9	181
Limulus	100	5.6	4.1	11.2	13.4	187
Cod	100	9.5	3.9	1.4		150
Man	100	6.8	3.1	0.7		129

Fig. 9-2

Distribution of ions in various extracellular fluids, with all values relative to sodium (Na^+) as 100.

The original discovery, as is so often the case in scientific work, was made as a result of chance. It was the practice at that time to use a simple salt solution (Na^+ and Cl^- ions) for bathing tissues. On one occasion, however, a particular batch of salt solution was found to keep frog hearts alive for many times the normal length of time. When it was found that an assistant in Ringer's laboratory had made that particular solution with tap water rather than with distilled water, the search was on for the other necessary ions. Ringer's solution resulted.

Another interesting fact about the ratio of ions in the ECF of animals can be seen by glancing at Fig. 9-2. Sea water, the ECF of marine invertebrates, and the ECF of vertebrates (including man) show a striking similarity in the relative amounts of the ions present. (The absolute amount of the different ions varies more widely; the concentration of salts in sea water and the ECF of marine invertebrates is roughly three times what it is in the ECF of vertebrates.) The similarity is sufficiently close that workers in the Woods Hole Marine Biological Laboratories often substitute diluted sea water for Ringer's solution in routine physiological experiments. This "Woods Hole Ringer's" serves the purpose admirably.

The similarity between the ratio of ions in sea water and in the blood plasma of animals lends strong support to the idea that life arose in the sea. (See Section 33-1.) Although animals now inhabit fresh water and the land, they must actively regulate the composition of their self-contained ECF so that its ionic composition continues to be compatible with the processes of life.

4. Foods and Vitamins. The ECF also contains organic compounds which serve as food or vitamins for the cells. Food substances serve as a source of energy and as a source of material for growth and repair. They include lipids, nitrogen-containing compounds such as amino acids, and perhaps most widespread of all, a carbohydrate source such as glucose. The blood plasma of man contains 0.1% of glucose or, as it is sometimes called, "blood sugar." In Chapter 26, we will examine some of the homeostatic mechanisms by which this level of glucose is maintained within fairly narrow limits in the ECF.

5. Hormones. Hormones are an important component of the ECF of vertebrates, higher plants, and perhaps all multicellular organisms. They are chemical substances, released into the ECF by certain cells, which affect the metabolic activities of other cells in the organism. Chapters 25 and 26 will be largely devoted to a consideration of these substances.

6. Wastes. The waste products of cell metabolism are also components of the ECF. Among the most important to animals are the waste products of protein and nucleoprotein metabolism. These nitrogen-containing wastes, such as ammonia and urea, are somewhat poisonous. Their level in the ECF must not be allowed to exceed certain limits or death will result. In most organisms, precise homeostatic devices (e.g. the kidney) have evolved which regulate the level of these wastes in the ECF. Although there are some cases where too low a level of a given waste in the ECF would be harmful, the major emphasis is on preventing too great an accumulation of the waste.

It is not always easy to distinguish clearly between cell wastes in the ECF and some of the chemical messengers mentioned above. A substance which is a waste product of the metabolism of one cell may well be necessary to the proper functioning of some other cell. For example, the carbon dioxide discharged into the ECF by all of our cells provides a necessary stimulus for that part of the central nervous system that controls the rate of our breathing. Here, then, is a case where too low a level in the ECF of a given waste would be as harmful as too high a level.

7. pH. An important requirement for the ECF is that it be neither too acid nor too alkaline. Degree of acidity is measured on a scale of pH units. Pure water, which is neutral, that is, neither acid nor alkaline, has a pH of 7. Acid substances are substances which produce more H^+ ions than are found in pure water. They have pH values of less than 7. Alkaline (or basic) substances are substances which combine with H^+ ions, thus leaving fewer than are found in pure water. They have pH values greater than 7 (Fig. 9-3). As we saw in Chapter 6 (see Section 6-9), both OH^- ions and HCO_3^- ions combine with H^+ ions:

$$OH^- + H^+ \rightleftharpoons H_2O$$

$$HCO_3^- + H^+ \rightleftharpoons H_2CO_3 \rightleftharpoons H_2O + CO_2.$$

Thus, when sodium hydroxide (NaOH) or sodium bicarbonate (NaHCO₃) is dissolved in water, a basic solution results.

The pH scale is a logarithmic one: each unit on the pH scale represents a tenfold increase or decrease in the concentration of H⁺ ions over the next lower or higher unit. For example, a solution with a pH of 5 is ten times more acid (has a concentration of H⁺ ten times greater) than a solution of pH 6.

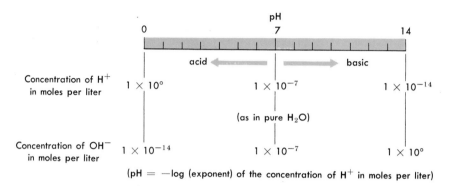

(pH = −log (exponent) of the concentration of H⁺ in moles per liter)

Fig. 9-3   The pH scale. A shift of one pH unit represents a tenfold shift in acidity. A solution of pH 7 is neutral.

Most living cells are extremely sensitive to changes in the pH of their ECF. The pH of human plasma is usually maintained at a value between 7.34 and 7.44. If these limits should be greatly exceeded (below pH 6.8 or above pH 7.8), serious illness and perhaps death would follow. Fortunately, our plasma is well supplied with substances called **buffers,** that act to prevent any sudden shift in pH. The proteins found in blood plasma act as buffers. If the pH should start to decrease (violent exercise or holding the breath will cause this), the proteins combine with the new H⁺ ions, thus keeping the pH constant. If the pH should start to rise, the proteins release H⁺ ions to the ECF, thus restoring the original condition. The plasma proteins thus serve as a homeostatic mechanism for maintaining a constant pH in the ECF.

Blood plasma also contains bicarbonate ions (HCO_3^-) which serve in the same capacity. In the presence of an increased concentration of H⁺ ions (and thus a decrease in pH), the following reaction occurs:

$$HCO_3^- + H^+ \rightleftharpoons H_2CO_3.$$

When the H_2CO_3 reaches the lungs, it decomposes into carbon dioxide (which passes into the air) and neutral water:

$$H_2CO_3 \rightleftharpoons H_2O + CO_2.$$

Thus the danger of too many H⁺ ions in the ECF is neatly avoided.

8.   Temperature. Another important characteristic of the ECF is its temperature. Protists have no control over the temperature of their ECF. It is simply a function of the climatic conditions around them. This is generally true of plants, invertebrate animals, and the so-called cold-blooded (or **poikilothermic**) vertebrates: the fishes, amphibians, and reptiles. In some of these cases, however, the organisms have a certain degree of control over the temperature of their ECF. When the temperature in a beehive becomes too high, the workers begin cooling the hive by bringing in water and fanning the air with their wings. Fanning brings in fresh air and also speeds the evaporation of the water, which is itself a cooling process.

Goldfish have been shown to seek water in a preferred temperature range. In fact, they have been trained in the laboratory to trigger the addition of cold water when their surroundings get too warm.

Many lizards also exert considerable control over the temperature of their ECF at least for the periods when they are active. Basking in the sun enables a lizard to raise its body temperature to the preferred range for its species even though the temperature of the surrounding air may be considerably cooler. When the air temperature becomes quite high, lizards can still maintain their preferred temperature by evaporating water from their tongue (panting) and retreating to shady locations.

It is among the birds and mammals, however, that we find the strictest control over the temperature of the ECF. Birds and mammals are able to maintain the temperature of their ECF within very narrow limits despite wide fluctuations in the temperature of the surrounding air. For this reason, they are often called "warm-blooded," or better, **homeothermic.** A healthy human is capable of maintaining the temperature of his ECF within a degree or so of 37.5° C (98.6° F) at rest or during violent exercise, in warm surroundings or cold. The homeostatic mechanisms by which this control is achieved will be discussed in Chapter 29.

EXCHANGE OF MATERIALS

At the beginning of this chapter it was stated that metabolism involves the exchange of matter and energy with the environment and the transformation of this matter and energy within the cell. The environment of an individual cell is its ECF. We must now examine the process by which substances are exchanged between it and the cell.

DIFFUSION   **9-3**

Some of the materials dissolved in the ECF enter the cell by diffusion across the cell membrane from the ECF into the cytoplasm. Similarly, other substances diffuse out of the cell into the ECF.

To help us understand the process of diffusion, consider what happens when a bottle of perfume is opened in one corner of a sealed room. Even with air currents completely eliminated, the odor of the perfume gradually spreads to every part of the room. Eventually the bottle of perfume becomes empty and the intensity of the odor is uniform throughout the room.

What has happened? The liquid perfume has evaporated. The molecules of which the perfume is composed have not, however, disappeared. At first they mix with the molecules of air in the vicinity of the bottle. Then, as time goes on, they spread to all parts of the room (Fig. 9-4). This process of diffusion continues until the molecules are uniformly distributed throughout the room. We can define diffusion as the net movement of molecules or ions from a region where they are in high concentration to a region of lower concentration.

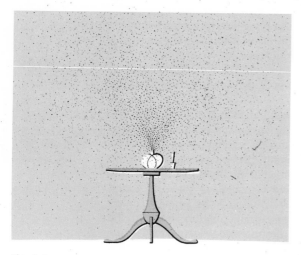

Fig. 9-4

Diffusion. Even in the absence of air currents, the perfume molecules will eventually become evenly distributed throughout the room. Their own random motion accounts for this.

What force accounts for this motion? It is believed that all the molecules in a gas (such as air) or in a solution are in constant random motion. This motion takes place in straight lines and continues in a given direction until one molecule collides with another and rebounds in a different direction.

One visible bit of evidence to support this theory is the phenomenon known as Brownian motion. If with a high-power microscope you examine a water suspension of tiny particles such as bacteria, you will see that the particles are in continual random motion or vibration. This motion is named after the English botanist Robert Brown, who first described it in 1827. It should not be confused with any swimming motions displayed by some bacteria. It is believed to be caused by continual collisions between the water molecules and the bacteria. It is thus an entirely physical process. Dead bacteria show Brownian motion just as well as living ones do. Why, though, do you suppose larger objects fail to show this activity?

The odds are that any object moving about entirely at random will gradually move away from its starting point. Furthermore, in the case of the perfume bottle, any molecule moving away from the bottle would be apt to travel farther than a molecule moving back towards the bottle. This is because there are more perfume molecules nearer the bottle and hence a greater chance of collisions to occur. Thus there will be a net movement of the molecules from the region of greater concentration to the region of lesser concentration. When the molecules are finally distributed evenly throughout the room, the process of diffusion ceases. This does not mean that motion of the molecules ceases. There is no longer a net movement or trend, however, and hence there is no more diffusion.

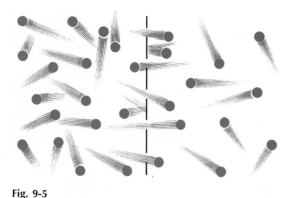

Fig. 9-5

Diffusion through a barrier. As long as there is a greater concentration of molecules on the left, more molecules will pass from left to right than from right to left.

In the case of the perfume bottle in the room, no barrier was placed between the region of high concentration and the region of low concentration. In the case of diffusion between cells and their ECF, a definite barrier, the cell membrane, is present. However, as long as there are pores in the membrane sufficiently large to let a given size of molecule pass through, diffusion of that substance can occur. A glance at Fig. 9-5 should make the mechanism clear. Whenever a small molecule strikes the macromolecules of which the membrane is made, it rebounds. If, however, it reaches the membrane in the vicinity of a pore, it can pass through to the other side. With a greater concentration of a given type of molecule on one side of the membrane than on the other, there will be more collisions with the membrane on that side. There will also be more successful passages through the membrane in this direction. Although molecules do pass through the membrane in both directions, diffusion is considered to occur only in the direction of greater movement.

Osmosis is simply a special case of diffusion. Chemists define osmosis as the diffusion of any solvent through a differentially permeable membrane. Cell membranes, having pores which permit the passage of some molecules but prevent the passage of others, are differentially permeable. The universal solvent in living things, as was mentioned earlier, is water. For our purposes, therefore, osmosis can be defined as the diffusion of water through a differentially permeable membrane from a region of high concentration to a region of low concentration. Note that concentration refers to the concentration of the solvent, water, and not to the concentration of molecules or ions which may be dissolved in the water. The exchange of water between the cell and its environment is such an important factor in cell function that it justifies the special name of osmosis.

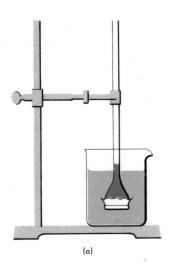 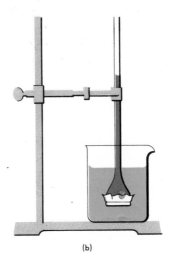

(a)　　　　(b)

Fig. 9-6

Osmometer. (a) At start. (b) A few hours later. The cellophane is a differentially permeable membrane; water molecules pass through it more readily than do sugar molecules.

An experiment that demonstrates osmosis is shown in Fig. 9-6. The lower opening of the glass tube is covered with a sheet of cellophane. This acts as a differentially permeable membrane, permitting the rapid passage of water molecules but obstructing the passage of larger molecules. The interior of the tube is filled with molasses, a concentrated solution of sugar in water. The whole apparatus is placed in a beaker containing distilled water. In which direction will osmosis occur? The water concentration in the beaker is 100%. The water concentration inside the tube is less than this because a given volume of molasses contains fewer water molecules than the same volume of distilled water. There is, therefore, a net movement of water molecules through the cellophane membrane and into the tube.

As additional water molecules enter the tube, the volume of fluid increases. The molasses is forced up the tube. This force arises from pressure exerted by the diffusion of water molecules into the tube. The pressure is called osmotic pressure. The greater the difference in water concentration on either side of the membrane, the greater the tendency for osmosis to occur and thus the greater the osmotic pressure. In fact, when the column of molasses stops rising, we have a rough measure of the osmotic pressure of the system. The weight of the column of water finally counterbalances the osmotic pressure and osmosis ceases. Note that the water concentrations on the two sides of the membrane are still not equal by any means. However, the increase of pressure on the inner surface of the membrane, created by the weight of the column of molasses above, causes water molecules to be forced or filtered back out through the pores. When the rate at which this filtration process occurs becomes equal to the rate at which water molecules are coming in because of the difference in concentration, osmosis ceases.

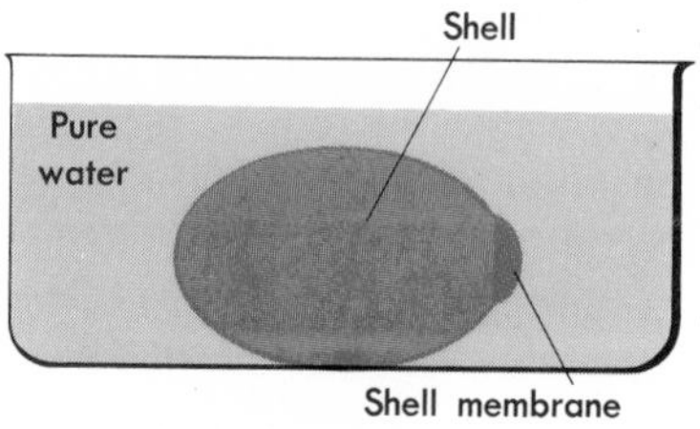

Fig. 9-7

Egg osmometer. The pores of the shell membrane permit water molecules to diffuse into the egg but are too small to let the macromolecules within the egg diffuse out. Consequently, the volume of materials within the egg increases until increasing pressure ruptures the membrane.

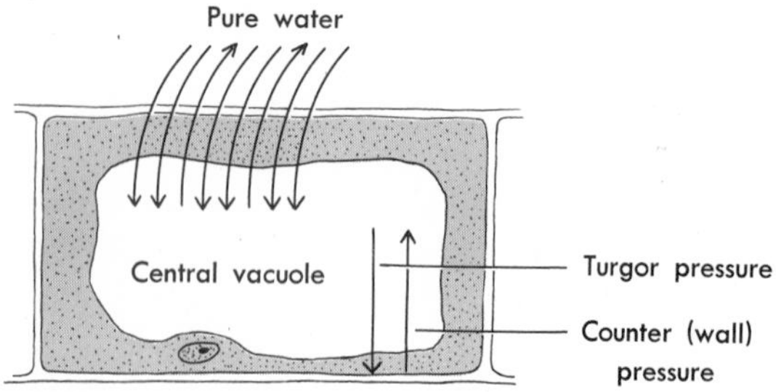

Fig. 9-8

When the pressure within the cell finally equals the osmotic pressure, the movement of water in and out of the cell will reach equilibrium.

Another experiment showing the effects of osmosis is depicted in Fig. 9-7. The shell membrane of a hen's egg is a differentially permeable membrane. Its pores are large enough to allow the easy passage of water molecules, but are not large enough to allow larger fat and protein molecules to get through. If after carefully removing a portion of the waterproof shell (by dissolving it away in dilute acid), one places the egg in pure water, water will diffuse into the egg. This osmosis occurs because there is a greater concentration of water outside the egg (100%) than within. The surrounding water is said to be **hypotonic** to the contents of the egg. As osmosis continues, more and more water accumulates within the egg and this crowding in of additional molecules results in a buildup of pressure. The development of pressure within a cell (and the egg *is* a single cell) as a result of the diffusion of water into it is called **turgor.** Although the remaining portion of the shell can resist the pressure, the unprotected membrane cannot. Ultimately it bursts.

What of organisms that spend their lives in fresh water? Certainly the water concentration of their cytoplasm can never approach that of the pure water surrounding them. In the case of the cells of freshwater plants, water passes into the cell by osmosis and turgor quickly develops. The strong cellulose walls of the cells are, however, capable of withstanding this pressure. Soon the pressure within the cell counterbalances the tendency of the water molecules to pass in by osmosis even though the two water concentrations are not equal. At this point, osmosis ceases (Fig. 9-8). Turgor is important in the life of many plants as it permits nonwoody tissues such as leaves to become rigid. Loss of turgor results in wilting.

Fresh-water animals and protozoans lack cellulose cell walls so they must cope differently with life in a hypotonic environment. Water enters their cells continually by osmosis but only slight turgor can safely be developed. The problem is solved by employing energy and some contractile structure to pump the excess water back out into the environment. The single-celled amoeba accomplishes this by means of a contractile vacuole (Fig. 9-9), in which water entering the cell by osmosis is collected. When the vacuole is filled, the amoeba contracts it forcing the water out through a pore which forms momentarily in the cell membrane. Note that the water, which had entered the cell as a result of the random molecular activity of osmosis, leaves the cell by flowing out because of a force generated by the cell. The creation of this force requires the expenditure of energy by the cell. In Chapter 16, we will examine some of the mechanisms by means of which fresh-water animals such as fishes cope with *their* hypotonic environment.

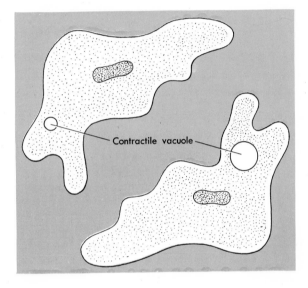

Fig. 9-9

The amoeba bails out the continual influx of water from its hypotonic surroundings by alternately filling and emptying its contractile vacuole. The contents of the vacuole may be discharged at any point on the surface of the cell.

Life in the oceans involves quite different osmotic conditions than life in fresh water. Sea water contains about 3.5% of various ions, especially Na^+ and Cl^-. This results in a water concentration which is approximately the same as that in the cytoplasm of marine plants and the invertebrate animals that live in the sea. Consequently, these organisms are able to exist in a state of equilibrium with respect to the water in their surroundings. They neither gain nor lose water by osmosis. We say that sea water is **isotonic** to their cytoplasm.

That a given volume of sea water is about 3% salt by weight, and thus 97% water, does not mean that the water concentration of the cytoplasm of these marine plants and animals is also 97% by weight. The speed with which diffusion or osmosis takes place is a measure of the difference in the number, not weight, of the molecules or ions involved. When osmosis occurs, the region of higher water concentration is simply the region which contains the greater number of water molecules in a given volume of the mixture. The cytoplasm of these marine organisms may contain as little as 80-90% water by weight. However, much of the remaining material in the cytoplasm consists of protein. These macromolecules make up a substantial fraction of the weight of the cytoplasm but contribute only a minor osmotic effect because of the relatively small number of molecules involved. Similarly, a 0.9% salt solution (99.1% water) is isotonic to human blood plasma although the latter contains only 90% water by weight. The number of water molecules in a given volume of each of the two solutions is, however, the same.

When a fresh-water (or terrestrial) plant is placed in sea water, its cells quickly lose turgor and the plant wilts. This is because a given volume of seawater contains a smaller number of water molecules than a given volume of the cytoplasm of these plants. The sea water is said to be **hypertonic** to the cytoplasm. As water continues to diffuse from the cytoplasm into the sea water, the protoplast gradually shrinks. This condition is known as **plasmolysis.** Note in the chapter opening illustration how the protoplasts have pulled away from the cell walls, which still retain their original shape.

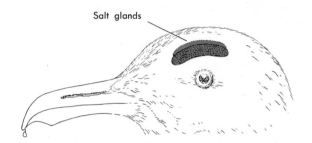

Salt glands

Fig. 9-10

The salt glands of the herring gull. The fluid excreted by the glands is saltier than the blood.

The ECF of bony fishes (Osteichthyes) has a water concentration substantially higher than that of sea water. Thus they live in a medium which is hypertonic. Whereas fresh-water organisms have to cope with water passing continually into their body by osmosis, the salt-water bony fish continually loses water by osmosis. Once again, however, survival depends upon the expenditure of energy to combat the force of osmosis. The fish drinks sea water and then uses metabolic energy to desalt it. The salt is transported back into the environment at the gills. Marine birds, which sometimes pass long periods of time away from fresh water, and sea turtles use a similar device. They, too, drink salt water to take care of their water needs and use metabolic energy to desalt it. The salt is extracted by two glands in the head and released (in a very concentrated solution) to the outside through the nostrils (see Fig. 9-10).

9-5   **ACTIVE TRANSPORT**

The ability of marine bony fishes and marine birds to transport ions from a region where they are in low concentration (the ECF) to a region where they are in high concentration (the ocean and the ducts of the salt glands, respectively) implies that some force other than diffusion is at work. In both cases, the transport of ions occurs against the concentration gradient and hence in a direction opposite to that which would occur by diffusion alone. This movement of ions or molecules against a concentration gradient is known as active transport.

It is described as active because the cell must expend energy to accomplish the transport against the passive force of diffusion. The ability of cells to accomplish active transport of ions and molecules to or from the ECF is a widespread one. Marine organisms frequently have certain ions in their cytoplasm in concentrations a thousand or more times greater than in the surrounding sea water. Iodine in brown algae and vanadium in certain tunicates are found concentrated in this way. This must mean that these cells have managed to transport ions actively from the sea water to their cytoplasm.

The cells lining the intestine of the rat can transport glucose actively from a lower concentration in the intestine to a higher concentration in the blood. Most cells actively transport sodium ions out of the cell and potassium ions into the cell. The transmission of nerve impulses (to be discussed in Chapter 28) depends upon this phenomenon. The filling of the amoeba's contractile vacuole requires the active transport of water molecules from the cytoplasm into the vacuole itself.

The mechanism by which active transport is accomplished is not yet clearly understood. There is no doubt that the cell must use some of the energy produced during its metabolism to carry out active transport. Anything that interferes with the cell's production of energy also interferes with active transport. It is probable that specific enzymes are required which serve to carry a given molecule or ion from one side of the cell membrane to the other. In any case, the plasma membrane cannot be considered as simply a passive barrier to the diffusion of molecules. It may exert a very decided influence on what substances pass through it.

PHAGOCYTOSIS AND PINOCYTOSIS 9-6

Still another mechanism by which the cell transports materials from the ECF into the interior is to engulf them by folding inward a portion of the cell membrane. The pouch that results then breaks loose from the outer portion of the membrane and forms a vacuole within the cytoplasm. In some cells, large particles the size of bacteria or diatoms may be engulfed in this manner. The process is called **phagocytosis** or "cell eating." The amoeba derives its nourishment by ingesting smaller microorganisms in this fashion (Fig. 9-11). Phagocytic cells in the blood of many animals serve the extremely valuable function of engulfing foreign particles, such as bacteria, that may get into the animal's body. Phagocytosis also permits any molecules present in the surrounding medium to which the cell membrane is normally impermeable to gain entry into the cell along with the ingested food particles.

The ability to engulf solid materials is found in only a few kinds of cells. Many cells, however, are able to carry on a similar action called **pinocytosis.** In pinocytosis ("cell drinking"), the cell engulfs droplets of the surrounding ECF by a mechanism quite similar to that of phagocytosis, although the pockets formed by the cell membrane are smaller. Figure 9-12 is an electron micrograph of a section of the wall of a capillary (the smallest type of blood vessel in our bodies). At the top is the interior or bore of the capillary. In the middle is the tissue space separating the capillary wall from a

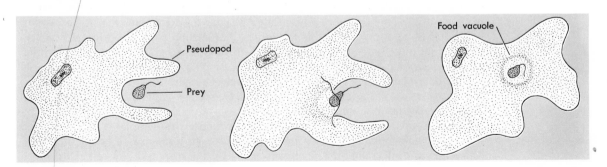

Phagocytosis in the amoeba. Even when totally engulfed, the victim is separated from the cytoplasm of the amoeba by a membrane around the food vacuole.

Fig. 9-11

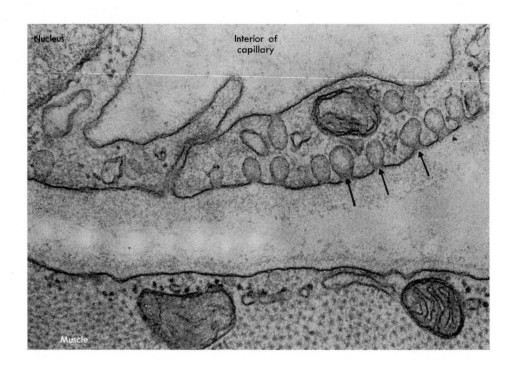

Labels in image: Nucleus, Interior of capillary, Muscle

Fig. 9-12 Pinocytosis in the thin cell that forms the wall of a capillary. Note that the inpocketings have formed on both surfaces of the cell. (Mag: 67,500 X, from Fawcett: *The Cell: Its Organelles and Inclusions,* W. B. Saunders Co., 1966.)

nearby muscle cell (bottom). The small inpocketings of the cell membrane are clearly seen. Most of these are engulfing the ECF of the tissue space, but some can also be seen on the other side of the wall, apparently engulfing fluid from within the capillary.

Pinocytosis requires the expenditure of energy by the cell and enables materials to enter the cell even though they are present in the ECF in a concentration less than that within the cell. In this sense, then, pinocytosis is a special case of active transport, although it is probably not the only mechanism by which active transport occurs.

While the size of the pockets formed in phagocytosis and pinocytosis is quite different, there is evidence to suggest that fundamentally the processes are similar. In cells such as the amoeba, where both phagocytosis and pinocytosis can occur, either activity temporarily inhibits the other. Presumably, an amoeba has only a certain amount of cell membrane to devote to this inpocketing activity at any one time. An amoeba which has been engulfing diatoms by phagocytosis is temporarily unable to carry on as much pinocytosis as usual. The reverse is also true.

The mere act of folding in a bit of the cell membrane with its content of materials from the ECF does not actually get these materials into the cytoplasm. They are still retained within vacuoles which, although surrounded by cytoplasm, are separated from it by a membrane. In the amoeba, the vacuole formed as a result of phagocytosis remains intact until it is finally discharged at the margin of the cell. During the period between its formation and discharge, however, some substances are certainly exchanged between it and the surrounding cytoplasm. Digestive enzymes enter the vacuole. This probably occurs when lysosomes (see Section 8-11) fuse with it. The small molecules produced by digestion pass through the vacuolar membrane

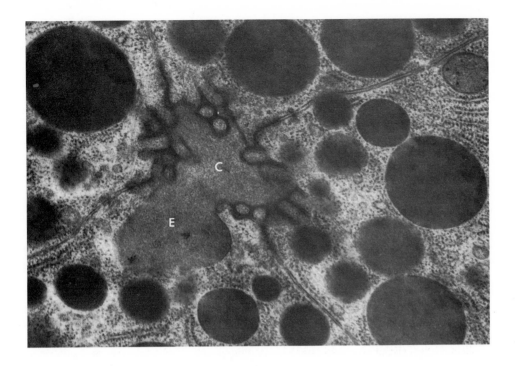

Reverse phagocytosis. The large spherical bodies contain digestive enzymes. One is seen in the process of discharging its contents (E) into the intercellular canal (C) where the corners of these four bat pancreas cells meet. (Mag: 30,000 X, from Fawcett: *The Cell: Its Organelles and Inclusions*, W. B. Saunders Co., 1966.)

Fig. 9-13

into the cytoplasm. As for pinocytotic vacuoles, a similar mechanism may be at work. There is good evidence that digestion of macromolecules occurs within them. The products of digestion (e.g. glucose) quickly enter the cytoplasm from the vacuoles although these same substances cross *cell* membranes far more slowly.

REVERSE PHAGOCYTOSIS AND PINOCYTOSIS

9-7

Just as materials can also *leave* cells by diffusion and active transport, so they may also leave by reverse phagocytosis or pinocytosis. The discharge of the old food vacuole of an amoeba, mentioned above, is an example of reverse phagocytosis. In cells that secrete large amounts of protein, the protein first accumulates in a membrane-bounded sac within the Golgi complex. This moves to the surface of the cell where its membrane fuses with the cell membrane, and it discharges its contents to the outside (Fig. 9-13).

Reverse pinocytosis has also been observed. The cells lining our intestine synthesize tiny droplets of fat and then discharge these from the cell by reverse pinocytosis. It may even be that some of the tiny vacuoles shown in Fig. 9-12 are not taking up material by pinocytosis, but are instead discharging material by reverse pinocytosis. In other words, the pinocytotic vacuoles formed at one surface of the cell may, after being detached, move through the cell to the other surface and there discharge their contents. In this way, materials can be moved efficiently through the capillary wall.

CELL CHEMISTRY

The exchange of materials beween a cell and the ECF is one aspect of metabolism. The chemical transformation of these materials within the cell is another. Literally hundreds of the chemical changes that occur within cells have been discovered and the list grows longer every year. In the remaining chapters of Part IV, several of the most common and most important of these will be described. Despite their variety, we will find that there is one feature they all share: each chemical change can occur only in the presence of a specific enzyme.

9-8   ENZYMES

In Chapter 6 we saw that even energy-yielding reactions, such as the burning of a strip of magnesium, require the input of some energy before they can proceed spontaneously. This energy is known as the energy of activation. Glucose exposed to oxygen in the air can become oxidized to carbon dioxide and water, but at room temperature the process goes on so slowly as to be imperceptible. When glucose is heated in a flame, however, a greater number of molecules receive their necessary energy of activation and the process proceeds more rapidly. Once a large number of molecules are being oxidized, the energy liberated supplies nearby molecules with their energy of activation. Soon the process becomes self-sustaining and the sugar burns rapidly.

The temperature necessary for this to occur is much higher than that which can be tolerated within living cells. Nevertheless, the oxidation of glucose can go on within living cells at a rapid rate and still at a low temperature. How is this accomplished? In Chapter 6 we saw that substances called catalysts are able to lower the activation energy of molecules and thus permit them to undergo rapid chemical change at lower temperatures. Respiration in living cells likewise requires the activity of catalysts to accomplish this same function. These catalysts are called **enzymes.**

Enzymes, like other types of catalysts, do not participate permanently in the chemical change that they promote. When the chemical change is completed, the enzyme is released unchanged. Because enzymes are not used up by the processes they catalyze, they may be re-used again and again. A single molecule of the enzyme catalase (see Section 6-11) is capable of catalyzing the breakdown of approximately 10 million H_2O_2 molecules every minute at the temperature of ice water ($0°$ C)! Because enzymes can be re-used, only small amounts of each enzyme are needed by a single cell. Since a single cell may be capable of carrying out over a thousand different chemical reactions, and each one of these probably requires its own special enzyme, it is fortunate that large quantities of enzymes are not necessary.

The fact that each chemical reaction in the cell requires its own special enzyme and, conversely, that a single enzyme can catalyze only one (or sometimes a few quite similar) chemical reactions requires some explanation. One theory which has been created to explain this specific relationship between an enzyme and the substance upon which it acts (its **substrate**) is called the **lock-and-key theory.** According to this theory, an enzyme actually combines with the molecule of its substrate for a brief period of time. Presumably the combination requires that each molecule have a shape complementary to that of the other. This would explain the specificity of enzymes. Different substrate molecules each possess a different shape and thus require a different enzyme. The combination between enzyme and substrate makes the substrate molecule more reactive; that is, it lowers the energy necessary for the substrate molecule to undergo chemical change. Once the chemical transformation in the substrate molecule is completed, the products leave the enzyme, which then is free to repeat the process with a new substrate molecule. Figure 9-14 shows how this process is thought to work.

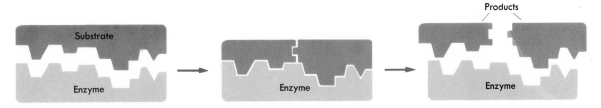

The "lock-and-key" theory of enzyme action. **Fig. 9-14**

There is quite a bit of experimental evidence to support the idea that the specific action of enzymes depends upon a brief union between the enzyme molecule and the substrate molecule. One type of evidence is the phenomenon of competitive inhibition of enzymes. Certain poisons exert their influence by blocking normal enzyme activity. It is thought that the shape of the poison molecule is so similar to that of the normal substrate molecule that the enzyme combines with it instead. However, the enzyme is not able to promote the chemical change of the new molecule. The poison molecule remains attached to the enzyme molecule, which is therefore no longer able to carry out its normal function. Among our vital enzymes is one that catalyzes the oxidation of succinic acid, a reaction which is an essential part of cellular respiration. The compound malonic acid blocks the activity of this enzyme. The molecular structure of malonic acid is sufficiently similar to that of succinic acid (Fig. 9-15) that it presumably combines with the enzyme but cannot then be transformed and released. The enzyme molecule is thus kept from combining with its normal substrate.

One difficulty that has been encountered in trying to support this picture of enzyme action has been the problem of determining what the actual shape of any enzyme molecule is. All enzymes are proteins and hence exceedingly complex molecules. Only recently has the chemical and physical analysis of certain proteins begun to reveal their shapes. One of these is an enzyme, lysozyme, that is found in

(a) Schematic representation of the action of the enzyme, succinic dehydrogenase, on succinic acid. (b) The competitive inhibition of the enzyme by malonic acid. **Fig. 9-15**

egg white and such body secretions as tears. It has a strong antibacterial action because its substrate is the polysaccharide that makes up the cell walls of bacteria.

The lysozyme molecule appears to be roughly globular in shape but with a long, narrow cleft on one surface. The long cellulose-like molecule (Fig. 7-5) of its substrate fits into this cleft. When in the cleft, one of the sugar units in the molecule is twisted out of its normal position. This seems to impart the necessary energy of activation, and the bridge between that sugar residue and the next is broken. In this way, the structure of the bacterial cell wall is broken down. (You can read an account of these discoveries in Reference 9 listed at the end of the chapter.)

So many enzymes have been discovered in living cells that some uniform system of naming them has become essential. Some enzymes are named by using a prefix taken from the name of the substrate and the suffix *-ase*. Thus fat-digesting enzymes are called lipases, and protein-digesting enzymes are proteinases. Some of the more recently discovered enzymes are named by giving the full name of the substrate, followed by the action carried out on the substrate and then the suffix *-ase*. Thus the enzyme which oxidizes triose phosphate (by removing two hydrogen atoms) is called triose phosphate dehydrogenase. Some of the enzymes that were discovered early in the history of enzyme chemistry still retain their early names and may not adhere to the principles just described. Pepsin and trypsin (see Section 10-7) are two examples in this category.

All of the enzymes that have been discovered so far are proteins and are quickly destroyed by high temperatures. Just as boiling water will denature or "cook" the proteins in an egg (see Section 7-3), so it will quickly inactivate enzymes. Enzymes are also sensitive to change in pH. Each enzyme operates most effectively at a certain pH, its activity diminishing at values above or below that point. The protein-digesting enzyme pepsin works most effectively at a pH of 1-2 while the related enzyme trypsin is quite inactive at that pH but functions effectively at a pH of 8 (Fig. 10-9).

Many enzymes require for their action some additional substance. This accessory substance may be a relatively small molecule attached firmly to the protein itself. It is then called a prosthetic group. Some of our vitamins (e.g. riboflavin) function as the prosthetic group of certain enzymes. Some trace element ions such as Zn^{++}, Cu^{++}, and Co^{++} are also found in the prosthetic group of enzymes. Sometimes enzyme activity requires only that the accessory substance unite briefly with the enzyme molecule, the rest of the time simply being present in the surrounding medium. Such substances are called coenzymes. Some of our vitamins function as parts of coenzymes. Some trace element ions (e.g., Mg^{++}) need only be present in the surrounding medium for enzyme activity to go on.

Considering the large number of enzymes in the living cell, one might well ask how their activity is regulated. A number of mechanisms play a part in making enzyme action within the cell efficient and well coordinated.

For those enzymes, such as proteinases, which can attack the very substance of the cell itself, we find that their action is inhibited while they are present within the cell. The proteinase pepsin, for example, is manufactured by the cell in an inactive form, pepsinogen. Only when exposed to conditions of low pH outside of the cell is the inhibiting portion of the enzyme molecule removed and the active pepsin produced. Other potentially destructive enzymes are sequestered in the lysosomes (see Section 8-11) and thus isolated from the rest of the cell.

Many of the cell's enzymes cannot move freely within the cell but are, instead, arranged in definite patterns. The enzymes within mitochondria and chloroplasts appear to be organized spatially in such a way that they interact with the greatest efficiency. It is quite likely that spatially organized enzyme molecules are also present on the cell membrane and the membranes of the endoplasmic reticulum.

The activity of enzymes within the cell is also closely regulated by the need for them. If the product of a series of enzymatic reactions (e.g., an amino acid) begins to accumulate within the cell, it specifically inhibits the action of the first enzyme involved in its synthesis. Thus further production of that amino acid is temporarily halted. On the other hand, the accumulation of a substance within the cell may specifically activate the enzyme for which it is the *substrate*. This action also reduces its concentration to normal levels.

The mechanisms mentioned above ensure that the activity of enzymes already present in the cell will be properly regulated. What of enzymes that may not be needed at all or that may be needed but are not present? Here, too, delicate controls are at work. These regulate the rate at which new enzymes are synthesized. If, for example, excess quantities of an amino acid are supplied to a cell from its ECF, the synthesis of all the enzymes by which the cell ordinarily would produce that amino acid for itself will be halted. Thus the cell enhances its efficiency by not producing enzymes that it does not need. Conversely, if a new substrate is made available to the cell, it will stimulate the synthesis of the enzymes needed to cope with it. Yeast cells do not ordinarily ferment the disaccharide lactose and ordinarily no lactase can be detected within their cells. If grown in solutions containing lactose, however, they eventually begin producing lactase and begin to metabolize the sugar.

In these cases where the *synthesis* of enzymes is being regulated, it is clear that this regulation works through the hereditary controls coded in the DNA of the nucleus. The mechanisms by which portions of the hereditary code are thought to be turned on and off in response to the needs of the cell will be examined in later chapters.

Whether acting on the enzymes already present within the cell or on the rate of synthesis of new enzymes, it is clear that these control mechanisms work together to stabilize the levels of substrates and products in the cell. In a sense, then, these mechanisms are homeostatic devices, working within the cell, that regulate enzyme activity with the utmost efficiency and in harmony with the changing needs of the cell.

Metabolism in plants and chlorophyll-containing protists includes the manufacture, by photosynthesis, of organic molecules from inorganic ones taken in from the environment. The nutrition of these organisms is said to be **autotrophic.** Animals and all the other organisms that lack chlorophyll must secure their organic molecules from the environment. This form of nutrition is referred to as **heterotrophic.** The way in which heterotrophic organisms secure their food molecules is the topic of the next chapter.

EXERCISES AND PROBLEMS

1 Describe three different ways in which materials in the human intestine might enter the cells lining it.

2 How can coenzymes be separated from their enzymes?

3 After the molasses reaches its maximum height (see Fig. 9-6), what will happen? Why?

4 Which will have the higher osmotic pressure, a 1-molar solution of glucose or a 1-molar solution of salt? Why?

5 A single molecule of catalase can decompose ten million molecules of H_2O_2 each minute at 0° C. What would you expect the approximate figure to be at 10° C?

6 What would happen if (a) red blood corpuscles, (b) plant cells, (c) an amoeba were placed in distilled water? Explain.

7 What would happen if (a) red blood corpuscles or (b) plant cells were placed in sea water? Explain.

8 What would happen if an amoeba were placed in an isotonic solution?

9 Distinguish between a coenzyme and a prosthetic group.

10 If a mole (28 g) of nitrogen molecules (N_2) and a mole (28 g) of ethylene molecules (CH_2CH_2) were released on opposite sides of a partition that divided a room into equal volumes and then the partition were removed, do you think diffusion of the molecules would occur? Explain.

REFERENCES

1 Wolf, A. V., "Body Water," *Scientific American*, Nov., 1958. Discusses the distribution of water in the body and the physiology of water balance.

2 Anderson, A. J., and E. J. Underwood, "Trace-Element Deserts," *Scientific American*, Jan., 1959. Discusses the importance of trace elements to plants and animals and tells how the addition of small quantities of these substances to the soil is bringing fertility to formerly unproductive regions of Australia.

3 Bogert, C. M., "How Reptiles Regulate Their Body Temperature," *Scientific American*, April, 1959.

4 Holter, H., "How Things Get into Cells," *Scientific American*, Reprint No. 96, September, 1961. An excellent review of the forces of passive and active transport across cell membranes.

5 Solomon, A. K., "Pores in the Cell Membrane," *Scientific American*, Reprint No. 76, December, 1960. A beautiful illustration of the way physical analysis and experimentation can unlock the secrets of biological function.

6 Schmidt-Nielsen, K., "Salt Glands," *Scientific American*, January, 1959. Shows how active transport enables marine reptiles and birds to desalt the sea water they drink.

7 Rustad, R. C., "Pinocytosis," *Scientific American*, April, 1961. Shows how molecules too large to enter the cell by diffusion can be actively engulfed by the cell.

8 Buchner, E., "Alcoholic Fermentation without Yeast Cells," *Great Experiments in Biology*, ed. by M. L. Gabriel and S. Fogel, Prentice-Hall, Inc., 1955. A report of the first demonstration (accidental) that the biochemical activities of a cell may be duplicated by enzymes extracted from the cell.

9 Phillips, D. C., "The Three-dimensional Structure of an Enzyme Molecule," *Scientific American*, Reprint No. 1055, November, 1966. Describes how the shape of the enzyme lysozyme was worked out and how this shape accounts for the antibacterial action of the enzyme.

10 Changeux, J.-P., "The Control of Biochemical Reactions," *Scientific American*, Reprint No. 1008, April, 1965.

Mycelium of a bread mold.

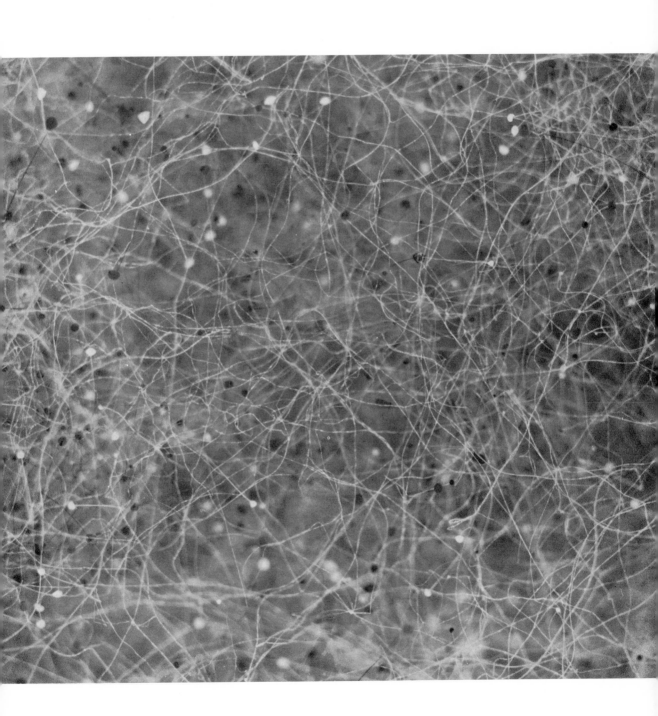

All organisms require a fairly steady supply of materials and energy from the environment in order to stay alive. For many, the chief supply of materials and the only supply of energy come from fairly complex, energy-rich, organic molecules secured directly or indirectly from the environment. (What is the ultimate source of these molecules?) Nutrition that involves dependence upon preformed organic molecules is called **heterotrophic** nutrition, and the organisms using this kind of nutrition are called heterotrophs. The nonchlorophyll-containing protists, the few nongreen plants, and all animals are heterotrophic.

10-1   REQUIREMENTS

The organic molecules that serve as a source of material and energy are the sugars, amino acids, fatty acids and glycerol, and (for purposes of synthesis only) the vitamins. Not all heterotrophs depend upon all these organic molecules. Some protists, for example the bacterium *E. coli,* thrive with just sugar as their source of energy. They must, however, take in some inorganic materials such as nitrates in order to synthesize all their other organic constituents. Man is quite demanding in his requirements for preformed organic molecules. He requires carbohydrates, eight of the twenty amino acids found in his body proteins (these are the "essential" amino acids—from them he can synthesize the other 12), and probably eight or more vitamins. Although he can manufacture fats from sugars, he seems to need certain special fats in his diet also.

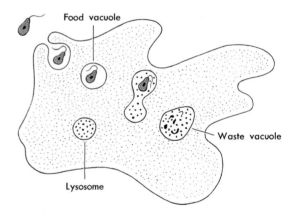

Fig. 10-1

Intracellular digestion in the amoeba. Digestive enzymes stored within lysosomes hydrolyze the food molecules of the prey into smaller molecules that can be absorbed through the vacuolar membrane into the cytoplasm.

10-2   INTRACELLULAR DIGESTION

Solid food materials must be broken down into a solution of relatively small, soluble, organic molecules before they can be used by heterotrophic organisms. This breakdown process is called **digestion.** In some protists and animals, digestion is intracellular, that is, it occurs after the solid material has actually been engulfed by a cell.

The protist *Amoeba* engulfs solid particles such as diatoms or small protozoans by phagocytosis (see Section 9-6). The prey, with a small amount of the ECF, is incorporated into a **food vacuole** within the cytoplasm of the amoeba. Next, the digestible portions of the food material are digested by enzymes secreted into the vacuole from lysosomes that fuse with it (Fig. 10-1). The soluble food molecules then pass through the vacuolar membrane into the rest of the cell. Indigestible parts, such as the silica shells of diatoms, are eventually discharged to the outside.

Although digestion in the amoeba can properly be described as intracellular, we should keep in mind the definite membrane that persists between the diatom in its food vacuole and the remainder of the cytoplasm.

It is obvious that phagocytosis can occur only if the food materials available to the organism are smaller than its phagocytic cells. It is not surprising, therefore, that feeding by phagocytosis is restricted to those animals that are adapted to secure food materials much smaller than themselves. In the sponge, as we have seen (Section 5-1), this is accomplished by filtering microscopic organisms from the surrounding water. Planarians eat much larger chunks of food but are able to break these up mechanically until they are sufficiently small to be engulfed by the phagocytic cells lining the gastrovascular cavity (Fig. 5-5).

EXTRACELLULAR DIGESTION   10-3

A second solution to the problem of digesting food is to secrete the digestive enzymes from the cell and digest the food outside the cell, that is, extracellularly. Once the food is digested, the small, soluble molecules produced (e.g., sugars, amino acids) can pass by diffusion or active transport across the cell membrane and into the cell.

Perhaps the simplest approach to extracellular digestion is that employed by **saprophytes.** Saprophytes secure their food from nonliving but organic matter, such as dead bodies of plants and animals, food products, excrement, etc. The nutrition of the common bread mold *Rhizopus nigricans* is typical of the group. It thrives on a sub-strate of moist bread kept in a dark location (Fig. 10-2). The bread, a man-made product of a once-living wheat plant, supplies all the dietary needs of the mold. The starch mole-cules in the bread are too large, however, to pass directly through the membrane surround-ing the cytoplasmic contents of the hyphae. To convert these large, insoluble starch mole-cules into smaller, soluble molecules that can enter the mycelium requires a starch-digesting enzyme, or **amylase.** *Rhizopus* secretes this en-zyme onto the bread and thus digestion occurs extracellularly. The sugar molecules produced are then absorbed into the mycelium.

This pattern of extracellular digestion of foods in the substrate is typical of all fungi and most bacteria. Puffballs growing on the stump of a dead tree and toadstools appear-ing above the humus-rich forest soil are just two other illustrations of this kind of nutrition (Fig. 3-11).

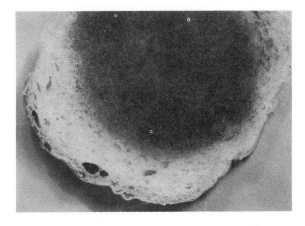

Fig. 10-2

A common bread mold, *Rhizopus nigricans*, growing on a piece of bread. This saprophyte secures all its nourish-ment by secreting digestive enzymes on the bread and absorbing the products of digestion.

Most animals, too, digest their food extracellularly. Rarely, though, do they live in a location where they are literally surrounded by a substrate of organic matter. Instead, they secure by one means or another food materials which appear from time to time in their surroundings. They place this food in a pouch or tube within their body, a process called **ingestion.** Then they secrete their enzymes there and diges-tion takes place. Thus the enzymes are localized where the food is, rather than secreted freely into the surroundings.

The fresh-water cnidarian *Hydra* paralyzes and seizes living prey, such as microscopic crustaceans, that swim into its nematocyst-laden tentacles. The hydra's mouth then opens and the prey is ingested into a gastrovascular cavity (Fig. 10-3). W. F. Loomis has discovered that this sequence of actions is triggered by low concentrations of the tripeptide (three amino acids linked together) glutathione. Apparently, when the prey blunders into contact with a tentacle, the penetration of its body by a nematocyst causes the release of glutathione and this, in turn, initiates the subsequent feeding action. A small quantity of glutathione purchased at a laboratory supply house and a few hydra can provide many interesting hours of observation and experiment.

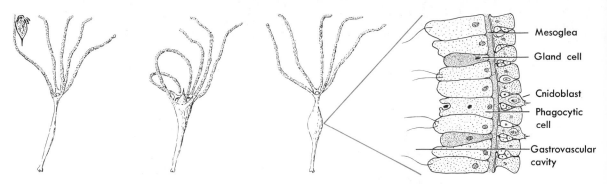

Mesoglea

Gland cell

Cnidoblast

Phagocytic cell

Gastrovascular cavity

Fig. 10-3   Feeding actions of the hydra. Preliminary digestion is accomplished in the gastrovascular cavity with enzymes secreted by the gland cells. Final digestion is intracellular following phagocytosis.

Among the cells lining the gastrovascular cavity are gland cells which secrete digestive enzymes into the fluid of the gastrovascular cavity. There the initial digestion of the prey takes place. When the prey has been reduced to small but still solid particles, these are engulfed by other, phagocytic, cells in the lining of the cavity. Final digestion is then completed within the food vacuoles just as it is in the amoeba. Thus the hydra uses both extracellular and intracellular digestion.

Although ingestion is described as the taking of food-containing solids into the organism, these solids are taken in only in a superficial sense. The cavity or tube that receives the solid food materials is really only a portion of the outside of the organism turned inward. A marble swallowed by a baby never enters any cell nor participates in any metabolic activity. A day or two later it emerges at the other end quite unchanged. The eating habits of the starfish serve as a good illustration of this principle. The starfish, which feeds upon bivalve mollusks such as oysters, must first attach itself by its tube feet to the two shells of its prey. It then applies a steady pull on the shells. Eventually, the shells become separated sufficiently to expose the soft, digestible parts of the oyster. When this occurs, the starfish pushes a portion of its stomach out through its mouth. Of course, the stomach turns inside out as it comes out. With the inner surface of the stomach applied to the soft body of the oyster, digestive enzymes are secreted and the process of digestion begins. When the process is partially completed, the starfish swallows its stomach back and with it the remains of the oyster. Digestion is then completed, but still quite outside of the lining of cells which serves as the barrier between the tissues and organs of the starfish and the external environment. There is no phagocytosis and hence no intracellular digestion.

The digestive apparatus of the starfish consists of a tube (alimentary canal) with an entrance (the mouth) and a separate exit (the anus). This system is an improvement over the saclike system of cnidarians and flatworms because it permits a one-way flow of food materials and consequently greater efficiency in their handling. Incoming food need not mix with food that is almost completely digested or with wastes. The various stages in chemical digestion can follow one another in an assembly-line fashion. Each portion of the alimentary canal may be modified to carry out one, or a few, special aspects of the entire process. Along with the increased efficiency which a tubular alimentary canal permits, we find that in more complex animals, portions of the alimentary canal are pushed out into accessory structures, the digestive glands. These produce digestive enzymes and other important substances which then flow through ducts to the main portion of the alimentary canal. Here the foods are completely digested into a solution of molecules which can be absorbed by the cells lining the alimentary canal.

A FILTER FEEDER: THE CLAM 10-4

Some fresh-water and many marine animals feed by taking in a stream of water and filtering from it any small organisms that may be present. These are then ingested into the alimentary canal for eventual digestion and absorption. The barnacle (a crustacean) and the clam (a mollusk) are two examples of filter feeders. In the case of the clam, the surfaces of the gills are covered with cilia. The rhythmic beating of these cilia draws fresh water in through an opening, the incurrent siphon (Fig. 10-4).

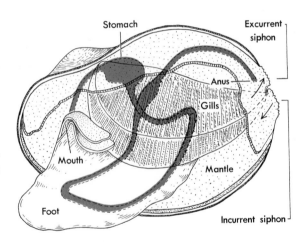

Fig. 10-4

The digestive apparatus of the clam. Food particles are filtered by the gills from the water drawn in through the incurrent siphon.

This water then passes through pores in the gills where it gives up oxygen to supply the respiratory needs of the clam. The gills are covered with a sticky mucus, and any solid particles in the water, including diatoms, bacteria, etc., are likely to be trapped in this mucus. Larger particles and indigestible particles drop from the gills and are swept out the excurrent siphon by cilia lining the mantle. The mucus with its load of carefully screened particles is swept forward to the mouth while the now-filtered water passes out through the excurrent siphon. The particle-laden mucus is then ingested. After digestion, any remaining material (the feces) is egested from the anus and passes out with the water flowing out the excurrent siphon.

ACTIVE FOOD SEEKERS: THE GRASSHOPPER AND THE HONEYBEE

Most insects and most vertebrates are capable of rapid locomotion and thus are able to seek their food actively. The grasshopper moves from plant to plant by walking, hopping, and flying. Specialized appendages around the grasshopper's mouth enable it to consume large quantities of plant leaves quickly and efficiently (Fig. 10-5). The plant material passes from the mouth into the alimentary canal for digestion and absorption. First it passes through the esophagus and into a temporary storage organ, the crop (Fig. 10-5). From here it travels to the muscular gizzard. The gizzard is lined with chitinous plates and the muscular action of the gizzard grinds the food material into still smaller particles. Efficient **mechanical breakdown** of food is thus one other advantage that a tubular alimentary canal can provide. The food then passes into the stomach where **chemical digestion** of it takes place. Digestive enzymes manufactured in six gastric glands (caeca) are secreted into the stomach to carry out this function. Some food may actually enter the caeca during the process.

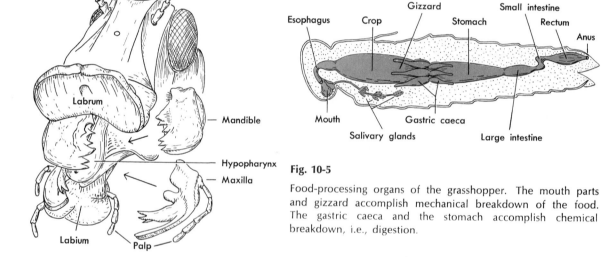

Fig. 10-5

Food-processing organs of the grasshopper. The mouth parts and gizzard accomplish mechanical breakdown of the food. The gastric caeca and the stomach accomplish chemical breakdown, i.e., digestion.

Digested food and a good deal of water are then absorbed in the intestine. The feces are stored temporarily in the rectum before being **egested,** relatively dry, through the anus.

The mouth parts of other insects, while homologous to those of the grasshopper, may be radically different in appearance and adapted for manipulating a different kind of food. The adult honeybee feeds on liquid food, either the nectar of flowers or the honey stored within the hive. Her maxillae and labium are modified to form a tube through which this food is drawn up into the mouth by the pumping action of the tongue. The whole apparatus is called a **proboscis** (Fig. 10-6).

Most of the nectar ingested by a honeybee is destined to be taken back to the hive to be converted into honey. After passing down the long, thin esophagus, it is stored in the honey stomach (Fig. 10-6). This structure is homologous to the crop and gizzard of the grasshopper but, there being no solid food to deal with, lacks the heavy muscles and chitinous plates found in the grasshopper. The nectar is normally prevented from passing from the honey stomach to the real stomach by a

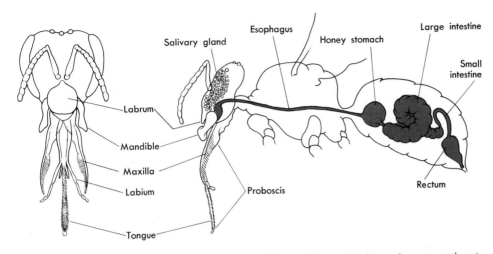

Food-manipulating structures of the honeybee. The maxillae and labium form a proboscis with which the bee sucks up liquid food such as nectar. The honey stomach holds this food while it is being transported back to the hive.

Fig. 10-6

valve located between the two. When the worker gets back to the hive, she regurgitates the nectar, and the process of converting it into honey begins.

The honey bee also uses her mouth to manipulate solids such as the wax out of which the hive is constructed. She uses her mandibles for this process and therefore it is not surprising that these mouth parts are rather like the mandibles of the grasshopper in their structure.

Vertebrates, too, are highly mobile and thus able to seek their food actively. The strong jaws of the pike, the modified tongue of the frog, the talons and curved beak of the eagle, the long canine teeth of the tiger, and the flat molar teeth of the herbivorous horse are just a few examples of the many structural modifications by means of which vertebrates secure their food.

THE DIGESTIVE SYSTEM OF MAN

INGESTION   **10-6**

Man, a mammal, uses his hands to assist him in preparing food and placing it in his mouth. His front teeth, the incisors, serve to cut off pieces of manageable size. His flat-topped molars then grind these into small bits. Here, as in the grasshopper, we see how mechanical breakdown of food precedes chemical breakdown (digestion). This is important because it makes the food more easily swallowed and at the same time greatly increases the surface area that will be exposed to the action of digestive enzymes.

While the food is within the mouth, it is moistened by saliva. Saliva is secreted into the mouth from three pairs of glands (Fig. 10-7) that are under the control of the nervous system. The sight, smell, taste, and even the thought of food can all trigger the passage of saliva from the glands through ducts into the mouth. Saliva is a somewhat sticky, "slippery" fluid because it contains a slimy carbohydrate-protein compound called mucin. The mucin enables the saliva to bind the small food particles together into a soft mass which can then be easily swallowed.

The saliva also contains an **amylase,** or starch-digesting enzyme, which catalyzes the hydrolysis of starch into the sugar maltose. This amylase is often called ptyalin, although under the rules for naming enzymes (see Section 9-8) the name salivary amylase is preferred. You can easily demonstrate its action by chewing an unsweetened cracker. After a short time, a distinctly sweetish taste will become noticeable.

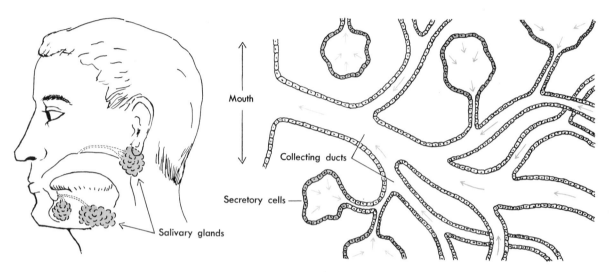

Fig. 10-7 Organization of human salivary glands. As in all exocrine glands, their secretions pass into a system of ducts which lead ultimately to the exterior of the body.

Saliva is only the first of a number of secretions that flow into the alimentary canal and aid the process of digestion. In each case, these secretions are synthesized within accessory structures called glands. Ducts carry the secretions from the glands to the alimentary canal. The inner surface of each gland is continuous with the inner surface of its ducts (Fig. 10-7) and also with the inner surface of the alimentary canal. In fact, all these digestive glands are formed during embryonic development from outfoldings of the alimentary canal.

When food is swallowed, it passes through the pharynx and into the esophagus. The esophagus is a thick-walled, muscular, straight tube leading from the pharynx to the stomach. It extends through the neck and the chest cavity. Its function can perhaps be best understood as a quick means of conveying food past the large, vital, but nondigestive organs of the chest cavity: the lungs and the heart.

The wall of the esophagus also contains glands that secrete mucin and thus lubricate the passage of food. Once the food mass is well into the esophagus, its movement is controlled by muscles in the wall of the esophagus that are not under our voluntary control. Those just in front of the food mass relax while those just behind it contract. As a result, the food mass is propelled downward. These rhythmic waves of muscular relaxation and contraction are called **peristalsis.**

Below the muscular diaphragm, which separates the chest cavity from the abdominal cavity, the esophagus joins the stomach. A ring of muscle, the cardiac sphincter, surrounds the esophagus at this point. It acts as a valve, relaxing to let into the stomach any food that approaches from above but remaining closed at other times. (The process of vomiting does, of course, also involve the opening of the cardiac sphincter.)

THE STOMACH 10-7

The stomach is a large pouch located high in the abdominal cavity (Fig. 10-8). Its wall is lined with millions of tiny gastric glands, which secrete 400-800 ml of gastric juice at each meal. The incoming food is thoroughly mixed with the gastric juice by vigorous muscular contractions of the stomach. (When these contractions occur in an empty stomach, hunger "pangs" result.)

There are several kinds of glands in the wall of the stomach. One secretes a dilute solution of hydrochloric acid. This gives the gastric juice a pH of about 1 to 2. Other glands secrete a solution containing the protein pepsinogen. In the presence of HCl, the pepsinogen is converted into the protein-digesting enzyme, **pepsin.** Pepsin hydrolyzes ingested proteins into peptide molecules by breaking the bonds between certain specific amino acid links in the chain. The peptide molecules produced may still contain dozens of amino acids.

Our present knowledge of the digestive activity of the stomach has been gained from the research of many men. As early as 1776, the Italian scientist Spallanzani discovered that human gastric juice digests meat. He built small cages of wire in each of which he placed a piece of sponge. After attaching a string, he would swallow a cage for a period of time and then retrieve it. The juice squeezed from the sponge digested meat readily.

The work of the American physician William Beaumont is also a landmark in the history of research on gastric activity. In 1822 he was called upon to treat a trapper, Alexis St. Martin, who had suffered a serious gunshot wound. The blast had penetrated both the muscular wall of the abdominal cavity and the wall of the stomach. Under Beaumont's care, St. Martin made an excellent recovery. However, the margin of the wound in the body wall healed to the margin of the wound in the stomach. As a result, a permanent opening into the stomach was formed. Beaumont recognized the research possibilities of this occurrence. For the next eight years (interrupted at intervals when St. Martin tired of his role) Beaumont supported St. Martin and his growing family while carrying on a classic series of investigations of his gastric activity.

In the 1890's, the Russian physiologist Ivan Pavlov discovered the mechanisms controlling the release of gastric juice. He found that after he cut nerves leading to the stomach of dogs, the amount of gastric secretion was reduced by about 25%. This showed definite, but incomplete, control of gastric secretion by the nervous system. What about the remaining 75%? Pavlov reasoned that a hormone might be liberated in the blood when food enters the stomach, which would also stimulate the production of gastric juice. He tested this theory by connecting the blood circulatory systems of two dogs. When one dog was fed, it was only a short time before the second dog began to secrete gastric juice also. The second dog, however, secreted only about 75% of the normal amount. We know now that a hormone, **gastrin,** is produced by certain cells in the stomach when food enters the stomach. This hormone diffuses into the blood stream and is carried throughout the body. When blood containing this hormone returns to the stomach, it stimulates the gastric glands to secrete gastric juice. In Pavlov's experiment, the hormone also passed into the blood stream of the second dog, causing its gastric glands to start functioning, too. The joining

Fig. 10-8   Digestive system of the human.

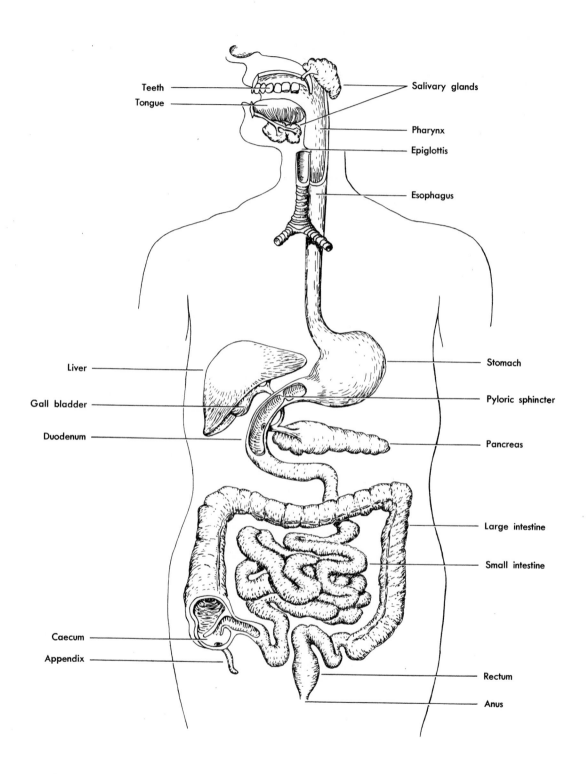

Teeth

Tongue

Salivary glands

Pharynx

Epiglottis

Esophagus

Liver

Stomach

Gall bladder

Pyloric sphincter

Duodenum

Pancreas

Large intestine

Small intestine

Caecum

Appendix

Rectum

Anus

of the circulatory systems of two animals in this way is called parabiosis. It is a very valuable tool for studying the action of the hormones, which are almost exclusively transported by the blood. The operation is always carried out with scrupulous care, under anesthesia, and every effort is taken to ensure that the animals suffer no unnecessary discomfort at any time during the procedure.

As the contents of the stomach become thoroughly liquefied, they pass through a sphincter at the lower end of the stomach, and into the small intestine, the first ten inches of which is called the **duodenum.** An opening in the wall of the duodenum leads to two ducts which, in turn, drain two large digestive glands, the pancreas and the liver.

THE PANCREAS   **10-8**

The pancreas is an elongated, whitish gland which lies in the loop formed by the duodenum and the under surface of the stomach. Secretory cells in the pancreas produce pancreatic fluid which then passes down the pancreatic duct and into the duodenum. The pancreatic fluid contains the following substances.

a)   **Sodium bicarbonate** ($NaHCO_3$). The sodium bicarbonate neutralizes the acidity of the intestinal contents, quickly raising the pH to about 8.

b)   An **amylase.** This pancreatic amylase hydrolyzes starch into maltose. Because it has a much longer period in which to act, it plays a more important role in starch digestion than does salivary amylase.

c)   A **lipase.** The pancreatic lipase hydrolyzes about one-third of the ingested fats into glycerol and fatty acid molecules. Its action is enhanced by a secretion of the liver called **bile.** Bile contains substances (steroids) called bile salts, which emulsify fats. Large drops of fat (oil) are broken into tiny droplets by the detergent action of these bile salts. This action increases the surface area exposed to the pancreatic lipase and thus hastens fat digestion.

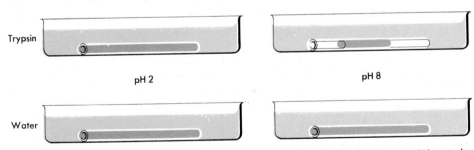

The effect of pH on the digestive action of trypsin. The contents of each bottom dish are the same as those of the one above it except that no enzyme is present. Thus the bottom dishes serve as "controls" for the experiment. The glass tubes contain cooked egg white.

Fig. 10-9

d)   **Two proteinases.** Trypsin and chymotrypsin are both enzymes that continue the work of protein digestion by hydrolyzing specific peptide bonds that were not attacked by pepsin. (The action of pepsin ceases when the sodium bicarbonate raises the pH of the intestinal contents.) Trypsin and chymotrypsin work most rapidly at the higher pH (Fig. 10-9). Like pepsin, both trypsin and chymotrypsin are secreted in an inactive form and only when within the duodenum are they converted into their active state.

e) **Carboxypeptidase.** This enzyme removes, one by one, the amino acids located at the acid end of peptide molecules (Fig. 10-10). Thus it aids in the hydrolysis of peptides into amino acids.

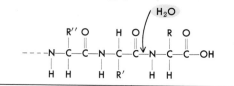

Pepsin or trypsin or chymotrypsin, depending on nature of R' and R''

Fig. 10-10

Hydrolytic action
of various proteases.

Carboxypeptidase

Aminopeptidases

f) **Nucleases.** These enzymes hydrolyze ingested nucleic acids (RNA and DNA) into their component nucleotides.

The secretion of pancreatic juice is under hormonal control. When the acidified contents of the stomach enter the duodenum, certain cells in the wall of the duodenum release the hormones secretin and pancreozymin into the bloodstream. When carried to the pancreas, these stimulate the production and discharge of pancreatic fluid. Secretin chiefly affects the secretion of sodium bicarbonate solution whereas pancreozymin stimulates the production of the digestive enzymes.

10-9   **THE SMALL INTESTINE**

As the mixture of food, bile, and pancreatic enzymes passes through the small intestine, maltose, peptides, fatty acids, glycerol, and fat droplets are produced. The final digestion and absorption of these materials is the function of the **villi,** which line the inner surface of the small intestine (Fig. 10-11). The villi increase the surface area of the small intestine many times what it would be if it were simply a tube with smooth walls. In addition, the exposed surface of the epithelial cells of each villus is covered with projections, the **microvilli** or "brush border." Thanks largely to these, the total surface area in the intestine is about 100 ft^2, five times the surface area of the exterior of the body.

Incorporated on the surface of the microvilli (or perhaps just inside them) are a number of enzymes that complete the digestion process. A number of **aminopeptidases** complete the hydrolysis of peptides into amino acids. These enzymes act in a manner similar to carboxypeptidase but attack the amino ($-NH_2$) end of the peptide molecules instead of the acid end (Fig. 10-10).

Three **disaccharidases** localized on or in the microvilli hydrolyze the disaccharides maltose, sucrose, and lactose into their component monosaccharides. Each maltose molecule is split into two glucose molecules and thus glucose is the end-product of the digestion of starch. Sucrose (common table sugar) gives a molecule of glucose and one of its isomers, fructose, while lactose (milk sugar) gives glucose and galactose (Fig. 7-2).

With the action of these enzymes, protein and carbohydrate digestion comes to an end. What were originally macromolecules have now been converted into small molecules (amino acids and monosaccharides) ready for passage into the bloodstream.

Each villus is richly supplied with blood which passes through a network of tiny tubes called capillaries. The sugars and amino acids as well as vitamins, salts and some water pass from the intestinal contents into the capillaries of the villus. Although this transport may be accomplished by diffusion in some cases, other mechanisms are involved, too. Glucose, for example, continues to be absorbed even when its concentration in the intestinal fluid becomes less than its concentration in the blood (about 0.1%). This absorption is accomplished by active transport.

Pinocytosis may also play a significant role in the absorption of digested foods. You remember that only about one-third of the ingested fats becomes hydrolyzed to fatty acids and glycerol. These molecules, acting with the bile salts, emulsify the remaining two-thirds into tiny droplets. The droplets are then absorbed, most likely by pinocytosis, into the epithelial cells of the villus. Once inside, many of the fatty acid and glycerol molecules become resynthesized into fat in the smooth endoplasmic reticulum of these cells. The fat droplets are then discharged into the interior of the villus by reverse pinocytosis. These droplets do not enter the capillary network.

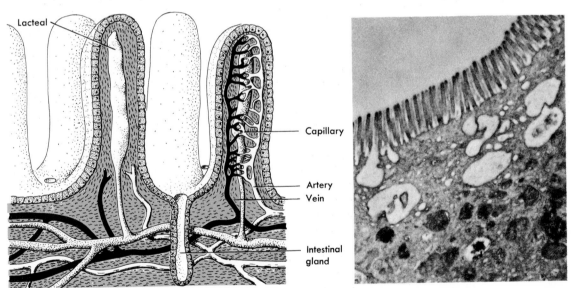

Villi. Left: Digested foods enter the capillaries. Oil droplets enter the lacteals. The villi, with their microvilli, provide approximately 100 square feet of absorbing area in the small intestine. Right: electron micrograph (8000✕) of the microvilli of mouse intestine cells. (Courtesy Dr. Sam L. Clark, Jr. Reprinted by permission from The Rockefeller Institute Press, *Journal of Biophysical and Biochemical Cytology* **5**, 41–50, 1959.)

Fig. 10-11

Instead they enter a duct, the lacteal, whose walls are more porous. The lacteals of the villi are part of the lymphatic system. The morphology and physiology of this system will be discussed in Chapter 14. Once inside the lacteals, the fat droplets are carried slowly through the lymphatic system until it joins with the regular blood circulatory system. After a fat-rich meal, the lacteals take on a whitish, milky appearance (*lac* is the Latin word for milk) because of the large numbers of fat droplets contained within them.

10-10   THE LIVER

Although the liver is not strictly an organ of digestion, its secretion, bile, does play an important role in the digestion of fats. Bile is produced continuously by the liver but between meals it accumulates in a storage organ, the gall bladder. When chyme enters the duodenum, a hormone (cholecystokinin) is released to the bloodstream from cells in the lining of the duodenum. Upon reaching the gall bladder, this hormone stimulates it to contract and expel its contents of bile into the duodenum. The action of this hormone, as well as the action of gastrin, secretin, and pancreozymin, illustrates nicely an important fact about hormonal control. In each case, the liberated hormone is carried by the blood to every organ, every tissue, every cell of the body. Only certain organs, however, are capable of responding to the presence of the hormone. These are called the target organs.

Bile contains other materials besides bile salts. Among these are the bile pigments. These are the products of the breakdown of the red blood pigment, hemoglobin, removed by the liver from old red blood cells. The brownish color of the bile pigments imparts the characteristic brown color of the feces.

The formation of bile is just one of several important nutritional functions carried out by the liver. Before the blood that leaves the villi reaches the general circulation, it passes through the liver. Here extraordinary components (e.g. nonnutritive molecules) that are picked up by absorption from the intestine, or excess amounts of ordinary components, are screened out. All monosaccharides except glucose (e.g. fructose, galactose) are removed by the liver and converted into glucose. Any glucose in excess of the normal 0.1% concentration found in the blood is removed and converted into the insoluble polysaccharide, glycogen.

Amino acids which are in excess of the body's anabolic needs are deaminated by the liver. In deamination, the nitrogen-containing amino ($-NH_2$) portion of the molecule is removed. This is then converted into a nitrogenous waste, urea. The mechanism of this process will be discussed in Chapter 16. The non-nitrogen-containing residue of the amino acid can then enter the metabolic pathway of cellular respiration and be oxidized for energy. The details of this mechanism will be considered in the next chapter.

Some fat-soluble vitamins, such as vitamins A and D, that reach the liver in greater than normal amounts are removed and stored by the liver. These vitamins can be released back into the blood later if inadequate supplies are secured in the diet.

The system of blood vessels that carries all blood received from the intestines through the liver before passing it to the general circulation is called the **hepatic portal** system. In a real sense, this system provides a gatekeeper between the intestines and the general circulation. In this role, the liver screens the blood passing through it so that the composition of the blood when it leaves will be that which is normal for the organism. For example, even after a meal rich in starches and sugars, the glucose level of the blood leaving the liver will not be much higher than the normal 0.1%.

On the other hand, if the concentration of glucose in the blood should start to fall between meals, the liver will hydrolyze enough of its glycogen reserves to maintain the level at 0.1%. In other words, the liver is one of the most important devices in the human body for maintaining the constancy of the ECF and thus for the preservation of homeostasis. In Chapter 26 the liver's role in maintaining homeostasis with respect to the sugar content of the ECF will be explored further.

THE LARGE INTESTINE 10-11

The small intestine leads into the large intestine. A sphincter controls the passage of materials from one to the other. Just beyond this sphincter is a blind pocket, the caecum. Attached to the caecum is a tiny projection, the appendix. The appendix has no known useful function in man. It is considered to be the vestigial remains of a structure which may have functioned in cellulose digestion in some very remote, prehuman ancestor. Its only other interest to man is the fact that it may become infected, causing appendicitis. A severe infection may cause the appendix to rupture, thus spreading the infection to the membranes lining the abdominal cavity and supporting the organs (the viscera) within it. This condition is known as peritonitis.

The large intestine receives the liquid residue of material left after digestion and absorption in the small intestine have been completed. This residue contains substantial quantities of water and indigestible substances such as cellulose. Some other food materials are invariably present and these serve to nourish the enormous population of bacteria that live in the large intestine. Usually these bacteria (of which the most common species is the much-studied *Escherichia coli*) are perfectly harmless. In the process of their metabolic activities they may produce gases and other odoriferous wastes. They flourish to such an extent that from 10% to 50% of the dry weight of the feces may consist of bacterial cells.

Some of the bacteria living in the large intestine may actually benefit man by producing vitamins which he can then absorb for his own needs. Vitamin B_{12}, mentioned in the previous chapter, is secured in this fashion. The bacteria also benefit from the relationship, of course, as they are supplied with food and a warm, moist, dark habitat.

Occasionally, harmful bacteria or protozoans may become established in the large intestine. Typhoid fever, Asiatic cholera, and amoebic dysentery are three diseases which are caused by intestinal parasites. These parasites may even invade other organs of the body such as the liver and cause extensive damage.

The chief function of the large intestine is the reabsorption of water. A great deal of fluid is secreted into the stomach and intestine by the various digestive glands. This fluid must be reclaimed if the individual is not to suffer from dehydration and thirst. Most of the water is reabsorbed in the large intestine during the 12 to 14 hours that the food residues remain there. Sometimes the large intestine becomes irritated and discharges its contents into the rectum and out of the anus before water reabsorption is complete. The resulting condition is called diarrhea. Perhaps you have noticed the thirst which accompanies a case of diarrhea. On the other hand, the large intestine may retain its contents for an extra long period. The fecal material, as it is now called, becomes dried out and compressed into dry, solid masses. This condition is known as constipation.

The feces pass from the large intestine through an S-shaped tube into the **rectum.** Here they remain until the two sphincters guarding the anus relax and vigorous peristaltic waves expel them in the process of defecation.

EXERCISES AND PROBLEMS

1 Outline the digestion of a bacon (protein and fat) sandwich (starch).

2 List six functions carried out by the liver.

3 Aquatic vertebrates such as fresh-water fishes and frogs have little or no large intestine. Can you think of an explanation for this?

4 By what mechanisms might amino acids in the small intestine enter the epithelial cells of the villi?

5 Is the digestion of macromolecules a process that occurs only in the digestive tract? Explain.

6 What is a nucleotide?

7 How does chewing or otherwise breaking food down mechanically aid digestion?

8 How can the amoeba digest the food it engulfs by phagocytosis without digesting itself?

9 How do cells that secrete extracellular enzymes avoid self-digestion?

10 What is sucrase?

11 Do any filter-feeders live on land? Explain.

REFERENCES

1 Beaumont, W., *Experiments and Observations on the Gastric Juice and the Physiology of Digestion,* Dover Publications, 1959. Dr. Beaumont's account of his own work.

2 Bayliss, W. M., and E. H. Starling, "The Mechanism of Pancreatic Secretion," *Great Experiments in Biology,* ed. by M. L. Gabriel and S. Fogel, Prentice-Hall, Inc., 1955. Deals with secretin and how it was discovered.

Mitochondria in epithelial cells of the gall bladder of a rabbit (17,000 X). In these structures the energy of food is made available to the cell. (Courtesy Dr. Gordon Kaye, Columbia University, College of Physicians and Surgeons.)

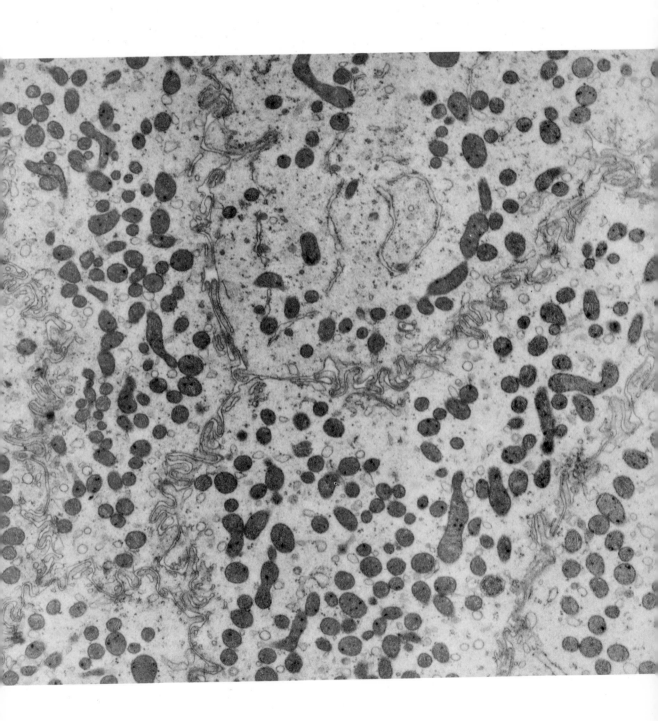

In the last chapter we examined some of the mechanisms by which heterotrophic organisms *ingest* large, insoluble, organic molecules and then *digest* these into smaller, soluble (but still organic) molecules. Very little energy is liberated in this process of hydrolysis. Most of the chemical energy stored in starches, proteins, and fats is still locked up in the end products of their digestion: sugars, amino acids, fatty acids, and glycerol. The process of digestion does accomplish a marked reduction in the size of the molecules, however, so that they may be absorbed readily from the ECF into the cytoplasm of cells.

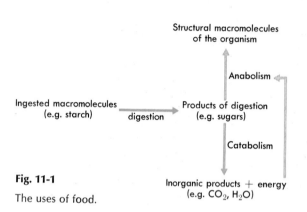

Structural macromolecules
of the organism

Anabolism

Ingested macromolecules
(e.g. starch)   digestion   Products of digestion
(e.g. sugars)

Catabolism

Fig. 11-1

The uses of food.

Inorganic products + energy
(e.g. CO_2, H_2O)

What is the fate of these small, organic molecules once they enter the cytoplasm? In general, two alternatives are available (Fig. 11-1). They may serve as the building blocks for the synthesis of more complex substances. Polysaccharides, lipids, nucleic acids, and proteins are all essential cell components which are synthesized within the cell from their units that have been absorbed from the ECF. This phase of metabolism in which larger, more complex molecules are built up from smaller, simpler ones is called **anabolism.**

Many of the digested food molecules absorbed by the cell do not participate in the synthesis of more complex substances, but are instead broken down chemically into still smaller molecules. This breakdown may continue until only simple, inorganic molecules (e.g. H_2O, CO_2, NH_3) remain. The total amount of energy stored in the end products of these decompositions is much less than the amount of energy present in the original molecule. Thus, at each step in the breakdown of sugars, amino acids, fatty acids, and glycerol, energy is released. This phase of metabolism in which relatively complex, energy-rich molecules (e.g. sugars) are broken down into simpler, energy-poor molecules (e.g. CO_2 and H_2O) is called **catabolism.**

ANABOLISM

11-1   **REQUIREMENTS**

The synthesis within the cell of proteins, nucleic acids, starches, and lipids from the end products of the digestion of these substances requires two additional factors: *energy* and one or more specific *enzymes.*

Energy is necessary as most of these synthetic reactions are energy-consuming. More complex molecules are being constructed from simpler ones and these constructive activities within the cell usually require energy for their accomplishment. The chemical syntheses within the cell of a gland such as the pancreas may require as much energy as a muscle cell uses in violent physical activity. Later in this chapter we will examine the specific mechanisms by which energy is provided for the anabolic, synthetic activities of the cell.

All chemical transformations within cells require specific enzymes in order to proceed rapidly and efficiently. The chemical changes involved in anabolism are no exception to this rule. In a few cases, the enzymes involved in synthesis may be the same as those involved in digestion. Theoretically, the action of enzymes is reversible. Whether a given reaction proceeds forwards or backwards depends upon other factors such as the relative concentration of reactants and products (see Section 6-12). For example, when one widely occurring enzyme, starch phosphorylase, is placed in contact with a high concentration of "activated" glucose, glucose-1-phosphate, starch synthesis results (Fig. 11-2). (The mechanism by which extra energy is incorporated in the glucose molecule will be discussed later in the chapter.) On the other hand, when the phosphorylase is placed in contact with a high concentration of starch, the breakdown of the starch into units of glucose-1-phosphate is promoted.

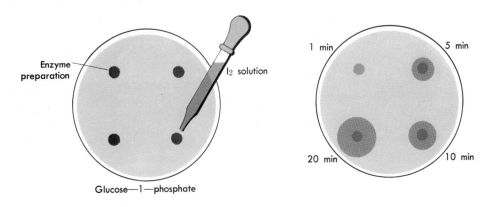

Testing the action of the enzyme starch phosphorylase on glucose-1-phosphate incorporated in a dish of agar-agar. The dark color produced with iodine reveals the progressive synthesis of starch.

Fig. 11-2

In other cases, the enzymes that catalyze the synthesis of large polymers such as proteins and starches are not the same as those involved in the digestion of these substances. In protein synthesis, especially, it is easy to understand why this is so. Man ingests protein from many sources (e.g. beef and beans) and digests these into their constituent amino acids. Once these amino acids are absorbed by his cells, they may be resynthesized into protein. The new protein is not beef or bean protein, however, but human protein. The sequence of amino acids in the protein chains, along with the folding of these chains, results in a protein unique to the species and, unless he happens to have an identical twin, perhaps unique to the individual. It is no wonder then that the enzymes that catalyze the synthesis of a specific protein are quite different from those that catalyze its digestion.

Another important point about the anabolic activities of the cell is that there may be considerable interconversions among the starting materials. For example, excess quantities of ingested glucose may be partially broken down, and then transformed into fatty acids and glycerol. These then can be synthesized into fats. People who get "fat" usually do so as a result of an excessive intake of carbohydrate rather than of fat. Nucleic acids may be synthesized from the absorbed products of nucleic acid digestion, or amino acids can serve as the starting materials instead. In the second case, a longer series of chemical transformations is required. Figure 11-3 illustrates some of the interconversions of the basic building blocks that are possible in the cell. Note that only plants and certain protists can manufacture amino acids from fatty acids plus an inorganic supply of nitrogen (e.g. NH_4^+, NO_3^-). Man, however, can manufacture about a dozen of his required amino acids from other amino acids. The amino acids that he cannot manufacture this way are called the "essential" amino acids. They must be ingested in his diet.

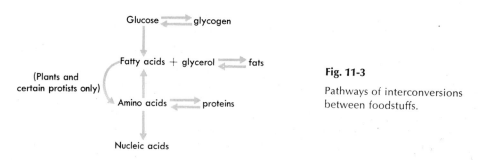

Fig. 11-3

Pathways of interconversions between foodstuffs.

The study of the anabolic activities of the cell is a very active field of research in biochemistry. Our understanding of the mechanisms and pathways involved is still only fragmentary. It is perfectly clear, though, that it is only through these activities that the amount of living matter increases. Growth of organisms requires an increase in the number of cells of which they are composed, or an increase in the size of the cells, or both. In each case, the quantity of those materials intimately associated with life (proteins, nucleic acids, polysaccharides, and lipids) must increase. This increase comes about as a result of the anabolism of the cell. Repair of damaged parts likewise depends upon the synthesis of these large molecules. And, of course, the production of new individuals in the process of reproduction depends directly upon anabolism.

Besides a supply of building blocks and the presence of the necessary enzymes, anabolism requires energy. Let us now examine the mechanisms by which energy is made available within the cell.

CATABOLISM

The catabolic activities of the cell are those in which the organic molecules absorbed by the cell (sugars, amino acids, fatty acids, and glycerol) are broken down into still simpler molecules. In the process of breakdown, some of the energy stored in the starting materials is released. Living organisms accomplish the breakdown by two different (but related) processes: fermentation and cellular respiration.

11-2 **FERMENTATION**

One method of securing energy from complex organic molecules is to fragment them into simpler molecules. An example of this process is the chemical breakdown of glucose into **ethyl alcohol** and **carbon dioxide.** This process is called alcoholic fermentation. It may be represented by the equation:

$$C_6H_{12}O_6 \rightarrow 2C_2H_5OH + 2CO_2.$$

Inspection of this equation shows that glucose is the only starting material. No other substance, not even oxygen, is required. Because oxygen is not required, the process is **anaerobic;** that is, it can go on in the absence of air. Every atom originally present in the glucose is accounted for in the products. The total energy stored in the products is, however, somewhat less than that stored in the glucose molecule. The energy difference is liberated in the process.

Although the process of alcoholic fermentation has probably been used by man through most of human history, it was not until about 100 years ago that scientists began to understand its nature. The great French biochemist Louis Pasteur found that alcoholic fermentation was always associated with the presence and growth of single-celled fungi, the yeasts. The converse was not true, however. He found that yeasts when exposed to adequate amounts of air produced mostly H_2O and CO_2 as the end products of their metabolism. Pasteur concluded that fermentation was an energy-producing mechanism used by organisms deprived of air. He called fermentation "life without air." Since Pasteur's time, the enzymes and coenzymes that carry out the chemical changes in alcoholic fermentation have been isolated and the details of the process determined. Because of the close relationship between these intermediate steps and those involved in the process of cellular respiration, we will defer a discussion of them until that topic is considered (see Section 11-4).

Other kinds of fermentation are also known. For example, when vigorous activity of the muscles of man outstrips the supply of oxygen available for cellular respiration, the muscles get energy from the fermentation of glucose. (The glucose is, in turn, derived from animal starch, glycogen, which is stored in muscles.) Fortunately for us, the end product of this fermentation is **lactic acid,** rather than alcohol and CO_2.

Both alcoholic and lactic acid fermentation are inefficient processes. Although the total energy in the products of fermentation is less than that in glucose, it is not much less. Not more than 4% of the energy stored in glucose is made available to the organism during fermentation. Most of the energy originally stored in the glucose molecule is still stored in the end products of ethyl alcohol or lactic acid. (The use of ethyl alcohol as a fuel component in some racing cars and rocket engines should make this clear.)

Not only is fermentation an inefficient method for securing energy, but it is potentially a hazardous one as well. Ethyl alcohol is poisonous in moderate concentrations. The activity of yeast plants ceases when the alcoholic concentration of the medium in which they are growing reaches about 14%. (This sets a limit on the alcoholic concentration of undistilled alcoholic beverages such as natural wines.) The accumulation of excessive amounts of lactic acid in human muscles is undesirable because it lowers the pH of the cell contents and ECF. Too high a concentration of lactic acid causes the muscle to become incapable of further action.

Fermentation is a wasteful process. Only a small fraction of the energy stored in the glucose molecule is made available to the organism. Most of it is still retained in the end products of fermentation. Therefore, organisms that rely on fermentation must have large amounts of glucose available to them in order to satisfy their needs. If, however, glucose could be broken down by cells into truly simple, energy-poor molecules (e.g. H_2O and CO_2), a much higher percentage of its energy would be released. Such a breakdown occurs when glucose is oxidized. Oxidation of glucose takes place within the cells of the vast majority of living organisms in the process of cellular respiration. It is carried out in the mitochondria (Section 8-8).

Cellular respiration can be defined as the oxidation of organic compounds that occurs within cells. In Chapter 6, we defined oxidation as the process of removing electrons from a substance. This occurs when oxygen atoms are added to a substance. When coal (carbon) is oxidized, oxygen atoms combine with the carbon atoms to form carbon dioxide: $C + O_2 \rightarrow CO_2$. The affinity of oxygen for the electrons present in the carbon atom is so great that the oxygen atoms "pull" these electrons close to them. This releases energy which, in the form of heat and light, can be used to heat homes, generate steam, etc. Oxygen is such a powerful and common electron acceptor that it has provided the name for the process: oxidation. Many other substances can, however, serve as oxidizing agents.

In cells, the most common type of oxidation involves the removal of hydrogen atoms (each with its electron) from a substance. The primary oxidizing agents in cells are the coenzymes nicotinamide-adenine dinucleotide, or **NAD,** and its close relative, nicotinamide-adenine dinucleotide phosphate (NADP). (These two substances have been known by a variety of other names of which DPN, for NAD, and TPN, for NADP, are still quite common.) Each of these is a complex molecule made up of (1) nicotinamide (a B vitamin), (2) two five-carbon ribose units, (3) the purine adenine, and (4) two (in NAD) or three (in NADP) phosphate groups (Fig. 11-4). Both of these substances can remove two electrons (usually associated with two hydrogen atoms) from certain organic compounds, thus oxidizing them.

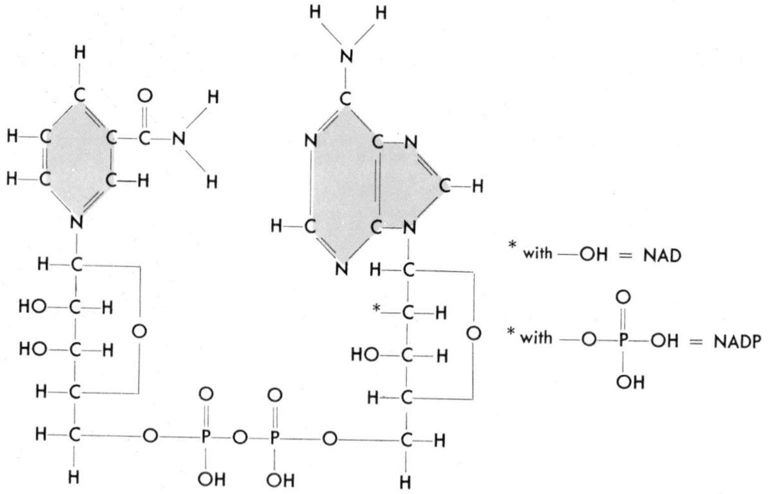

Fig. 11-4

Structural formula of nicotinamide adenine dinucleotide (NAD) and its phosphate (NADP).

The two electrons actually unite with the NAD (or NADP), thus reducing it. You remember that in Chapter 6 (Section 6-9) we pointed out that the process of reduction is always inseparable from the process of oxidation. An oxidizing agent (e.g. NAD) is reduced by the substance it oxidizes. Because NAD and NADP are so similar in activity, we will refer to either simply as NAD. The reduced form will be indicated as $NADH_2$.

There is another important way in which the oxidation that goes on within cells differs from the burning of coal. The latter process proceeds rapidly with most of the energy being released as heat. The high temperatures involved could not be tolerated by a living organism. The oxidations that occur in living cells proceed rapidly, too, but at low temperatures. Instead of being released as heat, over 40% of the energy liberated in the course of respiration is conserved by the cell as chemical energy. In this form it is available to run the energy-consuming activities of the cell.

The over-all chemistry of cellular respiration has been known for many years. The primary fuel in most living things is the sugar molecule, glucose. With the aid of oxygen taken in from the ECF, cells oxidize glucose to the simple, energy-poor compounds carbon dioxide and water. The reaction can be expressed by the equation:

$$C_6H_{12}O_6 + 6O_2 \rightarrow 6CO_2 + 6H_2O.$$

Knowing what goes in and what comes out of a process is only part of the story, though. When ignited by a flame, glucose combines directly with oxygen, forming CO_2 and H_2O according to the equation just given. In living cells, however, the process proceeds in a more orderly and controlled fashion. The gradual discovery of the way in which glucose in living cells is oxidized to CO_2 and H_2O has been one of the great achievements of biochemistry.

Anaerobic Breakdown   **11-4**

Glucose molecules must be activated by heating before they will begin to burn. In cells, also, glucose molecules must be activated before they can be respired. The activation is not accomplished by heat, but instead the energy of the molecule is increased by joining to it a phosphate group,

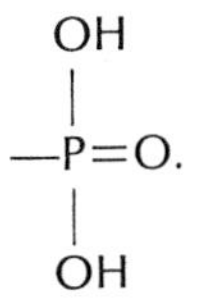

$$\begin{array}{c} OH \\ | \\ -P=O. \\ | \\ OH \end{array}$$

This process is called phosphorylation. Like all chemical reactions in cells, it requires an enzyme. It also requires a source of phosphate. The phosphate is supplied by a substance called adenosine triphosphate, or **ATP** for short. ATP consists of the purine adenine (what other substances contain this molecule?), a five-carbon sugar, ribose, and three phosphate groups (Fig. 11-5). The bonds by which the second and third phosphate groups are attached are known as high-energy bonds because

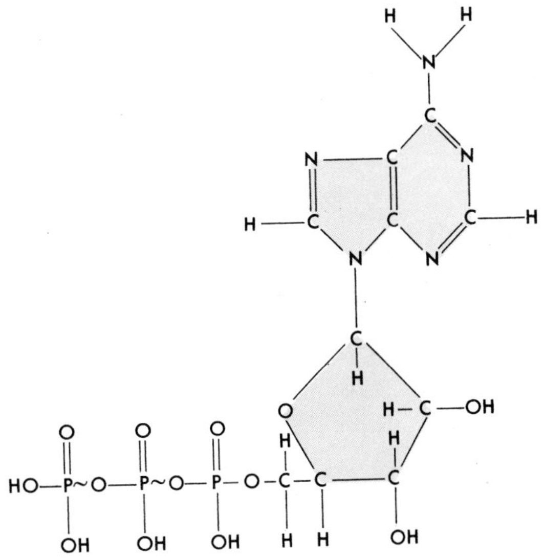

Fig. 11-5

Structural formula of ATP. How does it compare with Fig. 7–14?

of the large amount of energy stored in them. (They are shown in Fig. 11-5 as wavy lines.) When glucose is phosphorylated, ATP transfers its third phosphate group and the energy of its bond to the glucose molecule. This results in an activated form of glucose, glucose-phosphate. In the same process, the ATP is changed to adenosine *diphos-phate* (only two phosphates are left) or **ADP.** A minor enzyme-catalyzed rearrangement of the glucose molecule and the addition of one more phosphate group from a second molecule of ATP results in the formation of fructose-diphosphate. (Fructose is an isomer of glucose; i.e. it has the same molecular formula but a different structural formula.)

Fig. 11-6   The pathway of cellular respiration.

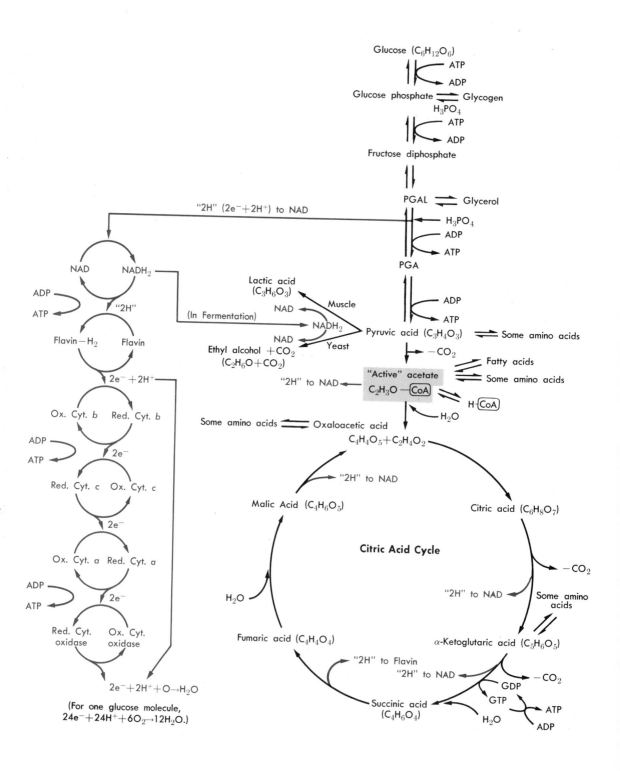

The fructose-diphosphate is then split into two halves. The resulting molecules, each containing three carbon atoms, are molecules of phosphoglyceraldehyde or **PGAL**. From this point on, we will trace the path taken by just one molecule of PGAL. Bear in mind, however, that two molecules of PGAL have been produced from the original glucose molecule and hence all reactants and products involved from this point on are actually doubled in the process of respiring a single glucose molecule.

PGAL is then oxidized, as two electrons (and their hydrogen nuclei) are removed by NAD. A second phosphate group (donated by a molecule of the inorganic acid phosphoric acid, H_3PO_4) is added and immediately removed and transferred to a molecule of ADP to form ATP. The compound that results from these reactions is phosphoglyceric acid or **PGA** (Fig. 11-6). Two more chemical transformations result in the formation of a second molecule of ATP. With all the phosphate groups removed, a molecule of **pyruvic acid** ($C_3H_4O_3$) remains.

Note that the conversion of glucose to pyruvic acid does not require the presence of oxygen. It is an anaerobic process. Note also that although energy in the form of two ATP molecules is needed to "prime" the process, four ATP molecules (two from each of the PGAL molecules) are produced. There is thus a net production of two molecules of ATP for each glucose molecule used. The total amount of energy stored in two pyruvic acid molecules is less than that stored in the glucose molecule. Some of the difference has been stored in the two molecules of ATP. Some of it is stored in the $NADH_2$. The remainder is liberated as heat.

The energy stored in $NADH_2$ may be used directly by some energy-consuming activity of the cell. One example is the reduction of pyruvic acid to lactic acid:

$$C_3H_4O_3 \rightarrow C_3H_6O_3.$$

$$NADH_2 \curvearrowright NAD$$

This reaction is carried on in the cells of some bacteria and in the cells of some muscles. In fact, this reaction is the final step in muscular fermentation (Section 11-2). Remember that the breakdown of glucose to pyruvic acid is an anaerobic process.

Careful biochemical studies have shown that the anaerobic breakdown of glucose to pyruvic acid proceeds in basically the same step-by-step fashion in both cellular respiration and muscle fermentation. In muscle fermentation, however, the $NADH_2$ formed by the oxidation of PGAL is used up in the reduction of pyruvic acid to lactic acid. There is, however, a net yield of two ATP molecules for every glucose molecule fermented, and it is this net yield which permits the muscle to continue to function for a time even when oxygen is not available.

It is interesting to note that alcoholic fermentation also proceeds by the same biochemical pathway that we have been discussing. In alcoholic fermentation, however, a carbon dioxide molecule is removed from the pyruvic acid before reduction by $NADH_2$ occurs. This reaction thus yields a molecule of CO_2 and a molecule of ethyl alcohol:

$$C_3H_4O_3 \rightarrow C_2H_5OH + CO_2.$$

$$NADH_2 \curvearrowright NAD$$

Again, the organism (e.g. yeast) must satisfy all its energy needs from the net production of two ATP molecules for each glucose molecule consumed. Is it any wonder that yeast cells deprived of air grow relatively slowly and consume large amounts of glucose?

Every step in the anaerobic breakdown of sugar—whether in muscles, yeast cells, or as the first steps in cellular respiration—requires the catalytic action of a specific enzyme. All the enzymes participating in this anaerobic process are present in the cytoplasm of the cell but they have not been found to be localized in any specific cell structures. We shall see, however, that all the remaining steps in the oxidation of sugar are accomplished by enzymes in the mitochondria.

11-5   The Cytochrome Enzyme System

In respiring cells, the usual fate of the $NADH_2$ is to be oxidized in turn by another coenzyme, a yellow substance called a flavin (Fig. 11-6). This oxidation, in some way as yet unknown, is coupled with the production of one ATP molecule from ADP and inorganic phosphate. The electrons received by the flavin are in turn passed on to another enzyme, called cytochrome b, thus reducing it. Cytochrome b is, in turn, oxidized by cytochrome c. This oxidation produces still another molecule of ATP. The electrons then pass to cytochrome a and then to the enzyme cytochrome oxidase. This last transfer results in the formation of a third ATP molecule. All these cytochrome enzymes are proteins with iron-containing prosthetic groups (Fig. 11-7). Iron, you remember (see Section 6-9), has a variable valence and thus is admirably suited to serve in REDOX systems. The prosthetic groups of the cytochrome enzymes are also quite similar to the prosthetic group, heme, of the red, oxygen-carrying pigment, hemoglobin, found in vertebrate blood. They also resemble the green plant pigment, chlorophyll, although the chlorophyll molecule contains an atom of magnesium rather than iron.

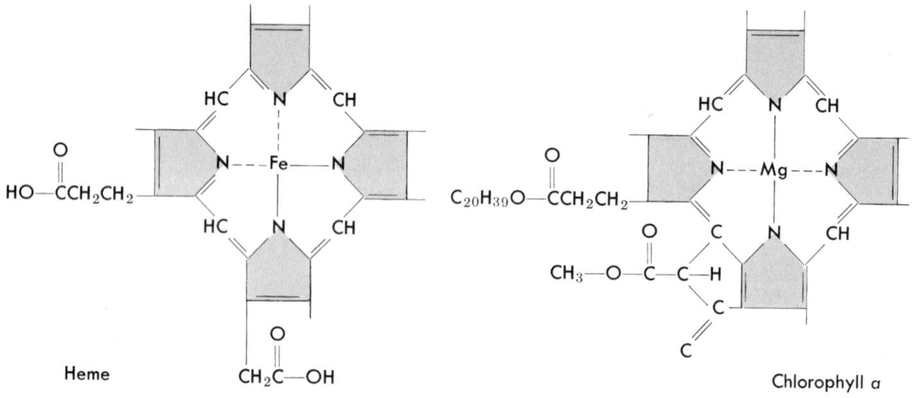

Fig. 11-7   Simplified structural formulas of heme and chlorophyll a.

Cytochrome oxidase donates its two electrons to an atom of oxygen which also picks up two H^+ ions to form a molecule of water. The ultimate electron acceptor then is oxygen just as it is when glucose is burned after being ignited by a flame. In the cell, however, the passage of electrons from the glucose to the oxygen proceeds in such small, separate steps, that over 40% of the energy released in the oxidation can be conserved as chemical energy stored in ATP, rather than being liberated as heat.

One might well expect that a system requiring the efficient passage of electrons through a whole sequence of enzymes would have to be highly organized. There is considerable evidence that this is indeed the case. The various cytochrome enzymes have been found to be fixed to the membranes of the cristae of the mitochondria (Fig. 11-8). This discovery was made by rupturing cells and spinning the cell contents at high velocities in a machine called a centrifuge. The centrifugal force developed

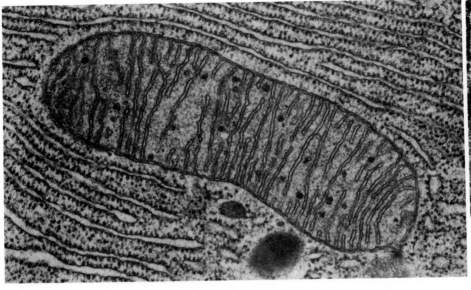

Organization of mitochondria. Left: The way in which the inner membranes project into the interior to form the cristae shows clearly in this mitochondrion from the pancreas of a bat (70,000 X, courtesy Keith R. Porter). Right: The subunits on the surface of the cristae can be seen in the mouse liver mitochondrion (200,000 X, courtesy Dr. Donald F. Parsons, *Science* **140** 985, May 31, 1963).

Fig. 11-8

in these machines causes the various cell components to fall to the bottom of the container, the heaviest ones first, the next heaviest after, and so on. In this way mitochondria have been isolated. The mitochondria can, in turn, be broken by subjecting them to powerful supersonic sound waves. When the outer membrane ruptures, the fluid contents of the mitochondrion are released. However, the membrane itself still possesses the ability to oxidize $NADH_2$ and ultimately to form H_2O. For this reason, we suspect that the various enzymes in the cytochrome system are arranged in an efficient, assembly-line fashion along the membranes of the mitochondrion. The discovery of rows of subunits projecting from the membranes of the cristae lends support to this view (Fig. 11-8). These subunits are thought to contain one or more molecules of enzymes used in cellular respiration.

The burning of 180 gm of glucose (**one mole**) yields 686,000 calories of energy in the form of heat. One mole of ATP stores about 8000 calories of energy. At this point in our story, a net of eight ATP molecules have been produced from one glucose molecule (a net of two from the anaerobic breakdown of glucose and six from the passage of two *pairs* of electrons through the cytochrome system). Only 64,000 calories (less than 10%) of the energy present in the glucose has been extracted. The explanation lies in the fact that pyruvic acid itself is a reasonably complex, energy-rich molecule. The oxidation of pyruvic acid is the next part of our story.

The Citric Acid Cycle   **11-6**

To extract the maximum amount of energy from a molecule of glucose, the glucose must be oxidized completely to CO_2 and H_2O. In converting glucose into two molecules of pyruvic acid, only a partial oxidation has been achieved: four electrons (and their associated H^+ ions) have been removed from the molecule and passed through the cytochrome enzyme system in the mitochondria. In the cellular respiration of glucose, however, the process does not stop with the formation of pyruvic acid. Instead, the molecule is oxidized still further until only the waste materials CO_2 and H_2O are left. This oxidation of pyruvic acid goes on in a step-by-step fashion just as does the breakdown of glucose to pyruvic acid. Each step in the process requires the presence of a specific enzyme. These are localized in the fluid contents of the mitochondria. Therefore, the electrons removed in each oxidation can be passed easily to the cytochrome enzyme system.

The first step in the oxidation of pyruvic acid is the removal of a molecule of CO_2 (Fig. 11-6). The residue is then "activated" by being combined with a coenzyme, called coenzyme A. This complex molecule is called active acetate. In the process of activation, two electrons (with H^+'s) are transferred to NAD and from NAD into the cytochrome system. With the aid of a molecule of H_2O, the active acetate complex is broken, coenzyme A is regenerated, and the acetate portion of the molecule ($C_2H_4O_2$) is united with a molecule of oxaloacetic acid ($C_4H_4O_5$). The new molecule ($C_6H_8O_7$) is **citric acid.** (This is the acid which is found in citrus fruits—lemons, grapefruit, etc. It has provided the name for the sequence of chemical changes we are discussing.) After a series of enzyme-catalyzed molecular changes, including removal of another molecule of CO_2 and the removal of another pair of electrons by NAD, alpha-ketoglutaric acid is formed. Another molecule of CO_2 and two more electrons (with H^+'s) are removed from the alpha-ketoglutaric acid by NAD. A molecule of H_2O enters the reaction at this step. The result of these changes is succinic acid. The molecular rearrangements involved in the conversion of alpha-ketoglutaric acid to succinic acid also result in the production of one molecule of ATP. The mechanism by which this occurs is not yet clear.

Two more electrons (and H^+'s) are removed from succinic acid to form fumaric acid.

Succinic acid   Fumaric acid

The oxidizing agent in this case is flavin. Do you suppose that as many molecules of ATP are produced when flavin donates electrons to the cytochrome system as when $NADH_2$ does? (Figure 11-6 can help you answer this.)

The addition of a molecule of H_2O to fumaric acid produces malic acid. NAD then removes two electrons (and two H^+'s) from malic acid with the formation of oxaloacetic acid. What do you suppose then happens to the oxaloacetic acid that has been formed?

In passing through the chemical changes of the citric acid cycle, the active acetate has been completely oxidized to H_2O and CO_2. When the process is completed, the "carrier" molecule, oxaloacetic acid, is regenerated and can then pick up another molecule of active acetate.

Importance of Cellular Respiration 11-7

You may well ask what is the significance of oxidizing glucose by such an involved sequence of chemical reactions. The answer should be clear once we see just how much ATP is produced during the respiration of one molecule of glucose (Fig. 11-6). Remember that a single molecule of glucose gives rise to two molecules of PGAL, whose fate we have just examined. At five different times in the breakdown of one PGAL molecule, NAD removes a pair of electrons and passes them through the cytochrome system. As each pair of electrons passes through the cytochrome system, three molecules of ATP are produced. Hence 15 molecules of ATP are produced from each PGAL molecule by this process, making a total of 30 ATP's for each glucose molecule. In addition one pair of electrons is removed by flavin, but these give rise to only two ATP molecules, since they pass down a shorter length of the chain of enzymes on the mitochondrial membranes. The shortage is made up, however, by the single ATP produced in the transformation of alpha-ketoglutaric acid into succinic acid. Again, as the cycle must "turn" twice for each glucose molecule oxidized, a total of six more ATP molecules are produced by these mechanisms. Adding the net yield of two molecules of ATP which are produced when glucose is broken down anaerobically to pyruvic acid, we end up with a grand total of 38 molecules of ATP produced by the oxidation of a single molecule of glucose.

As mentioned in Section 11-5, a mole of glucose yields 686,000 calories of energy when fully oxidized. In the rapid, uncontrolled oxidation which we call burning, all this energy is liberated as heat and light. The controlled, step-by-step oxidation of glucose in cellular respiration, in contrast, permits a substantial part of this energy to be conserved in the form of chemical energy. This chemical energy, stored in the high-energy phosphate bonds of ATP, can then be used to carry out the many energy-consuming activities of the cell. The efficiency of the process can be calculated easily. The conversion of a mole of ADP to ATP requires about 8000 calories. The respiration of a mole of glucose gives rise to 38 moles of ATP. Thus about 304,000 calories are conserved, or 44% of the energy (686,000 calories) available in the glucose molecule. An efficiency of 44% in the conversion of the chemical energy of glucose into the chemical energy of ATP compares very favorably with the 15-30% efficiency of internal combustion engines in converting chemical energy into mechanical energy.

Not only can we set up a balance sheet to study the energy conversion process, but we can also set up a balance sheet indicating the substances consumed and the substances produced by respiration. Obviously we start with one molecule of glucose. As this is broken down, it gives rise to 12 pairs of electrons (and H^+'s) which pass through the cytochrome enzyme system and unite with 6 molecules of oxygen to form 12 molecules of H_2O. Although only 12 hydrogen atoms and 6 oxygen atoms are present in the original glucose molecule, the deficit is made up by the introduction of 6 (three at each turn of the cycle) water molecules into the citric acid cycle. Six molecules of CO_2 are also produced during these transformations, three from each pyruvic acid molecule entering the cycle. Thus the overall chemical change in cellular respiration can be expressed by the equation:

$$C_6H_{12}O_6 + 6O_2 + 6H_2O \rightarrow 6CO_2 + 12H_2O + 304,000 \text{ calories}$$

stored in ATP. See whether you can verify the correctness of this equation by studying Fig. 11-6.

The step-by-step oxidation of glucose into H_2O and CO_2 has another important function. Several of the *intermediate* compounds formed in the process link glucose metabolism with the metabolism of other foodstuffs. Thus PGAL is a breakdown product of glycerol (a component of fats) as well as an intermediate in the breakdown of glucose. Active acetate is produced by the breakdown of the fatty acid component of fats. It is also produced when certain amino acids have their nitrogen removed in the process of **deamination.** Pyruvic acid, alpha-ketoglutaric acid and oxaloacetic acid also may be formed from amino acid breakdown. These links thus permit the oxidation of excess fats and proteins in the diet. No special mechanism of cellular respiration is needed by those animals that depend largely on ingested fats (e.g. many birds) or proteins (e.g. carnivores) for their energy supply. These links between carbohydrate metabolism and the metabolism of fats and proteins are useful in still another way. Fatty acids, glycerol (and then fats), and some amino acids can be synthesized using these intermediates. As mentioned in Section 11-1, a human can become fat as a result of eating excess amounts of carbohydrates. A knowledge of the links between carbohydrate metabolism and fat metabolism shows us how this is possible (see Fig. 11-6).

The steps in the processes of fermentation and cellular respiration are also interesting because they are found in such a wide variety of living things. While some differences have been found in different organisms, most of the enzymes and intermediate compounds in the processes are common to almost all organisms from bacteria to men.

11-8 ## HOW THESE DISCOVERIES WERE MADE

You may be puzzled as to how biochemists have been able to discover all the intermediate steps in fermentation and cellular respiration. The discovery has required many years, the work of many men, and the use of a variety of ingenious techniques.

One technique in studying intermediary metabolism is to supply a suspected intermediate substance and see (1) whether it is used up and (2) what new substance begins to accumulate. Sometimes this technique is applied to the intact organism, but usually it is applied to isolated organs, tissues, or even cell extracts. The discovery by Hans Krebs that oxaloacetic acid ($C_4H_4O_5$) added to isolated pigeon breast muscle is converted into citric acid ($C_6H_8O_7$) enabled him to work out the reactions in the citric acid cycle or, as it is sometimes called, Krebs' cycle.

Another technique is to attempt the isolation of a specific enzyme. Grinding up a piece of tissue, such as liver tissue, releases the cell contents. The biochemist can then attempt to extract and purify a single enzyme. If this is accomplished, he can then determine the single substrate upon which that enzyme acts and the substance produced by its action.

The use of enzyme poisons has also provided information on intermediary metabolism. A poison that interferes with cellular respiration may actually affect only a single enzyme in the process. For example, the poisonous effect of malonic acid (see Section 9-8) is due to its inhibition of the enzyme that catalyzes the conversion of succinic acid to fumaric acid in the citric acid cycle. When such a situation occurs, the normal substrate (succinic acid in this case) of the poisoned enzyme accumulates and may be identified. Then if the substance normally *produced* by that enzyme can be discovered, using the techniques mentioned above, this substance can be added to the poisoned system. If respiration begins again, as it does when fumaric acid is added to tissues poisoned by malonic acid (Fig. 11-6), another link in the chain has been established.

One of the best techniques for studying intermediary metabolism is to introduce into an enzyme system molecules which have been "tagged" with radioactive atoms. The gradual appearance of radioactivity in other chemical substances will indicate the pathway by which the chemical changes have occurred. In the next chapter, we will see how this technique was used to determine one of the important steps in the process of photosynthesis.

Finally, all of these special techniques depend for their success upon the multitude of analytical tests that chemists have devised through years of experimentation and logical reasoning. Some of the techniques for determining the identity of chemical substances and for determining the arrangement of the atoms in their molecules were mentioned in Chapter 6.

THE USES OF ENERGY   11-9

The processes of cellular respiration and fermentation transform chemical energy stored in the glucose molecule into chemical energy stored in the high-energy phosphate bonds of ATP. ATP, in turn, serves as the immediate source of energy for all the energy-requiring activities of the organism. These fall into several categories.

1) **Mechanical Work.** One of the most important ways in which energy is used by living organisms is to carry on mechanical work. This is especially true of animals. Running, swimming, flying, and climbing are just a few common animal activities in which work is accomplished and energy is consumed. In most cases, the mechanical work is brought about by the contraction of special cells, the muscle cells. The force exerted when muscle cells contract can then be transmitted to organs of locomotion, etc. The energy needed to accomplish muscular contraction is supplied by ATP. In Chapter 29 we will study details of this process.

2) **Electrical Work.** Energy is also used by living things to accomplish electrical work. The electric eel is a dramatic example of this. Special electric organs in this fish are capable of converting the energy of ATP into a brief current sufficient to stun an adult human. On a less dramatic (but far more important) scale, the energy of ATP is used to create the voltage which exists between the interior and exterior surfaces of most cell membranes. All nervous activity, as you will see in Chapter 28, depends upon this kind of electrical activity.

3) **Active Transport.** A third way in which cells use energy is to counteract the passive forces of diffusion and osmosis. The active transport of ions or molecules from regions of low concentration to regions of high concentration seems to be closely linked to the production and use of ATP by the cell. Several specific examples of active transport were mentioned in Section 9-5. The periodic filling (and contraction) of the contractile vacuole of the amoeba, for example, requires the energy of ATP.

4) **Bioluminescence.** Many organisms are able to give off light. Although the firefly is a common example, the majority of luminescent organisms are found in the oceans.

These include certain marine bacteria, protozoans, cnidarians, crustaceans, mollusks, echinoderms, and even fishes. Biochemists do not yet fully understand the bioluminescent process. One thing that is clear, however, is that energy in the form of ATP is essential for the process to occur. Other aspects of bioluminescence will be discussed in Chapter 29.

5)   **Heat.**   Energy is also a source of heat for living things. The mammals and birds are especially dependent upon internally generated heat. They can maintain a fixed body temperature despite fluctuations in the environmental temperature. Generally, the production of heat occurs simply as a by-product of other energy transformations within the cell. As we have already seen, no energy transformation is 100% efficient. For example, when chemical energy is converted into mechanical energy (as in muscular contraction) a substantial amount (70-80%) of the energy is lost in the form of heat. The involuntary muscular contraction which we call shivering exploits this inefficiency to prevent our body temperature from falling below normal. Thus although heat cannot do work for an organism, its production may be vital to the organism in cold surroundings.

6)   **Anabolism.**   As we have seen, the synthesis of large complex molecules from smaller, simpler ones is an energy-consuming process. From the absorbed products of digestion, cells are able to synthesize proteins, polysaccharides, lipids, and nucleic acids. Energy is needed to accomplish these syntheses. The source of energy here, too, is ATP. You have seen (Section 11-1) that before glucose units can be linked together to form starch, they must first be activated. This activation is accomplished by transferring a phosphate group from ATP to the glucose molecule. A specific enzyme is also necessary. In Chapter 20, you will learn that a similar mechanism is employed by the cell in the synthesis of its proteins. The constituent amino acids must first be activated before they can be assembled into a chain. This activation is also accomplished by ATP and specific enzymes. It is interesting that the activation of each of our 20-odd amino acids requires a separate enzyme, but the single substance ATP supplies the energy requirement for them all. Thus the many anabolic activities of the cell (as well as the other energy-requiring activities discussed above) are all linked to the catabolic, energy-producing activities of the cell by one substance: ATP.

It is as a result of the anabolism of the cell that an increase in the amount of living material (growth) takes place. The process of converting ingested food into more living substance is not 100% efficient, although in some organisms, such as carefully bred varieties of poultry, the percentage of conversion may be remarkably high. Broilers can gain about half a pound of live weight for every pound of food ingested. There are several reasons why one would not expect the rate of conversion to exceed this value by any great amount. First, of course, some of the ingested food must be catabolized in order to provide the energy for the anabolic use of the remainder. Second, although the energy transformations of the cell are remarkably efficient, a sizable part of the energy involved in every chemical change is lost as heat. Third, a great deal of the energy produced in catabolism is used in a multitude of other ways, as we have seen. An adult human may maintain a constant weight for a long period of time, but still is dependent, of course, upon ingested food materials as a source of energy for other activities. It is interesting to note in this connection that the high conversion ratio noted for broilers is achieved only when the animals are reared in relative confinement. The more physical activity carried on by an organism, the smaller will be the percentage of its food actually assimilated, that is, used in growth.

This inability of heterotrophic organisms to convert 100% of their ingested food materials into the constitutents of their own cells has other important consequences. All heterotrophic organisms depend ultimately upon autotrophic organisms for their food. Animals that eat plants directly (herbivores) will assimilate a small percentage (generally no more than 10%) of the food materials. Most of the ingested food will be broken down, as we have seen, into inorganic substances (e.g. CO_2 and H_2O). Animals that feed upon these animals (carnivores) will, in turn, be able to assimilate only a portion of the ingested food and thus just a tiny fraction of the food originally manufactured by the autotroph. Man includes both plants and animals in his diet. (He is an omnivore.) Whenever he consumes meat in his diet, however, he is indulging in the luxury of food whose manufacture has already involved substantial losses of matter and energy back to the environment. It is no accident that a pound of beefsteak is more expensive than a pound of corn. It took many pounds of the latter to produce one pound of the former. In Chapter 37 we will examine still other consequences of this fundamental law—that energy cannot be transformed with 100% efficiency.

In this chapter and Chapter 10, we have examined how heterotrophic organisms secure and use the complex, energy-rich, organic molecules which we call food. Whether eaten by herbivore or carnivore, the ultimate source of all these organic molecules is the life activities of autotrophic organisms. Only autotrophs can manufacture organic, energy-rich molecules from inorganic, energy-poor raw materials. How they do this is the topic of the next chapter.

EXERCISES AND PROBLEMS

1 Pound for pound, what food yields the most energy when oxidized?

2 In what ways is alcoholic fermentation similar to cellular respiration?

3 In what ways is it different?

4 Into what forms of energy can the chemical energy of ATP be transformed?

5 What parallels can you draw between the process of bread making and the process of brewing? What differences are there?

6 List the substances in the cell that participate in REDOX reactions.

7 Why is the calorie, a unit of heat energy, also used as a measure of chemical energy?

8 How many moles of oxygen are consumed when two moles of glucose are respired? How many moles of carbon dioxide are produced?

9 What is the ratio of moles of oxygen consumed to moles of CO_2 produced when glucose is respired?

10 What happens to this ratio when fats are used as the fuel in cellular respiration?

11 Why are alcoholic beverages usually brewed in sealed containers?

12 What is the maximum weight of alcohol that yeast cells can produce from 90 gm of glucose?

13 What is the net yield of ATP molecules when glycogen rather than glucose is used to produce the glucose phosphate used in cellular respiration?

REFERENCES

1 Siekevitz, P., "Powerhouse of the Cell," *Scientific American,* Reprint No. 36, July, 1957. Describes the structure of mitochondria and how they are studied.

2 Lehninger, A. L., "Energy Transformation in the Cell," *Scientific American,* Reprint No. 69, May, 1960. How mitochondria convert the energy stored in glucose into ATP.

3 Green, D. E., "The Mitochondrion," *Scientific American,* January, 1964. Attempts to relate the chemical activities of the mitochondrion to its internal construction.

4 McElroy, W. D., *Cellular Physiology and Biochemistry,* 2nd ed., Foundations of Modern Biology Series, Prentice-Hall, 1964. Chapters 4–7 discuss metabolic energy and how it is transformed in fermentation and respiration. Structural formulas are used in the equations.

Chloroplast (35,000 X). The structures that look like stacks of coins are the chlorophyll-containing grana. (Courtesy Dr. A. E. Vatter.)

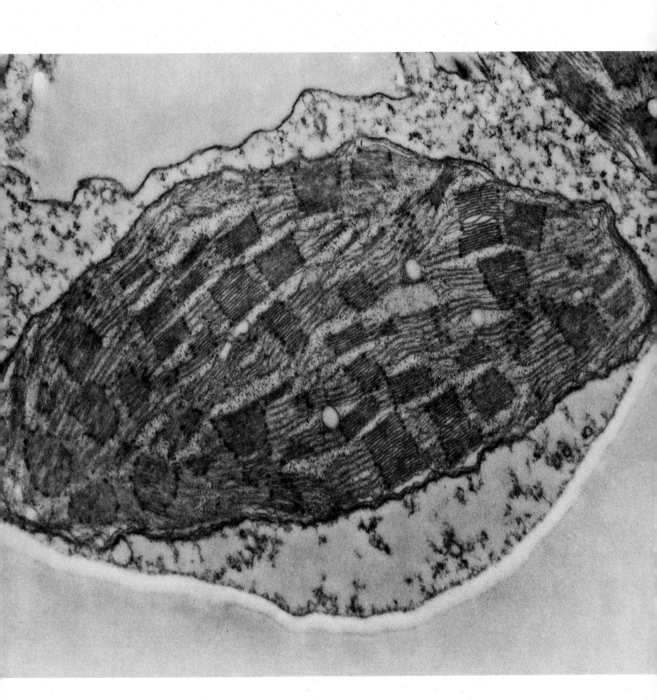

The life of every living organism depends upon a steady supply of materials and energy. The materials are necessary to provide for the growth and repair of the organism. The energy is necessary to permit the organism to maintain its structure in opposition to the tendency of all things (from molecules—see Section 9-3—to bureau drawers!) to become randomly arranged and disordered. In Chapter 8, we saw how intricately organized is the living cell. Even its constituents, such as the cell membrane, the mitochondria, and the parts of the nucleus, reflect an orderly arrangement of the protein, lipid, and nucleic acid molecules of which they are composed. Cells, in turn, are organized into tissues, the tissues into organs, etc. All these levels of organization depend ultimately upon energy to preserve their pattern. The maintenance of these complex, orderly patterns is one of the main features that distinguish living from nonliving things. With additional energy, additional materials can be organized into these patterns, resulting in growth.

Energy is also necessary for living things to cope with changes in their environment. The activity of nerves and the contraction of muscles permit you to respond to changes in your environment. These activities require energy. Do you think that there is any connection between using energy for this purpose and using energy to preserve the complex organization of matter which we discussed in the last paragraph?

Heterotrophic organisms supply their needs for both matter and energy by taking in complex, energy-rich, organic molecules from their environment. In Chapter 10, we examined some of the mechanisms by which these are taken in by heterotrophs and made available to individual cells. In Chapter 11, we examined the way in which these molecules serve not only as a source of materials for the repair and growth of the cell but also as a source of energy for it.

Where do these complex, energy-rich, organic molecules come from? They are manufactured by green plants and protists. These organisms are capable of synthesizing organic molecules from simple, inorganic materials in the environment such as CO_2 and H_2O. This type of nutrition is referred to as **autotrophic.** Organisms that are capable of autotrophic nutrition not only supply all their own needs for materials and energy but, directly or indirectly, the needs of all heterotrophic organisms. The Bible's statement "All flesh is grass" reflects a crucial biological truth: heterotrophic organisms depend for their existence upon autotrophic organisms. We may dine on beefsteak, but the steer dined on grass.

The kind of autotrophic nutrition upon which almost all heterotrophic organisms (including ourselves) depend is photosynthesis. In photosynthesis, light energy is harnessed for the synthesis of organic compounds from inorganic ones.

PHOTOSYNTHESIS

12-1 EARLY EXPERIMENTS

Our present knowledge of photosynthesis is the outcome of experiments performed and theories created during the past 300 years. Perhaps the first experiment designed to explore the nature of photosynthesis was that reported by the Dutch physician van Helmont, in 1648. Some years earlier, van Helmont had placed in a large pot exactly 200 pounds of soil that had been thoroughly dried in an oven. Then he moistened the soil with rain water and planted a five-pound willow shoot in it. He then placed the pot in the ground and covered its rim with a perforated iron plate. The perforations permitted water and air to reach the soil but lessened the chance that dirt would be blown into the pot from the outside (Fig. 12-1). For five years, van Helmont kept his plant watered with rain water or distilled water. At the end of that time, he carefully removed the young tree and found that it had gained 164 pounds, 3 ounces. (This figure did not include the weight of the leaves that had been shed during the previous four autumns.)

He then redried the soil and found that it weighed only 2 ounces less than the original 200 pounds. Faced with these experimental facts, van Helmont theorized that the increase in the weight of the willow arose from the water alone. He did not consider the possibility that gases in the air might also be involved.

Fig. 12-1

Van Helmont's experiment. Over a five-year period the willow gained more than 164 lb, while the weight of the soil was practically unchanged.

It was the English chemist Priestley and the Dutch physician Ingen-Housz who discovered that photosynthesis also involves gases in the air. Priestley found that green plants give off oxygen. Thus he was the first to see this important role that plants play in the lives of animals. As we saw in the last chapter, almost all animals require oxygen for cellular respiration. It was Ingen-Housz who, in 1778, showed that the ability of plants to liberate oxygen was entirely dependent upon light. In fact, he found that in the shade or at night, plants consume oxygen, just as animals do. This discovery that plants are capable of respiration plagued later generations of plant physiologists. They could never be sure that their measurements of photosynthetic activity represented true values or simply the difference between an unknown rate of photosynthesis working in one direction and an unknown rate of respiration working in the other. It was not until 1954 that photosynthesis was finally accomplished in isolated chloroplasts and thus free from the presence of mitochondria. Only then could the process be studied independently of the effects of respiration.

That CO_2 plays a part in photosynthesis was first demonstrated (in 1804) by the Swiss chemist de Saussure. He sealed the tops of plants in glass chambers to which he added measured amounts of CO_2. He found that when the plants were exposed to light, they consumed the CO_2 and grew. He also found that they released O_2 at the same rate that they consumed CO_2. By further experiment, de Saussure determined the fate of the carbon atoms in the CO_2. Beans germinated in an atmosphere containing CO_2 grew and increased their total carbon content. Beans germinated in a sealed container free of CO_2 did not increase the amount of carbon present. The total carbon content of the young root, stem, and leaves was no greater than that of the original seed.

THE PIGMENTS

Ingen-Housz also showed by experiments that only the green portions of plants liberate oxygen. He found that nongreen portions, such as woody stems, roots, flowers, and fruits, actually consume oxygen in the process of respiration. We now know that this is because photosynthesis can go on only in the presence of the green pigment **chlorophyll.** Chlorophyll is a magnesium-containing compound which shows a distinct chemical relationship to the prosthetic group of the cytochrome enzymes (Fig. 11-7). Its chief distinguishing features are the presence of a magnesium (instead of iron) atom and a side chain of carbon atoms called the phytol group. Actually, several kinds of chlorophyll molecules are known. Chlorophyll a is found in all green plants and all algae. Chlorophyll b is found in plants and green algae (Chlorophyta) along with chlorophyll a. Still other chlorophylls are found in other algae and in the photosynthetic bacteria.

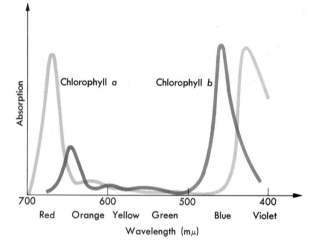

Fig. 12-2

Absorption spectra of chlorophyll a and b.

Many algae contain other pigments in addition to chlorophylls. These impart the special colors we find in the blue-green algae, the red algae, and the brown algae. They are accessory to the process of photosynthesis.

Chlorophyll is a green pigment because it does not absorb green light. White light (such as sunlight) contains light of all the colors of the visible spectrum from red to violet, but all these colors are not absorbed equally by the pigment. It is possible to determine how effectively each color is absorbed by (1) illuminating a solution of chlorophyll with light of a single color and (2) measuring with a sensitive light meter the amount of light that passes through the solution. By repeating this process with colored lights of the entire visible spectrum, it is possible to draw an **absorption spectrum** (Fig. 12-2). Note that chlorophyll absorbs light most strongly in the red and violet portions of the spectrum. Green light is very poorly absorbed. Hence when white light shines upon chlorophyll-containing structures, such as leaves, green rays are transmitted and reflected, with the result that the structures appear green.

Other pigments are found associated with the chlorophylls in green plant cells. Chief among these are the carotenoids. While carotenoids of many colors are known, in plant cells they range in color from yellow to red. Although their presence in green leaves is usually masked by the greater abundance of the chlorophylls, they often become the dominant pigment in flowers and fruits. The red of the ripe tomato and the orange of the carrot are produced by carotenoids. Even in leaves, the carotenoids may become visible. The brilliant yellows of autumn foliage are produced by the carotenoids which become visible as the supply of chlorophyll in the leaf dwindles.

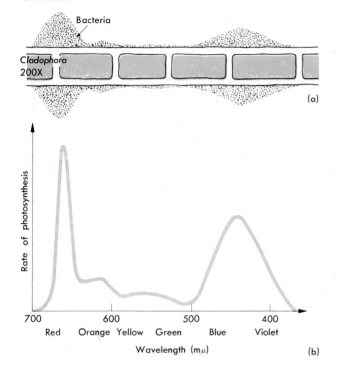

Fig. 12-3

(a) Engelmann's experiment and (b) action spectrum of photosynthesis.

In most green plant cells, the carotenoid content is less than one-quarter that of the chlorophylls. This does not necessarily mean that the carotenoids are not important in photosynthesis. However, the relative importance of the two kinds of pigments can be determined by finding out which colors of light are most effective in causing photosynthesis. In 1881, the German plant physiologist T. W. Engelmann performed a series of experiments to discover this. He placed a filamentous green alga under the microscope and illuminated the strand with a tiny spectrum. In the medium surrounding the strands were motile, aerobic bacteria. After a few minutes of illumination, the bacteria were found to be congregated and most active around the portions of the filament illuminated by red and blue light (Fig. 12-3). Assuming that the bacteria were congregating in the regions where oxygen was being evolved, Engelmann concluded that the red rays and the blue rays are the most effective colors for photosynthesis. By plotting the effectiveness of each color of light in stimulating photosynthesis, one can draw an **action spectrum** (see Fig. 12-3). The similarity of the action spectrum of photosynthesis and the absorption spectrum of chlorophyll suggests that the chlorophylls are the most important pigments in the process. The spectra are not identical, however, and this suggests that the carotenoids play some role in photosynthesis.

CHLOROPLASTS

The chlorophylls (along with some carotenoids) are contained within cell structures called chloroplasts. In the cells of plants, these are disk-shaped. In some of the green algae they may occur in a variety of shapes. For example, the chloroplast in *Spirogyra* is a spiral filament. There are no chloroplasts in the blue-green algae. In these organisms, the pigments are confined to membranes arranged concentrically within the cell (look back at the opening illustration in Chapter 8).

Fig. 12-4

Seedlings of the common garden bean grown in light (left) and in darkness (right). The pale color of the dark-grown plant is caused by its lack of chlorophyll. When the food reserves of its seed are used up, the seedling will die. Each seedling shows three nodes, but the internodes are greatly elongated in the dark-grown seedling, a condition known as etiolation.

In addition to the photosynthetic pigments, chloroplasts contain substantial quantities of lipids and proteins. The latter include many enzymes, among them cytochrome enzymes similar to those found in the mitochondria.

Chloroplasts arise from tiny, colorless structures in the cells called proplastids. Light is necessary for the development of proplastids into chloroplasts. This explains the pale color of seedlings grown in the dark (Fig. 12-4). Proplastids are capable of duplicating themselves. In fact, this is the only way in which additional proplastids are formed. The nuclei of green plant cells cannot manufacture them. Thus whenever green plant cells undergo mitosis, it is important that both daughter cells receive proplastids in the cytoplasm as well as the normal chromosome content of the nucleus. It is probably significant that these self-duplicating structures also contain some of the hereditary material, DNA. In the laboratory, *Euglena* cells have been produced that contain neither chloroplasts nor proplastids. These cells give rise to populations of colorless cells, which never regain the ability to carry on the process of photosynthesis.

The disk-shaped chloroplasts of higher plants average about 7 micra in diameter. Under the light microscope, these tiny bodies appear to be perfectly uniform in structure. With the aid of the electron microscope, however, it has been found that the chloroplast itself is a highly organized structure. The chlorophyll (and accessory pigments such as the carotenoids) are confined in flat layers, the **lamellae.** Viewed in cross section (Fig. 12-5), these lamellae seem to consist of pairs of modified unit membranes with chlorophyll and carotenoids as well as lipid molecules sandwiched between the layers of protein. Viewed on their flat surface, the pigments of the lamellae appear to be organized into distinct particles called **quantasomes.** Stacks of lamellae are called **grana** (Fig. 12-5). Surrounding them is a colorless material, the **stroma.** As mentioned above, the intact chloroplast is capable of carrying out the entire process of photosynthesis.

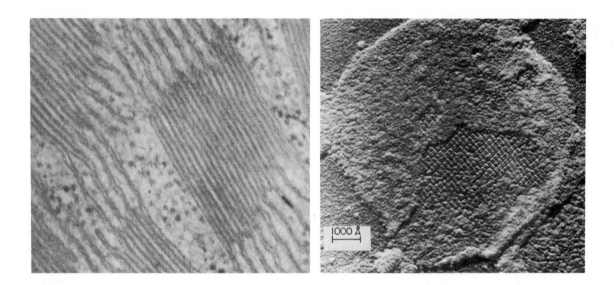

Organization of a chloroplast. Left: Under high magnification (60,000 X), the stacks of lamellae that form the grana can be seen clearly. (Courtesy Dr. A. E. Vatter.) Right: Lamellae are thought to be modified unit membranes. When viewed on their surface, the membranes of the lamellae can be seen to be composed of subunits, the quantasomes. (Courtesy Dr. R. B. Park. From R. B. Park and J. Biggins, *Science* **144,** 1009–1011, May 22, 1964.)

Fig. 12-5

THE LEAF 12-4

In higher plants, chloroplasts are generally confined to parenchyma cells of young stems, immature fruits, and leaves. It is the leaves which are the real photosynthetic factories of the plant. A cross section through the blade of a typical leaf reveals several distinct tissue layers (Fig. 12-6). The top surface of the leaf is covered by a single layer of cells which makes up the **upper epidermis.** These cells contain few or no chloroplasts. They are therefore quite transparent and permit most of the light which strikes them to pass through to the underlying cells. They also secrete a waxy, transparent substance called cutin. This material makes up the cuticle. It serves as a moisture barrier on the upper surface of the leaf, thus reducing water loss from the leaf.

Beneath the cells of the upper epidermis are arranged one or more rows of cells which make up the **palisade layer.** These cells are cylindrical in shape and oriented so that their long axis is perpendicular to the plane of the leaf. Each one is filled with chloroplasts (50 or more) and, as you might guess, these cells carry on most of the photosynthesis in the leaf. The form of the cells is well suited to this function. They are arranged so that a large number of cells are exposed to the sun's rays. Furthermore, their length increases the chance that the light entering the cell will be absorbed by a chloroplast.

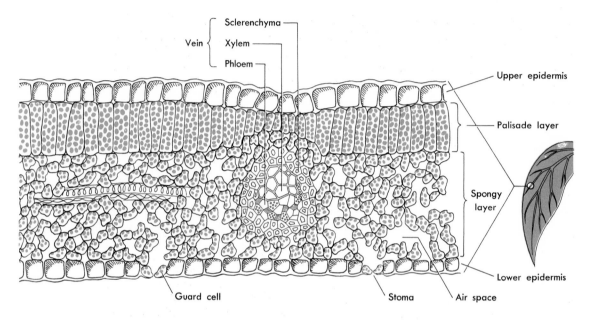

Fig. 12-6   Structure of a typical leaf as seen in cross section. The cells of the palisade layer carry on most of the photosynthesis in the leaf. In some leaves, especially those exposed to bright sun, there may be two or three layers of palisade cells.

Beneath the palisade layer is the **spongy layer** of the leaf. The cells of the spongy layer are irregular in shape and loosely packed. Although they contain a few chloroplasts, their main function seems to be the temporary storage of the food molecules produced by the cells of the palisade layer. They also aid in the exchange of gases between the leaf and the environment. During daylight hours, these cells give off O_2 and water vapor to the air spaces which surround them. They also pick up CO_2 from the air in the air spaces. The air spaces are interconnected with one another and eventually open to the outside of the leaves through special pores called **stomata.**

In most plants, the stomata are located chiefly in the **lower epidermis** of the leaf. Ingen-Housz himself first demonstrated that photosynthesizing leaves give off O_2 more rapidly from their lower surface than from their upper surface. The presence of as many as 100,000 stomata per square centimeter in the lower epidermis of some oak leaves and none in the upper epidermis easily accounts for this observation.

Most of the cells of the lower epidermis resemble those of the upper epidermis. Around each stoma, however, are located two sausage-shaped cells called **guard cells.**

The guard cells differ from the other cells of the lower epidermis not only in their shape but also in their having large numbers of chloroplasts. The guard cells regulate the opening and closing of the stomata. Thus they exert a considerable control over the exchange of gases between the leaf and the surrounding atmosphere. The mechanism of their action will be considered in the next chapter.

The leaf also has veins. The veins contain conducting vessels (xylem and phloem) which transport materials to and from the cells of the leaf and the rest of the plant. A detailed analysis of the structure and function of these conducting vessels will be presented in Chapter 15. The conducting vessels of the veins are often surrounded by sclerenchyma cells. These thick-walled cells not only provide mechanical support for the conducting tubes which they surround, but also provide a substantial amount of rigidity to the whole blade of the leaf.

FACTORS LIMITING THE RATE OF PHOTOSYNTHESIS 12-5

With the discovery that the first product of photosynthesis to accumulate in any substantial amount is glucose, it became possible to establish an equation for the process:

$$6CO_2 + 6H_2O \rightarrow C_6H_{12}O_6 + 6O_2.$$

This equation shows the relationship between the substances used in and produced by photosynthesis. It does not, however, tell us anything about the intermediate steps in the process. That there are intermediate steps was first pointed out by the British plant physiologist F. F. Blackman. You, too, can easily repeat his experiment, using the apparatus shown in Fig. 12-7. The green water plant *Anacharis densa* (available wherever aquarium supplies are sold) is the test organism. When a sprig is placed upside down in a dilute solution of $NaHCO_3$ (which serves as a source of CO_2) and illuminated with a flood lamp, oxygen bubbles are soon given off from the cut portion of the stem. You then count the number of bubbles given off in a definite interval of time at each of several light intensities. Plotting this information should produce a graph similar to that in Fig. 12-8. That the rate of photosynthesis does not continue to increase indefinitely with increased illumination led Blackman to the conclusion that at least two distinct processes are involved: one, a reaction that requires light and the other, a reaction that does not. This latter is called a "dark" reaction although

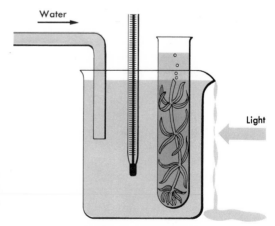

Fig. 12-7

Apparatus for determining the rate of photosynthesis in *Anacharis*. Measurements are made by counting the rate at which bubbles of oxygen are given off at the stem.

it *can* go on in the light. Blackman theorized that at moderate light intensities, the "light" reaction limits or "paces" the entire process. In other words, at these intensities the dark reaction is capable of handling all the intermediate substances produced by the light reaction. With increasing light intensities, however, a point is eventually reached when the dark reaction is working at maximum capacity. Any further illumination is ineffective and the process reaches a steady rate.

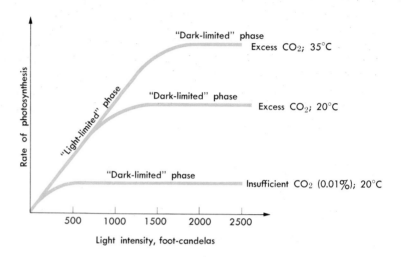

Fig. 12-8

Rate of photosynthesis as a function of light intensity, CO_2 concentration, and temperature. At low light intensities, light is the limiting factor. At higher light intensities, temperature and CO_2 concentration are the limiting factors.

This theory is strengthened by repeating the experiment at a somewhat higher temperature. As we have mentioned, most chemical reactions proceed more rapidly at higher temperatures (up to a point). At 35°C, the rate of photosynthesis does not level off until greater light intensities are present. This suggests that the dark reaction is now working more rapidly. The fact that at low light intensities the rate of photosynthesis at 35°C is no greater than at 20°C also supports the idea that it is a light reaction which is limiting the process in this range. All the light reactions known to chemists depend, not on the temperature, but simply on the intensity of illumination.

The increased rate of photosynthesis with increased temperature does not occur if the supply of CO_2 (in the form of HCO_3^-) is limited. As illustrated in Fig. 12-8, the overall rate of photosynthesis reaches a steady value at lower light intensities if the amount of CO_2 available is limited. Thus CO_2 concentration must be added as a third factor regulating the rate at which photosynthesis occurs. As a practical matter, however, the concentration of CO_2 available to terrestrial plants is simply that found in the atmosphere: 0.03%.

12-6

THE DARK REACTIONS

As you might expect, the dark reaction in photosynthesis is actually a series of reactions. These reactions involve the uptake of CO_2 by the plant and the reduction of CO_2 by hydrogen atoms. Dr. Calvin and his associates at the University of California have devoted years to working out the step-by-step sequence of chemical reactions involved. Their basic experimental procedure has been to expose suspensions of the

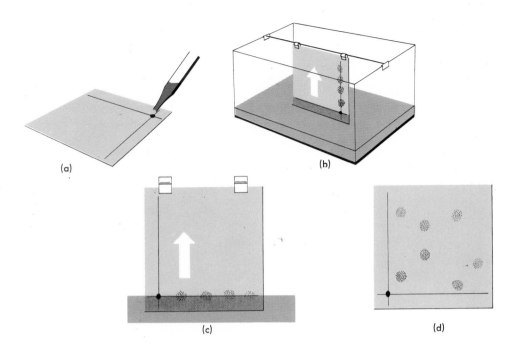

Separation of a mixture by two-dimensional paper chromatography. (a) and (b) Placed in a suitable solvent, the substances in the drop of material at the lower right-hand corner of the paper will be partially separated as they migrate upward. (c) and (d) Further separation can be achieved by turning the paper 90° and using a different solvent.

Fig. 12-9

green alga *Chlorella* to light and to radioactive carbon dioxide. The use of radioactive carbon (C^{14}) in the carbon dioxide "tags" the atom and allows its chemical transformations to be studied. After various intervals of illumination, the *Chlorella* suspension is inactivated and the contents of the cells extracted. These are then separated by a process called paper chromatography. A drop of the cell extract is placed along one edge of a square of absorbent paper. The paper is then dipped into a solvent. The solvent migrates up the sheet because of capillary attraction (Fig. 12-9). As it does so, the chemical substances in the drop of cell extract are carried along at different rates. Generally, each compound migrates at a unique rate in a given solvent. When the process is completed, the various substances will be separated at distinct places on the sheet of paper, thus forming what is called a *chromatogram*. The identity of each substance may be determined simply by comparing its position with the positions occupied by known substances under the same conditions. Or, the particular portion of the paper can be cut from the sheet and delicate analytical tests run on the tiny amount of substance present.

To determine which, if any, of the substances separated on the chromatogram are radioactive, a sheet of x-ray film is placed next to the chromatogram. If dark spots appear on the film (because of the radiation emitted by the C^{14} atoms), their position can be correlated with the positions of the chemicals on the chromatogram. Using this technique of *radioautography*, Calvin found that C^{14} turned up in glucose molecules within 30 seconds after the start of photosynthesis. When he permitted photosynthesis to proceed for only five seconds, however, he discovered radioactivity in many other, smaller, intermediate molecules. Gradually the pathway of carbon fixation was established.

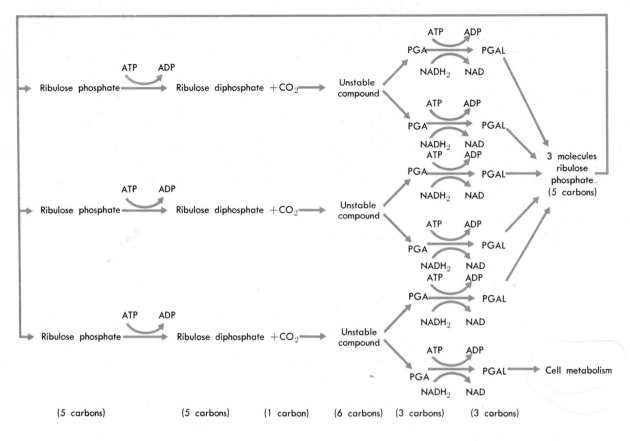

Fig. 12-10 Pathway of carbon fixation in photosynthesis: the "dark" reactions.

One of the key substances in this process is the five-carbon sugar ribulose phosphate. When it is "activated" by ATP, the resulting compound, ribulose diphosphate, is capable of combining with CO_2. The resulting six-carbon sugar molecule then breaks down to form two molecules of phosphoglyceric acid (PGA) (Fig. 12-10). Then, in what is fundamentally a reversal of the reaction in cellular respiration (see Section 11-4), the PGA molecule is reduced by $NADH_2$ to form phosphoglyceraldehyde (PGAL). (The energy of ATP is also needed to "drive" this reduction.) Starting with three molecules of ribulose phosphate, six molecules of PGAL are formed. Of these six, five are used to re-form the three starting molecules of ribulose phosphate. The remaining PGAL molecule, whose three carbon atoms represent the net gain from one turn of the cycle, stands right at the crossroads of cell metabolism. It can enter the mitochondria and continue "down" the pathway of cellular respiration. This will lead to the production of energy for the cell and/or the production of intermediates that can be used immediately for amino acid and lipid synthesis. On the other hand, an excess of PGAL will tend to reverse the reactions of cellular respiration. The PGAL then travels "up" the pathway to form fructose and then its isomer, glucose. Glucose and fructose can be combined to form the common table sugar, sucrose. This can then be transported to other regions of the plant. Excess glucose can be stored as the polysaccharide starch.

Hardly had the dark reactions in plant photosynthesis been worked out when it was discovered that these dark reactions are not unique to plants at all. The process of reducing carbon dioxide to form glucose is essentially the reverse of the anaerobic stage of cellular respiration. It has been found to go on in a variety of animal cells, including those of the human liver. However, just as the anaerobic breakdown of glucose produces energy (ATP and $NADH_2$), so its reversal *requires* ATP and $NADH_2$. (As you can see from Fig. 12-10, nine molecules of ATP and six of $NADH_2$ are needed for a net gain of one PGAL molecule.) Animal cells can thus never hope to accumulate glucose by this method. Remember that they must respire glucose to get their ATP and $NADH_2$ and that the process is only 44% efficient.

The discovery that the dark reactions of photosynthesis are not unique to green plants does, however, focus our attention on the light reaction. The secret of autotrophism must lie here.

THE LIGHT REACTIONS 12-7

It was the American microbiologist Van Niel who first glimpsed the role that light plays in photosynthesis. He arrived at his theory through studying photosynthesis in the purple sulfur bacteria. These microorganisms produce glucose from CO_2 as do the green plants, and they need light to accomplish the synthesis. Water, however, is not used as a starting material. Instead, these bacteria use a gas (which is poisonous to us), hydrogen sulfide (H_2S). Furthermore, no oxygen is liberated during this photosynthesis but rather the element sulfur. Van Niel reasoned that the action of light caused a decomposition of H_2S into hydrogen atoms and sulfur. Then, in a series of dark reactions, the hydrogen atoms were used to reduce CO_2 to carbohydrate:

$$CO_2 + 2H_2S \rightarrow (CH_2O) + H_2O + 2S.$$

(The parentheses around CH_2O signify that no specific molecule is being indicated but, instead, the ratio of atoms in some more complex molecule, e.g. glucose, $C_6H_{12}O_6$.)

In these reactions Van Niel envisioned a parallel to the process of photosynthesis in green plants. He reasoned that in green plants the energy of light causes water to break up into H_2 and O. The hydrogen atoms are then used to reduce CO_2 in a series of dark reactions:

$$CO_2 + 2H_2O \rightarrow (CH_2O) + H_2O + O_2.$$

If this theory is correct, it follows that all of the oxygen produced in photosynthesis is derived from water just as all the sulfur produced in bacterial photosynthesis is derived from the H_2S. This conclusion directly contradicts an earlier theory that the oxygen liberated in photosynthesis is derived from the carbon dioxide. If the equation for photosynthesis in Section 12-5 is correct, then at least some of the oxygen released must come from the CO_2. If, however, Van Niel's theory is correct, the equation for photosynthesis would have to be rewritten:

$$6CO_2 + 12H_2O \rightarrow C_6H_{12}O_6 + 6H_2O + 6O_2.$$

Faced with conflicting theories of this sort, scientists try to devise new experiments to test them. The usual method of procedure is to deduce from each theory a "fact" which must be so if the theory is sound. Then experiments must be devised to see which of the deduced "facts," if any, is actually a fact. In this case, the crucial experiments to test the two theories had to await the time when the growth of atomic research made the isotope O^{18} available for general scientific use. You remember that isotopes are atoms whose weight differs but whose chemical properties do not. O^{18} does not happen to be radioactive, but its presence in a compound can be measured. In 1941, a group of biochemists at the University of California allowed *Chlorella* cells to carry on photosynthesis (1) in the presence of water which had been "tagged" with O^{18} and (2) in the presence of CO_2 which had been tagged with O^{18}. If the earlier theory was correct, they would have expected the O^{18} atoms to appear in the liberated oxygen gas in the second experiment but not in the first. If Van Niel's theory was correct, however, the O^{18} atoms should appear in the liberated oxygen in the first experiment but not in the second. The latter proved to be the case. Therefore, we now express the process of photosynthesis by the equation:

$$6CO_2 + 12H_2O \rightarrow C_6H_{12}O_6 + 6O_2 + 6H_2O.$$

These experiments lent great support to Van Niel's idea that the role played by light in photosynthesis was the splitting of H_2O into hydrogen atoms and oxygen atoms. They gave no clue, however, as to the mechanism by which the hydrogen atoms then reduced the carbon dioxide to glucose.

As you have seen (Section 12-6), it was through the work of Calvin and others that this process and the other steps in the sequence of dark reactions were worked out. You also remember that in the dark reactions, the reducing agent is not hydrogen itself, but $NADH_2$. In 1951 it was discovered that chloroplasts illuminated by light reduce NAD to $NADH_2$, which can then be used as the reducing agent in the dark reactions. But there still remained the problem of determining how $NADH_2$ could be manufactured from the hydrogen atoms liberated from H_2O.

The problem has yet to be completely solved. However, Fig. 12-11 illustrates a mechanism which has received considerable experimental support. To understand this mechanism, it is necessary to understand the effect which light has upon chlorophyll.

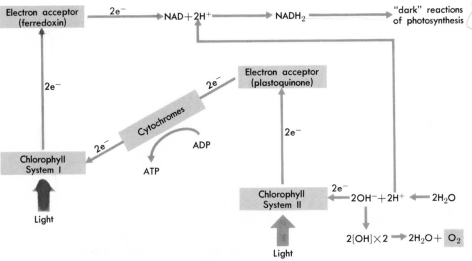

Fig. 12-11   Noncyclic photophosphorylation. The most important light-absorbing pigment in System I is chlorophyll *a*. In System II, most of the light is trapped by chlorophyll *b*. In the red, brown, and blue-green algae, the pigments responsible for their respective colors take the place of chlorophyll *b* in System II.

When a solution of chlorophyll is placed in a beam of white light, it gives off light of a deep red hue. This phenomenon is called fluorescence. It can be demonstrated easily. A crude chlorophyll extract can be prepared by soaking grass leaves in ethyl alcohol. When placed in a beam of white light, the solution fluoresces.

The explanation of the phenomenon of fluorescence is that the energy of the absorbed light is transferred to an electron in the chlorophyll molecule. The electron is "excited" and raised to a higher energy level. In the chlorophyll solution, the electron drops back to its former energy level after a fleeting instant. In so doing, it gives up most of the energy that had excited it in the first place. The energy is released as red light.

When *intact* chloroplasts are illuminated, no fluorescence is observed. This could mean that the excited electrons are removed from the chlorophyll by some other substance before they can drop back. This other substance is called ferredoxin. The excited electrons picked up by ferredoxin are sufficiently energetic to transfer to a molecule of NAD, thus reducing it. H^+ ions, present at all times because of the dissociation of water molecules, can then join with the electrons to give $NADH_2$. Finally, $NADH_2$ transfers its hydrogens to PGA in a dark reaction to form PGAL (Fig. 12-10).

You remember that plants and green algae have two kinds of chlorophyll in their chloroplasts. Chlorophyll a appears to play the dominant role in the reduction of ferredoxin. Other pigments may also participate in the trapping of light energy for this process, however; the complex of these pigments is called System I.

To maintain the process of $NADH_2$ production, fresh electrons must be supplied to the chlorophyll molecules in System I to replace the electrons expelled in the reduction of ferredoxin. These fresh electrons come from OH^- ions. Note that in the dissociation of a water molecule, for every H^+ that joins with NAD, an OH^- is left behind (Fig. 12-11). The electron that gives the OH^- its charge is held tightly, and its removal requires a substantial amount of energy. The source of this energy, like that for the reduction of ferredoxin, is light. Light absorbed by pigments in System II causes the chlorophyll molecules to lose electrons and thus become positively charged. In this condition, they are, a sufficiently powerful oxidizing agent to remove electrons from the OH^- ions. For every four OH^- ions which lose their electrons (become oxidized), two molecules of water and one molecule of oxygen are formed. The electrons are, in turn, raised to a high energy level as light continues to be absorbed by the pigments in System II.

Although chlorophyll a is probably responsible for the energizing and transport of electrons in both pigment systems, in System II it acquires much of its energy by transfer from chlorophyll b rather than by its own absorption of light. The difference in the absorption spectra of chlorophyll a and b (Fig. 12-2) increases the range of wavelengths useful in photosynthesis.

Chlorophyll b is found only in plants and green algae. The red, brown, and blue-green algae have chlorophyll a plus other pigments which give them their respective colors. These other pigments are used in System II, and by transferring their absorbed energy to chlorophyll a they markedly extend the range of wavelengths that can be used for photosynthesis by these algae.

The pathway of electrons from System II to System I is not yet entirely clear. At least part of the journey, however, involves cytochrome enzymes in the chloroplasts. As the electrons pass through these cytochrome enzymes, some ATP is manufactured. Then the electrons are further energized during the absorption of light by System I and $NADH_2$ is formed. This process is called **noncyclic photophosphorylation.** It is noncyclic because electrons must be continually supplied by the decomposition of water. It is a photophosphorylation because light energy results in the production of ATP. Clearly, the pigments of System I and II as well as the cytochrome enzymes and the special electron acceptors must be properly oriented with respect to one another so that the flow of electrons can proceed with maximum efficiency. Although the details have yet to be worked out, it is likely that these molecules *are* precisely arranged in the lamellae of the chloroplasts. Perhaps each **quantasome** (see Section 12-3) contains a single set of the molecules necessary to carry out all the steps in the light reactions.

At first glance, it would seem as though noncyclic photophosphorylation accounted for all the substances needed to convert CO_2 to glucose, namely $NADH_2$ and ATP. Probably not enough ATP is produced by this method, however, to satisfy the needs of all the various dark reactions in photosynthesis.

One possibility for making up the deficit would be to use some of the $NADH_2$ as a reducing agent for the cytochromes in the mitochondria. You remember (Section 11-5) that in cellular respiration, $NADH_2$ donates its electrons (and hydrogen ions) to the cytochrome enzyme system, which eventually passes them on to oxygen. In the process, ATP is manufactured. This possibility seems somewhat unlikely, though, when we see that most green plant cells have a relatively small number of mitochondria compared with the number of chloroplasts they contain.

This possibility was eliminated in 1954 when Dr. Daniel Arnon and his associates at the University of California showed that illuminated chloroplasts can manufacture substantial quantities of ATP even when isolated from other cell components (including mitochondria). Furthermore, this can be done even when no CO_2 is supplied to the chloroplasts and hence no dark reactions can occur. Even when the production of $NADH_2$ itself is stopped (by depriving the chloroplasts of NAD), the chloroplasts continue to produce large quantities of ATP as long as they are supplied with ADP, inorganic phosphate, and light. The energy of light is thus being converted directly into the chemical energy of ATP.

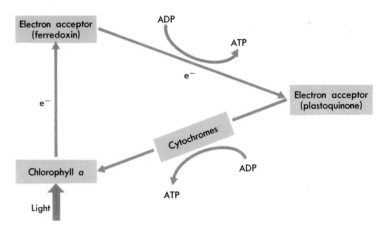

Fig. 12-12
Cyclic photophosphorylation.

Dr. Arnon named this process **cyclic photophosphorylation.** A possible mechanism is shown in Fig. 12-12. Light absorbed by chlorophyll a energizes and expels electrons from the molecule so that they can be trapped by ferredoxin. This then passes the electrons to the cytochrome enzymes in the chloroplast. As they pass "down" the system, their energy is used to produce ATP (just as in the cytochrome enzymes of the mitochondria). The cytochromes then return the electrons to the chlorophyll molecule where they can once again be energized by absorbed light and passed through the cycle.

The process is truly cyclic because no outside source of electrons is required. The chlorophyll is simply trapping light energy and using it to energize its electrons sufficiently to transfer them to the cytochrome enzymes in the chloroplast. On their route back to the chlorophyll molecule, they give up their acquired energy to form ATP. Thus chloroplasts can produce ATP as long as light shines upon them. This remarkable mechanism for converting light energy directly into the chemical energy of ATP more than makes up for the scanty production of ATP during the production of $NADH_2$ in noncyclic photophosphorylation. In fact, cyclic photophosphorylation probably provides (during daylight) the energy for many other energy-consuming reactions of the green plant cell. Not only the dark reactions of photosynthesis, but the energy for starch synthesis, protein synthesis, etc., can be supplied by the ATP produced in cyclic photophosphorylation.

In several respects, cyclic photophosphorylation resembles the second stage of noncyclic photophosphorylation, that is, the stage energized by the pigments in System I. Furthermore, there is some evidence that System II can absorb enough light to carry out noncyclic photophosphorylation without the help of System I. If this turns out to be the case, the role of System I will be simply the manufacture of ATP by cyclic photophosphorylation.

In any case, these light reactions (both noncyclic and cyclic) are thus the key to the ability of green plants (and the photosynthetic protists) to manufacture complex, energy-rich molecules from simple, energy-poor ones. As we have seen, heterotrophic organisms (such as ourselves) fulfill their energy requirements by converting the chemical energy of the glucose molecule into the chemical energy of ATP. The photosynthetic organisms can take care of their energy requirements by converting directly the energy of light into the chemical energy of ATP. In so doing, they produce organic molecules to supply themselves with energy in times of darkness. In producing a surplus of these organic molecules, they make possible the existence of all the heterotrophic organisms on this planet.

In the course of studying the light reactions and dark reactions in photosynthesis, methods were found to disrupt the chloroplasts and separate the pigment-containing lamellae from the stroma. Although the isolated lamellae retained the ability to carry on both cyclic and noncyclic photophosphorylation, they could not convert CO_2 into carbohydrate. These dark reactions were readily carried out by the colorless stroma, however, when it was supplied with CO_2, $NADH_2$, and ATP.

As we saw in the case of the mitochondria, the efficiency of cell reactions cannot be properly understood without considering the physical arrangement of the enzymes that carry them out. When you consider that the green plant chloroplast can manufacture glucose from CO_2 and H_2O after only 30 seconds of illumination, you can appreciate that the many enzymes and pigments involved must be carefully arranged with respect to one another.

CHEMOSYNTHESIS

THE CHEMOAUTOTROPHIC BACTERIA   12-8

A consideration of autotrophic nutrition would not be complete without examining the chemoautotrophic bacteria. Certain bacteria share the ability of chlorophyll-containing organisms to manufacture carbohydrates from inorganic raw materials, but do not need light energy to do this. Our study of photosynthesis has shown us that in itself there is nothing unique about this. The conversion of CO_2 into carbohydrate can go on in animal cells as well as plant cells. The same "dark" reactions are found to go on in the cells of the chemoautotrophic bacteria. The question is: what is the source of the energy that drives these energy-consuming reactions? How do the colorless chemoautotrophic bacteria manufacture sufficient ATP to produce glucose from CO_2?

In every case, chemoautotrophic bacteria have been found to secure the energy for these reactions by carrying out an oxidation of some substance present in their environment. Oxidation is an energy-yielding process, and the bacteria are able to harness this energy for the manufacture of carbohydrates. The chemoautotrophic **sulfur bacteria** oxidize H_2S in their substrate (e.g. the water of sulfur springs) to produce energy:

$$2H_2S + O_2 \rightarrow 2S + 2H_2O + \text{energy.}$$

This energy can then be used to reduce CO_2 to carbohydrate in the same manner as the purple photosynthetic sulfur bacteria do:

$$2H_2S + CO_2 \rightarrow (CH_2O) + H_2O + 2S$$

(Section 12-7). Which organism do you suppose uses up more H_2S in the production of a molecule of glucose, the photosynthetic sulfur bacteria or the chemoautotrophic sulfur bacteria?

Another group of chemoautotrophic bacteria are the **iron bacteria.** (These are responsible for the brownish scale that forms inside the water tanks of flush toilets.) They complete the oxidation of partially oxidized iron compounds. In some way, they are able to couple the energy produced by this oxidation to the synthesis of carbohydrate.

The **nitrifying bacteria** are also chemoautotrophic. They accomplish the oxidation of NH_3 (produced from proteins by the heterotrophic bacteria of decay) to nitrates. These oxidations provide the energy to drive the synthetic reactions of the bacteria. The nitrates produced as a by-product supply the nitrogen needs of plants. From them, plants produce amino acids and proteins. These proteins, in turn, supply the amino acids for heterotrophic organisms. While it is true that most organisms do not depend directly upon foods produced by the chemoautotrophic bacteria, here is an example where they do depend indirectly upon the metabolic activities of one group of these organisms. The role of the nitrifying bacteria in the over-all cycle of nitrogen on the earth will be considered again in Chapter 35.

Nevertheless, chemosynthesis cannot compare with photosynthesis in its general importance to the economy of life on this earth. Were photosynthetic organisms to disappear from the earth, almost all heterotrophic organisms would soon follow. Truly, "All flesh is grass."

The seat of photosynthesis is the chloroplast, *inside* the green plant cell. The seat of respiration is the mitochondrion, found *inside* almost all cells. Photosynthesis requires CO_2 and produces O_2. Respiration requires O_2 and produces CO_2. We must now turn our attention to the way in which these gases are brought to and removed from cells.

EXERCISES AND PROBLEMS

1 The oxygen released in photosynthesis comes from which of the two raw materials used by the plant?

2 When green algae are illuminated simultaneously by two beams of single-wavelength light (about 45 $m\mu$ apart at the red end of the spectrum), the amount of photosynthesis that takes place is markedly greater than when just a single wavelength of the same total intensity is used. How does this support Arnon's hypothesis? *Hint:* Refer to Fig. 12–2.

3 Life can be said to be fundamentally a matter of the transport of electrons between energy levels. Defend this view.

4 Distinguish between an autotroph and a heterotroph.

5 What is the most important reducing agent in living cells?

6 What color of light do green leaves absorb least well?

7 Do you think that the rate of photosynthesis would continue to increase indefinitely with increasing temperature? Explain.

8 Do you think that the rate of photosynthesis would continue to increase indefinitely with increasing carbon dioxide concentration? Explain.

9 When students perform the experiment illustrated in Fig 12–7, starting with minimum light intensity, they often find that the rate of photosynthesis does not level off sharply at higher light intensities. What factor have they neglected to keep constant?

10 Students who have taken an extra-long time to carry out the experiment in Fig. 12-7 often find that the rate of photosynthesis begins to drop at high light intensities. Can you think of an explanation for this?

11 In two columns, contrast photosynthesis and respiration in as many ways as you can.

12 Do green plants need digestive enzymes? Explain.

13 How many electrons are removed from water molecules for each molecule of O_2 produced in photosynthesis?

14 How many electrons are needed for each molecule of CO_2 assimilated in the process of photosynthesis? How many $NADH_2$ molecules? How many ATP molecules?

15 How many ATP molecules are produced when 4 electrons pass from System II to System I? Relate this to the inadequacy of noncyclic photophosphorylation alone to meet the needs of the dark reactions.

REFERENCES

You can read brief firsthand reports of the experiments of van Helmont, Priestley, Ingen-Housz, de Saussure, Engelmann, and van Niel as well as of the O^{18}-tracer experiments done at the University of California in:

1 *Great Experiments in Biology,* ed. by M. L. Gabriel and S. Fogel, Prentice-Hall, Inc., 1955.

Several excellent articles on various aspects of photosynthesis have appeared in *Scientific American.* All of those cited are available in inexpensive reprints:

2 Rabinowitch, E. I., "Photosynthesis," *Scientific American,* Reprint No. 34, August, 1948. A clear introduction to the subject written before the details of the light and dark reactions had been worked out.

3 Wald, G., "Life and Light," *Scientific American*, Reprint No. 61, October, 1959. Discusses the properties of light and the chlorophyll molecule that absorbs it.

4 Arnon, D. I., "The Role of Light in Photosynthesis," *Scientific American*, Reprint No. 75, November, 1960. The light reactions.

5 Bassham, J. A., "The Path of Carbon in Photosynthesis," *Scientific American*, Reprint No. 122, June, 1962. The dark reactions.

6 Lehninger, A. L., "How Cells Transform Energy," *Scientific American*, Reprint No. 91, September, 1961. Emphasizes the reciprocal relationship between photosynthesis and respiration.

7 French, C. S., "Photosynthesis," *This Is Life*, ed. by W. H. Johnson and W. C. Steere, Holt, Rinehart and Winston, New York, 1962. A summary that treats all aspects of the process.

8 Rabinowitch, E. I., and Govindjee, "The Role of Chlorophyll in Photosynthesis," *Scientific American*, Reprint No. 1016, July, 1965.

Insect tracheae.
(Courtesy General Biological Supply House, Inc.)

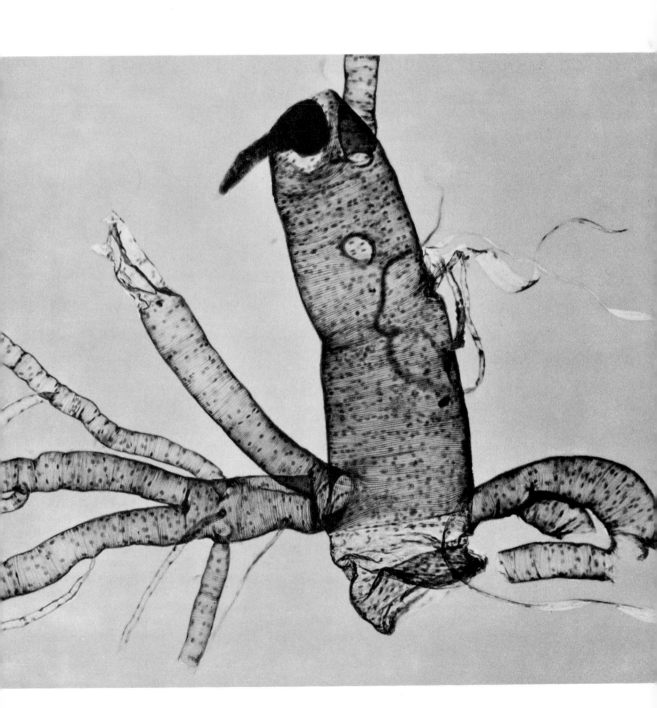

In order to carry on respiration, cells need a continuous supply of oxygen and a means of disposing of carbon dioxide. In order to carry on photosynthesis, green plant cells need a supply of carbon dioxide and a means of disposing of oxygen. Almost all cells are therefore involved in the problem of exchanging gases with the environment.

As you learned in Chapter 9, the environment of cells is the fluid which bathes them, the ECF. For gases to enter and leave cells, they must be dissolved in the ECF.

13-1   GAS EXCHANGE IN AQUATIC ORGANISMS

Among aquatic protists such as the amoeba, the ECF is simply the surrounding water. The ratio of surface area to volume in the amoeba is sufficiently great that simple diffusion of the gases between the cell and the water is adequate to take care of its needs. As the amoeba respires, the consumption of oxygen by its mitochondria lowers the oxygen concentration within the cell. If the concentration of oxygen is greater in the water outside than within the cell, oxygen passes into the cell by diffusion. The oxygen concentration of the water is, in turn, maintained by: (a) diffusion of oxygen from the air into the water and (b) production of oxygen during photosynthesis by aquatic plants (Fig. 13-1).

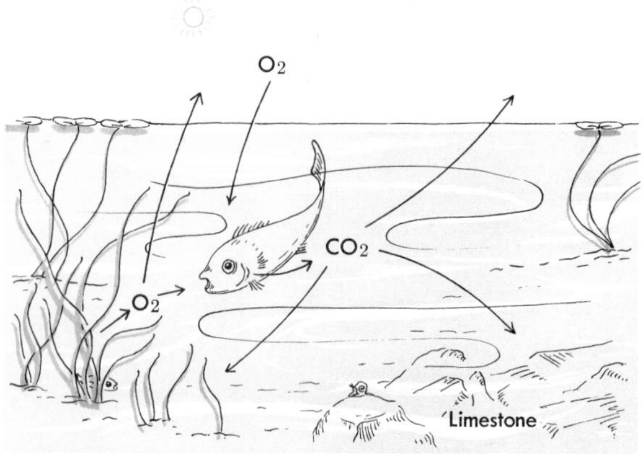

Fig. 13-1

Gas exchange in a fresh-water pond. Oxygen is released and carbon dioxide is consumed during photosynthesis. Carbon dioxide is released and oxygen is consumed in cellular respiration.

While the amoeba is consuming oxygen, it is producing carbon dioxide. When the concentration of this gas within the cell becomes greater than its concentration in the surrounding water, it passes out of the cell by diffusion. The carbon dioxide concentration of the water is kept at reasonably low levels by three mechanisms: (1) Aquatic plants consume it in photosynthesis. (2) It diffuses into the air. (3) It is converted into bicarbonate and carbonate ions: $CO_2 + H_2O \rightleftharpoons H_2CO_3 \rightleftharpoons H^+ + HCO_3^-$ $\rightleftharpoons 2H^+ + CO_3^=$. The latter are then converted into an insoluble mineral, limestone, which forms when carbonate ions and calcium ions are present together in the water: $Ca^{++} + CO_3^= \rightarrow CaCO_3$ (Fig. 13-1).

Even among the smaller plants and animals that live in the water, the surface-to-volume ratio may be sufficiently large so that simple diffusion will take care of the needs of gas exchange. Every cell in the hydra is in direct contact with water, either that of the pond or that in the gastrovascular cavity. And in the planarian, although many cells are buried beneath the surface, simple diffusion to and from the surface

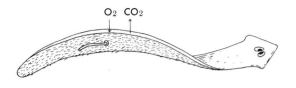

O₂ CO₂

Fig. 13-2

Every cell in the thin planarian body is close enough to the surface for its gas-exchange needs to be satisfied by diffusion.

cells provides adequately for them. Perhaps the very flat, ribbonlike shape of the planarian is an adaptation to allow for the easier exchange of gases between the interior cells and the environment (Fig. 13-2).

Among the larger aquatic animals, the ratio of surface to volume is smaller. Many cells, tissues, and organs of these animals are located too deep within the body to carry on adequate gas exchange with the environment by diffusion alone. An actively respiring interior cell cannot receive oxygen sufficiently rapidly if the oxygen must come to it by diffusion from cell to cell.

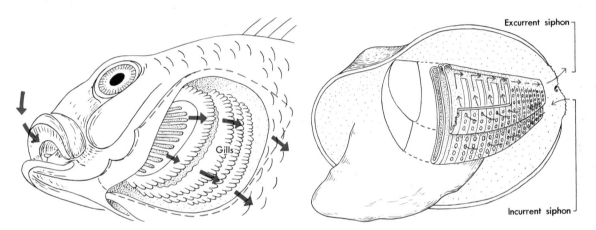

Gills

Excurrent siphon

Incurrent siphon

Two gill-breathers: the fish and the clam. Part of the fish has been cut away to reveal the gills. In the clam the left shell and portions of the left gills have been cut away to show the pathway taken by the water.

Fig. 13-3

The most widespread solution to this problem is to bathe the interior cells in an ECF, blood or lymph, contained within the organism's body. This fluid bathes each cell and, in so doing, brings oxygen to it and removes carbon dioxide from it. It must also be able to pick up fresh supplies of oxygen from the surrounding water and to discharge its accumulation of carbon dioxide into it. This requires a specialized organ for **gas exchange.** Among the crustaceans, some aquatic insects, mollusks, and all fishes, the gas exchange organs are **gills.** Gills present a large surface to the water in which they are bathed. Oxygen present in the water diffuses into the cells of the gills. The gills are supplied with blood which transports oxygen from them to the interior tissues of the body. The same fluid picks up carbon dioxide from the interior tissues and transports it to the gills. From the gills the carbon dioxide passes into the water by diffusion. Figure 13-3 shows how this system works in a clam and in a fish. Note that there are three distinct and essential parts to the system: (1) A **circulating fluid** which transports the gases. (The fluid is kept moving with the help of a muscular pump, the heart.) (2) **Gills** which exchange gases between this circulating fluid (the internal environment) and the water (the external environment). (3) A mechanism for drawing a continuous **supply of fresh water** over the gills. In the clam, the rhythmic beating of the cilia which cover the gills draws water in through the incurrent siphon, through pores in the gills, and out through the excurrent siphon. In the fish, "yawning" movements draw water into the mouth. The mouth is then closed. Contraction of the mouth cavity then forces the water through the arches which support the feathery gills. The water is finally expelled through the slits at the rear of the gill chamber (Fig. 13-3).

13-2 **WATER VERSUS AIR**

In one respect, the problem of gas exchange is simpler for a multicellular, terrestrial organism than for an aquatic one. Oxygen represents about 21% of a given volume of air. Therefore, a terrestrial organism in the process of passing 100 ml of air over its gas-exchange organ has come in contact with 21 ml of oxygen. On the other hand, even in well-aerated water the oxygen concentration seldom exceeds one ml of gas in every 100 ml of water. Consequently, the aquatic organism must expose its gills to a relatively large flow of water to satisfy its oxygen needs. Do you think that this difference in the availability of oxygen in air and water may be related to the fact that the only "warm-blooded" animals on earth are the air-breathing birds and mammals?

On the other hand, terrestrial organisms are faced with the problem of keeping their gas-exchange organ moist even while it is exposed to dry air. As we discussed earlier, diffusion of gas into a cell only occurs from the ECF. The ECF may be only a thin film of moisture, but it must be there. The most general solution to this problem has been to have the gas-exchange organ extend inward into the interior of the organism. In this way, air passing into the gas-exchange organ can be pre-moistened by accessory membranes and its drying effect lessened.

GAS EXCHANGE IN TERRESTRIAL PLANTS

Among the tracheophytes, no single gas-exchange organ supplies all the needs of the organism. Furthermore, there is very little transport of gases from one portion of the plant to another even though the plant has an elaborate fluid transport system, as we will see in Chapter 15. For this reason, we find that each organ of the plant (root, stem, leaf) takes care of its own gas-exchange needs.

13-3 **GAS EXCHANGE IN ROOTS AND STEMS**

The gas-exchange needs of roots and stems are not great. Plant respiration usually proceeds at much lower rates than in animals. While photosynthesis does impose substantial gas-exchange demands, roots do not participate in this process. The oxygen needs of roots are met by diffusion of oxygen from the air into the spaces between the soil particles. From here the oxygen diffuses into the film of moisture that surrounds the soil particles and then into root hairs (extensions of the epidermal cells of the root tips) which are in contact with this film of moisture (Fig. 13-4). From the cytoplasm of the root hairs, the oxygen passes by diffusion to the other cells of the root. Carbon dioxide produced by the cells of the root leaves by diffusion in the reverse direction.

The thicker, older portions of roots do not have any root hairs. Here the roots are covered with a protective layer of dead cells, the cork. It contains many tiny openings, the **lenticels,** which permit gases to pass quickly to and from the soil and the inner, living cells of the root.

Soil that is thoroughly soaked with water does not have any air between the soil particles. Most land plants will die if their roots are exposed to such waterlogged soil for a long period of time. Some plants do thrive, however, in boggy, swampy locations. In their case, special modifications enable them to survive. Usually the roots grow very close to the surface of the soil and thus closer to the oxygen which dissolves in the water from the air. Is it surprising, then, that hurricanes often blow down more trees in low, wet locations than in higher, more exposed locations?

Another adaptation to life in swampy places is the presence of loosely packed parenchyma cells within the root and stem. Air spaces between these cells (the tissue is called the cortex) are interconnected with one another. This system of air spaces enables oxygen to diffuse internally from the stem (above water) to the roots. While this is not a very efficient system, it is, at least, adequate to supply the moderate gas-exchange needs of roots.

Woody perennial stems likewise have only moderate needs for gas exchange. Only the cells of the bark region (epidermis, cortex, phloem, cambium, and young xylem) are alive and thus in need of oxygen for respiration. The outer cells of the bark are dead cork cells which are impregnated with a waxy, waterproof (and airproof) substance called suberin. As is the case in mature roots, though, lenticels are present, which enable oxygen to reach the living cells of the stem and carbon dioxide to be released to the atmosphere (Fig. 13-5).

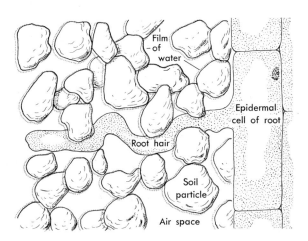

Fig. 13-4

The increased surface area provided by the root hairs aids not only in gas exchange but also in the absorption of water for use throughout the plant.

Fig. 13-5

Lenticels in the bark of a young stem. These openings enable the living tissues beneath the cork to exchange oxygen and carbon dioxide with the air.

In many annual plants, the stems are green and almost as important in carrying out photosynthesis as the leaves. In these stems, the gas-exchange mechanism is quite similar to that of the leaves.

13-4 GAS EXCHANGE IN THE LEAF

In the last chapter, we studied how the structure of the leaf adapts it for carrying out its main function, photosynthesis. A leaf photosynthesizing rapidly needs a substantial and steady supply of carbon dioxide. It also must release an equivalent volume of oxygen during the process. The exchange of gases occurs through pores in the leaf surface, the **stomata** (singular, stoma). When the leaf is actively photosynthesizing, the carbon dioxide content of the air in the air spaces of the spongy layer falls below the 0.03% present in the outside air. As a result of the difference in concentration, carbon dioxide then diffuses from the outside air through the stomata into the air spaces of the spongy layer. Here it dissolves in the film of moisture that covers the surface of every cell in the interior portion of the leaf. Once dissolved, most of it forms bicarbonate ions:

$$CO_2 + H_2O \rightleftharpoons H_2CO_3 \rightleftharpoons H^+ + HCO_3^-.$$

These enter the cells of the spongy and palisade layers by diffusion, where they are incorporated into the dark reactions of photosynthesis. Oxygen produced by the photosynthesizing cells diffuses from the cells into their surface film of moisture. From here it diffuses into the air in the air spaces and ultimately to the outside by means of the stomata.

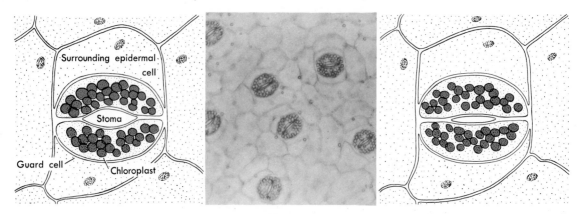

Surrounding epidermal cell

Stoma

Guard cell

Chloroplast

Fig. 13-6   Stomata: open (left) and closed (right). Stomata open when turgor builds up within the guard cells. Light striking the leaf initiates the reactions leading to this effect.

Under most circumstances, the stomata open when light strikes the leaf in the morning and close during the night. A great deal of experimentation has been carried out in an effort to discover how light actually controls the opening of the stomata. The immediate cause seems to be a change of turgor in the **guard cells.** The inner wall of each guard cell is thick and elastic. The outer wall is much thinner. When turgor develops within the two guard cells flanking a stoma, the thin outer walls bulge out and force the inner walls into a crescent shape (Fig. 13-6). This opens the stoma. When the guard cells lose turgor, the elastic, inner walls restore the original shape and the stoma closes.

As you learned in Chapter 9, the buildup of turgor in a cell depends upon the development of a difference in osmotic pressure between that cell and its surroundings. Figure 13-7 shows the osmotic pressure at different times of day measured within the guard cells of one plant. The osmotic pressure within the other cells of the lower epidermis remained steady at 150 lbs/in². When the osmotic pressure of the guard cells became substantially greater than that of the surrounding lower epidermal cells, the stomata opened. In the evening, when the osmotic pressure of the guard cells dropped close to that of the surrounding cells, the stomata closed.

Osmotic pressure in typical guard cells   Fig. 13-7

Time	Osmotic pressure (lbs/in²)
7 a.m.	212
11 a.m.	456
5 p.m.	272
12 midnight	191

(The osmotic pressure of the other lower epidermal cells remained constant at 150 lbs/in² during this experiment.)

In order for the osmotic pressure within the guard cells to increase, their water concentration must decrease with respect to that in the surrounding cells. Put another way, there must be an accumulation of small, soluble molecules in the cytoplasm. This seems to be the case. During the day, glucose molecules and phosphate ions accumulate within the guard cells and exert a strong osmotic effect. You might assume that the glucose arises from photosynthesis going on within the guard cells. (The guard cells have chloroplasts within them, unlike the other cells of the lower epidermis.) This is probably not the most important source, though. Several plant physiologists have found that considerable starch is stored within the guard cells during the night. Starch is a large, insoluble molecule and exerts no osmotic effect. During daylight hours, however, the amount of starch decreases, accompanied by an increase in the amount of glucose:

$$\text{starch + inorganic phosphate}$$
$$\updownarrow \text{ phosphorylase}$$
$$\text{glucose-1-phosphate.}$$
$$\downarrow$$
$$\text{glucose + inorganic phosphate}$$

As you learned in Section 11-1, the enzyme, phosphorylase, that catalyzes the first step of this reaction also catalyzes the reverse reaction. Which direction will be favored depends upon several factors. One of these is the pH of the medium. At pH 5, the formation of starch is promoted. At pH 8, the formation of glucose-1-phosphate is promoted.

Interestingly enough, when leaves are placed in solutions with a pH lower than 6.3, the stomata close. When they are placed in solutions of a higher pH (pH 8 seems to be optimum), the stomata open. What could cause a raising of the pH during daylight hours and a falling of pH during the night? Remember that when carbon dioxide dissolves in water, carbonic *acid* is formed. This acid lowers the pH, of course. However, as mentioned above, the carbon dioxide content of the air in an actively photosynthesizing leaf decreases. This, in turn, raises the pH. One bit of evidence to support the idea that it is the amount of carbon dioxide present that controls pH (and thus stomatal opening) is that the stomata of leaves in the dark will open if exposed to air containing less than 0.03% carbon dioxide. Thus it seems that light stimulates the opening of the stomata by (1) stimulating photosynthesis in the leaf, which (2) causes a reduction in the carbon dioxide concentration of the air in the air spaces, which (3) increases the pH of the cytoplasm of the guard cells, which (4) promotes the conversion of starch into glucose, which (5) causes water to enter the guard cells by osmosis from the surrounding epidermal cells, which (6) causes a build-up of turgor, and the stomata open!

The actual gas-exchange structures of the leaf are primarily the moist cells of the spongy layer. As suggested above, one of the great problems of gas exchange in terrestrial organisms is keeping the cells of the gas-exchange organ or tissue moist in opposition to the drying effect of the air. The solution in the green leaf is typical of the solution in all truly terrestrial organisms. The cells involved in gas exchange are housed in a cavity within the organism. Air is brought to the moist cells by means of openings in the waterproof and otherwise gas-proof exterior. The epidermal cells of the leaf are covered with cutin. This material greatly cuts down water loss from the leaf, but also prevents any appreciable gas exchange from occurring. The stomata, however, allow for the controlled passage of gases to and from the interior of the leaf. Even a leaf richly supplied with stomata (the cucumber may have as many as 400,000 per square inch) has no more than 3% of its surface open to the passage of gases.

Any air that is not fully saturated with water vapor (100% relative humidity) will tend to dry the surfaces of the cells with which it comes in contact. Therefore, the photosynthesizing leaf, despite its protective modifications, will still lose substantial quantities of water to the air by evaporation. This water vapor then passes out of the leaf (through the stomata) in the process called **transpiration.** The transpired water must be replaced by transport of additional water from the soil to the leaves by way of the roots and stem. We will see in Chapter 15 that the necessity of keeping the cells of the gas-exchange organ continually supplied with moisture may have secondary benefits to the plant.

On a hot summer day, the rate of transpiration may exceed the capacity of the root system to supply replacement water. This potentially hazardous situation is usually remedied by a nice self-protective mechanism. When the water supply to the leaf is diminished, the cells of the leaf lose turgor. When the guard cells lose turgor, they close the stomata. This results in a big drop in the rate of transpiration and hence the retention of an adequate moisture content within the leaf. Of course, the closing of the stomata also stops effective exchange of carbon dioxide and oxygen, so that the rate of photosynthesis is forced to a low level.

GAS EXCHANGE IN TERRESTRIAL ANIMALS

The solution of most terrestrial animals to the problem of gas exchange with the air has been solved in a manner analogous to that used by the green plants. The gas-exchange organ is located within the body cavity. Here it is protected from mechanical damage and, even more important, from the excessive drying effect of the air. Frequently, the gas-exchange organ is liberally supplied with glands which replace the water unavoidably lost by evaporation.

Earthworms are something of an exception to this pattern in that they simply use their skin as their gas-exchange organ. The skin must, of course, be kept moist at all times. This is accomplished by (1) glands which secrete mucus and (2) tiny pores located on the dorsal side between the segments, which exude fluid from the body cavity of the worm. Oxygen from the air dissolves in this moisture and diffuses into the cells of the skin. The skin is well supplied with blood vessels. The blood has a pigment (hemoglobin) dissolved in it which combines with the oxygen. In this manner, oxygen is transported to all the interior tissues of the body. Carbon dioxide is picked up by the blood from these tissues and transported back to the skin. Here it diffuses out into the air.

The two devices for maintaining skin moisture would be insufficient for the job if the worm did not live in burrows in damp soil. The relative humidity of the air in these burrows is high, and this retards the rate of evaporation of moisture from the skin. You have surely seen what happens to earthworms that get stranded on the pavement the morning after a rain. Exposed to dry air, their mucus glands and dorsal pores cannot keep up with the rate of evaporation from the skin, and the worm suffocates.

Thus, survival in a truly terrestrial environment requires that the gas-exchange organs be located within the body. This requirement has been met in two main ways. Among most terrestrial arthropods (insects, spiders, centipedes, and millipedes), gases are exchanged between the tissues and the air by means of an elaborate network of tubes, the **tracheae.** Among the air-breathing vertebrates, **lungs** are used as the gas-exchange structures.

The tracheal system of the grasshopper is fairly typical of that found in all the vast numbers of kinds of insects (Fig. 13-8). The **tracheae** open to the outside through small holes in the exoskeleton called **spiracles.** The first and third segments in the thorax have two spiracles, one on each side. Another eight pairs of spiracles are found arranged in a line on each side of the abdomen. The spiracles are guarded by bristles which aid in filtering dust and other foreign matter from the air before it enters the tracheae. The spiracles are also guarded by valves. These are controlled by muscles and enable the grasshopper to regulate the opening and closing of the spiracles.

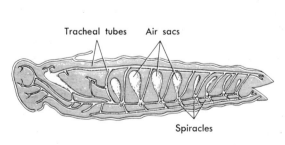 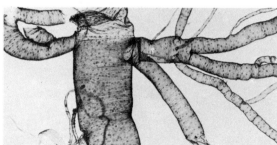

Left: tracheal system of the grasshopper. Right: a photomicrograph of tracheal tubes. (Courtesy General Biological Supply House, Inc.)   **Fig. 13-8**

The spiracles lead to major tracheal tubes which lead, in turn, to ever-finer branches. These branches penetrate to every portion of the insect's body. At their extreme ends, they may be only one micron in diameter. At this end they are filled with liquid. Oxygen, diffusing through the system, dissolves in this fluid and then diffuses into nearby cells. Perhaps every cell in the insect's body is adjacent to at least one of these tiny tubes.

The construction of tracheae is quite interesting. Their walls must be fairly rigid in order not to be forced together by the weight of the surrounding tissues. This rigidity is imparted by spiraling strands of chitin in the walls of the trachea (Fig. 13-8). Nevertheless, there is a limit to the pressures which this kind of construction can withstand without deforming and closing the air passageway. This may be one reason why insects are all relatively small in size. The increased weight of the tissues of an animal the size of a rabbit, for example, would crush a system of tubes filled only with air.

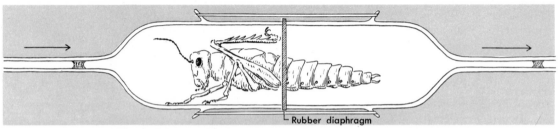

Rubber diaphragm

Fig. 13-9   Fraenkel's experiment demonstrating the one-way flow of air through the grasshopper. The liquid seals in the tubing move to the right as air enters the first four pairs of spiracles and is discharged through the last six pairs. The rubber diaphragm prevents air flow except through the grasshopper.

Among the smaller or less active insects, the passage of oxygen through the tracheal system is by simple diffusion. On the other hand, large or active insects like grasshoppers forcibly ventilate their tracheae. Contraction of muscles in the abdomen compresses the internal organs and forces air out of the tracheae. As the muscles relax, the abdomen springs back to its normal volume and air is drawn into the system. Large air sacs attached to portions of the main tracheal tubes increase the effectiveness of this bellowslike action. By means of an experiment such as the one illustrated in Fig. 13-9 (first performed by the insect physiologist Gottfried Fraenkel), one can show that this action is coordinated so that a one-way flow of air is set up.

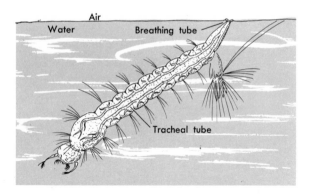

Fig. 13-10

The mosquito "wiggler" breathes air even though it lives and feeds under water.

Air enters the first four pairs of spiracles at the anterior end of the system and is discharged through the last six pairs in the abdomen. This one-way flow increases the efficiency of gas exchange, as oxygen-deficient air can be expelled without mingling with the incoming flow of fresh air.

Even the aquatic insects possess a tracheal system. Some of them (e.g. the mosquito "wigglers") secure their air by poking a breathing tube through the surface of the water (Fig. 13-10). This tube is connected with the tracheal system. Other insects can submerge for long periods, but in so doing, they carry with them a bubble of air from which they can breathe oxygen. Still others possess spiracles mounted on the tips of spines. With these they pierce the leaves of underwater plants and obtain oxygen from bubbles formed within the leaves. Even in those aquatic insects that have gills, after the oxygen diffuses from the water into these outgrowths, it then diffuses into a gas-filled tracheal system for transport to the tissues of the body.

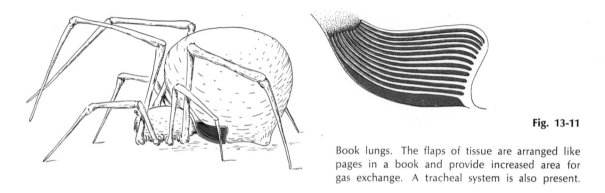

Fig. 13-11

Book lungs. The flaps of tissue are arranged like pages in a book and provide increased area for gas exchange. A tracheal system is also present.

Many spiders also breathe by means of tracheae. In some, this system is supplemented by a pair of **book lungs.** Each of these consists of a tiny chamber which opens to the outside through a narrow hole. Within these chambers are several flaps of tissue arranged like the pages of a partially opened book (Fig. 13-11). Oxygen diffuses from the air in the chamber into the fluid that circulates within these structures. This fluid then carries the oxygen to the other tissues of the spider's body. Carbon dioxide is removed by the reverse route. Note that the system of book lungs, in contrast to the tracheal system, requires the additional feature of a circulatory fluid to transport gases to and from the exchange organ and the interior tissues.

LUNG BREATHERS 13-7

Among the terrestrial vertebrates (amphibians, reptiles, birds, and mammals), the organs of gas exchange are two **lungs.** In the **frog,** the lungs are two thin-walled sacs suspended in the body cavity and connected to the mouth cavity through an opening, the glottis (Fig. 13-12). The surface area of the lungs is increased by a system of inner partitions which are richly supplied with blood vessels. To inflate the lungs, the frog must first fill its mouth with air by opening its two nostrils and lowering the floor of its mouth. (This, in itself, may at times satisfy the frog's oxygen needs. The lining of the mouth is also well supplied with blood vessels and serves as a gas-exchange organ.) Then the frog closes the internal openings to its nostrils, opens its glottis,

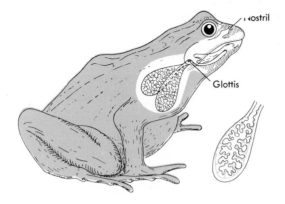

Fig. 13-12

Frog lungs. They are inflated by forcing air down through the glottis. The skin and the lining of the mouth are also used in gas exchange.

and raises the floor of its mouth. These actions force air from the mouth into the lungs, inflating them. In fact, the frog may force so much air into the lungs that they expand throughout the entire body cavity.

Oxygen in this air dissolves in the film of moisture on the surface of the epithelial cells of the lungs. The oxygen then diffuses through the epithelial cells and into tiny blood vessels, the **capillaries.** Once in the blood, most of the oxygen enters the myriads of oval-shaped red blood corpuscles. These floating cells contain the red pigment **hemoglobin.** Under the conditions that exist in the lungs, the hemoglobin combines chemically with the oxygen. The oxygen is then distributed throughout the frog's body in the circulating blood. When the blood reaches the various internal organs and tissues, the hemoglobin releases its oxygen. The oxygen is then free to leave the blood and enter the cells of the body to supply the needs of respiration. Carbon dioxide produced by cellular respiration enters the blood at the tissues and is then carried to the lungs and skin for release to the atmosphere.

The **skin** serves as a supplementary organ of gas exchange in most of the amphibia. It is richly supplied with blood vessels, and permeable to both water and gases. It can, however, function in gas exchange only if it is kept moist. Mucus-secreting cells in the skin assist in this function, but they are not adequate to cope with the drying effects of hot air of low humidity. Thus most amphibians are confined to moist locations such as ponds, swamps, damp soil, etc. This is just one of the reasons why they cannot be considered truly terrestrial animals.

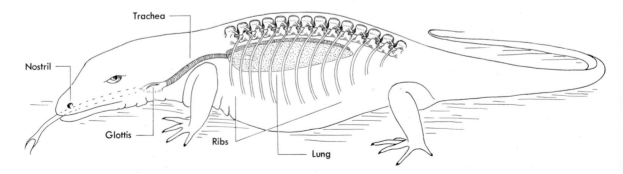

Fig. 13-13   Lizard lungs. They are inflated by expanding the rib cage.

Reptiles possess a scaly, dry skin. It is rather impervious to the passage of water so that little moisture is lost from the animal by this route. Thus reptiles are not confined to damp locations, although many do, in fact, live in such places. Lizards and snakes are abundant in the deserts, one of the driest habitats. While a scaly skin is an adaptation permitting safe exposure to dry air, it is of no use whatsoever as a gas-exchange organ. Reptiles depend upon their lungs for this function. Not only do their lungs have a relatively greater surface area than those of amphibians, but the ventilation of the lungs is considerably more efficient. The lungs are surrounded by a cage of rib bones (Fig. 13-13). These may alternately be spread apart and then drawn together by opposing sets of rib muscles. When they are spread apart, the volume of the rib cage increases. This expansion creates a partial vacuum within the lungs which is relieved by an inrush of fresh air. The fresh air, of course, brings a fresh supply of oxygen to the moist tissues of the lungs. Contraction of the rib cage then forces air out of the lungs. This exhaled air is depleted of oxygen but contains the carbon dioxide given off at the lungs. Some snakes exhale with great force when disturbed. The resulting hissing noise may frighten away an intruder.

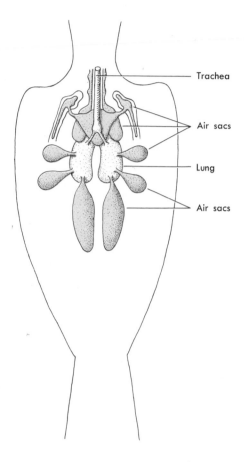

Trachea

Air sacs

Lung

Air sacs

Fig. 13-14

Air sacs in the pigeon. Although no gas exchange goes on in the air sacs, they are arranged so that fresh air passes through the lungs during exhalation as well as inhalation.

Although the ventilation of **bird** lungs is similar in principle to that of reptile lungs, the vigor of the action is intensified during flight by the beating of the wings. Unlike reptiles, birds are homeothermic ("warm-blooded"). They maintain a constant body temperature (usually around 104°F) despite wide fluctuations in the temperature of the external environment. Birds maintain their body temperature chiefly through the heat produced by muscular activity. Muscular activity, in turn, depends upon the energy liberated by cellular respiration. It is no wonder, then, that the oxygen demands of a small, active bird are very great. Outgrowths of the lungs, the **air sacs** (Fig. 13-14), help birds satisfy these extraordinary demands. Although no gas exchange actually occurs in them, their anatomical arrangement increases the efficiency of lung ventilation by enabling fresh air to pass through the lungs during *both* inhalation *and* exhalation. The air sacs also aid in reducing the weight of the body by substituting air for tissue or fluid in many locations. For example, some of the bird's bones are hollow and penetrated by air sacs.

Among the mammals, the efficiency of lung ventilation is improved by the presence of a **diaphragm.** This is a dome-shaped, muscular partition that divides the body cavity into two compartments: the abdominal cavity (which contains the viscera—the stomach, intestines, etc.) and the thoracic cavity (which contains the heart and lungs) (Fig. 13-15). The inner surface of the thoracic cavity and the outer surface of the lungs are lined with thin membranes, the **pleural** membranes. With the aid of a film of moisture between them, the lung pleura adhere tightly to the cavity pleura.

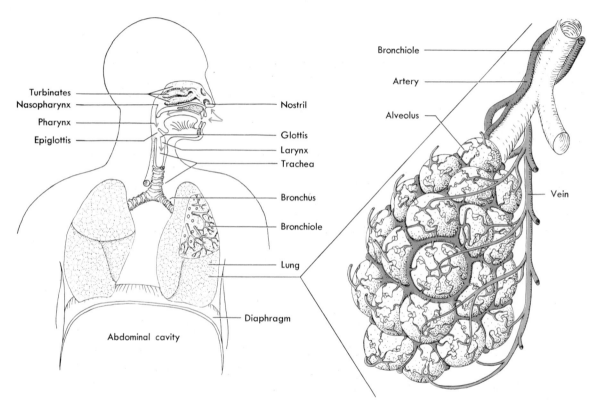

Fig. 13-15   Gas-exchange system in man. Transfer of oxygen and carbon dioxide between air and blood occurs at the alveoli.

The necessity for adhesion between the lungs and the walls of the thoracic cavity is vividly illustrated when air is introduced between the pleural membranes. The force of adhesion is broken and the natural elasticity of the lung causes it to collapse. This procedure is often done deliberately when a lung has been damaged by a disease such as tuberculosis. Collapsing the lung allows it to rest and thus heal more rapidly. Reinflation of the lung is no problem because the air between the pleural membranes is gradually absorbed by the tissues and the lung assumes its normal size once more.

Any action which increases the volume of the thoracic cavity increases the volume of the lungs because of their adhesion to the walls of the cavity. Spreading of the rib cage accomplishes this as it does in the reptiles and birds, but in mammals (including man) the action is enhanced by contraction of the diaphragm. Contraction lowers the diaphragm, resulting in a corresponding increase in the volume of the thoracic cavity. This, in turn, stretches the lungs, and air rushes into them. When the diaphragm relaxes, it returns to its former position, permitting the lungs to return to their former size. As they do so, air is forced out of them.

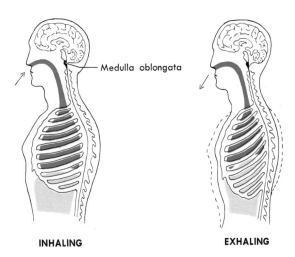

Fig. 13-16

During inspiration (inhaling), the ribs are lifted up and outward; the diaphragm is lowered. The rate and depth of breathing are controlled by nerve impulses originating in the medulla oblongata.

INHALING

EXHALING

The motion of the diaphragm in breathing accompanies, but does not substitute for, the action of the rib cage. The motion of the ribs is controlled by the external and internal intercostal muscles. During inspiration (inhaling), the external intercostal muscles contract, lifting the ribs up and outward (Fig. 13-16). This motion increases the volume of the thoracic cavity and hence draws air into the lungs. During expiration (exhaling), the external intercostal muscles relax and this, aided by the natural elasticity of the lungs, returns the thoracic cavity to its normal dimensions. The cycle of inspiration and expiration is repeated about 15 to 18 times each minute in the resting adult. About 500 ml of air is drawn in and then exhaled during each cycle.

It is, of course, possible to breathe more deeply, either consciously or as the result of exercise. Vigorous inspiration occurs simply as a result of more vigorous contraction of the diaphragm and the external intercostal muscles. Vigorous expiration depends, however, upon more than the elastic recoil of these muscles and the lungs. The *internal* intercostal muscles draw the ribs down and inward, thus reducing the volume of the thoracic cavity still further. At the same time, the muscular wall of the abdomen contracts, forcibly pushing the stomach, liver, etc., upwards against the diaphragm and reducing the volume of the thoracic cavity from that direction. With vigorous inspiration and expiration, an average adult male can flush his lungs with about 4 liters of air at each breath. This is known as the **vital capacity** of the lungs. Well-trained athletes usually have a vital capacity substantially greater than that of nonathletes. Even at the point of maximum expiration, about 1200 ml of air ("residual air") remain in the lungs.

Ventilation of the lungs is, of course, also dependent upon an unobstructed passageway between them and the outside air. During inspiration, air enters the **nostrils,** passes through the **nasal cavities** (one behind each nostril), through the **nasopharynx** and (merging with any air taken in through the mouth) the oral pharynx (Fig. 13-15). From the oral pharynx, the air passes through the **glottis** into the voice box, or **larynx.** From here it passes into the major air tube, the **trachea.** The walls of the trachea are stiffened by horseshoe-shaped bands of cartilage. These bands prevent the trachea from collapsing as a result of compression under the weight of surrounding tissues. The trachea branches into a right and left **bronchus,** leading to the right and left lungs, respectively. The bronchi, in turn, branch into many **bronchioles.** The walls of the bronchi and the major bronchioles are also stiffened with cartilage. Each bronchiole terminates in a grapelike cluster of tiny sacs, the **alveoli.** It is only in the alveoli that gas exchange actually takes place. It has been estimated that the total surface area for gas exchange provided by the 300 million alveoli in two adult lungs ranges from 400 to 800 ft^2. Compare this remarkable value with the total skin surface area of a 150-lb, 5'10'' human: 20 ft^2.

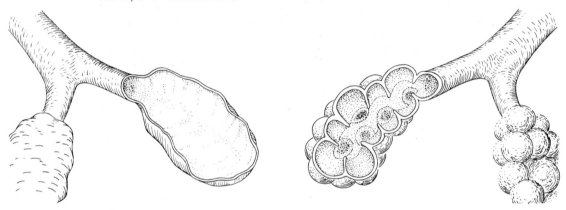

Fig. 13-17   Structure of the alveoli in a normal lung (right) and the lung of a victim of emphysema (left). Breakdown of the alveolar walls reduces the surface area for gas exchange.

The large area provided by the alveoli is sufficient to take care of the gas-exchange needs of the body both at rest and during exertion. Under certain conditions, however, the gas-exchange area of the lungs may be seriously reduced. For example, virus or bacterial infections of the alveoli result in **pneumonia.** In pneumonia, lymph and mucus accumulate in the alveoli and bronchioles, reducing the area exposed to air. In critical cases, the patient may turn blue from oxygen starvation. Allowing the patient to breath pure oxygen under an oxygen tent may save his life. The increased concentration of oxygen inhaled makes possible the most effective use of the gas-exchange area still available.

Another disease of the lungs in which the gas-exchange area is reduced is **emphysema.** In this disease, many of the walls separating the alveoli become irritated and break down. This greatly reduces the surface area available for gas exchange (Fig. 13-17). Unlike pneumonia, this condition develops very slowly and is seldom a direct cause of death. However, the gradual loss of gas-exchange area forces the heart to pump ever larger quantities of blood to the lungs in order to satisfy the gas-exchange needs of the body. The added strain this imposes on the heart often leads to heart failure.

Public health officials have made several studies of emphysema. They have accumulated a good deal of evidence to show that breathing polluted air severely aggravates the disease. Air polluted generally by industrial wastes and automobile exhaust and air polluted within the individual by cigarette smoke both seem to be involved. A few health officials even feel that air pollution may actually cause the disease in some cases.

During its passage from the outside to the alveoli, inhaled air is "conditioned." In the nasal cavities, the incoming air is warmed, moistened, and filtered. These operations are hastened by the **turbinates** (Fig. 13-15), which provide additional surface for contact between the air and the moist membranes of the nasal cavities. Mucus-secreting cells provide moisture which raises the humidity of the inspired air. The mucus also provides a sticky trap for dust particles that may .be inhaled. Ciliated cells then sweep the mucus with its accumulation of debris down into the pharynx where it can be expectorated or swallowed. It should be noted that air that is drawn in through the mouth is not as well-conditioned as the air that enters through the nostrils.

Air from either source passes through the oral pharynx, from which leads not only the glottis but also the opening to the esophagus (Fig. 13-15). A flap of tissue above the glottis, the epiglottis, seems to aid in avoiding a conflict in function. When food is swallowed, the epiglottis automatically projects over the glottis, thus insuring that no food gets into the larynx and trachea. On the rare occasions when food or water does go down the "wrong way," a violent spasm of coughing usually expels the offending material quickly.

The **larynx,** or voice box, is an enlarged portion of the trachea. Like the rest of the trachea, it is pro-

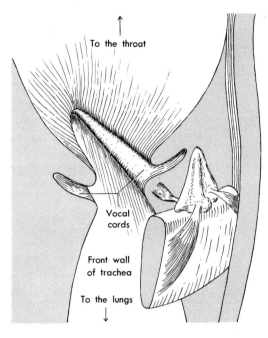

Fig. 13-18

The vocal cords. The rear wall of the larynx has been cut away. The pitch of the voice is altered by changing the tension on the vocal cords.

tected by cartilage. Associated with the deepening of the voice, which occurs during adolescence in boys, is an enlargement of the larynx. As a result of this enlargement, the cartilage covering protrudes at the front of the neck, forming the "Adam's apple."

Stretched across the larynx are two folds of tissue, the **vocal cords** (Fig. 13-18). These can be placed under varying degrees of tension through a system of muscles and cartilaginous levers. When air (usually as it is exhaled) passes over the tensed vocal cords, it causes them to vibrate. These vibrations, in turn, set the air in the larynx, pharynx, and mouth vibrating in sympathy. The air vibrations produce the sounds we use in speech and singing. Changing the tension on the vocal cords changes the pitch of the sound. Use of the tongue and other mouth parts breaks the sounds up into the various phonetic units that make up spoken language. Occasionally the vocal cords may become infected and inflamed. Inflammation thickens them so that they do not vibrate cleanly. The result is the husky voice, or even temporary loss of voice, associated with **laryngitis.**

Fig. 13-19

	% by volume	
Component	Atmospheric air	Expired air
N_2 (plus inert gases)	78.62	74.9
O_2	20.85	15.3
CO_2	0.03	3.6
H_2O	0.5	6.2
	100.0	100.0

Composition of atmospheric air and expired air in a typical subject

The inner walls of the trachea, bronchi, and bronchioles are all covered with a mucus-secreting ciliated epithelium. Fine dust particles that are not filtered out by the nose are trapped in the mucus. The cilia then sweep this material up the trachea. When it nears the glottis, the forceful exhalation of coughing is initiated, and the material is propelled into the mouth. This **sputum** can then be disposed of by expectoration or swallowing.

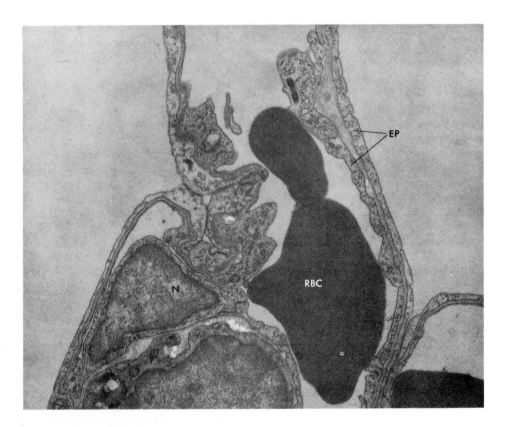

Fig. 13-20 Alveoli and an adjacent capillary from the lung of a laboratory mouse (10,500 X). Note the thinness of the epithelial cells (Ep) that line the alveolus and capillary (except where the nucleus, N, is located). The dark gray object is a red blood corpuscle (RBC). (Reproduced with permission from Keith R. Porter and Mary A. Bonneville, *An Introduction to the Fine Structure of Cells and Tissues,* 2nd ed., Lea & Febiger, Philadelphia, 1964.)

It is only in the alveoli that actual gas exchange goes on. A glance at the table in Fig. 13-19 shows what happens in a typical case to the composition of the air when it reaches the alveoli. Some of the oxygen dissolves in the fluid that moistens the thin epithelium of the alveoli. From here, the oxygen diffuses into the blood contained within the numerous capillaries present in the alveoli. As in the frog, most of the oxygen then combines with the hemoglobin contained within the red blood corpuscles. Simultaneously, some of the carbon dioxide in the blood diffuses out into the alveoli, from which it can be exhaled. The circulation of the blood then carries the oxygen to all the cells of the body. In so doing, it picks up carbon dioxide from these cells for transport back to the capillaries in the alveoli. Additional details of the chemical mechanisms by which oxygen and carbon dioxide are transported efficiently by the blood will be considered in the next chapter.

The ease with which oxygen and carbon dioxide pass between the air of the alveoli and the red blood corpuscles in the capillaries can be appreciated by examining Fig. 13-20. Portions of two alveoli are visible at the top, one on the left, the other on the right. Each is lined by a remarkably thin, elongated epithelial cell. The partition between the two alveoli is almost completely occupied by a capillary. Note, too, how thin is the cell that forms the wall of the capillary—except where its nucleus is located. The dark gray object within the capillary is a red blood corpuscle. At the closest point, its surface is only 0.7μ away from the air in the alveolus, less than one-tenth of the diameter of this tiny cell!

CONTROL OF BREATHING 13-10

The rate at which cellular respiration takes place (and hence oxygen is consumed) varies with the general state of activity of the body. Vigorous exercise may increase by 20 to 25 times the demands of the tissues for oxygen. This increased demand is met by increasing the rate and depth of breathing.

It would be reasonable to assume that lack of sufficient oxygen triggers this response. It is quite easy to show, however, that oxygen deprivation plays a very minor role in regulating the rate at which ventilation of the lungs occurs. Figure 13-21 illustrates an experimental setup by means of which a human subject can inspire various precise gas mixtures. While the subject is inhaling the gas mixture, his rate and depth of breathing can be checked constantly. The subject begins the experiment by breathing pure air (21% oxygen, 0.03% carbon dioxide, and about 79% inert gases by volume). He breathes first from the room and then from the tank. This procedure provides a "control." It reveals what, if any, changes in the subject's responses can be expected just by having him breathe from the tank. Nervousness, an unpleasant taste imparted to the air by the equipment, or increased air resistance are just three factors that might alter the subject's responses. These alterations would have to be taken into account in interpreting any changes brought about by varying the composition of the inhaled gases.

The two graphs in Fig. 13-22 show that no appreciable change does, in fact, occur in this particular experiment. When 100% oxygen is substituted for air, no marked change in rate or depth of breathing occurs either, although there is a tendency for depth of breathing to decrease slightly. When the subject inhales a gas mixture consisting of 92% oxygen and 8% carbon dioxide, however, a most dramatic increase in rate and depth of inspiration takes place. Note that there is no question here of the subject's tissues suffering from a lack of oxygen. He is inhaling a gas mixture over four times as rich in oxygen as the air. The experiment suggests that the concen-

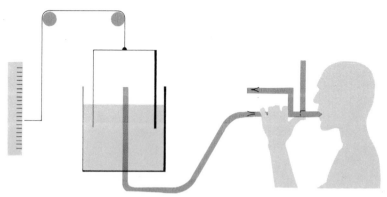

Fig. 13-21   Apparatus for determining the effects of different gas mixtures on rate and depth of breathing.

tration of carbon dioxide plays a decided part in governing the rate and depth of breathing.

Other physiological experiments have shown that carbon dioxide achieves this effect through its action on a portion of the brain called the **medulla oblongata** (Fig. 13-16). When blood passes through the alveoli, its carbon dioxide content becomes the same as that of the alveolar air. Moments later, the blood reaches the medulla oblongata, which contains cells that are very sensitive to the concentration of carbon dioxide in the blood. If this carbon dioxide content rises above normal levels, the medulla oblongata responds by increasing the number and rate of nerve impulses which control the action of the intercostal muscles and diaphragm. The result is an increased rate of lung ventilation, which quickly brings the carbon dioxide concentration of the alveolar air, and then of the blood, back to normal levels.

We all know that rate and depth of breathing are also under conscious control, but this conscious control has definite limits. You can hold your breath for only a limited period of time. Eventually, the carbon dioxide content of the blood reaching the medulla oblongata becomes so high that the medulla overrides conscious control. This is the "breaking point."

Figure 13-23 illustrates an experimental setup with which this type of response can be studied. Movements of the subject's chest are detected by a hollow bellows (the pneumograph) strapped around the chest. Expansion and contraction of the bellows cause decreases and increases in the pressure of the air within. These pressure changes can then be transmitted to a recording stylus, which writes on a slowly revolving, smoked drum (the kymograph). Note that after a period of breath-holding, the rate and depth of inspiration are markedly greater than before the period of breath-holding began. This can be accounted for by the build-up of carbon dioxide during the breath-holding period. The length of time that one can hold his breath to the breaking point can be increased substantially by breathing extra fast and extra deeply just prior to the period of breath-holding. Vigorous, forced ventilation reduces the carbon dioxide content of the alveolar air and blood to below its normal value, and thus it takes longer for the carbon dioxide content to build up to the breaking point. If the subject simply breathes naturally after a period of extra-vigorous breathing (hyperventilation), we find that his depth of breathing is markedly less than that which preceded the period of hyperventilation.

The medulla oblongata, then, is an extremely efficient mechanism for controlling the carbon dioxide content of the blood. Any increase in carbon dioxide is quickly

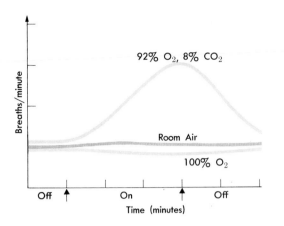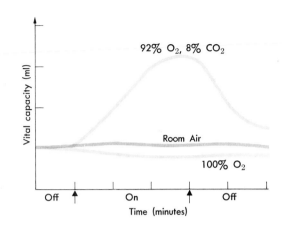

Graphs showing effect of inspiring room air, 100% oxygen, and 92% oxygen, 8% carbon dioxide on breathing rate (left) and depth of breathing (right).

Fig. 13-22

reduced by increased ventilation of the lungs. Any reduction in carbon dioxide content is quickly compensated for by a decreased ventilation of the lungs. The medulla is thus one of the homeostatic devices of the body. Through its activity, the carbon dioxide content of the blood is maintained within very narrow limits, and as a result, the constancy of the internal environment (ECF) with respect to carbon dioxide content is maintained.

It may seem curious that the rate at which one breathes and thus supplies oxygen to the body is controlled by the carbon dioxide content of the blood rather than the oxygen content. Remember, though, that in the breakdown of glucose by cellular respiration, carbon dioxide is produced as fast as oxygen is consumed. The muscles of the body need increased amounts of oxygen during vigorous exercise, but they produce increased amounts of carbon dioxide at the same time. This triggers increased ventilation of the lungs and thus automatically provides for the greater oxygen need.

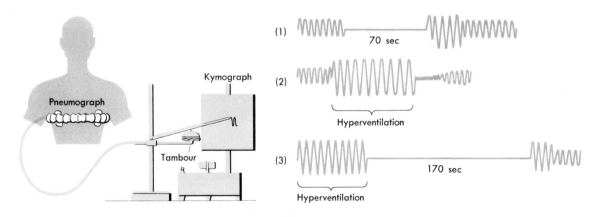

Operation of the pneumograph and typical kymograph records showing the effect upon rate and depth of breathing of (1) breath-holding, (2) hyperventilation, and (3) hyperventilation followed by breath-holding.

Fig. 13-23

Knowledge of the mechanism by which breathing is controlled has led to advances in the use of resuscitators. Victims of drowning accidents, electrocution, or carbon monoxide poisoning may have their breathing stopped but not their heartbeat. Quick action in forcing air into the lungs may save their lives. In such circumstances, the tissues, especially of the heart and brain, need oxygen. Many ambulances are equipped with resuscitators containing tanks of compressed oxygen which can be forced into the victim's lungs. It is also important that the victim's natural breathing movements be restored. To this end, it is now common practice to equip resuscitators with tanks containing a mixture of 95% oxygen (for the needs of the tissues) and 5% carbon dioxide (to stimulate the medulla oblongata).

There is one situation in which man may find himself suffering from a shortage of oxygen without a corresponding increase in the production of carbon dioxide. When suddenly transported (e.g. in a nonpressurized airplane) to altitudes above 13,000 ft, he may begin to suffer oxygen deprivation. With decreased amounts of oxygen for cellular respiration there is, however, a corresponding decrease in the amount of carbon dioxide. Consequently the medulla is not stimulated to step up the rate of lung ventilation. Fortunately, the body does possess a mechanism to cope with this situation. In the aorta and carotid arteries (Fig. 14-7) there are receptors which detect reduced levels of oxygen in the blood. These receptors send impulses to the medulla oblongata and stimulate it to increase the rate of lung ventilation. Although this increase in rate and depth of breathing is not so dramatic as that brought about by carbon dioxide excess, it does bring increased quantities of oxygen to the alveoli.

To carry on respiration, cells must receive oxygen and eliminate carbon dioxide. For most multicellular organisms, this requirement can be met only through the use of (1) an organ which exchanges these gases with the environment and (2) a circulatory system which can transport these gases to and from the gas-exchange organ and the individual cells. Gas exchange is, however, only one of many functions which a circulatory system can accomplish. The nature and functioning of animal circulatory systems is the topic of the next chapter.

EXERCISES AND PROBLEMS

1   List, in order, the sequence of steps that cause stomata to open up in the morning.

2   Trace the pathway taken by a molecule of oxygen from the time it enters a nostril until it enters a red blood corpuscle.

3   List three ways in which the CO_2 necessary for photosynthesis by aquatic plants is replenished in the water.

4   How do reptiles, birds, and mammals improve the efficiency of lung ventilation over that of amphibians?

5   How do amphibians compensate for their low efficiency of lung ventilation?

6   What biochemical advantage is there in the mouth-to-mouth method of artificial respiration that is not found in the older methods?

7   Using a microscope with a 43x-objective and a 10x-eyepiece, a student sees six stomata on the lower epidermis of a lily leaf. The diameter of the field of view is 0.4 mm. How many stomata are present per square centimeter?

8 Highway construction often interferes with the natural drainage of water, causing water to accumulate in formerly well-drained woods. Soon dead trees are to be seen in these areas. Explain.

9 Why are gills poorly adapted for life on land?

10 Which of the following gas mixtures would you use in an attempt to revive a victim of drowning: (a) 100% O_2, (b) 80% N_2, 20% O_2, (c) 95% O_2, 5% CO_2, (d) 50% O_2, 50% CO_2?

REFERENCES

1 Williams, C. M., "Insect Breathing," *Scientific American*, February, 1953. The mechanics of tracheal systems.

2 Fenn, W. O., "The Mechanism of Breathing," *Scientific American*, January, 1960. The mechanics of lung ventilation.

3 McDermott, W., "Air Pollution and Public Health," *Scientific American*, Reprint No. 612, October, 1961. Considers the relationship between general air pollution and pulmonary disease.

4 Hammond, E. C., "The Effects of Smoking," *Scientific American*, Reprint No. 126, July, 1962. Includes a description of the functional and structural changes of the bronchi and alveoli in smokers.

5 Meyer, B. S., D. B. Anderson, and R. H. Böhning, *Introduction to Plant Physiology*, D. Van Nostrand Company, Inc., Princeton, N.J., 1960. Chapter 6 discusses the physics of gas exchange through the stomata and the factors involved in the opening and closing of stomata.

6 Comroe, J. H., Jr., "The Lung," *Scientific American*, Reprint No. 1034, February, 1966.

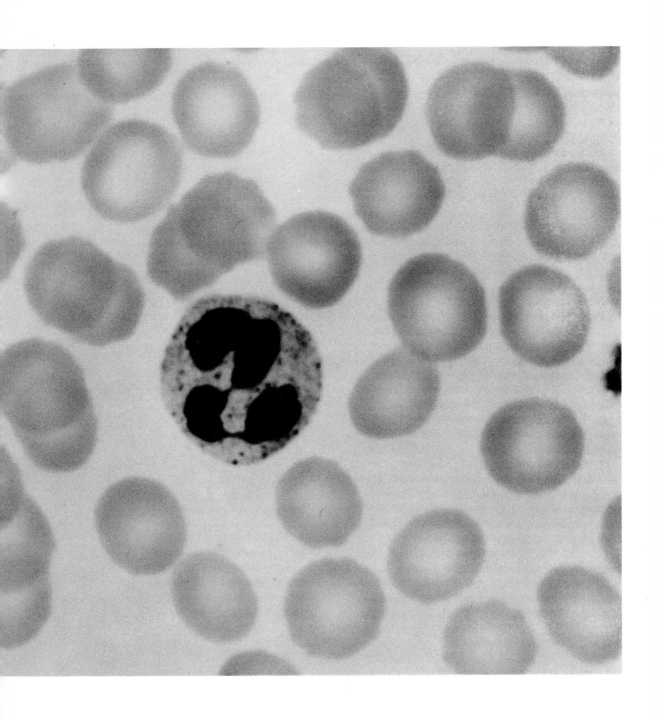

Among the protists and simple animals, there is no need for a special transport system. In these organisms, the processes of diffusion and cytoplasmic streaming are sufficient to insure that every portion of the body is adequately supplied with materials.

The food vacuoles formed in the amoeba (Fig. 9-11) are swept by streaming cytoplasm throughout the cell as digestion of the food contents occurs. The digested food molecules then pass by diffusion or by active transport into the cytoplasm.

Simple animals such as sponges and the hydra take care of their transport needs in a similar way. Because their cells are organized into thin sheets of tissue, no cell is ever far from the environment. Gas exchange and the elimination of metabolic wastes can proceed by simple diffusion between the cell and the environment. All digestion in the sponges and final digestion in the hydra are accomplished intracellularly. Small food particles are ingested by phagocytosis and food vacuoles are formed. The end products of digestion can then pass by diffusion or by active transport into any adjacent cells that are not phagocytic.

To insure that all the phagocytic cells are presented with food particles for ingestion, both the sponges and hydra have developed a type of external circulatory system. In each case, the phagocytic cells also possess flagella which maintain a current of water within the gastrovascular cavity. (Look again at Figs. 5-1 and 10-3.) In one sense, such a system resembles the circulatory system of higher animals: there is a fluid which bathes the individual cells and is kept in motion. The parallel is not really close, though, because the fluid in both the sponges and hydra is part of the *external* environment. In those animals with a true circulatory system, the fluid is retained within the tissues of the animal's body and is part of the internal environment.

The planarian has no circulatory system. There is, however, a small amount of fluid which bathes the internal organs of the worm. The only motion imparted to the fluid is that which results from the random body movements of contraction and expansion. We have seen (Section 13-1) that the shape of the planarian makes it unnecessary to have a special system for the transport of oxygen and carbon dioxide. The necessity for extensive transport of digested food materials is eliminated by the highly branched gastrovascular cavity. Digestion in the planarian is intracellular, and no portion of the body is far removed from the phagocytic cells which line the gastrovascular cavity and accomplish this work.

A "CLOSED" SYSTEM: THE EARTHWORM 14-2

The earthworm is relatively large and complex. It has a true circulatory system for the transport of materials, and all of the features essential to an efficient circulatory system are found in it. These are: (1) a fluid in which the materials to be transported are dissolved, (2) a system of conducting vessels or channels in which the fluid flows, (3) a pump for maintaining the flow of the fluid, and (4) specialized organs to carry out exchanges between the fluid and the external environment. These include organs (such as the skin and intestine) that add materials to the fluid, and organs (such as the skin and excretory organs) that remove materials from the fluid and deposit them back into the external environment.

◀ Human blood cells, 2000 X. (Courtesy General Biological Supply House, Inc.)

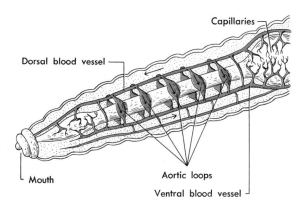

Fig. 14-1

Circulatory system of the earthworm. The blood is confined to the blood vessels at all times. Contraction of the dorsal blood vessel and the five pairs of aortic loops keeps the blood flowing.

The circulating fluid of the earthworm is blood. It is mostly water in which are dissolved gases, sugars, amino acids, salts, and many other molecules and ions that play a role in the metabolism of the earthworm. The efficiency of the earthworm's blood as a medium for oxygen transport is increased by the presence of the red, oxygen-carrying pigment **hemoglobin.** The earthworm's hemoglobin is not contained within red blood corpuscles as ours is, but is simply dissolved in the blood.

The blood of the earthworm is transported by an elaborate system of blood vessels. It can only carry on its function of exchanging materials with individual cells, however, when it passes through the finest of the blood vessels, the **capillaries.** Because the blood is always retained within the system of blood vessels, we say that the earthworm has a "closed" system. The pump that forces the blood to the capillaries consists of five pairs of aortic loops (Fig. 14-1). Muscular contraction of the walls of these aortic loops forces blood into the ventral blood vessel. The ventral blood vessel transports blood towards the rear of the worm and distributes the blood to an elaborate system of lesser blood vessels. All of these terminate in capillaries, and it is here that exchanges between the *exchange organs* and the *blood* and between the *blood* and the *tissues* take place. Once through the capillary beds, the blood is picked up by a second system of vessels leading into the dorsal blood vessel. This vessel contracts rhythmically, forcing the blood back to the aortic loops at the anterior end of the worm.

14-3 **AN "OPEN" SYSTEM: THE GRASSHOPPER**

The circulatory system found in the arthropods differs from that in the annelid worms in one important respect. The blood is confined to vessels during only a portion of its circuit through the body. The remainder of its journey takes place within the body cavity itself. Such a system is known as an "open" circulatory system. The volume of blood required for such a system is kept to a practical level by a marked reduction in the size of the body cavity. This reduced body cavity of arthropods is called a **hemocoel.** The efficiency of flow and distribution of the blood is maintained by having the hemocoel divided into chambers called sinuses.

In the grasshopper, the closed portion of the system is confined to a single long tubular heart and aorta running along the dorsal side of the insect (Fig. 14-2).

Fig. 14-2

The circulatory system of the grasshopper is "open." The blood is confined to vessels during only a small part of its circuit through the body.

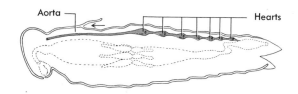

The heart pumps blood into the sinuses of the hemocoel, where exchanges of materials take place. Coordinated movements of the body muscles gradually bring the blood back to the sinus surrounding the heart, the dorsal sinus. Between contractions, tiny valves in the wall of the heart open and permit the blood to enter the heart from the dorsal sinus, thus completing the circuit.

The open circulatory system of the grasshopper might seem to be quite inefficient in comparison with the closed system of the earthworm. It should be kept in mind, however, that there is a decided difference in the function accomplished by the two systems. Remember that in the grasshopper the exchange of oxygen and carbon dioxide is accomplished by means of the tracheal system. Blood plays no part in this process. There is not even an oxygen-carrying pigment in the blood of the grasshopper. A good deal of experimentation and study has shown clearly that it is the problem of gas transport that poses the most serious demands upon a circulatory system. In animals such as the grasshopper and other insects, where the gas-exchange system is quite independent of the circulatory system, the demands upon the latter are far less severe than in animals (e.g. the earthworm) where the functions are combined.

Among the aquatic arthropods, such as the crayfish, the circulatory system does serve to transport oxygen and carbon dioxide to and from the tissues. An oxygen-carrying pigment (hemocyanin), which is dissolved in the blood, enables a given amount of it to carry more oxygen than could be carried simply in water solution. You remember that the gas-exchange organs in the crayfish are the gills. Although the crayfish circulatory system is an open one, it is significant that the "closed" portion —the system of vessels—is a good deal more extensive than in the grasshopper.

THE SQUID   **14-4**

Among the mollusks, both open and closed circulatory systems are found. The closed system of the squid is especially interesting because there are three separate pumps to maintain circulation (Fig. 14-3). One heart pumps blood to all the internal organs and tissues of the body. The other two hearts simply serve to pump blood from these internal organs and tissues to the gills, where gas exchange takes place. To understand the advantage of such a system, it is important to understand that the pressure produced by the contraction of a heart is almost entirely dissipated when blood enters

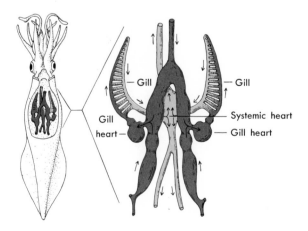

Fig. 14-3

Circulatory system of the squid. The gill hearts pump oxygen-deficient blood (dark color) to the gills where gas exchange takes place. The systemic heart pumps oxygen-rich blood (light color) to all parts of the body.

the capillaries. Although capillaries are tiny, the total cross-sectional area of all the capillaries supplied by a single major blood vessel is considerably greater than the cross-sectional area of the blood vessel itself. The situation can be compared to that which occurs when a rapidly flowing, narrowly confined stream is allowed to spread out over a flat plain. The force and velocity of flow diminish rapidly. The same situation occurs in a network of capillaries. Note, too, that gas exchange must take place in two different locations: the gills and the tissues. In both cases, the exchanges occur only while the blood is passing through capillaries. Thus, in passing through the gills, the blood loses the pressure which could then distribute it quickly to the tissues. On the other hand, in passing through the capillaries of the tissues, the blood loses the pressure which could then force it quickly back to the gills. The squid's system of separate hearts thus copes with the problem very nicely.

It is worth noting here that a closed circulatory system with separate pumps is also found in the birds and mammals, but the two pumps are located together. One half of the bird or mammal heart pumps blood to the lungs; the other half pumps blood to the tissues. The development of separate pumps in these animals was entirely independent of that in the squid.

14-5   **SINGLE PUMP: THE FISH**

Actually, the earliest vertebrates had only a single pump. This arrangement still persists among the modern fishes. Blood collected from throughout the fish's body enters a thin-walled receiving chamber, the **atrium.** During relaxation of the heart, the blood passes through a valve into a thick-walled, muscular **ventricle.** Forcible contraction of the ventricle forces the blood out to the capillary network of the gills.

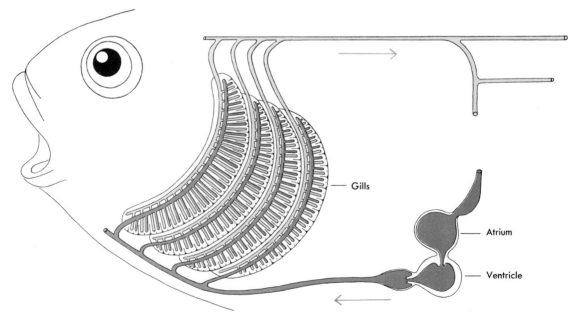

Gills

Atrium

Ventricle

Fig. 14-4   Circulatory system of a fish. Oxygen-deficient blood (dark color) is pumped forcibly to the gills. Little pressure remains to move the oxygen-rich blood (light color) to the rest of the body.

Here gas exchange takes place. From the gills, the blood passes to the many capillary networks in the remainder of the fish's body, where exchanges with the tissues take place. Then the blood returns to the heart. The system is "closed," as the blood is contained within vessels throughout its entire circuit (Fig. 14-4).

The circulatory system of fishes, while obviously adequate to their needs, is not very efficient. As mentioned above, there is a marked pressure drop when blood flows through a capillary network. In the fishes, after the blood passes through the gills, it is no longer transported vigorously by the force of the heartbeat.

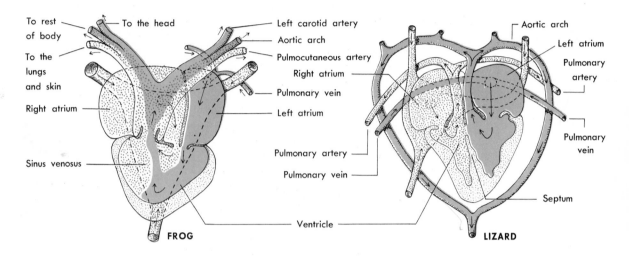

Comparison of an amphibian heart (left) and a reptile heart (right). No mixing of oxygen-deficient blood (stippled) and oxygen-rich blood (light color) occurs in the reptile heart.

Fig. 14-5

THREE CHAMBERS: THE FROG AND THE LIZARD 14-6

The situation in this respect is somewhat improved in the amphibian heart. The frog heart consists of three main chambers, two atria and a ventricle. The right atrium receives oxygen-deficient blood from the blood vessels (veins) that drain the various tissues and organs of the frog's body. Blood from the lungs, rich in oxygen, is carried to a separate atrium on the left. The blood from both atria passes into a single ventricle (Fig. 14-5). Contraction of the ventricle forces the blood into a vessel which immediately divides into a left and a right branch. Each of these immediately branches again into three main arteries. The anterior arteries carry blood to the head and brain of the frog. The middle ones, the systemic arches, carry blood to the internal tissues and organs in the rest of the body. The posterior arteries carry blood to the skin and lungs.

At first glance, it might seem that whatever advantage had been gained by returning oxygen-deficient blood to one part of the heart and oxygen-rich blood to another would be lost by mixing the two bloods in the single ventricle. To some extent this is true. However, the ventricle is partially divided into narrow chambers which tend to reduce mixing of the two bloods. When the ventricle contracts, most of the oxygen-deficient blood is deflected, with surprisingly little mixing, into the two arteries leading to the skin and lungs. Here a fresh supply of oxygen will be picked up. Oxygen-rich blood from the left atrium is sent, relatively pure, into the arteries leading to the brain. Only the blood passing into the systemic arches leading to the rest of the frog's body has been thoroughly mixed, but even so it contains enough oxygen to supply the needs of the organs to which it is carried.

Note that the problem created by pressure drop in the capillaries has been solved by the arrangement of the frog circulatory system. Both the gas-exchange organs *and* the interior tissues of the body receive blood under full pressure from the contraction of the ventricle.

Reptiles have a further modification of the heart. In the lizard, a muscular **septum** partially divides the ventricle (Fig. 14-5). When the ventricle contracts, the opening in this septum closes and the ventricle is momentarily divided into two entirely separate chambers. This prevents mixing of the two bloods. The left half of the ventricle pumps oxygen-rich blood (received from the left atrium) to the body. The right half of the ventricle pumps the oxygen-deficient blood (received from the right atrium) to the lungs.

14-7   **FOUR CHAMBERS: BIRDS AND MAMMALS**

In the hearts of birds and mammals, the septum is complete. This provides two entirely separate pumps. The right atrium receives oxygen-deficient (deoxygenated) blood from the body, and the right ventricle pumps this blood forcibly to the lungs, where it gives off carbon dioxide and picks up a fresh supply of oxygen. This oxygenated blood then returns to the left atrium, passes into the left ventricle, and is pumped out forcibly to all the other organs and tissues of the body. It is probably no coincidence that the only two groups of animals to develop warm-bloodedness (homeothermy) are the birds and mammals, with their two separate circulatory systems. One system is responsible for gas exchange with the environment; the other is responsible for gas exchange with the tissues. The efficiency provided by having these separate systems makes possible the high rate of cellular respiration upon which homeothermy depends.

THE PATHWAY OF CIRCULATION IN MAN

14-8   **THE HEART**

The heart is located roughly in the center of the thoracic cavity. It is surrounded by a protective membrane, the **pericardium** (Fig. 14-6). Deoxygenated blood from the body enters the right atrium. When this atrium contracts, the blood is forced through the **tricuspid valve** into the right ventricle. The name *tricuspid* refers to the three flaps of tissue that guard the opening between the right atrium and the right ventricle. These flaps or cusps are controlled by strands of connective tissue, the papillary tendons. They, in turn, are pulled by the papillary muscles in the wall of the ventricle. When the papillary muscles contract, the tricuspid valve opens so that blood can pass from the atrium to the ventricle. Contraction of the ventricle then closes the tricuspid valve but forces open the **semilunar valve** at the entrance to the **pulmonary artery.** Blood enters the pulmonary artery, which immediately divides into right and left

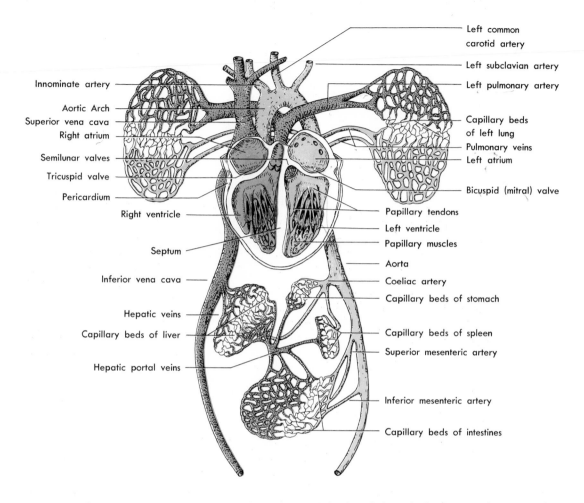

Left common carotid artery
Left subclavian artery
Left pulmonary artery
Capillary beds of left lung
Pulmonary veins
Left atrium
Bicuspid (mitral) valve

Innominate artery
Aortic Arch
Superior vena cava
Right atrium
Semilunar valves
Tricuspid valve
Pericardium
Right ventricle
Septum
Inferior vena cava
Hepatic veins
Capillary beds of liver
Hepatic portal veins

Papillary tendons
Left ventricle
Papillary muscles
Aorta
Coeliac artery
Capillary beds of stomach
Capillary beds of spleen
Superior mesenteric artery
Inferior mesenteric artery
Capillary beds of intestines

The human heart with a schematic view of the pathway of the blood through the lungs and the viscera. Oxygenated blood is shown in light color, deoxygenated blood in dark color.

Fig. 14-6

branches leading to the right and left lungs, respectively. These arteries branch and rebranch to form **arterioles.** The arterioles supply blood to the capillary networks of the lungs. Here the blood gives up carbon dioxide and takes on a fresh supply of oxygen. The capillary networks of the lungs are drained by vessels called **venules.** These serve as the tributaries of the **pulmonary veins.** Four pulmonary veins (two from each lung) carry the oxygenated blood to the left atrium of the heart. This completes the portion of the circulatory system that is known as the **pulmonary system.**

From the left atrium the blood passes through the **bicuspid valve** into the left ventricle. Contraction of the ventricle closes the biscuspid valve and opens the semilunar valve at the entrance to the **aorta.** The first branches from the aorta occur just beyond this semilunar valve. Two openings lead to the right and left **coronary arteries** which supply blood to the heart itself.

Although these coronary arteries arise where the aorta is still within the mass of the heart, they pass directly out to the surface of the heart and extend down across it. They lead to arterioles which in turn supply blood to the network of capillaries that penetrate every portion of the heart. These capillaries are drained by venules which lead to two coronary veins that empty into the right atrium. This portion of the circulatory system is known as the **coronary system.**

Its importance can be seen from the fact that the heart muscle must have a continuous supply of oxygen in order to continue beating. Anything which interferes with the proper operation of the coronary system will have drastic, and often fatal, effects upon the organism. Unfortunately, the coronary system is especially liable to malfunctions. The coronary arteries arise at the point of maximum blood pressure in the circulatory system. The continual high pressure to which they are subjected all too frequently causes a premature wearing of these vessels. This may take the form of a loss of elasticity in the arterial walls, which reduces the amount of blood that can surge through the coronary arteries and hence diminishes the oxygen supply to the heart. Frequently, fatty deposits accumulate on the interior wall of the coronary arteries reducing their bore and thus the amount of blood that they can carry. In either case, the oxygen supply of the heart may be inadequate in times of stress. Painful symptoms of **angina pectoris** result.

Fatty deposits in a coronary artery or arteriole may also lead to the formation of blood clots. These solid masses stop the flow of blood through the vessel and the capillary network it supplies. This is called a **coronary occlusion,** or heart attack. That portion of the heart whose blood supply is cut off quickly dies of oxygen starvation. If the area is not too extensive, the remaining portions of the heart can, in time, compensate for the damage. All too often, however, the plugged artery supplies such a large portion of the heart that the heart fails and death follows. Over 25% of the deaths of adult American males are caused by coronary occlusion.

14-9   **THE SYSTEMIC BLOOD VESSELS**

The remainder of the circulatory system of man is referred to as the systemic or body system. Figure 14-7 shows the path of the major branches of this system. Blood from the aorta passes into various major arteries which lead to all portions of the body. The blood moves because of the force exerted by the contraction of the left ventricle. The surge of blood which occurs at each contraction is transmitted through the muscular, elastic walls of the entire arterial system, where it can be detected as the **pulse.** Even during the moments when the heart is relaxed (diastole) there is a definite pressure in the arterial system. When the heart contracts (systole), the pressure increases.

The measurement of blood pressure is a common clinical test. This measurement is always expressed as a fraction, e.g. 120/80. The numerator of the fraction represents the pressure of the arterial blood during systole. The unit of measure is millimeters of mercury, in this example the pressure equivalent to that produced by a column of mercury 120 mm high. The denominator represents the pressure during diastole. Although blood pressure varies considerably in a given individual at different times, continual high pressures may be the symptom or cause of a variety of ailments.

When an artery is severed, the blood flows out in spurts because of the pressure exerted by the left ventricle. Severe bleeding may result. Fortunately, arteries are apt to lie somewhat deeper in the body tissues than veins and hence are not so likely to be damaged. If serious arterial bleeding should occur, however, it is important that pressure be applied on the side of the break *nearest* the heart.

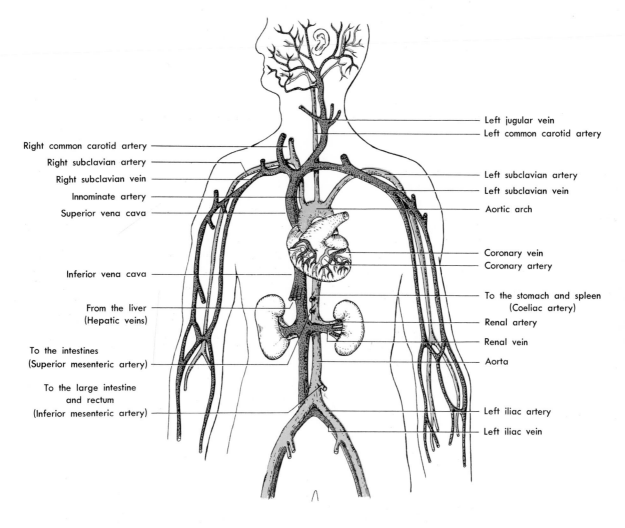

Major blood vessels in the human. Arteries are shown in light color. Veins are indicated in dark color.

Fig. 14-7

THE CAPILLARIES   14-10

As was mentioned earlier, the pressure of the arterial blood is largely dissipated when the blood enters the capillaries. Capillaries are tiny vessels whose diameter is just about that of a single red blood corpuscle (8 μ). Hence these corpuscles must pass through the capillary in single file (Fig. 14-13). Although the diameter of a single capillary is quite small, the number of capillaries which arise from a single arteriole is sufficiently great that the total cross-sectional area available for the flow of blood is increased. It has been estimated that there are 60,000 miles of capillaries in the adult human.

The walls of the capillaries consist of a single layer of epithelial cells. Through these walls all the exchanges between the blood and the tissues take place. Although networks of capillaries are not so conspicuous as the heart and major vessels, it is in these networks that the exchange functions of the circulatory system are carried out. In a real sense, the heart and major blood vessels are just accessory parts of the circulatory system. They simply serve to supply blood to and remove blood from the vast network of capillaries.

It has been estimated that the total surface area available for exchanges in the capillary networks is roughly one acre (43,560 ft²). And, in addition to impressive length and area, the capillary networks (or "beds" as they are often called) of the human body have considerable volume. In fact, their total volume is greater than the volume (about 5 liters) of blood itself. This means that not all the capillary beds can be open and functioning at once. As we will see, several mechanisms operate in the healthy individual to control which capillary beds will be open and which closed at any given time.

14-11   ## RETURN OF BLOOD TO THE HEART

When the blood leaves the capillaries and enters the veins, there is little pressure to force it along. How then does blood in the veins below the heart get back up to the heart? Two mechanisms play a role in this. One is the partial vacuum produced in the thoracic cavity during inspiration. You remember (Section 13-8) that this vacuum is created by the enlargement of the thoracic cavity during inspiration. It not only permits ventilation of the lungs but also aids in getting blood up from the lower portions of the body. A more important factor in returning blood through the veins is the **muscle pump.** This is simply the squeezing effect that active muscles have upon the veins running through them. Of course, this squeezing effect would be useless if there were not some mechanism to insure that the blood travels in one direction.

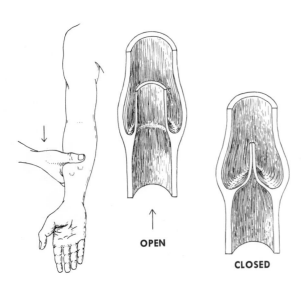

OPEN

CLOSED

Fig. 14-8

Demonstrating valves in the arm veins. Forcing blood back against a closed valve causes the vein to bulge at that point.

This mechanism is a system of valves that permit venous blood to flow towards the heart but prevent backflow. You can demonstrate these valves for yourself by firmly stroking the veins near the inner surface of your forearm. If you stroke away from the heart, you will force the blood back against the valves. They will close and a bulge will appear at that point (Fig. 14-8). (The walls of veins are quite thin and flabby.)

The importance of the muscle pump is dramatically illustrated when soldiers faint after standing "at attention" for long periods of time. The loss of consciousness results from an insufficient supply of blood (and hence of oxygen) to the brain. This develops because of a gradual accumulation of blood in the legs as a result of inactivity of the leg muscles. Fainting is a very nice self-protective mechanism in these cases. As the body moves from the vertical to the horizontal position, the heart reaches the same level as the legs. The blood in the legs no longer has to return several feet against gravity, and soon proper circulation is re-established. Fainting is more apt to occur among recruits than among seasoned soldiers. The latter know that un-locking the knees slightly and inconspicuously flexing the calf muscles will prevent fainting. These actions aid in maintaining the flow of venous blood back to the heart.

The development of high-speed aircraft (including rocket capsules) has posed a number of problems of human physiology for the occupants. One of these is the gravity (or "G") force set up in pulling out of a dive or on leaving and re-entering the earth's atmosphere. These G forces can seriously impede the return of blood from the lower portion of the body to the heart and cause fainting or "blackout" at a very critical time. This problem has been solved by the development of anti-G suits. The walls of these suits are inflated with compressed air when the number of G's begins to build up. The pressure exerted on the body (and hence on the veins, which gen-erally lie quite close to the surface) forces the blood back to the heart in opposition to the G forces.

Because of the modest forces involved in getting blood through the veins, the flow is quite even. Blood leaves a cut vein in a smooth, steady stream. For this reason and because the veins lie near the surface, it is relatively easy to check the bleeding. This must be done, however, by applying pressure on the side of the cut *away* from the heart.

It is a common error to think of arteries as the blood vessels that carry oxygenated (bright red) blood and the veins as the vessels that carry deoxygenated (dark red) blood. While this is usually the case, there is one striking exception in humans. Can you think of what it is? Arteries must therefore be defined as those vessels that carry blood *away from* the heart. Veins are those vessels that carry blood *toward* the heart.

BLOOD

The medium of transport in the circulatory system is blood. Not only does the blood transport oxygen and carbon dioxide to and from the tissues and lungs, but it also transports other materials throughout the body. These include soluble food molecules (e.g. glucose, amino acids), metabolic wastes (e.g. urea), ions of various salts (e.g. Na^+, Ca^{++}, Cl^-, HCO_3^-), and the hormones. Blood also serves to distribute heat in the body. In addition to its function as a transport agent, blood plays an active part in combating infective disease agents (e.g. certain bacteria) that gain access to the body.

THE BLOOD CORPUSCLES   14-12

Blood is a liquid tissue. It consists of cells (and cell fragments) suspended freely in a watery medium, the plasma. The cells and cell fragments constitute the so-called "formed" elements of the blood. They are sufficiently large that they can be observed under the light microscope. There are three types of "formed" elements: the red blood corpuscles, or erythrocytes, the white blood corpuscles, or leucocytes, and the platelets, or thrombocytes.

1. The **red blood corpuscles** (RBC's) are the most numerous of the three types. Normal women possess about 4.5 million of these cells in each cubic millimeter of blood. In normal men, the average runs somewhat higher: about 5 million. However, these values can fluctuate over a considerable range, depending upon such factors as

the altitude at which the individual lives (Peruvians living at an altitude of 18,000 feet may have values as high as 8.3 million) and the individual's state of health.

The RBC's are disk-shaped. They have a diameter of 7.5 μ and a thickness at the rim of 2 μ. The center of the disk is thinner (1 μ) than the rim. This interesting "biconcave" shape increases the surface area of the cell and thus speeds up the exchange of gases between it and the plasma.

In the adult, the RBC's are produced by special cells (Fig. 14-9) located in the marrow of bones, particularly in the ribs, sternum (breast bone), and vertebrae. When first formed, the RBC's have a nucleus and not very much hemoglobin. However, as they mature, the quantity of hemoglobin in the cell increases until some 280 million molecules—representing about 90% of the dry weight of the cell—are present. Toward the end of this process of hemoglobin synthesis, the nucleus is discharged from the cell. The absence of a nucleus seems to impose a definite limit, about 120 days, on the life span of these cells.

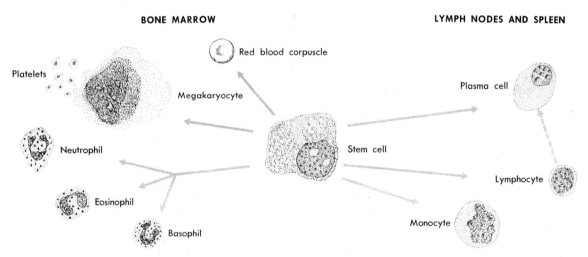

Fig. 14-9 The cells of the blood. Red blood corpuscles transport oxygen and carbon dioxide. Platelets participate in blood clotting. The rest of the cells aid the body in combating infection.

The death of a red blood corpuscle occurs when its cell membrane ruptures as the cell is squeezed through a capillary. The fragments of the ruptured cell are then ingested by phagocytic cells present in the liver and in a sac-shaped structure called the spleen. Most of the iron of the hemoglobin is reclaimed for re-use. The remainder of the hemoglobin molecule is broken down. Some of the breakdown products—the bile pigments—are excreted by the liver in the bile. It has been estimated that from one to two million RBC's die and are scavenged by the liver and spleen every second.

The continual loss of RBC's is normally compensated for by the action of the bone marrow. In fact, healthy bone marrow can, when necessary, produce RBC's at four or more times the normal rate of cell destruction. Thus, after severe bleeding (or blood donations), the bone marrow quickly brings the RBC content of the blood back to normal.

Under some circumstances, the rate of RBC loss exceeds the rate of RBC formation. When this occurs, the concentration of RBC's in the blood decreases and the individual is said to suffer from **anemia.** Most forms of anemia respond well to medical treatment.

2. The **white blood corpuscles** (WBC's) are much less numerous than the red, the ratio between the two types being approximately 1:700. There are actually five distinct types of WBC found in the circulating blood (Fig. 14-9). All possess nuclei. They range in size from the lymphocytes, which are not much larger (10 μ) than RBC's, to the monocytes, which may be three times as large (25 μ). The shape of the WBC's is quite variable, especially when they are being carried through the capillaries.

The general function of the WBC's is to protect the body from infection. The **neutrophils** and **monocytes** accomplish this by ingesting, by phagocytosis, foreign particles (e.g. bacteria) that get into the body. To carry out this function these leucocytes, in response to the release of a chemical substance, migrate to the capillary networks near areas where tissue destruction is occurring. Then they squeeze themselves through pores in the walls of the capillaries. Once free in the tissues, they begin phagocytosis. The bacterium or other particle is engulfed in a vacuole. This fuses with a lysosome, the enzymes of which proceed to destroy the bacterium. The granules which are so abundant in the cytoplasm of neutrophils are the lysosomes. As phagocytosis proceeds, their number decreases rapidly. Usually phagocytosis ends with the death of the WBC. An accumulation of dead WBC's and products of tissue destruction is called pus.

Although neutrophils possess a nucleus and all other cell structures, their life span is relatively short. Even in a healthy person, they die within a few days. You might well ask why these cells die so soon if there is no active infection to combat. The answer is that our phagocytes are constantly engaged in the control of bacteria that are permanent residents in our mouths, air passages, large intestine (see Section 10-11), and elsewhere. Generally, this control is sufficiently good that we can tolerate the presence of these bacteria. However, a variety of circumstances (e.g. exposure, improper diet, serious fatigue) may temporarily lower our resistance and permit these organisms to invade our tissues. A dramatic illustration of this is the disease *agranulocytosis*. In this disease, the production of new leucocytes ceases. Heavy exposure to radiation, such as accompanies an atomic bomb blast, is one of several causes of agranulocytosis. With leucocyte production stopped, the bacteria normally held in check in our bodies soon begin to multiply. After two days, ulcers of the mouth and large intestine, or serious lung infection, result. These infections soon spread throughout the body. Unless treatment with antibiotics is started quickly, death follows within a few days. Agranulocytosis is one more peril in our atomic age. It is also a fine illustration of the importance of our leucocytes in maintaining an uneasy truce with the various species of bacteria we harbor within our bodies.

Lymphocytes generally do not carry on phagocytosis. They do, however, combat disease by participating in the formation of **antibodies.** Antibodies are proteins that are produced whenever foreign macromolecules enter the body. Such foreign molecules are called **antigens.** Foreign protein, polysaccharide, and nucleic acid molecules can all act as antigens.

The relationship between antigens and antibodies is very specific. Each antigen stimulates the production of an antibody molecule that is capable of combining directly with that antigen and, generally, no other. When antigen and antibody do combine, the resulting complex has properties different from those of its components. For example, the complex may settle out of solution and/or be more easily engulfed by phagocytes.

An invading parasite, such as a bacterium or a virus, has on its surface macromolecules that are foreign to the host and hence antigenic. The ability to manufacture antibodies against these antigens and thus deactivate them is clearly an important weapon against invasion by disease-producing organisms.

Lymphocytes appear to carry the information for the manufacture of a given antibody but do not actually manufacture the antibody as they circulate in the blood. The nucleus of the lymphocyte practically fills the cell. There is very little cytoplasm and hence no extensive endoplasmic reticulum. Antibodies are proteins and there must be an endoplasmic reticulum for their synthesis.

There is evidence, however, that when lymphocytes are carried by the blood to the region containing the antigen molecules, they enter the area and become transformed into antibody-producing plasma cells (Fig. 14-9). The cytoplasm enlarges markedly and an elaborate endoplasmic reticulum develops. It can be demonstrated that large amounts of antibody are present within the endoplasmic reticulum of plasma cells.

The percentage of **eosinophils** and **basophils** in the blood is normally very low. Their function is not yet understood although there is indirect evidence that each plays a role in combating disease. The number of eosinophils rises markedly in certain diseases, especially those caused by parasitic worms. The number of basophils also increases during infections. Those at the site of infection appear to release substances that increase the flow of blood in the area and reduce its tendency to clot (Section 14-22). Although there is a great deal yet to be learned about the functions of the various white blood corpuscles, it seems fairly certain that each in its own way contributes to the body's defense against disease. Additional evidence to support this view will be presented in Chapter 36.

Lymphocytes and monocytes are manufactured in the spleen and in the lymph nodes (Section 14-17) from the same kind of cell that gives rise to the other leucocytes. The others are manufactured in the bone marrow. Rarely, the cells which manufacture leucocytes become cancerous. As a result, the number of leucocytes becomes far greater than normal, a condition known as **leukemia.** A variety of harmful symptoms (often including severe anemia) follow. In some forms of the disease, medical care can slow down the development of symptoms and prolong the patient's life for many years. As yet there is no cure, however.

3. The **platelets** are simply cell fragments produced by large cells in the bone marrow. They are disk-shaped and much smaller (2 μ) than the RBC's. Normally, there are 150,000-400,000 platelets in each cubic millimeter of blood. As we will see (Section 14-22), they are very important in the process of blood clotting.

14-13   THE PLASMA

The fluid in which all these "formed" elements are suspended is a straw-colored liquid called plasma. Figure 14-10 shows the chemical composition of the plasma. Most of it is water. Water is an excellent solvent and it is this property that makes it such an excellent transport medium. A variety of molecules and ions are found dissolved in the water of the plasma. They are transported by the blood from an exchange organ (e.g. intestine) or reserve supply (e.g. liver for glucose, bone for Ca^{++}) to the tissues that need them.

In addition to the small molecules and ions in solution, the plasma contains a substantial quantity (7%) of proteins. There are three major protein fractions in the plasma.

Chemical composition of blood plasma

Component	Percent
H_2O	90
Inorganic salts	less than 1
Major proteins	7 —(serum albumin 4%, serum globulin 2.7%, fibrinogen 0.3%)
Other substances (foods, wastes, hormones, etc.)	2

Fig. 14-10

1. **Serum albumin.** Serum albumin is manufactured by the liver. It aids in the maintenance of blood volume and hence blood pressure. The way in which this effect is achieved is discussed below.

2. **Serum globulin.** This protein fraction is not homogeneous; that is, there are many specific proteins in the blood which are collectively referred to as serum globulins. Some of these are enzymes and some, the gamma globulins, are circulating antibodies. Perhaps you have received at some time an injection of gamma globulin to give you temporary protection against measles or polio.

3. **Fibrinogen.** Fibrinogen is an essential component of the clotting process (Section 14-22).

In addition to their specialized functions, all the plasma proteins serve as buffers. Their presence in the plasma suppresses any marked change in its pH. The proteins can combine with both acids and bases, and in so doing, prevent drastic shifts in the acid-base balance of the plasma (Section 9-2, 7).

Functions of the Blood

The two major functions of the blood are: (1) to transport materials to and from all the tissues of the body and (2) to defend the body against infectious disease. The second function was mentioned in the discussion of the white blood corpuscles and will be considered further in Chapter 36. The first function concerns us here. As mentioned above, it is the great solvent power of the water in the plasma that makes blood such an effective transport medium. Glucose, amino acids, short-chain fatty acids, glycerol, vitamins, hormones, nitrogenous wastes (e.g. urea), and many ions are all transported dissolved in the plasma of the blood. Only in the case of gas transport is the plasma incapable of handling the job alone. It is the RBC's that carry out the bulk of oxygen and carbon dioxide transport.

Oxygen Transport   **14-14**

As much as 90% of the dry weight of a red blood corpuscle consists of the red pigment **hemoglobin.** Hemoglobin (Hb) is a protein consisting of four polypeptide chains to each of which is attached a prosthetic group, *heme* (Fig. 11-7). At the center of each heme is an atom of iron.

Oxygen and hemoglobin combine readily, one molecule of oxygen combining with each heme group. Thus the presence of Hb in the bloodstream greatly increases the amount of oxygen that can be carried by it. The affinity of Hb for oxygen is, however, only part of the story of oxygen transport. Many substances combine vigorously with oxygen. What makes hemoglobin useful as an oxygen transport agent is that it releases the oxygen again to the tissues. In other words, the reaction between hemoglobin and oxygen is freely reversible (Fig. 14-11). Under the conditions of temperature, pH, and increased oxygen pressure existing in the capillaries of the lungs, the reaction proceeds to the right. The purple-red hemoglobin of the venous blood becomes converted to the bright red oxyhemoglobin of the arterial blood. Under the conditions of temperature, pH, and reduced oxygen pressure that exist in the capillaries of the tissues, the reverse reaction is promoted and the oxyhemoglobin gives up its oxygen. Actually, the reverse reaction in the tissues never becomes completed. One hundred ml of arterial blood carries about 20 ml of oxygen. (Of this only 0.3 ml is carried in solution in the plasma; all the rest is carried in the RBC's.) In the resting human, only about one-fourth (5.3 ml) of this oxygen is released to the tissues. About 5000 ml of blood are pumped every minute by a resting human and hence about 275 ml of oxygen are transported from the lungs to the tissues in that time.

Fig. 14-11

Reversible reaction between oxygen and hemoglobin.

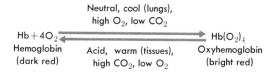

During vigorous exercise, as much as three-fourths of the oxyhemoglobin in the tissues gives up its oxygen. Furthermore, the heart of a trained athlete may pump seven or eight times as much blood during exercise as during rest. Thus the amount of oxygen delivered to the tissues may increase up to 5775 ml per minute or over 20 times that delivered during rest.

Such a performance would be impossible without the presence of the RBC's. One hundred ml of plasma alone can carry only 0.3 ml of oxygen. About 0.18 ml of this dissolved oxygen is released in the tissues. A quick calculation will show that a human depending on plasma alone for oxygen transport would have to pump 30 times as much blood every minute, even when at rest, to satisfy the demands of his tissues.

The importance of the loose, reversible association between hemoglobin and oxygen is dramatically illustrated in carbon-monoxide poisoning. Carbon monoxide, like oxygen, combines readily with hemoglobin, but, in so doing, prevents the Hb from also combining with oxygen. Carbon monoxide is not, however, released readily by the hemoglobin. Thus an individual exposed to carbon monoxide (such as in a closed garage with a running automobile engine) soon has more and more of his hemoglobin inactivated for the transport of oxygen. The affinity of Hb for carbon monoxide is 230 times that for oxygen. Hence, in air containing just 1/230 as much carbon monoxide as oxygen, the carbon monoxide competes on equal terms with the oxygen. One-half of the hemoglobin in the bloodstream will become incapable of transporting oxygen. The skin of the victim of carbon-monoxide poisoning develops a cherry-red color because this is the color which hemoglobin becomes when it combines with carbon monoxide. The prompt removal of the victim from the fouled atmosphere and the application of oxygen may save his life.

Carbon dioxide is much more soluble in water than is oxygen. One reason for this is that carbon dioxide combines chemically with water, forming carbonic acid,

$$CO_2 + H_2O \rightleftharpoons H_2CO_3.$$

This then dissociates into a hydrogen ion (H^+) and a bicarbonate ion,

$$H_2CO_3 \rightleftharpoons H^+ + HCO_3^-.$$

If all the carbon dioxide transported by our bloodstream were simply carried in the plasma this way, the pH of the blood would be lowered from its normal level of pH 7.41 to about pH 4.5. This would be instantly fatal. However, not more than 5-10% of the carbon dioxide produced by the tissues is actually transported in this fashion. The red blood corpuscles accomplish the transport of the rest. Forty to forty-five percent of the carbon dioxide actually combines with hemoglobin in the RBC's, forming carbaminohemoglobin. The carbon dioxide probably does not join the hemoglobin at the same place on the molecule that oxygen does, but the release of oxygen from hemoglobin in the tissues does increase somewhat its ability to carry carbon dioxide. Similarly, in the lungs, the pickup of oxygen by hemoglobin promotes the release of carbon dioxide from it.

The RBC's assist in the transport of carbon dioxide in still another way. When carbon dioxide enters the red blood corpuscle, some of it combines with water within the cell, forming carbonic acid. The reaction is greatly speeded by an enzyme, carbonic anhydrase, found within the corpuscle. (Fortunately, this enzyme is not present in the plasma and, thus, as we have seen, not much carbonic acid is found there.) The hydrogen ions released by the carbonic acid then combine with the protein portion of hemoglobin. Thus combined, they do not lower the pH. Most of the remaining bicarbonate ions then diffuse back out into the plasma. When the RBC's reach the lungs, these reactions are reversed and carbon dioxide is released to the alveolar air. Fifty percent of the carbon dioxide transported by the blood is carried in this fashion. Thanks to these two important mechanisms provided by the red blood corpuscles, we are able to transport carbon dioxide quickly and safely from the tissues to the lungs.

Exchanges Between the Blood and the Cells   14-16

The medium of transport in the human body is blood. Man's circulatory system is a closed one, however, and blood does not come in direct contact with the cells. (An exception, of course, is the epithelial cells that line the walls of the arteries and veins and make up the walls of the capillaries.) The number and distribution of capillaries is such that probably no cell is ever farther than 50 μ from a capillary (Fig. 14-12). Nevertheless, materials must cross this gap between the blood and the cells. When blood enters the arteriole end of a capillary, it is still under the pressure (about 35 mm Hg) produced by the contraction of the ventricle. As a result of this pressure, some filtration of the blood through the walls of the capillaries takes place. Between the epithelial cells that make up the wall of the capillary are tiny pores. It is through these pores that filtration of the blood occurs. The pores are sufficiently small that no formed elements get through (except when migration of WBC's occurs). Similarly,

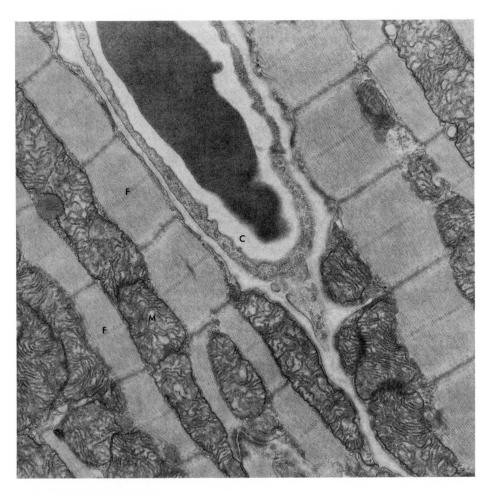

Fig. 14-12   Capillary between two adjacent heart muscle cells (17,000 X). Rows of the energy-producing mitochondria (M) can be seen between the contractile units (F). Note the thinness of the epithelial cell that forms the wall of the capillary (C). The object within the capillary is a red blood corpuscle. (Reproduced with permission from Keith R. Porter and Mary A. Bonneville, *An Introduction to the Fine Structure of Cells and Tissues,* 2nd ed., Lea & Febiger, Philadelphia, 1964.)

most of the proteins in the blood plasma are retained within the capillary. But the watery portion, with all the small molecules dissolved in it, passes easily through the capillary wall and into the cell-containing region, the tissue space (Fig. 14-13). This fluid is called **lymph.** It is simply blood plasma minus most of the proteins. In the tissue space, it bathes the cells. Any substances present in the lymph can then pass into the cells by diffusion or active transport. Also, any materials present in excess amounts in the cells (e.g. carbon dioxide or nitrogenous wastes) can diffuse out into the lymph.

Near the venous end of a capillary, as we have seen, the blood pressure is greatly reduced (about 15 mm Hg). Here, another force comes into play. Although the

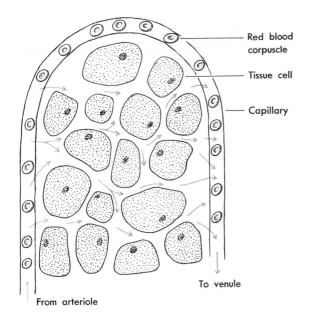

Red blood corpuscle

Tissue cell

Capillary

Fig. 14-13

Mechanism of exchange between blood and cells. The cells are bathed in lymph which is filtered from the blood.

To venule

From arteriole

composition of lymph is similar to that of blood plasma, it does contain a smaller quantity of proteins than plasma and, thus, a somewhat larger quantity of water. Because of this difference, an osmotic pressure is established. The osmotic pressure is quite small (about 25 mm Hg) but it is greater than the blood pressure at the venous end of the capillary. Consequently, lymph re-enters the capillary here. In so doing, it takes with it the cell wastes picked up from the cells of the tissue space. It is interesting to note that most capillaries curve around a tissue space in a horseshoe shape. Thus lymph formed at the arteriole end of a capillary flows across the tissue space, bathing the cells, and re-enters the same capillary at the venule end. Where this structural arrangement is not found, the venule end of some other capillary is located across the tissue space.

THE LYMPHATIC SYSTEM   **14-17**

From one-third to two-thirds of the plasma entering a capillary passes into the tissue space. Although most of this returns to the venule end of the capillary, some does not.

The small amount of lymph that remains is apt to be particularly rich in serum globulins which filtered through the capillary walls during lymph formation. These do not pass back into the capillary by diffusion. Fortunately, the bloodstream does not lose this fluid and protein for very long. Excess lymph in the tissue spaces is picked up by tiny vessels called lymph capillaries. These are very porous and easily pick up the proteins present in the lymph. (In Chapter 10 you studied the lymph capillaries in the villi: the lacteals.) The lymph capillaries lead into still larger vessels which make up the lymphatic system. The flow through the lymph vessels is quite slow. It is accomplished in a manner similar to that of venous blood. Muscular activity compresses the lymph vessels and squeezes the lymph along. The lymph can flow in only one direction because of the many valves present.

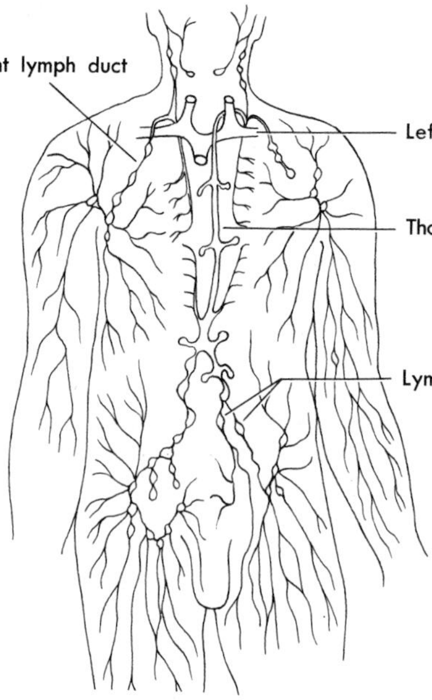

Fig. 14-14

Lymphatic system of man. It returns valuable plasma proteins to the blood and aids in combating infection.

Right lymph duct

Left subclavian vein

Thoracic duct

Lymph nodes

All the lymph collected from the entire left side of the body, plus the lymph collected from the digestive tract and the right side of the lower part of the body, flows into a single major lymph vessel, the **thoracic duct.** This duct empties about 100 ml of lymph every hour into the left subclavian vein (Fig. 14-14). The lymph produced in the right side of the head, neck, and chest is collected by the right lymph duct and empties into the right subclavian vein. In this way, lymph with its content of protein is returned to the bloodstream.

A number of things may upset the normal production or flow of lymph. An increase in blood pressure in the capillaries or a decrease in plasma proteins (such as may follow prolonged malnutrition) will result in the production of abnormally great quantities of lymph. (Why?) The lymphatic system may be unable to handle the increased lymph production successfully, and the lymph will begin to accumulate in the tissues and to distend them. This condition is known as **edema.** Another cause of edema is blockage of the lymph vessels. In the tropics this may occur as a result of infection with a parasitic roundworm, the filarial worm. The resulting edema may cause portions of the body, such as the legs or arms, to become grossly enlarged, a condition known as elephantiasis (Fig. 14-15).

Fig. 14-15

Elephantiasis. A heavy infection with filarial worms (nematodes) has so damaged the lymph vessels of one leg that they can no longer drain lymph from it. The resulting chronic edema and thickening of the skin cause increasing deformity. The worms are transmitted from person to person by mosquitoes.

Scattered at various places in the lymphatic system (especially in the groin, arm-pits, abdomen, and neck) are several hundred lymph nodes (Fig. 14-14). These contain cavities, or sinuses, into which the lymph flows. The walls of the sinuses are lined with phagocytic cells which engulf any foreign particles that might be present in the lymph. This mechanism protects the bloodstream from invasion by bacteria. It is one of the important body defenses against infectious disease. When combating a heavy infec-tion, the lymph nodes may swell, resulting in "swollen glands." Lymph nodes also manufacture lymphocytes and monocytes which then enter the bloodstream at the subclavian veins.

THE CONTROL OF CIRCULATION

Earlier in the chapter we mentioned that the amount of blood pumped by the heart increases with exercise and that the blood supply in the capillary beds varies from time to time over wide ranges. It is not surprising that a system as important as the circulatory system should be flexible in its operation so as to meet the changing needs of the body. This flexibility arises from a well-integrated system of controls.

THE HEART   **14-18**

The heart itself plays an important role in determining how much blood is pumped in a given period of time. During rest, the heart beats about 70 times a minute in the adult male while pumping about 5 liters of blood. The stimulus that maintains this rhythm is entirely self-contained. Embedded in the wall of the right atrium is a mass of specialized heart tissue called the sino-atrial (S-A) node (Fig. 14-16). The S-A node is often called the **pacemaker** of the heart because it establishes the basic rhythm at which the heart beats. The fibers of heart muscle, like all cells, are charged positively on the outside and negatively on the inside. In the pacemaker this charge breaks down spon-taneously about 70 times each minute. This, in turn, initiates a similar breakdown in the nearby muscle fibers of the atrium. A tiny wave of current sweeps over the atria, causing them to contract. When this current reaches the region of insulating connective tissue be-tween the atria and the ventricles, it is picked up by the atrial-ventricular (A-V) node. This leads to a system of branching fibers that carry the current to all parts of the ventricles, which then contract vigorously. The entire operation constitutes **systole.** A period of recovery fol-lows in which the heart muscle and S-A node become recharged. The heart muscle relaxes and the atria fill during this period **(diastole).**

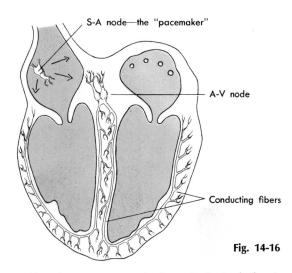

S-A node—the "pacemaker"

A-V node

Conducting fibers

Fig. 14-16

Although nerves run to the heart, its basic rhythm is established by impulses arising in the S-A node.

Damage to the pacemaker does not necessarily result in heart failure. Even without the pacemaker, the ventricles can maintain a beat, although it is considerably slower. There is, however, a danger that impulses arising in the ventricles may become disorganized and random. When this happens, the ventricles begin to twitch spasmodically and cease to pump blood. This is known as ventricular fibrillation. Death follows quickly unless immediate measures are taken to start rhythmic beating again. In the past this has meant opening up the chest cavity and massaging the heart by hand. Obviously such heroic measures have usually been confined to cases of ventricular fibrillation occurring while the patient was under surgery.

Ventricular fibrillation is probably the immediate cause of death in 25% of all cases. Although most cases arise spontaneously in damaged hearts, moderately severe electric shocks can also cause fibrillation. Unfortunately, the 60-cycle alternating current in such widespread use today is especially effective at this.

Recent advances in electronic technology have resulted in the development of artificial pacemakers. These instruments produce electrical impulses which, when led to the heart through properly implanted electrodes, can substitute for a damaged pacemaker. Some of the most recent devices, employing transistors and long-lived batteries, have actually been placed entirely within the body.

14-19 AUXILIARY CONTROL OF THE HEART

Although the pacemaker sets the basic rhythm of the heart, the rate and strength of beating can be modified by other factors. Located in the medulla of the brain are two auxiliary control centers. These initiate impulses which travel to the heart by way of nerves.

Impulses travelling to the heart by way of the *accelerator* nerves cause an increase in the rate and strength of the heartbeat and hence an increase in the rate of flow of blood through the body. These impulses are most likely to arise when the individual is subject to some stress such as fear or violent physical exertion. The heartbeat may increase to 140, or even more, beats per minute. Simultaneously, the strength of contraction increases. The total quantity of blood pumped by the heart may thus increase up to 35-40 liters per minute. Have you ever noticed your heart start to "pound" rapidly when you were frightened? The accelerator nerves are responsible for this.

Vigorous exercise accelerates heartbeat in two ways. As cellular respiration increases, so does the carbon dioxide content of the blood. This stimulates special carbon dioxide receptors located in the carotid arteries and aorta (Fig. 14-7), and these transmit impulses to the medulla for relay, by way of the accelerator nerves, to the heart. Furthermore, as muscular activity increases, the muscle pump (Section 14-11) drives more blood back to the right atrium of the heart. The atrium becomes distended with blood, thus stimulating stretch receptors located in its wall. These, too, send impulses to the medulla for relay to the heart. Working together, these two mechanisms thus insure that the increased demands on the heart during vigorous exercise are met.

Two *inhibitory* nerves also run from the medulla to the heart. Impulses passing down these, the **vagus** nerves, cause a slowing down of the heartbeat. Pressure receptors are present in the aorta and in the carotid arteries. When the blood pressure increases above normal levels, these receptors send impulses back to the medulla. The medulla, in turn, relays these through the vagus nerves to the heart. Heartbeat and blood pressure diminish. The vagus nerves thus act antagonistically to the accelerator nerves and protect the heart from unnecessary or excessive overactivity.

Nerves also affect the flow of blood through the arteries and arterioles. The walls of these vessels are muscular. Their constriction reduces the bore of the vessels, thus increasing blood pressure but reducing blood flow. Dilation of the vessels has the opposite effect. For example, in times of danger or other stress, the arteries and arterioles supplying blood to the skeletal muscles will be dilated while the bore of the vessels supplying the digestive organs will be decreased. This action is carried out by nervous stimulation and also by a hormone, adrenaline, which is released into the blood itself. On the other hand, after a full meal, the blood supply to the digestive organs will be increased at the expense of that to the skeletal muscles.

Many chemical substances in addition to adrenaline have been discovered in the blood which affect the bore of the arteries and arterioles and hence blood pressure. The brain and the kidneys both release substances that constrict arteries and thus raise blood pressure. On the other hand, cells where infection or other damage is occurring release substances, e.g. *histamine*, that dilate the arterioles and thus increase blood flow in the area. You remember (see Section 14-12, 2) that basophils probably do this but other cells participate in the process, too. A great deal of research remains to be done on the action and interrelationships of these substances.

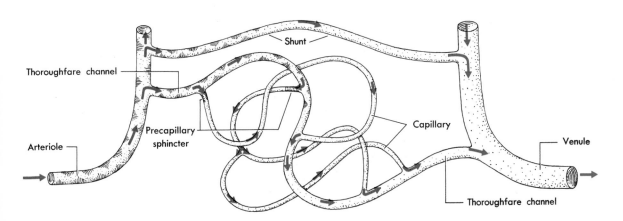

Organization of the capillary bed. Control of blood flow is achieved by changes in the diameter of the arteriole, shunt, thoroughfare channel, and precapillary sphincters. Only *their* walls are muscular.

Fig. 14-17

Although the walls of the capillaries have no muscles and hence cannot be controlled directly, the over-all action of the capillary bed is under precise control. Running between the arterioles and venules is a vessel called the "thoroughfare channel" (Fig. 14-17), from which arise the true capillaries. There is a ring of muscle, the precapillary sphincter, at the point where each capillary branches from the thoroughfare channel. When it is relaxed, blood flows into the capillary. When it is contracted, blood flow through the capillary ceases. Generally, the stimuli which cause constriction of the arteries and arterioles in any given portion of the body also cause constriction of the precapillary sphincters. The same is true for stimuli which cause dilation of the arteries and arterioles.

There is also a considerable degree of *local* control over the capillary beds. When cells in a tissue space are metabolizing rapidly, they release substances that relax the precapillary sphincters. This is a very nice control mechanism because rapidly metabolizing cells need additional supplies of glucose and oxygen. They also need to have their wastes carried away more quickly. Both these needs are taken care of by increasing the blood flow through the nearby capillaries.

As mentioned in Section 14-10, the total volume of the capillary beds of the body is considerably greater than the quantity of blood (about 5 liters) present in the body. In order to maintain adequate blood pressure and blood flow, it is important that as capillary beds open in one portion of the body, they close in another. Under a few circumstances, this may not occur. Some drugs, pain, even emotional upsets may cause a general dilation of the arteries and opening of capillary beds throughout the body. Although the volume of blood remains normal, the blood pressure decreases markedly and the victim may go into "shock." If the victim is placed in a horizontal position, the brain and heart will continue to receive sufficient quantities of blood and the chances of recovery are excellent. If maintained in a vertical position, however, the victim will eventually die from lack of oxygen in the brain and heart. This may be the mechanism responsible for death by crucifixion.

Shock can also result from severe bleeding. The heart can pump only as much blood as it receives. If insufficient blood gets back to the heart, the output of the heart (and thus blood pressure) drops. The tissues, especially of the brain and heart, fail to receive adequate supplies of oxygen and glucose. To combat the effects of severe bleeding, the arteries and arterioles become constricted and the capillary beds shut down (except in the brain and heart). This reduces the volume of the system and helps maintain normal blood pressure. The flow of blood through the capillary beds may be circumvented completely. Short lengths of vessel, normally closed, make a direct connection between arterioles and venules. These shunts can pass arterial blood directly into the venules and thus hasten its passage back to the heart (Fig. 14-17).

Air-breathing vertebrates that spend long periods of time under water (such as seals, penguins, turtles, and alligators) employ a similar mechanism to insure that the oxygen supply of the heart and brain is not seriously diminished. When the animal dives, the blood supply of the rest of the body is sharply reduced so that what oxygen remains in the blood will be available for those organs that need it most: the brain and the heart. The anatomy of the turtle heart provides an additional mechanism to help with this adjustment. While underwater, a good deal of the blood entering the right side of the ventricle passes through the opening in the septum (see Fig. 14-5) and right back out to the vital parts (e.g. brain) of the body. In so doing, this blood bypasses the lungs, which become less useful anyway as their oxygen content is depleted.

14-21   **BLOOD RESERVOIRS**

The body can maintain blood pressure not only by reducing the volume of the vessels but also by adding blood to them. As much as 15% of the total blood in the body is normally stored in tiny chambers, the sinuses, of the liver and spleen. Both these organs are muscular and in times of stress they contract. This forces their reserves of blood into the system. The liver stores more blood than the spleen, but the blood in the spleen is especially rich in RBC's. Extra blood is also stored in the skin in tufts of veins. All these blood reservoirs not only help to maintain blood volume (and thus pressure) after bleeding, but they also function under normal conditions. Whenever a greater volume of circulating blood is needed (such as during vigorous exercise), their emptying satisfies this need.

Still another protective mechanism of the circulatory system is the blood clot. When blood vessels are cut or ruptured, it is vital that loss of blood from the system be stopped before shock and death follow. Solidification, or clotting, of the blood is able to accomplish this in all but the major vessels. As blood flows out of a damaged vessel, the platelets adhere to the inner surface of the vessel wall. Both they and damaged cells in the area release a fatty material which is activated by proteins in the blood to form a complex of substances known as "thromboplastin." Some six to ten of these clotting "factors" seem to be needed to form active thromboplastin. Some act catalytically and others are actually consumed in the process. In the presence of calcium ions (Ca^{++}), thromboplastin then catalyzes the conversion of prothrombin (a serum globulin manufactured continuously by the liver) to **thrombin.** Thrombin is an enzyme that catalyzes the conversion of the soluble plasma protein fibrinogen to the insoluble protein **fibrin.** The fibrin gradually forms a mesh in which the blood corpuscles become embedded. Soon a dam (the clot) is constructed which stops loss of blood from the broken vessel.

The various steps in the clotting process are not yet fully understood, and Fig. 14-18 gives no more than an over-all picture. A shortage of any component in the process, e.g. platelets, a plasma clotting factor, or prothrombin, may lead to serious external and/or internal bleeding, even with minor injuries such as a slight cut or the rupture of small blood vessels by a bruise.

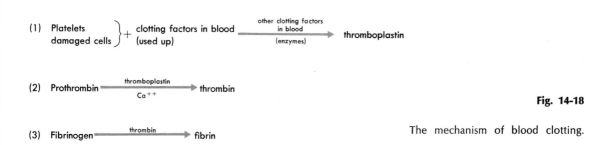

Fig. 14-18

The mechanism of blood clotting.

As pointed out in Chapter 9, the environment of each of the trillions of cells that make up our bodies is a fluid. This fluid, lymph, along with the blood, makes up the ECF of the body. Although lymph is perhaps a less conspicuous part of our circulatory system than blood, it is lymph that actually provides the internal environment in which our cells live. Lymph is manufactured from the blood, however, and returns, after bathing the tissues, to the blood. Any change in the physical or chemical properties of the blood immediately results in a corresponding change in the lymph. In the past few chapters, we have examined several mechanisms that operate to preserve a steady, unvarying chemical composition (and a steady physical state) in the blood. Its temperature, pH, and concentration of glucose, oxygen and carbon dioxide are all held remarkably constant by means of finely adjusted regulatory mechanisms. This constancy of the blood insures the homeostasis of the lymph and hence of the true environment, the internal environment, of our bodies. Despite great changes in the external environment, in diet, and in the general activity of the body, our cells continue to operate under conditions that are relatively unvarying and optimum.

In the chapters ahead, we will examine still other mechanisms by which homeostasis is maintained in the human body. But, before turning to these, let us examine how plants accomplish the transport of materials throughout their bodies.

EXERCISES AND PROBLEMS

1   Why are iron pills prescribed for mild cases of anemia?

2   Citrate ions ($C_6H_5O_7^{\equiv}$) combine with calcium ions (Ca^{++}) to form an insoluble product, $2C_6H_5O_7^{\equiv} + 3Ca^{++} \rightarrow Ca_3(C_6H_5O_7)_2$. Why do you suppose that a small quantity of sodium or potassium citrate is added to blood collected for storage in blood banks?

3   Trace the path taken by a red blood corpuscle from a capillary bed in your right thumb, to your lungs, and then back to the same capillary bed. Include all vessels, valves, and chambers through which it passes.

4   What substances are found in plasma but not in lymph?

5   General edema is characteristic of extreme cases of protein deficiency. Can you account for this?

6   Why is it difficult to see platelets in stained blood slides?

7   In what ways do arteries and veins differ?

8   Which arteries in the human carry deoxygenated blood?

9   How much blood would an adult human need to pump every minute in order to meet his oxygen needs during strenuous exercise if he had no hemoglobin?

10   Summarize the various mechanisms by which our circulatory system adjusts to the demands of strenuous exercise.

11   Trace in detail the path taken by a molecule of O_2 from an RBC into the mitochondrion of a liver cell. Explain what processes are involved at each step.

12   Do the same for a molecule of CO_2 going from a mitochondrion to an RBC.

13   Why are valves needed in veins but not in arteries?

14   Oxygen-transport pigments are found in crustaceans but not in insects. Explain this difference.

REFERENCES

1   Wiggers, C. J., "The Heart," *Scientific American,* Reprint No. 62, May, 1957.

2   Zucker, Marjorie B., "Blood Platelets," *Scientific American,* February, 1961.

3   Mayerson, H. S., "The Lymphatic System," *Scientific American,* Reprint No. 158, June, 1963.

4   Zweifach, B. W., "The Microcirculation of the Blood," *Scientific American,* Reprint No. 64, January, 1959.

5 Scholander, P. F., "The Master Switch of Life," *Scientific American,"* Reprint No. 172, December, 1963. Describes how air-breathing vertebrates reduce the blood supply to all organs but the heart and brain while underwater.

6 Scher, A. M., "The Electrocardiogram," *Scientific American,* November, 1961. How analysis of the electrical activity of the heart can aid in the diagnosis of heart damage.

7 Lillehei, C. W., and L. Engel, "Open-Heart Surgery," *Scientific American,* February, 1960. How the heart-lung machine makes surgical repair of the heart possible.

8 Chapman, C. B., and J. H. Mitchell, "The Physiology of Exercise," *Scientific American,* Reprint No. 1011, May, 1965. Describes the mechanisms by which the human body meets the demands on the circulatory system that occur during violent exercise.

9 Adolph, E. F., "The Heart's Pacemaker," *Scientific American,* March, 1967.

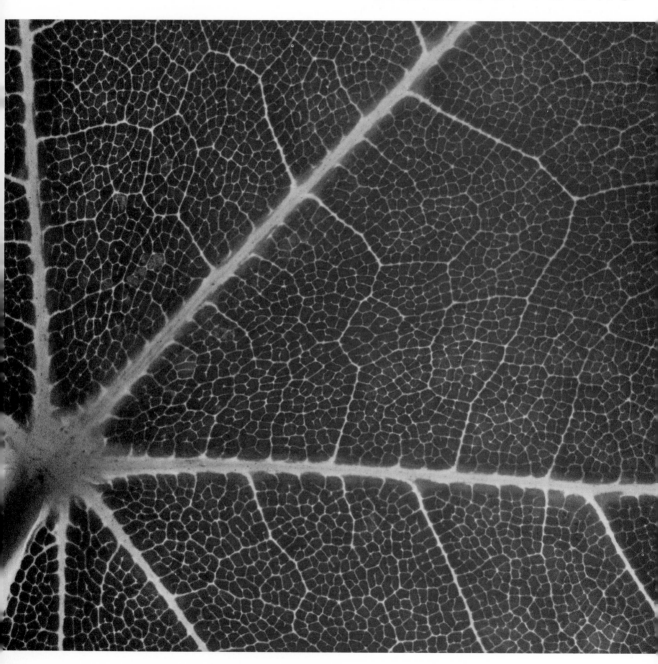

Our largest and most complex plants, the tracheophytes, are also faced with the problem of transporting materials throughout their bodies. The problem of supply to and from internal tissues is not so acute in plants as it is in animals. As we will see, the living tissues of a plant are usually quite close to the surface. The real demand for a transport system comes about because of the curious dilemma in which land plants find themselves. A plant cannot carry on photosynthesis without both water and sunlight. It secures its water by sending a root system into the soil. It secures its light by displaying leaves in the air. The greater its success in displaying its leaves above those of competing plants, the farther it has removed them from their supply of water in the soil. An efficient vascular system is needed, therefore, to bridge the gap and transport water quickly from roots to leaves. The vascular system is also needed to insure that food is transported efficiently from the leaves to the living cells of the stem and roots in order to satisfy their food requirements for metabolism and growth.

The transport of materials in plants is called **translocation.** In the tracheophytes, it takes place in a special system of conducting vessels. These are located in groups known as **vascular bundles** which extend through all the organs of the plant: root, stem, leaf (in the veins), and flower. All the vascular bundles are interconnected so that transport between organs is carried on rapidly and efficiently. Within the vascular bundles, two distinct types of tissue are found, the xylem and the phloem.

The most important part of the xylem tissue of angiosperms is the xylem **vessels** (Fig. 15-1). These are thick-walled tubes which extend vertically through several feet of xylem tissue. They range in diameter from only 20 μ to as much as 700 μ (0.7 mm), depending upon their location and the species in which they are present. The walls of the xylem vessels are thickened with secondary deposits of cellulose and are usually further strengthened by impregnation with a cementing material, lignin. The secondary walls of the xylem are not deposited evenly, but in spirals, rings, etc. The walls of xylem vessels may also be perforated by pits.

The xylem vessels arise from individual, cylindrical cells usually oriented end to end. At maturity, the end walls of these cells dissolve away and the cytoplasmic contents die. The result is the xylem vessel, a continuous nonliving duct. The xylem vessels function in the upward transport of water and minerals.

Also present in the xylem tissue of many angiosperms are xylem **tracheids.** These are individual cells about 30 μ in diameter and several millimeters in length. In cross section, they can be distinguished from the xylem vessels by their angular walls and, in many cases, smaller size. They taper at each end and the tapered ends of one cell overlap the tapered ends of the adjacent cells. Like xylem vessels, they possess thick, lignified cell walls and, at maturity, no cytoplasm. Their walls are perforated so that water and dissolved minerals can, and do, flow readily from one tracheid to the next.

◀ Veins in a maple leaf.

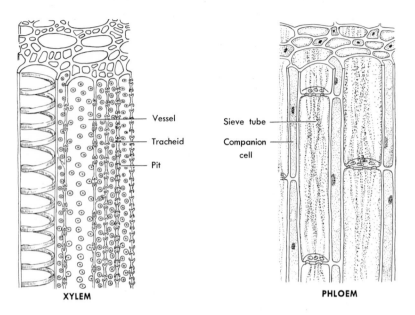

XYLEM   PHLOEM

Fig. 15-1   Vascular tissues. Xylem vessels and tracheids (left) contain no cytoplasm at maturity.

Like the xylem vessels, they transport water and minerals upwards through the vascular bundle. In the gymnosperms, the xylem tracheids are the only water transport ducts. Vessels are not present.

15-3   **PHLOEM**

The major conducting vessels of the phloem are the sieve tubes. These consist of cylindrical cells (about 25 μ in diameter and 100 μ long) oriented end to end. The end walls of mature sieve-tube cells are perforated, permitting strands of cytoplasm to extend between adjacent cells. The appearance of these end walls under the microscope has caused them to be called sieve plates (Fig. 15-1). The side walls of the sieve-tube cells are also perforated. Fine strands of cytoplasm, the plasmodesmata, extend through these pores, connecting sieve-tube cells that lie side by side. Like the xylem vessels and tracheids, the sieve tubes form ducts extending unbroken from the bottom to the top of the plant.

The sieve tubes differ from the xylem vessels and tracheids in that the constituent cells do not lose their cytoplasm at maturity. They do, however, lose their nucleus. In many plants, the cells of the sieve tubes lie adjacent to companion cells (Fig. 15-1) which do retain their nucleus at maturity and may possibly exert some control over the activities of the cells of the sieve tube. The sieve tubes transport foods and plant hormones both upwards and downwards in the plant.

The xylem and phloem make up the vascular bundles of the plant. The organization of these vascular bundles is different in the root, stem, and veins of the leaf. Furthermore, the arrangement of vascular bundles within a single organ varies considerably from species to species. In considering the internal organization of the root, stem, and the leaf we will necessarily restrict ourselves to just a few representative types.

Figure 15-2 shows the structure of a typical young dicot root. At the tip of the root is a meristem that produces the cells from which the first (primary) root structures will develop. Mitosis in this meristem increases the length of the root. Because of the frequency with which mitosis occurs in this "embryonic" region, root tips are frequently used to demonstrate and study this type of cell division. The meristem is protected from abrasion and damage in the soil by the root cap.

As soon as cells are manufactured by the meristem, they undergo a period of elongation. The region of the root in which this occurs is known as the region of elongation.

Once the root cells are fully elongated, they begin the process of **differentiation.** Differentiation involves the development of specialized structures. Cells at the surface of the root differentiate to form epidermal cells. Most of these develop long extensions of the wall, the **root hairs.** These greatly increase the surface area of the root and are the main point of entrance for water.

Within the epidermis develops a ring (as viewed in cross section) of parenchyma cells, the **cortex.** The cortex serves as a food storage area. Its inner surface is bounded by a single layer of cells, the **endodermis.** Within the endodermis is the central cylinder containing the vascular bundles. The other boundary of the central cylinder, the **pericycle,** is important because branches of the root (secondary roots) arise from it. Within the pericycle of the young root are xylem tissue, phloem tissue, and parenchyma or pith. The xylem tissue is arranged in bundles in a radial or spokelike fashion. The phloem tissue alternates with the xylem tissue (Fig. 15-2).

In the older root, another meristem, the cambium, develops between the xylem and phloem. Mitosis in the cambium produces new (secondary) xylem to the inside and new (secondary) phloem to the outside (Fig. 15-2).

The vascular bundles of the stem are simply extensions of those in the roots. They are, however, arranged somewhat differently. Furthermore, the arrangement of bundles in the monocot stem is markedly different from that in the dicot stem. (The organization of tissues in monocot roots and dicot roots is essentially alike.) Even among the dicots, the arrangement of tissues in those that develop woody stems (perennials) is somewhat different from those whose stems are herbaceous (annuals).

THE WOODY DICOT STEM   15-5

A cross section of a young twig of the basswood or American linden (*Tilia*) provides a good example of the organization of tissues in the typical woody dicot (Fig. 15-3). The twig is made up of three distinct regions, the bark, the wood, and the pith. The outer surface of the bark region is protected by layers of dead cork cells impregnated with suberin. Suberin (Section 13-3) is a waxy material which markedly cuts down water loss from the stem. A great many openings, the lenticels, are present in the cork and it is by means of these openings that oxygen and carbon dioxide can be exchanged between the stem tissues and the air. Beneath the cork are layers of parenchyma cells which make up the cortex. These cells store food in the stem just as they do in the root. In the very young stem (before cork has developed) they may have chloroplasts and carry on photosynthesis. In the older stem a meristem develops between the cortex and the cork. Mitosis in this meristem (the cork cambium) replaces the cork cells that are lost by weathering.

Fig. 15-2   Organization of a young dicot root in longitudinal section (left) and cross sections (right). The longitudinal section has been shortened to enable each stage in root development to be shown. (Photo courtesy General Biological Supply House, Inc.)

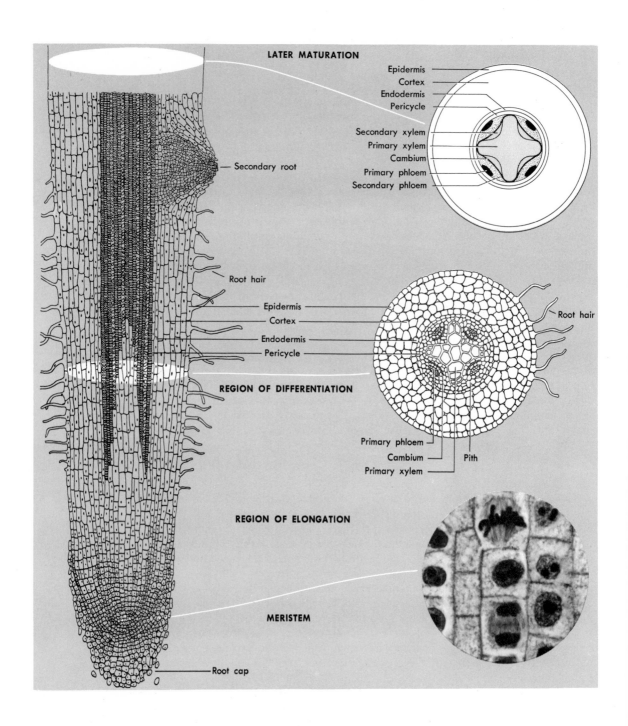

LATER MATURATION

Epidermis
Cortex
Endodermis
Pericycle

Secondary xylem
Primary xylem
Cambium
Primary phloem
Secondary phloem

Secondary root

Root hair

Epidermis
Cortex
Endodermis
Pericycle

Root hair

REGION OF DIFFERENTIATION

Primary phloem
Cambium
Primary xylem
Pith

REGION OF ELONGATION

MERISTEM

Root cap

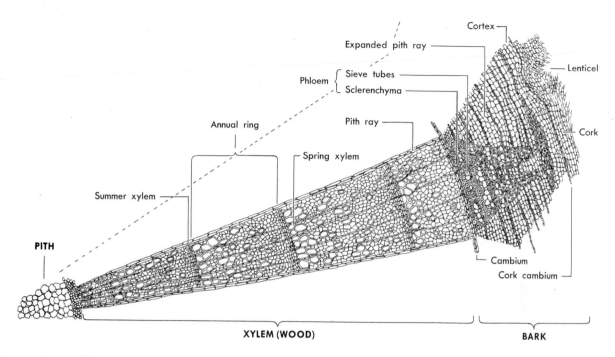

The woody dicot stem. A cross section showing a single vascular bundle of *Tilia*, the American linden (basswood). How old was this twig when it was cut?

Fig. 15-3

The inner portion of the bark is marked by alternating areas of phloem tissue and parenchyma. The parenchyma makes up the terminal portion of the horizontal rays that run between the pith and the bark. These rays carry on lateral transport of materials between the two regions. The enlarged portion in the bark also serves as a food storage area. The phloem tissue consists of bundles of sieve tubes surrounded by and supported by sclerenchyma cells.

The inner boundary of the bark region is marked by a meristem, the cambium. As a result of its activity, new phloem is continually produced in the bark region during the growing season. The cambium also produces new xylem towards the interior.

Xylem makes up the wood region. The xylem vessels produced during the spring, when water is plentiful, have larger diameters than those produced later in the summer. During the dormant season, no xylem whatsoever is formed. The visual contrast between the summer xylem of one year and the spring xylem of the next year permits the easy counting of annual rings. The entire band of xylem formed in one growing season makes up one annual ring. How old was the basswood twig shown in Fig. 15-3 when it was cut?

The xylem serves a dual function: support and transport. In older stems, only the most recent rings of xylem participate in the transport of materials. These make up the **sapwood.** The inner rings of xylem cease to function in transport, but provide ever-increasing support for the weight of the tree above. This portion of xylem is called the **heartwood.** The lumber and paper industries depend upon the xylem of our woody dicots and gymnosperms.

The innermost portion of the young basswood twig is the pith. It contains parenchyma cells and serves as a food storage area. In the older woody stem, the pith disappears.

THE HERBACEOUS DICOT STEM

The basic arrangement of the herbaceous dicot stem (Fig. 15-4) is similar to that of the woody dicot, although the surface of the stem is protected only by a layer of epidermis rather than by cork. Beneath the epidermal cells are cortex cells. These often possess chlorophyll and carry on photosynthesis. The interior of the stem is packed with parenchyma cells, the pith. The outer portions of the vascular bundles contain phloem tissue, just as in the woody dicot. On the inner side, the phloem is separated from the xylem by a cambium. Although the cambium does produce additional xylem and phloem during the growing season, no annual rings are formed. Why not?

As its name implies, the herbaceous dicot stem lacks the strength and rigidity of the woody dicot stem. This is because there are no rings of woody xylem present. The stem does receive some mechanical support, however, from masses of sclerenchyma located between the phloem and the cortex.

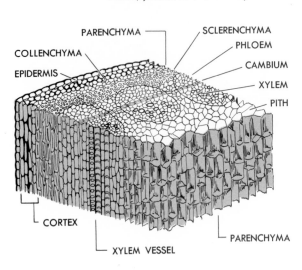

PARENCHYMA — SCLERENCHYMA
COLLENCHYMA — PHLOEM
EPIDERMIS — CAMBIUM
— XYLEM
— PITH
CORTEX
PARENCHYMA
XYLEM VESSEL

Fig. 15-4

Anatomy of a typical herbaceous dicot stem. Why are there no annual rings?

THE MONOCOT STEM

The organization of the monocot stem is quite different from that of the dicot. A cross section of a corn stem (*Zea mays*) (Fig 15-5) shows these differences nicely. The corn stem consists of an external rind and an interior filled with pith. The rind provides most of the mechanical support for the stem. Scattered pretty much at random through the pith are the vascular bundles. In cross section, they remind one of a caricature of a human face. Each is surrounded by a layer of sclerenchyma cells that provides mechanical support for the cells within. The phloem is located in the forehead region. Careful examination reveals companion cells located between the sieve tubes. Four xylem vessels are present, making up the two "eyes," the "nose," and "mouth." Much of the bottom xylem vessel is surrounded by air in the air space. Xylem tracheids are present in the "cheek" areas.

THE LEAF VEINS

The vascular bundles of the leaves are direct extensions of the vascular bundles of the stem. They pass from the stem into the leaf petiole and then into the various veins of the leaf. These branch into ever-finer veins. Probably no cell in the spongy layer of the leaf is more than two cells away from the end of a vein. The xylem and phloem of the vein (Fig. 12-6) are often surrounded by layers of sclerenchyma cells which impart strength to the vein. The veins, in turn, provide a rigid framework to support the remaining soft tissues of the leaf blade.

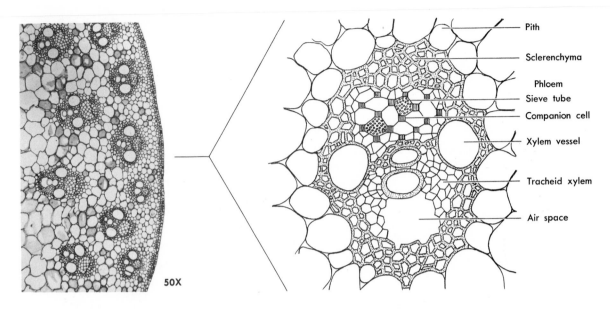

Organization of a typical monocot stem. Left: a cross section of a portion of a corn stem
(Zea mays). (Courtesy General Biological Supply House, Inc.) Right: detail of a single vascular
bundle.

Fig. 15-5

THE TRANSPORT OF WATER

THE PATHWAY   **15-9**

Water enters the plant through the root hairs. These extensions of the epidermal cells
have sticky walls and adhere tightly to soil particles. This places them in direct contact
with the film of water that also adheres to the soil particles of all but "bone-dry" soils
(Fig. 13-4).

Although the quantity of water absorbed by a single root hair is not large, the
amount absorbed by all the root hairs present in the root system is usually adequate to
supply the needs of the plant. Root hairs are found only at the tips of the roots, but
there may be a great many of them. Careful measurements have been made of the root
system of the grass, rye. After four months of growth, a single plant was found to have
387 miles of roots. There were approximately 13 million root tips possessing an estimated total of 14 billion root hairs (Fig. 15-6).

Although some minerals may also enter the root hairs, the most rapid uptake of
minerals occurs in the embryonic region of the root. The passage of minerals from the
soil into the cells of the root occurs by active transport. As in all cases of active transport, energy (ATP) is necessary for the process to occur.

Once within the epidermal cells, water passes through the cells of the cortex. It
enters the central cylinder by passing through the endodermis and pericycle. In many
roots, the endodermis contains specialized cells, the passage cells, which provide an

Fig. 15-6   Absorptive area of roots. Left: After two years of growth, a single plant of crested wheat grass had produced 319 miles of roots. (Courtesy "Science Service.") Right: The surface area for water absorption is increased further by the root hairs at the tip of each root (seen on the primary root of a germinating radish).

easy pathway for the movement of water into the central cylinder. In the young root, water then enters the xylem directly. In older roots, it may have to pass first through a band of phloem and cambium. It does this by travelling through horizontally elongated cells, the xylem rays.

Once in the xylem, water moves upwards in the vessels and/or tracheids. These run up through the root and the stem. At any level the water can leave the xylem and pass laterally to supply the needs of other tissues. At the leaves the xylem passes into the petiole and then into the veins of the leaf. A glance at the scars left on woody stems after the leaves have dropped in the autumn will reveal the severed ends of the vascular bundles that had supplied the leaves (Fig. 24-3).

At the ends of the veins, water leaves the xylem and enters the spongy layer and palisade layer cells of the leaf. Here the water may be used in photosynthesis or may be evaporated from the leaf in the process of transpiration.

THE GRAFT   **4 YEARS LATER**

Fig. 15-7

A bridge graft. Without it, the roots would die for lack of food.

Several bits of evidence lead to the conclusion that the upward transport of water takes place in the xylem. For example, if a ring of bark is carefully removed from the trunk of a tree, thus removing all the phloem, the upward passage of water is not interrupted. Such an operation is called girdling. Young fruit trees are all too frequently girdled during the winter by hungry field mice feeding upon the bark. With the arrival of spring, the tree develops leaves normally, suggesting that the upward movement of water and minerals has not been interfered with. Unless a special graft (Fig. 15-7) is made, however, the tree will ultimately die. (Why?) Additional evidence is obtained when the severed top of a plant is placed in water containing a dye. The water is drawn up into the stem for some period of time; microscopic examination of the vascular tissue shows that the dye is localized in the xylem vessels.

MAGNITUDE OF FLOW; TRANSPIRATION

The forces responsible for the movement of water through the xylem are not yet fully understood. Any theory to explain the upward movement of water in the xylem must take into account the large volume of water transported and the speed with which the water travels. Herbaceous plants may absorb a volume of water each day equal to several times the volume of the plant itself. Water that contains a marker (for example a radioactive mineral) has been shown to move up the stem as much as 75 cm each minute.

Only 1-2% of all this water is used in photosynthesis or in other metabolic activities of the leaf cells. The remainder evaporates from the leaf in the process of **transpiration.** In Chapter 13, you learned that the surfaces of the cells of the spongy layer are always covered with a film of water. This evaporates into the air spaces of the spongy layer. When the stomata open, the water vapor diffuses out of the leaf. If the leaf is to continue to function properly, fresh supplies of water must be brought to the leaf to replace that lost in transpiration.

Figure 15-8 illustrates a device with which it is possible to approximate the amount of water vapor given off in transpiration. As water is absorbed by the roots of the plant, it is replaced by water drawn through the graduated tube from the reservoir on the right. A small bubble introduced into the system serves to mark the volume consumed. Although this device, a potometer, measures the total water use of the plant, 98-99% of this is accounted for by transpiration.

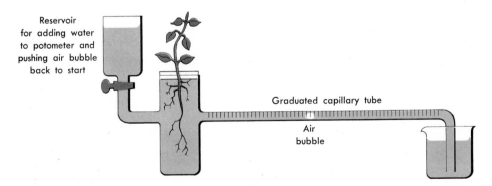

Reservoir for adding water to potometer and pushing air bubble back to start

Graduated capillary tube

Air bubble

Potometer in use. As water is transpired and otherwise used by the plant, it is replaced from the reservoir on the right. This pushes the air bubble to the left and permits the amount of water used to be measured accurately.

Fig. 15-8

Using a potometer, it is possible to study the effect of various environmental factors upon the rate of transpiration.

1) **Light.** Plants transpire much more rapidly when exposed to light than in the dark. This is chiefly because light stimulates the opening of the stomata (see Section 13-4) and thus greatly increases the transfer of moisture-laden air from the air spaces of the spongy layer to the outside. Light also speeds up transpiration by warming the leaf.

2) **Temperature.** Plants transpire more rapidly at higher temperatures than at low. At 30°C a leaf may transpire three times as fast as it does at 20°C. This is because water evaporates more rapidly as its temperature increases and, in this case, thus increases the humidity of the air in the air spaces with respect to that outside.

3) **Humidity.** Rate of transpiration is also affected by the relative humidity of the air surrounding the plant. The rate of diffusion of any substance is decreased as the difference in concentration of the substance in the two regions decreases. The reverse is also true. Therefore diffusion of water from the moisture-laden air spaces of the leaf to the outside goes on rather slowly when the surrounding air is quite humid. When the surrounding air is dry, diffusion proceeds much more rapidly.

4) **Wind.** The presence of gentle air currents also increases the rate of transpiration. When none are present, the air immediately surrounding a transpiring leaf becomes increasingly humid. As it does so, it causes a decrease in the rate of transpiration for the reason just mentioned. When a breeze is present, however, the humid air is carried away and replaced by fresh, drier air.

5) **Soil Water.** A plant cannot continue to transpire rapidly if its moisture loss is not made up by absorption of fresh supplies of water from the soil. When absorption of water by the roots fails to keep up with the rate of transpiration, loss of turgor occurs, and the stomata close. This immediately reduces the rate of transpiration greatly. Often the loss of turgor may extend to other plant parts and wilting occurs.

Under optimum conditions, the loss of water through transpiration is truly impressive. It has been estimated that over the course of the growing season an acre of corn plants may transpire 400,000 gallons of water. In liquid form this would be enough to cover the field with a lake 15 in. deep. The quantity of water transpired per acre by the trees of a mature deciduous forest is probably even greater.

Not only must a theory of water transport in the xylem account for the large quantities of water involved, but it must also account for the great height to which the water may be transported. The sequoias and Douglas firs of the Pacific coast regularly attain heights of 300 ft or more. The weight of a column of water this high exerts a pressure of almost 140 lb/in². Taking into account the speed at which water moves up the xylem and the resistance to this flow created by the walls of the tracheids, it seems likely that a push (or pull) of 300-400 lb/in² is called for.

Any theory to explain the upward transport of water must be based on purely physical principles. Remember that the xylem vessels and tracheids are quite lifeless. This was shown dramatically by a German botanist who sawed down a 70-ft oak tree and placed the base of the trunk in a barrel of picric acid solution. The solution was drawn up the trunk, killing nearby tissues as it went. Three days later water, to which a dye had been added, was still moving successfully to the top of the tree.

THEORIES OF WATER TRANSPORT

Three theories that have been proposed to explain the upward transport of water in the xylem deserve mention.

When a glass tube of narrow bore is placed in water, the water rises spontaneously in the tube. The narrower the bore of the tube, the greater the rise (Fig. 15-9). This phenomenon is called capillarity. It depends upon the property of water molecules to cling or adhere to any surfaces which they can wet. The bore of xylem vessels and tracheids is sufficiently small that water can rise in them several feet by capillarity. Several feet is not several hundred, however, and there seems little likelihood that capillarity plays any significant role in the upward transport of water.

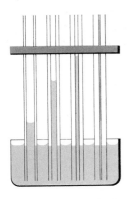

Fig. 15-9

Demonstration of capillarity. The water is drawn up in the tubes because of the adhesive force between water molecules and glass.

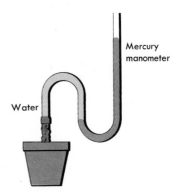

Mercury manometer

Water

Fig. 15-10

Measuring root pressure in the tomato.

ROOT PRESSURE   **15-13**

When a tomato plant is carefully severed close to the base of the stem, a fluid—sap — oozes from the stump. If a pressure-measuring device is connected to the stump, it is found that the sap is being pushed out under considerable pressure (Fig. 15-10). This is known as root pressure. Although the experiment is not an easy one to perform, careful workers have reported root pressures in the tomato as high as 130 lb/in^2. While this pressure would not lift sap to the top of a sequoia, it would easily lift it to the top of the tomato plant and even to the top of most trees.

The origin of root pressure is thought to lie in the difference in water concentration of the soil water and the sap in the xylem ducts. Xylem sap may be hypertonic to soil water because of the presence of a small quantity of dissolved sugars, or salts that have been actively transported into the central cylinder. This is particularly apt to be true in woody perennials like the sugar maple when, in very early spring, they hydrolyze the starches stored in their roots into sugar. At such a time, it is theorized, water would pass by osmosis from the root hairs, through the cortex and endodermis, to the xylem ducts. The inflow of water into the sap-filled xylem ducts would create a pressure, which could then be relieved by movement of the sap up the ducts. This is basically the same mechanism by which the molasses solution rose in the osmometer described in Section 9-4.

While root pressure is now a demonstrated fact, it seems unlikely that it can account completely for the upward transport of water in the xylem. Although substantial root pressures have been measured in the tomato, practically no other plants have been found to develop root pressures greater than 30 lb/in^2. Furthermore, it has been impossible to demonstrate any root pressure at all in many plants.

The volume of fluid transported by root pressure is also not adequate to account for the measured movement of water in the xylem. Furthermore, those plants whose roots produce a reasonably good flow of sap are apt to have the lowest pressure, and vice versa.

There is still another difficulty with the root pressure theory of water transport. Even in those plants that show root pressures, the highest values occur in the spring when the sap is strongly hypertonic to soil water but the rate of transpiration is low. In summer when transpiration is proceeding rapidly, and hence water is moving through the xylem rapidly, often no root pressure can be detected at all.

Thus, while root pressure may play a significant role in water transport in certain species (recent studies indicate that it may be the most important factor in the coconut palm) and at certain times, we must look for an alternative mechanism.

15-14   THE DIXON-JOLY THEORY

In 1895, the Irish plant physiologists H. H. Dixon and J. Joly proposed another theory to explain the rise of water in plants. They thought that water, instead of being pushed up by root pressure from below, was pulled up by tension (negative pressure) from above. As we have seen, water is continually being used at the leaves. Transpiration accounts for most of this, but photosynthesis and other biochemical activities in the cell account for some consumption of water, too. According to the Dixon-Joly theory, the use of water in the leaf exerts a pull on the water in the xylem ducts and draws more water into the leaf. The pull on the water in the xylem vessels is, in turn, transmitted to the roots and pulls water from the soil into the xylem ducts of the root.

Anyone who has studied physics knows that even the finest vacuum pump can only pull water up to a height of 32 ft. This is because a column of water that high exerts a pressure (about 15 lb/in^2) just counterbalanced by the pressure of our atmosphere (Fig. 15-11). How, then, can water be drawn up 300 or more feet under tensions of 300-400 lb/in^2?

The answer to this question lies in the property of water molecules to cling to each other. This property is know as **cohesion.** When water is confined to tubes of very small bore, the force of cohesion between the water molecules imparts great strength to the column of water. It has been found experimentally that tensions as great as 3000 lb/in^2 are necessary to break such a column of water. This compares very favorably with the strength of steel wires of the same diameter. According to the Dixon-Joly theory, the great cohesive strength of the tiny filaments of water in the xylem ducts, coupled with the property of water molecules to *adhere* to the walls of

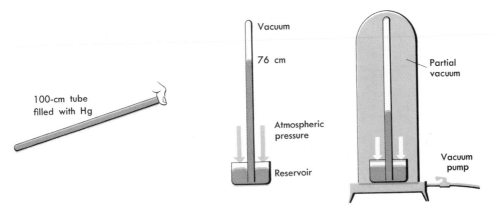

Establishment of Torricellian barometer and effect of placing the barometer in a vacuum chamber.

Fig. 15-11

the ducts, enables the filament of water to be pulled to the top of the tallest trees without breaking or pulling away from the walls of the ducts. Water use at the leaves, chiefly in transpiration, creates the tension which is then transmitted back down the xylem all the way to the root hairs. (The Dixon-Joly theory has often been called the transpiration pull-cohesion theory.) In a real sense, the tiny filaments of water in the xylem possess the physical properties of solid wires.

EVIDENCE FOR THE THEORY   **15-15**

What evidence is there to support this theory? Figure 15-12 illustrates an experimental model which shows that it is physically possible to raise water by such a mechanism. Evaporation of water at the porous clay cup creates a tension which is transmitted to the water and mercury in the glass tube. When great care is taken to see that no dissolved air is present in the water, it has been possible to draw the mercury column as high as 226 cm. This is equivalent to raising a column of water almost 100 ft into the air, and is three times greater than the height that atmospheric pressure working against a perfect vacuum could attain.

The model shows only that the phenomenon is possible. It does not prove that it takes place. When a cedar twig is substituted for the porous cup, however, the mercury is again lifted higher than the height (about 76 cm) that could be attained with a perfect vacuum.

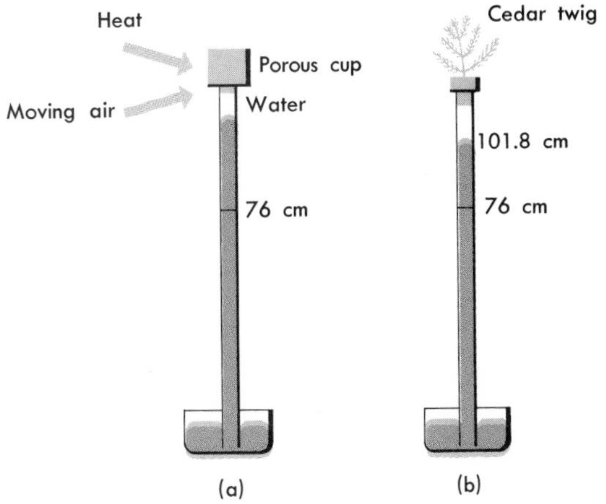

Fig. 15-12

Rise of mercury column in excess of 760 mm as a result of evaporation from (a) a porous cup and (b) a cedar twig.

Accepting the theory that the water in the xylem ducts is indeed under tension rather than pressure, it is possible to deduce certain facts which must follow from this. By checking to see if these predicted facts are indeed so, one is able to test the validity of the theory. If the water in a xylem vessel is under tension, we would expect the column to snap apart if air is introduced into the vessel by puncturing it. This has been found to be so.

Fig. 15-13

Diurnal (daily) variation in the diameter of the trunk of a Monterey pine. The diameter of the trunk reaches its minimum when the rate of transpiration reaches its maximum.

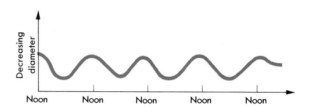

Furthermore, if the water in all the xylem ducts is under great tension, there should be a resulting inward pull (because of adhesion) on the walls of the ducts. The inward pull on the walls of all the ducts in the band of sapwood in an actively transpiring tree should, in turn, result in a decrease in the diameter of the tree. This deduction can be *tested* by continuously measuring, with suitable equipment, the diameter of tree trunks. Figure 15-13 shows the results that the American plant physiologist D. T. MacDougal obtained with the trunk of a Monterey pine tree. The diameter of the tree did indeed fluctuate, with its minimum diameter being reached just after midday, the time of greatest transpiration.

In 1960 a team of plant physiologists working in the jungles of Northeastern Australia carried out experiments on the rattan vine which lent additional support to the Dixon-Joly theory. The rattan vine climbs upon the trees of the jungle. In order to get its foliage into the sun, it may have to climb as high as 150 ft into the air. When the base of the vine is severed while immersed in a basin of water, water continues to be taken up by the vine. Obviously, root pressure is playing no part in the process, because the vine has been detached from its root system. A rattan vine less than 1 in. in diameter will "drink" water indefinitely at a rate of about 12 ml each minute. If forced to take up water from a sealed container, the vine does so without any decrease in rate even though a high vacuum is quickly produced in the container. In fact, the vacuum becomes so great that the remaining water begins to boil spontaneously. (The boiling temperature of water decreases as the air pressure over the water decreases.)

The Dixon-Joly theory provides an explanation for the ability of certain vascular plants to live in salt water. The roots of the coastal mangrove grow immersed in salt water, a solution markedly hypertonic to the cytoplasm of their cells. On the basis of respective water concentrations, we could expect water to leave the cells of the mangrove with resulting plasmolysis. Remember how the cells of *Anacharis* become plasmolyzed in salt water (see the opening illustration of Chapter 9). However, remarkably high tensions have been measured in the vascular system of coastal mangroves. These tensions (on the order of 500–800 lb/in^2) are so great that they can pull water molecules into the plant against the osmotic gradient. By this mechanism, mangroves literally desalt sea water to satisfy their water requirements.

On the basis of all the evidence, the Dixon-Joly theory seems to provide a satisfactory explanation of the rise of liquids in plants. Though several questions remain to be answered, most plant physiologists feel that the theory has been well tested and best describes the mechanism by which most, if not all, plants transport water and dissolved minerals from the soil to the leaves.

THE TRANSPORT OF FOOD

THE PATHWAY   **15-16**

Foods and other substances manufactured by the plant are also transported in the vascular bundles. Glucose is manufactured in the leaves by photosynthesis. During the day, much of this is converted into starch and stored in the cells of the spongy layer. You can easily demonstrate the presence of starch in a leaf. The variegated coleus, a common house plant, has chlorophyll only in certain regions of the leaf (Fig. 15-14). Remove a leaf from a healthy plant that has been in the light. Scald the leaf in boiling water and then place it in a small quantity of denatured alcohol. This procedure will dissolve out the chlorophyll. When the leaf has been adequately bleached, cover it with a dilute solution of iodine. A deep purple coloration reveals the presence of starch. The area of the leaf containing starch will be found to correspond closely, but not exactly, to the area of the leaf that had contained chlorophyll.

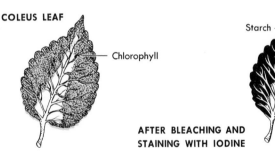

COLEUS LEAF — Chlorophyll

Starch —

Fig. 15-14

During the day, a leaf stores starch in the areas where photosynthesis is taking place. At night, most of the starch is hydrolyzed and translocated out of the leaf.

AFTER BLEACHING AND STAINING WITH IODINE

It is sometimes thought that this experiment proves that chlorophyll is necessary for photosynthesis. It really does not prove this because starch may be formed in any cell of the plant. (The cells of the underground tubers of the white potato are filled with starch.) For starch to form in nongreen portions of the plant, however, soluble sugar molecules must first have been translocated there.

Some of this translocation goes on in the night. Starch formed in the leaves during the day is hydrolyzed into soluble sugar molecules. The sugar then enters the cells of the phloem tubes. This entry is speeded up by the plasmodesmata which connect the cells of the spongy layer with the cells of the phloem.

Once within the phloem, the sugar may be transported either up or down to any region of the plant. In the case of sugar destined to be stored in the roots, it passes in solution through the phloem of the petiole, stem, and root. Once within the root, the sugar then passes out of the phloem, through the pericycle and endodermis and into the cells of the cortex. Here it can be reconverted into insoluble starch and stored as a food reserve.

That food is translocated out of the leaf during the night was first demonstrated late in the last century by the German botanist Julius Sachs. He found that the dry weight of leaves diminishes during the night. To show that most of this weight loss was due to translocation and not respiration, he cut leaves from the stem of the plant and placed them in water. The resulting weight loss was only 20% of what it was when the leaves remained attached to the rest of the plant. By careful chemical analyses, Sachs was able to show that over 90% of the normal weight loss was accounted for by loss of sugars.

Actually, more translocation from the leaves occurs during the day, but it is rather difficult to measure because sugar is being manufactured continuously by photosynthesis. Nevertheless, it can be shown that the weight of *nongreen* portions of a plant increases more rapidly during the day than during the night. This, of course, occurs at the expense of the green portions.

That food transport occurs in the phloem is suggested by girdling experiments. In summer, when a tree is girdled so that the phloem is removed but the xylem remains intact, the tree continues to live. There is, however, no further increase in the weight of the roots. Furthermore, chemical examination of the bark just above the girdle shows an extraordinary accumulation of carbohydrates. (This accumulation does not occur after girdling in the dormant season when no leaves are on the tree.) No accumulation of sugar occurs in the bark below the girdled region.

The transport of food materials through the phloem proceeds quite efficiently. Some fruits, such as the pumpkin, receive over half a gram of food each day through the phloem. Other fruits have been found to do even better. Bearing in mind that the food is being transported in a fairly dilute water solution, an appreciable flow must occur. In fact, studies with radioactive tracers have revealed that substances can travel through as much as 150 cm of phloem in an hour.

15-17   MECHANISM OF FOOD TRANSPORT

The mechanism by which sugars and other molecules manufactured by the plant are translocated through the phloem is not yet understood. It seems to be dependent upon the metabolic activity of the phloem cells, because any condition that slows down their metabolism also slows down the rate of translocation. Figure 15-15 illustrates apparatus with which one can show the effect of lowered temperature on the rate of food translocation. Oxygen lack similarly depresses it. Anything that kills the phloem cells puts an end to the process.

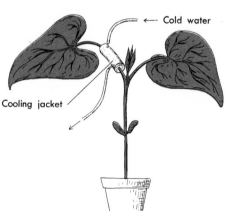

Fig. 15-15

Lowering the temperature of the petiole reduces the rate at which food is translocated out of the leaf.

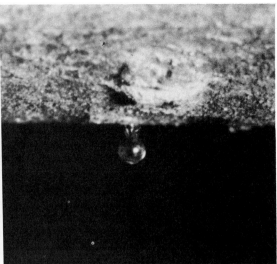

Left: aphid feeding on the branch of a linden tree. Excess sugar is released as a drop of honeydew that serves as food for ants or bees. The sap in the phloem enters the insect's mouth parts under pressure. Right: It will continue to exude from the mouth parts after the aphid has been cut away from them. (Courtesy Martin H. Zimmermann, *Science* **133**, 73–79, Jan. 13, 1961.)

Fig. 15-16

Two theories have been proposed to explain the movement of food materials through the phloem. According to one of these, water containing the food molecules in solution flows under **pressure** through the phloem. The pressure arises from the difference in water concentration of the solution in the phloem and the relatively pure water in nearby xylem ducts. With the accumulation of sugars and other products of photosynthesis in the phloem, water enters by osmosis. Pressure thus builds up in these cells something like root pressure in reverse. As the sap is pushed down the phloem, sugars are removed by the cortex of both stem and root and converted into starch. Starch is insoluble and exerts no osmotic effect. Consequently, the osmotic pressure of the contents of the phloem decreases. Finally, relatively pure water is left in the phloem, and this is thought to be drawn back into nearby xylem vessels by the suction of transpiration pull.

How well does this theory fit the observed facts? According to it, the contents of the sieve tubes must be under pressure. This has been found to be true. When sieve tubes are punctured by such sap-eating insects as aphids, the sap flows through the insect's mouth parts and into its body without further assistance. In fact, if the body of the aphid is cut away from its mouth parts, sugar-rich sap continues to ooze from the cut end (Fig. 15-16). This theory also requires that the osmotic pressure in the phloem of the leaves be greater than in the phloem of food-receiving organs such as the roots. Generally this seems to be true although apparent exceptions have been found.

On the other hand, this theory involves a purely physical mechanism. One would predict on the basis of it that factors affecting the rate of metabolism of the phloem cells would have no effect upon translocation. As we have seen, however, this is definitely not the case. Furthermore, this theory fails to account for the evidence that transport in young phloem can occur in both directions (up as well as down) simultaneously.

A second theory that has been set forth to explain the facts of phloem transport is based upon the process of **cytoplasmic streaming.** According to this theory, there is no flow of *solution* from one sieve-tube cell to another. Instead, food materials, incorporated in the cytoplasm, are swept along from cell to cell in strands of streaming cytoplasm. These strands of cytoplasm run longitudinally through the sieve-tube cells, interconnecting with adjacent cells through the sieve plates.

Microscopic examination of young sieve-tube cells in the petiole of primrose leaves has revealed cytoplasm moving through as many as ten consecutive cells. Furthermore, strands of cytoplasm have been seen to move in opposite directions even within a single duct, thus accounting for simultaneous two-directional transport in the phloem. The streaming theory also provides an adequate explanation for the biological aspects of phloem transport. Anything (including chilling and reduced oxygen supply) that has been found to reduce streaming in plant cells has generally been found to reduce translocation in the phloem, too. On the other hand, the rates of streaming that have been measured so far are not adequate to account for the measured rates of transport in the phloem, and only in the youngest phloem cells has streaming been observed. As yet, then, no single theory has been proposed that adequately explains all the known facts of phloem transport. Such a theory still awaits fresh observations, better measuring techniques, new experiments and, especially, the creative imagination capable of welding all these into a comprehensive scheme.

The xylem and the phloem of the tracheophytes represent one of the most important adaptations of plants to a land environment. In order to carry on photosynthesis, plants must expose a broad chlorophyll-containing surface to the sun's rays. For land plants, this means exposing a broad surface to the drying effect of the air. In order to remain functioning, the land plant must secure water for photosynthesis and replace water lost through transpiration with fresh water from the soil. As we have seen, the structure and functioning of the xylem permits this. On the other hand, the water-absorbing roots need food in order to remain alive. The phloem solves this transport problem. These two tissues have played a crucial role in the successful invasion by the tracheophytes of almost all the exposed land on our planet.

EXERCISES AND PROBLEMS

1 Trace the path taken by a hydrogen atom from the time it enters a root hair incorporated in a molecule of water until it is stored in the root cortex incorporated in a molecule of starch.

2 In what ways does the circulatory system of a plant differ from that of a vertebrate?

3 Many low-growing plants secrete drops of water along the edges of their leaves. This phenomenon, called guttation, is particularly apt to occur during damp spring nights. Which of the forces by which water rises in the xylem do you think is responsible for guttation? Why?

4 What functions in the maple tree are carried out by roots?

5 Why is it good practice to prune off some of the branches of a tree or shrub that has just been transplanted?

6 If in counting the annual rings of an ancient elm, several narrow rings are found just within several wide ones, what conclusions might you draw?

7 What is cohesion? What role does it play in the upward transport of water?

8 What is adhesion? What role does it play in the upward transport of water?

9 What is the function of the upward transport of maple sap to the maple tree?

10 Summarize the factors that influence the rate of transpiration.

REFERENCES

1 Zimmermann, M. H., "How Sap Moves in Trees," *Scientific American,* Reprint No. 154, March, 1963. A brief, up-to-date review of our knowledge of translocation in both the xylem and the phloem.

2 Meyer, B. S., D. B. Anderson, and R. H. Böhning, *Introduction to Plant Physiology,* D. Van Nostrand Co., Princeton, N.J., 1960. Provides a detailed analysis of translocation and the experiments upon which current theories are based. Chapter 8 discusses transport in the xylem; Chapter 17 deals with translocation in the phloem.

3 Salisbury, F. B., and R. V. Parke, *Vascular Plants: Form and Function,* Wadsworth Publishing Co., Inc., Belmont, Calif., 1964. Chapters 7 and 9–12 expand on the topics treated in this chapter.

4 Steward , F. C., *About Plants: Topics in Plant Biology,* Addison-Wesley, Reading, Mass., 1966. Chapter 10 examines the problems of translocation with emphasis on the role played by the active transport of salts and organic molecules.

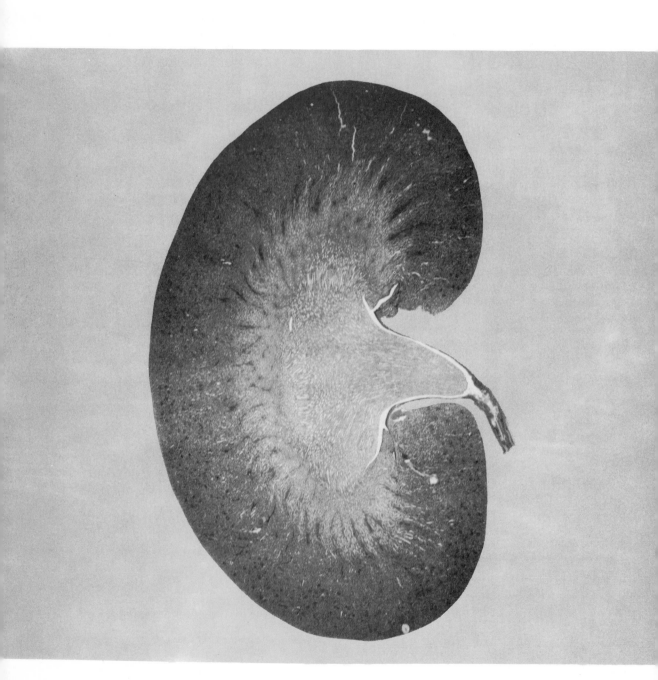

In the preceding chapters of Part IV, we have considered the ways in which living things (1) acquire materials (and energy) from their environment, (2) transport materials throughout their bodies, and (3) transform these materials within their cells. These operations are all part of an organism's metabolism. To complete our story of metabolism, we must now examine the ways in which living things return the waste products of their metabolism to the environment. In general, the most abundant products of metabolism are carbon dioxide, water, and ammonia. These substances should not, however, be considered simply as wastes. Each has important roles to play in the regulation of body activities (recall, for example, the effect of CO_2 on the rate of breathing) and in various anabolic cell syntheses. Even ammonia, a very toxic substance, is an essential reactant in a number of biochemical transformations of amino acid metabolism. It is, then, only as these substances accumulate to levels *in excess of the organism's needs* that they must be eliminated. The return of these unneeded products of metabolism to the environment is called **excretion.** As we have already studied (in Chapters 13 and 14) the ways in which plants and animals return gaseous wastes to the environment, we will not stress these in the present discussion.

EXCRETION IN PLANTS

16-1

Excretion in plants does not pose any serious problems. There are several reasons for this. First, the rate of catabolism in plants is generally much lower than in animals of the same weight. Consequently, metabolic wastes accumulate more slowly. Second, green plants use much of the waste products of catabolism in their anabolic processes. Water and carbon dioxide, produced by respiration, are used in photosynthesis. Waste nitrogen compounds, whose excretion makes such demands upon animals, can be used by green plants in the synthesis of new protein. Finally, the metabolism of plants is based mainly on carbohydrates rather than proteins. This reduces their excretory needs, as the end products of carbohydrate metabolism are far less poisonous than the nitrogenous wastes produced by protein metabolism. Of course, plants do produce protein from which a variety of important cell structures and all their enzymes are made. Nevertheless, protein metabolism plays a much smaller role in plants than in animals, whose general body structure is based to such a great extent upon protein.

Among the aquatic plants, metabolic wastes are free to diffuse from the cytoplasm into the surrounding water. No cell is far removed from the water and the concentration of wastes within the cell exceeds the concentration of these substances in the water. The only product of metabolism for which this is not true is water itself. As we saw in Section 9-4, fresh-water plants live surrounded by a water concentration greater than that within their cytoplasm. Not only does this eliminate diffusion (osmosis) as a means of getting rid of waste water, but (and far more important) it also exposes them to a continual inflow of water from the environment. As water enters the cell by osmosis, the pressure within the cell rapidly increases. The rigid cellulose cell wall withstands this pressure and turgor results. When the pressure within the cell becomes equal to the osmotic pressure, equilibrium is achieved between the cell contents (especially the central vacuole) and the environment.

◀ Rat kidney, longitudinal section.

Among the terrestrial plants, the waste products of metabolism, such as salts and organic acids, are simply stored in the plant. These wastes may be stored in solid form in crystals or they may be dissolved in the fluid of the central vacuoles. In herbaceous species, the wastes simply remain in the cells until the tops of the plants die in the autumn. In perennial plants, wastes are deposited in the nonliving heartwood and are also eliminated when the leaves are shed.

16-2   ## EXCRETION IN PROTOZOANS

Most protozoans live in a watery environment and eliminate their metabolic wastes by diffusion, just as the aquatic plants do. For many, the chief end product of protein metabolism is ammonia. This substance (in the form of its ion, NH_4^+) diffuses readily out of the cell before reaching a dangerous concentration.

Fresh-water protozoans, like fresh-water plants, cannot handle excess water in this way, though. Lacking a rigid cell wall, they cannot combat the continual inflow of water by building up turgor either. As we have seen (Section 9-4), the problem is solved by the **contractile vacuole.** Energy is used to force water back out of the cell and into the surrounding water. The contractile vacuole probably plays no significant role in the excretion of other substances. Protozoans that live in an isotonic environment (marine and parasitic forms) do not have a contractile vacuole. When placed in a hypotonic environment, however, they may develop one. This evidence suggests that the contractile vacuole serves simply to regulate water balance within the organism.

The so-called waste vacuole of protozoans like *Amoeba* and *Paramecium* is not really involved in excretion either. Its contents (e.g. diatom shells) never participated in the biochemistry of the cell and thus cannot be considered metabolic wastes. Their elimination is properly referred to as **egestion.**

16-3   ## EXCRETION IN THE INVERTEBRATES

Among the simpler animals, diffusion is still adequate to handle the elimination of metabolic wastes. In the hydra, for example, almost every cell has at least part of its surface exposed to water—either that surrounding the animal or that within the gastrovascular cavity. Thus cell wastes can diffuse directly into the water. Random body movements maintain a steady exchange of water between the gastrovascular cavity and the surroundings and thus prevent too great an accumulation of wastes within the cavity.

The hydra is a fresh-water animal and, like all other fresh-water animals, faces the problem of how to deal with its hypotonic environment. Presumably, there is a continual inflow of water into its cells. But as yet we do not know how the hydra handles the problem. Contractile vacuoles have not been observed in its cells. (In this connection, it is important to realize that the elimination of water from the gastrovascular cavity has nothing to do with the problem. The contents of the gastrovascular cavity are *outside* of the hydra in the sense that they do not have to cross a cell membrane to get to and from the environment.)

The planarian is considerably more complex than the hydra. It has fairly elaborate digestive, nervous, and reproductive systems. The planarian is also considered to have an excretory system. This consists of excretory canals, the blind ends of which terminate in a curiously shaped cell, the flame cell (Fig. 16-1). Water passes into the cavity within the flame cell. How this is accomplished is not yet known, but presumably energy is required, as the water is moving against the osmotic gradient. Once within the cavity of the flame cell, the water flows into the excretory canals. This process is aided by the action of cilia within the cavity of the flame cell. Under the microscope, these cilia create a flickering effect which has given rise to the name *flame* cell. The water in the excretory canals then passes to the outside through a series of pores.

Although this system is described as an excretory system, its real function is simply preserving water balance. It bails out the continual influx of water just as the contractile vacuole bails out the amoeba and paramecium. Nitrogenous and other wastes are excreted into the gastrovascular cavity and discharged at the mouth. The highly branched nature of the gastrovascular cavity enables all portions of the animal's body to liberate these wastes without the intervention of a circulatory system.

The earthworm has a true excretory system. It is a particularly interesting one because in its structure and function it resembles the excretory apparatus of many other animals, both invertebrate and vertebrate. This does not necessarily mean that all these animals have inherited the structure from a common ancestor. It may be that such an efficient mechanism has arisen more than once in the course of animal evolution. In other words, the organs may be analogous rather than homologous.

In the earthworm and many other invertebrates, these excretory structures are called **nephridia** (Fig. 16-2). There is a pair of these in each segment of the earthworm (except the first three and the last). Each nephridium consists of a ciliated funnel, the nephrostome, which is mounted on the septum, the membrane that separates the segments. It leads through the septum into a long tubule which lies coiled in the next posterior segment. The far end (distal end) of the tubule enlarges to form a temporary storage structure, the bladder. The bladder opens to the outside through a pore, the nephridiopore, on the ventral surface of the worm.

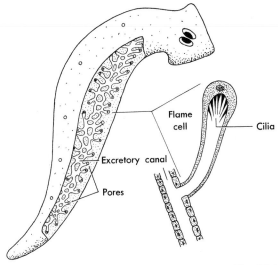

Fig. 16-1

Excretory system of a planarian. Its main function is to counteract the continuous influx of water from the worm's hypotonic surroundings.

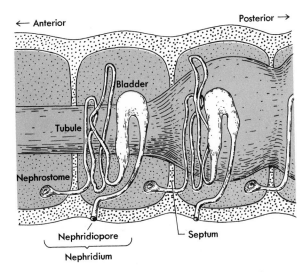

Fig. 16-2

Excretory system of the earthworm. A second nephridium is present in each segment. The nephridia pick up fluid containing both wastes and useful materials, but the useful materials are reclaimed as the fluid moves through the tubule.

The nephrostome lies within the body cavity. This cavity is filled with fluid which is chiefly lymph filtered from the closed circulatory system. This fluid is the ECF of the cells of the earthworm's body. It contains useful materials (e.g. glucose) and useless or harmful materials (e.g. nitrogenous wastes). The fluid enters the nephrostome and passes down the tubule. It is pushed along by cilia and muscular contractions of the tubule. As it moves along, materials useful to the worm are reclaimed by the cells lining the tubule. The tubule is richly supplied with blood vessels so that these useful materials are quickly placed back in circulation. Useless or waste materials are not reclaimed and they ultimately leave the worm by way of the nephridiopores. We will see that many other animals solve their excretory problems in a similar way. *All* the components of the ECF are sorted over, the useful materials being reclaimed while the rest are not.

In addition to this indirect sort of excretory activity, the nephridia may also function in a more positive fashion. Secretory cells in the tubule probably can transfer wastes from the blood capillaries directly into the cavity of the tubule. This is called tubular excretion.

Among fresh-water animals, there are adequate quantities of water to flush away toxic nitrogenous wastes as fast as they accumulate. In fact, the chief problem of these animals seems to be coping with the problem of too much water entering their bodies from the hypotonic environment. Among terrestrial animals, the situation is quite different. Every effort must be made to conserve water. In the terrestrial arthropods, such as the insects, we get our first glimpse of the problems of excretion in a dry environment. The grasshopper solves the problem by means of both structural and biochemical modifications. The nitrogenous waste of the grasshopper (and other insects) is **uric acid.** This biochemical adaptation is extremely important because uric acid combines high nitrogen content with low toxicity. This low toxicity is partly a result of low solubility. Just as soon as the concentration of uric acid begins to increase appreciably, it settles out of solution as a solid precipitate. As a solid, it exerts no biochemical effect and can be removed from the body with only a small amount of water.

Fig. 16-3

The excretory wastes (chiefly uric acid) of the grasshopper are deposited in the intestine, where almost all moisture is reabsorbed. The grasshopper can thus excrete its metabolic wastes with practically no loss of water.

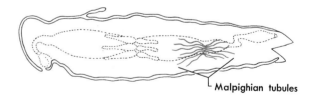

Malpighian tubules

Structurally, the insect's excretory system is made up of **Malpighian tubules.** These lie in the hemocoel and are bathed in blood (Fig. 16-3). Although there is no direct opening to the blood, the cells of the tubules extract soluble substances from it and pass them into the cavity of the tubules. Then valuable materials, including water, are reabsorbed. As the water concentration within the tubule decreases, uric acid precipitates. Instead of opening directly to the outside, the Malpighian tubules lead into the intestine where still more water is reabsorbed. The uric acid then passes to the outside with the feces. This excrement is quite dry. Thus the grasshopper is able to dispose safely of its nitrogenous wastes without losing valuable water in the process.

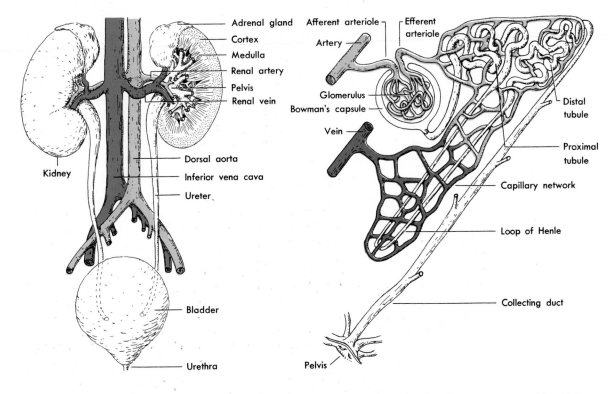

Human excretory system. Left: gross anatomy. Right: a single nephron (enlarged). There are approximately one million nephrons in each kidney.

Fig. 16-4

EXCRETION IN MAN

The main excretory organs of the vertebrates are the kidneys. Because more is known about the function of the mammalian kidney than any other type, we will first examine it, using man as an example. Later in the chapter we will examine some of the structural and functional modifications found in the kidneys of other vertebrates.

STRUCTURE OF THE HUMAN KIDNEY 16-4

The human kidneys are two bean-shaped organs each about the size of a clenched fist. They are located against the dorsal body wall on either side of the backbone.

Although the total weight of the kidneys is only 0.5% of the weight of the body, the kidneys receive an extraordinarily rich supply of blood. About 20% of the blood pumped by the heart each minute flows through them. This blood reaches the kidneys by way of a right and left renal artery and leaves by the right and left renal veins (Fig. 16-4).

A transverse section of the kidney shows it to be composed of three distinct regions. The outer region is the **cortex**. Beneath this is the **medulla**. Within the medulla is a hollow chamber, the **pelvis** of the kidney.

The cortex and medulla of each kidney are made up of approximately one million nephrons. The **nephron** is the structural and functional unit of the kidney. To understand the physiology of the kidney as a whole we need only learn the physiology of a single nephron.

The nephron consists of a long, coiled tubule closed at one end and open at the other (Fig. 16-4). At the closed end of the tubule, in the cortex, the wall of the nephron is expanded and folded into a double-walled chamber, the Bowman's capsule. Within the infolded portion of the Bowman's capsule is a network of capillaries, the **glomerulus.** The tubule itself consists of three distinct segments. The first segment, the **proximal tubule,** is coiled near the Bowman's capsule. The cells of which its walls are constructed are richly supplied with mitochondria. Many microvilli extend from these cells into the interior (the lumen) of the tubule. The proximal tubule leads to a long, thin-walled segment, the **loop of Henle.** This portion runs down into the medulla, makes a hairpin turn and returns to the region of the Bowman's capsule. Here the tubule expands again to form the **distal** (far) **tubule.** Like the proximal tubule, it is highly coiled.

16-5

THE FORMATION OF URINE

The nephron manufactures **urine.** It does this by filtering the blood and then reclaiming useful materials back into the blood. This leaves the useless material to pass out of the nephron in a solution which we call urine.

Each glomerulus receives blood from an afferent arteriole and discharges its blood into an efferent arteriole. The blood within the glomerulus, like that at the arteriole end of any capillary, is under pressure from the contraction of the left ventricle. This pressure causes water and the soluble molecules present in the blood to filter through the capillary walls. The fluid produced is called **nephric filtrate.** A glance at Fig. 16-5 will show that it is simply blood plasma minus almost all of the blood proteins. Essentially, then, it is no different from lymph (see Section 14-16).

Composition of plasma, nephric filtrate, and urine
gm/100 ml of fluid

Component	Plasma	Nephric filtrate	Urine	Concentration
Urea	0.03	0.03	2.0	60X
Uric acid	0.004	0.004	0.05	12X
Glucose	0.10	0.10	none	—
Amino acids	0.05	0.05	none	—
Total inorganic salts	0.72	0.72	1.50	2X
Proteins and other colloids	8.00	none	none	—

Fig. 16-5

The nephric filtrate collects within the Bowman's capsule and then passes into the proximal tubule. Here the reabsorption of glucose, amino acids, vitamins, hormones, and a large quantity of mineral ions (Na^+, K^+, Ca^{++}, Cl^-, HCO_3^-, $PO_4^=$, $SO_4^=$) takes place. This reabsorption proceeds by active transport. The details of how this is accomplished are not yet known, but enzymes and ATP are required. As mentioned above, the cells of the proximal tubule are richly supplied with mitochondria. Their rate of metabolism is equal to that of any cell in the body, including active muscle cells. Furthermore, their microvilli greatly increase the surface area exposed to the nephric filtrate. Thanks largely to the microvilli, the total surface area that participates in urine formation in man is over 60 square feet or three times the surface area of the exterior of the body.

The materials reabsorbed by the proximal tubule are returned to the blood system by a capillary bed which surrounds the tubules. In the mammals, this capillary bed receives its entire blood supply from the efferent arteriole of the glomerulus. The bed is drained by venules which lead into the renal vein.

As the various solutes are removed from the nephric filtrate and returned to the blood, a great deal of water follows them. This reabsorption of water is due entirely to the passive process of osmosis. The transfer of solutes from the nephric filtrate to the blood increases the water concentration of the nephric filtrate. Water then passes by osmosis into the blood and restores osmotic equilibrium.

Although the amount of nephric filtrate produced by a single nephron is not great, the quantity produced by two million of them is truly impressive. About 180 quarts of nephric filtrate are produced in the kidneys each day. This volume of fluid may represent more than twice the weight of the individual. About 80% of the water in the nephric filtrate is reabsorbed by the proximal tubules. Up to a pound of sodium bicarbonate, two and a half pounds of sodium chloride, a third of a pound of glucose and lesser amounts of other useful materials are absorbed along with the water. It is easy to see that life could not be sustained for very long if this amount of material simply passed out of the body.

Not all of the solutes in the nephric filtrate are reclaimed by the proximal tubule. Most of the nitrogenous waste, urea, remains behind. Substantial quantities of salts also remain dissolved in the fluid within the tubule.

As this fluid passes into the loop of Henle, it is approximately isotonic with the blood. The solutes and water have been absorbed in equivalent proportions by the proximal tubule. This situation may be altered in the distal tubule. Here a more selective, precisely regulated reabsorption of materials takes place. Additional quantities of salts and additional quantities of water may be absorbed. Furthermore, the exact amount of each substance reclaimed in the distal tubule is directly related to the level of that substance in the bloodstream. If the water content of the blood is lower than normal, additional quantities of water will be absorbed from the distal tubule until the concentration in the blood regains the normal value. So, too, with the various salt ions. The reabsorption of Na^+ ions in the distal tubule is particularly interesting, because H^+ ions can be exchanged for them. In other words, the distal tubule helps to preserve a constant pH in the blood by exchanging H^+ ions for Na^+ ions when the acidity of the blood tends to rise. In the rare instances when the blood becomes too alkaline, the distal tubule also acts to correct this. Consequently, in helping to maintain the pH of the blood within the normal limits of 7.3-7.4, the kidney can produce a urine whose pH drops as low as 4.5 or rises as high as 8.5.

Although urine formation in man occurs primarily by the filtration-reabsorption mechanism just described, an auxiliary mechanism is also involved. This is **tubular excretion.** The cells of the tubules remove certain substances from the blood in the surrounding capillaries. These substances are then excreted directly into the interior of the tubules and added to the urine. In all probability this process is of little importance in man. A nitrogenous waste, creatinine, and potassium ions are two of the few normal plasma constituents to be excreted in this fashion. Even without tubular excretion, the kidney could probably handle the elimination of these substances easily. Physiologists have discovered that tubular excretion does play an important role in the elimination of certain abnormal constituents, such as penicillin and some other drugs. This is particularly surprising because tubular excretion presumably involves active transport and special enzyme systems. How do we happen to have enzyme systems capable of dealing with the latest product of the drug manufacturers?

CONTROL OF THE KIDNEY

We do not know yet just what controls the selective reabsorption of most materials in the distal tubule. In some cases our chemical regulators, the hormones, are involved. A hormone that regulates the reabsorption of Ca^{++} in the distal tubule and one that regulates the reabsorption of Na^+ have been discovered. The details of their activity will be examined in Chapter 26.

Still another hormone, **vasopressin,** has been found to regulate the reabsorption of water in the tubules and also in the collecting ducts that drain them (Fig. 16-4). Vasopressin is produced by a gland located at the base of the brain, the pituitary gland. The secretion of this hormone is controlled by the water concentration of the blood. Anything which tends to dehydrate the body, such as perspiring heavily, causes a drop in the water content of the blood. This is detected by special receptors in the brain which stimulates the pituitary gland to produce vasopressin. Vasopressin is then carried by the blood to the kidney. There it increases the reabsorption of water. This tends to restore the normal water level in the blood. It also leads to the production of a scanty, concentrated urine. When vasopressin is being actively secreted, the concentration of solutes in the urine may become as much as four times that of the blood. Man shares this ability to produce a hypertonic urine with the other mammals and the birds. No other vertebrates can do it.

On the other hand, if the blood starts to become too dilute (as would occur after drinking a large quantity of water), the secretion of vasopressin is inhibited. The tubules and collecting ducts fail to absorb as much water, and a great deal of watery urine is produced. The concentration of solutes in this urine may be as little as one-fourth that in the blood.

Occasionally people lose the ability to secrete vasopressin. They become victims of the disease **diabetes insipidus.** As you might guess, the most dramatic symptom of this ailment is an enormous production of watery urine. It is accompanied by terrible thirst. Sufferers may urinate as much as 20 liters of urine each day (10 to 20 times the average amount). To avoid fatal dehydration, they must constantly replace this water loss by drinking fresh water.

Our study of the physiology of the tubules should make it quite clear that the kidney is far more than just an excretory organ. Certainly it removes nitrogenous and other wastes. However, it also removes foreign substances from the blood and normal plasma constituents that are present in the blood in greater than normal concentration. When excess water, sodium ions, chloride ions, etc. are present, the excess quickly passes out in the urine. On the other hand, the kidney steps up its reclamation of these same substances when they are present in the blood in less than normal concentration. In this way, the kidneys continually regulate the chemical composition of our blood within very narrow limits. Excretory products are eliminated simply because they naturally tend to accumulate to excess levels. The maintenance of a constant blood composition in turn assures a stable lymph. In short, the kidney is one of the most important of our organs for maintaining constant the composition of the internal environment. It is one of the major homeostatic devices of the body.

MECHANICS OF ELIMINATION

The process of urine formation continues unceasingly. When the urine leaves the distal tubule, it flows into a collecting duct, which passes through the medulla. The collecting duct drains urine from several nephrons into the pelvis of the kidney (Fig. 16-4). The urine then flows down from the kidney to the bladder by means of a duct, the **ureter.** The **bladder** is a hollow, muscular organ which expands as urine flows into it from the two kidneys. When the bladder becomes filled with urine, the muscular sphincter guarding its outlet relaxes and urine flows to the outside through the **urethra.** In the infant, relaxation of this sphincter occurs automatically. In older people, the sphincter is usually under conscious control.

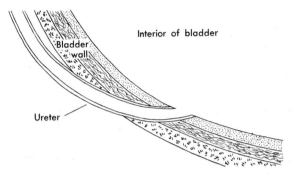

Interior of bladder

Bladder wall

Ureter

Fig. 16-6

Pressure within the bladder closes the ends of the ureters, causing urine to accumulate in them.

The two ureters enter the bladder in such a way that their exits become forced shut when the pressure in the bladder begins to build up (Fig. 16-6). If urination is delayed for some time, urine begins to accumulate in the ureters and even in the pelvises of the kidneys. When the bladder is finally emptied, this accumulation is permitted to flow down. Thus the individual finds that a long-delayed urination is quickly followed by the need for a second.

OTHER ORGANS OF EXCRETION IN MAN 16-8

In the process of maintaining the chemical constancy of our internal environment, the kidney eliminates many waste products of our metabolism. It is assisted in this function by four other organs.

(1) The **skin.** The skin acts as an organ of excretion because of the action of the sweat glands. These glands remove water, urea, and some salts from the blood and excrete them on the surface of the skin. The excretion of water by the sweat glands is part of the temperature-regulating mechanism of the body. Sweat is produced when vigorous muscular exertion, a high external temperature, or both, tend to raise the temperature of the blood. Evaporation of sweat cools the skin and aids the body in maintaining a constant internal temperature. The details of this homeostatic mechanism will be considered in Chapter 29.

The excretion of urea and salt by the sweat glands is really incidental to the excretion of water. In fact, the elimination of salt by this method may seriously deplete the body's reserves. People whose work forces them to sweat profusely are advised to ingest additional quantities of salt in their diet.

(2) The **lungs.** The lungs serve as organs of excretion in that they eliminate carbon dioxide and water. The latter can be easily demonstrated by breathing on a cold window pane. As in the case of the skin, however, the elimination of water occurs as an unavoidable consequence of another process. The alveoli of the lungs must remain moist if they are to function in gas exchange. However, the constant inflow of dry air causes a steady loss of this water. For animals living under desert conditions, the loss of body water from the lungs may be a critical factor in their survival.

(3) The **intestine.** Certain salts (e.g. those of iron and calcium) are excreted directly into the cavity of the intestine by the epithelial cells lining it. These salts leave the body in the feces. Of course, the undigested food materials (and bacteria) which make up most of the feces are not in any sense excretions. Undigested food is material which has never participated in the metabolism of our cells. **Egestion,** not excretion, is the proper term for the elimination of this material.

(4) The **liver.** The liver is also an excretory organ. The liver manufactures bile pigments in the process of breaking down the hemoglobin from dead red blood corpuscles. These bile pigments pass into the intestine by way of the common bile duct. Along with the metal salts mentioned above, they are the only constituents of the feces which are true metabolic wastes.

16-9   **NITROGENOUS WASTES OF MAN**

Although the liver plays only a small role in excreting wastes directly from the body, it is very important as an accessory organ in excretion. The chief nitrogenous waste in man is urea and it is manufactured in the liver.

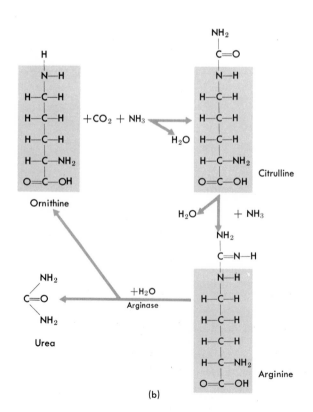

Most of the nitrogenous wastes in the body arise from the breakdown of amino acids. As you saw in Chapter 10, this breakdown, **deamination,** occurs in the liver. Deamination results in the accumulation of ammonia (Fig. 16-7). Ammonia is an extremely poisonous substance and its accumulation in the body would quickly prove fatal. Fortunately, the liver contains a system of carrier molecules and enzymes which quickly convert ammonia (and carbon dioxide) into urea. As each molecule of urea is synthesized, the carrier molecule, ornithine, is regenerated for re-use. Although our bodies cannot tolerate high concentrations of urea, it is much less poisonous than ammonia. As we have seen, the kidney removes it efficiently from the body.

Fig. 16-7

(a) Deamination and (b) the synthesis of urea. The action of arginase on arginine produces a molecule of urea and regenerates ornithine for recycling.

The presence of small quantities of uric acid in the urine is interesting. Uric acid is the main nitrogenous waste of insects, lizards and snakes, and birds. Of all the mammals, however, only man, the higher apes, and the Dalmatian dog excrete any of it. What we do excrete arises from the breakdown of nucleic acids rather than proteins. Other mammals produce uric acid by the breakdown of nucleic acids, but they also have an enzyme which then decomposes the uric acid. As mentioned earlier, uric acid is very insoluble. In some humans, the concentration of uric acid may be sufficiently high that it begins to precipitate out of solution. Needlelike crystals of uric acid accumulate in the joints, producing excruciating pain. The ailment is known as gout.

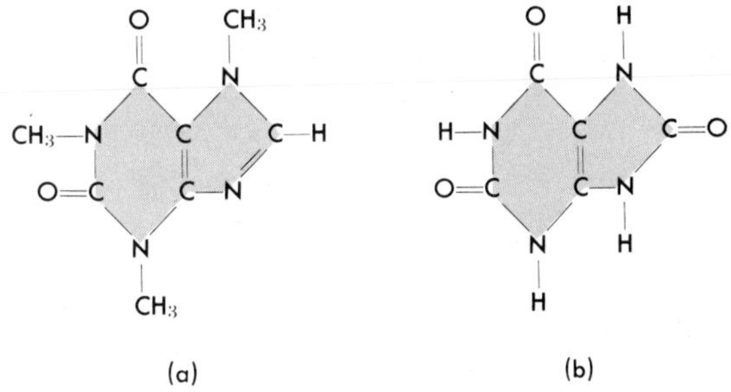

Fig. 16-8

Structural formulas of (a) caffeine and (b) uric acid.

The uric acid molecule is quite similar in structure to the caffeine molecule (Fig. 16-8). Caffeine is the ingredient in coffee which, for many people, seems to be a mental stimulant. One scientist has suggested that when the loss of the ability to break down uric acid occurred in our early ancestors, their mental activities were heightened by the accumulation of this substance in the blood. Unquestionably, the dominant feature in the evolution of man has been the development of the brain. Did uric acid play a role in this? We do not know. However, the fact that many of the famous (and brilliant) men of history were known to suffer from gout is used as a support for this interesting speculation. Do you see any weaknesses in this notion?

EXCRETION IN THE OTHER VERTEBRATES

All vertebrates have kidneys. Like the human kidney, they are made up of masses of nephrons. There are, however, some differences in the structure and functioning of the nephrons in the various vertebrate kidneys. These differences can be related to the environment in which the animals live.

AQUATIC VERTEBRATES   **16-10**

The fresh-water fish, like all fresh-water animals, suffers a continual inflow of water from its hypotonic environment. The scales of the fish are impervious to water, but the delicate gill membranes provide ready access for water to enter the body. In order to avoid serious dilution of its body fluids, the fresh-water fish must excrete this excess water. It does this by substantially the same mechanism as the amoeba: the use of energy to force the water back into the environment. In the fish, ATP provides the energy for the contraction of the heart. The contraction of the heart provides the pressure to force blood out of the glomerulus into the Bowman's capsule. Of course, valuable solutes (e.g. salts, glucose) pass into the nephric filtrate, too. These must then be reclaimed by the tubules. They pass into the blood in the capillaries surrounding the tubules. The blood supply in these capillaries comes from the glomerulus (as

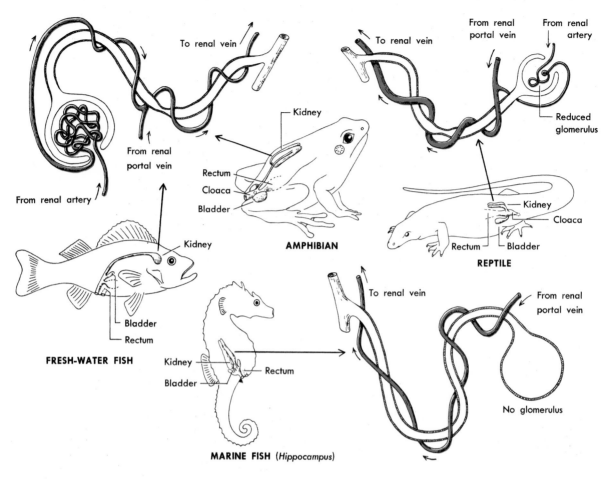

To renal vein

From renal portal vein

From renal artery

Kidney

Rectum
Cloaca
Bladder

AMPHIBIAN

From renal portal vein

From renal artery

To renal vein

Reduced glomerulus

Kidney

Cloaca

Rectum

Bladder

REPTILE

Kidney

Bladder

Rectum

FRESH-WATER FISH

Kidney

Bladder

Rectum

To renal vein

From renal portal vein

No glomerulus

MARINE FISH (*Hippocampus*)

Fig. 16-9   A comparison of vertebrate kidneys. In each case, the structure of the nephron is related to the role it plays in maintaining a suitable water content within the animal.

in man) and also from the veins which drain the posterior portion of the fish's body (Fig. 16-9). This part of the blood supply is called the renal portal system. What other example have you studied of a vein leading to a capillary bed rather than directly back to the heart?

After salt reabsorption is complete, the urine is little more than just water. Most of the nitrogenous wastes (including large amounts of NH_3) of the fish actually leave the body by diffusion out of the gills. The kidney is really a device for maintaining proper water balance in the animal rather than an organ of excretion.

Marine fishes face just the opposite problem from that of the fresh-water fishes. The salt content of sea water is so high that, physiologically, the marine fishes actually live in a dry environment. They are in continual danger of loss of vital body water to the hypertonic environment.

The marine fishes have solved this problem in two ways. The cartilaginous fishes, the sharks, skates, and rays (Class Chondrichthyes), have developed a tolerance to extraordinarily high levels of urea in their blood stream. Shark's blood may contain 2.5% urea in contrast to 0.01–0.03% in other vertebrates. This urea level is so high that the shark's blood is isotonic with the sea water. It lives in osmotic balance with its environment and has a kidney which functions similarly to man's (with the exception that far more urea is reabsorbed in the shark's tubules than in man's).

The marine bony fishes (Class Osteichthyes) have solved the problem differently (Section 9-4). They lose water continuously but replace it by drinking sea water and desalting it. The salt is returned to the sea by active transport at the gills. Living in constant danger of dehydration by the hypertonic sea, the bony fish has no reason to pump out large quantities of nephric filtrate at the glomerulus. The less water placed in the tubules, the less water that has to be reabsorbed. It is not surprising that many of these fishes have very small, weakly functioning glomeruli. Some have no glomeruli at all (Fig. 16-9).

With a reduction in the filtration-reabsorption mechanism, these fishes rely more on tubular excretion for eliminating undesired solutes. Tubular excretion requires a good blood supply to the tubules. Lacking efficient glomeruli, the renal portal system must carry most of the burden.

TERRESTRIAL VERTEBRATES   16-11

The **amphibian** kidney, like that of the freshwater fish, functions chiefly as a mechanism for excreting excess water. The permeable skin of the frog provides an easy site for the surrounding water to enter by osmosis. As the name amphibian suggests, however, these animals may spend some time on land. As we saw in Chapter 13, the problem then becomes one of conserving water, not eliminating it. The frog adjusts to the varying water content of its environment by adjusting the rate of filtration at the glomerulus. A renal portal system is present to carry away materials reabsorbed by the tubules during those periods when the blood flow through the glomerulus is restricted (Fig. 16-9). Furthermore, the frog is able to use its urinary bladder as a water conservation device. When in the water, the frog's bladder quickly becomes filled with a copious, watery urine. On land this water is reabsorbed into the blood thus replacing water lost by evaporation through the skin. The reabsorption mechanism is under the control of a hormone quite similar to vasopressin.

Many **reptiles,** e.g., desert rattlesnakes, live in extremely dry environments. Among the many adaptations that enable them to do so is their ability to convert waste nitrogen compounds into uric acid. As we have noted, uric acid is quite insoluble. Therefore, it can be excreted without the use of too much water. Accordingly, the reptile glomeruli are quite small. In fact, some reptiles have no glomeruli at all. Those that do have glomeruli filter just enough fluid to wash the uric acid, which is excreted by the tubules, into the **cloaca.** (The cloaca is a chamber through which the feces and the sex cells, as well as urine, pass on the way to the outside. The name comes from the Latin word for sewer.) Within the cloaca, most of the water is reabsorbed. Periodically, the reptile empties its cloaca. The feces are brownish in color; the uric acid forms a white paste. These water conservation mechanisms enable the reptile to survive even though little or no fresh water is available. The water content of its food coupled with the water produced in cellular respiration is usually sufficient for its needs.

It is important to note that the ability of these reptiles to convert waste nitrogen into uric acid is just as much an adaptation to dry-land living as their waterproof skin and their lungs. One is a physiological adaptation, the others are morphological. But note, too, that the excretion of uric acid is accompanied by structural changes in the kidney. Structure and function in living organisms are completely interrelated. One cannot appreciate the structural organization of cells, tissues, organs, and systems without understanding how they function. On the other hand, the physiological activitives of living organisms can only be accomplished by properly organized structures. The student who studies the way in which living things are put together without any concern for the way these structural components function glimpses only half the story of life. Just as restricted is the view of the student who studies physiological activities with no concern for the structures which accomplish these.

Birds solve the problem of dry-land living in a way similar to that of the lizards and snakes. Uric acid is their nitrogenous waste product, too. It is the whitish material that pigeons leave on statues. Although their glomeruli are very small, they do function actively and a substantial amount of nephric filtrate is produced. There are probably two reasons for this. Birds (like mammals) have no renal portal system, so the blood needed for tubular reabsorption and excretion must come from the glomeruli. Furthermore, birds (again like mammals) have high blood pressures and thus cannot avoid substantial filtration rates at the glomeruli. However, the increased production of nephric filtrate is more than compensated for by an increased absorption of water in the tubules. The concentration of uric acid in bird urine may be as high as 21%. This is over 3000 times the concentration of uric acid in the blood. Tubular excretion of uric acid is important in this process of concentration, but the reabsorption of water in the tubules is vital, too.

Fig. 16-10   The kangaroo rat (*Dipodomys spectabilis*). This little mammal is so well adapted to life in the desert that it never needs to drink water. (Courtesy Dr. Knut Schmidt-Nielsen.)

Although **mammals** are also terrestrial animals, their chief nitrogenous waste is urea. This substance requires a good deal more water for its elimination than does uric acid. As we have seen, mammals excrete large quantities of nephric filtrate but are able to reabsorb most of this in the tubules. But even with maximum reabsorption of water in the tubules, man must excrete several hundred milliliters each day in order to flush urea out of his body.

Some mammals have developed kidneys more efficient than man's in this respect. Water reabsorption in the tubules of the kangaroo rat (Fig. 16-10) is so effective that it can produce urine 17 times as concentrated as its blood. The most hypertonic urine that man can produce is only about four times as concentrated as his blood. The kangaroo rat also conserves water by remaining in its burrow during the heat of the day, thus reducing water loss through evaporation. This combination of behavioral and physiological adaptations makes it unnecessary for the kangaroo rat to drink water. The small amount of moisture in its food and the water produced by cellular respiration are fully adequate to its needs.

We have been discussing the various kidneys found in vertebrates of today. It is thought that all of these vertebrates have evolved over a vast period of time from a common ancestor. Probably the fishes have evolved the least in this period. The mammals and birds represent a much greater change from the earliest vertebrates. As the various vertebrate classes evolved on earth, new ways of life developed, too. The amphibians took to the land. The birds took to the air. It would be surprising if the evolution of an organ as important as the kidney did not reflect these changes. In this chapter we have seen how the various vertebrate kidneys are adapted to the way of life of their owners. In Chapter 34, we will re-examine these adaptations as part of the broader picture of the many structural and functional changes that occurred during the evolution of the various classes of vertebrates.

EXERCISES AND PROBLEMS

1   What is the chief nitrogenous waste of the (a) rattlesnake, (b) dog, (c) chicken, (d) shark?

2   Name the chief nitrogen-excreting organs of the (a) earthworm, (b) grasshopper, (c) frog.

3   How does the kidney maintain homeostasis of the blood with respect to (a) Cl^- concentration, (b) urea concentration, (c) pH?

4   Trace the path traversed by a molecule of urea from the time it enters a renal artery until it leaves the body.

5   Do you suppose evergreens are able to eliminate wastes by shedding their leaves ("needles")?

6   Compare lymph and nephric filtrate with respect to (a) composition, (b) method of formation.

7   What substances are found in blood plasma but not in nephric filtrate?

8   Distinguish between ureter and urethra.

9   Synthesis of urea occurs in what organ?

10   Why is the problem of excretion less complex in the maple tree than in the dog?

11   List the most important structures for maintaining water balance in the (a) amoeba, (b) trout, (c) planarian, (d) man, (e) Anacharis.

12   How does the quantity of urine formed by a frog change when it moves from a pond onto land? Would the quantity of urine formed by a beaver change under the same circumstances?

13   Distinguish between excretion and egestion.

14   Carnivorous mammals excrete a higher concentration of urea than herbivorous ones. Explain.

15   During the formation of urine, why does the concentration of salts not increase in proportion to the concentration of urea?

16   Name five organs of man that have an excretory function.

REFERENCES

1 Smith, H. W., "The Kidney," *Scientific American,* Reprint No. 37, January, 1953. This beautifully written article reviews the anatomy and physiology of the mammalian kidney, its evolutionary history, and how the various vertebrate kidneys are adapted to the homeostatic needs of their owners.

2 Schmidt-Nielsen, K., *Animal Physiology,* 2nd ed., Foundations of Modern Biology Series, Prentice-Hall, Inc., 1964. Chapter 4 examines the various ways in which animals solve the problems of water balance and excretion.

3 Schmidt-Nielsen, K. and Bodil, "The Desert Rat," *Scientific American,* Reprint No. 1050, July, 1953. Describes the observations and experiments from which it was learned how the kangaroo rat conserves body water.

4 Merrill, J. P., "The Artificial Kidney," *Scientific American,* July, 1961. How these life-saving devices work in temporarily replacing or supplementing natural kidney function.

PART V

REPRODUCTION

Dividing cells as seen with a differential interference microscope, 700 X.
(Research photograph of Drs. R. D. Allen and A. Bajer, 1966.)

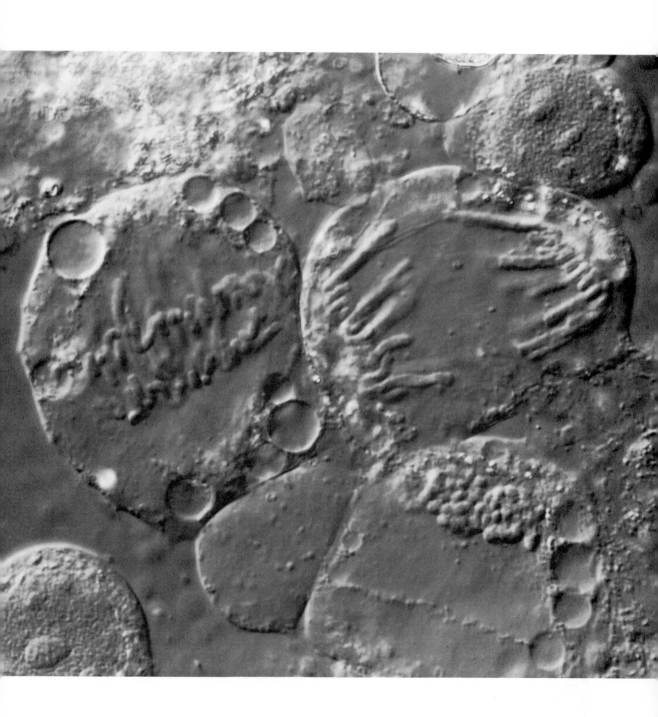

One of the most important aspects of living things is their ability to reproduce their kind. For every organism, there comes a time when its powers of metabolism, growth, and responsiveness are insufficient to maintain its complex organization against other forces. Attack by predators, parasites, starvation, other harmful changes in the environment, or simply those ill-defined processes that we call aging, result ultimately in the death of the organism. However, the species survives for periods far greater than the lifetime of any individual in it. This is accomplished with the production of new individuals by the old before the old die. Many of the major questions in biology concern this ability of living things to produce copies of themselves.

Two quite distinct methods for producing offspring are found among living things. One method is sexual reproduction. This is the production of new individuals that combine the hereditary information contributed by two different cells, generally representing two different parents. In most organisms, these cells are the gametes. The other method of reproduction involves only one parent. It is called asexual reproduction.

ASEXUAL REPRODUCTION

Asexual reproduction is the formation of offspring without the union of two gametes. Widely used by the protists, plants, and lower animals, it may be accomplished by a variety of specific methods.

17-1   ## ASEXUAL REPRODUCTION IN UNICELLULAR PROTISTS

The most common method of asexual reproduction among unicellular organisms is **fission.** The organism divides into two roughly equal halves. Each of these then grows to full size and the process may then be repeated. Under ideal conditions, bacteria can divide by fission every 20 to 30 minutes. *Amoeba* and most of the other protozoans also reproduce by this method (Fig. 17-1).

Asexual reproduction in yeast cells is by *budding.* Budding differs from fission in that the two parts produced are not of equal size. In the yeast plant, a bulbous projection, the bud, appears at one portion of the cell wall (Fig. 17-1). The nucleus of the parent cell divides and one of the daughter nuclei passes into the bud. Under favorable conditions, the bud may in turn produce another bud before finally separating from the parent cell.

17-2   ## ASEXUAL REPRODUCTION IN MULTICELLULAR ORGANISMS

1. Budding

The term budding is also used to describe asexual reproduction in certain multicellular organisms. In the hydra, a projection consisting of many cells forms on the side of the animal. This projection grows, developing tentacles and all the other structures of the adult. It eventually pinches off and takes up an independent existence (Fig. 17-2).

The tapeworms (Platyhelminthes) also reproduce asexually by budding. Undercooked pork may contain living "bladder worms" of the pig tapeworm, *Taenia solium.* These consist of a capsule containing a scolex (Fig. 17-3). When man ingests one of these, his gastric juice dissolves the wall of the capsule. The scolex turns inside out and attaches itself by suckers and hooks to the wall of the intestine. It then proceeds to produce buds, called **proglottids,** at its posterior end. These remain attached to one

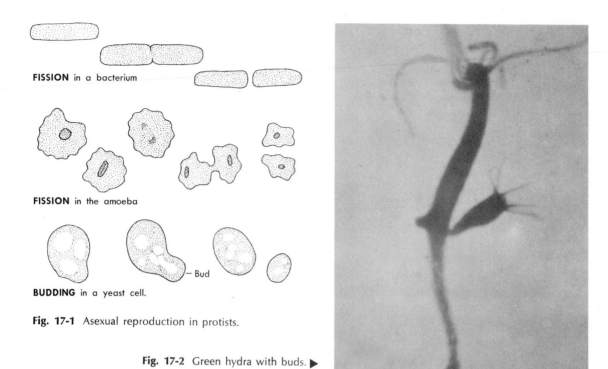

FISSION in a bacterium

FISSION in the amoeba

BUDDING in a yeast cell.

Fig. 17-1 Asexual reproduction in protists.

Fig. 17-2 Green hydra with buds. ▶

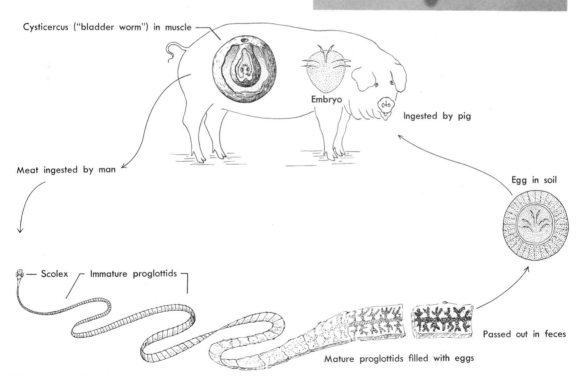

Cysticercus ("bladder worm") in muscle

Embryo

Ingested by pig

Meat ingested by man

Egg in soil

Scolex — Immature proglottids

Passed out in feces

Mature proglottids filled with eggs

Life cycle of the pig tapeworm *Taenia solium*. Asexual reproduction of proglottids by the scolex may produce a chain 20 ft long containing over 1000 proglottids. Each proglottid can be considered a separate individual. The proglottids reproduce sexually.

Fig. 17-3

Fig. 17-4   Asexual reproduction in the strawberry. The daughter plants form along the horizontal stems (stolons).

another. As they mature, they develop organs for sexual reproduction. The most mature proglottids eventually break loose and are passed out in the feces. Before this happens, the chain may reach a length of 20 feet and contain over 1000 proglottids. Although there are rudimentary nervous, excretory, and muscular structures shared by the proglottids, each proglottid can be considered a separate individual.

Similar *vegetative* methods of reproduction are found in plants. In some species, horizontal stems form which give rise to new individuals. These stems may extend underground (*rhizomes*) or along the surface of the ground (*stolons*) (Fig. 17-4). The houseplant *Bryophyllum* uses its leaves as organs of asexual reproduction. Along the margins, miniature copies of the plant form, complete with roots and stem (Fig. 17-5).

2. Sporulation

Among certain protists and plants, asexual reproduction is often accomplished by the formation of spores. These are small bodies containing a nucleus and a small amount of cytoplasm. The spores of terrestrial organisms are usually very light and have a

Fig. 17-5

Leaves of the common ornamental plant *Bryophyllum*. Note the miniature plants that have formed by asexual reproduction along their margins.

protective wall around them. These two features make sporulation more than just a special reproductory mechanism. The small size and light weight of spores enable them to be carried great distances by air currents. Spores thus serve as agents of dispersal, spreading the organism to new locations.

The resistant coat of the spore often serves another useful function. It enables the species to be maintained in a protected and dormant state over periods of unfavorable conditions which would be fatal to the active, vegetative organism. It is not surprising that this type of spore is produced most rapidly when conditions of temperature, moisture or food supply become less favorable.

Many bacteria are spore formers. This cannot be considered a reproductory mechanism for them, however, for each cell simply forms a protective case around its "nucleus" and part of its cytoplasm. No new individuals are produced. The spore merely provides a means of survival during unfavorable conditions.

In some of the green algae and aquatic fungi, the spores are not resting stages. In *Chlamydomonas,* the contents of a single cell divide 1 to 3 times, forming 2 to 8 small **zoospores,** each with its nucleus, cytoplasm, and 2 flagella (Fig. 17-6). After being released each zoospore grows to the full size of the parent cell. Some nonmotile algae use zoospores not only for reproduction but as a method of dispersal. Swimming by means of their flagella, the spores disperse the species to new locations.

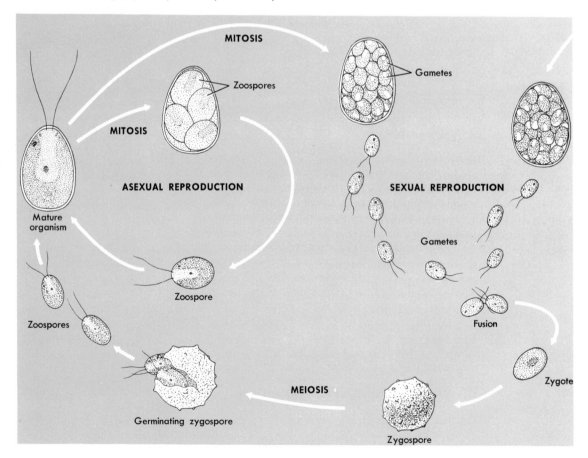

Life cycle of *Chlamydomonas.* Although all its gametes look alike, two gametes from the same parent cell will not fuse with each other.

Fig. 17-6

The fungi are prolific spore producers. A single *Lycoperdon* mycelium produces approximately 700,000,000,000 spores in one season in its puffballs (Fig. 3-11). Spores of the wheat rust fungus have been recovered by aircraft flying 14,000 feet above the earth. If one leaves a piece of moistened bread (which does not contain a mold inhibitor) in a warm, dark place exposed to air currents, a luxurious growth of mycelium soon reveals how widely distributed fungus spores are (Fig. 17-7). The mosses, club mosses, and our common ferns also produce enormous numbers of tiny, windblown spores which serve to disperse the species to new locations.

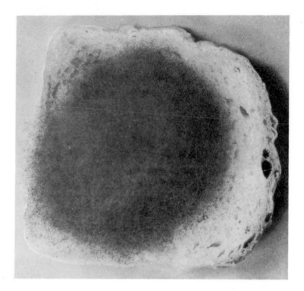

Fig. 17-7

This slice of bread was exposed to the air in a dusty room and then placed in a warm, moist, dark location. The mold is *Rhizopus nigricans.*

3. Fragmentation

Some plants and animals accomplish asexual reproduction by fragmentation. In these species, the body of the organism breaks up into several parts. Each of these can then regenerate all the structures of the mature organism. In the case of some tiny annelid worms, the process occurs spontaneously. After the worm grows to full size, it breaks up into 8 or 9 pieces. Each of these then develops into a mature worm and repeats the process.

Most cases of fragmentation depend upon outside forces. Green and brown algae at the seashore are often broken into pieces by the action of the waves. Each of these pieces can then grow to full size. Even in fresh water, filaments of algae (e.g. *Spirogyra*) are frequently broken apart. Fission of the cells remaining in a fragment quickly rebuilds the filament.

Man has learned to fragment plants deliberately in order to reproduce desired varieties asexually. This is often done by making *cuttings* (see Fig. 25-15). With proper care, these develop roots and leaves and can take up an independent existence.

17-3   **THE NATURE OF ASEXUAL REPRODUCTION**

Grafting is another asexual method of reproduction, which man uses to produce additional individuals of a desired variety. Only nurserymen deliberately grow apple trees by planting apple seeds. They do not raise these seedlings for the fruit they could produce but simply for a strong root system. After a year's growth, the portion of the plant above ground is removed and a twig (the **scion**) taken from a mature tree of the desired variety is inserted in a notch in the cut stump (the **stock**) (Fig. 17-8). So long as the cambiums of scion and stock are united and precautions are taken to prevent infection and drying out, the scion will grow. It will get all its water and minerals from the root system of the stock. However, the fruit that will be eventually produced will be identical (assuming it is raised under similar environmental conditions) to the fruit of the tree from which the scion was taken.

The need to specify similar environments is nicely illustrated in the wine industry. Most French vineyards are planted to grapes propagated vegetatively from California vines. However, the grapes of France (and the wines produced from them) are somewhat different from those of California.

The McIntosh apple is one of many popular varieties of apple grown in the United States and Canada. The first McIntosh tree was found over 150 years ago growing on the farm of John McIntosh in Ontario, Canada. It had grown from a seed. McIntosh's daughter-in-law appreciated the desirable qualities of the fruit. Moreover, she knew that it would be useless to try to grow other trees of the same kind from the seeds of the apples growing on this particular tree. Seeds, as we will see in Chapter 21, develop as a result of sexual reproduction. Two parents are involved, and while one would be the McIntosh tree, the other parent would probably be some other apple tree growing in the vicinity. The offspring would possess characteristics of both parents. Perhaps it might produce better apples, perhaps worse. But it would not be a McIntosh. The only way in which the McIntosh could be made available to other apple growers was by *asexual* reproduction. Scions removed from the original tree and grafted onto stocks of any apple variety would produce McIntosh apples. Every one of the hundreds of thousands of McIntosh apple trees growing today is descended from a scion of that first tree.

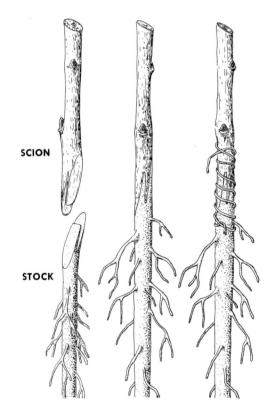

This example of man-controlled asexual reproduction is useful because it points out the essential feature of this method of reproduction. In all kinds of asexual reproduction, the offspring are identical in every way to the parent so long as they are raised under environmental conditions similar to those of the parents. If a given species is successful in its habitat, any inheritable variation in the offspring may be disadvantageous. Asexual reproduction is a method for producing new individuals which will probably not show any such variations. It tends to preserve the *status quo*.

SCION

STOCK

Fig. 17-8

Apple trees are propagated asexually by grafting. A piece of stem (the scion) from the desired variety is inserted into a notch cut in the stump of the stock. The fruit eventually produced will be characteristic of the variety that supplied the scion, not the variety that supplied the stock.

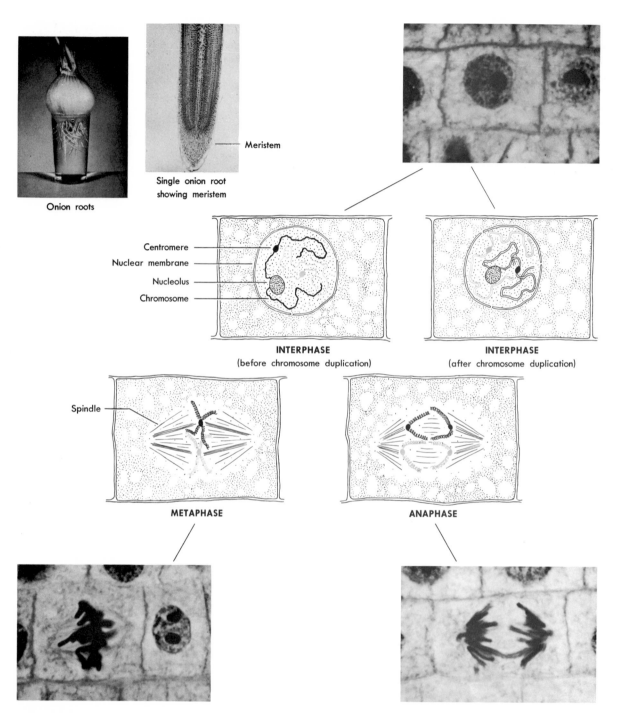

Onion roots

Single onion root
showing meristem

Meristem

Centromere
Nuclear membrane
Nucleolus
Chromosome

INTERPHASE
(before chromosome duplication)

INTERPHASE
(after chromosome duplication)

Spindle

METAPHASE

ANAPHASE

Fig. 17-9   Mitosis in a plant. The photographs show the stages as they occur in the dividing cells of the onion root tip. (Courtesy Carolina Biological Supply Co.) The drawings show the stages in a semidiagrammatic fashion. For the sake of clarity, only one pair of homologous chromosomes is shown: one member in black, the other in color.

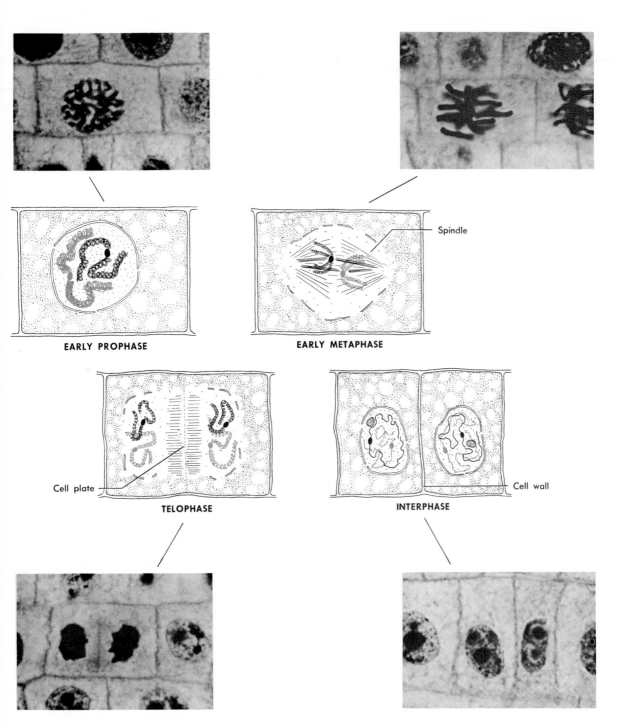

EARLY PROPHASE

EARLY METAPHASE

Spindle

Cell plate

TELOPHASE

Cell wall

INTERPHASE

Fig. 17-9 (cont.)

In all forms of asexual reproduction, new cells are produced by old. As our example of the McIntosh tree has shown, these new cells retain the same hereditary blueprints as their parents. In Chapter 8 (Section 8-4) we saw how Boveri's experiment showed that these hereditary blueprints reside in the nucleus. What in the nucleus contains them? When a cell divides, how is the information contained in the hereditary blueprints transmitted to its two daughter cells? As we will show in Chapter 19, the answer to the first question is the *chromosomes*. The answer to the second question is *mitosis*.

17-4   MITOSIS

One of the most convenient tissues in which to study mitosis is the meristem at the growing point of an onion root. By squashing this meristem and staining with an appropriate dye, we can make the chromosomes in dividing cells visible (Fig. 17-9). Unfortunately, the fine details of chromosome structure and activity cannot be seen without better methods of specimen preparation and higher magnification. Workers with the skill and equipment to apply these more refined methods to not only the onion meristem but other dividing cells have gradually pieced together a complete picture of what happens in mitosis.

A newly formed onion root cell contains 16 chromosomes; 8 of these had originally been contributed by the "father" of the onion plant, that is, the plant that supplied the male gamete. These chromosomes are often called *paternal* chromosomes. The other 8 were originally supplied by the onion's "mother," that is, the onion that produced the egg. These are the *maternal* chromosomes. For each of the maternal chromosomes, there is a paternal chromosome which looks (and, as we will see, functions) just like it. These similar chromosomes make up a **homologous pair.** Each member of a given homologous pair is often referred to as the *homologue* of the other member of the pair.

When a cell is not actually in the process of dividing, the chromosomes (which are housed within the nucleus) cannot be seen under the light microscope. They are too tenuous to absorb very much stain and reveal their true nature. When the chromosomes are in this condition, they are sometimes referred to collectively as the *chromatin* of the nucleus. In many cells, including the onion, one or more of the chromosomes has a nucleolus attached to it. This *can* be easily observed under the light microscope. The tenuous state of the chromosomes during the period between cell divisions should not suggest that they are inert at this time. Far from it. They are quite active in RNA synthesis and, at some time before (usually just before) the next cell division, DNA synthesis as well. In fact, chemical analysis shows that the DNA content is exactly *doubled.*

The various events which occur during mitosis have been divided into four consecutive phases: prophase, metaphase, anaphase and telophase. The period between divisions is called interphase. It is important to realize that these phases are simply a convenient way of describing mitosis. The actual process involves (with a few exceptions) an unbroken sequence of events which merge smoothly with one another. The photomicrographs in Fig. 17-9 are "snapshots" of these various phases. Motion pictures would impart a better appreciation of the process.

Prophase.   The onset of mitosis is marked by several changes. The nucleoli begin to disappear while the chromosomes themselves begin to appear. The previously extended strands of the chromosomes coil up into a helix, that is, like a cylindrical spring

(Fig. 17-9). In so doing, they become shorter and thicker and thus more easily visible. At this time, the nuclear membrane begins to disappear.

The significance of the doubling of the DNA content of the cell before mitosis now becomes apparent. Each of the 16 chromosomes (8 homologous pairs) that was present in the cell when it was first formed now reappears, *doubled* (Fig. 17-9). The duplicates are attached to each other by a small body called a **centromere.** Although the term is not a technical one, we can refer to these duplicated chromosomes as making up a *doublet* (Fig. 17-10). The more common practice is to call the entire structure a chromosome and each of its strands a *chromatid.* This terminology is not so satisfactory because it obscures the fact that each member of a doublet is a *complete* chromosome equivalent in every way to the chromosome that the cell received when it was formed by a prior mitosis. In this sense, the onion cell in prophase has not 16 but 32 chromosomes consisting of 8 *pairs* of homologous *doublets.*

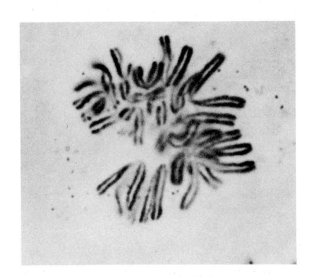

Fig. 17-10

Chromosomes in a dividing epidermal cell of a salamander. The duplicated chromosomes are still attached to each other by centromeres. (Courtesy General Biological Supply House, Inc.)

Metaphase. Metaphase is marked by the appearance of the **spindle.** This structure consists of an array of microtubules (see Section 8-13) which extend between the ends or "poles" of the cell. The centromere of each doublet becomes attached to a microtubule and migrates to a point exactly midway between the poles. The loose ends of the chromosomes may be oriented randomly, but the centromere of each chromosome lies exactly in a plane called the **equatorial plate** (Fig. 17-9).

Anaphase. Anaphase begins when the centromeres duplicate themselves. Each of the two resulting centromeres remains attached to one of the chromosomes of the doublet. They now move apart, still on the spindle, and migrate to opposite poles, dragging their attached chromosome behind them. The metaphor seems especially apt because the free ends of the chromosomes now turn toward the equatorial plate just as though friction with the surrounding cytoplasm were impeding their motion toward the poles.

Telophase. Telophase is roughly the reverse of prophase. Once the chromosomes reach their poles, they begin to uncoil and coalesce. The nucleoli reappear. A nuclear membrane begins to form around the chromosomes. Finally, a structure called the **cell plate,** which will become the middle lamella between the 2 daughter cells, appears at the equator. A cell wall is secreted on each side of the cell plate and cell division is thus completed.

Mitosis, as described here, is found universally among the plants. Animal cells, too, divide by mitosis. The phases are similar to those in plant cells, and the behavior of the chromosomes is the same. Two striking differences can, however, be observed. One is the appearance of the **asters.** Animal cells contain centrioles (see Section 8-14), and in prophase these migrate to the opposite sides of the nucleus. Here they seem to organize the formation of the spindle. Around each centriole also develops a system of radiating fibers, the aster (Fig. 17-11). The function of the aster is unknown. The second difference is that no cell plate is formed in animal-cell mitosis. Instead, in telophase, a furrow appears in the cell membrane, forming at the equator. The furrow deepens, and the two daughter cells simply become pinched apart. The cell plate in plants is probably a consequence of the rigid cell wall which prevents furrowing from taking place.

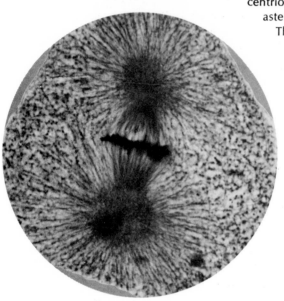

Fig. 17-11

Metaphase in a cell of the embryo of a whitefish. Note the prominent aster at each pole of the cell. (Courtesy General Biological Supply House, Inc.)

How long does mitosis take? The entire sequence of phases may be completed in from 9 minutes to many hours. The exact length of time varies considerably with different kinds of cells, different species of organism, and temperature.

In many protists and in some animal tissues, cell division occurs without the visible chromosome behavior that has been described here. This process has been called *amitosis*. In the case of these protists, at least, duplication and orderly separation of a small number of extended chromosomes is probably going on without the formation of the shorter, more easily stained forms. As techniques of observation have been improved, many cases of cell division formerly classed as amitotic have now been seen to be mitotic.

What is the significance of mitosis? The most dramatic activity in mitosis is the organized behavior of the chromosomes. In fact, this aspect of the process is so important that we still use the term mitosis even when the chromosomal activity occurs without actual division of the cell. This occurs in coenocytic organisms such as the molds and a few green algae (see Section 8-17). Nuclear division without cell division also occurs under certain conditions in other organisms and in these cases, too, is called mitosis.

We know that the nucleus contains the information that controls the development and activities of the cell. The evidence of mitosis suggests that the chromosomes play an important part in this. Viewed in this light, mitosis can be considered a device for the orderly duplication (in interphase) and separation (in anaphase) of the chromosomes and thus of the hereditary information. Each daughter cell gets a complete set of chromosomes identical to those of the mother cell. Mitosis thus provides a way of transmitting this information unchanged and undiminished from parent cells to daughter cells.

How is mitosis used by living things? All the kinds of asexual reproduction discussed earlier are carried out by mitosis. In addition, growth, regeneration, and cell replacement in multicellular organisms are all accomplished by mitosis of the cells concerned.

SEXUAL REPRODUCTION

THE NATURE OF SEXUAL REPRODUCTION   17-5

In sexual reproduction, new individuals arise from the union of two sets of hereditary information (DNA). Usually, each of these sets is contained within a specialized cell called a **gamete.** In order to combine their hereditary information, the two gametes must first unite, a process known as fertilization. Among some simpler organisms such as the green alga, *Chlamydomonas,* the two gametes are indistinguishable from each other. Such similar-appearing gametes are called **isogametes.**

The nucleus and cytoplasm of a single *Chlamydomonas* cell divide 5 or 6 times to form 16 or 32 isogametes. These are simply miniature copies of the adult. The cell wall of the adult breaks open and releases the flagellated gametes into the surrounding water. These then fuse with the gametes produced by other *Chlamydomonas* cells. There are no visible differences between the fusing gametes (Fig. 17-6).

In most organisms, two quite distinct kinds of gametes are produced. **Sperm** are tiny gametes which consist of little more than a nucleus and a flagellum. The flagellum enables the sperm to swim. Sperm are the male (♂) gametes. **Eggs,** the female (♀) gametes, are larger and nonmotile. They contain substantial quantities of food in addition to the nucleus. Because sperm and eggs are so dissimilar in appearance, they are called **heterogametes.**

The product of fertilization is the **zygote.** In the case of the union of heterogametes, the zygote is frequently referred to as a fertilized egg.

One of the most striking features of sexual reproduction is that each of the gametes involved is usually produced by a separate individual. Thus, two individuals, the parents, contribute to the formation of the offspring. If the two parents differ in any way (and often, as you will see, even if they don't), the offspring will possess new combinations of characteristics. Many times these new characteristics may be disadvantageous to the offspring. Many times they will have no effect on the welfare of the possessor. Sometimes the new combination will result in an individual better suited than its parents to the habitat in which it lives. It is this latter category that permits gradual structural and functional improvements in a species, that is, evolution.

In many organisms, both male and female gametes are produced in one individual. Such organisms are said to be hermaphroditic. Some species of hydra, the common earthworm, some fishes and the majority of our flowering plants are examples of hermaphroditic organisms. Even in these cases, two individuals usually contribute to the formation of the zygote. Sperm cells from one individual unite with the eggs of another individual. **Cross-fertilization** is the result, and variability in the offspring is thus promoted. Some hermaphrodites, such as the earthworm, never fertilize their own eggs. Others, such as many of the flowering plants, engage in self-fertilization only when cross-fertilization fails to occur. In Chapter 21 we will examine some of the mechanisms by which cross-fertilization in plants is promoted and self-fertilization is avoided.

SEXUAL REPRODUCTION IN BACTERIA

The essence of sexual reproduction, then, is newness, change, variability. This is perhaps best illustrated by the process as it occurs in some bacteria. For many years, bacteria were believed to reproduce by fission only. No evidence of sexual reproduction in them was detected until 1947. In that year, J. Lederberg and E. L. Tatum discovered that the common intestinal bacterium *Escherichia coli* could reproduce sexually. Although the cells were not actually observed in the process for some time after, Lederberg and Tatum did find definite, if indirect, evidence that sexual reproduction was taking place.

The particular strain of *E. coli* that they used is not at all fussy about its food supply. Given glucose as a source of energy and carbon, and some inorganic salts to supply nitrogen, sulfur, and phosphorus atoms for the synthesis of amino acids and nucleic acids, the organism grows well. Within its tiny cell, it contains all the enzymes with which to carry out the biochemical reactions needed to convert glucose and inorganic salts into all the organic molecules necessary to life.

E. coli, like all bacteria, is quite sensitive to exposure to ultraviolet light. A moderately heavy dose is lethal. In fact, this is why ultraviolet lamps are sold as "germicidal" lamps to be used for killing bacteria in hospital operating rooms, etc. Lesser exposures to ultraviolet light may not kill the bacterium outright but, instead, destroy its ability to manufacture one or more important organic compounds. These compounds must then be added to the bacterium's diet if it is to survive. Furthermore, this loss of synthetic ability is hereditary. All the offspring produced by the fission of a *nutritionally deficient* bacterium will suffer the same disability.

A strain of *E. coli* has been developed by ultraviolet irradiation that lacks the ability to synthesize one of the B-vitamins, biotin, and one of the amino acids, methionine. These two substances must be added to its diet in order for it to live. Another strain has been developed that can still synthesize biotin and methionine from glucose and salts but is incapable of synthesizing another B-vitamin, thiamin, and the two amino acids, threonine and leucine.

If these two strains of bacteria are allowed to mingle freely with each other and then placed on a culture medium containing only glucose and salts, colonies of cells soon appear. These cells thrive despite the absence of the vitamins and amino acids needed by their parents. Furthermore, descendants of these cells continue to be able to live on glucose and salts alone.

What has happened? Evidently, members of each strain have in some way managed to combine their hereditary blueprints. The first strain with blueprints for making the enzymes needed to synthesize thiamin, threonine, and leucine (as well as all the other organic molecules except biotin and methionine) has combined these blueprints with those of the second strain which included the instructions for making biotin and methionine. Thus, a bacterium was produced which, like the original strain, is capable of satisfying all its needs from glucose and salts alone. The evidence indicates that a bacterium of one strain actually injects part of its single chromosome into a cell of the other strain when the two cells come in contact.

Note that in this example, sexual reproduction has been reduced to its essence. No gametes are formed; one cell simply attaches temporarily to another and donates some of its hereditary blueprints to it. Nor have *additional* bacteria been created by this process. A *new* bacterium has, though, a bacterium capable of living under conditions neither of the parental types could survive in.

A problem remains. Sexual reproduction in bacteria involves the transfer of a piece of chromosome from one cell to another. It is not reciprocal: that is, no exchange is involved. Thus one cell acquires a greater total hereditary blueprint. This must be followed sometime by the elimination of an equivalent amount. Otherwise, over a period of time, there would be a steady accumulation of chromosomal material in the species. It is not yet certain by just what mechanism a bacterial cell re-establishes its normal chromosome content. The same problem faces other sexually reproducing organisms, however, and its solution in them *has* been discovered.

Each species of organism has a characteristic number of chromosomes. The little fly *Drosophila melanogaster* has 8, the onion 16, and man has 46. (Lest you assume from this that the number of chromosomes in a species is necessarily a function of the complexity of the organism, you should note that the crayfish has at least 200 chromosomes in its cells.) All these numbers are even. This reflects that fact that the chromosomes are present in homologous *pairs*. These cells are said to contain the **diploid** or 2n number of chromosomes.

Mitosis results in the formation of cells that have exactly the same number of chromosomes as the parent cell. This would create difficulties if the cells being formed were to serve as gametes. A human sperm with 46 chromosomes uniting with an egg containing 46 chromosomes would result in a zygote with 92 chromosomes—twice the normal number for the species. Development of the zygote by mitosis would result in all subsequent cells having the new number. You can readily see that after a few generations of this, there would be no room in the cell for anything but chromosomes.

Actually, this situation rarely arises in living things. At some point between the formation of the zygote and the formation of gametes, a special kind of cell division occurs, called **meiosis.** Meiosis consists of two consecutive cell divisions with but one duplication of the chromosomes. When a cell divides by meiosis, then, four cells are produced, each containing just one-half the normal diploid or 2n number of chromosomes. This half-number is called the **haploid** or n number. The reduction in chromosome number is not a random process. In cells produced by meiosis, only one member of each of the homologous pairs of chromosomes of the diploid cell is present. Thus when two gametes unite, the resulting zygote (2n) gets one member of each pair of homologous chromosomes from each gamete and thus from each parent.

Each of the two meiotic divisions can be separated into phases similar to those occurring in mitosis. However, significant differences in the behavior of the chromosomes can be observed in the first of the divisions.

Prophase of the first meiotic division is a much slower and more complex process than in mitosis. The most striking event during this stage is the fusing together of each pair of homologous doublets, a process called **synapsis.** As they lie united lengthwise, two of the chromosomes, one from each doublet, "cross over." In so doing, they exchange one or two sections (Fig. 17-12).

In metaphase, the centromeres of each homologous pair become attached to the spindle, one above, the other below the equatorial plate. With the onset of anaphase, each centromere moves toward its respective pole without duplicating. Thus telophase produces two cells, each of which has just one member of each homologous pair of chromosomes that was present in the original cell.

The second meiotic division occurs at varying lengths of time after the first division, depending on the species. It is similar to a mitotic division. The chromosomes are still present as "doublets." The two chromosomes of each doublet are not likely to be identical, however. A glance at Fig. 17-12 will show why this is so. In the first

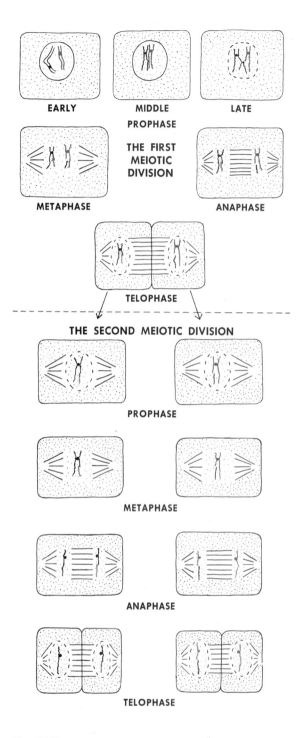

EARLY   MIDDLE   LATE

PROPHASE

THE FIRST
MEIOTIC
DIVISION

METAPHASE   ANAPHASE

TELOPHASE

THE SECOND MEIOTIC DIVISION

PROPHASE

METAPHASE

ANAPHASE

TELOPHASE

Fig. 17-12

Meiosis. The behavior of just a single pair of homologous chromosomes is shown with one homologue black, the other in color.

meiotic division, crossing over between the paternal and maternal homologues resulted in one chromosome of each doublet no longer being identical to the other chromosome of the doublet.

Each centromere then moves to the equatorial plate, attaches to the spindle, and is duplicated. As in anaphase of mitosis, the daughter centromeres now move apart and pull their attached chromosome to their respective pole. These nonidentical chromosomes thus become separated, one going to each daughter cell.

With the completion of the second meiotic division, a total of four cells has been produced. Each contains just one member of each homologous pair of chromosomes present in the original cell. These cells thus contain just one-half (the haploid number) of the chromosomes of the parent cell. Furthermore, in our simplified case, two of the four cells produced have an unchanged maternal or paternal chromosome; the others have a chromosome containing *both* maternal and paternal parts.

Crossing over is not the only way by which meiosis produces cells whose chromosome content differs. In Fig. 17-12, for the sake of simplicity, only one pair of chromosomes ($2n = 2$) is shown. In most living things, the diploid number is larger. The parasitic roundworm, *Ascaris bivalens,* has a diploid number of 4. These four chromosomes make up two homologous pairs. One member of each pair came from the worm's father, the other from its mother. Thus we can indicate the two pairs as $A^m A'$ and $B^m B'$. When *Ascaris* undergoes the first meiotic division, the homologous pairs orient themselves on either side of the equatorial plate. If A^m and B^m orient on one side and A' and B' on the other, the gametes will be the same (neglecting crossing over) as those the worm received from its parents. It is just as likely, however, that A^m and B' will orient on one side of the equatorial plate and A' and B^m on the other. (Fig. 17-13). The gametes produced by this arrangement will contain a new combination of chromosomes. Any organism whose diploid number is 4 can thus produce four kinds of gametes: $A^m B^m$, $A' B'$, $A^m B'$, or $A' B^m$. The fly *Drosophila melanogaster* has 8 chromosomes in its diploid cells, 4 derived from its mother and 4 derived from its father. A little figuring with pencil and paper will show that in distributing one of each homologous pair to the gametes, 16 different combinations can be produced. The number of different kinds of gametes produced by **random assortment** of the chromosomes is equal to 2^n where $n =$ the haploid number of chromosomes in the organism. Human mothers and fathers, each with a haploid number of 23, can each produce by random assortment alone 2^{23} or 8,388,608 different kinds of gametes. When you consider further that crossing over will have occurred between their own paternal and maternal chromosomes in the first meiotic division, it is not surprising that no two people ever resemble each other exactly. (An exception to this is the special case of identical twins; but it is only an apparent exception since they arise from a *single* fertilized egg.)

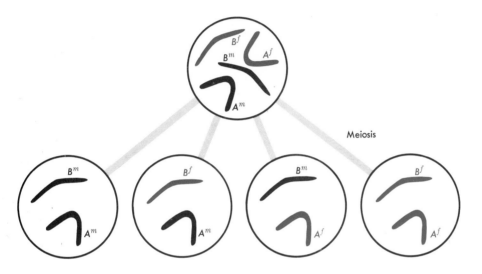

Random assortment of maternal (black) and paternal (color) chromosomes during meiosis in *Ascaris bivalens* (2n = 4).

Fig. 17-13

What, then, is the significance of meiosis? First, the number of chromosomes is reduced from the diploid number to the haploid number. This sets the stage for the union of two gametes and thus provides a mechanism by which traits of two different parents can be combined. Second, meiosis provides for variation in the gametes produced by each parent. **Random assortment** of the paternal and maternal chromosomes *plus* the **crossing over** of portions of the maternal and paternal chromosomes make it likely that no two gametes of even one parent will be exactly alike.

How is meiosis used by living things? You have seen the necessity for meiosis to occur sometime between fertilization and gamete formation in sexually reproducing forms. In animals, meiosis leads directly to the production of gametes. Among the protists that reproduce sexually, on the other hand, meiosis is apt to occur very soon after the formation of the zygote. The zygote formed by the fusion of two *Chlamydomonas* gametes develops a heavy wall and becomes dormant. When favorable conditions exist, the zygote undergoes meiosis, producing four haploid zoospores (Fig. 17-6). These are released and soon grow to full-sized *Chlamydomonas* cells. Most of the life cycle of this organism is thus spent in the haploid condition. In plants, too, meiosis is used in the production of spores. Only later are gametes derived from these.

The occurrence of meiosis well before the formation of gametes in protists and plants illustrates two additional points about cell division. First, *mitosis* can occur in haploid cells as well as diploid ones. Second, the haploid number of chromosomes is sufficient to control cell functions in these organisms. Seen in this light, re-establishment of diploidy by fertilization simply provides a double set of the hereditary information. This double set does, however, lay the basis for a reorganization of the hereditary information at the next meiosis. Once again, we see sexual reproduction serving one major function: the production of variability in the species.

Earlier in the chapter it was pointed out that asexual reproduction usually results in offspring that are exact copies of their parents. Sexual reproduction, on the other hand, was described as a method of producing offspring with characteristics different from those of the parents and thus of producing variability within the species. Assuming that the information that controls the development of the characteristics of an organism is located in its chromosomes, it is easy to see how mitosis makes the first possible and meiosis, followed by fertilization, make the second possible.

Throughout this chapter, we have referred often to the hereditary blueprints within the nuclei of cells. One of the most active fields of biological research is that concerned with the nature and operation of these hereditary blueprints. This study is called genetics. It is the topic of the next three chapters.

EXERCISES AND PROBLEMS

1   The haploid number of horse chromosomes plus the haploid number of donkey chromosomes can produce a healthy mule. The mule is sterile. With rare exceptions (see Question 2), it cannot breed with either another mule or a horse or a donkey. Can you explain why in terms of the behavior of the chromosomes during meiosis?

2   Although mules are generally sterile, a few cases are known where a female mule has given birth to a horse (after mating with a horse) or another mule (after mating with a donkey). Using your knowledge of meiosis, can you think of an explanation for these rare events?

3   How does the behavior of the chromosomes in mitosis differ from their behavior in the first meiotic division?

4   Name 3 kinds of asexual reproduction and give an example of each.

5   Asexual reproduction preserves the *status quo*. Sexual reproduction promotes change. Describe how mitosis makes the first possible and meiosis followed by fertilization makes the second possible.

6   Explain why the minimal medium for growing *E. coli* contains (a) glucose or some other carbohydrate, (b) KH_2PO_4, (c) $MgSO_4$, (d) NH_4NO_3.

7   In what ways are budding in yeast and budding in the hydra similar? In what ways are they different?

8   If a hermaphroditic organism fertilizes its own eggs, must all its offspring be identical? Explain.

9   How many kinds of gametes can the onion ($2n = 16$) produce by random assortment alone?

10   What kind of cell division is used in the production of sperm cells in honeybees?

11   What functions do spores accomplish in the bread mold, *Rhizopus nigricans*?

REFERENCES

1 Swanson, C. P., *The Cell,* 2nd ed., Foundations of Modern Biology Series, Prentice-Hall, Inc., 1964. Mitosis and meiosis are treated in Chapters 5 and 6, respectively.

2 Mazia, D., "How Cells Divide," *Scientific American,* Reprint No. 93, September, 1961.

3 Wollman, E. L., and F. Jacob, "Sexuality in Bacteria," *Scientific American,* Reprint No. 50, July, 1956. Describes how the occurrence of conjugation in *E. coli* is demonstrated.

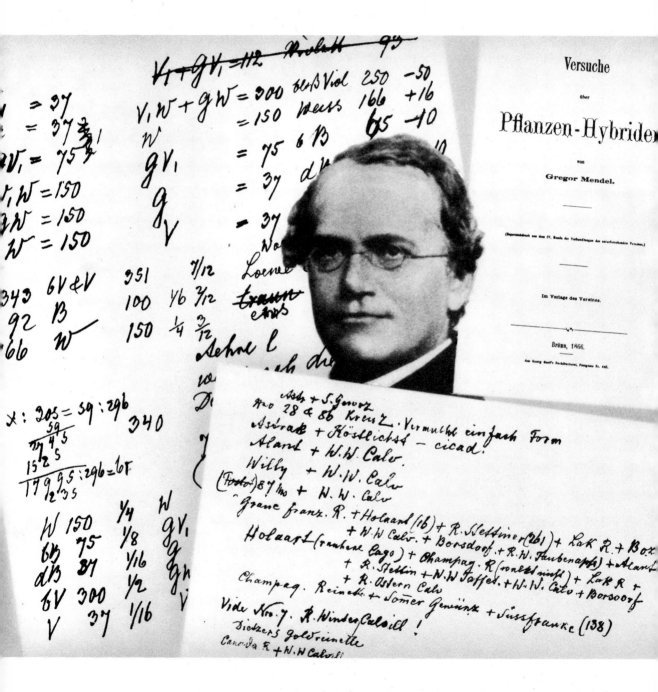

When living things reproduce asexually, their offspring develop into exact copies of their parents so long as they are raised under similar conditions. On the other hand, when living things reproduce sexually, their offspring develop traits different from one another and different from those of either parent. When a Collie and a German Shepherd mate, their offspring are dogs, not some other species of animal. Their offspring are, however, clearly neither Collies nor German Shepherds. Long before biologists discovered many of the facts of mitosis and meiosis, they tried to discover rules which would explain how the observable characteristics of offspring are related to those of their parents and even their parent's parents.

Of the several theories that have been formulated to explain how traits are inherited, two deserve special mention. One of these, Mendel's theory, has provided the foundation upon which all later work in genetics has been built. The other, the theory of the inheritance of acquired characteristics, has failed to pass scientific tests but, despite this, has continued to have its defenders.

THE THEORY OF THE INHERITANCE OF ACQUIRED CHARACTERISTICS 18-1

This theory states simply that traits *acquired* by parents during their lifetime can be passed on to their offspring. The theory is usually associated with the name of Lamarck, a French biologist, who used it in an attempt to explain the many striking adaptations to their environment shown by plants and animals. His most famous illustration was the giraffe. He claimed that the long neck of the giraffe has evolved as a result of generations of giraffes stretching their necks to browse on the leaves of trees. Each generation has passed on to its offspring the small increase in neck length caused by continual stretching.

Is there any evidence that such a phenomenon occurs? Despite repeated attempts to prove that changes in the body acquired by an individual can be passed on to its offspring, no evidence for it has yet been discovered. The earliest experiments that attempted to settle the question were those in which some body part, such as the tail of a mouse, was removed surgically. Even after generations of tail removal, young mice were born with as long tails as ever. Actually, the experimenters could have simply looked about them for corroboration of their findings. Sheep raisers have been removing the tails of lambs through uncounted generations, but the process must still be carried out with each new generation. Even when more sophisticated attempts were made to alter heredity by altering the environment, it could not be done.

Why not? In order for changes carried out on the body to be transmitted to the offspring, they would have to become incorporated into the sperm and egg cells, the only link between the bodies of the parents and the bodies of the children. Perhaps such a thing might occur if the specialized cells of the body, upon which some alteration could be made, then produced the gametes. But they do not. For many years it has been known that in animals the gamete-producing cells of the body are set aside very early in embryonic life. In fact, a newborn girl already has formed by meiosis all the eggs that she will ever have.

◀Gregor Mendel (1822–1884), with the title page of the paper in which he published his work, and some of his notes on plant genetics and hybridization. (Photo courtesy Professor Verne Grant.)

The German biologist, Weismann, expressed these thoughts in the form of his theory of the *continuity of the germplasm.* Multicellular organisms, according to his theory, are made up of gamete-producing cells or **germplasm** and the cells of the rest of the body, the **somaplasm.** Weismann considered the germplasm immortal, an unbroken chain of gametes and embryos going right back to the dawn of life (Fig. 18-1). At each generation, the embryo that develops from the zygote not only sets aside some germplasm for the next generation but also produces the cells that will develop into the body, the somaplasm, of the organism. In this view, the somaplasm simply provides the housing for the germplasm, seeing to it that the germplasm is protected, nourished, and conveyed to the germplasm of the opposite sex in order to create the next generation. The old riddle about which came first, the chicken or the egg, would have been no puzzle to Weismann. In his view, the chicken is simply one egg's device for laying another egg.

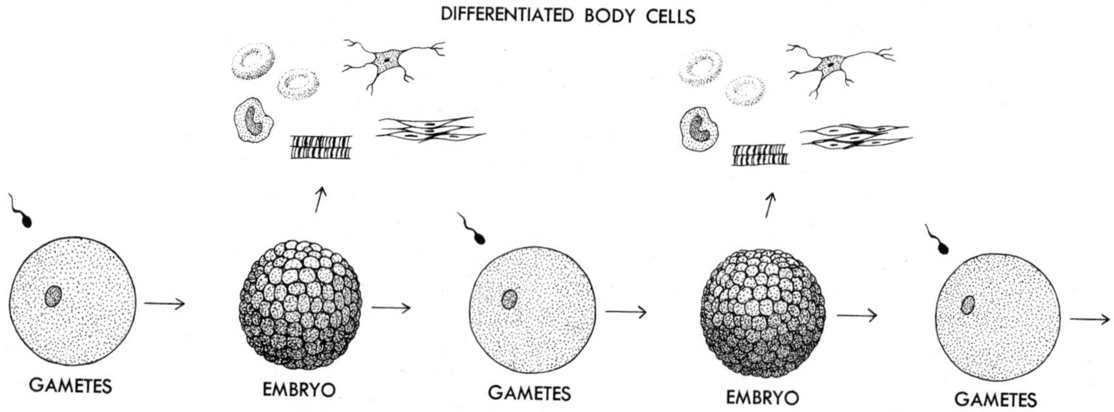

DIFFERENTIATED BODY CELLS

| GAMETES | EMBRYO | GAMETES | EMBRYO | GAMETES |

Fig. 18-1   Weismann's hypothesis. While true for most animals, it does not hold true for plants. Plants *can* produce gamete-forming cells from differentiated body cells.

The essential truth of Weismann's theory was beautifully demonstrated in 1909 by the Americans W. E. Castle and John C. Phillips. They removed the ovaries from an albino guinea pig and substituted the ovaries from a black guinea pig. Then they mated this albino guinea pig with an albino male. Instead of getting albino babies as might normally be expected, the babies were black. (Matings between albino and black guinea pigs always produce black offspring.) The hereditary blueprints of the eggs had not been altered by their maturation in the body of a different animal.

Despite this and many other experiments refuting the idea that what happens to the somaplasm can affect the germplasm, some scientists still persisted in trying to prove otherwise. This has been particularly true of those who were believers in Communism. They seem to feel that the physical and mental benefits that one generation acquires through its hard work *ought* to be transmitted to its offspring. In an effort to prove that such a thing can occur, one scientist went so far as to falsify his experimental results. Fortunately, one of the cornerstones of the scientific process is that if other men cannot duplicate certain scientific findings, they will not be accepted as valid. In this case, when the findings were finally proved to be fraudulent, the perpetrator of the hoax committed suicide.

Despite its setbacks, the theory is not dead yet. Under the leadership of Trofim Lysenko, it was made the *official* theory of inheritance in the U.S.S.R. in 1948. Geneticists who adhered to Mendel's theories of inheritance were at one time literally exiled and, in some cases, put to death. Since the death of Stalin, geneticists pursuing Mendel's theories have once more been allowed to work in the U.S.S.R. and thus to join in the scientific work of geneticists elsewhere. Let us now look at the theory which, having met test after test, is accepted by the vast majority of geneticists and forms the basis upon which most of the useful discoveries in genetics have been made.

MENDEL'S THEORY: THE BACKGROUND   18-2

Our present theories of inheritance were first worked out by the Austrian monk, Gregor Mendel. From 1858 to 1866, Mendel worked in the garden of his monastery, in the town of Brünn (now Brno) breeding garden peas and examining the offspring of these matings. Mendel was not the first man to carry on controlled breeding experiments in an attempt to discover rules of inheritance. He succeeded where others had failed, however, because (1) he chose his experimental organism with care, (2) he limited the scope of his investigation, and (3) he recorded his data carefully and subjected them to mathematical analysis. Mendel's decision to work with the common garden pea was an excellent one. The plant is hardy and fast growing. As in many legumes, the petals of the flower entirely enclose the sex organs. These are the **stamens,** which produce pollen (the bearer of the male gametes) and the **pistil,** which produces the female gamete, the egg. Although insects may occasionally penetrate to the sex organs, self-fertilization is the rule. Mendel found he could open the buds and remove the stamens before they ripened. Then, by dusting the pistil with pollen from another plant, he could effect cross-fertilization between them.

The choice of the garden pea was a happy one also because many varieties existed which differed from one another in clear-cut ways. Some produced (after drying) wrinkled seeds. Others produced smooth, round seeds. Some produced seeds with green cotyledons; others with yellow cotyledons. Some produced green pods; others, yellow pods. Some produced white flowers; others reddish flowers. These paired characteristics (and three others) Mendel chose to study because they were so easily distinguishable and because they "bred true" generation after generation. That is, so long as they were maintained by normal self-pollination, these varieties continued to produce offspring identical to the parents in the characteristics being studied.

There were other characteristics in which Mendel's pea varieties differed, such as leaf size and flower size. Mendel wisely ignored these differences in his studies simply because they did not fall into a clear-cut "either-or" classification. Mendel's peas produced either round seeds or wrinkled seeds. There were no intermediate types. On the other hand, the size of leaves and flowers varied over quite a range. There were not just two distinct categories in which they could be placed. Mendel's decision to thus limit the scope of his experiments was certainly an important factor in his success.

Finally, Mendel recognized the need to keep careful records of the various kinds of offspring produced by his experimental breeding. After counting the different kinds produced, he subjected the figures to statistical analysis. This analysis led him, as we shall see, directly to his theory of inheritance.

MENDEL'S EXPERIMENTS   18-3

In one of his first experiments, Mendel crossbred a round-seeded variety with a wrinkle-seeded variety. This parental generation he called the P_1 generation. Pollen from the stamens of the round-seeded variety was dusted on the pistils of the wrinkle-seeded variety. The reciprocal cross was carried out: pollen from the stamens of the wrinkle-seeded variety was placed on the pistils of the round-seeded variety. In both cases, every one of the seeds produced by these cross-fertilized flowers was round. There were no seeds intermediate in shape. (Seed shape and cotyledon color were particularly rewarding characteristics to study. Their form could be determined in the same season that the fertilization was carried out. The seeds *were* the next generation. Pod shape, stem length, and flower color in the second generation could not be determined until the following season when the seeds had germinated and developed into the mature plants.) Mendel called the second generation the **hybrid** generation because it was produced by dissimilar parents. It is also called the F_1 generation.

Mendel planted all his F_1, round seeds; 253 F_1 plants grew to maturity. The F_1 flowers were allowed to self-fertilize themselves in the normal way. In effect, Mendel was breeding the F_1 (or hybrid) generations together. From the pods of these F_1 plants, Mendel recovered 7324 seeds, the F_2 generation. Of these, 5474 were round, 1850 wrinkled. Dividing the larger number by the smaller, a ratio of 2.96 round to 1 wrinkled is derived.

Mendel then planted some of these two kinds of F_2 seeds. From the wrinkled seeds, he raised plants which produced (by self-fertilization) a new crop (F_3) of seeds. These were exclusively of the wrinkled type. From the round-seeds, he raised 565 plants and allowed these also to produce an F_3 crop by self-fertilization. In this case, 193 of the plants produced round seeds only. The other 372 plants produced both round and wrinkled seeds and in a 3 to 1 ratio (Fig. 18-2).

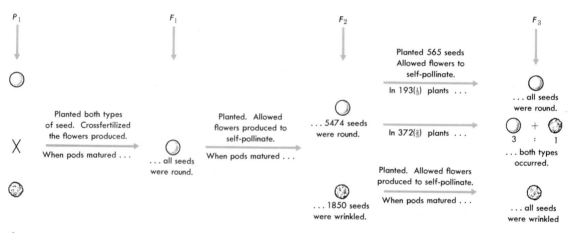

Fig. 18-2   Mendel's results.

What is the significance of these facts? Clearly, when round-seeded peas are cross-bred with wrinkle-seeded peas, the round-seeded ones pass some controlling factor on to the offspring (F_1). Further, it does not matter whether the round-seeded factor is supplied by the male gamete or by the egg. The results are the same in either case.

The reappearance of wrinkled peas in the F_2 generation can only mean that at least some of the F_1 plants were also carrying a factor for the wrinkle-seeded condition. Its presence was, however, obscured in the F_1 generation. Traits which are transmitted unchanged to the F_1 generation (e.g. round seeds) Mendel called **dominant.** Those which are hidden in the F_1, but reappear in the F_2 (e.g. wrinkled seeds), he called **recessive.**

In an attempt to explain these facts, Mendel made a series of assumptions. These as-sumptions we call a hypothesis. They were not observations; they were not facts. They were simply statements which, if true, would provide an explanation for the observed results. They were:

1) In each organism there is a pair of factors which control the appearance of a given characteristic. (Today we call these factors **genes.**)
2) The organism gets these factors from its parents, one from each.
3) Each of these factors is transmitted as a discrete, unchanging unit. (The wrinkled seeds in the F_2 generation were no less wrinkled than those in the P_1 generation, although the factors controlling this trait had passed through the round-seeded F_1 generation.)
4) When the reproductive cells (sperm or eggs) are prepared, *the factors separate* and are distributed as units to each gamete. This is often called *Mendel's first law,* the *law of segregation.*
5) If an organism has two unlike factors for a given characteristic, one may be ex-pressed to the total exclusion of the other. Today, we use the term **allele** to describe *alternative forms of a gene* controlling a given characteristic. Thus, in the case discussed, there are two alleles (round-seeded and wrinkle-seeded) of the gene which controls seed shape.

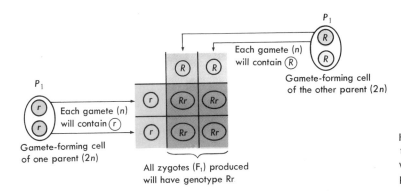

Fig. 18-3

How Mendel's hypothesis explains the results of mating a purebreeding wrinkle-seeded pea plant with a purebreeding round-seeded one.

How well does this hypothesis explain the observed facts? According to Mendel's scheme, the pure-breeding round-seeded plants of the P_1 generation contained two identical genes for round seeds. We can designate these as *RR.* The pure-breeding wrinkle-seeded plants contained two of the wrinkle-seeded genes, *rr.* Today we say that each of the P_1 plants is **homozygous** for its respective trait. In the formation of gametes, the genes separate. Since the genes are alike in each plant, however, all the gametes of one plant are the same. Any sperm nucleus or egg from the round-seeded plant will carry the allele *R.* Likewise, any gamete from the wrinkle-seeded plant will carry the allele *r.* The only possible zygotes that can be formed when these two vari-eties are crossbred would contain both, *Rr.* All the cells of the F_1 plant thus carry one of each of the two alleles. Today we would say that each of the F_1 plants is **heterozygous.** All the F_1 seeds are round according to Mendel because in the hetero-zygous state, the allele *R* is expressed to the total exclusion of the allele *r.* In other words, *R* is dominant over *r.* We can describe this cross by means of a so-called Punnett's square (Fig. 18-3).

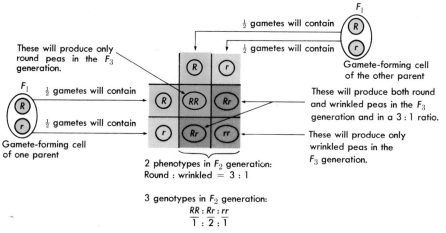

Fig. 18-4   How Mendel's hypothesis explains the results of mating two F_1 plants.

When the F_1 plants form gametes, the alleles again separate, only one allele being transmitted to a given gamete. This means that half of the total number of gametes formed will contain the allele R; half will contain r. When these gametes are allowed to unite at random, roughly one-half of the zygotes will be heterozygous, one-quarter homozygous for R, and one-quarter homozygous for r (Fig. 18-4). Three different combinations are thus probable (RR, Rr, rr), and the expected ratio would be 1:2:1. Because of the dominance of R over r, however, there is no way to distinguish visibly between seeds containing RR and those containing Rr. Both would have round coats. Today we say that they have the same **phenotype**, that is, *appearance with respect to some trait*. However, they have different **genotypes**, *actual gene content*, for the trait. This explains the interesting results Mendel achieved when he grew his F_3 generation. All the wrinkled seeds bred true. One-third (193) of the round seeds also bred true, indicating that they were homozygous for RR. However, two-thirds (372) of the round seeds produced both round and wrinkled seeds and in a 3:1 ratio just as in the F_2 generation. Thus, they must have been heterozygous.

It is important to note that these ratios are only approximate. Far more pollen is produced than is ever used in fertilization. Many eggs may never be fertilized. One would no more expect that four F_1 fertilizations would always produce $1RR$, $2Rr$, and $1rr$ than one would expect a coin flipped four times to always come up heads twice and tails twice. But as the size of the sample gets increasingly large, chance deviations

Actual seed production by each of ten of Mendel's F_1 plants

	Round	Wrinkled
1.	45	12
2.	27	8
3.	24	7
4.	19	16
5.	32	11
6.	26	6
7.	88	24
8.	22	10
9.	28	6
10.	25	7
Total	336	107

Fig. 18-5

Actual seed production by each of ten of Mendel's F_1 plants. Note that individual plants deviated widely from the expected 3:1 ratio but that the group as a whole approached it quite closely.

become minimized and the ratios approach the theoretical prediction more and more closely. Figure 18-5 shows the actual count of round and wrinkled seeds produced by ten of Mendel's 253 F_1 plants. In many cases, the ratio is far from the expected 3:1. By the time the seeds of all the plants have been counted, however, the ratio (3.14:1) is very close to that predicted.

HOW HYPOTHESES ARE JUDGED 18-5

Mendel's hypothesis provides a reasonable explanation for the results of his breeding experiments. While it is not the only scheme which can be devised to explain these results, it is the simplest scheme that anyone has yet thought up. We cannot ask if Mendel's hypothesis is true. All we can say is that it provides an adequate explanation of all the facts observed and that it is the simplest explanation which does this. "Reasonable," "adequate," "simplest" are all standards which are extraordinarily difficult to measure. Hypotheses, especially when newly created, must frequently be judged by just such subjective criteria as these, however. In the popular view, scientists lead working lives of complete objectivity. When dealing with facts, this is generally true. When dealing with hypotheses, however, they are also guided by subjective, aesthetic, even emotional considerations. The reasoning proceeded in Mendel's case from the concrete details of numbers of different kinds of seeds to the generalizations that explain the facts, that "make sense" out of them. We call this kind of reasoning **inductive.** No simple rules of logic lead in this direction; one needs intuition or insight. The ability to make these inductive generalizations requires more art than science, but science would not exist without them.

There is one further criterion that any good hypothesis should meet. It should be able to predict new facts. This prediction of new facts involves reasoning which is called **deductive.** If the generalizations are valid, then certain specific consequences can be deduced from them.

THE BACKCROSS: A TEST OF MENDEL'S HYPOTHESIS 18-6

Mendel appreciated fully the importance of this step. To test his hypothesis, he tried to predict the outcome of a breeding experiment he had never carried out. He crossed his heterozygous round peas (Rr) with homozygous wrinkled ones (rr). He reasoned that the homozygous recessive parent could only produce gametes with r. The heterozygous parent should produce equal numbers of R and r gametes. Mendel predicted that one-half of the seeds produced from this cross would be round (Rr) and one-half would be wrinkled (rr) (Fig. 18-6). This kind of mating, using as one parent a known homozygous recessive, is called a backcross or testcross. It "tests" the genotype in those cases where two different genotypes (like RR and Rr) produce the same phenotype. Note that to the casual observer in the monastery garden, the cross appeared no different from the P_1 cross described earlier. Round-seeded peas were being crossed with wrinkle-seeded peas. But Mendel, believing that round-seeded pea plants in this cross were actually heterozygous, predicted that both round and wrinkled seeds would be produced and in a 50:50 ratio. He performed the matings and harvested 106 round peas and 101 wrinkled peas from his plants.

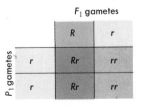

Fig. 18-6

Mendel's backcross. Although it superficially resembled a P_1 mating, Mendel's prediction that two phenotypes would be produced and in equal numbers was verified.

Mendel's hypothesis had explained all the known facts. It also led to the prediction of other facts as yet undiscovered. When these predicted facts were discovered, his hypothesis was greatly strengthened. A hypothesis that explains all the known facts in the situation and successfully predicts new ones is soon referred to as a **theory.** If a theory continues to serve its explanatory and predictive functions, it may eventually come to be called a **law.** Two of Mendel's assumptions (one of which we have already discussed) are now referred to as Mendel's laws.

18-7 DIHYBRIDS—THE LAW OF INDEPENDENT ASSORTMENT

During the same period of time that Mendel was investigating inheritance in round- and wrinkle-seeded peas, he ran similar experiments with pea varieties differing in six other clear-cut ways. The results from all these other experiments also supported his hypothesis. Next, he crossed pea plants differing in two characteristics. A pure-breeding, round-seeded, yellow-cotyledon pea variety was cross-pollinated with a pure-breeding, wrinkle-seeded, green-cotyledon variety. All the seeds produced from the mating were round and had yellow cotyledons. This bore out Mendel's previous finding that the allele for yellow cotyledons, like the allele for round seed shape, was dominant. (This F_1 generation is said to be *dihybrid* because it is produced by crossing parents differing in two traits.) Then Mendel planted these seeds and allowed the resulting flowers to self-pollinate. Either of two possibilities might be expected. The alleles for round shape and yellow cotyledons, which had been inherited from one parent, might be inseparable and thus passed on as a single unit to the F_2 generation.

	RY	ry
RY	RRYY round -yellow	RrYy round -yellow
ry	RrYy round -yellow	rryy wrinkled -green

or

	RY	Ry	rY	ry
RY	RRYY	RRYy	RrYY	RrYy
Ry	RRYy	RRyy	RrYy	Rryy
rY	RrYY	RrYy	rrYY	rrYy
ry	RrYy	Rryy	rrYy	rryy

Round		Wrinkled	
yellow	green	yellow	green
9 :	3 :	3 :	1

Fig. 18-7

Alternative predictions of the results of mating two dihybrids. In this case, the second prediction (right) turned out to be correct.

If the same were also true for the wrinkled-green alleles, one would expect that three-fourths of the F_2 generation would be round-yellow and one-fourth wrinkled-green (Fig. 18-7). If, on the other hand, the genes for seed shape and cotyledon color were distributed to the gametes independently of each other, then one would expect in the F_2 generation to find some peas that were round with green cotyledons and some that were wrinkled with yellow cotyledons as well as those resembling the P_1 types. According to this latter assumption, then, four phenotypes would be produced in the ratio 9:3:3:1 (Fig. 18-7).

Mendel performed this cross and harvested 315 round-yellow peas, 101 wrinkled-yellow peas, 108 round-green peas and 32 wrinkled-green peas. It is characteristic of Mendel's careful work that he then proceeded to plant all of these peas and verify the presence of four separate genotypes among the round-yellow peas and two separate genotypes among each of the peas with the new combination of characteristics.

Only the 32 wrinkled-green peas were of a single genotype. These results led Mendel to frame his last hypothesis (Mendel's second law): the distribution of one pair of factors is independent of the distribution of the other pair. This has come to be known as his *law of independent assortment*.

MENDEL'S THEORY: THE SEQUEL 18-8

The experiments described in this chapter were carried on from 1858 to 1866. In 1866 Mendel published the results as well as his analysis of them. Little attention was paid to them by other biologists. No one tried to repeat any of the experiments or carry them on with different traits or different organisms. Mendel himself soon gave up his experiments and became increasingly involved with the administration of his monastery.

Mendel died in 1884. In 1900, thirty-four years after he had published his work and sixteen years after his death, Mendel's work was brought to light once more. Three men, working entirely independently of one another, discovered the same principles we have been describing. Only after their work was done did they discover that they had been anticipated by an obscure monk a third of a century before.

Several reasons have been proposed for the failure of Mendel's work to gain acceptance. Whatever the reasons, it did not. It is indeed ironical that the present development of genetics dates only from the year 1900, not 1866. Mendel's brilliant work failed to become part of the scientific world of his time. When scientists were ready to pursue his findings further, they had already rediscovered them on their own.

What is the status today of Mendel's *laws?* Although important exceptions to them have been discovered in the years since 1900, they still form the foundation upon which the science of genetics rests.

CONTINUOUS VARIATION: THE MULTIPLE-FACTOR HYPOTHESIS 18-9

One of these exceptions arose from a study of the inheritance of traits which vary quantitatively among different individuals. Mendel had restricted his studies to traits which varied in a clear-cut, easily distinguishable, *qualitative* way. But men are not *either* tall *or* short; nor are they *either* heavy *or* light. Many traits differ in a continuous, quantitative way throughout a population (Fig. 18-8). Some of the variation can be explained by differences in diet and perhaps other factors in the environment. Environ-

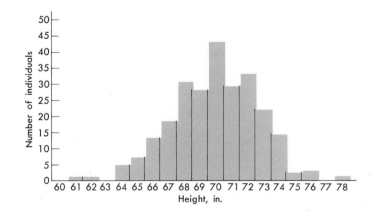

Fig. 18-8

Histogram showing distribution of heights among a group of male secondary-school seniors.

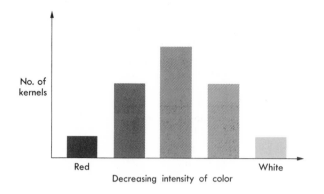

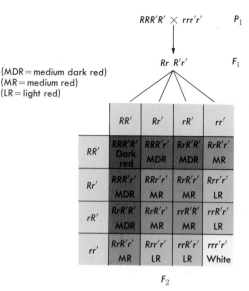

Fig. 18-9

Multiple-factor inheritance in wheat. The alleles at one locus are indicated with prime marks; at the other, without. They affect the phenotype additively.

ment is not, however, sufficient to explain the full range of heights or weights. No theory of inheritance could be regarded as completely successful until this kind of variation could be accounted for.

By 1908 the information was available which provided a solution to the problem. The Swedish geneticist, Nilsson-Ehle, studied the inheritance of kernel color in wheat. Using Mendel's methods, he mated pure-breeding red-kernel strains with pure-breeding white-kernel strains. The offspring were all red, but the intensity of the color was much less than in the red parent. It seemed as though the effect of the red allele in the F_1 generation was being modified by the presence of the white allele. This phenomenon, which had not occurred in Mendel's studies, is called **incomplete dominance.**

Furthermore, when Nilsson-Ehle mated two F_1 plants, he produced an F_2 generation in which red-kerneled plants outnumbered white-kerneled plants 15:1. Close examination revealed that the red kernels were not all alike. They could quite easily be sorted into four different categories. One-fifteenth of them were deep red, like the P_1 type. Four-fifteenths were medium dark red, six-fifteenths were medium red (like the F_1 generation) and four-fifteenths were light red. These results could be explained by assuming that kernel color in wheat is controlled by not one, but two pairs of genes, the effects of which add up *without* distinct dominance (Fig. 18-9). Four genes for red produce a deep red kernel. Four genes for white produce a white kernel. Just one red gene out of the four produces a light red kernel. Any two out of the four produce a medium red kernel. Any three out of the four produce a medium dark red kernel. If one plots the numbers of the different colored offspring in the F_2 generation against color intensity, a graph similar to that in Fig. 18-9 results.

In other wheat varieties, Nilsson-Ehle found F_2 generations with a ratio of red kernels to white of 63:1. These could be explained by assuming that three pairs of alleles were involved. In these cases, six different shades of red could be detected. Can you work out the genetics of this cross for yourself? The color differences were very slight. Environmental influences also caused alterations in intensity so that in practice the collection of kernels displayed a continuous range of hues all the way from deep red to white.

The occurrence of continuous variation of a trait in a population can thus be explained by assuming it is controlled by several pairs of genes, the effects of which are added together. This hypothesis is called the Multiple Factor Hypothesis. It suggests that (1) when two extreme types are mated (e.g. *AABB* and *aabb*), the offspring are intermediate in type; (2) when two intermediate types are mated, most of their offspring are also intermediate, but some extreme types will be produced; and (3) the results of random matings in a large population will be a wide range of types with the greatest number in the middle range and the fewest at the extremes. These three effects are actually observed in most cases of quantitative variation in living things.

When Mendel carried out his experiments on heredity, the nature of the nucleus, the chromosomes, and meiosis was not understood. In formulating the idea of genes, Mendel made no attempt to describe them as physical structures or to say precisely where in the gametes they were located. For Mendel, the genes were simply hypothetical entities which explained observed patterns of inheritance. With the rediscovery of his work, biologists immediately attempted to relate the behavior of his genes to visible features in the cell. Their efforts will be the topic of the next chapter.

EXERCISES AND PROBLEMS

1 What terms did Weismann use to distinguish the body cells of an animal from its reproductory cells?

2 Do these terms apply equally well to bacteria? To plants?

3 Give the gene content of the different kinds of eggs produced by a woman whose genotype is JjKkLl.

4 Is it correct to say that crossing 2 heterozygous red-flowered peas will produce 8 seeds, 2 of which will be homozygous for the trait? Explain.

5 The gene for tallness in peas is dominant over the gene for dwarfism. A cross between a tall pea and a dwarf pea produced 86 tall plants and 81 dwarf plants. What was the probable genotype of the tall plant? What is this kind of cross called?

6 Why was Mendel's choice of the pea plant as an experimental organism such a good one?

7 Distinguish between fact and a hypothesis. Are the two always easily distinguishable?

8 Is it a fact or a hypothesis that the earth is spherical?

9 In *Drosophila* sepia eye is recessive to red eye, and curved wing is recessive to straight wing. If a pure-breeding sepia-eyed, straight-winged fly is mated with a pure-breeding red-eyed, curve-winged fly, what phenotypes will appear in the F_1 generation? If two F_1 flies are allowed to mate, what phenotypes will occur in the F_2 generation and in what ratio?

10 How many different genotypes will occur in the F_2 generation described in Question 9?

11 When plant A (pure-breeding tall) is crossed with plant B (pure-breeding short), the offspring are all intermediate in height. When two of the offspring are crossed, 1/16 of the next generation is as tall as the tall grandparent. How do you account for this?

12 While continuous variation can be accounted for by multiple factor inheritance, cases involving three or more pairs of genes have been difficult to demonstrate conclusively. Why?

13 Define a gene.

REFERENCES

1 Castle, W. E., and J. C. Phillips, "A Successful Ovarian Transplantation in the Guinea-Pig, and its Bearing on Problems of Genetics," *Great Experiments in Biology,* ed. by M. L. Gabriel and S. Fogel, Prentice-Hall, Inc., 1955. A brief report of their experiment.

2 Mendel, G., "Experiments in Plant Hybridization," *Classic Papers in Genetics,* ed. by James A. Peters, Prentice-Hall, Inc., 1959. A clear presentation of Mendel's experiments and his interpretation of his results.

3 Sinnott, E. W., L. C. Dunn, and Th. Dobzhansky, *Principles of Genetics,* McGraw-Hill, New York, 1958. A basic text on the subject, including a thorough treatment of Mendel's work and the multiple-factor hypothesis.

Human chromosomes.
(Courtesy Dr. T. T. Puck and Dr. J. H. Tjio.)

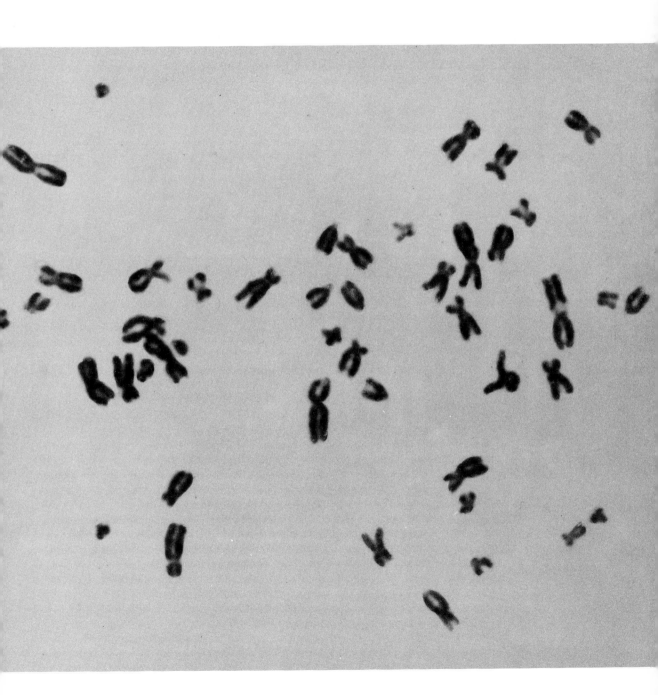

The 35 years during which Mendel's discoveries lay unnoticed saw many important discoveries in cytology—the study of cells. The importance of the nucleus in controlling the traits of the organism was revealed by Boveri's work with sea-urchin eggs, discussed in Chapter 8. The behavior of the chromosomes in mitosis and meiosis, discussed in Chapter 17, was also discovered.

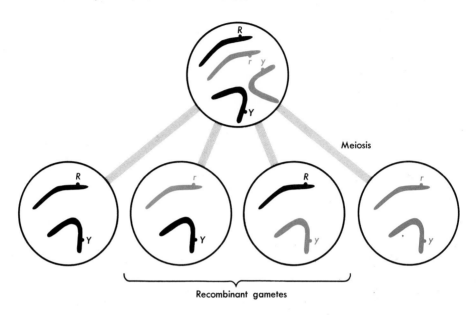

Meiosis

Recombinant gametes

Fig. 19-1   Mechanism of Mendel's *law of independent assortment*. If the gene loci in a dihybrid are on different chromosomes, the random assortment of these chromosomes during meiosis would account for the independent assortment of the genes.

19-1   **PARALLEL BEHAVIOR OF GENES AND CHROMOSOMES**

Shortly after the rediscovery of Mendel's "laws," several workers, among them Sutton and Boveri himself, realized that certain of Mendel's rules of gene behavior could be explained if the genes were located on or in the chromosomes. Mendel had said that genes occur in pairs, one member of which is received from each parent. Chromosomes also exist in pairs, one member of which is received from each parent. Mendel had said that when the reproductive cells are produced, the paired factors (genes) separate and are distributed as units to each gamete (*law of segregation*). In meiosis, the homologous pairs of chromosomes separate and only one member of each pair goes to a given sex cell. Mendel had stated further that in a dihybrid cross, the distribution of one pair of factors is independent of the distribution of the other pair (*law of independent assortment*). In meiosis, the distribution of maternal and paternal chromosomes is entirely at random. If we assume that the genes for one trait, say seed shape, are located on one pair of chromosomes and the genes for the other trait (cotyledon color) on another pair, then the independent assortment of the chromosome pairs in meiosis will also result in the independent assortment of the two traits (Fig 19-1). Because there are so many more traits in an organism than there are chromosomes, the chromosomes cannot be identical to the genes. Instead each chromosome must contain many genes. If we mated dihybrids in which both traits were controlled by genes in the same chromosome, would you expect Mendel's *law of independent assortment* to still hold? Later in the chapter we will see that many dihybrids are of this sort and this law does not hold for such cases. Instead, these genes are said to show "linkage."

The fact that the behavior of the hypothetical units of heredity (genes) is parallel to the behavior of the chromosomes that can actually be seen under the microscope suggested to Sutton that the genes are located in or on the chromosomes. He reasoned that the two alleles controlling a given trait are located at corresponding sites (**loci**— singular, **locus**) on each of the two homologous chromosomes. While the parallel behavior of genes and chromosomes suggested that they were associated in this way, it did not prove that this was so.

For more direct proof it was necessary to be able to associate the presence or absence of a given trait or traits in an organism with the presence or absence of a given chromosome in the body cells of this organism. But the two alleles controlling the expression of a given trait are, according to the chromosome theory, located at corresponding loci on each of two homologous chromosomes. Homologous chromosomes may be visually distinguishable from other chromosomes in the cell but are not distinguishable from each other. So it is not possible to tell by visual inspection of a member of the pair whether it carries a given allele or not.

TESTS OF THE CHROMOSOME THEORY

SEX DETERMINATION 19-2

The first solution to this dilemma came as a result of studies on the fruit fly (more properly but less commonly called a vinegar fly) *Drosophila melanogaster* (Fig 19-2). Thomas Hunt Morgan pioneered in the use of this tiny organism as a subject of research in genetics. It was an admirable choice for several reasons. First, the flies are small and thus sizable populations of them can be reared easily in the laboratory.

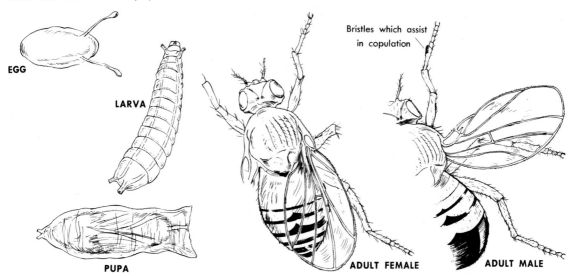

EGG

LARVA

Bristles which assist in copulation

PUPA

ADULT FEMALE

ADULT MALE

Stages in the development of the fruit fly *Drosophila melanogaster*. **Fig. 19-2**

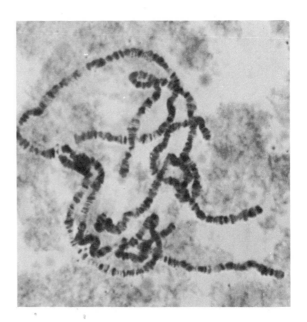

Fig. 19-3

Giant chromosomes from the salivary glands of the fruit fly *Drosophila melanogaster*. Such chromosomes are found in other large, active cells as well. (Courtesy General Biological Supply House, Inc.)

Second, the life cycle is completed quite rapidly. A new generation of adult flies can be produced every two weeks. Third, the flies are remarkably fecund; that is, a female may lay hundreds of fertilized eggs during her brief life span. The large populations thus produced make statistical analyses easy and reliable. Still a fourth virtue was discovered: the presence of giant chromosomes in the salivary glands of the larvae. These chromosomes show far more structural detail than do normal body chromosomes (Fig. 19-3). Although the pattern of bands may not represent genes themselves, eventually it became possible to associate specific genes with specific bands in the chromosomes.

Although a female fruit fly has four pairs of homologous chromosomes (Fig. 19-4), the male fly has only three pairs of homologous chromosomes. The remaining two chromosomes are not homologous. One of the fourth pair of chromosomes is identical in appearance to the chromosomes of the fourth pair in the females. It is called the X-chromosome. The other chromosome in the male is quite different in appearance. It is called the Y-chromosome (Fig. 19-4). Collectively, these X- and Y-chromosomes are called **sex chromosomes** because their presence is always correlated with the sex of the fly. The other chromosomes are called **autosomes.**

As a result of the separation of homologous pairs in meiosis, fruit-fly *eggs* contain one of each of the autosomes plus one X-chromosome. The sperm cells produced by male fruit flies contain three autosomes and either an X- or a Y-chromosome. We can depict the results of random union of these sperm and eggs by setting up a Punnett's

Fig. 19-4

Chromosomes of *Drosophila melanogaster*. Both sexes have three homologous pairs of autosomes. In addition the females have two X-chromosomes (left), the males have an X- and a Y-chromosome (right). These are the sex chromosomes.

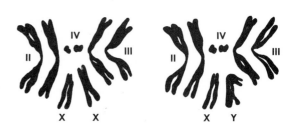

square (Fig. 19-5). (Note that the symbols now refer to whole chromosomes, not genes.) One can quickly see that the offspring should be about equally divided between males and females, and this indeed is the case.

Glancing at Fig. 19-2, we can immediately see that the matter of sex differences is one of inherited traits. The pigmentation on the abdomen of the male, the penis, the bristles on the first tarsal segment of the foreleg are just a few of the visible traits that distinguish the male fruit fly from the female. The mere fact that the presence or absence of these traits is always related to the sex chromosomes present is evidence of the chromosome theory of heredity.

Fig. 19-5

Sex determination. A fruit fly (or human) with 2 X-chromosomes is ♀; ♂'s have 1 X- and 1 Y-chromosome.

It is tempting to think of the Y-chromosome as carrying the genes which determine maleness. In mammals, including man, this is the case. In many insects, including the fruit fly, however, the Y-chromosome seems to be genetically inert. Only a few genes have been associated with it and these are not directly related to sex. Probably the autosomes carry the male determinants and it takes two X-chromosomes to mask their effect and produce a female. The fact that the male grasshopper has no Y-chromosome at all, just one X-chromosome, while the female has two, is one bit of evidence to support this idea.

In still other insects, like the honeybee, as you will remember, sex is determined by whether the chromosomes are present in the haploid or diploid condition. The drone bee arises from an unfertilized egg and his cells are haploid.

Whatever the specific mechanism involved, sex in the animal kingdom seems to be directly related to the arrangement of specific chromosomes and thus serves to support the general theory that the chromosomes carry the determinants of the traits of an organism.

SEX LINKAGE   **19-3**

The discovery of the mechanism of sex determination in fruit flies quickly paved the way for another test of the chromosome theory, this one involving the inheritance of one specific trait. In one of Morgan's *Drosophila* cultures there appeared a male fly with white eyes instead of the brilliant red eyes characteristic of the species. When this fly was mated with normal red-eyed females, the offspring all had red eyes. This suggests that if the white-eyed trait is determined by a specific gene, it must be recessive. According to Mendel's *law of segregation*, all the red-eyed F_1 offspring must have been hybrid for the trait. (Why?) We can then predict that if two red-eyed F_1 flies were mated, white-eyed flies would appear in the F_2 generation in about 25% of the offspring. When Morgan made this cross, he found that this indeed occurred but all the white-eyed offspring were *males*. Not a single white-eyed female appeared. Morgan reasoned that this peculiar sex-related type of inheritance could be explained if one assumed that the alleles involved were located on the X-chromosomes. The female flies, having two X-chromosomes, would have to be homozygous for white eyes to show the trait. The males, on the other hand, having only one X-chromosome, would show the trait for whichever allele they had on that chromosome. Even if it were the recessive allele (*r*), the Y-chromosome contains no allele that would be dominant to it. Figure 19-6 shows diagrammatically Morgan's idea of what had occurred in his first two crosses. Note again that the symbols X and Y stand for the visible chromosomes and the superscripts R and r for the dominant and recessive alleles, respectively.

If this hypothesis is correct, it should be possible to produce white-eyed females by mating white-eyed males with F_1 females. Morgan made this cross and produced all four kinds of flies in approximately equal numbers (Fig. 19-7). Today we call this type of inheritance *sex-linked*. In humans, red or green color blindness and the blood disease hemophilia are both produced by sex-linked genes. These ailments are rare in females because they must inherit the recessive alleles from both their father and their mother in order to show the trait. This would be especially unlikely in the case of hemophilia because a man possessing the allele is a hemophiliac or "bleeder," and his chances of ever becoming a father are quite dim. Figure 19-8 shows a pedigree of the descendants of Queen Victoria. Note that the allele for hemophilia, which has plagued the royal houses of Europe since her time, was nearly always passed on by the mothers who were heterozygous for the trait and thus showed no symptoms. We call them "carriers" because, while free from symptoms, they passed the recessive allele on to approximately one-half their sons, who became bleeders.

Fig. 19-6

	X^r	Y
X^R	$X^R X^r$	$X^R Y$
X^R	$X^R X^r$	$X^R Y$

Sex linkage. Any recessive allele (e.g., r-white eyes) on the X-chromosome will be expressed in males because no corresponding gene loci are found on the Y-chromosome.

Fig. 19-7

	X^R	Y
X^R	$X^R X^R$	$X^R Y$
X^r	$X^R X^r$	$X^r Y$

	X^r	Y
X^R	$X^R X^r$	$X^R Y$
X^r	$X^r X^r$	$X^r Y$

Morgan's backcross. By mating a white-eyed ♂ fruit fly with a "carrier" ♀, Morgan was able to produce white-eyed ♀'s, too.

Although females who are "carriers" for a sex-linked trait usually appear to be perfectly normal, their heterozygous condition can sometimes be determined without waiting to study their male offspring. For example, women who are carriers of one of the sex-linked genes producing red or green color blindness do show some reduction in their sensitivity to these colors. There are at least two possible explanations for this. One is that there might be *incomplete* dominance (see Section 18-9) of the normal gene over the abnormal allele. A second possibility stems from the discovery that only *one* X-chromosome is functional in most of a woman's cells.

You remember that during interphase the chromosomes are so tenuous that they cannot be stained and observed. In 1949, however, a dense, stainable structure was found to be present in virtually all the interphase nuclei of *female* mammals. It was never found in males. This structure (called a Barr body after its discoverer) turned out to be one of the X-chromosomes. Its compact appearance was a reflection of its inactivity.

It now appears that early in embryonic development, one or the other of a female's X-chromosomes becomes inactivated and converted into a Barr body. Which of the two X-chromosomes becomes inactivated in a given cell is probably a matter of chance. However, after it has taken place, all the descendants of that cell will have the same chromosome in the inactive state.

Now if a woman is heterozygous for a sex-linked trait, one of her X-chromosomes will contain the normal, usually dominant, allele. The other will contain the recessive allele. However, the dominant allele will not be able to exert its effect in any *cell* in

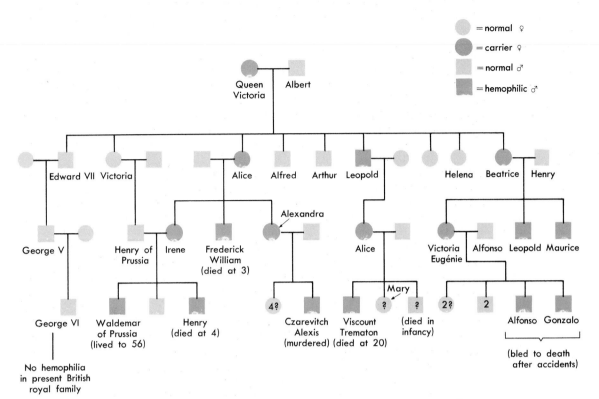

Legend:
= normal ♀
= carrier ♀
= normal ♂
= hemophilic ♂

Queen Victoria — Albert

Edward VII — Victoria   Alice   Alfred   Arthur   Leopold   Helena   Beatrice — Henry

George V   Henry of Prussia — Irene   Frederick William (died at 3)   Alexandra   Alice   Victoria Eugénie — Alfonso   Leopold   Maurice

George VI   Waldemar of Prussia (lived to 56)   Henry (died at 4)   4?   Czarevitch Alexis (murdered)   Viscount Trematon (died at 20)   Mary   ?   (died in infancy)   2?   2   Alfonso   Gonzalo

No hemophilia in present British royal family

(bled to death after accidents)

Pedigree showing inheritance of hemophilia, a sex-linked trait, in the descendants of Queen Victoria. Many of the descendants in the third and fourth generations (3rd and 4th rows) have been omitted because the mutant gene was not transmitted to them.

Fig. 19-8

which the X-chromosome carrying that allele has been inactivated. In those cells, the recessive allele will be the only active one and hence may express itself in the phenotype. Perhaps, then, the slightly impaired color vision in women who are carriers of the gene for this trait results from the presence of two different phenotypes among the color-sensitive cells of their eyes. Some cells would contain the normal gene in the *active* state and would respond to color normally. Others would contain the normal gene in the *inactive* state and would not respond to color at all.

Although it has been difficult to establish with certainty the existence of these two types of receptor cells in carriers for color blindness, other examples of such a phenomenon are well known. For example, women who are heterozygous (i.e., carriers) for a sex-linked genetic defect involving an enzyme in their red blood corpuscles actually have two kinds of RBC's in their bloodstream: those that have the enzyme and those that don't. Presumably the latter were produced by cells in which the normal gene and the X-chromosome of which it was a part became inactivated.

An organism whose cells vary in their *effective* gene content and hence in phenotype is said to be a genetic mosaic. Not only are human females genetic mosaics for any sex-linked trait for which they are carriers, but the phenomenon has been observed in some other animals.

The gene for yellow coat color in cats is present on the X-chromosome and is recessive. A male inheriting his single X-chromosome with this gene on it will have a yellow coat. However, females who are carriers of the gene have neither the normal nor a yellow coat but a mixture of the two. Some patches of hair are normal in appearance, some are yellow (producing a "tortoise-shell" effect). Once again, the patches with yellow hair can be explained as those in which the cells are all descended from an embryonic cell in which the X-chromosome carrying the dominant allele for normal coat color became inactivated.

The discovery and analysis of sex-linked traits, and of their peculiar mosaic expression in certain cases, serves to corroborate further the chromosome theory of inheritance. Each example described can now best be explained by assuming that the alleles involved are located on a specific chromosome.

19-4 **NONDISJUNCTION**

Additional proof of the chromosome theory came in 1916 as a result of closely observing the offspring produced by mating white-eyed *Drosophila* females with red-eyed males. Because of sex linkage, one would expect that all the female offspring would have red eyes and all the male offspring would have white eyes (Fig. 19-9). The American geneticist C. Bridges noticed, however, that out of every 2000 to 3000 offspring, a white-eyed female or a red-eyed male would be found. He could explain the rare appearance of these individuals only by assuming that something had gone wrong in the production of eggs by the white-eyed mothers. If, during either meiotic division, the X^r-chromosomes failed to separate normally, they would both travel to one pole of the cell. The result would be either an egg containing two X^r-chromosomes (instead of the usual one) or, just as often, an egg with no X^r-chromosome at all. This failure of two homologous chromosomes to separate from each other in cell division is called *nondisjunction*. When these abnormal eggs were fertilized by normal sperm from the red-eyed males (X^R and Y), four kinds of zygotes would be expected (see Fig. 19-10).

	X^R	Y
X^r	$X^R X^r$	$X^r Y$
X^r	$X^R X^r$	$X^r Y$

Fig. 19-9

Expected results of crossing a white-eyed ♀ fruit fly with a red-eyed ♂.

Fig. 19-10

Bridges' hypothesis to explain the occasional appearance of a white-eyed ♀ and a red-eyed ♂. The XXX genotype is seldom viable, and the single Y is never so.

The zygote containing no X-chromosome would not develop because of the absence of the many genes associated with the X-chromosome. The zygote containing the three X-chromosomes is known to have a very small chance for survival probably because of a lack of proper balance between the autosomes and the X-chromosomes. The zygote containing the two X^r- and one Y-chromosomes would develop into a female. She would have white eyes, being homozygous for *r*. Remember that in fruit flies, the Y-chromosome is apparently empty and that it is the presence of two X-chromosomes that determines femaleness. In the case of the zygote with just one X-chromosome, the situation would be similar to that described for the grasshopper earlier in the chapter. One X-chromosome permits the autosomes to determine maleness and the single *R*-allele results in production of red eyes.

Bridges' hypothesis provided a neat explanation of these rare flies and, at the same time, could be tested. Microscopic examination of the chromosomes of the white-eyed females should reveal nine of them: six autosomes, two X-chromosomes and one Y-chromosome. It did. Microscopic examination of the chromosomes of the red-eyed males should, and did, reveal just seven of them: six autosomes and one X-chromosome.

Bridges' discovery was exceedingly important because it provided the most direct evidence up to then of the chromosome theory of heredity. The presence of a given trait was directly associated with the presence of an abnormal number of chromosomes —the sex chromosomes. His discovery was also important in that it illustrates beautifully how dependent biologists are on abnormal phenomena for clues to the method of operation of normal phenomena. Over and over again in biology, knowledge of basic life activities has been gained through studying examples of the improper functioning of these activities. Charles Darwin's son once said of him, "There was one quality of mind which seemed to be of special and extreme advantage in leading him to make discoveries. It was the power of never letting exceptions pass unnoticed."

Nondisjunction has since been found to occur in other animals including mice and men. When it occurs in meiosis, the resulting gametes may have one too many or one too few chromosomes. In fertilization, such a gamete will transmit its chromosome excess or deficiency to the zygote. The cells of humans suffering from mongolism have recently been found to contain 47 chromosomes instead of the usual 46 (Fig. 19-11). Humans suffering from certain sexual abnormalities have been found to have more or less than the usual number of sex chromosomes. Although cases such as XYY and just a single X have been studied (what sex would they be?), most of these abnormalities involve extra X's. One might expect a sex chromosome constitution such as XXXX to be so abnormal as not to be viable, but this is not the case. You remember that even in normal women one X-chromosome is inactivated and forms a Barr body (see Section 19-3). In individuals with additional X-chromosomes, the extras are also inactivated. The number of Barr bodies in their cells is equal to the number of X-chromosomes minus one.

OTHER CHROMOSOMAL ABERRATIONS 19-5

The nondisjunction of homologous chromosomes is only one of several abnormal events which can happen to chromosomes during cell division. These abnormalities fall into two groups: (1) changes in chromosome number and (2) changes in chromosome structure. In both cases, the abnormality is inheritable and may be associated with distinct changes in the phenotype of the individuals possessing it. For this reason, these abnormal events (aberrations) are sometimes referred to as chromosomal mutations. They should not be confused with the gene or "point" mutations which will be discussed in the next chapter.

Changes in Chromosome Number

Among the several kinds of wheat grown by man are species with 14, 28, and even 42 chromosomes in the body cells. The species in the latter two cases contain four sets ($4n$) and six sets ($6n$) of chromosomes, respectively, instead of the usual two sets ($2n$). They are said to be **polyploid.** Other cases are known among both plants and animals where this condition occurs. There is a species of grass in New Zealand that is 38-ploid ($38 n$, with $n = 7$).

Polyploidy probably occurs during the process of mitosis. If, after division of the centromeres, something prevents the division of the cell into two, the nuclear membrane will re-form around four sets of chromosomes ($4n$) instead of the usual two sets.

Fig. 19-11

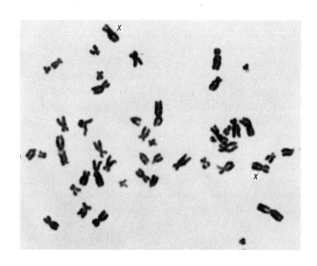

(a) The 46 chromosomes of a human female. The two *X*-chromosomes are marked. (Courtesy Drs. T. T. Puck and J. H. Tjio.) *Karyotypes* (b and c) are prepared by cutting the photograph into pieces containing single chromosomes and arranging these by homologous pairs.

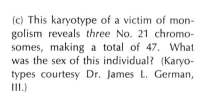

(b) This karyotype is of a normal male. The *X*- and *Y*-chromosomes are marked.

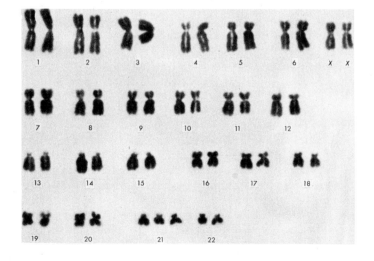

(c) This karyotype of a victim of mongolism reveals *three* No. 21 chromosomes, making a total of 47. What was the sex of this individual? (Karyotypes courtesy Dr. James L. German, III.)

This cell would be polyploid. Geneticists have discovered a chemical, colchicine, which is quite effective in inducing polyploidy. The chemical prevents cell division, but the chromosomes duplicate normally. Onion cells exposed to colchicine for several days have been found with over a thousand chromosomes.

Although the effect of polyploidy on the organism varies from species to species, it is often associated with larger size and greater vigor. For this reason, plant breeders have worked extensively to develop polyploid species. The giant chrysanthemums, so popular at autumn football games, are one outcome of these efforts.

As we have already seen, plants and animals are sometimes found in which only one or two chromosomes in the normal set are present in greater than normal numbers (e.g. $2n + 1$ or $2n + 2$). In other cases, a chromosome may be missing ($2n - 1$). Nondisjunction is one way in which these exceptional forms may be produced. Would you expect to find individuals in which one *pair* of homologous chromosomes was missing?

Changes in Chromosome Structure

1. Deletions. From time to time, geneticists have observed chromosomes which are shorter than normal because of a missing segment. When such a chromosome undergoes synapsis with its homologue, only corresponding portions come together. The result is a loop in the normal chromosome (Fig. 19-12). An organism may reveal such a deletion by a change in its phenotype. For example, a recessive allele on the normal chromosome may express itself if its dominant allele was located in the missing segment of the chromosome with the deletion. The ability to associate a specific gene locus with a microscopically observable loop of a chromosome provides strong support for the chromosome theory.

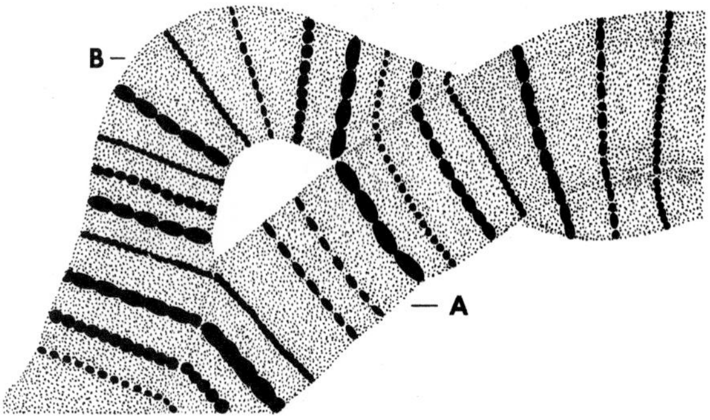

Fig. 19-12

Synapsis of a chromosome having (A) a deletion with (B) its normal homologue. The buckled portion in (B) corresponds to the deleted portion of (A).

2. Duplications. Sometimes chromosomes are found in which a given segment has been duplicated. These, too, are best observed during synapsis with the normal homologue. In this case, which chromosome will form the loop? The extra genes present as a result of a duplication may also affect the phenotype of the organism and permit a definite correlation between the gene loci and the structure of the chromosome.

3. Inversions. Occasionally, chromosomes are found in which a segment of the chromosome is turned around. These inversions are best studied in giant chromosomes such as those found in the salivary glands of the fruit fly. They seldom have drastic effects upon the phenotype of the organism because all the genes are still present. Difficulties may arise, however, when a chromosome with an inversion undergoes synapsis with its normal homologue.

The fact that an inversion has *any* effect on the phenotype is quite interesting. It shows that the action of genes is not just a matter of their presence or absence; it is also affected by their position in the chromosome. This phenomenon is called the "position effect."

4. Translocations. Occasionally a segment of one chromosome breaks loose and becomes attached to a chromosome with which it is not homologous. This is called a translocation. Again the only changes in the phenotype result from the position effect. Organisms with translocations are frequently partially sterile, however. One-half or more of the gametes formed by meiosis will have deletions of certain gene loci and may not be able to survive.

Each of these chromosomal aberrations results in changes which can be observed under the microscope. Whenever these changes in chromosome number or structure can be associated with a change in the traits of the organism, the chromosome theory of heredity is supported further.

19-6	**LINKAGE**

Earlier in the chapter, it was pointed out that the large number of genes and the relatively small number of chromosomes in an organism require that each pair of chromosomes possess many gene loci. In considering the inheritance of two different traits controlled by genes located on the same chromosome, it is obvious that Mendel's *law of independent assortment* can no longer hold. You will remember from the previous chapter that Mendel developed several strains of peas which were dihybrids; that is, they were heterozygous for two different traits, such as seed shape and cotyledon color. When a dihybrid plant (*Rr Yy*) was mated with the homozygous recessive P_1-type (a backcross), the resulting generation contained not only individuals of the P_1-types, round-yellow and wrinkled-green, but also individuals displaying new combinations of the traits, i.e. round-green and wrinkled-yellow. These latter individuals are called *recombinants*. The four kinds of offspring were produced in approximately equal numbers. Today we know that this independent assortment of genes occurred because the gene loci for the two traits were located on different pairs of chromosomes. Because of the random arrangement of maternal and paternal chromosomes on either side of the equatorial plate in first meiosis, random distribution of the genes resulted. This must have been true of all the cases that Mendel

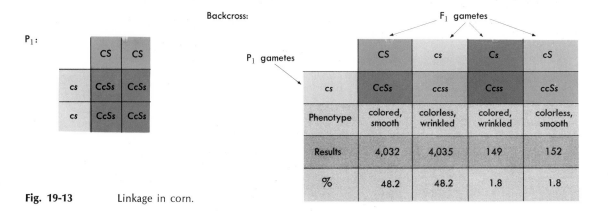

Fig. 19-13   Linkage in corn.

studied and as a result, he framed his second law, the *law of independent assortment:* the distribution of one pair of factors is independent of the distribution of the other pair.

Shortly after the rediscovery of Mendel's work, it became apparent that his second law does not account for inheritance in many dihybrids. In many cases, two alleles inherited from one parent show a strong tendency to segregate together in the formation of gametes and the two alleles inherited from the other parent do the same. This phenomenon is called **linkage.** One of the clearest examples of linkage is found in corn. A strain of corn can be developed which produces kernels that are yellow in color and well filled with a food reserve tissue called endosperm. This strain breeds true, indicating that it is homozygous for these traits. Another strain can be developed which breeds true for colorless kernels that are quite wrinkled in appearance because they contain shrunken endosperm. When the pollen of the first strain (P_1) is dusted on the silks of the second (P_1) (or vice versa), the kernels produced (F_1) are all yellow and full. This tells us that the genes for color (C) and fullness (S) are dominant over those for colorlessness (c) and shrunken endosperm (s) (Fig. 19-13). The plants grown from the F_1 kernels are then backcrossed with the homozygous recessive (P_1) strain ($ccss$) to find out what kinds of gametes are produced by the F_1 plants. According to Mendel's second law, the inheritance of the genes determining color should be entirely independent of the inheritance of the genes determining the appearance of the endosperm. The heterozygous F_1 should thus produce the following gametes in approximately equal numbers: (1) CS, as inherited from one parent, (2), cs as inherited from the other parent, (3) Cs, a recombinant, and (4) cS, a recombinant. All the gametes produced by the double homozygous recessive in the backcross would be cs.

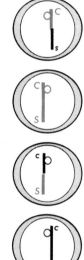

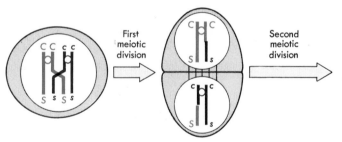

Fig. 19-14

Schematic representation of genetic recombination in a dihybrid cross.

Random union of these gametes would result in four kinds of individuals: (1) colored, smooth, as in the original strain, (2) colorless, wrinkled, as in the other original strain, (3) colored, wrinkled, a recombinant, and (4) colorless, smooth, another recombinant. The genetics of this cross and the actual results achieved are shown in Fig. 19-13. Obviously, Mendel's *law of independent assortment* does not hold. There is a very strong tendency for the gene for colored (C) to remain associated with the gene for smooth texture (S), and similarly, for the gene c to remain associated with the gene s. As we have seen, it can be explained by assuming that the loci of the genes controlling kernel color are on the same chromosome as the loci of the genes controlling kernel texture. In the F_1 generation, when the chromosomes separate in the first meiotic division, the paternal chromosome (CS) goes to one pole and the maternal chromosome (cs) goes to the other (Fig. 19-14).

One question remains. If the gene loci for color and texture are on the same chromosome, how can one explain the 301 recombinant individuals (3.6%) produced by the backcross? The answer is clear when one remembers precisely what happens in the prophase of the first meiotic division. Pairs of duplicated homologous chromosomes unite in synapsis and then one chromosome of each homologue exchanges one or more segments in the process of "crossing over." It is this process of crossing over that gives rise to recombinant gametes. In this case, whenever the crossover occurs between the gene locus for kernel color and the gene locus for kernel texture the original combination of alleles (CS and cs) will be broken up and a chromosome containing Cs and one containing cS will be produced. Note, however, that the other 2 homologues do not participate in this process. Thus only one-half of the gametes produced after second meiosis will contain the recombinant genotype. Remembering that 3.6% of the total gametes produced by the F_1 generation were recombinants, in what percent of the meiotic divisions did crossing over occur between the C and S loci? (The answer is 7.2%. Do you see why?)

19-7   CHROMOSOME MAPS

Other linked traits have been studied in corn. In some, the percentage of recombinant gametes formed by F_1 individuals is even less than the 3.6% found above. In most, the percentage of recombinant gametes is higher. Assuming for a moment that the gene loci are in a linear order from one end of a chromosome to the other, we may deduce that the higher the percentage of recombinant gametes formed for a given pair of traits, the greater the distance separating the two loci. The opposite is also true. Using this knowledge, one can plot a linkage map for as many of the gene loci on a given chromosome as can be discovered. For example, we have seen that about 3% recombinant gametes are produced as a result of crossing over between gene loci C and S. A dihybrid can then be developed for another pair of linked traits, say kernel color (C) and waxy endosperm (wx). This dihybrid produces 33% recombinant gametes, indicating that the loci C and wx are farther apart than the loci C and S. However, one does not yet know whether the locus wx is on the same side of C as S or on the opposite side (Fig. 19-15). The answer can be determined by developing a dihybrid for S and wx. If the percentage of recombinant gametes produced by this individual is less than 33%, then the gene locus wx must be on the same side of locus C as locus S. The opposite is true if the percentage of recombinant gametes turns out to be greater than 33%. Actually the number of recombinant gametes formed is about 30%. Thus we know that the sequence of gene loci on this chromosome is C-S-wx. Furthermore, the fact that the sum of the percents of recombinants between C and S and S and wx is so close to the percent between C and wx lends strong support to the idea that the gene loci are arranged in a line along the length of the chromosome (Fig. 19-15). A straight line is the only geometric arrangement in which this simple numerical relationship can exist.

By pursuing this method with as many linked genes on a given chromosome as can be discovered, it is possible to plot chromosome maps. These maps show the

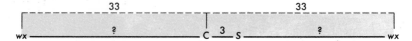

Fig. 19-15   Plotting a linkage map. The production of 30% recombinant gametes as a result of crossing over between the S and wx loci tells us that locus wx is on the same side of locus C as is locus S.

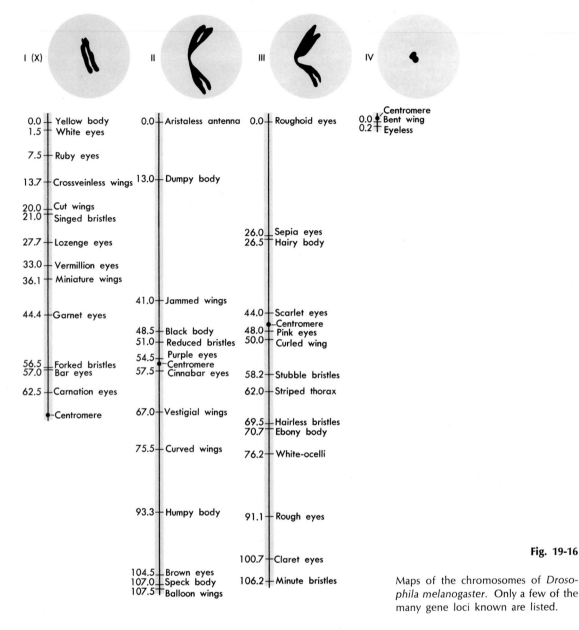

I (X)

0.0	Yellow body
1.5	White eyes
7.5	Ruby eyes
13.7	Crossveinless wings
20.0	Cut wings
21.0	Singed bristles
27.7	Lozenge eyes
33.0	Vermillion eyes
36.1	Miniature wings
44.4	Garnet eyes
56.5	Forked bristles
57.0	Bar eyes
62.5	Carnation eyes
	Centromere

II

0.0	Aristaless antenna
13.0	Dumpy body
41.0	Jammed wings
48.5	Black body
51.0	Reduced bristles
54.5	Purple eyes
	Centromere
57.5	Cinnabar eyes
67.0	Vestigial wings
75.5	Curved wings
93.3	Humpy body
104.5	Brown eyes
107.0	Speck body
107.5	Balloon wings

III

0.0	Roughoid eyes
26.0	Sepia eyes
26.5	Hairy body
44.0	Scarlet eyes
	Centromere
48.0	Pink eyes
50.0	Curled wing
58.2	Stubble bristles
62.0	Striped thorax
69.5	Hairless bristles
70.7	Ebony body
76.2	White-ocelli
91.1	Rough eyes
100.7	Claret eyes
106.2	Minute bristles

IV

	Centromere
0.0	Bent wing
0.2	Eyeless

Fig. 19-16

Maps of the chromosomes of *Drosophila melanogaster*. Only a few of the many gene loci known are listed.

sequence in which the gene loci occur and the relative spacing between them. Such maps have been produced for the chromosomes of the fruit fly (Fig. 19-16), corn, certain bacteria, the mouse, the silkworm, the tomato, and *Chlamydomonas*.

The discovery of linkage has also provided support for the chromosome theory. For example, in the fruit fly all gene loci that have been discovered are found to fall in one of four groups. All the gene loci in a given group show linkage with respect to one another. They do not show linkage with respect to gene loci in other groups. Remembering that fruit flies possess four homologous pairs of chromosomes, the presence of four linkage groups is strong evidence that these four sets of gene loci are, in fact, located on the four pairs of chromosomes.

Perhaps the most convincing proof of the chromosome theory came in 1932 from the work of geneticists Harriet Creighton and Barbara McClintock. During the course of their studies of linkage in corn, they developed a strain of corn that had one chromosome (out of 10 pairs) with two unusual features: a knob at one end of the chromosome and an extra piece of chromosome on the other. This extra piece of chromosome was the result of a translocation that had occurred in an earlier generation. These workers saw immediately the use to which their discovery could be put. Here, at last, was an organism with a pair of homologous chromosomes which could easily be distinguished from each other by microscopic examination. Furthermore, this unusual chromosome carried the dominant allele for colored kernels (C) and the recessive allele for waxy endosperm (wx). Its normal-appearing mate carried the recessive allele for colorless kernels (c) and the dominant allele for normal (starchy) endosperm (Wx). Thus the plant was a dihybrid for these two linked traits and, in addition, one chromosome of the pair was visibly marked at each end. Creighton and McClintock reasoned that this plant would produce four kinds of gametes: the parental kinds (Cwx and cWx) and the recombinant kinds (cwx and CWx) produced by crossing over. Fertilization of these gametes by gametes containing a chromosome of normal appearance and both recessive alleles cwx (a typical backcross) should produce four kinds of kernels: (1) colored waxy (Ccwxwx) kernels, (2) colorless kernels with normal endosperm (ccWxwx) and the two recombinant types, (3) colorless waxy (ccwxwx), and (4) colored kernels with normal endosperm (CcWxwx). Furthermore, microscopic examination of each of the plants resulting from these four kinds of kernels should reveal the following kinds of chromosomes. In the first case, there should be one normal chromosome and one extra-long chromosome with the knob at the end. In the second case, both chromosomes should be of normal appearance. However, in the third case, where genetic crossing over had occurred, one would hope to find evidence that a physical exchange of parts between the homologous chromosomes of the dihybrid parent had occurred. Either a chromosome of normal length but with a knob at one end should be present or an extra-long chromosome with no knob.

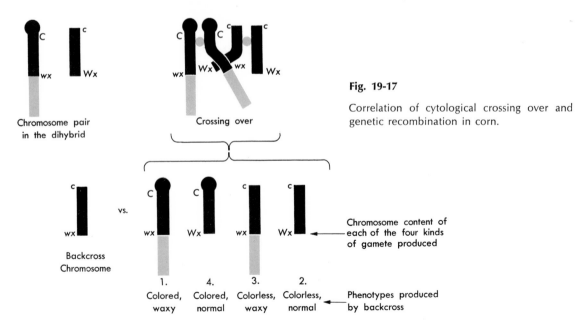

Chromosome pair
in the dihybrid

Crossing over

Fig. 19-17

Correlation of cytological crossing over and genetic recombination in corn.

Backcross
Chromosome

Chromosome content of
each of the four kinds
of gamete produced

1.   4.   3.   2.
Colored,   Colored,   Colorless, Colorless,
waxy   normal   waxy   normal

Phenotypes produced
by backcross

Actually Creighton and McClintock found the latter, thus indicating that the gene locus for *wx* was associated with (and thus near) the end of the chromosome with the extra segment. The gene locus for kernel color must then be nearer the end with the knob. Examination of the plants in Class 4 (colored kernels-C and normal endosperm-*Wx*) revealed a chromosome of normal length but with a knob at one end (Fig. 19-17).

Thus, behavior of the genes as revealed by study of the phenotypes produced was shown to be directly related to the behavior of the chromosomes as revealed by microscopic examination. The recombination of genes is now shown to occur at the same time that homologous chromosomes exchange parts. This is perhaps the most elegant demonstration of the chromosome theory. The determinants of the hereditary traits, genes, whose existence was first hypothesized by Mendel, are shown indeed to be located in these visible structures, the chromosomes.

EXERCISES AND PROBLEMS

1 The garden pea has 7 pairs of homologous chromosomes. If Mendel had mated all possible dihybrid combinations of 8 pairs of contrasting traits instead of 7, would his *law of independent assortment* still have held? Explain.

2 In man, normal vision is a sex-linked trait and its gene is dominant to the allele for red-green colorblindness. When a color-blind woman marries a man with normal vision, what would be the expected distribution of color vision among (a) their sons and (b) their daughters?

3 How many pairs of homologous chromosomes are found in the human male?

4 Summarize the parallelism between the behavior of genes as described by Mendel and the behavior of chromosomes in meiosis and fertilization.

5 Nondisjunction may lead to zygotes containing *XXY*. What sex would this produce in a fruit fly? In a human?

6 When tall tomatoes with red fruit are crossed with dwarf tomatoes with yellow fruit, all the offspring are tall-red. When these F_1's are mated, only the two P_1 phenotypes are found in the F_2. What do we conclude about the genetic control of these two traits?

7 Define a gene.

8 For some reason (not yet fully understood) more male babies are conceived than female. By childhood, the number of boys and girls is the same. Can you think of a possible explanation for the higher mortality (both before birth and after) of male babies?

9 By backcrossing the following dihybrids, it is shown that each produces recombinant gametes in the percentage indicated.

AaBb	31%	AaXx	36%
XxYy	22%	AaYy	14%
XxBb	5%		

From these data determine the linear sequence and relative spacing of each gene locus on the chromosome.

10 Predict the sex of humans with the following chromosome abnormalities (all of which have been observed): *XXY, XXX, X, XYY, XXXX, XXXY, XXXXY*.

11 How many Barr bodies would you expect to find in the cells of each of the individuals in the previous problem?

REFERENCES

1 Hannah-Alava, Aloha, "Genetic Mosaics," *Scientific American*, May, 1960. Explains how nondisjunction and crossing-over may occur during *mitosis*, providing another mechanism for producing genetic mosaics, that is, individuals with cells of differing genotypes.

2 Bearn, A. G., and J. L. German, III, "Chromosomes and Disease," *Scientific American*, Reprint No. 150, November, 1961. Describes the mechanisms by which certain chromosome abnormalties arise and the diseases that may result.

3 Gabriel, M. L., and S. Fogel, eds., *Great Experiments in Biology*, Prentice-Hall, Inc., 1955. This paperback contains several original papers on the chromosome theory, including the report by Harriet Creighton and Barbara McClintock of their experiments.

4 Mittwoch, Ursula, "Sex Differences in Cells," *Scientific American*, Reprint No. 161, July, 1963. Discusses the significance of the sex chromosomes and Barr bodies in both normal and abnormal conditions.

Polysomes. They manufacture proteins according to the instructions coded in the genes. (Courtesy Alexander Rich.)

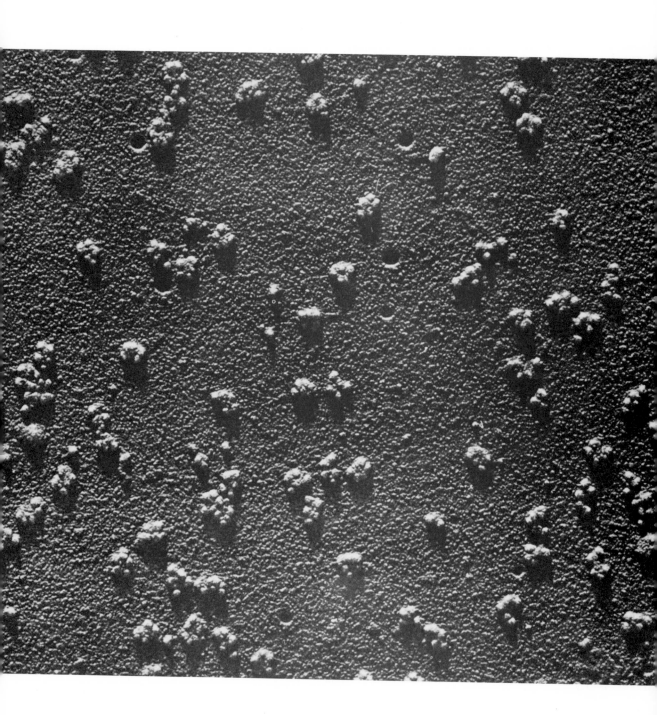

The idea (though not the name) of the gene was developed by Mendel in an attempt to explain certain rules of inheritance. Mendel made no attempt to visualize the gene as a specific structure, in a specific location, with a specific chemical nature, and a specific method of action. Once it was fully established that the genes are located on the chromosomes, however, it became possible to make this attempt. Chromosomes are visible structures in a specific location. It is possible to isolate them from the rest of the cell and to study their chemical composition.

THE CHEMICAL NATURE OF THE GENES

Chromosomes are made of nucleoprotein. By gentle chemical treatment it is possible to break a nucleoprotein into two constituent parts: a protein and a nucleic acid. The chemical nature of each was discussed in Chapter 7. You remember that proteins are macromolecules made up of 20 kinds of repeating units called amino acids. Although all proteins have this same basic structure, the sequence of amino acids is almost infinitely variable. Thus it is not surprising that proteins from different species, proteins from different individuals within a species, and proteins from different locations within the individual all show physical and chemical differences.

Nucleic acids are also macromolecules, and they, too, have a basic structure of repeating units. These units are of three types: bases, sugars, and phosphate groups. The nucleic acid found in chromosomes is DNA. Its bases are generally restricted to four kinds: 2 purines (adenine and guanine) and 2 pyrimidines (thymine and cytosine). For convenience, we will henceforth refer to these as A, G, T, and C, respectively. The sugar is deoxyribose and it supplies the name, deoxyribonucleic acid, for DNA. A second nucleic acid, ribonucleic acid (RNA), is found chiefly outside of the nucleus. In RNA, ribose is the sugar unit rather than deoxyribose. Ribose differs from deoxyribose in having one more oxygen atom in its molecule. Another pyrimidine, uracil (U), substitutes for thymine in RNA.

Having found that the chromosomes are made up of two kinds of macromolecules, protein and DNA, the question is whether the hereditary information is carried by one or both of these substances. A series of experiments with bacteria called pneumococci provided a clear answer. Pneumococci are coccus bacteria than can infect man and cause pneumonia. There are over 30 strains of pneumococci known. A given strain can cause infection only when its cells have a gummy capsule around them. When these encapsulated forms are grown in culture dishes, they produce glistening smooth (S) colonies. Strains which lack the capsule cannot cause the disease and produce rough (R) colonies.

As early as 1928 an English bacteriologist, Fred Griffith, had discovered that if a mouse were injected with living R cells of one strain and *dead S* cells of another strain, the mouse became infected and died of pneumonia. Somehow, the mere presence of the dead S cells had given the R cells the characteristics of the S strain. Furthermore, the transformation was permanent. The transformed cells could be recovered from the mouse and cultured. They passed their newly acquired traits on from generation to generation.

Later, it was discovered that the transformation of R cells to S cells could even be accomplished in a test tube with *extracts* from ruptured S cells. In other words, some ingredient of the dead S cells was capable of permanently altering the heredity of the R bacteria. This ingredient, called the "transforming principle," actually introduced new genes into the R cells. In 1944, after months of tedious, elaborate chemical purifications, Doctors Avery, MacLeod, and McCarty at the Rockefeller Institute

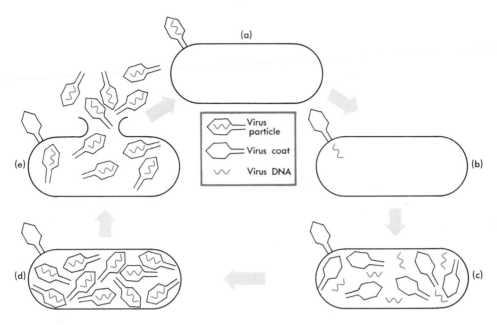

Cycle of infection of bacterial cells by bacteriophages. After the virus attaches to an uninfected bacterial cell (a), its content of DNA is injected (b). New viral DNA molecules *and* new viral protein coats are produced (c). From these are assembled infective bacteriophages (d), which are released when the bacterial cell bursts (e).

Fig. 20-1

finally succeeded in isolating the "transforming principle" as a pure substance. It was DNA.

In 1952, geneticists A. D. Hershey and Martha Chase performed a series of experiments with viruses that gave further proof that DNA is the basic hereditary material. In many ways viruses resemble small chromosomes. They, too, are made of nucleoprotein and when they enter a host cell, the latter goes to work duplicating the virus particles. It is as if the normal genetic control of the cell has been taken over by foreign, invading genes. Bacteria may be infected with viruses called **bacteriophages.** The process of entry has been observed under the electron microscope. Only an inner portion of the virus particle actually enters the cell (Fig. 20-1). The exterior part, the virus coat, probably serves to inject the infecting portion.

Bacteriophages produced within bacteria growing in radioactive culture medium will themselves be radioactive. If radioactive sulfur atoms are present in the medium, they will be incorporated into the proteins of the bacteriophage, since two of the twenty amino acids found in proteins contain sulfur atoms. There are no sulfur atoms in DNA. On the other hand, radioactive phosphorous atoms will be incorporated into the DNA exclusively, for it alone contains phosphorus atoms. When bacteriophages containing radioactive phosphorous atoms are allowed to infect *non*radioactive bacteria, all the bacterial cells become radioactive. Much of this radioactivity is then passed on to the next generation of bacteriophages. However, when bacteria are infected with viruses containing radioactive sulfur atoms and then the virus coats are removed (by whirling in the Waring blendor), practically no radioactivity can be detected in the cells. It is retained in the virus coats.

From these experiments we conclude that the DNA component of the bacteriophage is injected into the bacterial cell while the protein component remains outside.

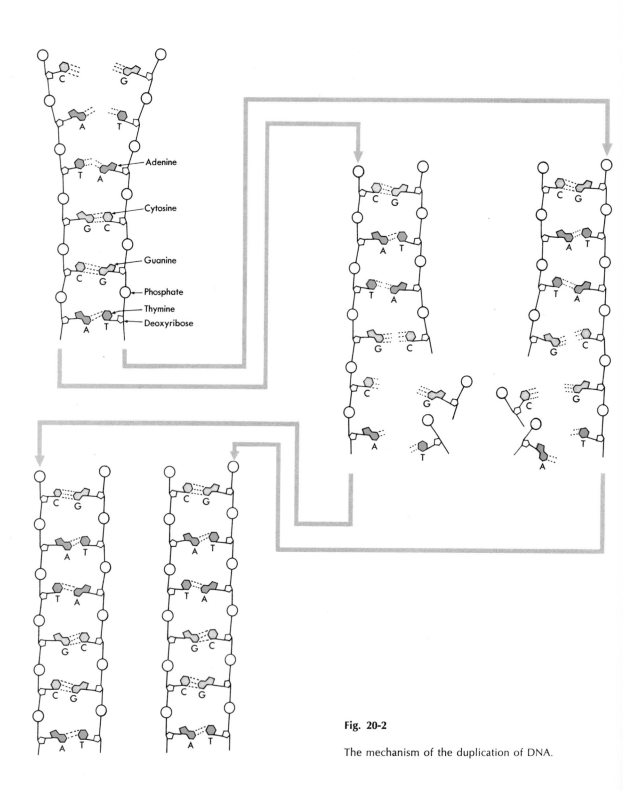

Fig. 20-2

The mechanism of the duplication of DNA.

The DNA is, however, able to direct the formation of new virus particles *complete* with protein coats. Clearly, DNA is the fundamental hereditary material, the substance of the genes. To understand how DNA carries out this function, it is necessary to know more about its chemistry.

In attempting to unravel the chemical nature of DNA, biochemists soon discovered an interesting fact about the relative amounts of the four bases that are present in it. Whatever the amount of A present (and it varies widely from species to species), the amount of T is precisely equal to it. Similarly, the amount of G present is always equal to the amount of C.

THE WATSON-CRICK MODEL OF DNA   20-2

It was the model proposed by Nobel prize winners James Watson and Francis Crick that first provided an idea as to the way these various constituents of DNA are attached to one another. They deduced that the sugar and phosphate groups alternate with one another in a long strand. Two of these strands are twisted around each other in the form of a double helix, something like a double "spiral" staircase. A base is attached to each sugar in the chain so that it projects in toward the axis of the staircase. There it joins with the base projecting from the other staircase. Because of the shape and chemical nature of the purine and pyrimidine bases, A can be attached only to T. Similarly, G can be attached only to C. This explains why the amounts of A and T (also C and G) in the molecule are always equal. Single DNA molecules may contain from hundreds of thousands to millions of base pairs.

The Watson-Crick model provides a clue to the manner in which hereditary information can be stored in the DNA molecule. Although the basic arrangement of parts in the DNA molecule seems to be the same for all organisms, there is an almost infinite variety of sequences in which these four kinds of base pairs, present by the hundreds of thousands, can be arranged. The International Morse Code provides an interesting parallel. It is made up of only three basic units: a dot, a dash, and a pause. Given sufficient patience and time, however, a telegraph operator could transmit the contents of an entire library by the sequences in which he combined these three units!

At one step on a single staircase, any one of the four bases may be present. Thus, there are four items in our code. Note, too, that whatever base is present at a given step, we know immediately what kind of base bridges the gap between it and the opposite staircase. Thus whatever sequence of bases is present on one strand of the DNA molecule, a complementary sequence is present on the other strand. The two sequences have the same relationship to each other as the "positive" and "negative" of a photograph. This repetitious nature of the code provides a nice mechanism to explain one of the fundamental properties of genes: their ability to duplicate.

The chromosomes are duplicated during interphase, the period between cell divisions. According to the Watson-Crick hypothesis, the DNA molecules become "unzipped" at this time; that is, the bonds between the base pairs break and the two halves of the molecule unwind. Once exposed, the bases on each of the separated strands can pick up the appropriate nucleotides (a base linked with deoxyribose and phosphate) floating freely in the nucleus. Each exposed C will pick up a G, each G a C, etc. When the process is completed, two complete DNA molecules will be present, identical to each other and to the original molecule (Fig. 20-2). This is precisely the description we used in discussing what happens to chromosomes in the process of mitosis.

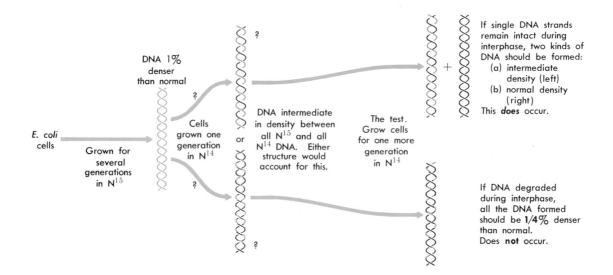

Fig. 20-3   The experiment of Meselson and Stahl. The results (right) suggest that during the process of duplication each strand of DNA remains intact and builds a complementary strand from the nucleotides available. This is consistent with the Watson-Crick model of DNA.

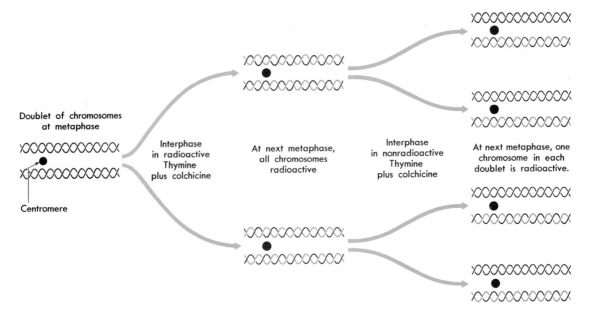

Fig. 20-4   The duplication of chromosomes. The results suggest that (1) each chromosome (chromatid) consists of two parts and (2) each of these two parts remains intact during the process of duplication. The parallel between this experiment and the one in Fig. 20-3 suggests that the two parts are the two strands of a DNA molecule and that they separate during interphase according to the Watson-Crick model. Exactly how the DNA is organized in the chromosome is not yet known. This experiment was first performed by Dr. J. Herbert Taylor of Columbia University.

This attractive hypothesis has received considerable experimental support. As we saw in Chapter 17 (see Section 17-6), *E. coli* cells can be grown in a culture medium containing just glucose and inorganic salts. Among the latter must be a source of nitrogen atoms for protein and nucleic acid synthesis. Nitrate ions (NO_3^-) serve nicely. Although the most common isotope of nitrogen is N^{14}, it is possible to synthesize nitrates containing a heavier isotope of nitrogen, N^{15}. When *E. coli* cells are grown for several generations in a medium containing $N^{15}O_3^-$, their DNA becomes about 1% heavier because of the incorporation of N^{15} atoms in it. Working at Caltech in 1958, M. S. Meselson and F. W. Stahl grew *E. coli* cells in this way and then let them divide once in a medium containing ordinary nitrate, $N^{14}O_3^-$. The DNA in the new generation of bacterial cells was exactly intermediate in weight between the heavier DNA in the previous generation and the normal. This, in itself, is not surprising. It tells us no more than that half the nitrogen atoms in the new DNA are N^{14} and half are N^{15}. It tells us nothing about their arrangement in the molecule. However, when the bacterial cells were allowed to divide *again* in normal nitrate ($N^{14}O_3^-$), two distinct weights of DNA were formed: half the DNA was of normal weight and half was of intermediate weight. As shown in Fig. 20-3, this indicates that DNA molecules are not degraded and re-formed at each interphase, but instead, each original strand remains intact as it builds a complementary strand from the nucleotides available to it.

Watson and Crick's theory of DNA duplication is reflected even at the level of the visible chromosomes. When plant root tips are grown in a solution containing radioactive T, the chromosomes in the rapidly dividing cells of the embryonic region become uniformly radioactive. If the root tips are then transferred from the radioactive solution to one containing nonradioactive T and colchicine, chromosome duplication takes place without cell division. After one duplication, the chromosomes are still uniformly radioactive. After a second duplication, however, one chromosome of each doublet is radioactive, the other is not (Fig. 20-4).

In seeking to relate the Watson-Crick model of DNA to the actual structure of the chromosome, it must be remembered that the two are of quite different sizes. Chromosomes are easily observed under the light microscope; isolated pieces of DNA can be seen only under the electron microscope (Fig. 20-5). If the single chromosome of *E. coli* does contain just one DNA molecule, the molecule would have to be over 1 mm long even though only 20 A in thickness. Such a molecule has actually been isolated, but in the intact cell (about 2 μ long) it must be greatly folded and twisted. If all chromosomes are made of single DNA molecules, separation of the two strands of DNA prior to duplication must require the unraveling of millions of turns. This probably is not the case. There is some indirect evidence that the chromosomes of higher organisms contain something on the order of 100 DNA molecules. However, no one yet knows exactly how DNA is organized to make up the chromosomes.

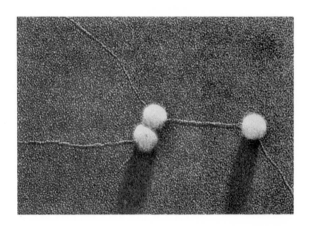

Fig. 20-5

Single strands of DNA. The white spheres are polystyrene latex with a diameter of 880 A. They provide a built-in measuring scale. (Electron micrograph made by Dr. Cecil E. Hall, M.I.T.)

The mechanism for the duplication of DNA must be remarkably precise. Genes may be passed on for thousands of generations without showing any change. Today certain species of organisms are found which are called living fossils because they are so little changed from fossil forms living millions of years ago. The mollusk *Neopilina* (Fig. 1-1), living in the ocean today, is little changed from *Pilina* which lived in the oceans over 500 million years ago. When you consider that our Rocky Mountains were formed 60 million years ago, you can appreciate the great precision by which this particular hereditary information has been passed on from generation to generation.

The structure of the DNA molecule is ideally suited to the long-term preservation of the sequence of bases coded in it. Because the two chains in a DNA molecule are complementary, the information in one is also coded in the other. In a sense, then, each DNA molecule contains two copies of its information. If for some reason the sequence of bases on one chain were disturbed, the correct message could still be determined from the complementary chain. Recently it has been discovered that bacteria, at least, have a mechanism by which they correct errors that occur in their DNA code. By means of enzymes, they remove damaged or incorrect bases from their DNA molecule. These are then replaced by the correct bases, that is, bases complementary to the bases on the opposite strand. In this way, their genetic code is preserved intact.

20-3　　　　　**MUTATIONS**

Although the organization of the DNA molecule makes it remarkably resistant to changes in its sequence of bases, such changes do occur. These changes we call gene or "point" mutations to distinguish them from the chromosomal aberrations discussed in the last chapter. They may occur in the body cells of an organism. In this case, the welfare of the species is little affected. The mutant gene may cause the cell to age or die or perhaps to become cancerous, but when the owner of the cell dies, the mutant gene dies with him.

On the other hand, mutations that occur in the gamete-producing cells may be of great significance. We have seen how a mutation that probably occurred in the gonads of Queen Victoria's father gave rise to genes which produced many hemophiliacs in the royal families of Europe.

The mutant gene for hemophilia illustrates two points about most mutations. They are usually recessive and they are usually harmful. Why this is so will be clear when we discuss the mechanism of evolution in Chapter 32.

Mutations such as the one that first appeared in Queen Victoria are called "spontaneous." This is another way of saying that we don't know what caused the change in the genetic code. But methods have been found to induce mutations. In 1927, H. J. Muller reported that he had increased by 15,000 percent the rate of mutations in *Drosophila* by treating them with x-rays. Muller ultimately received the Nobel Prize for this work. Since that time other radiations of short wavelength such as ultraviolet rays and cosmic rays have been found to induce mutations when they penetrate to the chromosomes. High temperatures and certain chemical substances, such as the nitrogen-mustard war gases, also produce mutations indistinguishable from those produced by radiation.

Mutations are of great importance and interest to the biologist and the layman alike. First, the biologist sees mutations as the basic source of the variability among living things that has permitted evolution to occur. Second, the biologist recognizes that the vast majority of mutations produce harmful effects on the organism. These harmful genes may be passed on to future generations, carrying with them their burden of illness and deformity. The biologist also sees that man, as he develops his technological civilization, is exposing himself to ever-increasing doses of radiation capable of causing mutations. All good citizens are becoming aware of this problem, although few laymen yet seem to appreciate the quantitative aspects of it. Since there seems to be no minimum dose below which mutations will not occur, all unnecessary exposure to radiation should be avoided. Nevertheless, a glance at Fig. 20-6 will show that the problems of the medical use of x-rays (chest x-rays, dental x-rays, wart therapy, etc.) perhaps need more urgent attention than those raised by radioactive fallout. Unnecessary exposure to radiation, as with x-ray shoe-fitting machines, seems indefensible.

K^{40} in body	20	mrem/yr	
Cs^{137}-fallout	1	mrem/yr	
Cosmic rays	30	mrem/yr	—at sea level
λ-background	45	mrem/yr	—value increased 1.5 times in sedimentary rock area or use of stone construction
λ-fallout	0.5	mrem/yr	
Medical	140	mrem/yr	—estimated
Total	236	mrem/yr	

Fig. 20-6

Estimated yearly radiation dosage to the gonads of man. (Courtesy Robert A. Dudley, *AAAS Publication* **59**, 1959, p. 87.)

Third, the biologist sees mutations as an extremely valuable tool for discovering more about genetics. The discovery of sex linkage, discussed in the last chapter, is just one example of how mutant genes make clearer the mechanism of heredity.

Mutant genes have also been of great importance in providing clues to the way in which genes act to produce a given phenotype. Red eyes, nonclotting blood, waxy endosperm, etc., are not made up of DNA. They are simply the expression or product of gene activity. A discussion of genetics would not be complete without considering the steps by which a given genotype produces a given phenotype.

THE ONE GENE-ONE ENZYME THEORY 20-4

The most widely accepted theory on the method of action of genes grew out of the work of the geneticists G. W. Beadle and E. L. Tatum with the red bread mold *Neurospora crassa*, an ascomycete. *Neurospora* is particularly well suited for genetic studies. Its life cycle is shown in Fig 20-7. Note that the only diploid stage in the organism is the zygote, and it quickly undergoes meiosis. The vegetative stage of the organism is haploid. Thus each gene is present only once and the geneticist does not have to worry about the effect of recessive genes being masked by dominant ones. Another great virtue is that the meiotic divisions of the zygote nucleus occur in an elongated structure, the ascus. The ascus is so narrow that the 8 nuclei produced by the first and second meiotic divisions followed by one mitotic division are not able to slip past one another. Consequently, if the original zygote nucleus is heterozygous for some pair of alleles, and no crossing over of that locus occurs, the alleles will segregate at first meiosis. After the next two divisions, the ascus will have four spores at one end containing one allele and four spores at the other end containing the other allele. (What patterns might occur if crossing over of the loci *should* occur in the first meiotic division?)

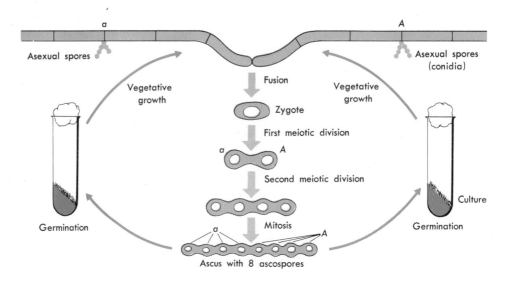

Fig. 20-7 Life cycle of *Neurospora*. The distribution shown here of the *A* and *a* alleles would occur only if no exchange of this locus took place during crossing over in the first meiotic division.

This segregation of alleles in the spores of the ascus silences one criticism sometimes made of genetic studies, namely, that their analysis is always statistical. Sperm, pollen, or eggs display Mendelian ratios only when large samples are considered, because the products of one meiotic division become mixed at random with the products of other meiotic divisions. On the other hand, in *Neurospora* the nuclei resulting from a given meiosis are held in a fixed position and show the Mendelian ratios directly and exactly.

Neurospora can be grown in test tubes containing a very simple ("minimal") culture medium. Sucrose, a few salts, and the one vitamin, biotin, provide all the nutritional requirements for *Neurospora* to live, grow, and reproduce. From these relatively few and simple substances, it is capable of synthesizing all the many complex substances, such as proteins and nucleic acids, necessary for life. Beadle and Tatum exposed some of the asexual spores of one mating type of *Neurospora* to ultraviolet rays. These spores were then allowed to germinate on a "complete" medium, that is, one enriched with various vitamins and amino acids. Once a vigorous mycelium had developed, it was allowed to mate with the other mating type. The ascospores produced as a result were then dissected out individually and each one placed on additional quantities of complete media. After growth had occurred, portions of the mycelium of each culture were placed on a minimal medium. Sometimes growth continued; sometimes it didn't. When it did not, the particular strain was then supplied with various vitamins, amino acids, etc., until growth did occur. Eventually, each deficient strain was found to be capable of growing on a minimal medium to which one accessory substance, for example, the vitamin thiamine, had been added. Beadle and Tatum reasoned that ultraviolet irradiation had caused a gene that permits the synthesis of thiamine to mutate to an allele that does not.

The manufacture of thiamine from the simple substances present in the minimal medium does not take place in a single chemical reaction but in a whole series of them. Like all chemical reactions in living things, each one requires the presence of

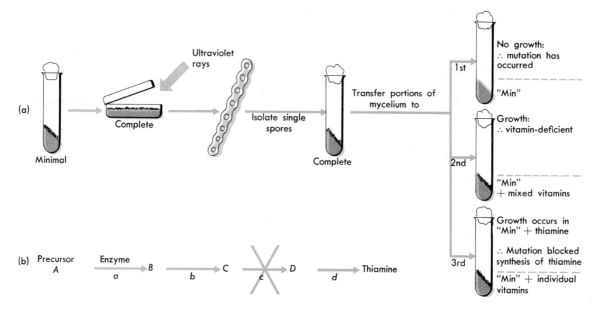

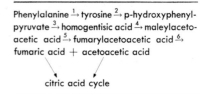

Beadle and Tatum's (a) experiment and (b) hypothesis. Crossing the mutant strain with a normal strain showed that the ability to convert thiamine precursor C into precursor D was controlled by a single gene. Presumably the mutant gene could not produce the necessary enzyme.

Fig. 20-8

a specific enzyme. By adding intermediate compounds (precursors) to the medium in which their mold was growing, Beadle and Tatum were able to locate just which step in the synthesis of thiamine was blocked in their mutant strain (Fig. 20-8). If they added to the minimal medium any precursor further along in the process, growth occurred. Any precursor before the blocked reaction did not permit growth. They reasoned that the change of precursor C to precursor D was blocked because of the absence of the specific enzyme required. On this basis they created the "one gene-one enzyme" theory of gene action: each gene in an organism controls the production of a specific enzyme. It is these enzymes which then carry out all the metabolic activities of the organism, resulting in the development of a characteristic structure and physiology, the phenotype of the organism.

One might argue that Beadle and Tatum's experiment does not prove that only a single gene was involved. When the thiamine-deficient mutant is mated with a normal strain, though, the resulting asci contain four mutant spores and four non-mutant spores. Would this 50:50 ratio have occurred if more than one gene locus were involved?

The discoveries of Beadle and Tatum (for which they shared a Nobel Prize) shed new light on some interesting human diseases which were known to be hereditary. One of these, alcaptonuria, is a rather rare ailment in which the chief symptom is that the urine of the patient turns black upon exposure to air. Biochemical studies have shown that the disease results when the enzyme that catalyzes the conversion of homogentisic acid to maleylacetoacetic acid is lacking in the individual (Fig. 20-9). These substances are intermediates in the breakdown of the amino acid phenylalanine into compounds that can be oxidized in the citric acid cycle. When Step 4 is blocked, homogentisic acid accumulates in the

Phenylalanine $\xrightarrow{1}$ tyrosine $\xrightarrow{2}$ p-hydroxyphenyl-pyruvate $\xrightarrow{3}$ homogentisic acid $\xrightarrow{4}$ maleylaceto-acetic acid $\xrightarrow{5}$ fumarylacetoacetic acid $\xrightarrow{6}$ fumaric acid + acetoacetic acid

citric acid cycle

Fig. 20-9

Pathway of phenylalanine metabolism in humans.

blood. The kidney then excretes this excess in the urine. Oxidation of homogentisic acid by the air turns the urine black.

Another hereditary disease, phenylketonuria (PKU), is caused by a blockage of Step 1. In this case, phenylalanine itself accumulates in the blood. The chief symptoms are a serious stunting of intelligence (most sufferers have to be confined to mental institutions), pale skin, and a tendency to epileptic seizures. The pale skin may result from a lack of tyrosine from which the pigment melanin (responsible for suntan and freckles) is formed. Both alcaptonuria and phenylketonuria are recessive traits. An individual must be homozygous for the mutant allele to show the trait. This is quite consistent with the one gene-one enzyme theory: so long as one nonmutant gene is present, the necessary enzyme is manufactured.

Another recessive hereditary disease is sickle-cell anemia. In individuals homozygous for the trait, the RBC's become crescent or sickle-shaped, particularly when passing through the capillaries (Fig. 20-10). This reduces the life span of the RBC's and a fatal anemia can result. Curiously, there is evidence that the mutant allele, when present in the single dose, confers on children some resistance to one kind of malaria. The allele is particularly prevalent among Negroes living in malarial regions. Studies of individuals having the allele show that they also have abnormal hemoglobin molecules in their RBC's. These are designated as Hb^s. Heterozygous individuals, with one normal allele and one mutant allele, have both normal hemoglobin (Hb^A) and Hb^s.

Fig. 20-10   Red blood corpuscles of a victim of sickle-cell anemia. Left: oxygenated. Right: deoxygenated. The shape of the cells when deoxygenated causes them to break easily. (Courtesy Dr. Anthony C. Allison.)

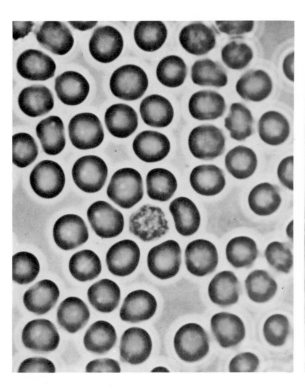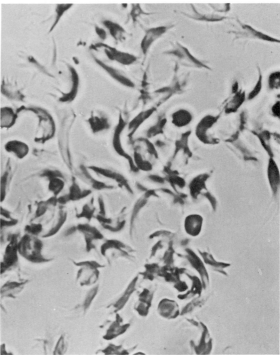

Hemoglobin molecules are proteins consisting of four poly-peptide chains (2 "alpha" chains and 2 "beta" chains), each with the prosthetic group, heme. Each of the polypeptide chains is made up of about 150 amino acids. Chemical analysis of Hb^A and Hb^S reveals that they have the same sequence of amino acids in their alpha chains. Their beta chains are also identical except that at one place in the chain, the amino acid valine is substituted for the amino acid glutamic acid normally found at that point (Fig. 20-11).

Other abnormal hemoglobins are known where alterations occur in the alpha chain of the molecule. These are produced by genes at a different gene locus from that of the sickle-cell allele. On this basis, the one gene-one enzyme theory can be refined into a one gene-one polypeptide theory. The evidence from sickle-cell anemia is that a gene not only controls the synthesis of a polypeptide but that its mutant allele may pro-duce a polypeptide in which only one amino acid in the sequence has been altered.

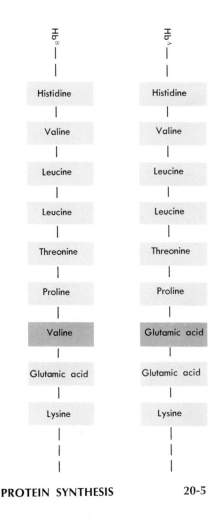

Fig. 20-11

Corresponding portions of the "beta" polypeptide chains of normal hemoglobin (Hb^A) and sickle-cell hemoglobin (Hb^S).

PROTEIN SYNTHESIS   20-5

Most of the DNA of a cell is located in the nucleus. Most of the protein synthesis in the cell goes on in the cytoplasm. How, then, do the genes control the synthesis of protein in such a precise way? Biologists, chemists, and physicists in laboratories throughout the world are cooperating in an attempt to answer this question.

Protein synthesis occurs at clusters of tiny (150 A) cytoplasmic particles called **ribosomes.** These are made up of two molecules of **ribosomal RNA,** each associated with protein. The RNA molecules are on the surface. There do not appear to be specific ribosomes for the manufacture of specific proteins. In fact, the ribosomes from organisms as diverse as yeast and the rabbit seem interchangeable. While they are essential to protein synthesis, we must look elsewhere for the key by which the nature of the protein being synthesized is determined.

This substance is another kind of RNA called **messenger RNA.** Molecules of mes-senger RNA are synthesized within the nucleus and then pass out into the cytoplasm. They transmit the hereditary message from the DNA within the nucleus to the ribo-somes out in the cytoplasm. Thus the name messenger RNA is well chosen.

DNA guides the synthesis of messenger RNA in the same way that it guides its own duplication (see Section 20-2). A single strand of DNA picks up *ribo*nucleotides from the surrounding medium and, with the aid of an enzyme, assembles them into

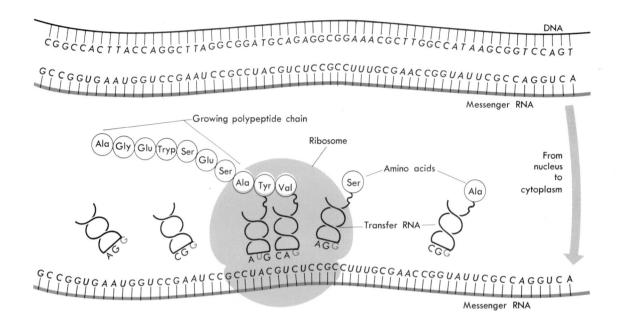

Fig. 20-12   Probable mechanism of the synthesis of a polypeptide according to the genetic instructions coded in DNA. The particular bases with which *transfer* RNA molecules are thought to "recognize" complementary codons on the *messenger* RNA molecule have been tentatively identified for the transfer RNA molecules shown. The use of colored letters for certain bases indicates that the actual base is a chemically modified form of the one indicated but forms base pairs in the same way.

a strand of RNA whose sequence of bases complements exactly the sequence of bases in the DNA molecules. For every C on the DNA molecule, a G is inserted into the complementary strand of messenger RNA. So, too, every G picks up a C-containing ribonucleotide and every T picks up an A-containing ribonucleotide. A's on the DNA strand code the insertion of a uracil (U)-containing ribonucleotide. (There is no thymine in RNA.) When the job is completed, the single strand of messenger RNA leaves the DNA as a faithful transcription of it.

This theory of messenger RNA formation has been nicely supported. When a synthetic DNA consisting solely of T-containing nucleotides ("poly-T") is supplied with all four ribonucleotides (A, U, C, and G), and the necessary linking enzyme, a messenger RNA molecule is formed which contains adenine only in the strand (poly-A).

Messenger RNA can thus serve to transmit the hereditary message in the nucleus to the protein-making machinery of the cytoplasm. Several unanswered questions still remain, however. Proteins are made up of amino acids. How is the sequence of amino acids in a protein related to the sequence of exposed bases on a strand of messenger RNA?

This requires a third kind of RNA called **transfer RNA.** There are at least 20 distinct kinds of transfer RNA molecules in the cell, one for each of the 20 amino acids. With the aid of a specific enzyme and ATP, each amino acid is activated and attached to its particular transfer RNA molecule.

The structure of several transfer RNA molecules has been determined. Each consists of a chain of from 75 to 85 ribonucleotides. Many of these are the normal RNA nucleotides (A, U, G, and C) and in places these bases link two portions of the chain in a double helix like the DNA molecule. Because of this, at least one loop is formed in the chain and, of course, it has two exposed ends (Fig. 20-12). The amino acid is attached to one of the free ends. It is thought that unpaired bases at a loop "recognize" complementary exposed bases on the messenger RNA molecule and unite with them according to the usual rules of base-pairing. Each of the 20 kinds of transfer RNA carrying its specific amino acid could unite, theoretically, with those portions of the messenger RNA molecule whose bases were complementary to the exposed bases on the transfer RNA. This would bring the amino acids into sequence ready to be joined to form a polypeptide. Furthermore, this sequence would be controlled by the sequence of bases in the messenger RNA molecule and thus, ultimately, in the DNA molecule in the nucleus (Fig. 20-12).

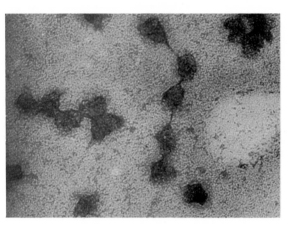

Fig. 20-13

Polysomes from cells engaged in the synthesis of the polypeptide chains of hemoglobin. Five ribosomes are connected by a strand thought to be a molecule of messenger RNA. The length of the polysome suggests that 3 bases in the messenger RNA molecule code 1 amino acid in the polypeptide. (Courtesy Dr. Alexander Rich.)

The union of transfer RNA and messenger RNA requires the presence of the ribosomes. Electron micrographs and biochemical analysis both suggest that the ribosomes attach to the end of a strand of messenger RNA and then move along its length, "reading" its sequence of bases. As they do this, they pick up the appropriate transfer RNA molecules, each with its amino acid. One at a time these amino acids become linked together to form the polypeptide chain. When the ribosome reaches the end of the messenger RNA strand, the polypeptide chain is complete. It and the ribosome are released.

Although a single ribosome can manufacture a polypeptide chain from a messenger RNA molecule, several ribosomes are usually engaged in the process at one time. One messenger RNA molecule with several ribosomes attached to it at various stages in assembling the polypeptide is called a polyribosome or **polysome.** These have been observed under the electron microscope (Fig. 20-13).

Here, then, is a mechanism by which a unique sequence of bases in the DNA of the chromosomes controls a unique sequence of amino acids in the proteins manufactured by the cell. The DNA of a cell may thus constitute the "master" copy of the hereditary information, while the messenger RNA is the "working" copy. An analogy may help to make this clear. In the recording industry, great care and expense go into the manufacture of a master negative of a record. It is far too valuable to be used in the molds that produce the thousands of wax impressions that will be sold to the public. Instead, working copies of the master are made from it. These copies, which are called "mothers," are then used in the molds to produce the final product.

A great deal of work has also been done in an effort to determine what sequence of bases in the messenger RNA molecule codes each of the amino acids. There are only four kinds of bases (A, U, C, and G) in the messenger RNA molecule, too few for each one to code a single amino acid. Pairs of bases could be arranged in 16 different ways (AA, UU, AU, UA, etc.), but this is still short of the necessary number. Triplets of bases could be arranged in 64 different ways (Fig. 20-14) and thus would provide ample possibilities for coding 20 amino acids. In fact, we might expect two or three different triplets to code a single amino acid.

UUU ⎫ Phenylalanine UUC ⎭ (Phe) UUA ⎫ Leucine UUG ⎭ (Leu)	CUU ⎫ CUC ⎮ Leucine CUA ⎧ (Leu) CUG ⎭	AUU ⎫ Isoleucine AUC ⎮ (Ileu) AUA ⎭ AUG—Methionine (Met)	GUU ⎫ GUC ⎮ Valine GUA ⎧ (Val) GUG ⎭
UCU ⎫ UCC ⎮ Serine UCA ⎧ (Ser) UCG ⎭	CCU ⎫ CCC ⎮ Proline CCA ⎧ (Pro) CCG ⎭	ACU ⎫ ACC ⎮ Threonine ACA ⎧ (Thr) ACG ⎭	GCU ⎫ GCC ⎮ Alanine GCA ⎧ (Ala) GCG ⎭
UAU ⎫ Tyrosine UAC ⎭ (Tyr) UAA ⎫ Chain UAG ⎭ terminators	CAU ⎫ Histidine CAC ⎭ (His) CAA ⎫ Glutamine CAG ⎭ (GluN)	AAU ⎫ Asparagine AAC ⎭ (AspN) AAA ⎫ Lysine AAG ⎭ (Lys)	GAU ⎫ Aspartic acid GAC ⎭ (Asp) GAA ⎫ Glutamic acid GAG ⎭ (Glu)
UGU ⎫ Cysteine UGC ⎭ (Cys) UGA—Chain terminator UGG—Tryptophan (Tryp)	CGU ⎫ CGC ⎮ Arginine CGA ⎧ (Arg) CGG ⎭	AGU ⎫ Serine AGC ⎭ (Ser) AGA ⎫ Arginine AGG ⎭ (Arg)	GGU ⎫ GGC ⎮ Glycine GGA ⎧ (Gly) GGG ⎭

Fig. 20-14   The genetic code. Although most of the codons have been assigned as a result of studies with *E. coli*, there is evidence that the code applies to all organisms. In most cases several codons code for a single amino acid, and one codon may be "preferred" by one organism, another by a different organism.

By manufacturing synthetic messenger RNA molecules and then supplying them with ribosomes, ATP, enzymes, and all 20 amino acids, it has been possible to establish tentatively the triplets that code the various amino acids. For example, a synthetic messenger RNA that has only uracil (poly-U) produces a polypeptide containing the single amino acid phenylalanine. This suggests that the triplet UUU guides the incorporation of phenylalanine into the growing polypeptide chain. Similarly, synthetic poly-A messenger RNA guides the synthesis of a polypeptide containing only the amino acid lysine. Using synthetic messenger RNA with two or more bases present in fixed ratios, it has been possible to correlate one or more triplets with each one of the 20 amino acids (Fig. 20-14). Because of this coding relationship, a triplet of bases is called a **codon.**

Three of the 64 possible codons (UAA, UAG, and UGA) have not been found to code for any amino acid. In *E. coli*, at least, these three codons serve as punctuation marks. When the ribosome reaches them, the growth of the polypeptide chain is halted, and the chain is released ready to carry out its function in the cell.

That the genetic code is indeed the simplest possible, that is, a triplet code, has been nicely supported by the discovery that the polysomes which synthesize the alpha and beta chains of hemoglobin are approximately 1500 A long. The alpha and beta chains each consist of some 150 amino acids. To code these by a triplet code would require 450 bases on the messenger RNA molecule. Since each base occupies about 3.4 A of the chain, this would produce a molecule whose length would be very close (1530 A) to the measured value.

Going back to our one gene-one polypeptide hypothesis, perhaps a mutant gene is simply a section of a DNA molecule in which one base pair has been altered. An alteration of a base pair in the DNA molecule would result in a corresponding alteration in the *messenger* RNA molecule. This, in turn, would provide a surface complementary to a different *transfer* RNA molecule. Thus a different amino acid would be inserted in the protein at this point.

The codons GAA and GAG are thought to code for glutamic acid (Fig. 20-14). In our example of Hb^A and Hb^S, the substitution of a single base, a U for an A in the middle position of the codon, would give a GUA or a GUG codon. Both of these have, indeed, been assigned to valine, the amino acid substitution in sickle-cell hemoglobin. Perhaps, then, the primary difference between a sickle-cell individual and a normal one is the presence of adenine (A) instead of thymine (T) at one spot in the part of a DNA molecule that stores the information for the synthesis of the beta chain of hemoglobin. Although a seemingly minor change, the resulting substitution of valine for glutamic acid so alters the physical properties of hemoglobin that a fatal anemia is produced in the individual homozygous for the trait.

Is the code universal? Probably so. It appears that the same codons are assigned to the same amino acids in such diverse organisms as *E. coli,* yeast, the tobacco plant, a species of toad, and the guinea pig. As you can see from Fig. 20-14, however, almost all the amino acids are coded by more than one codon. *Which* of the alternative codons for a particular amino acid is most often used may vary from species to species.

INCOMPLETE DOMINANCE   20-7

If a dominant gene produces one polypeptide, does its recessive allele simply not make any polypeptide at all? Clearly this is not the case in sickle-cell anemia. A person heterozygous for the trait produces both Hb^S and Hb^A. There are many other cases known where hybrids produce a phenotype distinguishable from that of either homozygous parent. This situation is called incomplete dominance. When pure-breeding red snapdragons (P_1) are mated to pure-breeding white snapdragons (P_1), the F_1 offspring produced are pink. Both alleles contribute to the phenotype and neither can be said to be dominant over the other. Note, however, that although their effects are somewhat blended in the F_1, the alleles themselves are in no sense blended. They will segregate normally in the formation of gametes and one-half of the F_2 offspring will show the P_1 traits completely. Note too, that the phenotype ratio in the F_2 for traits showing incomplete dominance is just the same as the genotype ratio: 1:2:1.

MULTIPLE ALLELES   20-8

Another illustration of incomplete dominance is found in the inheritance of the Landsteiner blood types. For many years, doctors have tried to save the lives of victims of severe bleeding by transfusing into their veins fresh blood from a healthy donor. Prior to 1900, the results were quite unpredictable. Sometimes the procedure worked successfully. Other times, the recipient died suddenly.

In 1900, Karl Landsteiner discovered the explanation for these erratic results. He found that many people have antigenic substances on the surface of their red blood corpuscles. Two different ones were discovered by him: the A antigen and the B antigen. People having the former are said to have Type A blood, people with the latter have blood Type B. Some people have both antigens (Type AB) and others (Type O) have neither (Fig. 20-15).

Blood group	Approx. % in U. S. population	Antigens on RBC's	Antibodies in plasma	Can donate to	Can receive from	Genotypes
A	42	A	Anti-B	A, AB	O, A	$L^A L^A$ or $L^A l$
B	10	B	Anti-A	B, AB	O, B	$L^B L^B$ or $L^B l$
AB	3	A and B	Neither	AB	O, A, B, AB	$L^A L^B$
O	45	Neither	Anti-A and anti-B	O, A, B, AB	O	ll

Fig. 20-15   The Landsteiner (ABO) blood groups and the genotypes that give rise to each.

When RBC's carrying one or both antigens are brought in contact with the appropriate **antibodies,** they agglutinate, that is, they clump together (Fig. 20-16). You remember (see Section 14-12) that antibodies are proteins and are found in the plasma of the blood. When anti-A antibodies come in contact with RBC's carrying the A antigen, they cause the RBC's to agglutinate. Fortunately, no one has antibodies in his plasma capable of clumping his own RBC's.

Figure 20-15 illustrates which bloods can and cannot be safely transfused. The basic principle to be observed is that the blood introduced into the patient's body must not contain RBC's which he can clump. It is not too serious if the introduced blood contains antibodies against his own RBC's because the antibodies will quickly be diluted by his own plasma. Hence, Type O blood has been called the "universal donor" because O corpuscles cannot be clumped and the antibodies will be quickly diluted by the recipient's plasma. Similarly, AB blood is called the "universal recipient" because it contains no antibodies to clump RBC's introduced into it. In actual practice, however, doctors prefer to match bloods exactly when carrying out transfusions.

The Landsteiner blood types are inherited. The type is controlled by two alleles, one inherited from each parent. However, there are three alleles, L^A, L^B, and l, present in the population as a whole. Figure 20-15 shows the genotypes that produce each of the blood types. For example, persons with either genotype $L^A L^A$ or $L^A l$ will have A antigens on their RBC's and hence Type A blood. Only the genotype $L^A L^B$ produces both A and B antigens and hence blood Type AB. A knowledge of how blood types are inherited has been used to solve cases of disputed fatherhood. For example, a Type AB man could not be the father of a Type O child. Of course, this kind of evidence can only disprove fatherhood. It cannot prove it. Why?

Inheritance of blood types illustrates the specificity of gene action very well. Both L^A and L^B produce a specific antigen. Any individual who is born with both the L^A and L^B alleles has both antigens. These alleles show no dominance with respect to each other.

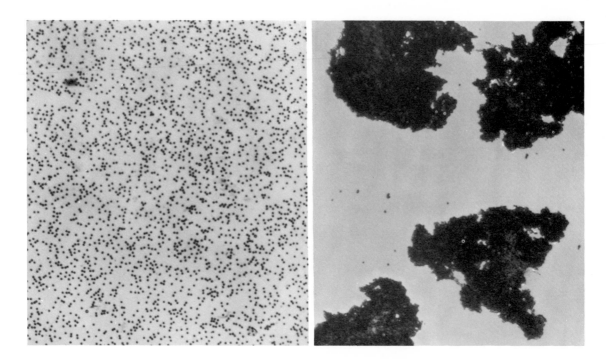

Red-blood corpuscles (left) before and (right) after adding serum containing anti-A antibodies. **Fig. 20-16**
The agglutination reaction indicates the presence of the A-antigen on the corpuscles.

Although the blood type of any one individual is controlled by just one pair of alleles, there are actually three different alleles present in the human population for that particular gene locus. This tells us that a given gene need not simply mutate from one dominant to one recessive form. Instead there may be a variety of mutant forms of a given gene. These are referred to as **multiple alleles.** Over a dozen alleles have been found in the fruit fly at a gene locus controlling eye color. Remember, though, that any individual fly can have only two of them.

Using mutagenic agents, some 300 different mutations have been produced in a single gene on a bacteriophage chromosome. In fact, just as crossing over separates linked genes, so it can separate the parts of a gene. As we saw in Chapter 19 (Section 19-7), the closer two genes are on a chromosome, the less frequently they are separated by crossing over. We might guess from this that the separation of parts of a gene would be rarer still. This is so. It is so rare, in fact, that for any particular gene under study it is not detectable in an organism such as the fruit fly whose offspring number only in the hundreds. On the other hand, this phenomenon *can* be detected among the billions of offspring produced in a short period when bacteriophages infect a culture of their host cells. It has, in fact, been possible to map a linear sequence of intragene mutations for a single bacteriophage gene in the same way that the linear sequence of genes in a single fruit fly or corn chromosome is mapped. Probably any base in the chain of several hundred to several thousand needed to code a single polypeptide can be altered and a mutation thus produced. We can feel confident that as the study of genetics progresses, multiple alleles will prove to be the rule rather than the exception.

THE ACTION OF THE TOTAL GENOTYPE

Mendel wisely knew that an understanding of the rules of inheritance could come only from the study of simple, clear-cut traits. Much of the later work in genetics has necessarily followed this tradition. However, clear-cut traits such as flower color, eye color, blood type, etc., are often rather superficial ones. Of vastly greater significance in the life of the organism is the complex ensemble of genes which guides the basic patterning of the embryo, the differentiation of cells, and the integration of tissues, organs, and systems into a smoothly functioning organism. Although the science of genetics has made only a beginning at relating the total organism to its complete hereditary blueprint, from the research carried out thus far three important features stand out:

1) a single gene may have many effects upon the organism,

2) all traits are influenced by a large number of genes, and

3) the expression of a trait is also modified by the environment of the organism.

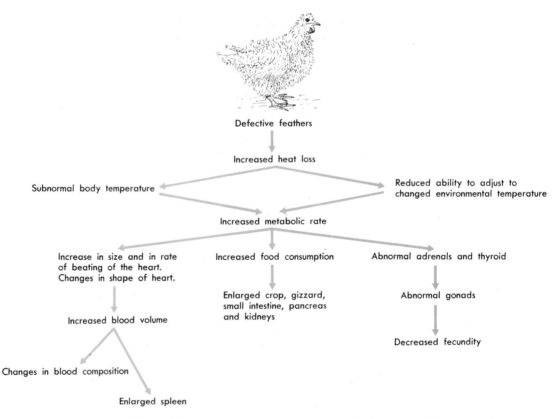

Fig. 20-17   Multiple effects of the gene for "frizzled" feathers in chickens. A whole series of secondary effects stem from the primary effect of the gene. (Adapted, with permission, from W. Landauer's "Temperature and Evolution," *Biological Symposia*, Vol. 6, The Jaques Cattell Press, Inc.)

1. Multiple Effects of a Single Gene

Although a single gene produces only a single polypeptide, the activity of that polypeptide (or the protein of which it is a part) in different parts of the organism may lead to different effects. Furthermore, effects produced in one part of the organism, as a direct result of gene action, may in turn upset natural balances in other parts of the organism. A whole series of functional and structural changes may thus follow indirectly from some primary gene action. The inheritance of the trait "frizzle" in chickens illustrates this. Chickens homozygous for the trait have defective feathers which break easily and provide little heat insulation for the bird. Presumably, the mutant alleles produce a protein which does not permit proper feather development. The poor insulating qualities of frizzle feathers lead to increased heat loss from the bird. This, in turn, triggers a whole sequence of homeostatic responses resulting in marked structural and functional changes (Fig. 20-17). The variety of symptoms found in many of man's hereditary diseases, for example the pale pigmentation and seriously lowered I.Q. in phenylketonurics, also illustrates this principle.

Some mutant genes produce so many and such important secondary effects in the course of embryonic development that the life of the embryo cannot be maintained. These are called **lethal genes.** Most of them cause death only when they are present in the double dose.

yy = gray—breeds true
Yy = yellow—heterozygous
YY = dies during embryonic
 development.

Fig. 20-18

Interpretation of results obtained by breeding mice that are heterozygous for the lethal gene Y. Two-thirds of the offspring have yellow coats; one-third, gray. The litters average three-fourths normal size.

Strains of gray-coated mice always breed true with respect to coat color. Strains of yellow-coated mice do not. About one third of all the offspring produced by mating two yellow-coated mice are gray. This suggests that yellow-coated mice are heterozygous. A backcross of a yellow-coated mouse with a gray-coated mouse confirms this. The ratio of gray to yellow coats in the offspring is the typical backcross ratio of 1:1. Thus yellow-coated mice are hybrid with the allele for yellow dominant (Yy). Gray-coated mice are homozygous recessives (yy) (Fig. 20-18). Why, then, the 2:1 ratio (rather than the normal 3:1 ratio) in the F_2 generation produced when two yellow-coated mice (F_1) are mated? A clue to the answer is that the F_2 litters are only about three-fourths normal size. Autopsies of the F_1 mothers show that the missing offspring have died in the uterus during embryonic development. Note that although the lethal allele Y is dominant with respect to one of its more trivial effects, coat color, it causes death only when present in the double dose.

2. Traits Are Influenced by Many Genes

One allele may result in a pea flower's being red rather than white. Many other alleles are necessary to produce the structure and arrangements of the petals. Going still further, no traits for flower color could be expressed without the coordinated activity of the many genes guiding the development of functional roots, stems, and leaves.

Twelve different pairs of alleles, at twelve different gene loci, have been found to influence color and pattern in the pelt of the mink. Mink farmers, breeding for various combinations of these alleles, are able to market a great variety of pelts for the fur-coat industry. Of course, as in the case of flower color, still other genes must be involved in the production of hair on the mink and even the production of the mink itself.

When the expression of one pair of genes can be shown to be modified by the presence in the genotype of another pair of genes, the gene pairs are said to show interaction. As our knowledge of genetics increases, we can expect to find that the interaction of gene loci is a very general phenomenon.

Even such a simple trait as the ability to metabolize a small molecule like phenylalanine (Fig. 20-9) requires the action of a number of enzymes. Each of these is constructed from one or more polypeptide chains which, in turn, are each synthesized by a specific gene. Genetics studies in a number of organisms have now shown that in some cases the genes responsible for the synthesis of *related* enzymes are located adjacent to one another on the chromosome. In *E. coli*, for example, the genes that produce the enzymes necessary for the organism to metabolize the disaccharide lactose are located adjacent to each other in one region of the organism's chromosome. At one end of this chain of genes is a special gene, the operator, which turns the others on and off as conditions within the cell dictate. The combination of an operator gene and the genes that it controls is called an **operon.** The close linkage of functionally related genes is surely of value to the organism. By grouping such genes in operons, the production of all the enzymes needed for a given metabolic activity can proceed simultaneously and in accurately coordinated amounts.

How many genes does it take to build an organism? No one knows exactly, but it is possible to compute the number of base pairs present in the total weight of DNA found in the chromosomes of an organism. Assuming that all of it is genetically active, one can then estimate the number of genes that could be present. The DNA of one of the well-studied bacteriophages contains some 200,000 base pairs. Assuming that most of its genes consist of 500 to 1000 base pairs, this would mean that 200 to 400 genes are present. *E. coli* DNA has over 5 million base pairs, giving it over 5 thousand genes if each of its genes averages 1000 base pairs in length. The number of genes in man, with the DNA of his chromosomes containing over 3 billion base pairs, may be close to 3 million.

3. Heredity and Environment

The action of genes is dependent also upon the environment. The ability to manufacture chlorophyll is under gene control, but plants cannot do the job unless they are exposed to light (look back at Fig. 12-4). If victims of the hereditary defect phenylketonuria (PKU) are identified very early, it is possible to prevent the mutant genes from expressing themselves. This is accomplished by reducing the amount of the amino acid, phenylalanine, in the diet of the patient.

A great deal has been said about the relative importance of heredity and environment in the development of the organism. Much of the discussion has been fruitless because of a basic misconception of the way in which these two factors are related. To say that the development of an individual is controlled 50% by heredity and 50% by environment (or any other such figures) is to assume that the effects of these two are added together in the development of an individual. A far better metaphor is to think of the organism as being the *product* of two factors, heredity and environment, the latter working through the former. Many farmers today raise hybrid corn varieties. The seeds, produced through extensive breeding programs, are of a very uniform and desirable genotype. The plants one farmer raises from the seeds may, however, vary greatly in phenotype from those raised by another farmer. Soil, temperature, water supply, and fertilizer are just a few of the many environmental influences that affect the ultimate phenotype.

The genes an individual organism inherits determine the potentialities that may be achieved in the course of the entire growth and development of that organism. The environment establishes to what degree these potentialities will actually be achieved. Clearly, the study of inheritance must always take into account the influence of environment on the action of the genes.

EXERCISES AND PROBLEMS

1 Outline the essay that you would write defending the "one gene—one enzyme" hypothesis.

2 Henry is blood Type O. So is his mother. What blood types may his father have?

3 An accident victim of blood type A should receive a transfusion from a donor of what blood type? What other blood types could be used without serious danger?

4 What are the possible blood types of children resulting from the marriage of a Type O father with a Type AB mother?

5 Distinguish between multiple factors and multiple alleles.

6 Neglecting crossing-over, how many different kinds of ascospores can *Neurospora crassa* form by random assortment of its chromosomes? The haploid number is 7.

7 Besides DNA and RNA, what other important biological substances contain the purine adenine?

8 Is it correct to say that in the ascus produced by a heterozygous (*Aa*) *Neurospora* zygote, 4 spores will contain *A* and 4 spores will contain *a*? Explain.

9 Why can a definite prediction be made in Question 8 when you could not make a definite prediction in Question 4 at the end of Chapter 18?

10 What sequence of bases in messenger RNA will be coded by the following triplets in the DNA molecule: GCT, GAT, CCA, AAA, AGT?

11 Why are haploid organisms especially useful in genetics studies?

12 It is possible to buy sorghum seeds ¾ of which germinate into green seedlings and ¼ of which germinate into albino seedlings. The albino seedlings soon die. Why?

13 What was the genotype of the sorghum plants that produced the seeds in Question 12?

14 Outline all the steps which must be taken by a plant breeder in order to be sure that he is offering sorghum seeds that will demonstrate the 3:1 ratio in Question 12.

15 Why are organisms that reproduce rapidly and produce large numbers of offspring so useful in genetics studies?

16 It has been suggested that pocket watches should not have luminous dials but it is all right for wrist watches to have them. Why the difference?

17 Would Weismann have appreciated this difference?

18 Why are most mutations recessive?

19 What inorganic ions would you expect to add to sucrose and biotin to make a minimal medium for growing unmutated *Neurospora?* Why?

20 Minimal medium for *Neurospora* requires the presence of biotin while minimal medium for *E. coli* does not. Does this mean that biotin does not participate in the metabolism of *E. coli* cells? Explain.

21 Define a gene. Is this the same way you defined it at the end of the previous two chapters?

22 Show how asexual reproduction in *Bryophyllum* (see Fig 17–5) depends on the duplication of (a) cells, (b) subcellular structures, (c) individual molecules.

23 Why are organisms (e.g. plants, *Neurospora, E. coli*) that can reproduce asexually so useful in genetics studies?

24 Using your knowledge of meiosis, predict what arrangements of *A* spores and *a* spores could occur in the ascus produced by a strain of *Neurospora* heterozygous for these alleles.

REFERENCES

1 Hotchkiss, R. D., and Esther Weiss, "Transformed Bacteria," *Scientific American,* Reprint No. 18, November, 1956. The alteration of bacterial heredity by treatment with DNA is described in detail.

2 Taylor, J. H., "The Duplication of Chromosomes," *Scientific American,* Reprint No. 60, June, 1958. Attempts to relate the structure of DNA to the structure of chromosomes.

3 Hanawalt, P. C., and R. H. Haynes, "The Repair of DNA," *Scientific American,* February, 1967. Describes how bacteria are able to exploit the complementarity of the two strands of DNA in the repair of damage to the molecule.

4 Muller, H. J., "Radiation and Human Mutation," *Scientific American,* Reprint No. 29, November, 1955.

5 Beadle, G. W., "The Genes of Men and Molds," *Scientific American,* Reprint No. 1, September, 1948. The techniques of using *Neurospora* as a tool for studying gene action are described in detail.

6 Peters, J. A., ed., *Classic Papers in Genetics,* Prentice-Hall, Inc., 1959. Includes the original papers on the discoveries made by H. J. Muller, Beadle and Tatum, Avery and his co-workers, and Watson and Crick. Other papers on the nature and action of genes are also included.

7 Ingram, V. M., "How Do Genes Act?," *Scientific American,* Reprint No. 104, January, 1958. Describes the evidence from sickle-cell anemia.

8 Nirenberg, M. W., "The Genetic Code II," *Scientific American,* Reprint No. 153, March, 1963. Explains how synthetic messenger RNA is used to determine the "letters" in the genetic code.

9 Crick, F. H. C., "The Genetic Code: III," *Scientific American,* Reprint No. 1052, October, 1966. The author, one of the co-discoverers of the structure of DNA, summarizes our current knowledge of the nature of the DNA code and how it is translated.

10 Holley, R. W., "The Nucleotide Sequence of a Nucleic Acid," *Scientific American,* Reprint No. 1033, February, 1966. Describes the steps by which the nucleotide sequence of alanine transfer RNA was worked out.

11 Gorini, L., "Antibiotics and the Genetic Code," *Scientific American,* Reprint No. 1041, April, 1966. Summarizes the mechanism of protein synthesis and shows how certain antibiotics interfere with the process by causing errors in the translation of the genetic code.

12 Yanofsky, C., "Gene Structure and Protein Structure," *Scientific American,* May, 1967. Demonstrates that the order and spacing of mutations within a single gene is directly correlated with the order and spacing of amino acid substitutions in the polypeptide produced by that gene.

Each of the following paperbacks presents a thorough treatment of genetics as seen in the light of recent discoveries.

13 Bonner, D. M., and S. E. Mills, *Heredity,* 2nd Edition, Foundations of Modern Biology Series, Prentice-Hall, 1964.

14 Levine, R. P., *Genetics,* Holt, Rinehart and Winston, Inc., New York, 1962.

Sexual reproduction involves the two processes of fertilization and meiosis. In fertilization, the nuclei of two gametes fuse, raising the chromosome number from haploid to diploid. In meiosis, the chromosome number is reduced again from the diploid to the haploid condition. Whatever variation there may be in the details from one organism to another, these two activities must occur alternately if sexual reproduction is to continue.

In plants, fertilization and meiosis divide the life of the organism into two distinct phases or "generations." The **gametophyte** generation begins with a spore produced by meiosis. The spore is haploid and all the cells derived from it are also haploid. Among the cells produced by this generation are the gametes. When two gametes fuse, the **sporophyte** generation begins. The sporophyte generation thus starts with a zygote. It contains the diploid number of chromosomes and all cells derived from it by mitosis are also diploid. Eventually though, certain cells will undergo meiosis, forming spores and starting the gametophyte generation once again.

THE PROBLEMS TO BE SOLVED   21-2

Plants probably evolved from aquatic ancestors, the green algae. Although plants can be found today growing in water, they are primarily associated with life on land. The members of each group of plants have a variety of morphological and physiological adaptations which enable them to live away from the aquatic environment. How plants solve the problem of securing water and keeping their cells moist was discussed in Part IV. In this chapter, we will examine the ways in which the plants have solved the problem of reproducing sexually on land.

The problem is really twofold. Gametes are single cells and quite delicate. In cross-fertilization, some mechanism must be present to enable the two gametes to reach each other safely. The problem is compounded in plants by their not having the power of locomotion. The inability of plants to move about also creates a problem of how to disperse the offspring produced by sexual reproduction to locations far enough away from the parent plant that they can receive the sunlight, water, and soil minerals they need. The twin problems of bringing the gametes together in a protected environment and dispersing the species to new locations have been solved in different ways by the various groups of plants.

MOSSES   21-3

A bed of moss consists of masses of leafy shoots which, being haploid, belong to the gametophyte generation (Fig. 21-1). In the common haircap moss, *Polytrichum commune*, the leafy shoots are of three kinds: female, male, and sterile. (The latter do not participate in sexual reproduction and need not concern us here.) The male shoots are easily distinguished from the other two by their flat top. A longitudinal

◄ Flower of American lotus. Flowers contain the organs of sexual reproduction.
(Courtesy John H. Gerard, National Audubon Society.)

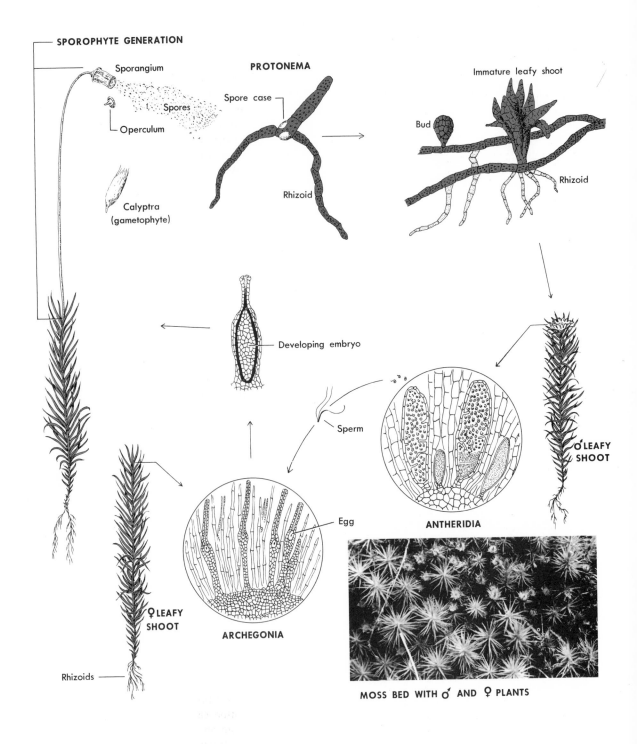

SPOROPHYTE GENERATION

Sporangium

Spores

Operculum

Calyptra
(gametophyte)

PROTONEMA

Spore case

Rhizoid

Immature leafy shoot

Bud

Rhizoid

Developing embryo

Sperm

ANTHERIDIA

♂LEAFY
SHOOT

Egg

♀LEAFY
SHOOT

ARCHEGONIA

Rhizoids

MOSS BED WITH ♂ AND ♀ PLANTS

Fig. 21-1   Life cycle of the common haircap moss *Polytrichum commune.* In order for fertilization to take place, there must be surface water in which the sperm can pass from the male plant to the female plant.

section through the tip of a male plant reveals several of the male reproductory organs, the **antheridia.** Each is filled with sperm. A similar section through the female plant reveals several bottle-shaped **archegonia,** the female reproductory organs. Each of these contains a single egg in a chamber near its base. In early spring, if there is plenty of water present, the sperm are released from the antheridia. The splashing of raindrops distributes the sperm to nearby plants. On female plants, the sperm swim to the archegonium, probably following a concentration gradient of malic acid diffusing from the archegonium. The sperm swim down the canal to the egg, and fertilization takes place. The resulting zygote is the start of the sporophyte generation.

Mitotic divisions of the zygote produce the mature sporophyte generation (Fig. 21-1). It consists of:

1) A foot, which absorbs water and minerals from the parent gametophyte. Although the cells of the sporophyte generation contain chlorophyll, some food materials may also be absorbed from the parent gametophyte.
2) A stalk, which grows a few inches up into the air.
3) A **sporangium,** which is formed at the tip of the stalk. Within it are located spore mother cells. The opening to the interior is sealed with a lid, the operculum. The entire sporangium is covered by a calyptra. (Curiously enough, the calyptra is derived from the wall of the old archegonium. Thus it is actually a part of the gametophyte generation.) It is the calyptra that is responsible for the common name of this species.

During the summer, each spore mother cell in the sporangium undergoes meiosis, producing four spores, the start of the gametophyte generation. Late in the summer, the calyptra and operculum become detached from the sporangium. Lowered humidity causes the ring of teeth within the opening to the sporangium to bend outward. In so doing the spores are ejected. Their small size enables them to be transported great distances by the wind.

If a spore comes to rest in a suitable location (moist and shady), it will germinate to form a filament of green cells called a **protonema.** A resemblance between the protonema and certain filamentous green algae has suggested to botanists that the mosses evolved from algae. Soon buds appear on the protonema and from these buds develop the leafy shoots—male, female, and sterile—that started our story.

What are the roles played by these two stages in the moss life cycle? The gametophyte generation produces the gametes and is responsible for the carrying out of sexual reproduction. The process requires ample water, however, and in a dry spring sexual reproduction often fails to occur.

Even though it may manufacture some of its own food, the sporophyte generation is completely dependent upon the gametophyte for its water and minerals. Its contribution to the success of the species is the myriads of wind-blown spores which it produces. These disperse the species, enabling it to colonize new habitats.

FERNS   21-4

In ferns, it is the sporophyte generation that we commonly see. The Christmas fern is a typical example (Fig. 21-2). The **leaves** (or fronds as they are often called) are the only part of the plant that is visible above ground. These arise from an underground stem—the **rhizome**—from which also extend the **roots.** All these structures make up the mature sporophyte generation. During early summer, brownish spots appear on the under side of the leaflets of the fronds. These dots do not signify that the plant

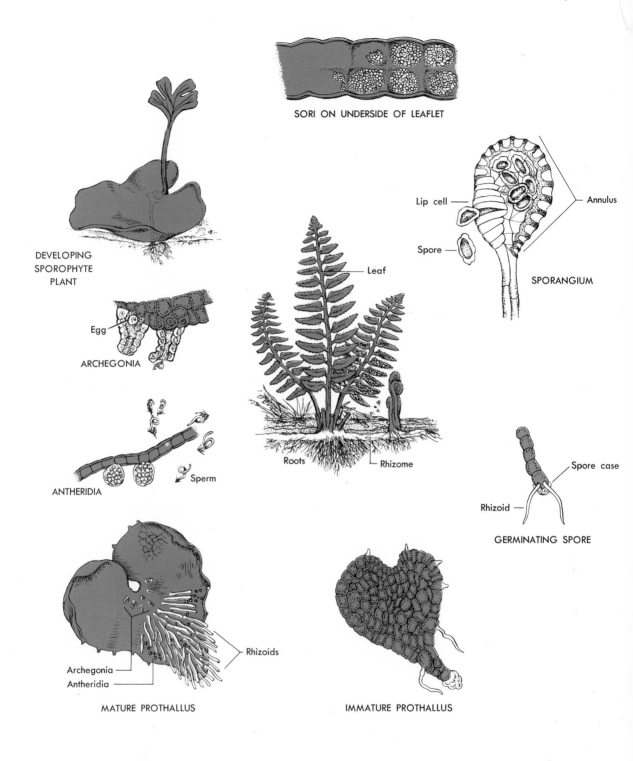

SORI ON UNDERSIDE OF LEAFLET

DEVELOPING
SPOROPHYTE
PLANT

Lip cell

Spore

Annulus

SPORANGIUM

Egg

ARCHEGONIA

Leaf

Roots

Rhizome

Spore case

Rhizoid

GERMINATING SPORE

Sperm

ANTHERIDIA

Archegonia

Antheridia

Rhizoids

MATURE PROTHALLUS

IMMATURE PROTHALLUS

Fig. 21-2   Life cycle of a typical fern. Cross-fertilization is the rule; that is, the sperm swim from one prothallus to another. Surface water must be present for this to occur.

has become diseased but are, instead, a normal development in its life cycle. Each dot is called a **sorus** and consists of many sporangia mounted on stalks (Fig. 21-2). Within each sporangium, the spore mother cells undergo meiosis, producing four spores each. When the humidity drops, the thin-walled lip cells of each sporangium separate, and the annulus slowly straightens out. Then with a quick motion, the annulus snaps forward, expelling spores.

You can easily demonstrate this action yourself. Soak a few fern leaflets with ripe sori in a small amount of rubbing alcohol for a day or two. Then scrape some of the sori onto a clean microscope slide with the blade of a knife. Under magnification, the details of the sporangia are easily seen. As the heat from the microscope illuminator passes through the moistened material, the alcohol will evaporate and spore ejection begin.

If the wind-blown fern spores reach a suitable habitat (again, moist and shady) they will germinate into filaments of cells. Each grows into a small (¼ in.), flat, green, heart-shaped structure called a **prothallus** (Fig. 21-2). It grows on the surface of the soil anchored by thin filaments of cells called rhizoids. These also absorb water and minerals from the soil. The cells of the prothallus are haploid and it is the mature gametophyte generation. On its under surface are the sex organs: **antheridia** for sperm production and **archegonia** for egg production. When moisture is plentiful, the sperm are released and swim to an archegonium, usually on another prothallus, because the two kinds of sex organs generally do not mature simultaneously on a single prothallus. This circumstance results in cross-fertilization and thus greater opportunity for variation in the offspring. Fertilization takes place within the archegonium and the new sporophyte generation is formed. The embryo sporophyte develops by repeated divisions of the zygote. One structure that develops in the embryo but is not found in the mature sporophyte is the foot. This organ penetrates the tissues of the prothallus and derives moisture and nourishment from it until the roots, rhizome, and leaves become self-sufficient. Note that the prothallus, though tiny in comparison with the mature sporophyte, is still an independent, autotrophic plant and even supports the embryo sporophyte during the early stages of its development.

GYMNOSPERMS 21-5

The gymnosperms are truly terrestrial plants. They can flourish in locations too dry for most mosses or ferns. They have several adaptations that make this possible. The sporophyte generation (which is the only part the casual observer ever sees) produces not one, but two, different kinds of spores. There are the small **microspores,** which will germinate to form the male gametophyte generation, and the somewhat larger **megaspores,** which will develop into the female gametophyte generation. Each of these is produced in its own sporangium. In our most common gymnosperms, the conifers, the two kinds of sporangia are produced in the **cones.** Almost everyone is familiar with female cones (Fig. 21-3). The male cones appear in the spring and are much shorter-lived. Within these cones, microspores are produced by meiosis to start the male gametophyte generation. Before being released, mitotic division of the nucleus of each spore takes place with the final production of a four-celled pollen grain. Then the pollen grain is released from the male cone into the air.

In the female cones, the megaspore similarly undergoes a period of development within the cone. The product of this is the mature female gametophyte generation (Fig. 21-3). This small structure is not released from the cone but is retained within the tissues of the parent sporophyte. This is seemingly a simple change, but it is one

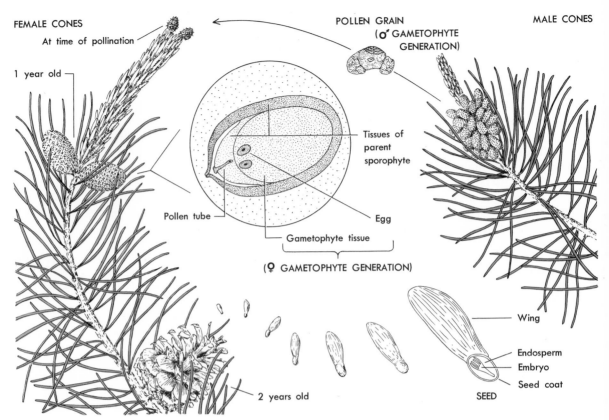

FEMALE CONES
At time of pollination

1 year old

POLLEN GRAIN
(♂ GAMETOPHYTE GENERATION)

MALE CONES

Tissues of parent sporophyte

Pollen tube

Egg

Gametophyte tissue

(♀ GAMETOPHYTE GENERATION)

2 years old

Wing

Endosperm
Embryo
Seed coat

SEED

Fig. 21-3   Life cycle of a typical pine. Fertilization of the egg occurs within the tissues of the parent sporophyte.

of vast significance to the success of gymnosperms in a dry environment. By retaining the female gametophyte within the tissues of the parent sporophyte, external moisture is no longer necessary for fertilization. The pollen grains are carried by the wind to the female cones. There they germinate. In the earliest gymnosperms, motile sperm were probably released. These could swim to the egg in the archegonium, propelling themselves in fluid supplied by the tissues of the parent sporophyte. This fluid was ultimately derived from a root system extending deep into the ground. The need for surface water for the sperm was thus eliminated. The ginkgo, commonly planted in city parks, is a gymnosperm that still uses this method of fertilization. For this reason the ginkgo is considered a very primitive type of gymnosperm. In modern gymnosperms, free-swimming sperm are not produced by the male gametophyte. Instead, the pollen grain germinates to form a thin tube, the pollen tube, which grows into the tissues of the female cone until it reaches the vicinity of the egg. (In the pines, this may take a full year.) Then the tube ruptures and a nucleus, the sperm nucleus, fuses with the egg to form the zygote. The basic situation remains unchanged, however. The delicate process of fertilization is carried out deep in the tissues of the parent sporophyte where it is protected from the possible harshness of the external environment.

With the production of two kinds of spores and two kinds of gametophytes, spores of the gymnosperms can no longer serve the function of dispersal as they do in mosses and ferns. In mosses and ferns, a single spore can germinate in the *soil* to form a gametophyte with both kinds of sex organs. Sexual reproduction can follow and soon the organism is established in the new environment. Dispersal of the species has occurred. Gymnosperm spores, in contrast, cannot be agents of dispersal. The only place the wind-blown microspore can germinate is on a female cone of the same plant or, better (why?), another plant of the same species. The microspore is simply transported from one plant to another. This does not accomplish dispersal of the species to a new location.

The function of dispersal is taken over by the **seed.** After fertilization, the zygote develops by repeated mitosis into a tiny embryo sporophyte plant (Fig. 21-3). Around the embryo develops accessory food-containing tissue called **endosperm.** It is derived from the cells of the female gametophyte generation and is haploid. Its food came, however, from the parent sporophyte. Around the embryo and endosperm develops a protective coat of parent sporophyte tissue. This coat usually develops a thin vane or wing on one side of the seed. All these developmental activities require another year for completion in the pines. At the end of this period, the female cone opens, releasing, one by one, its contents of seeds. The "wing" of the seed coat serves as a propeller and increases the distance the seed may be carried by the wind. The seed coat itself also serves to protect the embryo from drying out. If the seed is carried to a suitable location (moderately moist), it will absorb water. The embryo starts metabolizing rapidly and then begins to grow. This resumption of growth is called **germination.** At first, growth occurs at the expense of food stored in the endosperm. When the young seedling grows up into the light, however, chlorophyll develops and the plant begins to manufacture its own food by photosynthesis. The endosperm is totally consumed and the seed coat drops away so that every cell of the maturing plant is descended from the zygote.

Compared with the gametophytes discussed earlier, the gymnosperm gametophyte is little more than a reproductory mechanism. Both the male and female gametophytes are tiny and entirely dependent upon the parent sporophyte for nourishment. The gametes can be brought together only through the use of structures of the parent sporophyte generation. The developing embryo is no longer protected by the gametophyte generation as in the mosses and ferns, but receives its nourishment and protection from the parent sporophyte. (The endosperm is gametophytic, but its food stores come from the sporophyte.) The sporophyte generation continues to accomplish dispersal of the species. This is no longer accomplished by wind-blown spores, however, but by wind-blown seeds.

ANGIOSPERMS

The life cycle of the angiosperms, the flowering plants, is similar to that of the gymnosperms. Although minor differences in detail occur in the many species of angiosperms, the major features of the angiosperm life cycle are shared in common.

THE FLOWER AND ITS POLLINATION 21-6

In the angiosperms, microspores and megaspores are produced in flowers. In most angiosperms the flowers are *perfect;* that is, each flower has both microsporangia and megasporangia and thus produces both kinds of spores. The microspores are produced in the **stamens.** The megaspores are produced in the **pistil** (Fig. 21-4).

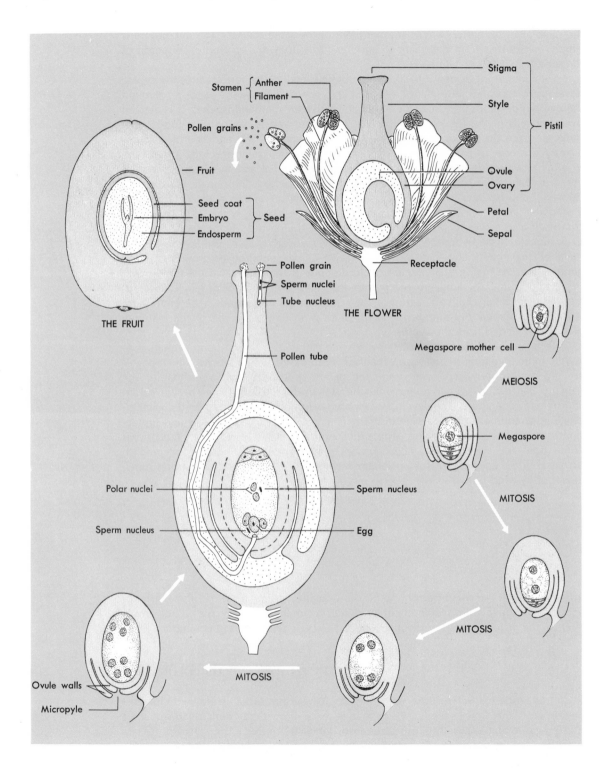

THE FRUIT

THE FLOWER

MEIOSIS

MITOSIS

MITOSIS

MITOSIS

The stamen consists of a lobed structure, the anther or microsporangium, supported by a filament. The pollen grains are formed in the anther. Meiosis of microspore mother cells results in the production of four microspores each. These then develop into a two-celled pollen grain with a tough, resistant outer wall.

The pistil consists of a stigma, style, and ovary. The ovary contains a chamber within which are located the megasporangia, the **ovules.** The number and arrangement of ovules within the ovary varies greatly from species to species. Meiosis of the megaspore mother cell produces four haploid cells: the large megaspore and three small cells which disintegrate. The nucleus of the megaspore undergoes three successive mitotic divisions. The eight nuclei produced are distributed and partitioned off by cell walls as illustrated in Fig. 21-4. This is the mature female gametophyte generation. The two most important cells are the **egg cell** and the large central cell which contains the two **polar nuclei.** From this latter cell will be derived the endosperm of the seed.

Although wind transfer of pollen grains is employed by certain groups of angiosperms (e.g. the grasses), the angiosperms are particularly noted for the variety of animals which assist in pollination. Associated with the stamen and pistil may be found accessory structures. Most obvious of these are the brightly colored **petals** (collectively called the corolla) supported by a whorl of **sepals** (the calyx). Along with the petals may be found glands which emit fragrant odors. It is these accessory structures which give such aesthetic pleasure to us. In woods and fields, gardens and hothouses, the extraordinary variety of corolla shapes and colors are a delight to man. Except for certain domesticated species, however, these shapes and colors do not exist for his pleasure. They serve instead to attract certain smaller animals which, as they pass from flower to flower, may incidentally transport pollen grains from the anther of one to the stigma of another.

Animal-pollinated flowers frequently contain nectaries which secrete a sugary solution (nectar) and reward the animal for its visit. Birds (e.g. the hummingbird) and bats pollinate some flowers, but the great majority are pollinated by insects. Beetles, flies, butterflies, moths, and bees are active pollinators. The relationship between the plant and the animal may be quite loose. Some angiosperms are pollinated by many kinds of insects, and some insects pollinate many kinds of plants. In other cases, the relationship is far closer. There is a tropical orchid that is pollinated by just one species of moth, which itself is limited to foraging that one kind of flower for its nectar. The moth has a 10-in. proboscis; the orchid has a nectary 10 in. deep. Other orchids have pistils whose shape and color pattern mimic the abdomens of certain female insects. In attempting to mate with several of these "dummy" females, the male insects effectively transport pollen from one flower to the next.

Generally, insect-pollinated flowers are perfect, both stamens and pistils being found within one flower. Two advantages follow from this. First, there is a greater likelihood of pollination occurring. At each visit by the pollinator, pollen from the last flower is deposited while fresh supplies of pollen are picked up. With **imperfect flowers,** which contain either stamens or pistils but not both, a pollinating insect has to visit staminate flowers and pistillate flowers alternately in order to achieve a comparable efficiency as a pollinator. Second, if pollination between different flowers (cross-pollination) should fail to occur, the flower may still be able to pollinate itself. Seed production will still occur, although the similar heredity of the gametes will diminish the amount of variability in the offspring.

The flowers of some angiosperms are actually modified in such a way that self-pollination is the rule rather than the exception. As we noted in Chapter 18, the corolla of the common pea completely encloses the stamens and pistil so that insects

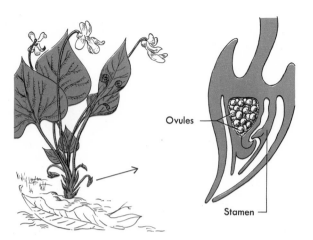

Fig. 21-5

Violet flowers. The petal-bearing flowers are cross-pollinated. The others (enlargement) are self-pollinated.

Ovules

Stamen

cannot easily reach these structures. Many violets produce, in addition to their conspicuous cross-pollinated flowers, smaller flowers that never open to expose their stamens and pistil to insect pollinators. A glance at Fig. 21-5 will show why only self-pollination occurs in these flowers.

Flower modifications to promote cross-pollination are more common than those to prevent it. In many species the stamens and pistil of a single flower mature at different times. In some species the floral parts are arranged so that there is little likelihood of a direct transfer of pollen from anther to stigma. The sage (*Salvia*) flower embodies both these mechanisms in addition to an unusual hinged stamen which bends downward to dust pollen on the bee which triggers it (Fig. 21-6). In many angiosperms, e.g. red clover and some apple varieties, pollen will not germinate on a stigma of the same plant. These plants are called self-sterile.

Still another mechanism that ensures cross-pollination is the occurrence of imperfect flowers on separate plants. Species in which this occurs, such as the willows, poplars, and the date palm, are called **dioecious.** (Species with imperfect flowers on one plant are called **monoecious.** Fertilization between these flowers produces no more hereditary variability than self-pollination within a single flower.)

In one locality all the plants of a given species flower at roughly the same time. This usually occurs even if the various individual plants have begun growing at different times. As we shall see in Chapter 25, such synchronous flowering seems to be a response to the changing length of day and night as the season progresses. It, too, is an important factor in encouraging cross-pollination.

Our emphasis on animal-pollinated angiosperms should not obscure the fact that many angiosperms are wind-pollinated. Poplars, oaks, elms, birches, plantains, ragweed, grasses, and many others are wind-pollinated. Their flowers are not apt to have petals, odor, or nectar. They are frequently imperfect (as are the cones of gymnosperms which, you remember, are also wind-pollinated). The stamens of the staminate flowers are exposed to the wind and produce large quantities of light, dry pollen. This wind-blown pollen may cause hay fever in allergic humans. The stigmas of the pistillate flowers are often long and sticky. The ovary usually contains only a few ovules.

Although the wind-pollinated flowers do not provide much aesthetic pleasure for man, they are largely responsible for man's ability to find time for any aesthetic pleasures at all. All our cereal grains come from wind-pollinated species. As a group, they provide, directly or indirectly, the major portion of the food consumed by mankind.

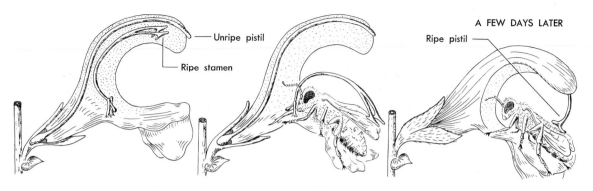

Pollination in *Salvia*. Cross-pollination is assured by (1) ripening of the stamen before the pistil, (2) a trigger mechanism that dusts pollen on the pollinator, (3) later growth of the pistil so that it brushes the bees that continue to forage the flower for nectar.

Fig. 21-6

When, by one means or another, the pollen grain reaches the stigma of a flower of the same species, it germinates into a pollen tube. The pollen tube contains two nuclei: the tube nucleus and the generative nucleus. As the pollen tube starts to grow down the style into the ovule chamber, the generative nucleus divides by mitosis, forming two sperm nuclei. The pollen tube, with its three nuclei, is the mature male gametophyte generation. It enters the ovule through the *micropyle* (Fig. 21-4) and ruptures. One sperm nucleus fuses with the egg, forming the zygote (2n). The other sperm nucleus fuses with two polar nuclei to form an endosperm nucleus containing 3n chromosomes. The tube nucleus disintegrates.

THE SEED   **21-7**

Mitotic divisions of the zygote and endosperm nucleus result in the formation of the seed (Fig. 21-7). It consists of:

1) A **plumule,** made up of two embryonic leaves, which will become the first true leaves of the seedling, and a terminal (apical) bud. The terminal bud is the meristem at which further growth of the stem will occur.

2) The **hypocotyl** and **radicle,** which will grow into the stem and primary root, respectively.

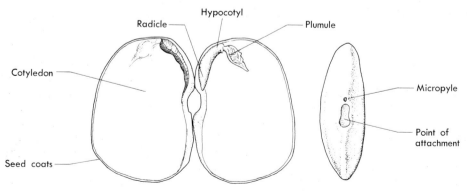

Structures of a typical dicot seed, the bean.   **Fig. 21-7**

3) The **cotyledons,** which store food that will be used by the germinating seed. This food is derived from the endosperm which, in turn, received it from the parent sporophyte. In many angiosperms (the common bean is one example), the endosperm has been totally consumed and its food stores transferred to the cotyledons by the time development of the seed is complete. In others, the endosperm persists in the mature seed. This is true of some dicots and all monocots. The latter, of course, have only one cotyledon in the seed (Fig. 21-8). The cells of the endosperm are triploid ($3n$) in contrast to the haploid (n) endosperm of the conifers and other gymnosperms (see Section 21-5). While these structures are developing, the walls of the ovule thicken to form the protective seed coats.

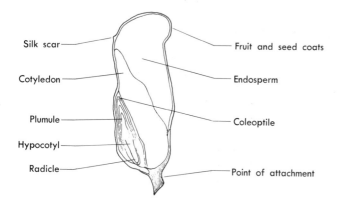

Silk scar

Cotyledon

Plumule

Hypocotyl

Radicle

Fruit and seed coats

Endosperm

Coleoptile

Point of attachment

Fig. 21-8

Structures of a corn kernel. Because its outer covering is derived from the ovary wall of the flower, the corn kernel is actually a fruit with a single seed inside.

The seed is thus a dormant embryo sporophyte with stored food and protective coats. Its two functions are: (1) dispersal of the species to new locations and (2) maintenance of the species over periods of unfavorable climatic conditions. "Annuals" (such as the bean, cereal grains, and many weeds) can survive as a species only by the production of resistant seeds. With the onset of freezing weather in the fall, the mature plants die. However, many of their seeds will remain alive, though dormant, throughout the winter. When conditions once more are favorable for the growth of the plant, germination of the seeds occurs and a new generation of mature plants develops.

21-8   **SEED DISPERSAL: THE FRUIT**

The fruit is a development of the ovary wall and sometimes other flower parts as well. It contains the seeds. To a biologist, the term *fruit* is not restricted simply to those succulent types which man enjoys eating. Figure 21-9 shows some of the many different types of fruits produced by angiosperms.

In every case these fruits aid in the dispersal of their content of seeds. The maple "key" and the dandelion parachute are examples of fruits which facilitate dispersal of the seeds by the wind. The cocklebur and sticktights are fruits which achieve dispersal of their contained seeds by sticking to the coat (or clothing!) of a passing animal. The animal's power of locomotion serves to transport the seeds to new locations.

The coconut is a fruit which achieves dispersal of its single seed by *floating* to new locations. Groves of coconut palms ring all the Pacific islands. Trees leaning out over the water may drop their coconuts in. The fruit does not germinate in salt water but it will remain viable (capable of germinating) for long periods as it is carried by ocean currents. Finally cast up on a beach, it will be washed by rain water and may germinate and develop into another mature palm.

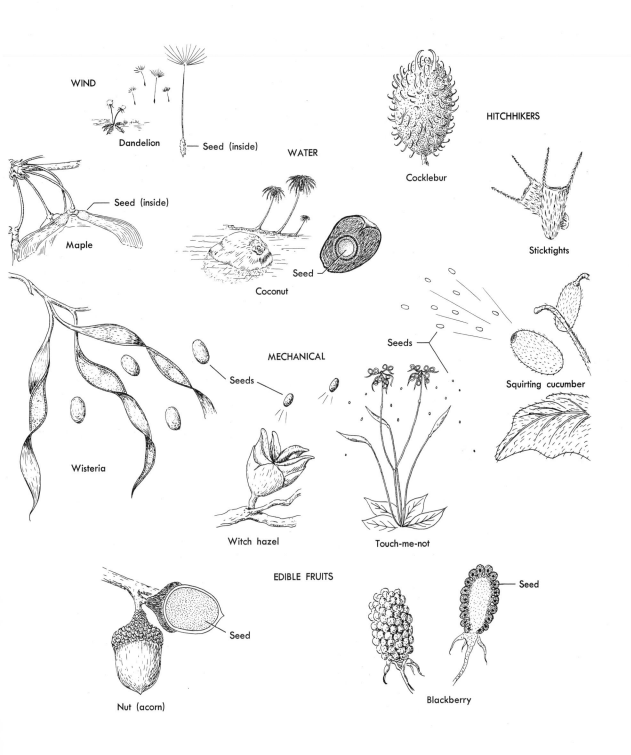

WIND

Dandelion

Seed (inside)

Seed (inside)

Maple

WATER

Seed

Coconut

Cocklebur

HITCHHIKERS

Sticktights

Seeds

MECHANICAL

Seeds

Squirting cucumber

Wisteria

Witch hazel

Touch-me-not

EDIBLE FRUITS

Seed

Nut (acorn)

Seed

Blackberry

Fruits and their role in seed dispersal.   **Fig. 21-9**

Some of the most interesting fruit adaptations are those which achieve mechanical dispersal. Legume pods (e.g. wisteria), witch-hazel pods, touch-me-nots and the squirting cucumber all forcibly eject their seeds as the fruit dries out in the fall. While the distances traveled by these seeds do not achieve rapid dispersal of the species, they do decrease the likelihood of the seedlings having to compete with the parents for sunlight, moisture, and soil minerals.

Edible fruits are very effective dispersal mechanisms. Squirrels, field mice, and other rodents seldom eat all the nuts and grains they store in the fall. With the coming of spring, the forgotten seeds may germinate and at considerable distances from the parent plant. The various kinds of berries are characterized by tiny seeds which can pass undamaged through the alimentary canal of the bird or other animal that eats them. When the animal expels the seeds in defecation, it is usually in quite a new location. The manure in which the seeds are defecated serves as a rich source of minerals and humus for the developing seedling.

21-9   GERMINATION

Germination is the resumption of growth of the embryo plant inside the seed (Fig. 21-10). Proper temperature, proper amounts of moisture, and an adequate supply of oxygen are all necessary for it to occur. What is proper or adequate for one species may not be for another, but for each species these three conditions must be met to some degree.

A period of dormancy is also a requirement for the germination of many seeds. For example, the seeds of apples and peaches will germinate only after a prolonged period of cold. There is evidence that some chemical inhibitor is present in the seed when it is first formed. This inhibitor is gradually broken down at low temperatures until finally there is no longer enough to prevent germination when the other conditions become favorable. Can you think of any survival value this mechanism may have for the plant? The seeds of many desert angiosperms possess inhibitors which prevent germination until the substance has been leached away by water in the soil. In this process more water is required than is necessary for germination itself to occur. Can you think of any survival value *this* mechanism may have for these species?

Fig. 21-10

Three stages in the germination of a bean seed, shown by time-lapse photography. The cotyledons protect the plumule from damage as it is lifted through the soil. (Courtesy Pittsburgh Plate Glass Co.)

Exposure to light of proper duration is also a condition for germination in some cases. The seeds of some plants which grow in marshy locations will germinate only after prolonged exposure to light. On the other hand, the germination of the seeds of some desert plants is inhibited by prolonged exposure to light. What survival value might these responses have?

The angiosperm life cycle is basically similar to that of the gymnosperm. Like that of the gymnosperm, it permits successful existence in a truly terrestrial environment. The angiosperms, however, are a far more varied and successful group than the gymnosperms. There are approximately 200,000 species of angiosperms today compared with approximately 650 species of gymnosperms. Further, the angiosperms have exploited far more kinds of habitat than have the gymnosperms. Arctic tundra, plains, temperate forests, deserts, and jungles are types of environment where angiosperms grow in far greater variety and numbers than do the gymnosperms. The greater abundance and variety of angiosperms and their wide distribution throughout the world is evidence of the survival value of their two unique structural adaptations: the flower and the fruit.

EXERCISES AND PROBLEMS

1 Where are the sporangia located in the (a) moss, (b) fern, (c) pine, (d) apple tree?

2 In what ways are the gametophyte generations of the moss, fern, and angiosperm alike?

3 In what ways are they different?

4 In what ways are the sporophyte generations of the moss, fern, and angiosperm alike?

5 In what ways are mosses well adapted to life on land? In what ways are they poorly adapted?

6 What three conditions are always necessary for germination of seeds to occur?

7 What additional factors are sometimes necessary for the germination of seeds?

8 Describe the experimental procedure that you would use to test the viability of bean seeds that had been stored for five years.

9 Describe the experimental procedure you would use to determine the optimum temperature for the germination of bean seeds.

10 In what ways is the alternation of generations in cnidarians similar to that in plants? In what ways is it different?

11 What plant tissue is normally triploid?

12 Which cells undergo meiosis in the (a) moss and (b) bean?

13 Reproduction in the closed flowers of the violet (see Fig. 21-5) is sexual because it involves the union of two gametes. Does it accomplish what sexual reproduction in the open flowers does? What would be the long-term consequence if the violet reproduced exclusively by means of its closed flowers?

14 In angiosperms, what do the ovules eventually become? What does the ovary become?

15 Summarize the adaptions found in angiosperms that prevent or minimize self-pollination.

REFERENCES

1 Bold, H. C., *The Plant Kingdom,* 2nd ed., Foundations of Modern Biology Series, Prentice-Hall, Inc., 1964. Chapters 7, 8, and 9 discuss reproduction in the ferns, gymnosperms, and angiosperms, respectively.

2 Grant, V., "The Fertilization of Flowers," *Scientific American,* Reprint No. 12, June, 1951.

3 Biale, J. B., "The Ripening of Fruit," *Scientific American,* Reprint No. 118, May, 1954.

4 Koller, D., "Germination," *Scientific American,* Reprint No. 117, April, 1959.

American chameleon emerging from egg.
(Courtesy Carolina Biological Supply Co.)

THE FORMATION OF GAMETES

Animals, unlike plants, do not exhibit an alternation of diploid and haploid generations. Fertilization is still preceded by meiosis, but the products of meiosis are the
gametes themselves. In all animals, **heterogametes** are produced. A moment's reflection will reveal the adaptive value of this modification. To carry out their function
most effectively, gametes should be motile (so they can meet and unite) and supplied
with food reserves to furnish energy and material for the developing embryo. These
two requirements are rather incompatible. The solution is: one gamete, the **sperm,**
that is motile and small and one gamete, the **egg,** that is filled with food reserves.

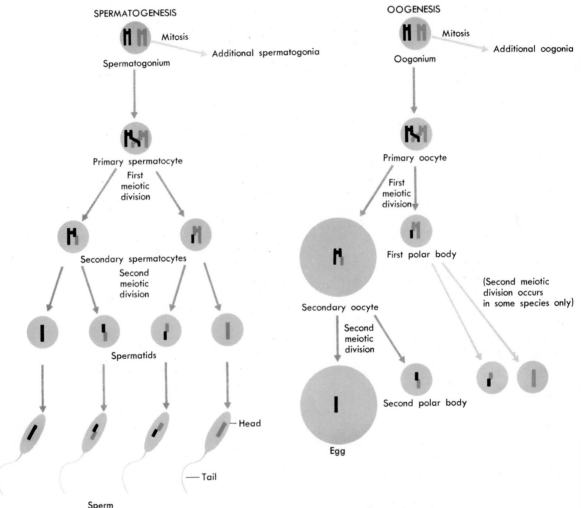

Fig. 22-1 Spermatogenesis and oogenesis. For the sake of simplicity the behavior of just a single pair
of homologous chromosomes is shown (cf. Fig. 17-12). With two or more pairs, random
assortment of the homologues contributes to the variety of gene combinations in the gametes.
Note that which chromosomes end up in the egg and which in the polar bodies is entirely
a matter of chance.

Sperm cells are little more than flagellated nuclei. They are produced in **testes** by specialized cells called spermatogonia. Spermatogonia, which are diploid, may divide by mitosis to produce additional spermatogonia or they may be transformed into *spermatocytes*. Meiosis of each spermatocyte results in the production of four haploid cells, the spermatids (Fig. 22-1). These then become transformed into sperm cells, losing most of their cytoplasm in the process.

A sperm cell consists of (1) a head, which contains the chromosomes in a compact, inactive state, (2) two centrioles, and (3) a flagellum. One of the centrioles will help to construct a spindle for the sperm and egg chromosomes following fertilization. The other serves as the basal body of the flagellum, which propels the sperm. Mitochondria surround the upper part of the flagellum and supply the energy for its lashing movements (Fig. 22-2).

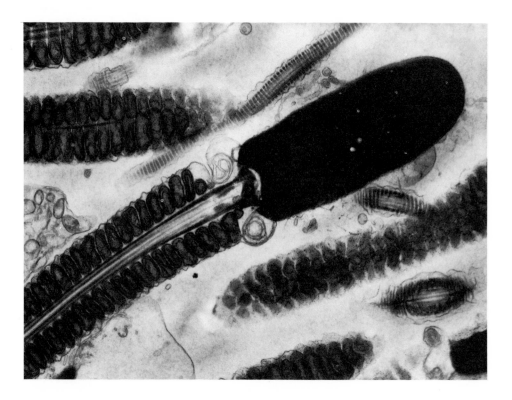

Sperm cell of a bat (15,000 X). Note the orderly arrangement of the mitochondria in the tail. They supply the energy for its motion. (Courtesy Don W. Fawcett and Susumu Ito.)

Fig. 22-2

Eggs are produced in **ovaries.** Diploid oogonial cells divide by mitosis to produce additional oogonial cells. This occurs once a year in most aquatic animals and in the amphibians. Among the reptiles, birds, and mammals, however, the process stops long before birth. In fact, by the time the female human fetus (a developing baby) is 15 weeks old, multiplication of oogonia is almost completed. No wonder Weismann emphasized the early isolation of the germplasm from the somaplasm!

Egg formation starts when the oogonial cells enter prophase of the first meiotic division. No further development of the resulting primary oocytes takes place until

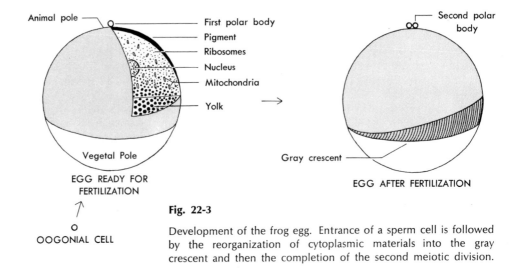

Animal pole — First polar body
Pigment
Ribosomes
Nucleus
Mitochondria
Yolk

Vegetal Pole

EGG READY FOR
FERTILIZATION

OOGONIAL CELL

Second polar
body

Gray crescent

EGG AFTER FERTILIZATION

Fig. 22-3

Development of the frog egg. Entrance of a sperm cell is followed by the reorganization of cytoplasmic materials into the gray crescent and then the completion of the second meiotic division.

just before the animal is ready to enter a period of reproductive activity. In frogs, this occurs once a year—usually in the spring—after adulthood is reached. Then thousands of primary oocytes begin a period of marked cell growth. Each is enclosed in a cluster of cells called a **follicle.** Food materials are transferred from the follicle cells to the growing oocyte. The volume of frog eggs increases over a million times during this period (Fig. 22-3).

When this phase of development is completed, the egg cell is a large sphere containing in its cytoplasm large quantities of DNA, RNA, yolk, mitochondria, and oil droplets. These materials are not distributed uniformly throughout the egg of the frog but in gradients extending from pole to pole. The dark hemisphere of the egg is topped by the so-called **animal pole.** Except for the yolk, most of the egg constituents are concentrated near this pole. The nucleus is also found here. The yolk concentration increases toward the opposite, light-colored **vegetal pole.**

As growth of the primary oocyte nears completion, the first meiotic division is completed, too. The cytoplasm is not distributed equally to the two daughter cells, but almost all of it passes to just one of them. The other cell is called a **polar body** (Fig. 22-4).

Fig. 22-4

Polar body formation during oogenesis in the whitefish. (Courtesy General Biological Supply House, Inc.)

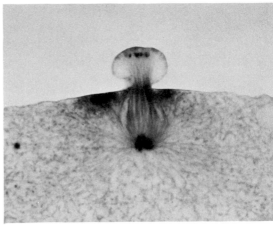

In most vertebrates, the second meiotic division gets only as far as metaphase and then stops. At this time, the egg is ready for release from the follicle, a process known as **ovulation.** The follicle and ovary walls rupture, allowing the egg to pass into the body cavity. It then enters an oviduct where accessory substances, such as gelatinous rings of albumen in the frog, may be added. Further development of the egg awaits fertilization.

The life span of both sperm and eggs is usually measured in hours. Furthermore, sperm are definitely limited in the distance they can swim. But, since most animals have the power of locomotion, the sperm themselves do not usually have to travel great distances to reach the egg. Successful locomotion of the sperm and successful fertilization do, however, require moist surroundings.

BRINGING THE GAMETES TOGETHER   22-2

Among aquatic animals, the problem of moist surroundings for fertilization does not exist. Fertilization can occur directly in the water after each parent releases its gametes. To improve the chances of the gametes meeting, they are usually released in fairly close proximity. This requires that the males and females of the species reach full sexual development at about the same time and in about the same place. Synchronous flowering achieved by response to definite photoperiods was discussed in the last chapter. Analogous periodic behavior is observed in many animals. In the California grunion (a fish), the two sexes swim into shallow water to spawn (release their gametes) at the time of full moon and new moon. In other species, a member of one sex (usually the male) carries out certain behavioral activities ("courtship") in the presence of the female. These activities trigger appropriate egg-laying behavior in the female.

The first terrestrial animals were probably arthropods such as arachnids and insects. Life on land created a problem in bringing the gametes together while protecting them from the drying action of the air. It was solved by internal fertilization. In insects, a special organ of the male, the penis, is inserted into the female in a process called **copulation** and transfer of the sperm takes place. The sperm are then stored in sperm receptacles until the female is ready to lay her eggs. As the eggs pass down her genital tract, they are fertilized by the sperm. The critical process of fertilization is thus accomplished entirely within the moist body of the female (Fig. 22-5).

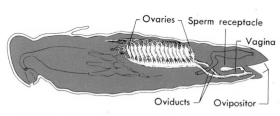

REPRODUCTIVE ORGANS OF ♀ GRASSHOPPER

Reproductive organs of the female (♀) grasshopper (above). Sperm are stored in the sperm receptacle following copulation with the male (♂) grasshopper. Fertilization takes place as the eggs pass through the vagina before being deposited in a capsule in the soil (below).

Fig. 22-5

The first terrestrial vertebrates were the amphibians. As the name implies, they are really only semiterrestrial. Most frogs and toads must return to the water to engage in sexual reproduction. Fertilization takes place in the water. The common male bullfrog, for example, clasps the female in an embrace called amplexus. As the female deposits her several thousand eggs into the water, the male deposits sperm over them. No copulation takes place.

The reptiles were the first vertebrates able to live in a truly terrestrial environment. They have several important adaptations, both structural and physiological, which permit them to flourish even in hot, dry climates. Some of these will be discussed in Chapter 34. As for sexual reproduction, the problem of moisture for the gametes is solved by internal fertilization. In most cases, the male copulates with the female, introducing sperm directly into her genital tract. Birds and mammals also solve the problem of bringing the gametes together in moist surroundings by copulation followed by internal fertilization.

22-3   FERTILIZATION

In contrast to the situation in mosses and ferns, there is no evidence that animal sperm are guided toward the egg. They find it entirely at random, but when we remember that millions of sperm may be released in the vicinity of the egg, it is not surprising that some do find it.

The process of fertilization begins when sperm actually become attached to the egg. In so doing, they may release digestive enzymes that dissolve an opening through the membrane or layer of residual follicle cells that usually cover eggs. Then the nucleus and one centriole of the sperm cell actually enter the egg. The egg seems to play an important part in this as these structures appear to be drawn inward. Entrance of the sperm head is followed by a rapid and dramatic transformation within the egg itself. Its cytoplasmic constituents quickly become reorganized. In the frog, certain cytoplasmic granules appear at the surface of the egg in a band called the **gray crescent** (Fig. 22-3).

In many eggs, the changes brought about by the entrance of one sperm immediately prevent, in some way, other sperm from entering, too. Just how this is accomplished is not fully understood. In animals with large eggs, such as reptiles, birds, and the duckbill platypus, it doesn't occur at all. Although many sperm gain entrance to these eggs, only one contributes its nucleus to the future zygote. In any case, entrance of a sperm cell also triggers the completion of the second meiotic division, and a second polar body forms.

The final event in fertilization occurs when the sperm centriole initiates the formation of a spindle upon which first the sperm chromosomes and then the egg chromosomes become arranged. At this point, a zygote with the diploid number of chromosomes has been formed and fertilization is complete. Within a short time, the first mitotic division of the cell will take place and embryonic development begin.

22-4   CARE OF THE YOUNG

An important relationship exists between the number of gametes, especially eggs, produced by different animals and the care given the embryos during development. For a population to continue at a stable size, an average of two offspring should reach maturity for every two parents. Very few aquatic animals take any care of their eggs once they are fertilized, and mortality of the developing young is extremely high. In compensation for this, a mature female American oyster, *Crassostrea virginica*, may release as many as one million eggs per season. The chances of any one egg ever developing into a mature oyster are exceedingly small. Most, even if successfully fertilized, will succumb at some stage of development to predators, infection, or other unfavorable happenings. Some aquatic animals, e.g. many fresh-water bivalves and some fish, do provide a certain amount of care for the eggs. The fresh-water clam retains fertilized eggs in the gills until they hatch. The male stickleback fish builds a nest and guards and aerates the eggs that the female deposits inside. Characteristically, these species do not produce such enormous numbers of gametes.

The eggs of most aquatic animals are relatively small. In a large number of species, the organism that hatches from the egg is not a miniature replica of the adult but a larval stage quite different in appearance. Usually the larvae are free-swimming and feed on miscroscopic plant and animal life called plankton. In so doing, they acquire additional food materials for further growth. After a period of growth, the larvae undergo metamorphosis, and the body structure is reorganized on the plan of the adult. Metamorphosis may occur in several stages (e.g. in crustaceans and mollusks) or it may be completed in a single brief, but extensive, transformation (e.g. in the echinoderms).

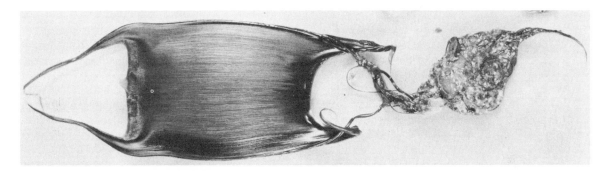

Egg case of a skate (almost life-size). The eggs are sealed inside. (Courtesy New York Zoological Society.) **Fig. 22-6**

An exception to these generalizations on aquatic animals is found in the cartilaginous fishes: the sharks, skates, and rays. Their interesting solution to the problem of dehydration by salt water was discussed in Chapter 16. You remember that the concentration of urea in the bloodstream is maintained at such a high level that the blood is isotonic to the sea water. This physiological adaptation cannot be achieved by their embryos. The cartilaginous fishes have, however, developed two techniques for avoiding fatal dehydration of their embryos. One is to enclose the fertilized egg and a suitable watery medium in a tough, waterproof case. Empty skate egg cases are a familiar sight among the debris washed up on our beaches (Fig. 22-6). The other solution is to retain the developing embryo within the female's body until it becomes physiologically capable of maintaining a high urea level. The young then are "born." Either solution requires internal fertilization of the eggs. (The egg case of the skate is as impervious to sperm as it is to water.) The sperm are introduced directly into the body of the female in the process of copulation. Modified fins on the male aid in clasping the female and in transferring the sperm.

Terrestrial animals all need some means of protecting the developing embryo from the drying action of the air. In insects this protection is provided by a waterproof covering deposited around each egg and, in some cases, a capsule or sac which is deposited around a cluster of eggs. The number of fertilized eggs laid each season varies from hundreds to thousands, depending on the particular species and the amount of care taken of the eggs. The smaller numbers reflect a somewhat greater chance of survival to adulthood for a given embryo than in the aquatic species discussed earlier. Care of the young is developed to an extreme in colonial ants and bees. In these species a very high percentage of the fertilized eggs develops to maturity. Significantly, most of the offspring of these species are sterile workers, which makes the maintenance of a stable population easier.

Most of our common amphibians take no care of their eggs. After fertilization, they are simply left to develop in the water. The gelatinous layers of albumen surrounding the egg absorb water, swell, and provide some physical protection for the egg. They also aid in keeping the egg somewhat warmer than the surrounding water. The clear jelly is transparent to the visible portion of the sun's rays. The dark upper surface of the developing egg absorbs these rays effectively. The light energy is converted into heat which warms the embryo. The jelly is, however, a good heat insulator and less energy radiates from the embryo than was received by it. This physical phenomenon is familiar to anyone who has entered an automobile that has been standing in the sun for some time with the windows closed.

The dark upper surface of the fertilized egg also provides protective coloration. When viewed from above, the egg is hard to distinguish against the dark background of the pond bottom. Similarly, the light underside of the egg blends with the sky when viewed from underneath.

Reptile eggs are fertilized in the genital tract of the female. Then a waterproof shell is deposited around each as it passes down the oviduct. This solves the problem of maintaining the embryo in moist surroundings after the egg is laid. In most species, the eggs are buried in a warm location and abandoned by the mother. There is a plentiful supply of yolk and when the young hatch, they are replicas, although smaller, of their parents. They are also quite self-sufficient.

In some reptiles, e.g. the common garter snake, the eggs are retained in the mother's body until the young hatch. Their nourishment throughout this period is derived chiefly from the yolk of the egg rather than directly from the mother's tissues.

Not long after reptiles first appeared on earth, some species returned to an aquatic environment. Today, one species of lizard (the marine iguana), some snakes and turtles, and the various crocodilians spend most of their lives in water. Nevertheless, they return to land to lay their eggs.

A loggerhead turtle lays about 125 eggs in a season. Althought left unprotected by the parents, the mortality rate is sufficiently low so that the population is maintained. Some reptiles are among the most long-lived animals on earth. An old female turtle has had a good many opportunities to contribute to the maintenance of the population.

Birds are also fully adapted to life in dry locations. Like many of the reptiles (from which they are descended), they lay shelled eggs. These are often carefully tended by the parents. The eggs are richly supplied with yolk, and the young hatch with most of the adult structures. The parents continue caring for the newly hatched young until they are ready to care for themselves. Appropriately, birds rarely lay more than 20 eggs in a season and the average is probably closer to four.

The shelled egg is obviously an important adaptation permitting bird and reptile embryos to develop away from water. A close examination of a common bird egg, the hen's egg, will reveal why this is so. The egg itself consists of a large quantity of yolk and a tiny bit of cytoplasm. After fertilization, but while still within the mother's oviducts, the egg is surrounded with thick layers of watery albumen (egg "white") and a shell made of calcium carbonate. The shell is permeable to gases, but practically impermeable to water. As the embryo develops from the zygote, four special membranes are formed (Fig. 22-7). These "extra-embryonic" membranes develop from the embryo but remain part of it only during its existence within the egg. These four membranes are:

The **yolk sac,** which surrounds the yolk. It connects the embryo with its major source of food. Fats constitute most of the food in the yolk. This is a valuable adaptation, since the oxidation of fats supplies large amounts of both energy and water.

2) The **amnion,** which grows around the embryo, enclosing it in a fluid-filled cavity.

3) The **chorion,** which lines the inner surface of the egg shell. It aids in the exchange of gases (O_2 and CO_2) between the embryo and the outside air.

4) The **allantois,** which serves as a reservoir for the metabolic wastes (chiefly uric acid) excreted by the embryo during its development. As the allantois grows larger, it also participates in gas exchange.

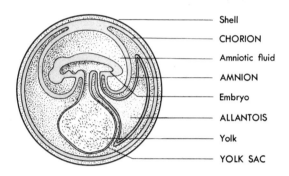

Shell
CHORION
Amniotic fluid
AMNION
Embryo
ALLANTOIS
Yolk
YOLK SAC

Fig. 22-7

The extra-embryonic membranes of the developing chick. Note that the yolk sac and allantois are outgrowths of the embryo digestive tract. The same membranes are produced by the embryos of reptiles and mammals.

With these four membranes, the developing embryo is able to carry on essential metabolism while sealed within the egg. Surrounded by the fluid in the amniotic cavity, the embryo is kept as moist as the fish embryo in a pond.

These four membranes are produced by the embryos of birds, reptiles, and also mammals. Except for the rare echidnas and duckbill platypus, though (Fig. 5-21), the membranes are not associated with a shelled egg in the mammals. Mammalian eggs, which are poorly supplied with yolk, are retained within an oviduct after fertilization. The extra-embryonic membranes penetrate the walls of an enlarged portion of the oviduct, the **uterus.** After the small supply of food within the egg is exhausted, additional nourishment is secured through exchange with the mother's circulatory system.

In the marsupials (of which only the opossum is found in this country), the yolk sac serves this function for a time. However, it does not become well-established, and as a consequence, the young are born in a very immature state (Fig. 22-8). They are able, though, to crawl into a special pouch on the mother's abdomen. There they attach themselves to her nipples and consume milk from her mammary glands until they are developed enough to fend for themselves.

Fig. 22-8

Newborn opossums. Eighteen of them fit easily into a teaspoon. (Courtesy Dr. Carl G. Hartman.)

In all other mammals, the extra-embryonic membranes form a **placenta** and **umbilical cord** which connect the embryo to the mother's uterus in a more elaborate and efficient way. The blood supply of the embryo is continuous with that of the placenta. Although the capillaries of the placenta are in close contact with the mother's blood supply to the uterus, actual intermingling of the blood of the mother and the embryo does not normally occur. The placenta extracts not only food but also oxygen from the uterus. Carbon dioxide and other excretory wastes (e.g. urea) are similarly transferred to the mother's circulatory system for ultimate disposal by her excretory organs.

Although development continues within the uterus for a longer time than is characteristic of marsupials, there is a great variation among the mammals in the degree of helplessness of the newborn. In all cases, however, a period of feeding on milk supplied by the mother's mammary glands occurs. In some species, care of the young may be extended to include training in behavior patterns characteristic of the species, as illustrated by the red fox demonstrating to her cubs the techniques of hunting.

HUMAN REPRODUCTION

22-5

THE SEX ORGANS OF THE MALE

Man, of course, is a mammal. The gamete-producing organs, the gonads, arise early in embryonic development. In both sexes they arise low in the abdominal cavity. The gonads of the male are the two **testes**. At about the time of birth, they descend through the body wall into a sac, the scrotum. Occasionally, they fail to descend and the condition of cryptorchidism results. Unless corrected by surgery, no viable sperm are produced even after sexual maturity has been reached. The major difference between the location in the abdomen and the normal one is temperature. In the scrotum the testes are maintained at a temperature a few degrees below 98.6°F; this lower temperature is essential for the production of viable sperm.

Each testis consists of myriads of **seminiferous tubules** embedded in a matrix of **interstitial cells.** Lining the walls of the seminiferous tubules are the spermatogonia that produce the sperm. The interstitial cells produce the male sex hormones, the **androgens.** Androgens, of which testosterone is the most important, produce the secondary male sexual characteristics such as deep voice and facial hair. Sperm produced in the seminiferous tubules are collected by a series of tiny ducts, the *vasa efferentia,* which lead to a long (20 ft) coiled *epididymis* (Fig. 22-9). Here they are stored.

22-6

THE SEX ORGANS OF THE FEMALE

The gonads of the female are the two **ovaries** (Fig. 22-10). At the time of birth, hundreds of thousands of oogonia have started the first meiotic division to produce the same number of primary oocytes. No further development takes place until a girl reaches the period known as puberty (9-15 years). Then the eggs mature, usually one at a time and once a month. The egg grows much larger and completes its first meiotic division. This occurs within a **follicle,** a fluid-filled envelope of cells surrounding the egg. The follicle serves also as an endocrine gland. It produces a mixture of

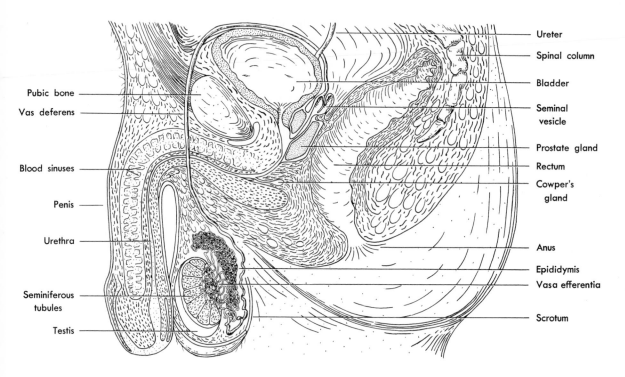

Reproductive organs of the human male. **Fig. 22-9**

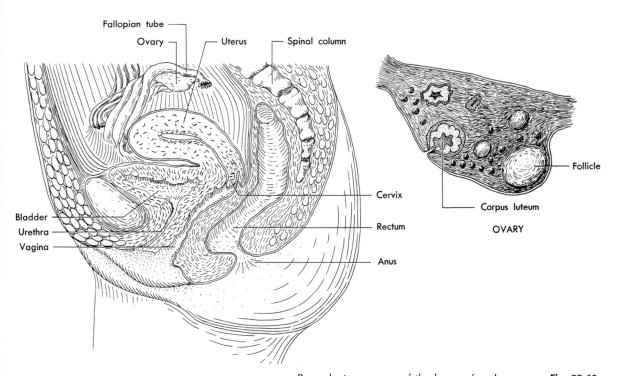

Reproductive organs of the human female. **Fig. 22-10**

female sex hormones collectively known as **estrogens.** These are responsible for the development in the girl of the secondary sexual characteristics of a mature woman, such as broadening of the pelvis and development of the breasts.

The estrogens produced by the follicle also play an important role in the monthly menstrual cycle of women. About once every 28 days (cycles somewhat longer or shorter or even irregular in length are found in perfectly healthy women), a small amount of blood and other products of tissue disintegration are discharged from the vagina. This process is called **menstruation.** It continues for four or five days during which time a new follicle begins to develop in one of the ovaries. After menstruation ceases, the follicle continues to develop, producing increasing amounts of estrogens as it does so. These stimulate an increase in the thickness and blood supply of the inner lining of the uterus. About two weeks after the onset of menstruation, **ovulation** occurs. The follicle ruptures and discharges its egg. The egg is then swept into the open end of the oviduct (called a Fallopian tube in humans) and begins to migrate slowly down the length of the tube.

The old follicle undergoes a reorganization of its cells and develops into a yellow body, the **corpus luteum.** The corpus luteum also functions as an endocrine gland by secreting another female sex hormone called **progesterone** (Fig. 7-9). For about ten days, the high level of progesterone in the bloodstream exerts the following effects:

1) It stimulates the further development of the lining of the uterus.

2) It inhibits contraction of the smooth muscle of the uterine wall.

3) It causes a slight enlargement of the mammary glands.

4) It inhibits the development of a new follicle.

If fertilization does not occur, the production of progesterone begins to drop off about the 26th day of the cycle. The corpus luteum shrinks, the lining of the uterus begins to break down, and by the 28th day, the menstrual flow begins again. Withdrawal of progesterone lifts the inhibition on uterine contraction. The "cramps" associated with the first day or two of menstruation result from vigorous contractions of the uterus. Withdrawal of progesterone also lifts the inhibition on follicle development so a new follicle begins to ripen and the cycle begins anew.

Menstruation in humans should not be confused with the periods of "heat" exhibited by many mammals, including the domestic dog and cat. These animals will allow copulation close to the time of ovulation only. In the process of ovulating the several eggs which a female dog may produce at one time, some blood is also produced. This flow is not related to that which occurs during menstruation.

22-7   **FERTILIZATION, PREGNANCY, AND BIRTH**

For fertilization to occur, sperm must be deposited in the vagina fairly near to the time of ovulation. This is accomplished during copulation. As a result of sexual excitation, the arteries supplying blood to the penis of the male dilate. Blood accumulates in sinuses in the penis and the resulting pressure causes the penis to become erect and thus able to penetrate the vagina of the female. Further sexual excitation results in ejaculation. Sperm pass from the epididymis into the vas deferens. Peristaltic contractions of the smooth muscle of the wall of the vas deferens propel the sperm forward. Glandular secretions are added to the sperm by the seminal vesicles, the prostate gland, and the Cowper's glands (Fig. 22-9). These secretions probably serve to activate the sperm and to provide optimum chemical conditions for them in the female. The mixture of sperm and glandular secretions is called **semen.** The semen passes into the urethra and is expelled from the penis into the vagina.

The sperm swim to the opening in the cervix of the uterus (Fig. 22-10), through the uterus itself, and up into the Fallopian tubes where fertilization takes place if a viable egg is present. Although only one sperm penetrates the egg, medical authorities agree that at least 60 million sperm should be present in each milliliter of semen if fertilization is to occur. Most of the sperm die during the trip through the female genital tract.

Embryonic development begins while the zygote is still within the Fallopian tube. The developing embryo continues to travel down the tube, reaching the uterus in about one week. Here implantation in the thick inner lining of the uterus takes place. The extra-embryonic membranes develop and form the amniotic cavity, placenta, and umbilical cord (Fig. 22-11).

With the implantation of the embryo, pregnancy is established. The corpus luteum continues to produce progesterone beyond the 26th day of the cycle and its effects are actually increased. After five months, however, the corpus luteum is no longer able to produce sufficient progesterone to maintain pregnancy. By this time, however, the placenta itself has become active as an endocrine gland, producing supplementary amounts of progesterone. This placental progesterone violates the usual rule that hormones are transported in the blood. Instead, it simply diffuses from the placenta into the wall of the uterus where it serves to inhibit its contraction.

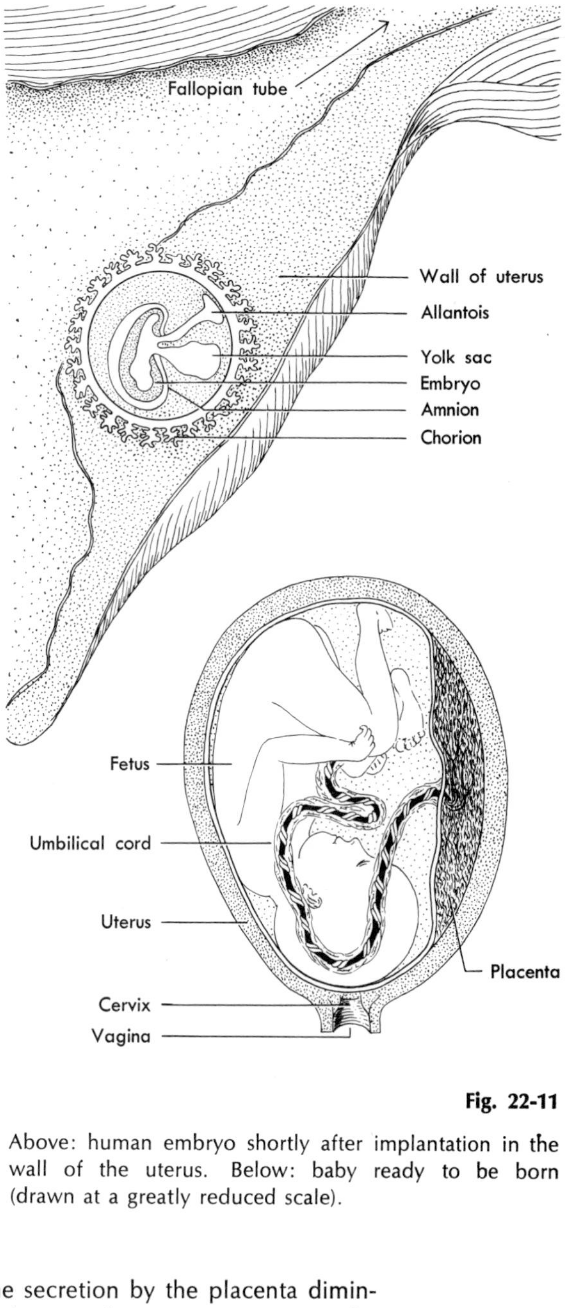

After about nine months of development, the baby is ready to be born. A hormone, **relaxin,** is produced by the ovaries, which causes the ligaments between the pelvic bones to loosen. This provides a more flexible passageway for the baby during birth. Progesterone secretion by the placenta diminishes with the result that contractions of the uterus begin. These contractions are the "labor pains." The cervix opens, the amniotic membrane ruptures and the amniotic fluid flows out. Finally, vigorous contractions of the uterus expel the baby through the cervix and out of the vagina. The umbilical cord must then be severed. The baby may have to be spanked to cause it to fill its lungs with air and commence breathing. Important changes also must occur in the baby's circulatory system so that a full supply of blood will be delivered to the newly inflated lungs. Occasionally, the changeover is not completed successfully. The opening which shunts blood directly

Fallopian tube

Wall of uterus
Allantois
Yolk sac
Embryo
Amnion
Chorion

Fetus

Umbilical cord

Uterus

Cervix
Vagina

Placenta

Fig. 22-11

Above: human embryo shortly after implantation in the wall of the uterus. Below: baby ready to be born (drawn at a greatly reduced scale).

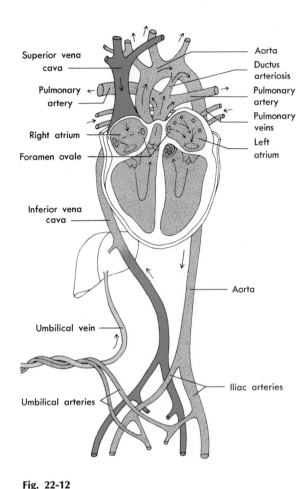

Superior vena cava

Pulmonary artery

Right atrium

Foramen ovale

Inferior vena cava

Umbilical vein

Umbilical arteries

Aorta

Ductus arteriosis

Pulmonary artery

Pulmonary veins

Left atrium

Aorta

Iliac arteries

Fig. 22-12

Circulation in the human fetus. Oxygen is picked up at the placenta, not at the lungs. Most of the blood bypasses the lungs by passing through the foramen ovale and the ductus arteriosus.

from the right side to the left side of the heart of the fetus (Fig. 22-12) may not close properly and thus the lungs will not receive sufficient blood for proper gas exchange. This condition results in "blue babies." Today the defect can be cured through surgery. Shortly after the arrival of the baby, the placenta and remains of the umbilical cord (the "afterbirth") are also expelled.

Within two or three days, the mammary glands of the mother begin to secrete milk. This is triggered by nervous stimulation provided by the baby's nursing and hormones produced by the pituitary gland, a tiny endocrine gland located at the base of the brain. (There are, in fact, a number of hormones produced by this gland which regulate the reproductory processes. Their precise role will be examined in Chapter 26.) Milk provides a rich, balanced diet for the young baby. (Some mothers prefer to substitute cow's milk for their own, and feed the baby from a bottle.)

In humans, care of the young continues for a very long period. This care involves training of all kinds in addition to feeding and cleaning the young. Such meticulous, protracted care makes it possible for humans to maintain the population easily with just one baby born at a time. (Multiple births occur, but not frequently.) The converse seems also to be true. Single births avoid the competition that would occur (during pregnancy as well as after) if twins, triplets, etc, were the rule. This, in turn, makes rapid development unnecessary. Perhaps some of the achievements of humans can be traced to the leisurely development of the young that single births permit.

EXERCISES AND PROBLEMS

1 Name the four extra-embryonic membranes of the chick.

2 The retention of fertilized eggs within the mother's body occurs commonly among the cartilaginous fishes and the reptiles. Why do you suppose no birds employ this means of protecting their eggs?

3 Distinguish between sperm and semen.

4 In what ways is egg formation in the frog similar to megaspore formation in the bean? In what ways is it different?

5 Spermatogenesis in the honeybee occurs by what kind of cell division?

6 What is the difference between amplexus and copulation?

7 Summarize the functions of progesterone.

8 Where does fertilization occur in (a) the trout, (b) the shark, (c) the queen bee, (d) the frog, and (e) the human?

9 If a family has had 7 daughters and no sons, what are the chances that their next child will be a son?

10 Neglecting crossing-over, how many kinds of sperm cells can be produced by *Ascaris bivalens* ($n = 2$)? How many kinds of egg cells can be produced?

11 Do drone bees have fathers? Grandfathers?

12 Few animals are hermaphroditic, while most plants are. Can you think of an explanation for this?

13 The number of eggs produced by the members of a species can be related to the amount of care given to the developing young. Is the same true of the number of sperm produced? Explain.

14 What functions do the centrioles of the spermatogonia carry out (a) in sperm formation, (b) in sperm transfer, (c) in fertilization?

REFERENCES

1 Rothschild, Lord, "Unorthodox Methods of Sperm Transfer," *Scientific American,* November, 1956. Deals with the sponge, bedbug, spider, and leech.

2 Guyton, A. C., *Textbook of Medical Physiology,* 2nd Edition, W. B. Saunders Company, Philadelphia, Penn., 1961. Chapters 78 through 81 describe in detail the physiology of the human sex organs, including the processes of copulation, pregnancy, birth and lactation.

3 Csapo, A., "Progesterone," *Scientific American,* Reprint No. 163, April, 1958.

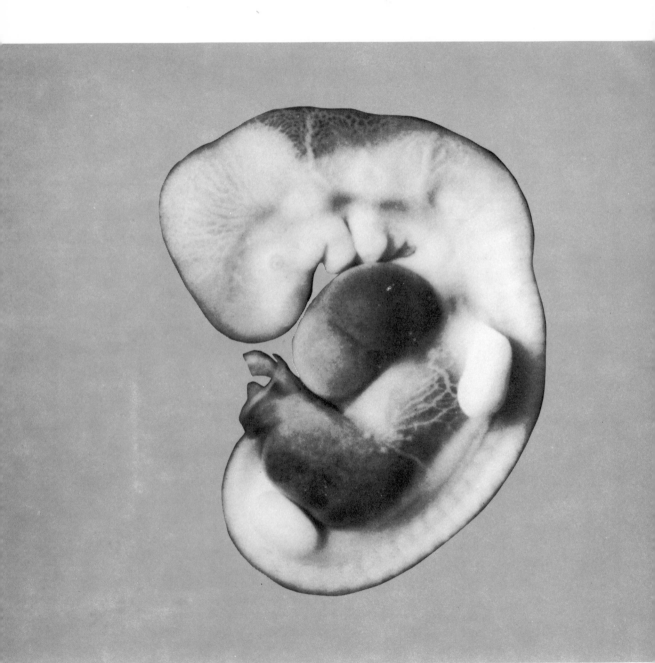

In the past two chapters we have examined the ways in which gametes are manufactured and brought together so that fertilization can occur. Fertilization is not the end of the process of sexual reproduction. It is, in fact, the start of a series of elaborate and well-organized changes which eventually give rise to a new adult of the species. We use the term *development* to describe these changes.

STAGES IN THE DEVELOPMENT OF THE ADULT   23-1

The development of an adult organism from a zygote proceeds by an orderly progression of stages. Although the exact pattern varies from one species to another (especially if they are not closely related) and there is some overlapping, one can usually distinguish the following stages.

1) **Cleavage.** During this stage of development, the zygote nucleus undergoes a long series of mitotic divisions. The resulting daughter nuclei usually become partitioned off in separate cells fashioned from the cytoplasm of the zygote. There is little or no growth during this stage.

2) **Morphogenesis.** During this stage, the many cells produced by cleavage continue dividing but also move about and organize themselves into distinct layers and masses. As a result, a definite pattern appears. It is this development of pattern that is called morphogenesis, and the organism at this stage is called the **embryo.** Although the cells of the embryo during this phase of development are organized into distinct groups, they are all rather similar in structure.

3) **Differentiation.** Soon, however, the cells of the developing embryo begin to take on the specialized structure and functions which they will have in the adult. Nerve cells, muscle cells, etc., are formed. This process is called differentiation. The differentiated cells are organized into tissues, the tissues into organs, and the organs into systems.

4) **Growth.** Even after all the body systems of the organism have been formed, there follows a period of growth. During this period, the organism becomes larger by continued cell division or by cell enlargement, or both. Whatever the exact mechanism, growth depends on the intake of more matter and energy than is needed simply to maintain the normal functions of the organism. There must be an accumulation of proteins, carbohydrates (especially in plants) and the many other kinds of molecules characteristic of living things. Let us now examine the first three of these developmental stages in more detail.

CLEAVAGE   23-2

As we saw in the last chapter, the entrance of a frog sperm into the frog egg initiates several events. The "gray crescent" appears, meiosis of the egg is completed, and then the sperm nucleus and egg nucleus fuse. Shortly after this vital part of the fertilization process is completed, the first cleavage takes place. The zygote nucleus divides by mitosis, and a furrow appears which runs longitudinally through the "poles" of the egg (Fig. 23-1). This soon divides the egg into two halves.

◀ Human embryo 31 days old (16 X).
   (From *Medical Radiography and Photography*, Carnegie Institution of Washington.)

Fig. 23-1   The stages in the development of a frog.

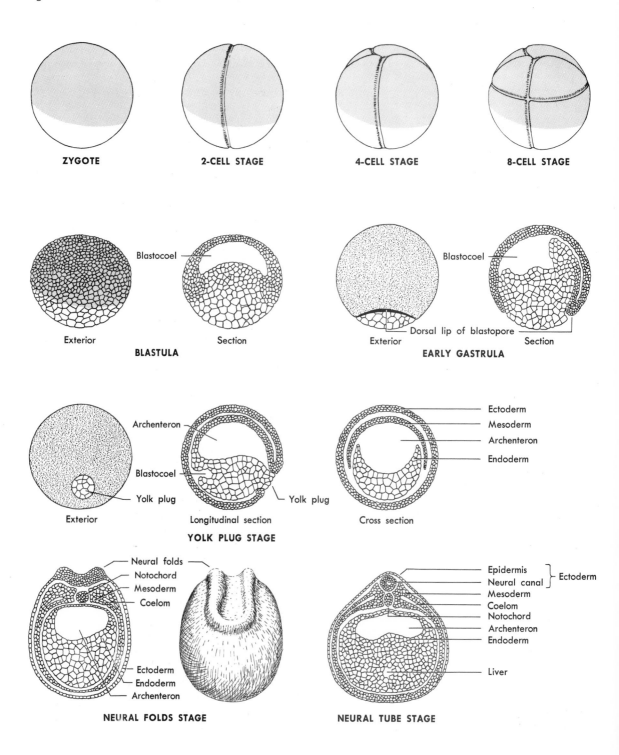

ZYGOTE   2-CELL STAGE   4-CELL STAGE   8-CELL STAGE

Blastocoel

Exterior   Section
BLASTULA

Blastocoel

Exterior   Dorsal lip of blastopore   Section
EARLY GASTRULA

Archenteron

Blastocoel

Yolk plug   Yolk plug

Exterior   Longitudinal section   Cross section
YOLK PLUG STAGE

Ectoderm
Mesoderm
Archenteron
Endoderm

Neural folds
Notochord
Mesoderm
Coelom

Ectoderm
Endoderm
Archenteron

NEURAL FOLDS STAGE

Epidermis ⎤ Ectoderm
Neural canal ⎦
Mesoderm
Coelom
Notochord
Archenteron
Endoderm

Liver

NEURAL TUBE STAGE

Fig. 23-1 (cont.)

Cleavage types. **Fig. 23-2**

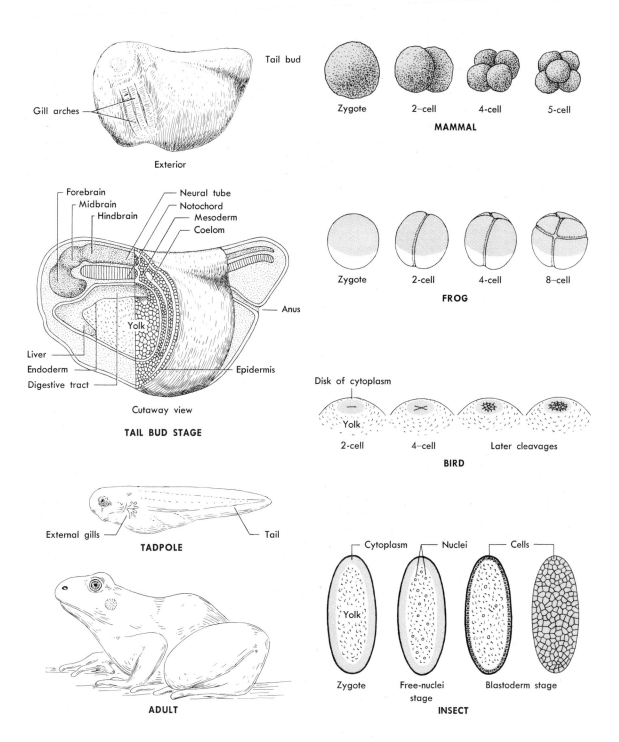

Gill arches

Tail bud

Exterior

Forebrain
Midbrain
Hindbrain

Neural tube
Notochord
Mesoderm
Coelom

Anus

Yolk

Liver
Endoderm
Digestive tract

Epidermis

Cutaway view

TAIL BUD STAGE

External gills

Tail

TADPOLE

ADULT

Zygote   2–cell   4-cell   5-cell

MAMMAL

Zygote   2-cell   4-cell   8–cell

FROG

Disk of cytoplasm

Yolk

2-cell   4–cell   Later cleavages

BIRD

Cytoplasm   Nuclei   Cells

Yolk

Zygote   Free-nuclei stage   Blastoderm stage

INSECT

Although the first cleavage normally follows the fusion of sperm and egg nucleus, we do not yet know exactly what "triggers" the process. We do know that cleavage can sometimes occur without fertilization. Pricking a frog's egg with a pin dipped in frog's blood may cause cleavage to occur. Electrical and chemical stimuli have also been used successfully to start the process. Tadpoles, fish, and even adult rabbits have been produced by artificially inducing cleavage in unfertilized eggs. This process is called **parthenogenesis.** It occurs naturally in a few species of lizards and in many species of insects. The domestic honeybee *(Apis mellifera)* provides a common example. All of the males (called drones) of the colony develop from unfertilized eggs.

Although an organism produced by parthenogenesis has hereditary information from only one parent, it is not necessarily haploid. The chromosomes of the egg nucleus may duplicate twice before the first cleavage so that the two daughter cells contain the diploid number of chromosomes. (This does not occur in the honeybee drone, which *is* haploid.)

About an hour after the first cleavage in the frog egg, each of the daughter cells divides again. The resulting cleavage furrow also runs through the poles but at right angles to the first. Each of the four resulting cells then simultaneously divides in a horizontal plane (Fig. 23-1). This plane is located closer to the animal pole than the vegetal pole. As a result, the cells of the animal pole are somewhat smaller than the yolk-filled cells of the vegetal pole. Simultaneous cleavage continues with the production of a 16-cell and then a 32-cell stage.

As cleavage continues, the animal pole cells begin to divide more rapidly than those of the vegetal pole. The former thus become not only smaller but also more numerous. During this period some migration of the cells of the animal pole takes place. These orient themselves so that a fluid-filled cavity, the **blastocoel,** forms inside the mass of cells. This hollow-ball-of-cells stage is called the **blastula.** It marks the end of the cleavage stage of development. Note that during this entire stage there has been no growth of the developing organism. The original mass of the egg has simply been partitioned into smaller and smaller units.

The frog egg is richly supplied with yolk, which is concentrated in the vegetal pole. This may account for cleavage becoming unequal and hence the cells of the animal pole becoming smaller and more numerous than those of the vegetal pole. The eggs of mammals are not so well supplied with yolk, and the yolk that is present is fairly evenly distributed throughout the egg. Because of this, cleavage produces cells that are quite uniform in size (Fig. 23-2).

Reptiles and birds produce the largest eggs of all living things. For example, the hen's egg consists of just a tiny patch of cytoplasm resting on the surface of a large ball of yolk. (The "white" of the egg is simply noncellular accessory protein.) When cleavage occurs in the hen's egg, the cleavage furrows do not continue down through the mass of yolk. As a result, each of the cells produced in the early cleavage stages is bounded on the top and on the sides by a cell membrane, but the bottom of the cell is in direct contact with the mass of yolk (Fig. 23-2).

The yolk of insect eggs is concentrated in the center of the egg. Cleavage of the egg does not accompany mitosis of the zygote nucleus. Instead, the daughter nuclei divide repeatedly but remain suspended within the single egg compartment (Fig. 23-2). After a large number of nuclei have been produced, they migrate to the cytoplasm-rich margin of the egg. Only then do cell membranes form around each one.

Development of the zygote in plants proceeds somewhat differently than in animals. Mitosis of the zygote is usually accompanied by cell enlargement. In the gymnosperms and angiosperms, some of the daughter cells elongate very rapidly. Their growth pushes the remaining cells up into the food-rich endosperm. The endosperm provides the materials for further development of the embryo (Fig. 23-3).

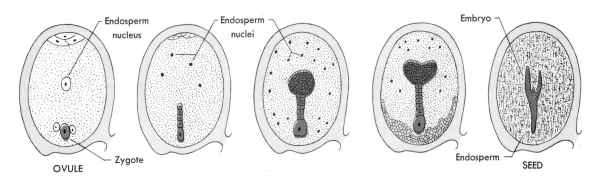

Cleavage and morphogenesis in the angiosperm. Nourishment for the developing embryo is secured from the endosperm. The scale of the drawings decreases from left to right.

Fig. 23-3

What does cleavage accomplish in the development of the organism? First, it provides a mass of cells out of which the embryo can be constructed. We have seen that cells are the structural unit of almost all living things. Cleavage establishes a supply of them. Second, cleavage establishes a normal relationship between the nucleus and the cytoplasm it regulates. Even small eggs are enormous when compared with other kinds of cells. The volume of the frog egg is about 1.6 million times larger than that of a normal frog cell. But it, too, contains only one nucleus. During the process of cleavage, thousands of new nuclei are produced by mitosis. Each of these eventually becomes established in a cell of normal dimensions. Remember that the frog blastula with its thousands of cells is no larger than the original zygote.

MORPHOGENESIS   23-3

Cell division does not cease with the blastula stage. In the frog the smaller, darker cells of the animal pole continue to undergo rapid mitosis. As the number of these cells increases, they begin to migrate down over the yolk-filled cells of the vegetal pole. Some of the vegetal pole cells also begin to migrate. In their case, they push into the interior of the cell mass, producing a small crescent-shaped depression known as the blastopore (Fig. 23-1). This pushing-in of cells marks the start of **gastrulation.** As the animal-pole cells migrate down over the surface of the cell mass, a large number of them also push into the interior at the region of the blastopore.

The inpocketed vegetal pole cells develop into a sheet of cells which grows upward and eventually encloses a cavity, the archenteron (Fig. 23-1). These cells are known as **endodermal** cells. From the archenteron will develop the alimentary canal, the liver and other digestive glands and, after metamorphosis, the lungs. At this stage, the only opening to the archenteron is at the blastopore. Ultimately, the anus will form here. The inner lining of all these organs will be made of endodermal cells directly descended from the first vegetal-pole cells.

The animal-pole cells growing down over the embryo also migrate inward. This occurs first at the upper (or dorsal) portion of the blastopore. The cells move in directly beneath the overlying animal-pole cells. They are now called **mesodermal** cells. From them develops a rodlike structure, the **notochord,** which runs lengthwise along the dorsal side of the developing embryo.

As gastrulation continues, animal-pole cells crowd in around the entire margin of the blastopore. These late arrivals also become mesoderm. Those nearest the notochord become organized into separate masses called **somites,** from which will develop muscles and the bones of the vertebral column. Nearer the ventral surface of the embryo, the mesodermal cells develop into the lining of the **coelom,** the main body cavity. The cavity itself arises by a splitting of this mesoderm (Fig. 23-1). This stage of development is often known as the yolk-plug stage because only a small disk of yolk cells is still visible at the exterior. The animal-pole cells that do not migrate into the interior are called **ectodermal** cells. From them will arise all the structures of the nervous system as well as the skin of the animal.

Shortly after the formation of the notochord, the ectodermal cells immediately above it undergo a period of rapid cell division. This results in a deep, flat layer of cells called the neural plate (Fig. 23-1). Then the edges of the neural plate grow up while the central region just above the notochord becomes depressed. This so-called neural-folds stage is followed by the formation of a neural tube. The two elevated folds grow over and fuse together along their entire length. From this structure develops the brain and spinal cord. In Fig. 23-1 you can see that three enlargements of the neural tube form at the anterior end of the embryo. These will develop into the brain. The neural tube then drops down into the embryo and is covered over by another layer of ectodermal cells which develops into skin.

Although the details of gastrulation vary considerably from species to species, the variations are superficial rather than fundamental. In every case, the process results in the three primary cell layers (often called "germ" layers), the **ectoderm, mesoderm,** and **endoderm.** From these three germ layers arise the various organs and systems of the animal body. Figure 23-4 lists the germ-layer origin of the various organs and systems in man. This list could serve as well for any other chordate.

Gastrulation also occurs in the course of embryonic development in the other animal phyla. Among the echinoderms, the process is basically similar to that described for the frog, with the exception, of course, that no notochord ever develops.

Gastrulation among the other invertebrates differs from that in the chordates and echinoderms in two important respects. Among the annelid worms, mollusks, and arthropods, the blastopore forms in the region that will become the mouth rather than the anus. Furthermore, the mesoderm does not result from an inpocketing of cells. Instead, special mesodermal cells arise within the interior of the embryo. From them develop all the structures made of mesoderm. The very fact that these diverse animals all produce mesoderm in this way gives strong support to the idea that they are much more closely related to one another than they are to the echinoderms and chordates.

ECTODERM

Skin, hair, nails
Entire nervous system, including receptor cells
Adrenal medulla

MESODERM

Muscles
Blood and blood vessels
Connective tissue, including bone
Kidneys, ureters
Testes, ovaries, oviducts, uterus
Mesenteries
Lymphatic system

ENDODERM

Lining of alimentary canal
Lining of trachea, bronchi, and lungs
Lining of urethra and bladder
Liver
Pancreas

Fig. 23-4

Germ-layer origin of the various body tissues.

The process of gastrulation establishes the basic pattern of the embryo. Cells are stockpiled in specific locations in preparation for the construction of the various tissues, organs, and systems of the organism. Their construction involves more than simply the migration and stockpiling of cells in the three germ layers, however. The unspecialized cells of ectoderm, mesoderm, and endoderm must all take on specialized shapes and internal organization to permit them to carry out the functions of the tissue or organ in which they are located. This conversion of unspecialized cells into specialized ones is called differentiation.

Although the later stages of morphogenesis and the process of cell differentiation overlap to a considerable extent, it is well to keep in mind the distinction between the two processes. Morphogenesis involves the organization of cells into the various layers and groups that will form the structures of the body. It involves cell division and the actual movement of cells from place to place within the embryo. Although the various layers of cells in the frog gastrula have definite and different fates ahead of them, they do not at first reveal these fates by any specialization of structure or function. In fact, it is possible for a careful experimenter to transplant cells from one location to another in the early gastrula; these transplanted cells readily adapt to their new location and go on to participate in the building of an organ appropriate to it.

As embryonic development proceeds, however, the cells of the developing embryo reach a "point of no return." They become committed to the formation of a specific kind of cell. Gradually they take on the appearance and function of the various kinds of cells discussed in Chapter 8. As they do this, each begins to synthesize a small number of proteins characteristic of that cell type and no others. Differentiating heart muscle cells start synthesizing a special contractile protein called heart myosin. Differentiating red blood corpuscles begin synthesizing hemoglobin. As connective tissue cells differentiate, they become committed to the synthesis of collagen and other extracellular proteins. And so on. This commitment to a specific fate seems to occur first in mesodermal and endodermal cells, then in the ectodermal cells.

Although the processes of cleavage, morphogenesis, and cellular differentiation can be distinguished from one another, the three operations share one fundamental similarity. In each case, unlike things are being made from like things. From the 8-cell stage of frog cleavage, the cells of the animal pole differ in appearance and chemistry from those of the vegetal pole. From the hollow sphere of the blastula arise three distinct germ layers. From the unspecialized cells of the three germ layers are formed all the differentiated cells of the mature organism. Furthermore, the development of all these diverse structures does not proceed in a random, haphazard way. The precise arrangement of the cleavage planes, the migration of cells in gastrulation, and the production of just the right kinds and numbers of cells in the process of cellular differentiation all reveal a wonderful degree of orderliness and organization. Indeed, at every stage of embyronic development it seems as though the operations are being carried out under the guidance of some master plan.

WHAT CONTROLS DEVELOPMENT?

What is the nature of this guiding plan? Although men have tried for years to discover the answer to this question, we are only just beginning to glimpse the mechanism by which the zygote gives rise to the adult. Of one thing we may be quite sure, however: the master plan of development must reside within the egg or sperm or both. When we consider the large number of organisms (including the frog) that develop far from any adult body, this conclusion seems inescapable. The only essential contribution that adults make to the formation of the next generation is the gametes—the egg and sperm.

THE GENES—A PROBLEM

Boveri's work with haploid sea urchins (see Section 8-4) suggests strongly that it is the nucleus which contains the master plan or blueprint for the development of the organism. After all, the sperm itself is little more than a flagellated nucleus. Within the nucleus are the chromosomes and, as we saw in Chapter 19, the evidence is overwhelming that they are the bearers of the genes. Genes control the traits of an organism, that is, its phenotype. But the phenotype is itself simply the ultimate expression of a long series of developmental stages. Assuming, then, that it *is* the genes that control the development of an organism, a crucial question still remains unanswered.

So far as we can tell, all the trillions of differentiated cells in the adult human have developed from the zygote by mitosis. If this is true, they all contain the same chromosomes that the zygote contained: no more, no less. This suggests that every cell contains *all* the genes for constructing an entire organism. How, then, can we explain the fact that during the course of embryonic development certain cells migrate and differentiate in one way while other cells develop quite differently? How can we explain the diverse fates of a trillion cells each of which contains the same genes that the zygote contained? This is one of the most important questions in biology.

CYTOPLASMIC FACTORS

Many of the tentative answers we now have to this question have come about as a result of the work of experimental embryologists. These are biologists who, by a variety of techniques, alter the path of normal embryonic development. By observing what happens under abnormal conditions, they gain clues as to the mechanisms that operate under normal ones.

One of the earliest experiments of this sort involved the physical separation of the cells produced in the early stages of cleavage. It is known that each of the two cells produced when the frog zygote undergoes its first cleavage will normally give rise to one-half the embryo. One might expect that in some way each of these two cells is able to use only one-half of the genes of the organism. Physical separation of the cells shows, however, that such is not the case. Reared separately, each goes on to produce a complete, although smaller, embryo.

This discovery provides an explanation for the occurrence of identical twins, those twins that show such a striking resemblance to each other. Identical twins are always of the same sex and even in their body chemistry seem to be identical in every way. We explain these rare individuals by assuming that they came from a single zygote which, after one or two cleavages, was separated into two parts. Identical triplets, quadruplets, and quintuplets undoubtedly arise in a similar fashion. The remarkable similarity of these individuals is understandable when we realize that they were formed from a single zygote and thus a single set of genes.

It is worth noting that identical twins are found only among the echinoderms and chordates. The cells produced by the first cleavage of annelid, arthropod and mollusk zygotes are incapable of producing a complete embryo when separated from each other.

When the cell-separation experiment is repeated at the 4-cell stage of cleavage, the results are quite different. None of the resulting cells, when isolated, can produce a complete embryo. What has happened? Have the daughter nuclei produced during the second cleavage lost some of the genes necessary to construct the total organism? The answer to this question was discovered by the German experimental embryologist, Hans Spemann. Using fine strands of baby hair, he tied tight loops around fertilized newt eggs (which are similar to frog eggs) so that they were constricted longitudinally into two halves (Fig. 23-5). The zygote nucleus was in one half. The other half had no nucleus but was in contact with its nucleus-containing partner by a narrow bridge of cytoplasm. Spemann found that only the half-egg with the nucleus in it would cleave. However, at some point during cleavage, a nucleus usually did get across the narrow connecting bridge of cytoplasm. As soon as this happened, the second half began to cleave, too. Even though its nucleus was the product of as many as five prior cleavages, it went on to form a complete embryo. Clearly, then, the nucleus, at the 32-cell stage at least, has not lost any of the genes for making the organism.

When Spemann repeated his experiment with the fertilized egg constricted so that all of the gray crescent lay in one half, the final results were quite different (Fig. 23-5). The half lacking the gray crescent but containing the nucleus began cleavage right away but never developed beyond an unorganized mass of intestinal, liver, and other abdominal cells. The other half, even though it did not get a nucleus until the fourth mitotic division on the cleaving side, went on to form a perfectly normal embryo. This again was proof that the nuclei, here at the 16-cell stage, had not lost any genes. But why, then, did a normal embryo fail to develop on the side with the original zygote nucleus?

We have already seen that the distribution of cytoplasm, mitochondria, RNA, ribosomes, and yolk in the amphibian egg is not uniform. Shortly after fertilization, some of the cytoplasmic constituents migrate and form the gray crescent. Perhaps the potentialities a nucleus can achieve are regulated by the cytoplasmic environment in which it finds itself. Thus, in Spemann's first experiment, each half of the egg contained all the normal egg constituents, because the longitudinal constriction was perpendicular to the gray crescent. However, in his second experiment, the hemisphere lacking the gray crescent may have lacked some essential cytoplasmic materials.

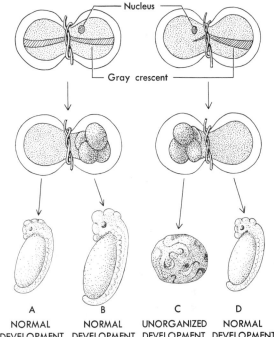

Fig. 23-5

Spemann's experiment. Even though Embryo C started development earlier than Embryo D, it never developed beyond an unorganized mass of belly tissues.

The importance of the cytoplasmic environment may explain the results of the cell-separation experiments described earlier. When the first cleavage in the frog egg occurs perpendicular to the gray crescent (as it often does), each of the two cells produced contains all of the normal egg constituents. The second cleavage, however, isolates the gray crescent in two of the four cells produced. Although all these cells contain nuclei with the complete hereditary blueprint, we may assume that the action of the genes is now limited by the cytoplasmic surroundings in which they find themselves. Though the nuclei are all alike, the nucleus-cytoplasm combinations are not, and we have our first clue as to the way in which dissimilar cells can arise from a single zygote.

The experiments we have been describing show that an unequal distribution of substances within the zygote gives rise to cells of diverse fates despite their identical nuclear controls. It is difficult to imagine, though, that the relatively simple gradients involved account for all the complex migration and differentiation of cells during embryonic development. Are there other guiding forces at work during embryonic development?

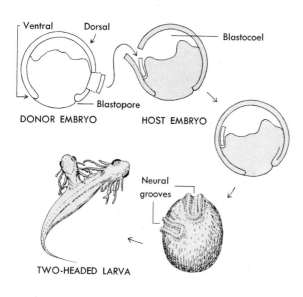

Fig. 23-6

Another of Spemann's experiments. Donor tissue (white) from the region of the gray crescent developed into a notochord and induced the formation of a second head in its host (gray).

To Hans Spemann must go the credit for discovering that there are indeed other guiding forces. You remember he had found that half a newt zygote would develop normally so long as it (1) contained the nucleus and (2) contained some of the region of the cytoplasm known as the gray crescent. Spemann knew that it is the cells that develop in the region of the gray crescent which migrate through the blastopore during gastrulation and form the notochord. With great surgical skill, he succeeded in cutting out the cells of the dorsal lip of the blastopore before their inward migration (Fig. 23-6). Then he transplanted this tiny bit of tissue into the ventral side of a normal newt gastrula. To make it easier for him to follow the fate of the transplant, he used the early gastrula of a pale variety of newt as the donor and the early gastrula of a dark variety as the recipient or host. He discovered that the transplanted piece of dorsal lip developed into a second notochord. Above the site of the transplant a neural groove appeared. This neural groove was made up almost exclusively of host (dark) cells. It underwent normal development, forming a neural tube and then a central nervous system. Ultimately a two-headed monster was produced.

The fact that most of the tissues of the second head were derived not from the transplanted cells, but from the host cells, suggested to Spemann that the transplanted cells had altered the normal course of development of the host cells around them. Instead of producing the belly of the newt, the host cells above the transplant were stimulated to produce a second central nervous system. We use the term **induction** for this process.

When Spemann transplanted portions of gastrulas other than the cells of the dorsal lip of the blastopore, no induction was observed. The transplanted tissue simply developed according to its new location. Because only the dorsal lip of the blastopore could induce altered development in the host, Spemann called it the *organizer*. He visualized the organizer as initiating the process of morphogenesis and differentiation by inducing the formation of the neural tube. The neural tube then might induce the formation of still other embryonic structures. For example, we know that as the brain develops, two masses of nervous tissue, the optic cups, grow forward from it. As these near the anterior surface of the embryo, skin cells just in front of them differentiate to form lenses (Fig. 23-7). The optic cups become the retinas of the finished products, the eyes.

The theory of induction explains very nicely this transformation of skin cells into lens cells. In fact, it is not hard to visualize the development of the entire embryo by this mechanism. As each structure is induced, it can then induce still other structures. Successive waves of induction could thus account for the complete, organized embryonic development of the animal.

Not long after Spemann's discovery, it was found that the inducing properties of the organizer were retained even if the cells were killed. This immediately suggested that induction is accomplished by the passage of some chemical substance from the organizer to the affected cells. It was thought that the inducing substance instructed the affected cells to organize and differentiate in a specific way. This idea thus provided another plausible answer to our question of how diverse cells arise from a single zygote. The peculiar cytoplasmic composition of the gray crescent region might stimulate the blastula cells produced in that region to liberate special chemical regulators. These cells would thus have a feature unique in the embryo and could become the organizer. The diffusion of chemical substances from them might then instruct adjacent cells to develop in a special way. As the latter developed, they in turn could release inducing substances which would program the differentiation of still other cells. In this way the entire embryo could be built.

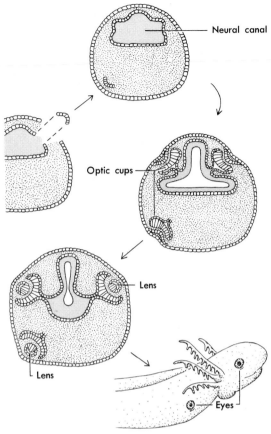

Fig. 23-7

Embryonic development of the salamander eye. A transplanted optic cup induces lens formation in the tissues of its host and an extra eye develops.

With such an attractive theory, it was natural that every effort be made to isolate and identify inducing substances, not only in amphibian embryos but in other organisms as well. In a number of cases it was found that induction could occur across a gap filled with agar-agar, but not across a sheet of cellophane. This suggested that a fairly large molecule was involved and, indeed, a number of inducers have turned out to be proteins. In some cases, a ribonucleoprotein has been implicated, that is, a complex of RNA and protein. In one case, RNA itself is able to induce a new pattern of protein synthesis in the recipient cells.

Although most inducers are macromolecules, there are some exceptions. Vitamin A, a small molecule, can induce altered development in the epidermal cells of a chick embryo. Other small molecules such as certain steroids and even the dye methylene blue (which is not a normal constituent of cells) can induce neural plate formation in the amphibian embryo.

The differentiation of cells seems also to be influenced by *inhibitory* substances that reach them from adjacent cells. When developing frog embryos are placed in cultures containing pieces of adult frog heart, the embryos fail to produce a normal heart. Similarly, embryos cultured with pieces of adult brain fail to produce a normal brain. This would suggest that differentiated cells can produce substances that inhibit adjacent cells from differentiating the same way.

Such a phenomenon accounts nicely for the fact that as embryonic development proceeds, developing organs become sharply separated from one another. It could also account for the uniform distribution of repeating units in many organisms. For example, the body surface of the larval "kissing bug" (*Rhodnius*) is covered with evenly spaced mechanoreceptors and glands (Fig. 23-8). If a group of these in one area is destroyed (for example, by applying a hot needle to the body surface), replacement cells eventually become differentiated in the same location. These reconstruct the receptors and glands with their normal spacing. No two receptors or glands develop right next to each other. Perhaps as each begins to develop, it gives off an inhibitory substance which prevents nearby cells from developing in the same way.

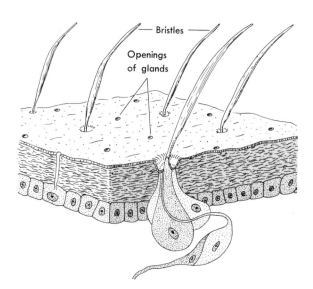

Fig. 23-8

Both the mechanoreceptors and the glands of the *Rhodnius* exoskeleton develop at evenly spaced intervals from one another.

It is becoming increasingly clear that the course of embryonic development depends not just on the induction or inhibition of some cells by other cells but on *interactions* occurring between both groups of cells. For example, in order for the mesoderm within the developing limbs of an embryo to become differentiated, it must have functioning ectoderm above it. On the other hand, continued differentiation of that ectoderm depends upon the continued activity of the underlying mesoderm. Perhaps, then, normal embryonic development depends not so much on the passage of a specific stimulating or inhibiting substance from one tissue to another but on the proper exchange of materials between the two.

The development of mouse kidney tubules requires two kinds of differentiated cells. One kind makes up the collecting portion of the tubule; the other, the secretory portion. It is possible to grow, in tissue culture, the embryonic cells that normally produce each of these differentiated types. When grown alone, they fail to do so, even when supplied with extracts of the other cell type. But when the two are allowed to grow together, each proceeds to differentiate into its adult form. Not only do they differentiate successfully, but the two kinds of cells then proceed to organize themselves into recognizable kidney tubules.

When, however, cells from two *unrelated* adult tissues are cultured together, the two kinds sort themselves out and unite, like with like, to form recognizable tissues. Some of these have even been grafted successfully into adult bodies and have functioned properly.

The ability of two like cells to recognize each other depends upon the presence of specific substances on their surfaces. As we have seen, embryonic cells migrate extensively, especially during morphogenesis. When they finally reach their destination, they adhere to other such cells, presumably by means of the mutual stickiness of these surface substances. Once together, portions of their respective cell membranes fuse so tightly that an easy path is formed for the rapid passage between them of ions, electrical charges, and probably large molecules. Thus each cell has a means of knowing what is happening in adjacent cells. Interestingly enough, cancer cells lack the sticky cell-surface substances and do not recognize other cells nor stop their migration and cell division. Thus they escape from the controls that regulate the normal cells of the body.

SELECTIVE TRANSLATION OF THE GENETIC CODE   23-8

Although the inducing substances that pass from one cell to another may be quite specific or quite general in their instructions, it seems clear that what a differentiating cell does is programmed by its own genes, not those of adjacent tissues. An experiment by one of Spemann's students, Oscar Schotté, vividly demonstrated the truth of this important point.

The larval salamander has bony teeth, and a balancing organ on each side of the head. The tadpole of the frog has horny teeth, and external gills at the sides of the head. Schotté carefully grafted a piece of tissue, destined to become belly skin, from a frog embryo to the part of a salamander embryo that would normally develop into mouth and balancers. The grafted frog tissue underwent development appropriate to its *new* location, but the mouth that was produced had the horny jaws characteristic of tadpoles. Instead of balancers, external gills were formed.

An inducing substance produced by the salamander must have been responsible for changing the fate of what would have been frog belly tissue. However, the instructions provided by the inducing substance must have been quite general. Instead of programming the development of salamander parts, it seems only to have instructed the transplanted tissue to use its own genes, although in a way appropriate to the new location. Thus we must look for the ultimate control of differentiation not in any *organizer* tissue but in the reacting tissue itself. When one considers the large number of substances, even such simple molecules as methylene blue, that can induce neural plate formation in the frog embryo, it begins to look as though the reacting tissue contains all the information required to specialize and simply needs some fairly unspecific influence to enable it to do so. The problem then becomes one of determining what makes a developing cell express certain of its genes (e.g. those participating in building horny jaws or external gills) and not others (in our example, those for belly skin).

Some workers have suggested that during the process of development, the genes contained in the original zygote nucleus become separated and are parceled out to the cells of the various tissues and organs. In Schotté's experiment, however, this is certainly not the case. The cells destined to become belly skin still had the genes for building jaws and gills. Furthermore, chromosome counts of adult cells are generally identical to those of the zygote.

How, then, are the genes within a cell controlled so that certain of them are active and the rest are not? Attempts at answering this question are being made in laboratories around the world. Curiously enough, the first clues came from studies on an organism that has no embryology and no differentiation: the intestinal bacterium *Escherichia coli.*

1. The Jacob-Monod Hypothesis

Within its tiny cell, *E. coli* contains all the genetic information it needs to metabolize, grow, and reproduce. As we saw in Chapter 20, it can synthesize everything it needs from glucose and a number of inorganic ions. We would expect it to need a large number of enzymes to accomplish so many syntheses, and there may well be 600-800 present in the cell. Some of these, such as the enzymes of cellular respiration, are present at all times. Others are produced only when they are needed by the cell. Among these is an enzyme, β-galactosidase, which (like the "lactase" of the human digestive system) hydrolyzes lactose into glucose and galactose. If lactose is substituted for glucose in the culture medium, *E. coli* cells are not able at first to metabolize it. After a period of time, however, they begin producing large quantities of β-galactosidase. At the same time, they produce a second enzyme, called a permease, which transports the lactose across the cell membrane from the medium into the interior of the cells.

The synthesis of each of the two enzymes is controlled by a specific gene. Genetic studies show that these two so-called **structural** genes, which are obviously related in function, are also closely linked on the bacterial chromosome. What causes them to begin the work of producing their enzymes? Or rather, what *keeps* them from producing the enzymes before the need arises? Another gene, called a **regulator** gene, is responsible for this. There is a good deal of evidence that the function of the regulator gene is to produce a protein which prevents the structural genes for β-galactosidase and the permease from expressing themselves. Curiously enough, the regulator substance, called the **repressor,** does not inactivate the structural genes directly; rather, it represses a gene immediately adjacent to them, called the **operator** (Fig. 23-9). The combination of operator and its structural genes is called the **operon** (see Section 20-9). Perhaps the role of the operator, when not repressed by the regulator, is to separate the two strands of DNA of the structural genes so that one of them can be transcribed into a single (probably) molecule of messenger RNA. Ribosomes moving down this molecule would translate the messages into the polypeptides of which the enzymes are to be constructed. (You can see why punctuation codons—UAA or UAG or UGA—would thus be needed to terminate polypeptide synthesis between the portion of the messenger RNA coding for β-galactosidase and that coding for the permease.)

What, then, determines whether the repressor substance produced by the regulator gene is active or not? In the case described, it is probable that the presence of lactose itself prevents the repressor substance from acting on the operator. Lactose unites with the repressor, and as a result the repressor may change its shape enough that it can no longer combine with and thus inactivate the operator. The synthesis of β-galactosidase and the permease may therefore begin. A system such as this, where a substrate (i.e., lactose) *induces* the synthesis of the enzymes needed to metabolize it, is one example of the mechanisms of enzyme control discussed in Chapter 9 (Section 9-8). This mechanism was proposed by the French scientists François Jacob and Jacques Monod to explain the genetics of enzyme induction. For their work, they shared a Nobel Prize in 1965.

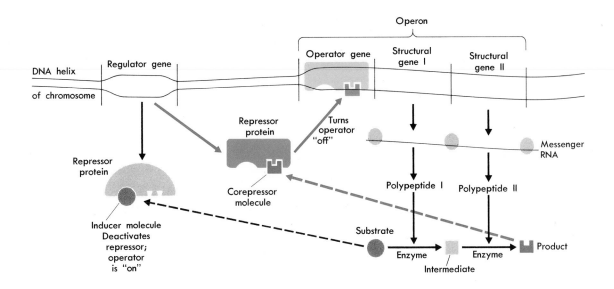

The Jacob-Monod hypothesis of gene control. When an inducer molecule is present, the repressor is unable to attach to the operator gene and polypeptide synthesis takes place. When a corepressor molecule is present, the operon is shut down (color).

Fig. 23-9

Examples are also known where the *products* of enzyme action *repress* enzyme synthesis. Ordinarily, *E. coli* is able to make all its amino acids from glucose and salts. A large number of enzymes are required to accomplish these syntheses. If, however, an amino acid is added to the culture medium, the bacteria soon stop producing the enzymes for the synthesis of that particular amino acid. In such a case, the repressor substance is thought to be unable to block the operators unless it has the amino acid attached to it as a **corepressor** (Fig. 23-9).

Several different operons participate in making the enzymes for the synthesis of the amino acid arginine. However, a single regulator gene, through its repressor molecules, is able to block all the operators (but presumably, only when these repressor molecules are combined with their corepressor, the amino acid itself).

Here then is a mechanism by which the genetic code in an organism can be selectively translated. It involves both protein molecules (the repressors) and small molecules (e.g. lactose, arginine). Thus it might be able to account for the inducing action of both proteins and small molecules in the embryonic development of higher organisms.

Is there any concrete, genetic evidence of regulator and operator genes in organisms that do have embryonic development, that do have cells that differentiate? Such genes have been found in plants (corn and the evening primrose) but have not yet been conclusively identified in animals.

2. Changing Patterns of Gene Action

In a bacterium, the genes are turned off and on in quick response to the changing needs of the cell. In embryonic development, the repression and derepression of genes appears to be a more complex process. Morphogenesis and differentiation require an orderly, sequential program of gene repression and derepression. The genes concerned with the synthesis of certain proteins in the fully differentiated cell cannot do their work unless that cell has passed through a number of earlier stages of selective gene activity.

Although the Jacob-Monod theory may not be directly applicable to the problems of embryonic development, some mechanism for selectively controlling the action of the genes is surely at work. Microscopic examination of the giant chromosomes found in the salivary glands of the fruit fly (Fig. 19-3) has provided some evidence of this. It has been shown that these chromosomes actually change their structure during the course of embryonic development. They develop enlarged regions, called "puffs," and it is these regions which are most active in RNA synthesis (Fig. 23-10). Inasmuch as messenger RNA synthesis is the first step in gene action, we may conclude that the enlarged regions of the chromosomes indicate genes or sets of genes that are especially active.

The exact location of the puffs varies over the course of the differentiation of a single kind of cell and also varies from one kind of cell to another. Transplanting a nucleus to another kind of cell or to the same kind of cell at a different stage of development leads to the disappearance of its characteristic puffs and the appearance of new ones. This, then, provides visible evidence of a sequential pattern of gene activity during the course of the differentiation of different cell types (Fig. 23-10).

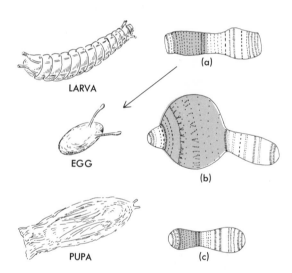

Fig. 23-10

Changes in equivalent portions of a giant chromosome of a fruit fly (a) in the larva, (c) in the pupa, and (b) when transplanted into an egg. (Eggs do not normally have giant chromosomes.) Enlargements ("puffs") in the chromosomes are associated with increased activity.

RNA synthesis also takes place in the less darkly staining regions of the giant chromosomes, that is, in the regions between the dark bands. Here the DNA seems to be in a tenuous, extended state. The dark bands themselves contain a much greater quantity of DNA, but they do not seem to be active in RNA synthesis. Perhaps the DNA in these regions is too tightly coiled and folded to serve as a template for the synthesis of messenger RNA. Perhaps the proteins with which it is united prevent it from being active. You remember that the chromosomes of higher organisms consist of both DNA and protein. Although we established in Chapter 20 (Section 20-1) that the genetic code resides in the DNA, the proteins turn out to have a function as well. These proteins, called **histones,** block the transcription of DNA into RNA. When they are removed from the chromosome, the rate of RNA synthesis increases markedly.

Could they *selectively* lock and unlock portions of the genetic code during embryonic development?

As embryonic development proceeds, the ability of bits of embryonic tissue to have their future altered by transplantation to new locations becomes more limited. Their cells become progressively less flexible in their potentialities. Once gastrulation begins, for example, the cells of one tissue layer generally cannot be converted into those of another. The conversion of potential belly skin into mouth parts or the lens of an eye (Fig. 23-7) simply involves a shift from one kind of ectoderm to another. Later, the number of alternatives open to differentiating cells decreases still more. Finally, the cells become committed to a definite fate. If transplanted after this time, they continue to develop as they would have in the old location, not in a way appropriate to the new one. For example, if the limb buds are removed from one salamander embryo and grafted onto a second, they form extra legs on the host. This occurs even though the cells of the limb bud are not visibly differentiated.

This progressive loss of developmental flexibility seems to run parallel to a progressive reduction in the amount of DNA in the cell that is active. In embryonic pea cells, about 80% of the DNA is complexed with histone and thus inactive. The remaining 20% is active in RNA synthesis. In the fully differentiated cells of the pea, on the other hand, the amount of active DNA drops to 10% or less. This is about the value found in most of the fully differentiated cells of other plants, such as corn, and also of animals such as the chick. In fact, one of the most fully differentiated, and thus specialized, cells of the chick is the red blood corpuscle. It really has only one protein to synthesize, hemoglobin. Virtually 100% of the DNA in the nucleus of chick RBC's is complexed with histone and carries on no RNA synthesis. As for mammals, you remember (see Section 14-12) that they do not even retain the nucleus once their RBC's are fully differentiated.

Are these progressive losses in the potentialities of differentiating cells utterly irreversible? Probably not. For plants, in fact, one can answer with greater certainty simply by examining Fig. 23-11. A fully differentiated carrot root cell when grown in a suitable culture medium divides repeatedly, losing its differentiated structure as it does so. Then its descendants begin, themselves, to differentiate and they finally form all the organs of a mature carrot plant. Probably any differentiated plant cell, if placed in surroundings resembling those found in endosperm (Fig. 23-3) can revert to an embryonic type and have all the genetic capabilities of its species once more unlocked.

The situation is not so clear with respect to animals. Attempts have been made to answer the question by means of nuclear transplant experiments. Using micromanipulators equipped to operate on

Fig. 23-11

The carrot plant in the flask grew from fully differentiated carrot root cells that had been isolated and induced to undergo mitosis. (Courtesy Roy De Carava and *Scientific American*.)

single cells, Robert Briggs and Thomas King succeeded in removing nuclei from the cells of frog embryos in various stages of development. To test the potentialities of these nuclei, they transplanted them into unfertilized frog eggs whose own nucleus had been removed. In this way, it could be determined whether a nucleus from the later stages of embryonic development was fully equivalent to the nucleus of the zygote or early cleavage cells. It was soon found that nuclei from frog blastulas still retain all the potentialities of the zygote nucleus. The nucleus from any one of the thousands of cells of the frog blastula initiates perfectly normal development when transplanted into a frog egg lacking its own nucleus.

This is understandable because there is good evidence now that the chromosomes of cells during cleavage have not begun to carry out any function except their own duplication during the interphases of the repeated mitotic divisions. All the control of the activities of the cleaving cells appears to be provided by the many messenger RNA molecules and ribosomes that were deposited in the unfertilized egg by the mother during oogenesis. In other words, the genetic code supplied by the father in the sperm cell seems to play no role during cleavage. It is only at the start of gastrulation that nucleoli form, new ribosomes are manufactured, and vigorous messenger RNA synthesis—using the maternal *and* paternal codes—begins.

When Briggs and King repeated their experiments with nuclei from later embryonic stages, quite different results were obtained. These nuclei were also capable of initiating embryonic development, but with widely varying degrees of eventual success. Many of the resulting embryos ceased developing at one stage or another. Furthermore, those that did develop were often abnormal. This evidence suggests that during gastrulation cell nuclei do become altered. Perhaps some of their genes have become permanently repressed with histone molecules.

Interestingly enough, when nuclei from newly hatched tadpoles are used in these experiments, the results are far more uniform. A few regain their full potentialities and go on to build a complete embryo. This is apt to occur especially with nuclei taken from such rapidly dividing cells as those of the intestinal epithelium. In most cases, however, the nuclei do not regain their full potentialities, and development of the egg ceases at a very early stage. Perhaps this change reflects the change in cell flexibility that we have already seen occurring late in gastrulation. Once the "point of no return" is reached, the nuclei may become strictly limited in the amount of embryonic development they can successfully regulate. On the other hand, it may simply reflect inability to pull the trick off. Possibly the nuclei from fully differentiated, nondividing cells are more easily damaged during the manipulations and are not really irrevocably repressed. Even the nucleus of the chick red blood corpuscle, the chromosomes of which *seem* totally and permanently repressed, have—under certain special conditions—been derepressed and made active once again in the synthesis of RNA.

While it is clear that histones block gene transcription, can they alone account for the precision with which specific genes or gene complexes are turned on and off during embryonic development? There are three possible mechanisms by which such precise control could be achieved. One is to have many different kinds of histones, each a specific repressor of one part of the genetic code. A number of different kinds of histones have been identified and, in the chick, different kinds are produced at different times during embryonic development. Nevertheless, the number is far too small for us to conclude that histones can do the job alone. A second possibility is that it is not individual genes that have to be selectively switched on and off, but simply clusters of related genes, i.e., operons. This simplifies the problem somewhat but probably not enough. A third possibility is that the gene repressors are not histones alone, but histones complexed with RNA. This is a particularly attractive possibility because it easily accounts for the precision of the gene repression. The RNA portion of the molecule could carry just the codons needed to "recognize" a given sequence of bases in DNA. There *is* evidence of a fourth kind of RNA (neither ribosomal, nor transfer, nor messenger) that is found attached to chromosomes and perhaps it is part of a ribonucleoprotein repressor.

Not only would a ribonucleoprotein repressor provide a means of recognizing specific genes (through its RNA portion), but its protein part could unite with small molecules that have inductive or corepressor properties (Fig. 23-9). Such a repressor molecule would thus resemble the repressors in bacterial cells. Furthermore, it could explain the data that has been acquired on embryonic induction. You remember (see Section 23-7) that macromolecules of protein and ribonucleoprotein have been implicated as agents of induction in embryonic tissues. Perhaps when these substances pass from one cell (e.g. notochord) to another (e.g. ectoderm), they act as repressors of *regulator* genes, thus turning on operons. As for the role of inhibitors in embryonic development, these could be repressor molecules that inactivate operons directly. Thus when frog embryos are cultured with pieces of adult heart, the latter may produce repressors of the operons that would otherwise have formed heart proteins in the embryo.

What about the many *small* molecules that alter embryonic development? Perhaps these (vitamin A, methylene blue, etc.) are *inducers* and when they unite with repressor proteins in the recipient cell, they block the repressors from joining with their operator genes. In this way, the operons to produce, say, the neural plate could go to work. In fact, it is becoming increasingly clear that among the small molecules that alter and guide the course of embryonic development, a large role is played by the hormones. As we will see in Chapters 25 and 26, many (if not most) of the hormones of higher organisms act on the genetic code, with the resulting transcription of specific genes producing specific proteins. While this is well established in adult organisms and is, as we shall see, one of the major coordinating mechanisms in adults, it is clear that hormones guide the path of embryonic development, too.

As this discussion should have shown clearly, attempts to find out what controls the development of living organisms have raised more questions than they have answered. Only time will tell how well the Jacob-Monod hypothesis will be able to account for the selective and sequential transcription of the genetic code that occurs during embryonic development. Whatever the outcome, though, it will have played a crucial role in suggesting new experiments to be performed and posing new questions to be asked. It is important that vigorous efforts continue to be made to answer these fundamental questions. Not only will the answers tell us more about the nature of life, but important practical problems will be nearer to solution, too. For example, the problem of cancer will be better understood when we know much more about the forces that control morphogenesis and differentiation. Cancers are tissues whose cells have, for some reason, escaped from the inductive and inhibitory influences of the adult body. Consequently, cancer cells do not differentiate, nor is their growth inhibited. The uncontrolled growth of these embryonic, undifferentiated cells is a frequent and tragic killer of humans of all ages. Vast efforts are being made to achieve control over cancer, but it seems likely that real success will have to await our learning a good deal more about the forces that control normal morphogenesis and differentiation.

EXERCISES AND PROBLEMS

1 From what embryonic germ layer is the optic nerve derived?

2 Distinguish between morphogenesis and differentiation.

3 Distinguish between identical and fraternal twins.

4 How do we know that the liver of a frog is derived from endodermal cells?

5 A tadpole ready to hatch is slightly larger than the fertilized egg was. What might account for this?

6 Female armadillos always give birth to four offspring of the same sex. Can you account for this?

7 Would you expect mutations in *regulator* genes to be inherited as dominants or recessives? Explain.

8 Would you expect mutations in *operator* genes to be inherited as dominants or recessives? Explain.

REFERENCES

1 Fischberg, M. and A. W. Blackler, "How Cells Specialize," *Scientific American*, Reprint No. 94, September, 1961. Shows how the sequence of changes occurring during embryonic development can be traced to specialization within the egg itself.

2 Spemann, H., "The Development of Lateral and Dorso-ventral Embryo Halves with Delayed Nuclear Supply," *Great Experiments in Biology*, ed. by M. L. Gabriel and S. Fogel, Prentice-Hall, Inc., 1955. A description of two of the author's famous experiments with constricted newt eggs.

3 Gray, G. W., "The Organizer," *Scientific American*, Reprint No. 103, November, 1957. Not only discusses the concept of the "organizer" but provides a brief, well-written history of experimental embryology and its implications.

4 Ebert, J. D., "The First Heartbeats," *Scientific American*, Reprint No. 56, March, 1959. The differentiation of cardiac muscle can be detected by biochemical changes even before morphological changes become evident.

5 Rose, S. M., "Feedback in the Differentiation of Cells," *Scientific American*, December, 1958. A discussion of the theory that embryonic development is controlled by inhibitory substances.

6 Bonner, J., *The Molecular Biology of Development*, Oxford University Press, New York, 1965. A superb account of Dr. Bonner's studies on the role of histones in embryonic development. He also shows how many of the results of experimental embryology can be interpreted in terms of the Jacob-Monod theory.

7 Moscona, A. A., "How Cells Associate," *Scientific American*, Reprint No. 95, September, 1961. Presents evidence that cells of a given kind are able to recognize one another and cluster together to form tissues.

8 Beermann, W. and U. Clever, "Chromosome Puffs," *Scientific American*, Reprint No. 180, April, 1964.

9   Steward, F. C., "The Control of Growth in Plant Cells," *Scientific American,* Reprint No. 167, October, 1963.

10 Sussman, M., *Growth and Development,* 2nd Edition, Foundations of Modern Biology Series, Prentice-Hall, Inc., 1964. Discusses single-celled organisms as well as multicellular ones.

11 Barth, Lucena J., *Development, Selected Topics,* Addison-Wesley, Reading, Mass., 1964. Examines many of the experiments that bear on the question of the role of nucleo-cytoplasmic interactions in embryonic development.

12 Ebert, J. D., *Development,* Holt, Rinehart and Winston, New York, 1965. A paperback.

Plant and animal development is not limited to morphogenesis and differentiation. Development also includes an increase in the size of the organism, that is, growth. Among animals, most growth takes place after the completion of morphogenesis and differentiation. These processes are essentially completed in the human embryo by the time it reaches a weight of 1.5 grams. This weight may, however, be increased some 45,000 times before the adult size is reached. You remember also that the newly hatched frog tadpole is little larger than the original frog egg.

In plants, there exists considerable overlap in these vital developmental activities. Apical growth in the monocots (in the region of elongation of roots and stems) precedes morphogenesis and differentiation. However, growth of stem thickness occurs by cell enlargement after morphogenesis and differentiation have taken place.

For growth to occur, the rate of synthesis of the complex molecules of the organism, proteins for example, must exceed the rate of their breakdown. This means that additional supplies of intermediate-size energy-rich molecules (e.g. amino acids, fatty acids, glycerol, and glucose) must be taken in by the organism from its environment. Some of these materials will serve as the building blocks for the anabolic reactions. The others will supply the extra energy needed to run them. In photosynthetic organisms, light supplies the energy for anabolism and inorganic molecules are the raw materials.

Growth thus involves gaining more material from the environment than is given back to it in the form of metabolic wastes. This is not just a simple process of accumulation. The amino acids which you assimilate after a meal of beefsteak are not reassembled in your cells into beef protein. Instead, they are assembled into your unique proteins. You grow by converting relatively unspecific molecules taken in from your environment into the specific cell materials that are characteristic of you.

The autotrophic organisms are even more remarkable in this respect. In growing, they convert the small, energy-poor inorganic substances of their environment (e.g. H_2O, CO_2, and nitrates) into the specific structures that form more maple tree, corn plant, etc. This ability of all living things to build more of their own specific, complex organization from relatively simple, disorganized materials in their environment is the ability to grow. It is one of the most characteristic features of life.

Growth in organisms may occur simply by an increase in the number of cells that make up the organism. The adult human is made up of some 60 trillion (6×10^{13}) cells, while the newborn baby contains only about two trillion (2×10^{12}). Growth may also occur as a result of an increase in the size of the cells that make up the organism. Most monocots, lacking a cambium, grow in thickness this way. Some species of rotifers (see Section 5-4) develop until a precisely fixed number of cells is reached. Further growth consists simply of enlarging these. Most organisms grow by both an increase in the number of cells and an increase in their size. All growth in woody dicots involves both activities. Tiny new cells are produced by the cambium and apical meristems. These cells then enlarge and differentiate.

◀ Starfish regenerating arm.
(Courtesy Dr. Charles Walcott.)

Several periods can usually be distinguished in the growth of an organism (Fig. 24-1). The first period, the **lag period,** is characterized by little or no actual growth. During this period, however, the organism is getting prepared for growth. A seed imbibing water, preparatory to germination, and an *E. coli* cell synthesizing the enzymes with which to metabolize its substrate are both in the lag period of growth.

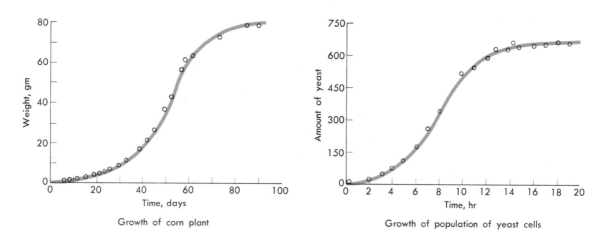

Growth of corn plant

Growth of population of yeast cells

Fig. 24-1   The *S*-shaped curve of growth occurs in both individuals (left) and populations (right).

The lag period is followed by the logarithmic or **exponential period** of growth. In this period growth begins, slowly at first, but then more and more rapidly. This gradually accelerating rate of growth is understandable when you remember that in most cases, the product of growth, living material, is itself capable of further growth. Thus the organism enlarges according to a geometric progression, doubling and redoubling in size. Such progressions are expressed in algebra by exponents (logarithms); hence this phase of growth is called the exponential or logarithmic phase. Different organisms vary greatly in the time that it takes them to double their size. The newly hatched housefly larva doubles its weight in 13 hours. The newborn baby usually requires 5 to 6 months to do the same. Whatever the amount of time required, all organisms pass through a constantly accelerating period of growth.

The exponential phase of growth does not continue indefinitely, and it is a good thing that it does not. The housefly larva, doubling its weight every 13 hours, would be an awesome creature indeed after a few days. Fortunately, the fly larva (as well as all other growing organisms) soon enters a period of **decelerating growth.** Growth now proceeds more slowly and finally ceases altogether. At this time the larva prepares for metamorphosis. In many organisms the rate of growth slows down but never ceases entirely. Many fishes and reptiles continue to grow year after year, although more and more slowly, until finally they die. A similar situation occurs in trees, which continue to grow until disease or accident strikes them down.

Mammals, including man, reach a certain size and then cease growing entirely. At this point, the rate at which more living substance is synthesized by anabolism is exactly counterbalanced by the rate at which it is broken down catabolically. In later years, humans may even enter a period of negative growth, that is, they shrink. Body constituents are then broken down more rapidly than they are synthesized.

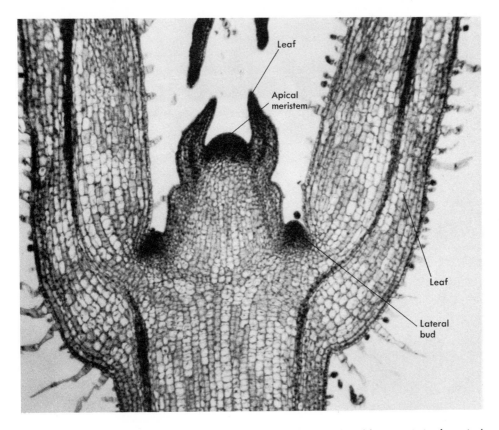

Terminal bud of a coleus stem, cut lengthwise. New cells are produced by mitosis in the apical meristem. Later, branching may occur at the lateral buds.

Fig. 24-2

If one plots a graph showing the growth of a single organism during the accelerating and decelerating phases, an S-shaped curve results (Fig. 24-1). It is interesting to note that this same curve expresses the growth of populations. If a few bacteria or a pair of rabbits are placed in a suitable and uncrowded environment, they will produce offspring. These offspring will, in turn, produce their own offspring. This will go on in an ever-expanding way until external conditions force a slowdown in the rate of growth of the population. Biologists have a good idea of what forces are involved in the stabilizing of population growth. We will consider these in Chapter 37. Biologists are not at all sure which forces cause a slowdown in the growth of individuals. Perhaps the controlling factors differ from one group of organisms to another. In any case, until these factors are identified, a large gap will remain in our knowledge of development.

Growth in plants occurs chiefly at the meristems. Here rapid mitosis provides the necessary additional cells. The stem and roots increase their length by mitosis at the apical meristems. In Chapter 15 (Section 15-4), we examined the way in which the apical meristem in the embryonic region of the root provides new cells which then elongate and differentiate.

A similar pattern of vertical growth occurs at the tips of stems. Mitosis in the apical meristem (Fig. 24-2) of the shoot apex or terminal bud produces a stockpile of new cells. Periodically these give rise to leaves. The point on the stem where the leaves develop is called a **node** (Fig. 24-3). The distance between the nodes (the internode) in the terminal bud is very short, and the leaves develop rapidly. As a result, the leaves grow above the apical meristem that produced them and thus protect it.

New meristems, the lateral buds, develop at the nodes, each just above the point where a leaf is attached. When the lateral buds develop, they produce new stem tissue and thus branches are formed.

Under special circumstances (which we shall study in the next chapter), the apical meristem is converted into a flower bud. This develops into a flower and thus enables the plant to carry on sexual reproduction. The formation of a flower bud "uses up" the apical meristem so that no further growth of the stem can occur at that point. Branching may, however, occur from lateral buds directly behind the flower (Fig. 24-3).

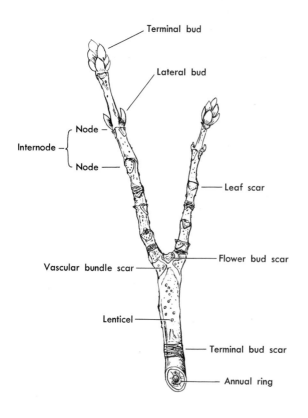

Terminal bud

Lateral bud

Node

Internode

Node

Leaf scar

Vascular bundle scar

Flower bud scar

Lenticel

Terminal bud scar

Annual ring

Fig. 24-3

External structures of a typical woody dicot stem, the horse chestnut, as seen during the dormant season.

In dicots, growth in diameter is accomplished by a band of cambium which separates the phloem from the xylem in both the root and the stem (Figs. 15-2 and 15-3). Except for a few palms and lilies, monocots lack a cambium. As we noted earlier, increase in their stem diameter can occur only by cell enlargement.

Growth in animals does not occur in such localized areas as it does in plants. All of the tissues and organs of the animal body participate in growth. They may not all grow at the same rate, however. Figure 24-4 shows how much faster the trunk and limbs of the human grow from infancy to adulthood than the head. The result is a marked change in body proportions.

Fundamental to the growth of the body is growth of its supporting skeleton. Bones are able to grow and lengthen only so long as they have a cartilaginous, nonbony region where further cell division and elongation can occur. In the long bones, this occurs at the epiphyseal lines just back of the hard ends of the bones (Fig. 8-14).

In humans, the growing regions of the bones become fully "ossified" during the late teens and early twenties. The cartilaginous matrix of these regions becomes replaced with a bony matrix and further skeletal growth ceases. Cessation of growth also occurs in the other mammals but usually at a younger age. On the other hand many of the fishes and reptiles continue to exhibit skeletal growth throughout their lives.

The problem of development is particularly interesting in those animals that undergo metamorphosis. Most aquatic invertebrates (e.g. starfish and barnacles), many aquatic vertebrates (e.g. frogs), and most insects develop from the zygote into a **larva.** Later the larva undergoes the drastic changes of metamorphosis and the adult body is produced.

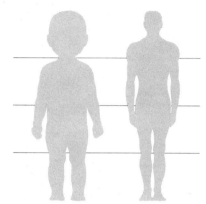

Fig. 24-4

Differential growth in the human. The head of a baby is roughly one-fourth the length of the body, while in the adult the fraction is closer to one-eighth.

The significance of this two-stage method of development is not entirely clear. For those animals, such as barnacles, whose adult bodies are sessile (anchored), free-swimming larvae permit dispersal. In cases such as the lobster and the frog, the larva serves as an intermediate stage in development during which food (usually of microscopic dimensions, e.g. algae, etc.) can be taken in from the environment. This permits more growth than is provided for by the food reserves in the egg itself and enables the animal eventually to reach the size necessary for it to have the characteristic diet of the adult.

While larvae are a stage in the development of many animals, it is wrong to think of them as incompletely developed or embryonic organisms. For example, the garden caterpillar is a highly specialized creature. It is the product of an elaborate morphogenesis and complete cell differentiation, that is, complete except for a few masses of embryonic cells, the imaginal disks, within its body. At the time of metamorphosis, most of the specialized cells of the caterpillar die. These dying cells supply the nourishment necessary for the cells of the imaginal disks to undergo an entirely new pattern of morphogenesis and differentiation. The result is the adult organism, a moth or butterfly. All growth in insects occurs during the larval stages. In fact, some adult insects do not even feed. They simply mate and die.

Another reason why larvae should not be considered incompletely developed forms is that cases are known in which certain species have abandoned metamorphosis entirely. The axolotl, an amphibian found in Mexico and the American Southwest, spends its entire life as a gill-breathing animal (Fig. 26-5). It reaches sexual maturity and mates without ever undergoing metamorphosis to an air-breathing form. While there is no evidence that the axolotl is going to lead to the evolution of a whole new group of animals, there is evidence that in the past, larval, rather than adult, forms have sometimes evolved into new species. Many biologists feel, for example, that the earliest vertebrates arose from the larvae of sea squirts (Fig. 5-16) living in brackish water.

During the lifetime of an organism, some of its parts may become damaged or lost. Most organisms have, to some degree, the ability to replace defective or missing parts. This process of replacement is called **regeneration.**

Plants generally have great powers of regeneration. Angiosperms can have many, sometimes all, of their branches and foliage removed by pruning. If the root system is healthy, however, buds soon appear on the stem or trunk. The buds develop into new branches, leaves, and flowers. In fact, many woody angiosperms (maples, birches, etc.) can be cut off right at ground level and sprouting at the margins of the stump will soon produce new stems and leaves.

The ability of animals to regenerate missing parts varies greatly from species to species. Sponges can regenerate the entire organism from just a conglomeration of their cells. This is also true of the hydra. A planarian can regenerate the entire organism from a middle section. Even the starfish can regenerate an entire organism from just one arm and the central disk. At one time oyster fishermen used to dredge up starfish from their oyster beds, chop them up in the hopes of killing them, and then dump the parts back overboard. They soon discovered to their sorrow the remarkable powers of regeneration in this group of animals.

Earthworms, crustaceans, fish, salamanders, and lizards do not possess such powers of regeneration that they can regenerate the whole organism from just one part. They can, however, regenerate fairly substantial parts. The earthworm can regenerate the first four or five segments of its head and even longer sections of its "tail." Lobsters and salamanders can regenerate a missing leg. Many lizards will part with their tail if caught by it. They then regenerate a new one at their leisure. Birds and mammals cannot regenerate entire organs. They can, however, regenerate tissues and thus repair damaged or missing parts. The healing of skin wounds and bone breaks is an example of regeneration in man. The replacement of blood after blood loss is another example. The digestive glands, especially the liver and pancreas, are capable of extensive regeneration after damage.

What happens in the process of regeneration? If a foreleg is removed from a salamander, the first repair process is the healing of the wound by means of skin growing over it. Then a bud of undifferentiated cells appears. This bud has the same appearance as a limb bud in the developing embryo. As time goes on, the cells of the regenerating limb become organized and differentiated into the bone, muscle, and other connective tissues which make up the functional leg. It is not yet clear just where the rapidly dividing, unspecialized, "embryonic" cells of the limb bud come from. Some workers feel that specialized cells near the wounded area lose their specialization and take on the job of regeneration. They call this process **dedifferentiation.** Other biologists feel that the cells which participate in regeneration are simply unspecialized mesodermal cells, the **mesenchyme cells,** which migrate to the region of the wound and then begin to divide rapidly. It may well be that both processes are involved.

In many ways, the process of regeneration is similar to the process of embryonic development. From rapidly dividing, unspecialized cells arises a complex organization of specialized cells. This involves morphogenesis and differentiation just as embryonic development does. There is, however, at least one way in which the process of regeneration differs from the process of embryonic development. Can you think of what it is?

The similarities between regeneration and embryonic development have caused some embryologists to study regeneration in the hope of gaining an understanding of how embryonic development "works." The discovery of **polarity** has shown that definite organizing forces, probably chemical, are at work in regeneration. A midsection of a planarian will regenerate a new head at the same cut edge at which a head was originally present. A tail will be regenerated at the other edge. It has been found that the cells at the "forward" cut surface have a higher metabolic rate than those at the "rear" edge. It seems to be this difference in metabolic rates in the cells of the regenerating piece that determines polarity. If the rear section of a worm is removed and the head is then treated with a solution containing a metabolic inhibitor, the polarity of the worm can be reversed and a second head will form at the posterior edge (Fig. 24-5).

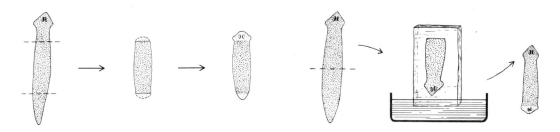

Regeneration in planarians. Left: Each cut surface of the planarian "remembers" its polarity. Right: When the head of a cut planarian is placed in agar and dipped in water containing a metabolic inhibitor, a second head develops at the cut surface.

Fig. 24-5

In comparing the regenerative abilities of different animals, there seems to be some relationship between the complexity of the organism and its ability to regenerate. The powers of regeneration in the sponge are practically complete. In man regeneration is limited to repair of certain organs and tissues. We wish we knew just why it is that regenerative powers diminish with increasing structural and physiological complexity.

Within a single organism, at least among the vertebrates, there also seems to be a progressive loss of regenerative ability with increasing age. When legs first appear on a frog tadpole, they can be regenerated easily if lost. After metamorphosis, however, a frog is normally unable to regenerate a missing leg. Everyone knows how much more quickly broken bones and skin wounds heal in a child than in an elderly person. What causes the loss of regenerative power as age increases? In the frog, it may be that the area of amputation fails to receive sufficient amounts of some substance released by the nerves. When extra nerves are moved surgically to the stump of a frog foreleg, regeneration does occur. It is known that the ratio of nerve tissue to other tissues decreases as the tadpole grows into a frog. It is also possible, though, to bring about leg regeneration in the frog simply by irritating the stump. This suggests an alternative explanation. Perhaps aging tissue simply loses the ability to respond to the regeneration-promoting substances released by nerves. If this is the case, irritation of the tissue may restore some of its sensitivity. While it is far too soon to predict the practical value of these discoveries to man, they should certainly stimulate a great deal more experimentation into the nature of the regenerative process. In addition to this, they may provide us with increased knowledge of the nature of the aging process.

Aging can be defined as the progressive deterioration, with the passage of time, of the structures and functions of a mature organism. This ultimately leads to the death of the organism. While perhaps no human has ever died of old age alone, the progressive loss of function makes the organism less able to withstand infectious disease or to repair damaged parts of the body.

The study of aging has long been neglected. But now that so many infectious diseases of humans have been brought under better control by vaccines, sulfa drugs, and antibiotics, more and more people are living to an age when the process of aging becomes quite obvious. Because of this, there recently has been a great surge of interest in the problem of aging. Doctors, social workers, physiologists, biochemists, embryologists, histologists, endocrinologists, and many others are turning their attention to this problem. Not only is aging in humans under direct study, but many other organisms are being examined for clues as to the nature of aging. As a result of these studies, one fact stands out already. The effects of increased age vary widely from one living thing to another.

Among the bacteria, the process of aging does not even occur. When a single cell is fully grown, it divides into two cells, which then repeat the process. Although a wide variety of changes in the environment may kill a bacterium, no cell has ever been known to die because of aging. For this reason, some biologists have described the bacteria as potentially immortal. They have also included all other kinds of single-celled organisms in this category. While the idea that the bacteria enjoy a kind of potential immortality may have some merit, it is probably not true that all single-celled forms can be included. For example, there is good experimental evidence that paramecia do age.

Everyone agrees that multicellular organisms are mortal. Presumably the loss of independence which occurs when cells specialize in a multicellular organism leads to eventual death. In specializing to carry out a certain function, cells abandon other vital functions to neighboring cells. If disease or other damage should strike down any one group of specialists, all the rest will fall, too. Thus heart failure results in the speedy death of all our cells no matter how vigorous and healthy they might otherwise be.

Although all multicellular organisms eventually die, it may not be accurate to say that they all age. Some seem to avoid aging and, in the process, may achieve remarkable records for length of life. Some sea anemones are known to have lived for as long as 78 years. They may achieve their longevity and avoid aging by periodically replacing all old body parts. Woody perennials fall into a similar category. Throughout their lives, they produce new vascular tissues, leaves, and flowers each year. They do not show signs of aging, although their rate of growth does decline with advancing years. Finally, disease or inability to support their ever-increasing size against wind or snow load lead to their death. This may not occur for a long period. Tree ring analysis shows that some of the bristlecone pines of eastern California are over 4,000 years old. At the moment, this seems to be a record for tree longevity. Note, however, that no *living* cells in these trees are more than a few years old.

Many fish and reptiles also seem to avoid aging by continuing to grow throughout their lives. We do not know just what brings on death, but it may simply be the same factors that cause death in younger members of the species: disease and predation. These challenges to life, acting in a completely random way, will eventually strike down all the members of a given generation (Fig. 24-6). It is probably also true that fish and reptiles become less well adapted to their environment when they exceed a certain size. In any case, the ability to grow steadily, even if slowly, does seem to

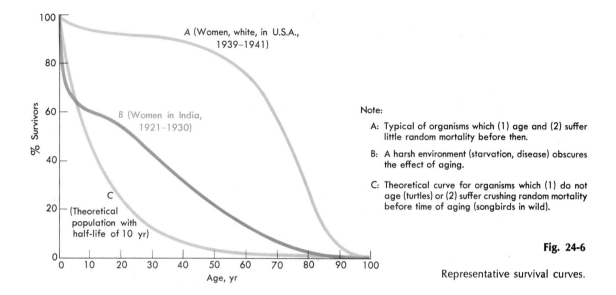

A (Women, white, in U.S.A., 1939–1941)

B (Women in India, 1921–1930)

C (Theoretical population with half-life of 10 yr)

Note:

A: Typical of organisms which (1) age and (2) suffer little random mortality before then.

B: A harsh environment (starvation, disease) obscures the effect of aging.

C: Theoretical curve for organisms which (1) do not age (turtles) or (2) suffer crushing random mortality before time of aging (songbirds in wild).

Fig. 24-6

Representative survival curves.

protect them from the harmful effects of aging. Some marine turtles are estimated to live more than 150 years.

The situation is quite different among the annual plants (such as the grasses and many "weeds") and the mammals. Most annual plants grow vigorously for a period and then form flowers followed by fruits. Fruiting is accompanied by a marked slowing down of growth. As the growth rate slows to a halt, other changes take place, too. A great deal of chlorophyll may disappear from the leaves. The rate of respiration (and thus, catabolism) rises markedly. Many other morphological changes follow. All of these changes constitute aging and end with the death of the plant. It is important to realize that these changes are not necessarily related to adverse changes in the physical environment. Aging in annual plants may occur in the midst of plentiful moisture, soil minerals, sunlight, and warm temperatures.

Mammals, as we have seen, also grow to a certain size and then stop. Some time after the cessation of growth, aging begins. The actual time span involved varies widely from species to species. A three-year-old laboratory rat is very old. In man, although the deterioration associated with aging can be detected by the age of 30 years, fatal loss of function may not occur until much later.

What are the symptoms of aging? Decreased muscular strength, decreased lung capacity, decreased pumping of blood from the heart, decreased urine formation in the kidney, and decreased metabolic rate are just a few of the many body changes which occur with aging. Figure 24-7 shows still other examples of the structural and functional deterioration that occurs between ages 30 and 75.

Fig. 24-7

Loss of structure and function in aging. Figures represent percentage of a given function remaining in an average 75-year-old man compared with that found in an average 30-year-old man, the latter value taken as 100%.

(a) Weight of brain	56%
(b) Blood supply to brain	80%
(c) Output of heart at rest	70%
(d) Number of glomeruli in kidney	56%
(e) Glomerular filtration rate	69%
(f) Speed of return to normal pH of blood after displacement	17%
(g) Number of taste buds	36%
(h) Vital capacity	56%
(i) Strength of hand grip	55%
(j) Maximum O_2 uptake during exercise	40%
(k) Number of axons in spinal nerve	63%
(l) Velocity of nerve impulse	90%
(m) Body weight in males	88%

Why do the various body organs gradually lose their ability to function well? One answer is that they lose the cells of which they are composed. Many organs of the body lose weight with age (Fig. 24-7), and even those that do not, do lose the specialized cells which enable them to carry out their function. These cells may then be replaced by connective tissue or fatty tissue cells, however, and the over-all weight of the organ remains constant. It is interesting to note that organs which lose so much of their ability to function (and thus show so much aging) are those organs whose cells are no longer dividing actively. These include the heart, brain, kidneys, and muscles. On the other hand, the organs in which cell division is actively maintained (e.g. the bone marrow, the liver, and the pancreas) show far less loss of function with age. The situation reminds us of the perpetual youthfulness of rapidly dividing bacterial cells.

24-4   **AGING—THE THEORIES**

What causes the degenerative changes of aging? This is one of the many unanswered questions in biology. A great many theories of aging have been proposed, but the known facts of aging are still too few either to substantiate or discredit any of them.

A few biologists feel that aging is largely a result of adverse changes in the environment. They are particularly concerned with the effects of radiation (e.g. cosmic rays, x-rays) on the genes in the body cells or somaplasm. Mutations in the somaplasm are not as easily detected as mutations in the germplasm. (Virtually the whole science of genetics has been based on the latter.) There is no reason to think, though, that the DNA in body cells is appreciably more resistant to mutations than the DNA in the germ cells. Remembering the one gene-one polypeptide theory (see Section 20-4), we would expect body cells with acquired mutations to produce defective polypeptides and proteins. This would naturally reduce their efficiency and might even cause their death.

In support of this theory, it has been shown that sublethal exposure to radiation does lower the life expectancy of many animals. However, radiation exerts its most drastic effects upon rapidly dividing cells and it is the tissues with rapidly dividing cells (e.g. liver, bone marrow) that seem the freest from the effects of aging. On the other hand, cell damage and death in such tissues can be compensated for. The defective cells can be destroyed by lysosomes and phagocytes and healthy replacements produced by mitosis. In organs such as the brain and muscles, where mitosis does not occur, the damaged cells become a permanent liability.

Many biologists feel that the tendency to age is intrinsic. They claim that even under the best environmental conditions, organisms will age at a rate determined by the nature of their genes. They point to the decrease in the level of sex hormones in the blood which seems to occur spontaneously in man after the active period of reproduction is over. They relate this drop in the level of sex hormones to a shift from anabolic to catabolic body chemistry. Unfortunately, the idea that the sex hormones may be related to the aging process has encouraged such questionable medical practices as grafting bits of monkey testes into men in an attempt to stimulate rejuvenation. Such experiments have not been effective.

There is a good deal of evidence to support the view that the aging process is intrinsic. We have seen that annual plants age despite the maintenance of suitable physical conditions around them. The widely different life expectancies from one species of mammal to another are difficult to explain without including hereditary factors. Even within a single species, some family lines show consistently greater longevities than others. The best way to assure yourself a long life is to have long-lived parents! The fact that, as a group, human females have an average life expectancy greater than males also suggests that hereditary factors are at work. (It does not prove this, however. Why not?) Not only do human females tend to outlive the males but female rats, mice, fruit flies (*Drosophila*), spiders, and many fish do, too.

Most biologists accept the idea that aging results from an interaction of both hereditary and environmental factors. Consequently, most of the many current theories on aging assume an interaction of these two forces. But if any aspect of aging is under the influence of the genes, it means that aging is as much a part of the over-all process of development as is, say, morphogenesis.

One popular theory explains aging as a consequence of living. That is, the more rapidly the organism lives, the sooner it begins to age. Rapid living is defined as rapid differentiation and growth. It may also involve a high rate of metabolism. It is certainly true that mammals, such as rats, which reach maturity weeks after birth, age far more rapidly than mammals, such as man, that take years to mature.

One way to test this theory is to find some way to slow down an organism's rate of development. It has been found that feeding young rats just enough to keep them alive does just this. When these rats are finally given adequate diets, they usually catch up to their normally raised cousins in almost all respects. In fact, they are apt to be living comfortably long after their well-fed cousins are dead!

Another theory that relates aging to living has been called the "clinker" theory. According to this theory, each cell unavoidably accumulates poisonous wastes during its lifetime. The accumulation gradually reduces the ability of the cell to function, and the cell thus ages. This theory is supported by the finding of large quantities of pigment in the cells of aged people, especially nondividing cells such as those of muscles and nerves. Rapidly dividing cells, such as are found in the liver, contain much less pigment. (You remember that it is the organs in which rapid cell division does not continue throughout life that age the most.) Although the exact chemical nature of this pigment is not yet known, there is evidence that it represents the remnants of old, worn-out cell structures (e.g. mitochondria) that have been incorporated into lysosomes.

Why is the cell unable to rid itself of these harmful substances? It may be that older cells are less able to rid themselves of any substance. Collagen, the chief structural protein of the body, is found in the extracellular coatings or matrix of most of the cells of the body. It has been shown to undergo progressive chemical and physical changes as an animal ages. Perhaps these changes reduce the ability of the cells to exchange all sorts of materials with the ECF. Of course, this would limit cell function especially if, as seems likely, the cell were forced to store harmful products of its metabolism.

One other theory of aging deserves mention. This is the theory that during the course of our lifetime we become allergic to certain substances produced by our own cells. This is the immunological theory of aging. You remember that our bodies have a mechanism to cope with foreign macromolecules (e.g. proteins on the surface of a virus) that gain entrance into it (see Section 14-12). The foreign macromolecules act as *antigens,* and inactivating *antibodies* are soon produced by our plasma cells. Normally, our antibody-producing machinery never produces antibodies against our own macromolecules. It is able to recognize "self" from "nonself." However, this protection often breaks down as an organism ages. Increasingly, doctors are finding that many of the degenerative changes of old age arise from the body's beginning to produce antibodies against its own components. This results in *auto-immune* diseases. Perhaps it is not too far-fetched to suggest that the same radiation-induced mutations with which we began this discussion are at work here. Mutant cells do produce defective proteins and perhaps these stimulate antibody production because they seem "foreign" to the antibody-producing machinery. Perhaps, on the other hand, it is the antibody-producing cells that become altered by mutation so that they fail to recognize that the body's own proteins are not foreign and should not be attacked.

You may feel dismayed that there are so many different theories to explain such a vital process as aging. Actually, this is a perfectly normal stage in the development of any science. The fewer the facts that are known, the more theories are plausible. It does not matter now which, if any, of these theories best explains the facts of aging. What is important is that each theory of aging that is concocted should suggest definite experiments by which the theory can be tested. Whether or not a given theory is successful in predicting the outcome of an experiment, it will at least have resulted in the acquisition of new knowledge. The more we know about aging, the fewer will be the theories that can explain all the facts. Only thus, by a process of closer and closer approximations, can we hope to discover the true nature of the aging process.

If aging is even partly controlled by our genes, is there any hope that we can increase our life span through evolution? It is not likely. As we will see in Chapter 32, the only traits upon which evolutionary forces can operate in a positive way are those that appear before the organism has finished raising its offspring. Unusual slowness in aging or unusual longevity will not be discovered until the chance to pass these traits on to a large number of offspring is gone. Unless the inherited traits that promote longevity also promote vigor during the years of reproduction, there is little likelihood of these traits becoming generally established in the population. In this connection, it is interesting to note how many species of living things begin aging as soon as their reproductory activities are completed.

There is at least one case where evolution has probably led to a shortening of the life span rather than a lengthening of it. Species of annual plants, whose individuals live for only one season, are probably better able to adapt to changing environmental conditions than perennial plants, because there is a complete population turnover each year. We have seen that sexual reproduction promotes variability within the species. Any one individual makes only a small contribution to the process. A 100-year-old elm tree has been producing for decades annual crops of offspring whose range of genotypes has most likely remained unchanged. Annual plants, on the other hand, remove themselves totally from the breeding population after a new generation is formed. The next season will find the field exclusively populated by the second generation and any variations appearing will have full opportunity to meet the tests of the environment. If successful, they will play a larger role in the formation of still another generation than if their parents were still in the game, too. In view of this, it is not surprising that the annual plants are among our most hardy and adaptable plants. In fact, we call many of them weeds because of these characteristics.

24-5 DEATH

The outcome of aging is death. As the organs of the body become less efficient, the body becomes less able to cope with the stresses of life. Infections are controlled less easily. Shifts in body chemistry are corrected less easily. Finally, a given organ fails to carry out its vital functions upon which all the other organs depend. Death results.

Although other organs may fail first, we mark death in man at the time the heart stops beating. When you consider the role it plays in supplying food and oxygen to the cells, this should not be surprising. Without food and oxygen the constituent cells of the body die. They do not, however, all die at once. Even after the human body is dead as a functioning organism, various cells survive for short periods of time. Nerve cells are among the first cells to succumb to lack of oxygen. Some of the skin cells are among the last. Eventually, though, every cell of the body dies.

With advances being made in heart-lung machines and other supportive measures, it may soon be necessary to reexamine our definition of death. With such devices, it is now possible to maintain a supply of food and oxygen to all the cells of the body even though the heart or breathing has failed. What, then, can we use as a criterion of death? As we will see in Part VI, it is the central nervous system that coordinates the actions of the body. Without a functioning brain, we are little more than an assemblage of cells. Therefore, irrevocable loss of brain activity is death, of the *organism* even if not of all its constituent cells.

The death of cells is accompanied by a rapid dissolving of the cell constituents. This process of cell degradation illustrates beautifully the need for continual supplies of energy to maintain the complex organization of matter that we call life. Once energy ceases to be made available to the cells, the precise organization of their parts becomes quickly and totally destroyed.

It is hard to visualize how the death of cells can also be considered a normal stage in development. Nevertheless, there are examples where cell death plays an important role in the life of the organism and presumably occurs as a result of definite genetic controls. One of the best examples is found in those insects that undergo complete metamorphosis. In the change from larva to pupa, almost all of the specialized cells of the larva die. These dying cells then supply the materials which enable the cells of the imaginal disks to develop into the pupa and then the adult. This widespread death of most of the cells of the larva is clearly a vital stage in the over-all development of these insects.

Genetically programmed death may also occur in certain fishes. The sea lamprey and the salmon are well-known examples. When they reach sexual maturity, these animals migrate from the ocean into fresh-water rivers and streams. Here the females lay their eggs, and the males fertilize them with their sperm. Once the task is done, the adults die. The phenomenon is really quite similar to that of the annual plants mentioned earlier in the chapter. The removal of the old generation seems as much a part of development as the embryology that now occurs in the fertilized eggs that are the new generation.

In the past eight chapters we have examined many aspects of the process of reproduction. Central to all of these has been the nature and expression of the hereditary controls within cells. These controls, the genes, guide the development of the individual into an adult and guide their own passage to the next generation through the mechanics of reproduction. We have looked for clues as to how the genes are regulated, over time and from cell to cell, so that the organism is maintained and the species preserved. It is not enough that the selective transcription of genes be able to produce a functioning adult organism. The genes must *continue* to act selectively so that the organism can respond to changes that it will meet until death finally occurs. Each differentiated cell in the organism's body must be able to modify the expression of its genetic potentialities in response to changes occurring both outside and within the organism. In other words, the ability of organisms to cope with changes in their environment and to coordinate the multitude of activities that occur in the diverse cells of which they are composed is, in the last analysis, a matter of the regulation of gene expression. How multicellular organisms integrate the activities of their cells as they respond to changes in their environment is the topic to which we now turn.

EXERCISES AND PROBLEMS

1   Summarize the mechanisms by which the beef protein you eat is converted into proteins characteristic of you.

2   What is the average number of times every cell in the newborn baby has to divide in order to produce an adult?

3   Which best describes an actively growing organism, an arithmetic progression or a geometric progression? Why?

4   A certain restaurant buys 1000 amber water tumblers. An average of 1 tumbler is broken every day and each broken tumbler is replaced by a new one made of clear glass. What is the shape of the survival curve of amber tumblers?

5   Which of the following organisms would you expect to have a survival curve like that in Question 4: (a) contemporary humans in the U.S., (b) humans living in prehistoric times, (c) parrots in cages, (d) sparrows in the wild, (e) alligators in the wild?

6   What food does a tadpole eat? What food does an adult frog eat? Of what significance is this difference in diet?

7   List all the factors you can think of that affect growth in humans.

8   Which human organs regenerate damaged portions most easily? Which human organs show the fewest degenerative changes in old age?

9   How do the two lists you prepared for Question 8 compare? What explanation can you give for this?

10   In what ways are the processes of regeneration and embryonic development similar? In what way are they different?

REFERENCES

1   Williams, C. M., "Metamorphosis of Insects," *Scientific American*, Reprint No. 49, April, 1950. A summary of the structural and hormonal changes in insect metamorphosis seen in the larger context of the regulation of growth and differentiation.

2   Singer, M., "The Regeneration of Body Parts," *Scientific American*, Reprint No. 105, October, 1958.

3   Shock, N. W., "The Physiology of Aging," *Scientific American*, January, 1962.

4   Verzár, F., "The Aging of Collagen," *Scientific American*, Reprint No. 155, April, 1963. Explains how the chemical and physical properties of this important structural protein change with its age.

5   Comfort, A., "The Life Span of Animals," *Scientific American*, August, 1961.

PART VI

RESPONSIVENESS AND COORDINATION

The sensitive plant, *Mimosa pudica*. Darkness, touch, heat, and certain chemicals cause the leaflets to fold together along the midrib (right).

One of the chief distinguishing features of living things, as opposed to nonliving things, is that living things are capable of actively responding to certain changes in their environment. These environmental changes serve as **stimuli** which trigger a definite response on the part of the organism. When the "sensitive plant" *Mimosa pudica* is darkened, the leaflets along each side of the midrib fold together (see chapter opening illustration). When the plant is illuminated once again, the leaflets spread out into their former position. The stimulus is the presence or absence of illumination; the response is the movement of the leaflets.

25-1   IMPORTANCE OF INTERNAL COMMUNICATION

Responsiveness in multicellular organisms requires a proper coordination of parts. Few responses could be accomplished successfully if every cell of the organism responded in the same way to the stimulus. For you to be able to run, you must contract certain muscle fibers while others relax. Your liver must provide additional fuel for your muscles. Your lungs must supply an extra amount of oxygen and take away a correspondingly increased amount of carbon dioxide. In other words, for your entire body to respond as a whole to a given stimulus, its constituent systems, organs, tissues, and cells must respond in a variety of special ways. Furthermore, the response of each of the various parts of your body must be carefully coordinated with the response of all the other parts. This ability of individual cells, tissues, organs, and systems to respond harmoniously to the activities of other parts requires some form of communication among them.

Two different, but related, systems of internal communication are found in animals. One of these, the **nervous system,** is a very fast-acting system. Specialized cells, **neurons,** conduct electrical impulses from one part of the body to another. These impulses accomplish quick, localized communication between parts. The impulses are of brief duration and quite separate from one another. Consequently, nervous responses are usually brief, intermittent, and do not continue for long periods unless the stimulus remains.

The second communication system, the **endocrine system,** is usually somewhat slower in its action. Specialized glands, the endocrine glands, release **hormones** to the blood stream or other circulating fluid. Hormones are chemical substances which are carried by the circulatory system to every cell of the body. Sometimes just a few, sometimes many, cells respond to the presence of these hormones. Usually the response occurs as a change in the metabolic activities of the "target" cell, tissue, or organ. These changes may persist for long periods of time.

Plants differ from animals in having no nervous system. Therefore, quick, localized responses are practically nonexistent in the plant kingdom. A few plants, however, do exhibit rapid movement. When *Mimosa* leaflets are pinched, they fold up. This change occurs as a result of a sudden loss of turgor in a special mass of parenchyma cells at the base of each leaflet. If one pinches just the tip leaflets of a *Mimosa* leaf, the leaflets fold up in pairs working from the tip back to the base. It certainly looks as though some stimulus is passing up the leaf. This may be a chemical moving through the vascular bundles. Although nerves are not involved, there is also evidence that a definite electrical impulse does pass up the leaf.

For the most part, plants achieve their responsiveness and coordination through a system of chemical coordinators, the plant hormones. Our knowledge of the nature and interplay of the various chemical regulators in plants is still quite fragmentary. In this chapter we will examine some of what has been learned from experimentation and some of the current theories on the coordinating mechanisms in plants.

With the exception of turgor movements, plants respond to changes in their environment by growth. Naturally this sort of response takes longer to occur than a turgor response or a nervous-system response in an animal. The growth response may consist in having one part of the plant grow faster than another. Such a response produces definite, if relatively slow, movement. Two kinds of growth movements in response to outside stimuli are recognized in plants.

1) **Nastic movements.** A nastic movement (or *nasty* as it is sometimes called) is a response to an external stimulus that is independent of the direction from which the stimulus strikes the organism. The opening of certain flowers after sunrise is an example of a nastic movement. Illumination from any direction whatever will trigger the response, and the response itself is not oriented with respect to the direction of the stimulus. Although most nastic movements involve differential growth, that is, more rapid growth in certain parts than in others, some, such as the response of *Mimosa* leaflets, are turgor movements.

2) **Tropisms.** A tropism is a growth movement whose direction is determined by the direction from which the stimulus strikes the plant. If the plant part grows in the direction from which the stimulus originates, the tropism is referred to as positive. Growth in the opposite direction constitutes a negative tropism.

It has been known for years that plants respond to both the stimulus of light and the stimulus of gravity. The former response is a **phototropism,** the latter a **geotropism.** Stems exhibit positive phototropism while roots are negatively phototropic. On the other hand, stems are negatively geotropic while roots are positively geotropic (Fig. 25-1). The value to the plant of these responses seems quite clear. Roots growing downwards and/or away from light are more likely to find soil, water, and minerals. Stems growing upwards or towards light will be able to expose their leaves so that photosynthesis can occur.

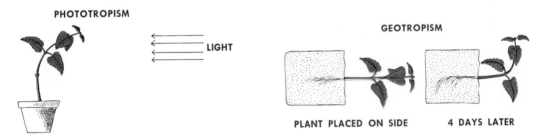

Tropisms. The direction of plant growth is affected by light (phototropism) and gravity (geotropism).   **Fig. 25-1**

In addition to growth movements, we know that several important *developmental* changes in plants occur in response to environmental stimuli. The germination of seeds, the resumption of growth of perennials in the spring, and the development of flowers all come about as a result of environmental triggers. The problem of understanding how plants respond to changes in their environment is twofold. First, we must discover how the plant detects the specific stimulus. Second, we must discover how the various tissues of the plant are coordinated in carrying out the response.

THE MECHANISM OF PHOTOTROPISM

The first clues to the coordinating mechanisms in plants came through a study of phototropism reported by Charles Darwin and his son Francis in 1880. They discovered that when the tip is removed from a growing shoot, the shoot ceases to exhibit phototropism. This was particularly surprising in view of their additional discovery: the bending action of the plant stem occurs in the region *behind* its tip. They found that if they placed an opaque covering over the tip of the plant, phototropism failed to occur even though the rest of the shoot was illuminated from one side. On the other hand, when they buried a plant in fine black sand so that only the tip of the shoot was exposed, there was no interference with phototropism. When the tip was illuminated from the side, the buried stem promptly bent in the direction of the light (Fig. 25-2). From these experiments, it seemed quite clear that the stimulus (light) was detected at one location (the tip) and the response (bending) was carried out at another (the region of elongation). This implied that the tip was, in some way, communicating with the cells of the region of elongation.

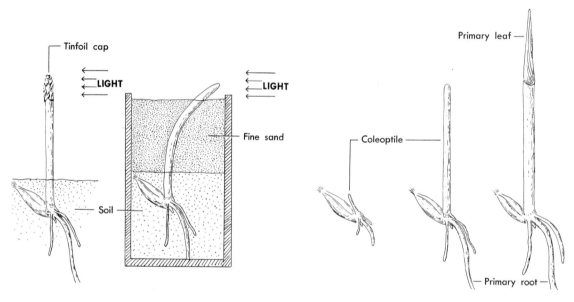

Fig. 25-2

The Darwins' experiments which showed that the response of phototropism is dependent upon light striking the tip of the plant.

Fig. 25-3

Stages in the germination of an oat (*Avena*) seed.

The Darwins confirmed these results with several different plant species. They found that grass seedlings were particularly easy subjects for this kind of experimentation. When grass seeds germinate, the primary leaf of the plant pierces the seed coverings and soil layers. It is protected from damage as it does so by a hollow, cylindrical structure, the **coleoptile,** which surrounds it (Fig. 25-3). Once the seedling has grown up above the surface of the ground, growth of the coleoptile ceases and **the** primary leaf pierces it.

The Darwins found that the tip of the coleoptile was necessary for phototropism in grass seedlings just as the shoot tip is necessary in older seedlings or in dicots such as the bean. Also, they found that the actual bending of the coleoptile occurs in the region below the tip. Thus a system of communication seems to be involved here, too.

In 1913, the Danish plant physiologist Boysen-Jensen showed that this communication must be accomplished by means of a chemical substance passing downward from the tip of the coleoptile. He cut off the tip of the coleoptile, covered the stump with a layer of gelatin, and then replaced the tip. Phototropism was still accomplished successfully. However, a piece of impervious material, such as mica, placed between the tip and the stump prevented the phototropic response. Interestingly enough, this interference occurred only when the sheet of mica separated the tip and stump on the shady side of the plant. When a horizontal incision was made in the illuminated side and the mica inserted, no interference with phototropism occurred. This suggested that the chemical coordinator was passing down the dark side of the seedling only. It also suggested that the chemical coordinator was a growth stimulator, as the phototropic response involves faster cell elongation on the shady side than on the sunny side (Fig. 25-4).

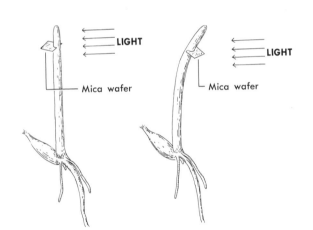

Fig. 25-4

Boysen-Jensen's experiments. The wafer of mica interfered with the phototropic response only when inserted on the shady side.

THE DISCOVERY AND ROLE OF AUXIN 25-4

F. W. Went first extracted this growth stimulator. He removed the tips from several coleoptiles of the oat plant (a grass), *Avena sativa*. He placed these tips on a block of agar and let them remain there for several hours. At the end of this time, the agar block itself was able to initiate resumption of growth in a decapitated coleoptile (Fig. 25-5). The growth was vertical because the agar block was placed completely across the stump of the coleoptile, and no light reached the plant from the side. This experiment showed that a chemical growth stimulator had diffused from the tips into the agar block. The name **auxin** was given to this material.

Unfortunately the quantity of active material in the coleoptile tips was far too small to be purified and analyzed chemically. Therefore, a search was made for other

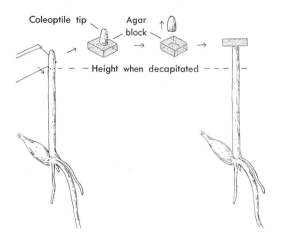

Fig. 25-5

Went's experiment showed that a chemical growth stimulator—auxin—can be extracted from coleoptile tips and still retain its effectiveness. Several tips should be placed on the agar block for a good response.

Fig. 25-6

The *Avena* test. The degree of bending is proportional to the amount of auxin activity in the agar block. The use of a living organism to determine the amount of activity of a substance is called a bioassay.

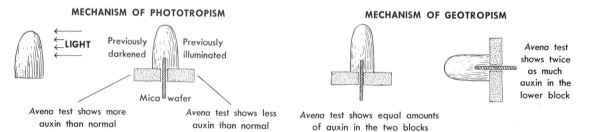

Fig. 25-7   Photographic record of an *Avena* test. (Courtesy Dr. Kenneth V. Thimann.)

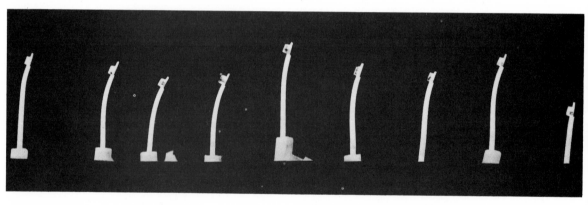

Fig. 25-8   Unequal distribution of auxin in phototropism and geotropism. In the intact plant, the side of the coleoptile receiving the greater concentration of auxin would grow more rapidly, resulting in bending toward light and away from the force of gravity.

sources of auxin. In this search, research workers were greatly aided by a technique, developed by Went, for determining the relative amount of auxin activity in a given preparation. The material in question is incorporated into an agar block and the block is placed on one side of a decapitated coleoptile (Fig. 25-6). As the auxin diffuses into that side of the coleoptile, it stimulates cell elongation and the coleoptile bends away from the block. The degree of curvature, measured at the end of 1½ hours, is proportional to the amount of auxin activity (e.g. number of coleoptile tips used) in the agar block. The use of a living organism to determine the amount of a given substance present is called a **bioassay** (Fig. 25-7).

Using Went's technique, it was soon found that auxins occur widely in nature. One of the most potent auxins was actually first isolated from human urine. It is indoleacetic acid or IAA. Although it is only one of many growth-promoting substances which have been discovered, there is good evidence that it is the most important auxin produced by plants.

To Went also goes the credit for discovering that an unequal distribution of auxin is responsible for the bending in phototropism. When a coleoptile tip that has previously been illuminated from one side is placed on two separated agar blocks (Fig. 25-8), the agar block on the side that had been shaded accumulates almost twice as much auxin as the block on the previously lighted side. This explains why cell elongation occurs more rapidly on the shady side of the plant. It seems as though light causes auxin to be translocated to the shady side.

Unequal distribution of auxin also explains the phenomenon of geotropism. When an oat coleoptile tip is placed on two separated agar blocks, as shown on the left in Fig. 25-8, there is no difference in the auxin activity picked up by the two blocks. When the two agar blocks are applied to a coleoptile tip placed on its side, however, the lower block accumulates twice as much auxin activity as the upper block. Under natural circumstances, this would result in greater cell elongation on the underside of the coleoptile. Thus the plant would bend upwards (Fig. 25-1).

How can one explain the negative phototropism and positive geotropism of *roots?* It seems as though exactly the same mechanism is at work in roots as in stems. The difference lies in the sensitivity of the cells of the root as compared with those of the stem (Fig. 25-9). Concentrations of auxin that stimulate growth in stems actually inhibit growth in roots. Concentrations of auxin which are too low to have any effect upon stems give some stimulation of cell elongation in the root. Therefore it is the illuminated side and the upper side of the root that grow more rapidly. As a result the root bends away from the light and downwards.

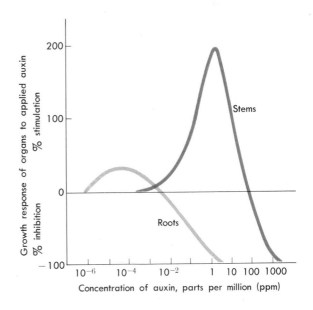

Fig. 25-9

The effect of auxin concentration on root and stem growth. Concentrations of auxin that stimulate stem growth inhibit the growth of roots. (Based on Fig. 2, K. V. Thimann, *Amer. Journal of Botany* **24,** 411, 1937.)

Although we have discovered a mechanism that coordinates these plant responses, we do not yet know how the environmental stimuli are actually received. In the case of phototropism, we assume that some light-absorbing *pigment* must be involved. IAA itself cannot fill this role as it does not absorb visible light. Because the phototropic response is most sensitive to blue light, the pigment is probably yellow in color, most likely a carotenoid (see Section 12-2).

25-5   ## OTHER AUXIN ACTIVITIES

The discovery of auxins opened up a very active field of research. Over a brief period of time, auxins were found to participate in the coordination of a variety of other plant activities.

1) Fruit development. Pollination of the flowers of angiosperms initiates the formation of seeds. Each seed contains the embryo of a new plant. As the seeds mature, surrounding flower parts form a covering, the fruit, around the seeds. It is now known that as the seeds develop, they release auxin into the surrounding flower parts, thus stimulating the growth of the fruit. In fact, it is possible to stimulate fruit development in nonpollinated flowers simply by the application of auxin to the flower. This is not just a laboratory curiosity. Many tomato and holly growers deliberately initiate fruit development in this way. Not only does this insure that all flowers will "set" fruit, but it also increases the likelihood that all the fruits will be ready for harvesting at the same time.

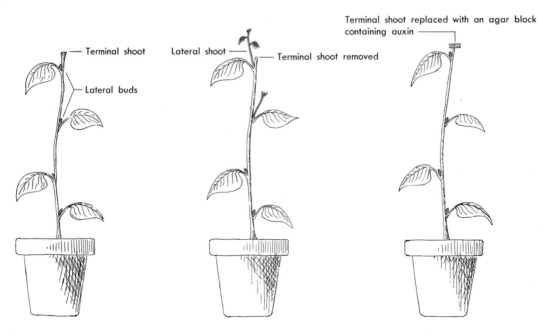

Fig. 25-10   Apical dominance. Translocation of auxin from the terminal shoot (left) or an auxin-containing agar block (right) inhibits development of the lateral buds. Absence of a source of auxin enables the lateral buds to develop (center).

When the white pines in this grove were young, their terminal shoots ("leaders") were killed by the white pine weevil. With the removal of apical dominance, two lateral branches succeeded in replacing the leader on the tree the boys are standing near. (Courtesy Owen MacNutt.)

Fig. 25-11

2) Apical dominance. As a general rule, growth of the shoot apex (terminal shoot) of a plant inhibits the development of the lateral buds on the stem beneath. This inhibition is called apical dominance. In trees which form a single, straight trunk (e.g. most pines), apical dominance is very pronounced. In low-growing, many-branched, shrubby plants, it is less noticeable. If the terminal shoot is removed, the inhibition is removed with it (Fig. 25-10). The lateral buds then commence growth. Gardeners regularly exploit this principle by pruning the terminal shoot of ornamental shrubs. The release of apical dominance enables lateral branches to develop and the shrub becomes fuller and less spindly. The process must be repeated periodically, though, because one or two of the "laterals" will eventually outstrip the others and reimpose apical dominance.

Apical dominance seems to result from the downward transport of auxin produced in the apical meristem. In fact, if the apical meristem is removed and a block of auxin-containing agar placed on the stump, inhibition of the lateral buds is maintained (Fig. 25-10). A plain block of agar has no such inhibiting effect.

White pines grown in warm, sunny locations frequently are parasitized by the white pine weevil. This insect lays eggs in the terminal shoot of the tree. After the young hatch, they consume the tissues of the shoot and kill it. Death of the shoot removes apical dominance and the lateral branches beneath begin to grow rapidly upward. If left alone, one or two laterals usually succeed in reestablishing apical dominance. Figure 25-11 shows the crotch formed in a white pine by the replacement of one terminal shoot by two.

The principle of apical dominance can easily be demonstrated in the laboratory. The common white potato is really a portion of the underground stem of the potato plant. It has a terminal (apical) bud or "eye" and several lateral buds. After a long

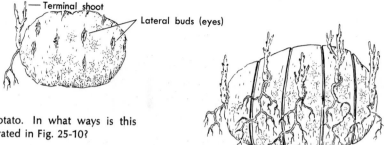

Fig. 25-12

Apical dominance in the white potato. In what ways is this experiment similar to the one illustrated in Fig. 25-10?

period of storage, the terminal bud usually sprouts but the other buds do not. However, if the potato is sliced into sections, one bud to a section, the lateral buds develop just as quickly as the terminal bud (Fig. 25-12).

3) Abscission. It has been found that auxins play an important role in the shedding of leaves and fruit. Young leaves and fruits produce auxin and as long as they do, they remain firmly attached to the stem. When auxin production diminishes, however, a special layer of cells forms at the base of the petiole or fruit stalk. This layer of cells is called the abscission layer (Fig. 25-13). Soon the petiole or fruit stalk breaks free at this point and the leaf or fruit falls to the ground.

One can demonstrate this nicely in the laboratory. If the blade of a coleus leaf is removed, as shown in Fig. 25-14, the petiole remains attached to the stem for just

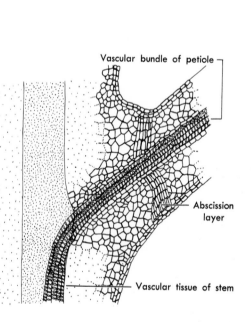

Fig. 25-13

The abscission layer. When leaves and fruits fall from a plant, the separation occurs at the abscission layer.

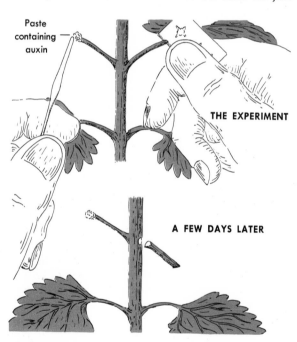

Fig. 25-14

The role of auxin in abscission. The petiole of a leaf whose blade has been removed soon drops from the stem unless auxin is applied to the cut surface.

Fig. 25-15

Top: American holly cuttings which have been treated with a synthetic auxin (beta-indole-butyric acid). Bottom: untreated controls. (Courtesy Paul C. Marth, U.S.D.A., Beltsville.)

a few more days. The removal of the blade seems to be the trigger here, as an undamaged leaf at the same node of the stem remains on the plant much longer, in fact, the normal length of time. If, however, auxin is applied to the cut end of the petiole (Fig. 25-14), abscission of the petiole is greatly delayed.

The ability of auxin to delay abscission has been exploited by apple and orange growers. The fruits of these species often drop off before they are ready for picking. This may result in a severe financial loss to the grower. Carefully applied auxin sprays greatly cut down loss by premature dropping.

Just what causes the lowered production of auxin in mature leaves and fruits is not completely clear. Leaves which are entirely shaded by others above them soon cease to produce auxin and drop off. This is a valuable adaptation of the plant because a shaded leaf needs nourishment but cannot manufacture it by photosynthesis. Thus it becomes a detriment to the plant.

In the fall, all the leaves of deciduous trees drop off. This, too, is a valuable adaptation because it reduces the surface area of the plant. This, in turn, diminishes water loss and snow load. As far as the plant's metabolism is concerned, freezing weather is equivalent to a drought. Leaf drop thus serves to conserve water and to minimize snow damage during the winter. (Most nondeciduous, cold-climate species have "needles" for leaves. These are very narrow and have a heavy, waterproof cuticle. The shape aids in the shedding of snow, and the cuticle cuts down on water loss.)

4) Root initiation. Auxins also stimulate the formation of **adventitious roots** in many species. Adventitious roots arise from stems or leaves rather than the regular root system of the plant. Gardeners may propagate desirable plants by cutting pieces of stem and placing them base down in moist sand. Eventually, adventitious roots grow out at the base of the cutting. Their development seems to depend, among other things, upon the presence of auxin which has been translocated down from the upper portions of the cutting. Many gardeners now hasten the process by pretreating their cuttings with solutions or powders containing synthetic auxins (Fig. 25-15).

HOW DO AUXINS WORK? A THEORY

As we have seen, auxins affect a variety of plant tissues in a variety of different ways. Some tissues (e.g. coleoptile, ovary wall of the pistil) are stimulated by auxin. Some (e.g. lateral buds) are inhibited. How can a single small molecule of this sort produce such a variety of effects?

The answer is not yet known with certainty. However, at least some of the effects of auxin on plant cells can be traced to its influence on the genes themselves. The stimulating effect of auxin on coleoptile and stem growth has been shown to be strongly inhibited by an antibiotic called **actinomycin D.** Actinomycin D exerts its lethal effect on cells in a remarkably precise way. It binds to the DNA molecules in the nucleus of the cell and prevents the two strands of DNA from separating. Thus the DNA molecule cannot serve as the template for the synthesis of either additional DNA (Fig. 20-2) or messenger RNA molecules (Fig. 20-12). Without fresh supplies of messenger RNA, the synthesis of new proteins (including all enzymes) by the cell soon comes to a halt. The inhibition of auxin action by actinomycin D thus suggests that at least one effect of auxin is on the transcription of the DNA code in the cell. This has been further verified by the discovery that when isolated plant nuclei are treated with IAA, there soon follows a marked increase in the production of RNA. However, when actinomycin D is added to the system, this increase is prevented.

Treatment of plant cells with auxin produces an increase not only in RNA production but in protein production as well. This is to be expected in view of the role that messenger, ribosomal, and transfer RNA molecules play in protein synthesis (see Section 20-5). At least one specific protein, an enzyme, has been found to be induced in pea stems exposed to auxin. This induction, too, is blocked by actinomycin D, and therefore we may conclude that auxin has a direct effect on the genetic code itself. A specific gene coding for a specific enzyme has been unlocked by the presence of IAA.

It is not yet known exactly how auxin interacts with the genetic code to unlock genes. There is evidence, however, that auxin is active within the cell only when joined to a protein molecule. Could the Jacob-Monod hypothesis of selective gene action apply here (see Section 23-8, 1)? Perhaps the auxin molecule is acting as an *inducer* by joining with a repressor protein molecule and preventing it from turning off one or more operons (look back at Fig. 23-9).

The foregoing discussion should not obscure the fact that *some* of the varied activities of auxin occur too rapidly to be a result of gene activation. Auxin must influence cell activities in other, more rapid, ways as well. Only further experimentation will show how these effects are achieved.

THE GIBBERELLINS

Other growth-promoting substances have been discovered in addition to the auxins. During the 1930's, Japanese scientists isolated such a substance from cultures of a fungus which parasitizes rice plants. They called this substance gibberellin. After the delay caused by World War II, plant physiologists in other countries took up the trail and succeeded in isolating several more closely related compounds. These are now known collectively as gibberellins.

Perhaps the most dramatic effect of the gibberellins is on stem growth. When applied in low concentrations to a bush or "dwarf" bean, the stem begins to grow very rapidly. The length of the internodes becomes sufficiently great that the plant becomes indistinguishable from climbing or "pole" beans. Gibberellin seems to overcome the hereditary limitations in many "dwarf" plant types.

Although gibberellins somewhat resemble auxins in their stimulation of stem growth, they are not classified as auxins. Not only is their molecular structure quite different from that of the auxins, but they do not give a response in the oat coleoptile test.

The gibberellins (like the auxins) were first isolated from sources other than the higher plants themselves. This, of course, raises the question of whether they are normal constituents of the higher plants and, if so, what role they play in the normal coordinating mechanisms of the plant. In recent years gibberellins have indeed been found to occur naturally in a variety of plant tissues. In addition to being implicated in the growth of stems, they seem to be the chief stimulants of root growth. The application of gibberellins to certain plants (e.g. spinach, cabbage) promotes the development of flowers. That this reflects a natural activity is suggested by the presence of increased quantities of gibberellins in the tissues of these plants when they are normally ready to flower.

Gibberellins also appear to play a role in the sprouting of buds. When white potatoes are first harvested, neither the terminal nor the lateral buds will sprout (Fig. 25-12). However, the application of gibberellin to the terminal bud will cause it to sprout immediately. In such woody species as the peach, birch, and sycamore, the synthesis of gibberellins in the spring seems to be the trigger for the sprouting of buds, which have been dormant during the cold winter months.

The germination of seeds is another stage of plant life in which gibberellins may play a major role. You remember that most of the food reserves of cereal grains such as barley, wheat, rice, and corn are stored in the endosperm (Fig. 21-8). One of the first steps in the germination process in these monocots is production of gibberellin by the embryo. The gibberellin acts on the cells surrounding the endosperm, causing them to produce a number of specific hydrolytic enzymes (e.g. amylase) that digest the starch and protein of the endosperm and thus make sugars and amino acids available to the growing embryo. These enzymes also break down the seed coats and thus make it easier for the radicle and coleoptile to break through them (Fig. 25-3). This effect of gibberellin can be blocked by actinomycin D, a fact suggesting that the gibberellin is activating genes within the cells surrounding the endosperm. In fact the application of synthetic gibberellin to these cells first produces a burst of messenger RNA synthesis. This is followed by the synthesis of the various hydrolytic enzymes.

THE CYTOKININS   25-8

Another group of plant growth regulators are the cytokinins. Each of these substances contains the purine, adenine, as part of their molecular structure. (What other substances have you studied that contain adenine?)

Cytokinins, when acting together with auxin, strongly stimulate mitosis in meristematic tissues. The food reserves of some seeds contain cytokinins. Presumably these provide the chemical stimulus for rapid mitosis in the developing seedling. Cytokinins also promote the differentiation of the cells produced in the meristems.

In addition to their growth-promoting effects, cytokinins have been shown to slow down the aging of plant parts, such as leaves, and to increase the resistance of plant parts to such harmful influences as low temperatures, virus infection, weed killers, and radiation.

As is the case with auxins and gibberellins, at least some of the effects of cyto-kinins are brought about by selective gene activation. Two enzymes have been shown to be specifically induced by cytokinins and this induction is blocked by actinomycin D. Furthermore, a marked burst of RNA (probably messenger RNA) synthesis occurs when plant cells or isolated nuclei are treated with cytokinins.

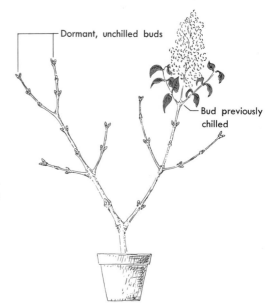

Fig. 25-16

Breaking bud dormancy in the lilac by localized cold treat-ment. Even under the best growing conditions, lilac buds will not develop without prior chilling.

25-9   DORMIN

Inhibitors also play a role in the coordination of plant activities. In the fall, the mature leaves of such trees as the birch and sycamore produce a substance which stops growth in the apical meristems of the stems and converts them into dormant buds. The newly developing leaves growing above the meristem (look back at Fig. 24-2) become converted into stiff bud scales that wrap the meristem closely and will protect it from mechanical damage and drying out during the winter months. The substance responsible for the conversion of the apical meristems into dormant buds has been identified and named *dormin*. Presumably it passes from its place of manu-facture, the mature leaves of the plant, to the apical meristems by way of the phloem.

Once a bud has become dormant, it usually cannot be reactivated simply by the return of warm temperatures and abundant moisture. In some cases, gibberellin synthesis is necessary (probably triggered by the lengthening days of spring). In some cases, a period of exposure to cold temperatures is necessary before bud dormancy can be broken. Apple trees and lilacs, for example, cannot be grown in tropical areas because the winters never get cold enough (a few days at 0–10° C) to break bud dormancy.

The value of enforced dormancy to the plant is quite clear. If inhibitors such as dormin were not present in the late fall and early winter, an unexpected warm spell might stimulate bud sprouting. The return of freezing weather would quickly kill this delicate growth. Enforced dormancy, which can only be ended after a period of prolonged cold or with the return of longer days, prevents the plant from being endangered in this way.

The dormancy of buds seems to be a very localized thing. By prior chilling, one bud on a lilac stem can be stimulated to grow while the other, nonchilled buds on the stem remain quite dormant (Fig. 25-16).

Many newly-formed seeds must also undergo a period of enforced dormancy before they can germinate. Dormin may be involved in some cases (e.g. in peach seeds) but other inhibitors have been discovered, too. Exposure to cold temperatures or, in some cases, exposure to sufficient amounts of water to leach the inhibitor out of the seed, is necessary before germination can occur. The value to the seed of a cold requirement is the same as for buds. As for a water requirement—beyond that needed for the process of germination itself—you remember (see Section 21-9) that this insures that the seeds of desert plants will not germinate if there has not been sufficient rainfall to enable them to complete their entire life cycle.

Dormin also has been found to speed up the abscission of aging plant parts such as leaves and fruits (Fig. 25-13). Because this discovery was made independently of the studies on dormancy, the name *abscisin* II was given to what turned out to be the same substance as dormin.

In contrast to auxins, gibberellins, and cytokinins, dormin appears to be a repressor of gene activity. It inhibits the synthesis of RNA (also DNA). However, this inhibition can be reversed by the presence of cytokinin. Possibly, then, we are dealing with a cellular control mechanism like that proposed by Jacob and Monod (Fig. 23-9). Dormin may be a corepressor which, when joined with a protein, blocks gene action. A cytokinin, on the other hand, may serve as the inducer in the same system. When joined to the repressor protein, it prevents the repressor from blocking operator genes, and messenger RNA synthesis followed by enzyme synthesis can begin.

ETHYLENE   **25-10**

When first harvested, lemons are often too green to be acceptable in the market. In order to hasten the development of a uniform yellow color, lemon growers used to store the newly harvested lemons in sheds which were kept warm and humid. The warmth was supplied by kerosene stoves. When one grower tried a more modern heating system, he found that his lemons no longer changed color properly. Following this clue, it was soon found that the important factor in the ripening process was not the heat, but the small amounts of ethylene gas (CH_2CH_2) given off by the burning kerosene.

Since that time it has been found that most fruits produce their own ethylene, and it is this which triggers the ripening process. Among the many changes that ethylene brings about is a change in the permeability of the membranes of the cell. One consequence of this is to allow a chlorophyll-destroying enzyme into the chloroplasts. With the breakdown of chlorophyll, the red and/or yellow pigments in the cells of the fruit are unmasked and the fruit assumes its ripened color.

THE FLOWERING PROCESS

One of the most important developmental activities of angiosperms is flowering. When a plant is in active growth, mitosis in the apical meristem produces cells which go on to form more stem tissues and cells which will form leaf buds (Fig. 24-2). The leaf buds grow into mature leaves. Eventually, though, a time comes (usually as active growth ceases) when the meristems form flower primordia. These are clusters of cells which develop into flower buds. The flowers, into which these buds mature, contain the sex organs of the angiosperms, without which sexual reproduction could not occur.

The importance of the flowering process has led many plant physiologists to try to find out what initiates it. The question is simply, "What causes the plant to stop producing leaf buds and start producing flower buds?"

In some cases, the stimulus seems to be purely internal. Certain tomato varieties automatically produce flower primordia after 13 nodes have been produced by the growing stem. Adequate food reserves must be present in the plant, however. If the plant has not been photosynthesizing actively, it will lack the energy reserves necessary for the flowering process.

In most cases, the stimulus which initiates the flowering process seems to be external. Temperature often serves as the critical stimulus. This is particularly true of biennial species, that is, plants that require two growing seasons in order to complete their life cycle. Beets, carrots, and cabbages are three common biennial plants. In the first growing season, they develop roots, a short stem, and a cluster of leaves. (Look back at Fig. 4-9.) During this season, food is stored in the root system. With the arrival of cold weather, the tops die back. The next season, flowers are produced on the new shoot growth. After the reproductory process is completed, the entire plant dies. Flowering will not occur in the second season, however, unless the plant has been exposed to cold weather during the winter.

Experiments have shown that the entire plant need not be chilled for successful flowering to follow. The terminal bud is the temperature receptor. Its exposure to temperatures in the range of 1–10°C sets the stage for subsequent flowering. Gibberellins may be involved in the process. When gibberellin is applied to a terminal bud that has not been exposed to cold, the plant proceeds to flower normally. Furthermore, when a cold-treated biennial is grafted to a non-cold-treated one, the latter also flowers vigorously. This suggests that the chilling of the terminal bud is followed by the production and translocation of a flower-promoting substance.

Still another factor that triggers the flowering process in many plant species is a change in the daily intervals of illumination to which the plant is exposed. This discovery was made in 1920 by two plant physiologists, W. W. Garner and H. A. Allard, employed by the United States Department of Agriculture. They were perplexed to find that a new variety of tobacco, Maryland Mammoth, did not flower during the summer as other tobacco varieties do. Protected in a greenhouse, however, this variety did flower successfully near Christmastime. After considerable experimentation with artificial lighting in the winter and artificial darkening in the summer, they concluded that the flowering response was governed by the length of the day. They called this behavior **photoperiodism.** Because Maryland Mammoth would flower only when exposed to short periods of light, they called it a short-day plant. Other species such as chrysanthemums, poinsettias, and the cocklebur are also short-day plants. Some plant species, e.g. spinach, sugar beets, and the radish, flower only after exposure to long days and hence are called long-day plants. Still other species, such as the tomato, are day-neutral, that is, their flowering is not closely regulated by the length of their exposure to light.

The discovery of photoperiodism explained several puzzling facts about plant development. First, it provided a mechanism to explain, partly at least, the regular succession of blooms which occurs during the growing season. From the first flowers of early spring to the last flowers in the fall, one plant species after another flowers in a sequence as regular as clockwork. Now one could understand why spinach "bolts" and flowers during the summer months while chrysanthemums produce their blooms in the autumn. Second, photoperiodism explains why the plants of a given species usually bloom simultaneously. Though some individuals may have commenced growth earlier than others in the spring, in a given area they all bloom at the same time. Third, photoperiodism explains why many plant species can be grown successfully only in a rather narrow range of latitude. Spinach, a long-day plant, cannot flower successfully in the tropics because the days never get long enough (14 hours). Ragweed, a short-day plant, fails to thrive in northern Maine because by the time the days become short enough (August) to initiate flowering, a killing frost is apt to occur before the reproductory process is completed and the seeds matured.

MECHANISM OF PHOTOPERIODISM 25-12

The discovery of photoperiodism stimulated a great many plant physiologists to explore the process further in an attempt to determine the mechanism of action. They soon found that the terms *short-day* and *long-day* were misnomers. Interrupting the daylight period with intervals of darkness had absolutely no effect on the flowering process. Interrupting the night period with artificial illumination was, however, quite a different story. When short-day plants like the cocklebur were illuminated even briefly at night, they failed to flower. Thus it became clear that it was not the length of day that was important to the flowering process, but the length of night. Short-day plants were really *long-night* plants. The cocklebur, for example, will flower only after it has been kept in the dark for 8½ hours. If it is illuminated by a flash of light at any time during this period, it fails to flower.

Although the development of flower primordia occurs at the meristems, the photoperiodic stimulus is not detected there. The leaves are the receptors of the stimulus. If only one leaf, in fact just a small portion of one leaf, of the cocklebur is subjected to an 8½-hour period of darkness, the entire plant will flower even though all the rest of its leaves fail to receive a sufficiently long exposure to darkness (Fig. 25-17). This suggests that some stimulus is passing from the leaf to the meristems.

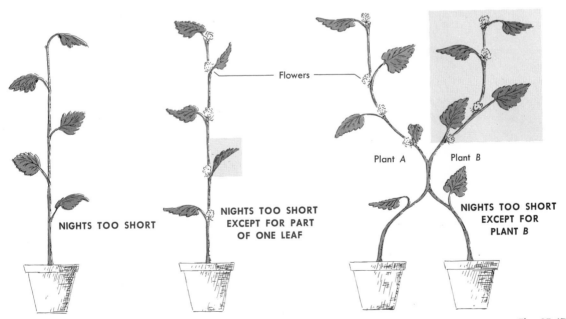

Experimental evidence that the flowering stimulus is initiated in the leaf (center) and is transported by the vascular system to the flower buds (right).

Fig. 25-17

Grafting experiments lend solid support to this idea. If a cocklebur exposed to a favorable photoperiod is grafted to a cocklebur exposed to an unfavorable photoperiod, both plants will flower (Fig. 25-17). By grafting a series of plants together, it is even possible to estimate how fast the stimulus is transported. A flower-inducing substance has now actually been isolated chemically and been given the name *florigen*. It is manufactured in the leaves and transported, in the phloem, to the meristems. Here it triggers their conversion into flower primordia. The process begins with a number of important biochemical changes within the cells of the meristems. The first of these is a drop in the amount of histone in the cells. If histones inhibit gene action, (as we suggested in Section 23-8, 2), then this first step appears to consist of unlocking genes within these cells. That this is so is suggested by the next event: a sharp rise in the production of RNA, including messenger RNA. This is followed, as one would expect, by an increase in synthesis of protein. It is only after this sequence of events has been completed that visible changes in the cells occur and the flower primordia develop.

In the cocklebur, at least, production of florigen is a one-time affair. Given one night of at least 8½ hours' duration, the plant will begin the flowering process even though it is subsequently placed back under unfavorable, short-night conditions.

The "long-day" plants are also misnamed. Spinach and other members of this group bloom successfully on a short-day schedule as long as the night periods are interrupted by a brief exposure to light. Thus, "long-day" plants are really *short-night* plants. They can bloom only if the nights are not too long.

The mechanism of action in short-night plants seems somewhat more complicated than in long-night plants. When the short-night plant henbane is placed under long-night conditions, it fails to flower. If, however, some of its leaves are removed, or the plant is chilled, or it is placed in an anaerobic atmosphere during the long night, the inhibiting effect of the long night can be overcome and the plant does flower. This suggests that some inhibiting substance (it may be dormin) is produced by the metabolism of the leaves during the hours of darkness. If too much of this substance accumulates, it inhibits flowering. Any interference, however, with the normal metabolism of the plant slows down the accumulation of this inhibitor.

On the other hand, there is evidence that a substance which *stimulates* flowering is released from leaves to meristems when the plant is under short-night conditions. In fact, this substance appears to be identical to the florigen produced by long-night plants. If a short-night plant is grafted to a long-night plant, both plants will flower under a short-night schedule, although the long-night plant would not normally do so. Can you think of any way to reconcile this evidence with that in the previous paragraph?

25-13   **THE DISCOVERY OF PHYTOCHROME**

Photoperiodism must involve a very sensitive light-detecting mechanism. We have seen that the cocklebur fails to flower on a long-night schedule if the night is interrupted by even a brief flash of light. The light flash can be very dim, exposure to light not much brighter than the light of the full moon being effective.

The most effective light rays for inhibiting flowering in the cocklebur are orange-red rays with a wavelength of 660 mμ. The same wavelength is most effective in promoting flowering of spinach when its nights are otherwise too long. These findings suggest that the plants contain a pigment which absorbs orange-red light most strongly.

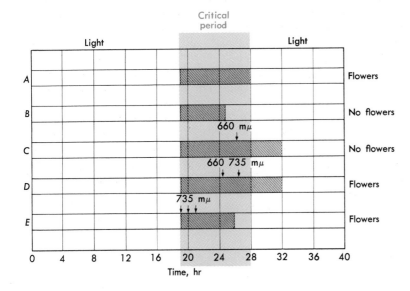

Photoperiodism in the cocklebur. An uninterrupted night at least 8½ hours long is needed for flowering to occur (*A* and *B*). Interruption of an otherwise long night by orange-red (660 mμ) light prevents flowering (*C*) unless it is followed by irradiation with far-red (735 mμ) light (*D*). An intense exposure to far-red light at the start of the night reduces the dark requirement by two hours (*E*).

Fig. 25-18

It has also been found that the inhibiting effect of orange-red (660 mμ) light on the cocklebur can be completely overcome by exposing the leaves of the plant to far-red light. This is light which is just beyond the visible spectrum. A wavelength of 735 mμ is most effective in reversing the inhibitory action of orange-red light.

The system is completely reversible. The 8½ hour night of the cocklebur can be interrupted any number of times by orange-red light alternating with far-red light. Whether flowering is inhibited or not depends upon the wavelength of the last flash. If the last flash is orange-red light, flowering will not occur. If it is far-red light, flowering will occur normally even though the plant has been exposed to substantial quantities of orange-red light prior to the final exposure (Fig. 25-18).

This reversible effect suggests the presence of a reversible pigment. In one condition, the pigment absorbs orange-red light. In so doing, it becomes converted to a form which absorbs far-red light. Exposure of the far-red absorbing form to far-red light reconverts the pigment to the orange-red absorbing form. The pigment has been given the name **phytochrome.** The orange-red-absorbing form is designated P_R. The far-red-absorbing form is P_{FR}. The two forms are interconvertible according to this scheme:

$$P_R \underset{\underset{735m\mu \text{ light}}{\uparrow\uparrow\uparrow\uparrow}}{\overset{660m\mu \text{ light}}{\overset{\downarrow\downarrow\downarrow\downarrow}{\rightleftarrows}}} P_{FR}$$

Although present in exceedingly small amounts, phytochrome has been isolated from plant tissue. It is a protein to which is attached a prosthetic group which gives it its light-absorbing property. As one could guess from the fact that phytochrome absorbs most strongly in the red end of the light spectrum, its color is blue.

The action of phytochrome in controlling photoperiodism seems to hinge on two factors. (1) Sunlight is richer in orange-red light (660 mμ) than in far-red (735 mμ) light. This means that at nightfall, all the phytochrome in the leaves of a plant is in the form of P_{FR}. (2) P_{FR} is unstable while P_R is stable. In the darkness, P_{FR} gradually becomes reconverted into P_R. This conversion thus serves as the clock by means of which the plant measures the length of the night. In fact, it is possible to induce the cocklebur to flower after a night as short as 6½ hours if it is first exposed to a large dose of far-red light (Fig. 25-18). Presumably the far-red light accomplishes immediately the P_{FR} to P_R transition, which would otherwise require two or more hours of darkness. That a large dose of far-red light does not do away entirely with the need for darkness indicates that other chemical reactions must also be carried out in the dark if flowering is to take place. What these are is not yet known.

The behavior of phytochrome provides a reasonable mechanism to explain the long-night requirement of the cocklebur. P_{FR} inhibits the chemical reactions necessary for the release of florigen from the leaves. P_R does not. Therefore the cocklebur needs 8½ hours of darkness in which (1) to convert all the P_{FR} present at sundown into P_R and (2) to carry out the unknown supplementary reactions leading to the release of florigen. If this process is interrupted by a flash of light (containing 660-mμ rays), the P_R is immediately reconverted to inhibitory P_{FR} and the night's work is undone. A subsequent exposure to far-red light will convert the pigment back to P_R and steps leading to the release of florigen can be completed. Exposure to far red light at the start of the night sets the clock ahead two hours or so by eliminating the need for the spontaneous conversion of P_{FR} to P_R.

In the case of short-night plants like spinach, P_{FR} is needed to stimulate the flowering process. A flash of orange-red light in the night will reverse the spontaneous conversion of P_{FR} to P_R which has been going on since sundown. This will permit flowering to occur even though the plant has been maintained under long-night conditions. In fact, spinach will bloom under continuous illumination (no night at all) when presumably all its phytochrome is in the P_{FR} form.

25-14   **OTHER PHYTOCHROME ACTIVITIES**

Phytochrome has been found to be involved in many other plant activities. The seeds of the Grand Rapids variety of lettuce will not germinate unless exposed to light. If shortly after exposure to visible light they are exposed to far-red light, they fail to germinate. Action spectra (see Section 12-2) for this stimulation and inhibition show that phytochrome is the light-absorbing pigment. P_{FR} stimulates germination while P_R inhibits it. The same mechanism has been found to operate in the seeds of many other angiosperms, both herbaceous and woody, and in some gymnosperm seeds, e.g. those of the Scotch pine. The situation is just reversed in the seeds of the California poppy. P_{FR} inhibits germination and P_R stimulates it. Under natural conditions, these are seeds which will not germinate when exposed to light. Phytochrome is probably responsible for the light-regulated germination of the species mentioned in Section 21-9.

Stem growth is also regulated by phytochrome. It has long been known that plants raised in the dark elongate very rapidly. (Look back at Fig. 12-4.) This phenomenon is known as etiolation. It is a mechanism that increases the probability of the plant's reaching the light. Once light shines upon it, the plant produces internodes of normal size and its leaves grow to full size. That this is not brought about by satisfaction of the plant's needs for photosynthesis is shown by the fact that exposure to light too dim to be useful in photosynthesis nonetheless halts etiolation. Orange-red light is especially effective in producing this response. This, plus the fact that exposure to far-red light causes a resumption of etiolation implicates phytochrome as the receptor in this response, too. The development of a red color in the skins of tomatoes and apples, the breaking of dormancy in some plant buds, and the straightening up of the hypocotyl arch when a dicot seedling grows above the surface of the soil (Fig. 21-10) also are triggered by light acting on phytochrome.

In the last chapter, we discussed the spontaneous aging and death that is so characteristic of annual plants once they have completed flowering and the production of seeds and fruits. In some cases, this process, too, may be a photoperiodic response involving phytochrome. Cocklebur plants that are given long nights age and die even if all their buds are removed before they can develop into flowers. If, however, the debudded plants have their long night interrupted by light, they live several weeks longer than they normally would.

Although plants have no nervous system, they do have a variety of mechanisms by which they respond to changes in the environment. They respond to the direction of light, its wavelength, and the duration of exposure to it. They respond to gravity and temperature. All of these responses require a means (e.g. phytochrome, carotenoids) of detecting the stimulus in the environment. The detector mechanism may be located in the terminal bud or leaf or elsewhere. Once the stimulus is detected, these plants then require a communication system to enable all parts of the plant to respond in an appropriate, coordinated way. This communication system is made up of chemical messengers (e.g. auxins, florigen) transported in the contents of the phloem.

Among animals, chemical messengers also play an important role in coordinating the various organs of the body. These substances are the hormones. Their chemical nature and action is the topic of the next chapter.

EXERCISES AND PROBLEMS

1 Why do gardeners not have to worry about planting seeds upside down?

2 List six ways in which auxins affect plant function both in nature and under the control of man.

3 What term would you use to describe the closing of a crocus flower on a cold spring day?

4 What is a controlled experiment?

5 A student sprays auxin on the flowers of a tomato plant growing in a greenhouse. Tomatoes develop. Is he right to conclude that auxin promotes fruit development?

6 What is the control in the experiment illustrated in Fig. 25-16?

7 What control should have been included in carrying out the experiment shown by the righthand plant in Fig. 25-10?

8 For each of the following responses of the cocklebur, tell (1) where and how the stimulus is detected, (2) where and how the response is carried out, (3) how the information is transmitted from the first region to the second. Cite experimental evidence to support your conclusions.
a) Phototropism of the shoot.
b) Production of flowers when nights become at least 8½ hours long.
c) Geotropism of the root.

REFERENCES

The following three papers have been republished in *Great Experiments in Biology,* ed. by M. L. Gabriel and S. Fogel, Prentice-Hall, 1955:

1a "Sensitiveness of Plants to Light: Its Transmitted Effects." Charles Darwin and his son Francis show that the phototropic response originates in the coleoptile (they call it a cotyledon) tip.

1b "Transmission of the Phototropic Stimulus in the Coleoptile of the Oat Seedling." P. Boysen-Jensen shows that a layer of gelatin separating a coleoptile tip from its base does not interfere with the phototropic response.

1c "On Growth-accelerating Substances in the Coleoptile of *Avena sativa.*" F. W. Went proves that a growth-promoting material can be extracted from coleoptile tips.

2 Galston, A. W., *The Life of the Green Plant,* 2nd ed., Foundations of Modern Biology Series, Prentice-Hall, Inc., 1964. Chapter 4 contains a brief review of auxins (both natural and synthetic), gibberellins, and the cytokinins.

3 Went, F. W., "Plant Growth and Plant Hormones," *This is Life,* ed. by W. H. Johnson and W. C. Steere, Holt, Rinehart and Winston, New York, 1962. A detailed account of the discovery of auxins, their role in plant physiology, and some of the problems of plant growth that still await solution.

4 Jacobs, W. P., "What Makes Leaves Fall," *Scientific American,* Reprint No. 116, November, 1955. The role of auxin in abscission.

5 Naylor, A. W., "The Control of Flowering," *Scientific American,* Reprint No. 113, May, 1952. Tells of the discovery of photoperiodism and the evidence that the stimulus is detected by the leaves and transmitted through the vascular system of the stem.

6 Salisbury, F. B., "The Flowering Process," *Scientific American,* Reprint No. 112, April, 1958. Describes experiments with the cocklebur which show that phytochrome supplies part of the clockwork by which photoperiod is measured.

7 Salisbury, F. B., and R. V. Parke, *Vascular Plants: Form and Function,* Wadsworth Publishing Co., Inc., Belmont, California, 1964. Chapter 16 describes a number of experiments that clarify the nature of photoperiodism.

Frogs vary the darkness of their skin by means of a hormone.

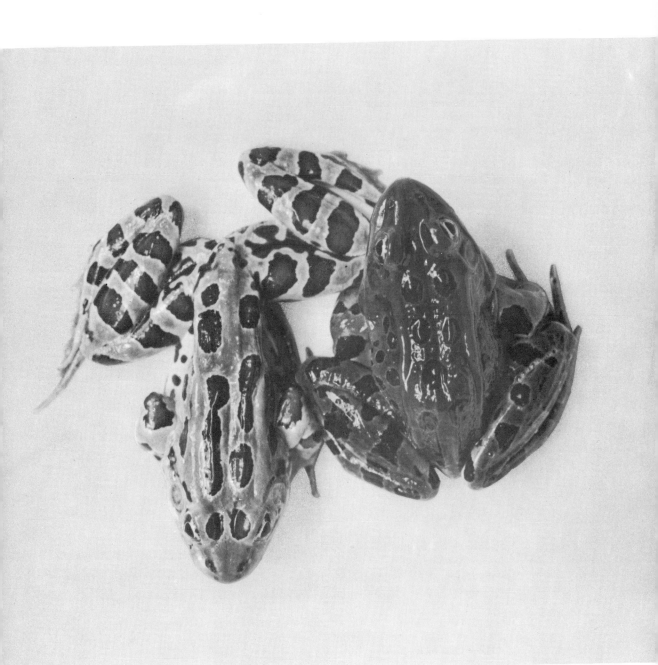

INTRODUCTION

Multicellular animals, like multicellular plants, must solve the problem of coordinating the activities of all the different kinds of cells of which they are made. They, too, need some mechanism by which the various cells, tissues and organs of the body can communicate. Only in this way can all these structures function in an efficient, well-coordinated way.

Two communication systems exist in most animals. One of these is the nervous system. It consists of specialized cells, neurons, which transmit electrical impulses from one part of the body to another. The other is the **endocrine** system. It achieves control of body functions through chemical substances, **hormones,** which are transported throughout the body in the blood. These two systems are not independent of one another. As we will see in this chapter and the ones to follow, a close connection exists between their activities.

Chemical coordination in animals, like chemical coordination in plants, involves: (1) the release of chemicals from cells into the ECF, (2) the transport, by one means or another, of these substances, and (3) the alteration of the activities of other cells by them. Probably every cell in a multicellular organism participates in chemical coordination of this sort. In fact, we have already studied an example of this in human physiology. Every cell of our body produces carbon dioxide as a result of cellular respiration. This carbon dioxide is released into the ECF and is then carried throughout the body by the bloodstream. When carbon-dioxide-rich blood reaches the medulla oblongata, it triggers the release of nerve impulses to the diaphragm and intercostal muscles. You remember (see Section 13-10) that the rate at which these impulses are generated governs the rate and depth of breathing. This, in turn, maintains a constant level of carbon dioxide in the blood.

There is reason to believe that all multicellular organisms carry on this kind of chemical coordination, that is, coordination achieved by release of chemical substances that are the *by-products* of other cell activities. Evidence is, however, very scanty on this point. For the present, therefore, we will narrow our view to those special clusters of cells whose sole function seems to be the release of chemical coordinators in the body. These are the endocrine glands. They are often referred to as ductless glands because their secretions, the hormones, pass directly into the blood that drains the gland (rather than into a duct as is the case with the *exocrine* glands discussed in Section 10-6). These hormones are then carried to all the other cells of the body. In some cases, they may influence the activities of all these cells. More often, the hormones exert their effect only on certain body structures, the "target" organs. So far, specific endocrine glands have been discovered only in the insects, crustaceans, certain mollusks, and all vertebrates.

INSECT HORMONES

In insects, hormones have been found which: (1) bring about color changes in the body, (2) stimulate development of eggs in the females, and (3) control growth and metamorphosis. It is interesting to note that some of these substances are produced by cells in the brain. Endocrine activity is closely related to nervous system activity in these animals.

Perhaps the control of growth and metamorphosis has been more carefully studied than any other endocrine activity in insects. Because of their rigid exoskeleton, insects can grow only by periodically shedding the exoskeleton in the process of **molting.** This process occurs repeatedly during the period of larval development. At

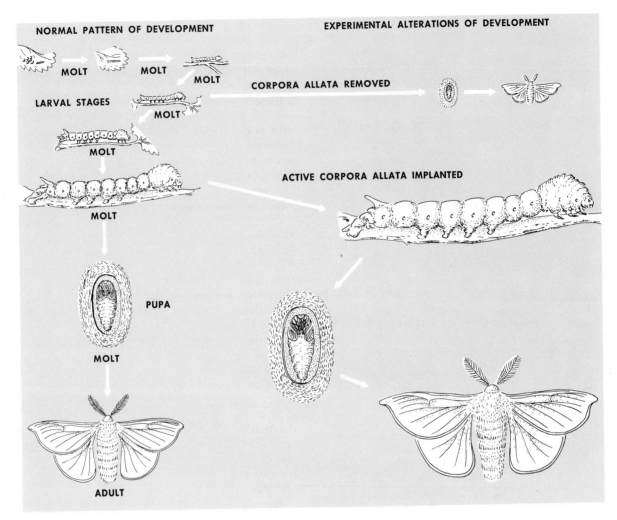

NORMAL PATTERN OF DEVELOPMENT

EXPERIMENTAL ALTERATIONS OF DEVELOPMENT

MOLT MOLT MOLT

LARVAL STAGES

MOLT

CORPORA ALLATA REMOVED

MOLT

ACTIVE CORPORA ALLATA IMPLANTED

MOLT

MOLT

PUPA

MOLT

ADULT

Left: normal pattern of development in the silkworm, *Bombyx mori.* This sequence can be shortened by removing the corpora allata from a young caterpillar and lengthened by introducing active corpora allata into a mature caterpillar. Pupation does not occur so long as the corpora allata secrete substantial amounts of juvenile hormone.

Fig. 26-1

the final molt, the organism which emerges is the adult. In several insect orders, it bears no resemblance whatsoever to the earlier larval stages. The marked transformation in body structure which occurs in these insects is called **metamorphosis.** Among the diptera, hymenoptera, and lepidoptera, it is accomplished during a dormant stage called the **pupa.** Figure 26-1 illustrates the larval, pupal, and adult stages in the development of the domestic silkworm moth, *Bombyx mori.* Metamorphosis occurs within a silken cocoon which is spun by the mature larva.

If the brain of a mature Cecropia caterpillar, one of several wild silkworms, is surgically removed before the caterpillar spins its cocoon, formation of the pupal stage does not occur. This cannot be simply a result of the shock of surgery because if the brain tissue is reintroduced into some other part of the body, pupation will proceed normally. In fact, just a tiny portion of the brain—about two dozen special cells—will do the trick. This experiment suggests that these special brain cells produce a hormone necessary for pupation to occur. This hormone does not trigger pupation directly, but instead acts upon a pair of glands in the thorax, the prothoracic glands. When stimulated by the brain cell hormone, they produce a second hormone, a steroid called **ecdyson,** which directly initiates molting and formation of the pupa.

These two hormones, acting together, promote not only the molt from larva to pupa, but also the earlier larva-to-larva molts. What, then, accounts for the sudden change in action which occurs at the time of metamorphosis?

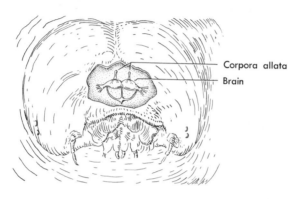

Corpora allata

Brain

Fig. 26-2

The corpora allata of the silkworm secrete juvenile hormone. The brain itself secretes a hormone that initiates growth and metamorphosis.

It has been found that if a tiny pair of glands located behind the brain, the **corpora allata** (Fig. 26-2), are removed from an immature silkworm, it spins a cocoon and undergoes pupation at its very next molt (Fig. 26-1). This raises the possibility that the corpora allata produce a third hormone which acts as a brake on metamorphosis. As long as substantial quantities of this hormone, which has been named the **juvenile hormone,** are present, ecdyson promotes larval growth. When the amount of juvenile hormone is reduced, ecdyson promotes development of the pupa. Complete absence of the juvenile hormone leads to development of the adult.

This hypothesis can be tested nicely. If the corpora allata of a young silkworm are introduced into the body of a fully mature larva, metamorphosis does not occur. Molting simply results in the production of an extra-large caterpillar (Fig. 26-1). Corpora allata from a *mature* caterpillar have no such effect. Thus normal pupation seems to occur when the output of the corpora allata diminishes spontaneously in the mature caterpillar.

The development of the characteristic structures of the larva, then the pupa, and finally the adult must require the sequential participation of different sets of genes within the cells of the insect. This raises once again the question of how genes can be selectively activated or repressed. You remember (see Section 23-8, 2) that the giant chromosomes of certain flies (such as the fruit fly) have enlarged regions or "puffs" which occur at different places on the chromosomes during the course of development (Fig. 23-10). For example, each time a larva prepares to molt, a definite sequence of puffing occurs in its chromosomes. If ecdyson is administered to a larva shortly *after* it has completed a molt (a time when its own level of ecdyson is very low), the normal pre-molt sequence of puffing begins again. It is in these puffs that vigorous RNA synthesis occurs and, accordingly, it is the genes in the puffed regions of the chromosomes that are active. In fact, a messenger RNA has been extracted from these ecdyson-treated chromosomes that serves as the template for the synthesis of a specific enzyme not found in the cells of untreated larvae.

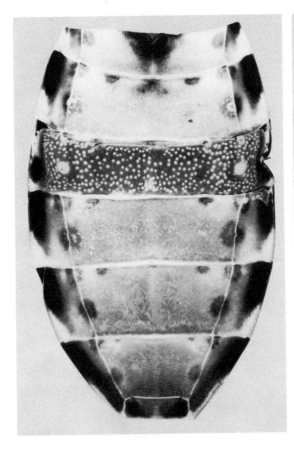

Wigglesworth's experiment. Left: Application of a band of juvenile hormone to the cuticle of an adult *Rhodnius* results in the formation of larval cuticle when the insect is forced to undergo an extra molt. Right: The experimenter has printed his initials with juvenile hormone. (Courtesy Dr. Wigglesworth.)

Fig. 26-3

The production of puffs following the injection of ecdyson is completely blocked by the simultaneous administration of actinomycin D. As you learned in the last chapter (see Section 25-6), actinomycin D blocks transcription of DNA, that is, the synthesis of messenger RNA. Here, then, is additional evidence that the hormone ecdyson acts by unlocking genetic information stored within the cell.

The response of the insect's cells to ecdyson is also influenced by juvenile hormone. As we have seen, ecdyson promotes a larva-to-larva molt when the level of juvenile hormone is high. When the level is diminished, the molt is larva-to-pupa. When juvenile hormone is absent, ecdyson promotes the development of the adult. It is as though the juvenile hormone has been repressing the genes for making adult structures. This role of juvenile hormone is beautifully illustrated by an experiment first performed by the English insect physiologist V. B. Wigglesworth. Adult insects do not normally molt, but if extra-normal amounts of brain hormone are administered to an adult "kissing bug" (*Rhodnius*), it can be forced to do so. If juvenile hormone is first applied to the insect's exoskeleton, the regions affected by it revert to larval type at this next molt (Fig. 26-3). This shows that the genes for the manufacture of larval structures are present in adult cells although normally their action is repressed.

In temperate climates, the pupal stage of many insects is formed in the fall (in response to the shorter days) and remains unchanged throughout the winter. Neither brain hormone nor ecdyson is produced during this period of **diapause.** When spring returns, so does the production of brain hormone and ecdyson. Metamorphosis is completed, and the adult emerges from its pupal case. In at least some insects, the resumption of brain hormone secretion does not occur unless the pupa has first been exposed to a period of cold temperatures and then to warmer temperatures and increasing length of day. Cells in the brain of the pupa of one species detect the light through a transparent area of the exoskeleton just above the brain. When the days become 16 hours long, diapause is ended and development and hatching of the adult are then completed. The phenomena of enforced dormancy, a cold requirement, and photoperiodism that we examined in the last chapter are not, then, restricted to plants.

The corpora allata of insects are too small to serve as a source from which juvenile hormone can be extracted. Fortunately, many insects begin to secrete juvenile hormone once again after they are fully adult. The hormone accumulates in relatively large quantities in the abdomen of the males of two species of silk moths. The amount accumulated is sufficiently great that it has been possible to extract the material and, after years of laborious work, to determine its chemical structure. The hormone has a relatively simple molecular structure, and we should eventually be able to synthesize substantial quantities of it or at least closely related substances. This is a particularly exciting possibility because at certain times in the life cycle of an insect, the presence of juvenile hormone leads to abnormal development and death. For example, when solutions containing juvenile hormone are sprayed on mature caterpillars, or on the foliage upon which they are feeding, normal pupation is prevented. The insect does not molt successfully into a giant larva either. Presumably this method of applying the hormone results in such an uneven distribution within the caterpillar's body that all the tissues do not respond alike. In any case, the animal soon dies. If insect eggs come in contact with even tiny traces of juvenile hormone, their normal embryonic development is upset. These phenomena have led to speculation that the juvenile hormone, if it could be synthesized cheaply and in large quantities, would make an effective insecticide. There would seem to be little chance that insects could develop resistance to a substance which is a normal constituent of their bodies. Nor does the juvenile hormone seem to have a toxic effect on other organisms (unlike such conventional insecticides as lead arsenate and DDT). On the other hand, many insects (e.g. honeybee) are beneficial to man and the use of a juvenile hormone as an insecticide might in some situations cause more problems than it cured. However, there do seem to be slight molecular differences in the juvenile hormones of different groups of insects, and different synthetic juvenile hormones show some selectivity in their action. Perhaps these differences can some day be exploited in man's unceasing warfare with the insects that destroy his crops and transmit diseases.

26-3   RESEARCH TECHNIQUES IN ENDOCRINOLOGY

The experiments which have led to our knowledge of hormonal control in insect metamorphosis provide an excellent illustration of the methods used in the study of endocrinology. The basic technique is simply this. First, an organ suspected of having an endocrine function is surgically removed from the animal's body. Second, a close observation is made of any changes or symptoms which may then occur. Third, the suspected gland is reintroduced into the animal's body to see if its presence will reverse these symptoms. If it does, the next step is to attempt to prepare an active extract (a mixture) that will duplicate the action of the missing gland. Although the extract is usually made from the gland itself, a few hormones have been extracted from such sources as urine. (The blood seldom contains enough hormone to serve as a source of supply.) Finally, an attempt is made to purify the extract and determine what single chemical substance within it produces the reversal of symptoms. This substance is the hormone.

These techniques have also been used successfully in the study of human endocrinology. Fortunately, many of the hormones found in humans are also found in the other vertebrates, so that the more drastic experimental studies can be performed on some other animal—frequently a dog or laboratory rat—with high hopes that the findings will be applicable to man. That vertebrates share many of the same hormones is also of great importance in the treatment of human endocrine disorders. Many hormones are too complex to be manufactured synthetically. They can, however, be extracted from the glands of slaughtered cattle, pigs, etc., and used in the treatment of human ailments.

The fact that vertebrates have many hormones in common does not mean that in every case they use them in the same way. As we take up the study of the hormones found in humans, we will find some which have different functions in other vertebrates.

HUMAN ENDOCRINOLOGY

THE THYROID GLAND　　　　　　　　**26-4**

The thyroid gland is a double-lobed structure located in the neck (Fig. 26-4). For its size, it has an extraordinarily rich blood supply. The most important hormone that it releases into the blood is the iodine-containing amino acid *thyroxin*. This substance has been isolated from thyroid tissue and is easily synthesized commercially. Injections of it counteract the symptoms produced when the thyroid gland is removed from experimental animals.

In humans, the most obvious function of the thyroid gland is the control of the rate of body metabolism. When thyroxin is administered, the amount of heat produced by the body is increased. Because energy production is a function of cellular respiration, we might expect the administration of thyroxin to increase the rate of oxygen consumption. Such is the case. In fact, measurements of oxygen consumption are used to diagnose malfunctioning of the thyroid gland.

In addition to its effect on body metabolism, the thyroid gland has effects on a large number of other body functions. Among these is its potent stimulating effect on protein synthesis. In fact, there is good evidence that the influence of thyroxin on protein synthesis may underlie many (not all) of its other functions. Within minutes after it is administered to a laboratory rat, thyroxin produces a sharp rise in the synthesis of messenger RNA and, shortly thereafter, protein. Furthermore, this effect is completely inhibited by actinomycin D. This indicates that thyroxin is acting on the translation of the genetic code, that is, it is stimulating gene action. The effect of thyroxin on certain other functions, such as oxygen consumption and growth, is also inhibited by actinomycin D.

Fig. 26-4 The endocrine glands of the human. They are the same in both sexes except for the gonads, which in the female are ovaries (color) and in the male are testes.

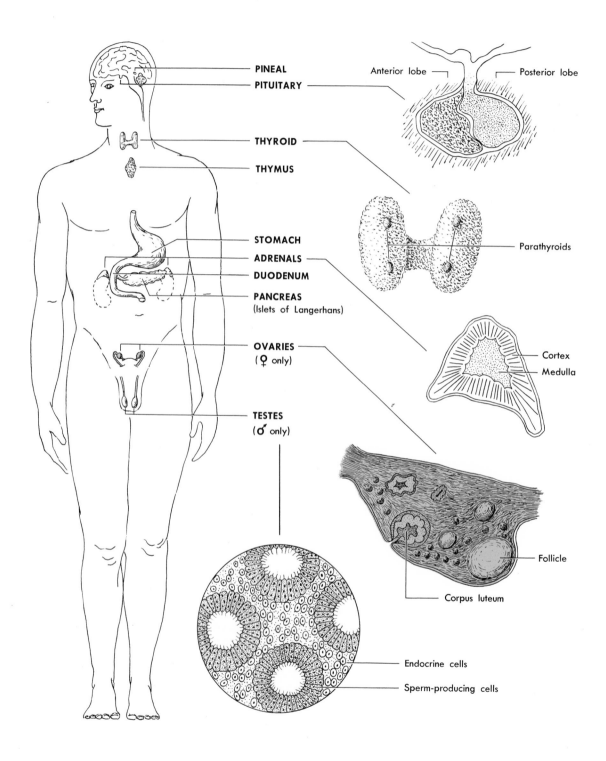

PINEAL

PITUITARY

Anterior lobe

Posterior lobe

THYROID

THYMUS

Parathyroids

STOMACH

ADRENALS

DUODENUM

PANCREAS
(Islets of Langerhans)

OVARIES
(♀ only)

Cortex

Medulla

TESTES
(♂ only)

Follicle

Corpus luteum

Endocrine cells

Sperm-producing cells

The axolotl, a salamander that reaches sexual maturity without undergoing metamorphosis into an air-breathing form. Note the external gills. (Courtesy New York Zoological Society.)

Fig. 26-5

Most of the effects of thyroxin are duplicated in all the vertebrate animals. However, a special function of the thyroid gland is found in amphibians. Their metamorphosis from the larval to the adult stage is triggered by thyroxin. If thyroxin (or even iodine) is administered to a small tadpole, it will undergo premature metamorphosis into a midget frog. On the other hand, surgical removal of the thyroid gland of a tadpole prevents metamorphosis.

Some races of the common tiger salamander never undergo metamorphosis from the gill-breathing larval stage to the air-breathing terrestrial form. (They reach sexual maturity and reproduce as larvae.) However, administration of thyroxin to these animals causes them to carry out metamorphosis into typical tiger salamanders. It is perhaps no accident that these so-called *axolotl* forms are found in mountain lakes in the western part of our country and in northern Mexico, where very little iodine is found in the soil and water (Fig. 26-5).

Several human diseases are associated with the improper functioning of the thyroid gland. In considering these ailments, it is important to distinguish between those associated with excessive production of the hormone (*hyperthyroidism*) and those associated with insufficient hormone production (*hypothyroidism*).

Hypothyroidism before maturity results in the disease cretinism. The victim fails to attain either normal physical or mental development. The cause of the disease is not clear. Although it is most prevalent in areas where insufficient iodine is present in the diet, other factors are probably involved, too. In any case, all symptoms can be prevented by the early and regular administration of thyroxin. If treatment is delayed until after the symptoms have become severe, only minor improvement can be secured.

Hypothyroidism in adults causes myxedema. The symptoms of this disease are a low metabolic rate, over-weight, and a coarsening of the features. Like cretinism, it is most prevalent in iodine-deficient areas, but other causative factors are probably involved, too. It is cured by administration of thyroxin.

Iodine-deficient areas of the world (around the Great Lakes and the Pacific Northwest in the United States) are often called **goiter** belts. This expression is used because of the large number of people with simple goiter found in these regions. A goiter is a swelling of the neck caused by a swelling of the thyroid gland. Although there is still disagreement as to the cause of simple goiter, most of the facts point to inadequate amounts of iodine in the diet. Now that iodine-rich foods (e.g. marine fish) are shipped throughout the country and iodized table salt (NaCl with traces of KI added) is used so widely, simple goiter is no longer a serious health problem.

It might seem surprising that inadequate amounts of iodine would lead to an enlargement (and hence extra activity) of the thyroid gland. It is probably a matter of compensation. The rate of activity of the thyroid gland is itself governed by another hormone, TSH, which is liberated by the anterior lobe of the pituitary gland (Fig. 26-4). An increase in the production of TSH causes an increase in the amount of thyroxin. However, an increased amount of thyroxin in the bloodstream depresses the output of TSH. This nice homeostatic device thus insures a steady supply of thyroxin. When there is insufficient iodine in the diet for the thyroid to synthesize thyroxin, however, this control mechanism breaks down. The pituitary gland is not inhibited and thus produces ever-larger quantities of TSH. This, in turn, stimulates the thyroid gland to work harder even though it has little or no iodine to work with. Thus it becomes enlarged, and a goiter results.

26-5   **THE PARATHYROID GLANDS**

The parathyroid glands are four tiny structures imbedded in the rear surface of the thyroid glands (Fig. 26-4). This inconspicuous location accidentally led to the discovery of their importance. Early attempts at treating goiters by surgical removal of the thyroid gland sometimes led to unpleasant symptoms of muscle spasms and twitching in the patient. Eventually these symptoms were traced to a loss of the parathyroid glands and a resulting drop in the level of calcium ions (Ca^{++}) circulating in the blood. As we have learned, the calcium ion is one of the most important mineral constituents in the body. In addition to its role in bone formation, an adequate level of Ca^{++} in the ECF is necessary for proper functioning of the nervous and muscular systems. Too low a level of Ca^{++} in the ECF leads to the symptoms associated with removal of the parathyroids.

In 1960 a chemically pure hormone, the parathyroid hormone or PTH, was finally extracted from the parathyroid glands of cattle. It is a small protein (M.W. = 8500) containing 83 amino acid units. It produces the following effects: (1) It promotes the release of Ca^{++} from the bones. (2) It promotes the absorption of Ca^{++} from food in the intestine. (3) It promotes the reabsorption of Ca^{++} in the tubules of the kidneys. All of these actions result in an increase in the level of Ca^{++} circulating in the blood. (The hormone also inhibits the reabsorption of $PO_4^{\equiv}$ in the kidney tubules and thus helps rid the body of the excess $PO_4^{\equiv}$ produced when bone—calcium phosphate— is decomposed to provide Ca^{++}.)

The maintenance of a constant level of Ca^{++} in the ECF (homeostasis) requires that the activity of the parathyroids be under precise control. This control is quite direct.

The amount of PTH secreted by the glands is regulated by the level of Ca^{++} in the ECF. When the level of Ca^{++} drops, the glands are stimulated to release the hormone and thus restore the normal level of Ca^{++}. If the level should rise above normal, the hormone output of the gland is depressed. Here, then, is another nicely adjusted mechanism by which the constancy of the internal environment is maintained.

In 1961 it was discovered that the response of the parathyroids to excess Ca^{++} (the response being a subsequent reduction in Ca^{++}) is much faster than could occur simply by shutting off the production of PTH. This has led to the discovery of another hormone (named thyrocalcitonin) that acts antagonistically to PTH. This second hormone (probably released by the *thyroid*) provides an additional control mechanism over the Ca^{++} level in the ECF. If, for example, the Ca^{++} level of the ECF drops below normal limits, the parathyroids will be stimulated to release PTH. This is a rather slow response, however, and there is a possibility that the system might overshoot and the Ca^{++} concentration reach too high a level. Of course, depression of the glands would eventually correct this, but it might be some time before fluctuations in the Ca^{++} level were "damped out." However, release of fast-acting thyrocalcitonin prevents this overshoot and restores a steady Ca^{++} level more quickly.

Humans rarely suffer from hypoparathyroidism. Most cases in the past have resulted from accidental or unavoidable removal of the parathyroids during thyroid surgery. The unpleasant (and occasionally fatal) symptoms of parathyroid deficiency can be successfully avoided by careful addition of Ca^{++} to the patient's diet. Vitamin D, which duplicates many of the functions of the parathyroid hormone, is also used successfully in treating this disease.

Occasionally one or more of the parathyroid glands becomes enlarged and extra-active. The *hyper*parathyroidism that results produces severe symptoms. The bones become brittle, weakened, and deformed. They break under the slightest stress. The great excess of Ca^{++} in the blood causes some to pass over into the urine where it may precipitate with phosphate ions and form kidney stones. These are dangerous because they occasionally block the urinary ducts. Surgical removal of the diseased glands usually brings about marked improvement.

THE STOMACH AND DUODENUM 26-6

There are cells in the walls of both the stomach and duodenum that display hormonal activity. As we saw in Chapter 10, the hormones produced in these cells stimulate a number of digestive processes. **Gastrin,** secreted into the blood by cells in the stomach wall, stimulates the production of hydrochloric acid by the exocrine glands of the stomach. **Secretin** and **pancreozymin** are secreted into the blood by cells in the duodenum. When these hormones reach the pancreas, they stimulate the secretion of the various components of the pancreatic digestive fluid. Secretin also stimulates the liver to secrete bile. Another duodenal hormone, **cholecystokinin** (CCK), stimulates the gall bladder to contract and force its accumulation of bile into the duodenum.

THE ISLETS OF LANGERHANS 26-7

The islets of Langerhans are small clusters of cells scattered throughout the pancreas in most vertebrates. There are well over a million of these clusters in the human pancreas. The cells of the islets of Langerhans are not connected to the ducts which drain pancreatic juice into the duodenum. They are, however, richly supplied with blood vessels.

As has so often been the case in science, the discovery that the islets of Langerhans are endocrine glands grew out of a chance observation. In 1889, the German physicians von Mering and Minkowski tried to learn more about the digestive functions of the pancreas by observing what digestive upsets occurred after surgically removing the organ from dogs. During the course of their studies, a laboratory assistant noticed many flies collected near the dog's urine. The urine was found to contain a large amount of the sugar glucose. The urine of normal dogs does not.

For many years, all attempts to extract a glucose-regulating hormone from the pancreas failed. However, in 1922 Dr. Frederick Banting finally succeeded in this venture. The hormone, named **insulin,** was found to be a protein. Can you see now why so many workers had failed to extract it from crude preparations of the entire pancreas? Banting succeeded where others had failed by first tying off the pancreatic ducts of his dogs. This operation caused the exocrine portion of the gland to degenerate rather quickly while the endocrine portion remained active. After the exocrine portion was destroyed, extracts could be made free from the digestive action of trypsin.

Insulin acts to lower the level of glucose in the bloodstream. Normally, 100 ml of blood contains about 0.1 gm of glucose. After a carbohydrate-rich meal, this level tends to rise. As it does so, it triggers the release of insulin from the islets of Langerhans. The insulin passes immediately to the liver (through the hepatic portal veins), where it speeds up the conversion of glucose into glycogen and fats. As a result, the blood-sugar level is quickly brought back to normal.

One of the effects of insulin is to make the cells of the body more permeable to the entrance of glucose. Once within cells, the glucose can then be metabolized. This effect is not inhibited by actinomycin D. However, insulin also stimulates the synthesis of proteins, including enzymes that participate in carbohydrate metabolism. This action does seem to involve the selective unlocking of genes. Within a few minutes after insulin is administered to isolated rat diaphragm muscle, there is a substantial rise in newly synthesized messenger RNA. Both this effect and the effect of insulin on enzyme synthesis are blocked by actinomycin D. Once again, therefore, we find a hormone that exerts at least some of its effects through the derepression of genes.

Insufficient production of insulin results in the disease **diabetes mellitus.** Victims of this disease are unable to cope with excess glucose in the blood by converting it to glycogen or fats. Worse still, the reverse reactions are promoted. Glycogen and body fats are converted into glucose which raises the blood sugar level further. The kidney tubules fail to reclaim much of this excess glucose and so it passes out in the urine. Even body proteins are converted into glucose and then excreted. The high glucose level in the nephric filtrate exerts a powerful osmotic effect, sharply reducing the transport of water back into the blood. Consequently, victims of the disease urinate frequently and copiously. Unless corrective measures are taken, the victim wastes away, his body gradually being converted into a flood of sugary urine. Coma and death eventually follow.

Fortunately, insulin is now available in large quantities from the glands of slaughtered livestock. The molecular structure of these animal insulins is so close to that of human insulin that they may be used to treat diabetes. Unfortunately, insulin must be given by injection rather than by mouth. (Why?) Despite this inconvenience, administration of insulin to a diabetic quickly restores normal sugar metabolism in the body. Of course, insulin injections are no cure. They simply provide temporary relief from the symptoms. Nevertheless, careful attention to diet and periodic injections of insulin have enabled thousands of diabetics to lead active useful lives. In recent years at least two nationally ranked U.S. tennis players have been diabetics.

The use of insulin is not without some danger. Insulin injected after a period of exercise or long after a meal may drive the blood sugar level down to abnormally low levels. This can result in an "insulin reaction." The victim becomes irritable, fatigued, and may lose consciousness. It is quite important that those associated with diabetics learn to distinguish between the symptoms of insulin reaction and diabetic coma so that they can take proper measures if either crisis should occur.

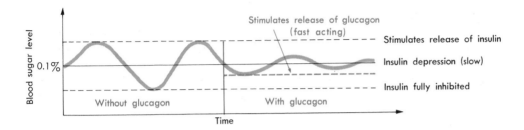

Effect of glucagon on the homeostatic control of blood sugar. Its quick release and fast action help to prevent fluctuation of the glucose level in the blood.

Fig. 26-6

Injection of commercial insulin preparations usually causes a brief rise in blood sugar before the longer-lasting fall. This has been found to be caused by a second pancreatic hormone, **glucagon,** which *stimulates* the conversion of liver glycogen into glucose. In the normal organism, glucagon may act to prevent insulin from lowering the blood-sugar level excessively. Its quick release and quick action dampens the tendency of the slower-responding insulin to overshoot in *its* action (Fig. 26-6). It thus plays an important role in establishing a constant level of glucose in the blood. This homeostatic role resembles that of thyrocalcitonin (see Section 26-5).

THE PITUITARY GLAND 26-8

The pituitary gland is a pea-sized structure located at the base of the brain (Fig. 26-4). In most vertebrates, it consists of three lobes: anterior, intermediate, and posterior. An intermediate lobe is present in the pituitary gland of human infants, but only a vestige remains in adulthood.

Although small in size, the pituitary plays a vital role in the chemical coordination of the body. It is often called the "master" gland because many of its secretions control the activity of other endocrine glands. Can you think of an example of this that you have already studied?

The Anterior Lobe

An extraordinary amount of research has been conducted on the pituitary gland. At least seven chemically distinct hormones have been isolated from the anterior lobe alone. These are:

1) **Human growth hormone (HGH).** This hormone, as its name implies, promotes growth of the skeleton and the body as a whole.

It is normally active in this respect only during the years of childhood and adolescence. A hyposecretion of HGH in the child results in stunted growth or dwarfism. A hypersecretion during the same period results in giantism (Fig. 26-7).

Some HGH is normally secreted throughout adult life, especially during periods of exercise or other stress. What function it serves at these times has been the subject of intensive research. One of its effects is an increase in the rate of protein synthesis. At this point, you should not be surprised to learn that this effect is inhibited by actinomycin D and is therefore dependent upon the synthesis of RNA, including messenger RNA. HGH must thus be added to the growing list of hormones—plant as well as animal—that regulate body activities through their action on the genetic code.

HGH has been shown to have a further function in adults: the stimulation of milk production in women after childbirth. In this it resembles the action of the next hormone to be discussed and, in humans, may be very similar or even identical to it.

Fig. 26-7

A giant and a dwarf with a man of average height. The amount of growth hormone produced during childhood and adolescence accounts for these differences.

2) Lactogenic hormone (LTH). Although it may not be true in man, in other mammals that have been studied the lactogenic hormone is a distinctly different substance from the growth hormone. It is produced by females following childbirth and stimulates the secretion of milk from their mammary glands.

LTH has even been found in nonmammalian vertebrates. It does not, of course, stimulate milk production in these animals, but instead some kind of maternal activity appropriate to the particular species. In some birds, for example, LTH stimulates broodiness, that is, an inclination to sit on the nest. In one species of newt, it stimulates the animals to return to the water to lay and fertilize their eggs.

3) Thyroid-stimulating hormone (TSH). This hormone stimulates the thyroid gland to secrete thyroxin. This effect probably depends upon first derepressing genes within the nuclei of thyroid cells. When TSH is administered to nuclei that have been isolated from thyroid cells, there is a quick increase in RNA (probably messenger) synthesis. This effect is completely inhibited by actinomycin D.

The secretion of TSH is depressed by thyroxin; thus there exists a homeostatic control mechanism over the level of thyroxin in the blood. Even the "master" gland has its controls! As we saw in Section 26-4, this mechanism can break down, producing a hypersecretion of TSH that results in goiter.

4) **Adrenocorticotropic hormone (ACTH).** ACTH is a polypeptide containing 39 amino acids. Its main function is to stimulate the cortex of the adrenal gland to release some of *its* hormones into the bloodstream. The vital role that these adrenal hormones play in human physiology will be considered in the next section.

5) **Follicle-stimulating hormone (FSH).** FSH acts upon the gonads or sex organs. In females, FSH promotes the development of follicles within the ovary (see Section 22-6). In conjunction with another pituitary hormone, LH, it stimulates the secretion of **estrogens** by the follicle and the ripening of the egg within it.

FSH is produced in human males, too. In them it stimulates the development of the seminiferous tubules and the production of sperm (see Section 22-5).

6) **Luteinizing hormone (LH).** As a human egg matures, it completes its first meiotic division and reaches metaphase of the second division (see Section 22-1). Then it breaks out of the follicle (ovulation) and is ready for fertilization by a sperm cell. The remaining cells of the follicle become transformed into the *corpus luteum* (see Section 22-6). Every one of these activities is triggered by LH. In some mammals (probably including humans), LH then stimulates the corpus luteum to secrete *its* hormone, progesterone.

LH is also found in human males. It acts upon the endocrine cells in the testes (the interstitial cells—see Section 22-5) causing them to release male sex hormones (androgens) into the bloodstream.

7) **Melanocyte-stimulating hormone (MSH).** MSH is a small polypeptide whose sequence of amino acids shows it to be closely related to ACTH. Its "target" cells are the melanocytes, cells which contain the black pigment melanin. Large numbers of them are present in the skin, where they are responsible for moles, freckles, and suntan. Although MSH does not seem to play an important role in the normal behavior of human melanocytes, under certain conditions, such as pregnancy, an increase in its secretion does cause some darkening of the body.

In most vertebrates MSH is produced in an intermediate lobe of the pituitary gland. Its secretion causes a dramatic darkening of the skin of many fishes, amphibians, and reptiles. The darkening occurs because of the spread of granules of melanin through the branches of specialized melanocytes in the epidermis. Figure 26-8 shows these cells (called melanophores) in the skin of a frog. When the melanin is concentrated in the center of the melanophores, the skin has a light appearance. When the melanin is dispersed throughout the branches, the skin becomes much darker. This mechanism is undoubtedly of value in enabling the animal to blend in with its surroundings.

When biologists wish to study the development of frog eggs "out of season," they initiate production of the eggs by injecting female frogs with pituitary extract. (Why?) Within minutes after the extract is injected into a frog, marked darkening of the skin occurs. This is caused by the MSH which is also present in the extract.

The Posterior Lobe

The posterior lobe of the pituitary is probably not a true endocrine gland at all. Instead of manufacturing hormones of its own, it seems simply to store those produced by nerve cells in the hypothalamus of the brain.

Two hormones have been isolated from the posterior lobe of the pituitary. **Oxytocin** is a polypeptide which stimulates contraction of smooth muscle, particularly the smooth muscle lining the uterus ("womb") of women. Its secretion initiates "labor" in women when the baby is ready to be born. Injections of this hormone

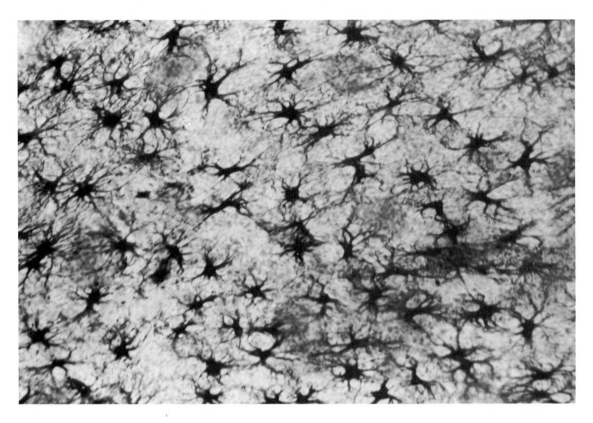

Fig. 26-8   Melanophores in the skin of a frog. The pigment melanin is dispersed throughout the branches of the cells, thus darkening the skin. The general term for any pigment-containing cell is *chromatophore*.

are sometimes given at this time to hasten delivery of the baby and to hasten the return of the uterus to its normal size. The new mother also secretes her own oxytocin, especially if she nurses her baby.

Vasopressin, a second polypeptide produced by the posterior lobe, has two functions in man. It causes the muscular walls of the arteries and arterioles to contract. This constricts the bore of these vessels and causes an increase in blood pressure. Vasopressin also stimulates the reabsorption of water from the tubules of the kidneys. As we mentioned when discussing kidney function (see Section 16-6), insufficient production of vasopressin causes an enormous loss of water through the kidneys. This ailment is called diabetes insipidus. The name is derived from an early diagnostic test for the disease. The copious urine produced by hyposecretion of vasopressin is very watery and has no marked taste (insipidus). The urine produced by victims of insulin deficiency, however, contains a large amount of glucose and thus has a sweet (mellitus) taste.

Both the structure and the function of the pituitary gland indicate that it serves as a vital connecting link between the nervous system and the endocrine system. The pituitary is located at the base of the brain and the posterior lobe has a direct nerve connection to the hypothalamus of the brain. The anterior lobe receives blood from the hypothalamus and there is evidence that stimulating substances pass from the hypothalamus to the anterior lobe by this route. Pituitary secretion can often be traced to the influence of nervous stimulation. Release of vasopressin from the posterior lobe occurs when special cells in the hypothalamus detect a lowering of the water content of the blood. Release of ACTH from the anterior lobe has been shown to be partly influenced by nervous activity in the hypothalamus and is often associated with emotional states such as anger and fear. In birds, visual stimuli such as increasing length of daylight or frequent sight of a member of the opposite sex have been shown to result in an outpouring of the gonad-stimulating hormones into the bloodstream.

THE ADRENAL GLANDS   26-9

The adrenal glands are two small structures situated one atop each kidney (Fig. 26-4). They are richly supplied with blood. Both in anatomy and in function, they consist of two distinct regions. The exterior portion is the adrenal **cortex.** The interior portion of the gland is the adrenal **medulla.**

The Adrenal Medulla

Although a true endocrine gland, the adrenal medulla is also considered to be a part of the nervous system. Its secretory cells seem to be modified nerve cells. It releases two hormones which pass into the bloodstream. The better-known of these is adrenaline. It is not yet clear what role, if any, adrenaline plays in the normal metabolism of the body. However, large quantities of this hormone are released into the bloodstream when the organism is suddenly subjected to stress such as anger, fright, or injury. As adrenaline spreads throughout the body, it promotes a wide variety of responses. The rate and strength of the heartbeat is increased, thus increasing blood pressure. A large part of the blood supply of the skin and viscera is shunted to the skeletal muscles, coronary arteries, liver, and brain. The level of blood sugar rises and the metabolic rate increases. The bronchi dilate, permitting easier passage of air to and from the lungs. The pupils of the eye dilate and there is a tendency for the body hair to stand erect. (This is particularly obvious in angered cats and dogs. Man, who is comparatively hairless, displays "gooseflesh" instead.) The clotting time of the blood is reduced, and the anterior lobe of the pituitary is stimulated to produce ACTH.

The second hormone of the adrenal medulla, noradrenaline, also causes an increase in blood pressure. It accomplishes this by stimulating the contraction of the arterioles.

Almost all of the body's responses to these two hormones can be seen to prepare the body for violent physical action. We have all heard accounts of heroic deeds accomplished in times of danger or other emergency. The secretion of adrenaline and noradrenaline by the adrenal medulla is an important mechanism for making such action possible.

The Adrenal Cortex

Several different hormones have been extracted from this gland. All of them are steroids (see Section 7-2). They are quite similar in molecular structure and seem to be freely converted from one to another by enzyme action. They fall into three categories.

1) The glucocorticoids. In man, the most important members of this group are **cortisone** and the closely-related **hydrocortisone.** These hormones promote the conversion of fat and protein into intermediary metabolites that are ultimately converted into glucose. Thus they cause the level of blood sugar to rise. One of the chief target organs in this response is the liver. If cortisone is administered to an animal whose own adrenal glands have been removed, it induces in the liver the synthesis of a number of specific enzymes involved in protein and carbohydrate metabolism. This induction is preceded by an increase in messenger RNA synthesis. Both of these responses are completely blocked if actinomycin D is administered before the cortisone. This effect of cortisone is, then, one that depends upon the activation of specific genes.

The glucocorticoids also act to suppress antibody formation. It is interesting to note that when cortisone is administered to white blood corpuscles (some of which are responsible for antibody-formation—see Section 14-12), *their* synthesis of RNA is almost completely *inhibited* within a minute or two. In these cells, cortisone is a repressor (or corepressor?—see Fig. 23-9) of gene action.

The glucocorticoids also act to suppress inflammation in the body. Cortisone has found widespread medical use in the treatment of inflammatory diseases ranging from arthritis to poison-ivy poisoning.

The glucocorticoid hormones are needed to maintain the body during periods of stress after the first brief, adrenaline-triggered response has worn off. This second, longer-lasting response seems to be quite independent of the nature of the stress. Exposure to extremes of temperature, poisoning, severe bodily injury, infection, even emotional turmoil all trigger a definite sequence of responses. The endocrinologist Hans Selye calls these responses the General Adaptation Syndrome. After the initial response to adrenaline, the body goes into a stage of "shock." The levels of glucose and salt in the blood drop sharply. Blood pressure is also reduced. Then, the adrenal cortex begins to pour glucocorticoids into the bloodstream in response to the increased secretion of ACTH by the pituitary gland. The release of ACTH is itself triggered by (1) the emotional state of the subject, (2) the lowered level of steroids in the blood, and (3) the adrenaline released by the adrenal medulla. During this phase of "countershock," the symptoms of the "shock" phase are reversed. The various body functions return to normal or even above-normal activity. The organism then enters a stage of resistance. It has become adapted to the stress.

2) The mineralocorticoids. The chief function of these hormones, of which **aldosterone** is the most important in man, is to promote the reabsorption of Na^+ and Cl^- ions in the tubules of the kidneys. Not only are these ions valuable for their own sake, but their retention in the blood keeps its osmotic pressure high. This, in turn, assures normal blood volume and pressure (see Section 14-16).

The rate of aldosterone secretion is controlled by a number of factors including ACTH and the level of Na^+ ions in the blood. A decrease in blood sodium stimulates increased aldosterone secretion and thus increased reabsorption of sodium ions in the tubules. An increase in blood sodium inhibits the release of aldosterone and thus releases more sodium in the urine. Thus the level of this important component of the ECF is under precise homeostatic control.

Mineralocorticoid hormones are found in other vertebrates, too. In every case, they also function in the control of salt and water balance in the animal. The exact action varies, however, according to the environment of the organism. In the fresh-water fishes, they act to retain salts but release water. This action is just reversed in the marine fishes, with the hormones promoting the excretion of salt by the gills and the reabsorption of water by the kidneys. The active excretion of salt by the nasal glands of marine birds and reptiles is also stimulated by them. (See Section 9-4.)

The active transport of Na^+ ions has been intensively studied in the bladder cells of the toad. It has been demonstrated that the phenomenon depends upon the induction, by aldosterone, of enzyme synthesis in the cytoplasm of these cells. However, when aldosterone is administered to the cells, it moves into the nucleus. Only after about an hour is the transport of Na^+ ions increased. The response to aldosterone is inhibited by actinomycin D, and this supports the idea that the primary effect of the hormone is on the genetic code.

3) Sex hormones. The adrenal cortex also produces a small quantity of sex hormones, especially **androgens,** the male sex hormones. A hypersecretion of these hormones promotes the development of masculine traits. The masculinization seen in some women (facial hair, deep voice, angular body contours) can frequently be traced to excessive secretion of androgens by the adrenal cortex.

Although the sex hormones secreted by the adrenal cortex seem to have no important function to carry out, the glucocorticoids and mineralocorticoids are essential to life. Under laboratory conditions, some animals can survive for about two weeks when their adrenal glands have been surgically removed, but they must be protected from stress. The slightest stress of any kind causes a sudden drop in the sugar and salt levels of the blood, and death follows quickly. Humans cannot survive even under the best conditions without their adrenal cortices. If absolutely no cortical steroids are present, death comes in a few days. A hyposecretion of these hormones results in Addison's disease. The symptoms are lowered blood pressure, loss of appetite, muscular weakness, and general apathy. Unless corrective measures are taken, death follows after about two years. Fortunately, administration of synthetic cortical steroids and/or ACTH can today restore the patient to a relatively normal life.

THE GONADS   26-10

Both the male and female gonads (Fig. 26-4) possess endocrine activity in addition to their prime function of producing the sex cells.

The Testes

The testes of males contain endocrine tissue, the interstitial cells. When stimulated by the anterior pituitary hormone LH, these cells release androgens (e.g. **testosterone**) into the bloodstream. This action commences at the start of adolescence. Testosterone triggers the development of the so-called secondary sexual characteristics found in adult males. The voice deepens. Hair begins to grow on the face, in the armpits, and around the genital organs. These organs become enlarged. The body takes on the general angular contours typical of adult males. The formation of fat deposits is inhibited.

Removal of the testes (castration) before this period prevents the development of the secondary sexual characteristics. Until close to the end of the nineteenth century, this operation was occasionally performed on Italian boys. The object was to preserve their soprano voices for church choirs. Castration has also been practiced in certain Near Eastern countries to provide guards for the royal harem. Castrated adults are called eunuchs. The response of adult males to castration varies, but generally there is only a moderate loss of masculine traits. Castration is frequently used in animal husbandry to provide animals with better meat quality and/or easier temperament. Geldings are castrated horses. Capons are castrated fowl. Male sheep and cattle are also regularly castrated.

Studies using immature or castrated laboratory animals have shown clearly that at the cellular level, testosterone causes a substantial increase in the synthesis of messenger RNA and protein. These effects are blocked by actinomycin D. Interestingly enough, when testosterone is administered to the cells of *female* rats, not only is the amount of messenger RNA synthesis increased but new *kinds* of messenger RNA molecules are synthesized. *Which* genes in a cell will be activated thus must depend not only on the nature of the inducing molecule but also on the state of differentiation of that cell, in this case, whether it is male or female.

The Ovaries

The ripening follicle in the ovary not only contains a ripening egg but also acts as an endocrine gland. The accessory cells of the follicle liberate several steroid hormones called **estrogens.** They are stimulated to do so by the combined influence of FSH and LH from the anterior lobe of the pituitary gland.

The estrogens have two major functions in the female body. First, they promote the development of the secondary female sexual characteristics. At the start of adolescence, the mammary glands (breasts) develop, the pelvis becomes broader, the genital organs enlarge, and hair develops around them and in the armpits. The estrogens are responsible for these changes. They also promote the development of fat deposits and these lead to the more rounded body contours characteristic of adult women.

The estrogens continue to be secreted throughout the reproductive years of women. During this period they participate in the monthly preparations of the body for possible pregnancy. This includes the preparation of the inner lining of the uterus to receive an embryo. The lining becomes thicker and more richly supplied with blood. In response to estrogens, its cells become very active, first in messenger and transfer RNA synthesis, then in ribosomal RNA synthesis, and finally in protein synthesis. All of these responses are blocked by actinomycin D, so they depend on the activation of genes. Each kind of messenger RNA, each kind of transfer RNA, and the two kinds of ribosomal RNA are coded by separate genes. In some way, estrogens are able to activate these genes with the result that all the proteins necessary for the development of the cell are produced.

The secretion of estrogens is stimulated by FSH and LH. The estrogens, in turn, act back on the pituitary to suppress the secretion of FSH and LH. This interaction (similar to that between TSH and thyroxin) serves to coordinate estrogen production with the needs of the monthly sex cycle.

At the end of a woman's reproductive years (the menopause), the production of eggs and estrogens ceases. Disappearance of the estrogens removes their brake on the pituitary, and large quantities of FSH are liberated into the bloodstream. The control mechanism has broken down. The elevated level of FSH causes a variety of unpleasant physical and emotional symptoms. Many doctors now administer estrogens at this time, in order to reimpose a brake on FSH secretion by the pituitary and thus relieve the symptoms.

The corpus luteum is also an endocrine gland. It secretes **progesterone** into the bloodstream. This hormone continues the preparation of the body for pregnancy and, if pregnancy does occur, prevents the premature birth of the developing young. The details of this action were considered in Section 22-6. **Relaxin,** which is produced just before birth and makes a more flexible passageway for the exit of the baby (see Section 22-7), is also secreted by the ovaries.

THE PLACENTA   26-11

Nourishment of the human embryo while within its mother's uterus is accomplished through the umbilical cord and placenta which connect the embryo indirectly to the mother's circulatory system (Fig. 22-11). After pregnancy is well established, the placenta takes on the secondary function of serving as an endocrine gland. It secretes estrogens, progesterone, relaxin, and another hormone quite similar to the gonad-stimulating hormones of the anterior lobe of the pituitary. These hormones supplement those produced by the corpus luteum and the pituitary gland.

THE PINEAL GLAND   26-12

The pineal gland is a small, pea-sized structure attached to the brain just above the cerebellum (Fig. 26-4). It produces a hormone called **melatonin.** When this hormone is injected into frogs, it causes a marked lightening of the skin. Its action on the melanophores (Fig. 26-8) is thus just the reverse of that of MSH. In the laboratory rat and the hamster, melatonin inhibits the gonads both as gamete producers and as endocrine organs. The secretion of melatonin in these animals is markedly increased when they are placed in the dark and decreased when they are exposed to light. Many mammals have inactive gonads during the winter. With the lengthening days of spring, their gonads become active once again and mating follows. Perhaps the pineal gland, through its secretion of melatonin, serves as a connecting link between the eyes and the gonads in this **photoperiodic** response. As for humans, its normal role is still uncertain.

THE THYMUS GLAND   26-13

The thymus gland consists of two lobes of tissue similar to that found in lymph nodes. It is located high in the chest cavity just under the breastbone (Fig. 26-4). It enlarges during childhood but then shrinks after the start of adolescence. Many techniques, including surgical removal, have been employed in attempts to find an endocrine function of the thymus, but none has been found in adult mammals. However, there is good evidence that the thymus in the infant mammal plays a major role in setting up the lymphocyte-producing machinery of the lymph nodes, thus providing the basis for the development of antibodies. (See Section 14-12.) This seems to involve, among other things, the release of a hormone (as yet unidentified) into the bloodstream. Once the job is completed, the thymus is ordinarily no longer needed.

HORMONES AND HOMEOSTASIS   26-14

Our study of the human endocrine system reveals what a variety of important roles are accomplished by chemical coordination. Most (but not all) of these chemical controls act in a rather slow, generalized way. Growth, sexual development, and metabolism are three body processes under hormonal controls that act gradually over a span of time.

The endocrine system also plays a major role in the maintenance of a constant internal environment. The concentration of sugar, water, and various salt ions in the ECF is maintained within narrow limits by hormonal action. There are at least three controlling mechanisms by which hormones maintain homeostasis in the body.

1) The secretion of some hormones is directly controlled by the need for that hormone. A high level of Ca^{++} in the blood suppresses the output of PTH. A low level of Ca^{++} stimulates it. The level of sugar in the blood acts directly on the islets of Langerhans, promoting the appropriate response from them. The osmotic pressure of the blood triggers (with the aid of the nervous system) the production of vasopressin and thus its own readjustment.

2) In some cases, the response of a gland to the level of the substance it regulates is apt to be slow. The resulting lag in response may cause undesirable fluctuations above and below the desired level. This situation may be improved by a second hormone acting antagonistically to the first. The antagonistic action of such pairs of hormones as insulin-glucagon and PTH-thyrocalcitonin provides a system of checks and balances for reestablishing homeostatic equilibrium quickly after any displacement.

3) A third system for achieving self-regulation of hormone production is illustrated by the relationship between TSH and thyroxin. Whenever one hormone stimulates the production of a second, we find that the second hormone acts, in turn, to suppress the production of the first. Another example of this is the way in which high levels of estrogens keep the production of FSH in check. Here again is a self-contained control system (analogous to the action of a governor on an engine) for maintaining homeostasis.

All the human hormones we have studied in this chapter are transported by the bloodstream. They are thus carried from the endocrine gland which produces them to every cell of the body. In some cases (e.g. thyroxin), every cell of the body responds to the presence of the hormone. More often, only certain cells, those in the "target organ," respond. This arrangement can be compared with that in radio broadcasting. We live surrounded by the electromagnetic radiation from a large number of broadcasting transmitters. However, only a correctly tuned receiver can respond to this energy. In a similar way, only certain of our cells may be competent to respond to a given hormone circulating in the blood.

The matter of cell competence cannot be overly stressed. Hormones, in themselves, cannot accomplish the various functions we have ascribed to them. Hormones simply release within the target cells their potentialities for dealing with the situation. Insulin added to blood in a test tube has no effect on the glucose content. In the living organism, however, it enables the cells to reduce the blood-sugar level.

Furthermore, our emphasis on the many cases where hormones exert their effects through the activation of genes should not delude us into thinking that that is all there is to the story. Remember that cortisone has one effect on messenger RNA synthesis in liver cells, quite a different effect on white blood cells. Testosterone produces certain kinds of messenger RNA molecules in the liver cells of male rats, but different kinds in the cells of female rats. The differing actions of FSH and LH in men and women further emphasize the essential role played by the responding cells in gene activation. While many (not all) of the actions of hormones can be traced to the activation of genes, we do not yet know why the genes in certain cells respond to the hormone while in other cells they do not. The secret must lie in the process of cellular differentiation itself. As we saw in Chapter 23, there is a progressive reduction in the capacity of differentiating cells to use the genetic information stored within them. When the mechanism responsible for this loss of developmental flexibility is understood, we shall be much closer to an understanding of the diverse effects that hormones have on the cells of the adult organism.

THE PHEROMONES   26-15

Hormones are chemical substances that are released into the *internal* environment (ECF) by *endocrine* glands. Carried throughout the body, they coordinate many of the activities of its various parts. This coordination provides, among other things, for a close regulation of the chemical properties of the internal environment and the activities of our internal organs.

In recent years, an entirely different category of chemical coordinators has also been receiving careful study. These are the **pheromones.** Pheromones are chemical substances which are released into the *external* environment by *exocrine* glands. They provide a means of communication with other members of the same species.

In some cases, the communication is quite subtle. The pheromones released by some members of the species simply initiate physiological changes in the others. These changes usually do not lead to any externally directed response for some time. Adult male grasshoppers of the species that migrates in locust plagues release a pheromone which, when detected by immature members of the species, hastens their growth. This, in turn, speeds the time when a migratory swarm will be formed and a locust plague will get under way. The queen bee in a honeybee colony secretes a substance which prevents the worker bees from developing ovaries and laying eggs. However, if the queen is killed or removed from the hive, the disappearance of this pheromone permits some of the workers to take over her egg-laying function.

Other pheromones have been discovered which trigger immediate action when detected. When an ant is disturbed, it secretes from glands in its head a volatile chemical that quickly diffuses in all directions. This chemical can be detected by other ants several centimeters from the spot. They are attracted by low concentrations of the substance and begin to move toward the area of increasing concentration. As they thus get nearer their disturbed nest mate, their response changes to one of alarm. The higher concentration of the pheromone causes them to run about actively as they remedy the disturbance. Unless additional quantities of this pheromone are released, it soon dissipates. This is important, too, so that once the emergency is over, the ants can return quietly to their former occupations.

Several other ant pheromones have been discovered, including one that is laid in a trail by a worker returning to the nest with food. This trail attracts and guides other ants to the food source (Fig. 26-9). It is continually renewed as long as the food holds out. When the supply begins to dwindle, however, trail-making ceases. The trail pheromone evaporates quickly so other ants stop coming to the site and will not be confused by old trails when food is located elsewhere.

Most of the pheromones discovered so far have been in insect species, although a few have been found in other animals. Furthermore, the most elaborate pheromone communication systems have been found in the social insects—the ants, termites, and bees. This should not be surprising when you remember the argument we examined in Section 8-21, that societies represent one *further* stage of biological organization

Fig. 26-9 A stick treated with the trail pheromone of an ant (left) can be used to make an artificial trail which is followed closely by other ants emerging from their nest (right). The trail will not be maintained by the other ants unless food is placed at its end. (Courtesy Sol Mednick and *Scientific American*.)

beyond the levels of tissue → organ → system → organism. Just as hormones help to coordinate the action of the tissues, organs, and systems within the organism, so pheromones help to coordinate the action of the individuals that make up a society.

A response to a pheromone is a response to one of many kinds of stimuli present in an animal's external environment. In order to detect the stimulus and to carry out an immediate, coordinated response, a nervous system must be present. We now turn our attention to the general topic of nervous coordination.

EXERCISES AND PROBLEMS

1 Summarize the mechanisms which participate in the control of the blood-sugar level in the body.

2 Cortisone therapy for children is undesirable because it may result in severe stunting of growth. What mechanism might be responsible for this?

3 Why must insulin be given by injection rather than by mouth?

4 How will each of the following affect the quantity and composition of urine formed in humans: (a) hypersecretion of vasopressin, (b) hyposecretion of insulin, (c) drinking copious amounts of water?

5 Which endocrine glands are controlled by the secretion of other endocrine glands?

6 What parallels can you find between the relationship of organs in an organism and the relationship of individuals in a society?

7 How is communication among the parts of an organism accomplished?

8 How is communication among the parts of a society accomplished?

9 What is the significance of diapause in insects?

10 Compare the mechanisms by which (a) the body regulates the concentration of water in the blood and (b) a steady temperature is maintained in your home.

REFERENCES

1 Williams, C. M., "Metamorphosis of Insects," *Scientific American,* Reprint No. 49, April, 1950. An excellent summary of the structural and hormonal changes in insect metamorphosis.

2 Beermann, W., and U. Clever, "Chromosome Puffs," *Scientific American,* Reprint No. 180, April, 1964. Presents evidence that the puffs are sites of gene activity and shows how the hormone ecdyson alters the pattern of puffing.

3 Beck, S. D., "Insects and the Length of Day," *Scientific American,* February, 1960. Discusses the influence of photoperiod on the life cycle of certain insects.

4 Williams, C. M., "Third-Generation Pesticides," *Scientific American,* July, 1967. Explores the potentialities of juvenile hormone as an insecticide.

5 Wilkins, L., "The Thyroid Gland," *Scientific American,* March, 1960.

6 Etkin, W., "How a Tadpole Becomes a Frog," *Scientific American,* Reprint No. 1042, May, 1966. Examines the interacting roles of the thyroid gland, pituitary gland, and brain in tadpole metamorphosis.

7 Rasmussen, H., "The Parathyroid Hormone," *Scientific American,* Reprint No. 86, April, 1961.

8 Banting, F. G., and C. H. Best, "The Internal Secretion of the Pancreas," *Great Experiments in Biology,* ed. by M. L. Gabriel and S. Fogel, Prentice-Hall, New York, 1955. A description of the method by which insulin was finally isolated. This work, for which Banting shared a Nobel Prize, led ultimately to the development of insulin therapy for diabetics.

9 Li, C. H., "The ACTH Molecule," *Scientific American,* Reprint No. 160, July, 1963.

10 Lerner, A. B., "Hormones and Skin Color," *Scientific American,* July, 1961. Describes the action of MSH and melatonin on melanocytes.

11 Wurtman, R. J., and J. Axelrod, "The Pineal Gland," *Scientific American,* Reprint No. 1015, July, 1965.

12 Guyton, A. C., *Textbook of Medical Physiology,* Second Edition, W. B. Saunders Company, Philadelphia, Penn., 1961. Chapters 73 through 80 include a thorough treatment of human endocrinology.

13 Davidson, E. H., "Hormones and Genes", *Scientific American,* Reprint No. 1013, June, 1965. Presents evidence that the primary effect of many hormones is the activation of genes within the target cells.

14 Wilson, E. O., "Pheromones," *Scientific American,* Reprint No. 157, May, 1963. A general discussion with emphasis on sex attractants and the pheromones of ants.

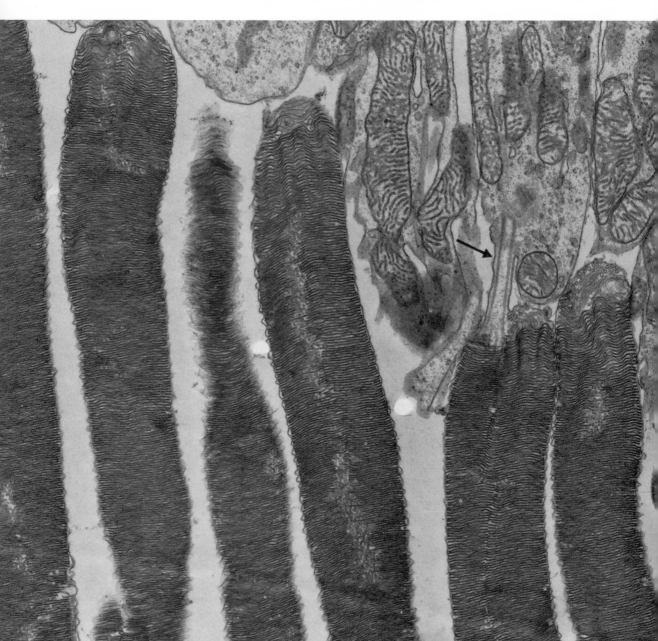

Nervous coordination differs from endocrine coordination in being faster and generally more localized in its action. It enables the organism to respond quickly to changes in the external as well as the internal environment. This is in contrast to the endocrine system which, as we know, is primarily concerned with internal changes. Although both plants and animals carry on chemical coordination by means of transported hormones, nervous coordination is characteristic of animals only.

THE THREE COMPONENTS OF NERVOUS COORDINATION 27-1

The ability of an organism to respond to changes in its environment requires the presence of three different components. *First,* there must be a stimulus **receptor.** This is a structure capable of detecting a certain kind of change in the environment and initiating a signal, the nerve impulse, in the nerve cell to which it is attached. Our sense organs are stimulus receptors. They enable us to detect such stimuli as light (the eye), sound (the ear), and chemicals (the odor receptors in the nose).

The *second* component in nervous responsiveness and coordination consists of the impulse **conductors,** the nerves themselves. Nerves are made up of bundles of conducting fibers in much the same way that a telephone cable is made up of bundles of wires. These fibers are greatly elongated extensions of special cells, the neurons. Two kinds of neurons make up most nerves. **Sensory** neurons transmit impulses from the stimulus receptor to the central nervous system, the brain and spinal cord. **Motor** neurons transmit impulses from the central nervous system to the part of the body that will take action.

In a few cases, sensory neurons may transmit their impulses directly to motor neurons, the junction occurring in the central nervous system. Most of the time, though, impulses from sensory neurons pass along one or many **association** neurons before finally reaching a motor neuron. The central nervous system is composed of millions of these interconnecting association neurons. Their complex arrangement provides a virtually unlimited number of routes by which impulses can travel through the central nervous system. This, in turn, enables a great variety of complex actions to be carried out in a well-coordinated way. If the nerves can be compared to telephone cables, the central nervous system should be compared to the switchboards of the telephone exchange.

The *third* component in nervous coordination consists of the **effectors.** These are the structures that carry out some action in response to impulses reaching them by way of motor neurons. The most important effectors in man are the muscles and the glands (both exocrine and endocrine).

◀ Rod cells of a kangaroo rat (25,000 X). The outer segments of the rods contain orderly stacks of unit membranes in which the visual pigment is incorporated. The inner portions contain many mitochondria. The two parts of the rod are connected by a stalk (arrow) that has the same structure as a cilium. (From Porter and Bonneville: *An Introduction to the Fine Structure of Cells and Tissues,* Lea & Febiger, 1964.)

In this chapter we will examine the various kinds of stimulus receptors. Some of these detect stimuli arising within the body. Often, but not always, the nerve impulses generated by them are not made conscious in the brain. Other receptors detect stimuli in the external environment. Generally, these stimuli give rise to conscious sensations. It is important to realize that sensations exist only in the brain and not in the organ that detects the stimulus. Under general anesthesia, there are no sensations. Stimuli are still detected and nerve impulses are still sent back to the central nervous system. But the brain is unable to assign any interpretation to these impulses and hence no sensation exists. On the other hand, a person whose leg has been amputated may still feel pain ("phantom" pain) in the missing leg. In such a case, remnants of sensory neurons in the stump continue to send impulses back to the brain. It is the brain alone which interprets these impulses as signifying pain in the now-missing structure.

Most animals have receptors of radiant energy **(photoreceptors)**, mechanical forces **(mechanoreceptors)**, and chemicals **(chemoreceptors)**.

PHOTORECEPTORS

Radiant energy exists in a range of wavelengths that extends from radio waves that may be thousands of yards in length to cosmic rays with wavelengths less than a millionth of an angstrom unit (Fig. 27-1). Over this long span, the only wavelengths that generally serve as stimuli for living things are light rays (about 400–700 mμ) and the somewhat longer infrared or heat rays.

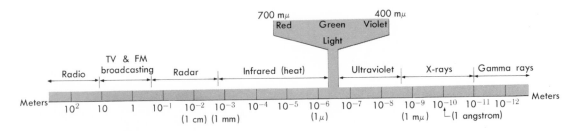

Fig. 27-1 The spectrum of electromagnetic radiation. The scale is logarithmic, every point representing a wavelength one tenth of that at the next point to the left.

Light receptors are common in the animal kingdom. They range in complexity from light-sensitive cells which simply detect the presence of light (as in the earthworm) to eyes that are capable of forming images. The latter are found in certain mollusks (especially the cephalopod mollusks, the squids and octopuses), most arthropods (insects, crustaceans, and arachnids) and the vertebrates.

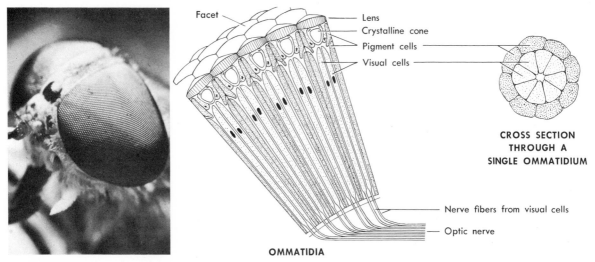

Facet
Lens
Crystalline cone
Pigment cells
Visual cells

CROSS SECTION THROUGH A SINGLE OMMATIDIUM

Nerve fibers from visual cells
Optic nerve

OMMATIDIA

Left: compound eyes of a tabanid fly. They are made up of thousands of ommatidia (center), each of which serves as a separate light receptor. In some insects, the visual cells of a single ommatidium (right) respond selectively to different colors of light, thus providing the basis for color vision. (Photo courtesy William H. Amos.)

Fig. 27-2

THE COMPOUND EYE   27-2

The structure and functioning of the arthropod eye is quite different from that of the mollusk and vertebrate eyes. It is called a compound eye because it is made up of repeating units, the **ommatidia,** each of which functions as a separate visual receptor. Figure 27-2 shows the arrangement of ommatidia in a compound eye. Each ommatidium consists of (1) a lens (the front surface of which makes up a single facet of the compound eye), (2) a transparent crystalline cone, (3) light-sensitive, visual cells arranged in a radial pattern like the sections of an orange, and (4) pigment-containing cells which separate the ommatidium from its neighbors. The location of the pigment-containing cells is such that only light entering the ommatidium parallel (or almost so) to its long axis reaches the visual cells and triggers nerve impulses. Light entering at an angle is absorbed by the screening pigments. Thus each ommatidium is pointed at just a single area in space. If that area is giving off light of sufficient intensity, the ommatidium (and adjacent ommatidia whose field of "view" overlap its own) will respond to it. If not, there will be no response. There may be thousands of ommatidia in a compound eye with their facets arranged over most of the surface of a hemisphere.

A favorite trick of nature photographers is to take a picture of some object as it would be seen through the cornea (all the facets, peeled off together) of a compound eye. Unfortunately, the results (Fig. 27-3) are not at all comparable to what the insect sees. In the photographer's setup, each facet acts as a lens, gathering light rays from all parts of the viewed object and passing them back to the film. As we have seen, however, the presence of screening pigments in the intact compound eye permits light from only one area on the viewed object to reach the visual cells. Thus each ommatidium contributes information about only one area on the object. The other ommatidia contribute information about the other areas. The composite of all the responses of all the ommatidia is a mosaic image—a pattern of light and dark dots which make up the total view.

The halftone illustrations used in newspapers (and in this book) are created in a similar fashion. If you look carefully at such an illustration (a magnifying lens will help) you will see a regular array of dots of black ink. The differing sizes of the ink dots provide for intermediate shades of gray and thus a rather faithful, but colorless, reproduction of the original scene. The finer the pattern of dots, the better the quality of the illustration. Grasshopper eyes, with relatively few ommatidia, must produce an exceedingly coarse, grainy image. The bee and the dragonfly possess many more ommatidia in their compound eyes and a corresponding improvement in the ability to discriminate ("resolve") detail. Even at that, the resolving ability of the bee eye is poor in comparison with most vertebrate eyes and only 1/60 as good as the human eye.

Fig. 27-3

Portrait of George Washington, as photographed through a portion of the cornea of the compound eye of a water beetle. (Photograph by Prof. Walter E. Flowers, from W. Davis, *Science Picture Parade*, Duell, Sloan and Pearce, 1940.)

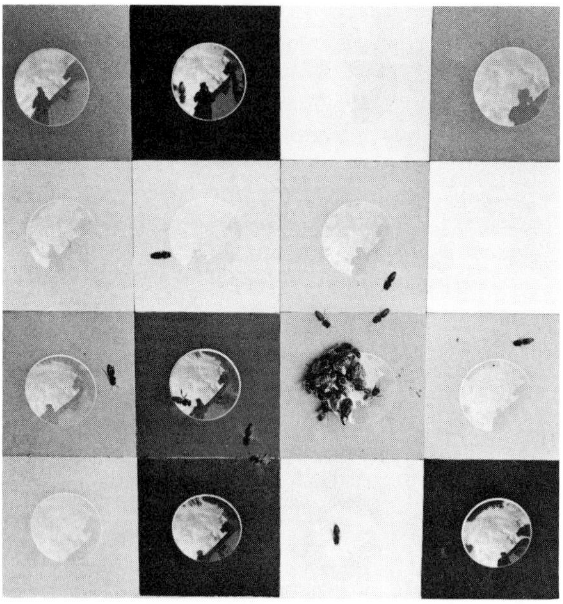

Fig. 27-4

A demonstration of color vision in honeybees. After a period of feeding from a dish placed on blue cardboard, the bees return to an empty dish on a clean blue card. They are able to distinguish the blue card from others of varying shades of gray. (Courtesy Dr. M. Renner.)

Because the compound eye does not permit good discrimination of points located close together in space, arthropods are quite nearsighted. Two objects which we could distinguish between at 60 ft could be distinguished by the bee only at a distance of 1 ft. On the other hand, the compound eye is well-adapted to detect motion. As an object moves across the visual field, ommatidia are progressively turned on and off. Because of the "flicker effect" produced, insects respond far better to moving objects than to stationary ones. Honeybees, for example, will visit windblown flowers more readily than still ones. The ability of the honeybee to perceive motion compares quite favorably with our own.

The quality of the compound-eye image gets even worse in dim light. Those arthropods which are apt to be active in dim light (e.g. crayfish, praying mantis) are able to concentrate the screening pigments of the ommatidia into the ends of the pigment cells. This shift then enables light entering a single ommatidium at an angle to pass into adjacent ommatidia and stimulate them, too. With many ommatidia responding to a single area in the visual field, the ability to form an image should deteriorate markedly. The praying mantis is probably able to do little more than distinguish light and dark in the evening. The shift in pigments does, however, make it more sensitive to light than it is during the daytime as more ommatidia can detect a given area of light.

Studies of insect behavior show conclusively that some insects, at least, are able to distinguish colors from varying shades of gray. They have true color vision (Fig. 27-4). In order for this to be possible, two or more light-absorbing pigments must be present in the eye, each of which absorbs best at a different wavelength. A single pigment can only provide information about the amount of light given off by an object, that is, its brightness. In such a case, the individual is totally colorblind, with all objects appearing in varying shades of gray. With two or more pigments, however, it becomes possible to distinguish colors because an object giving off rays of predominantly one wavelength will selectively stimulate the receptors containing the pigment which absorbs that wavelength best. Although the actual pigments that permit color vision in certain insects have not been conclusively identified, there is strong evidence for their existence. It has been found, for example, that some of the visual cells in the ommatidia of blowflies respond best to green light, some to blue, while others are most sensitive to yellow-green rays of light. This would enable these insects to discriminate colors. This ability probably does not begin to compare with ours. A well-trained human can distinguish over 17,000 different hues. Honeybees, on the other hand, can distinguish only four: yellow-green (as a single color), blue-green, blue-violet, and ultraviolet. The human eye cannot normally detect ultraviolet light, but on the other hand, the honeybee cannot see red light.

STRUCTURE OF THE HUMAN EYE 27-3

The eyes of both mollusks and vertebrates operate on the same basic principle as a camera. A single lens focuses light from all parts of the visual field onto a sheet of light-sensitive cells (Fig. 27-5). Despite the close similarity in structure and function between the eyes of mollusks and vertebrates, all the evidence indicates that they arose and evolved quite separately in the two phyla.

The human eye is roughly spherical in shape. It is bounded by three distinct layers of tissue (Fig. 27-6). The outer layer, the **sclerotic coat,** is extremely tough. It is white in color (the "white" of the eye) except in the front. Here it forms the transparent **cornea** which admits light into the interior of the eye and bends the light rays so that they can be brought to a focus. The surface of the cornea is kept moist and dust-free by the secretion of the tear glands.

The middle coat of the eye, the **choroid coat,** is deeply pigmented with melanin and well-supplied with blood vessels. It serves the very useful function of stopping the reflection of stray light rays within the eye. This is the same function accomplished by the dull black paint within a camera.

In the front of the eye, the choroid coat forms the **iris.** This, too, may be pigmented and is responsible for the "color" of the eye. An opening, the pupil, is present in the center of the iris. The size of this opening is variable and under automatic

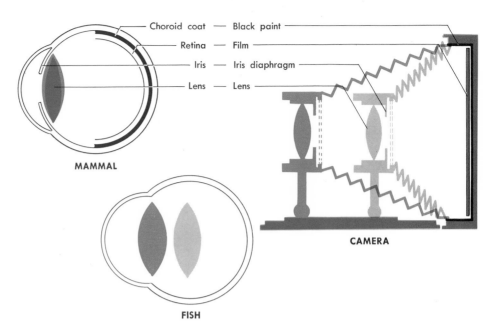

Choroid coat	Black paint
Retina	Film
Iris	Iris diaphragm
Lens	Lens

MAMMAL

CAMERA

FISH

Fig. 27-5   A comparison of two vertebrate eyes and a camera. Each is shown focused on a distant object (black) and a near object (color). The eyes of amphibians, snakes, and most mollusks
work like that of the fish; that is, focus is changed as it is in a camera. Birds and mammals
accommodate by changing the curvature of the lens.

control. In dim light (or times of danger—see Section 26-9) the pupil enlarges, letting
more light into the eye. In bright light, the pupil closes down. This not only protects
the interior of the eye from excessive illumination, but improves its image-forming
ability and depth of field. Photographic enthusiasts, too, make a practice of "stopping
down" the iris diaphragm of their cameras to the minimum permitted by the amount
of light available in order to get the sharpest possible pictures.

The inner coat of the eye is the **retina.** It contains the actual light receptors, the
rods and cones, and thus functions in the same way as the film of a camera.

The **lens** of the eye is located just behind the iris. It is held in position by suspen-
sory ligaments (Fig. 27-6). Ordinarily, these are kept under tension and the lens is
correspondingly flattened. However, contraction of muscles attached to these ligaments relaxes them and permits the lens to take on a more nearly spherical shape.
These changes in lens shape enable the eye to shift its focus (accommodate) from far
objects to near objects and vice versa.

Some people have a difficult time bringing light rays to focus on the retina. If
the eyeball is too short, or the lens too flat or too inflexible, the light rays entering the
eye will not be brought to a focus by the time they strike the retina (Fig. 27-7). This
condition is known as farsightedness because nearby objects are particularly difficult
to bring into focus. The use of eyeglasses fitted with convex lenses corrects the
condition by helping the eye's own lens to converge light rays more rapidly. Aging
people are particularly apt to become farsighted as their lenses become less flexible.

Too long an eyeball or too spherical a lens cause nearsightedness. The image of
distant objects is brought to a focus in front of the retina and is out of focus again
before the light actually strikes the retina (Fig. 27-7). Nearby objects can be seen more

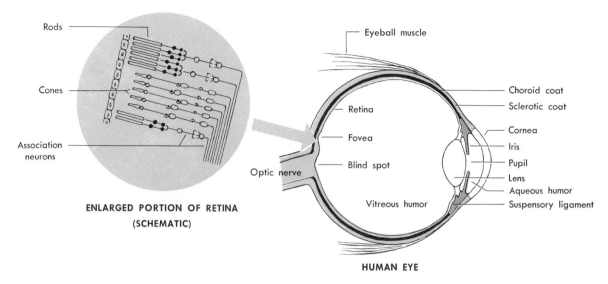

ENLARGED PORTION OF RETINA (SCHEMATIC)

HUMAN EYE

The human eye. The actual light receptors are the rods and cones.

Fig. 27-6

easily. Eyeglasses with concave lenses correct this condition by diverging the light rays somewhat before they enter the eye.

The method of changing focus by changing the shape of the lens has no parallel in photography. Focus is changed in cameras by moving the position of the entire lens with respect to the film. This method is also used in the eyes of some fishes, amphibians, snakes, and some mollusks.

If either the lens or the cornea has any irregularities in its curvature, all the light rays entering the eye will not be brought to a focus together. This defect is known as **astigmatism.** It may be diagnosed by observing a pattern of radial lines as shown in Fig. 27-7. It is corrected by specially ground eyeglasses which compensate for the irregularities.

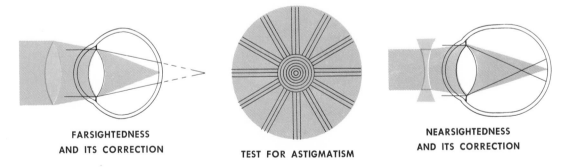

FARSIGHTEDNESS AND ITS CORRECTION

TEST FOR ASTIGMATISM

NEARSIGHTEDNESS AND ITS CORRECTION

Common eye defects. The path of light rays without glasses is shown in black; with glasses, in color. The lenses of modern eyeglasses are not so simple in shape as those shown but function in the same way. Irregularities in the cornea or lens of the eye will prevent all the lines in the pattern (center) from appearing equally sharp. This eye defect is known as astigmatism.

Fig. 27-7

For reasons which are still obscure, some people develop cloudy areas in one or both lenses. These are called **cataracts** and they cause partial or complete blindness. Today eye surgeons can usually restore vision by removing the defective lenses surgically and giving the patient extra-"strong" eye glasses to compensate for their loss.

The iris and the lens divide the interior of the eyeball into two main chambers. The anterior one is filled with a watery fluid, the **aqueous humor.** The posterior chamber is filled with a jellylike material of marvelous clarity, the **vitreous humor.**

Movement of the eyeball is accomplished by three pairs of muscles, the members of each pair working antagonistically. The coordinated action of these muscles enables the eyeball to be rotated in any direction. Thus we are able to train both eyes in a single direction. This produces two slightly differing views of the same scene which our brain is able to fuse into a single, three-dimensional (stereoscopic) image. Improper coordination of the muscles controlling the eye produces such defects as "cross-eyes."

27-4   **DETECTION OF LIGHT**

The actual visual receptors of the eye are the rods and cones. These are cells which are stacked closely together just beneath the surface of the retina.

1)   The **rods.** There are approximately 100 million rods in each eye. They are used chiefly for vision in dim light and are extremely sensitive to light. The image produced by the rods is, however, not a sharp one. Careful microscopic study of the structure of the retina provides an explanation for this. The rods function in groups. In other words, several nearby rods share a single nerve circuit to the brain. A single rod can initiate an impulse in that circuit but there is no way for the brain to determine which rod in the cluster was involved (Fig. 27-6).

For light to be absorbed, there must be a light-absorbing substance, a pigment. The pigment in the rods is **rhodopsin.** It is incorporated in unit membranes that are neatly stacked in the outer portion of the rod (see chapter opening illustration). This arrangement is similar to that which we found in the lamellae of chloroplast grana (See Section 12-3), another light-absorbing device.

Rhodopsin consists of a protein molecule, opsin, to which is attached a molecule of the carotenoid retinal (formerly called retinene). Retinal itself is light orange, but when attached to opsin, the deep reddish-purple color of rhodopsin is produced. When light is absorbed by rhodopsin, the opposite reaction occurs. The retinal is split from the protein, and the rod becomes partially bleached. At the same time, a nerve impulse is initiated. It has been shown that several steps are involved in the breakdown of rhodopsin. The first is a "light" reaction. The latter steps are "dark" reactions, that is, they do not require light. A similar situation occurs in photography. Opening of the camera shutter exposes the film, but no visible image is produced. Only the subsequent chemical changes of the developing process can convert this "latent" image into the visible image of the negative.

Although the rods provide us with a relatively coarse, colorless image, they are extremely sensitive to the presence of light. They are capable of detecting light a billion times less intense than that which our eyes receive on a bright, sunny day. The more light which strikes the rods, however, the more rhodopsin is bleached and the less sensitive the rods become. Fortunately, the process is reversible. Some rhodopsin may be resynthesized directly from its breakdown products, retinal and opsin. There is also evidence that fresh retinal is continually being manufactured in the eye by the oxidation of vitamin A. The body reserves of vitamin A thus provide a large reservoir for the synthesis of retinal. It is no wonder, then, that vitamin A deficiency is usually associated with nightblindness, the inability to see in the dark.

In order for the rods to become as sensitive as possible ("dark-adapted") it is necessary that the rate of rhodopsin synthesis exceed the rate of its breakdown. This means that bright light must be excluded from the eye. We all are aware of how difficult it is to see in a dimly lighted room immediately after entering from a brightly lighted one. It takes some thirty minutes in the dark for our eyes to become fully adapted to the dark. For night-flying aviators during the second world-war, the necessity of remaining in the dark for a period before the start of a dangerous mission was nerve-racking indeed. The realization that the rods are insensitive to red light produced a nice solution, however. Red goggles permitted the aviator to carry on normal activity while still enabling his rods to become dark-adapted. The goggles permitted only red light to reach his retina; this stimulated his cones but not his rods.

2) The **cones.** We know less about how the cones work than about how the rods work. The cones are especially abundant (about 150,000 in each square millimeter) in a single region of the retina, the **fovea,** a region just opposite the lens. Unlike the rods, the cones operate only in bright light. Furthermore, they enable us to see colors. As we noted in Section 27-2, at least two kinds of cones must be present in order to detect any colors at all. Each must contain a pigment that absorbs a certain wavelength best. Actually, with just three kinds of cones, it would be possible to have full color vision if each kind contained a pigment that best absorbed one of the three primary colors: red, green, and blue. Theoretically, the brain could mix three primary color sensations to produce any of the more than 17,000 different hues that the well-trained eye can distinguish. There is good evidence of the presence of a red-absorbing, a green-absorbing, and a blue-absorbing pigment in the fovea. Retinal is the prosthetic group for each of these. It is differences in the protein, opsin, to which the retinal is attached that account for the differences in absorption. The pigments seem to be located in different cones.

These discoveries relate nicely to our knowledge of color blindness. As you learned in Section 19-3, red-green color blindness is a sex-linked, recessive trait. Actually, there are two kinds of color-blind people who confuse reds and greens: those lacking the red-absorbing pigment and those lacking the green-absorbing pigment. Since this is a sex-linked trait, most of the victims in each group are men. Perhaps the recessive gene on their X-chromosome is coding for a defective opsin and hence a functional red- or green-absorbing pigment is not produced. There is good evidence that the gene for each of these pigments is located at a separate locus on the X-chromosome.

Far rarer is the case of color blindness involving an absence of the blue-absorbing pigment. The few cases that have been found involve women almost as often as men, so the defective gene is probably located on an autosome. Furthermore, this gene appears to be inherited as a dominant.

In addition to providing the basis for color vision, cones provide us with our most acute vision. Unlike the rods, they operate individually. Each cone triggers a specific nerve impulse that travels by its own circuit to the brain. Furthermore, the cones are very densely packed in the fovea. Other tissues, such as blood vessels, are absent from this portion of the retina and thus do not interfere with the reception of a distinct image. The image is, however, distinct (and colorful) over just a small area of view. Our ability to direct our eyes quickly to anything in view that interests us tends to make us forget just how poor our peripheral vision is.

All the nerve impulses generated by the rods and cones travel back to the brain by way of neurons in the **optic nerve.** At the point on the retina where the approximately one million neurons converge on the optic nerve, there are no rods or cones at all (Fig. 27-6). This spot, the blind spot, is thus insensitive to light. With the marks in Fig. 27-8 you can demonstrate the presence of the blind spot for yourself. The blind spots of our two eyes do not receive the same portions of the visual image, so that each eye compensates for the blind spot of the other.

Fig. 27-8   A demonstration of the blind spot. Cover your left eye with your hand and, holding the book at arm's length, stare at the cross with your right eye. What happens to the circle as you slowly move the book toward you?

27-5   **HEAT RECEPTORS**

Heat is electromagnetic radiation of wavelengths longer than those of light (Fig. 27-1). The human skin is very sensitive to gain or loss of heat. Distributed discretely through the skin are receptors that, when warmed, give rise to the sensation of warmth. Other receptors give rise to the sensation of cold when they are appropriately stimulated. The location of these two classes of receptors can be mapped by using blunt metal probes dipped in hot water and a salt-ice-water mixture respectively. The skin is richly supplied with sensory neurons, many of which are connected to specialized receptor structures (Fig. 27-10). However, it has not yet been possible to show with certainty whether any of these are exclusively responsible for detecting changes in temperature.

Some snakes contain remarkably sensitive heat receptors located in two pits on the face. These so-called pit vipers include the rattlesnakes (Fig. 27-9), cottonmouth, and copperhead found in this country. The receptors aid the snakes in detecting warm-blooded prey in the dark. Rattlesnakes can strike accurately at a mouse in complete darkness.

The human body also has receptors that detect internal temperature changes. Two sensitive "thermostats" are located in the hypothalamus (Fig. 28-7) of the brain. The receptor cells in one of these respond to small (0.01°C) increases in the temperature of the blood. As a result of their response, all the activities by which the body cools itself (dilation of the blood vessels in the skin, sweating, etc.) are brought into play when the temperature of the blood begins to rise. It is this temperature-detecting center which enables us to maintain a constant body temperature (homeothermy) during periods of exertion and/or high environmental temperatures. A second receptor in the hypothalamus maintains homeothermy when the body is exposed to chilling. The action of the skin temperature receptors supplements, but cannot replace, the action of the temperature receptors in the hypothalamus.

The western diamondback rattlesnake. Note the sense receptors concentrated in the head. **Fig. 27-9**
The eyes respond to visible radiation. The pits, which are located below the nostrils, detect
infrared (heat) radiation. The tongue samples the air for molecules of odorous substances.
(Courtesy New York Zoological Society.)

MECHANORECEPTORS

A wide variety of receptors of mechanical stimuli are found in animals. Each initiates
nerve impulses when it is physically deformed by an outside force.

TOUCH AND PRESSURE **27-6**

In man, light **touch** is detected by receptors located close to the surface of the skin.
These are often found next to a hair follicle (Fig. 27-10). Even if the skin is not touched
directly, movement of the hair is detected by the receptor. Touch receptors are not
evenly distributed over the surface of the body. The skin of the fingertips may contain
as many as 100 per square centimeter and the tip of the tongue is similarly well supplied. The concentration of touch receptors in other locations is apt to be much
lower. The back of the hand, for example, has fewer than 10 per square centimeter.
The exact location of touch receptors can be determined by gently touching the skin
with a stiff bristle and marking those spots where the subject detects a distinct touch.

An interesting variation on this technique can be carried out with a pair of dividers such as are used in mechanical drawing. With a blindfolded subject, determine the minimum separation of the points which will give rise to two separate touch sensations. You will find that the subject's ability to discriminate the two points is far better on the fingertips than on, say, the small of the back.

Lying deep in the skin are the Pacinian corpuscles (Fig. 27-10). These respond to **pressure.** The mechanism of action of the Pacinian corpuscle has been studied very carefully. It has been found that any mechanical deformation of the corpuscle (such as would be produced by pressure) creates a tiny current of electricity in the sensory neuron originating within it. The greater the deformation of the corpuscle, the greater this "generator current." If the generator current becomes sufficiently large, it initiates a nerve impulse in the sensory neuron. The **threshold** has been reached.

Pacinian corpuscles are also found scattered throughout the interior of the body. Some of these provide the brain with information on the movement of internal organs. We rarely become conscious of this information.

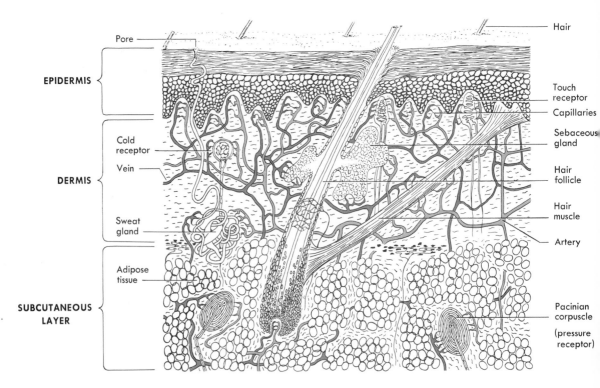

Fig. 27-10   Human skin and its sense receptors. Stimulation of the various receptors shown *probably* gives rise to the sensations indicated for each.

Other pressure receptors exist in the walls of the aorta and carotid arteries. When stimulated by high blood pressure, these initiate nerve impulses which ultimately bring about an inhibition of the heartbeat (see Section 14-19).

Muscular coordination is aided by the **proprioceptors.** These are sense receptors which are found scattered throughout skeletal muscle and tendons. Stretching or contraction of muscles triggers these receptors to initiate nerve impulses. These, in turn, enable the brain to determine the state of contraction of the muscle. If one starts to lose his balance, the brain is informed by the proprioceptors of the legs and corrective action is taken at once. Complex muscular movements, such as are involved in typing, catching a ball, playing the violin, etc., would be impossible without the proprioceptors. The properly timed, coordinated action of a variety of muscles requires that the brain be continually informed of the performance of each. If you ever have had one or both legs "go to sleep," you have some idea of how difficult locomotion would be without proprioceptors.

Massive mechanical stimulation of the skin produces the sensation of pain. Excessive heat, cold, and certain chemicals do this also. The sensation may be produced by the stimulation of a network of nerve fibers in the skin that are not attached to specialized stimulus detectors and thus do not respond unless the stimulus is very strong. On the other hand, pain may be felt as a result of a change in the frequency and pattern of the signals passed to the central nervous system by the specialized skin receptors of touch, pressure, heat, and cold. Perhaps both mechanisms participate in the process.

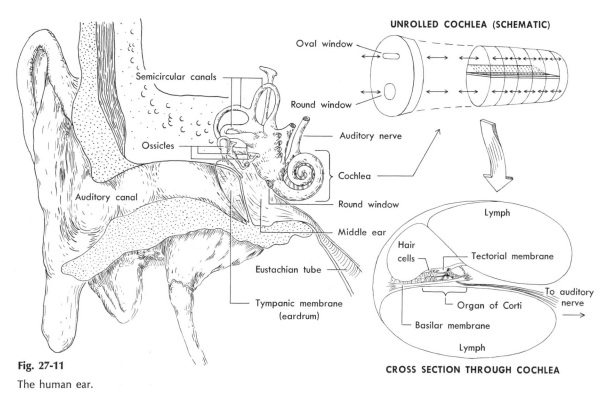

Fig. 27-11

The human ear.

CROSS SECTION THROUGH COCHLEA

HEARING   27-7

The ability to hear is the ability to detect mechanical vibrations which we call sound. Under most circumstances, these vibrations reach us through the air. The external ear (Fig. 27-11) may aid somewhat in concentrating sound waves. These then pass down the auditory canal and strike the eardrum or **tympanic membrane,** causing it to vibrate. The vibrations of the tympanic membrane are transmitted across the middle ear by three tiny, linked bones, the **ossicles,** which also serve to concentrate the vibrations.

The middle ear is filled with air and is connected to the outside air by means of a **Eustachian tube** opening into the nasopharynx. This opening permits the air pressure on both sides of the tympanic membrane to be kept equal. The "popping" of our ears that we feel when we rapidly change altitude in an unpressurized airplane or an elevator results from the sudden equalizing of pressure when the Eustachian tubes open during swallowing or yawning. Victims of head colds may have inflamed Eustachian tubes which are temporarily prevented from opening. Change in altitude may be very painful at such times because of unequal pressure against the tympanic membranes.

Mechanical vibration of the innermost ossicle, the stirrup, is transmitted through a flexible membrane (the oval window) to the **cochlea** of the inner ear. The cochlea is a tube, about 3 cm in length, which is coiled like a snail shell (Fig. 27-11) and filled with lymph. Running through the cochlea for almost its entire length is a plate of bone and an inner tube which is also filled with lymph. These structures divide the outer tube of the cochlea into two separate chambers. Vibrations of the oval window are transmitted to the fluid in these outer chambers. Because liquids are practically incompressible, it is necessary to have some way of relieving the pressures created when the oval window is pushed in and out. The flexible *round* window accomplishes this by moving the opposite way (Fig. 27-11).

Lying within the inner, or middle, chamber of the cochlea is the **organ of Corti.** It contains thousands of sensitive "hair" cells which are the actual vibration receptors. They are located between the basilar and tectorial membranes (Fig. 27-11). Vibrations in the cochlear fluid cause vibrations in the basilar membrane. This moves the sensitive hair cells against the tectorial membrane, thus stimulating them. Electrical impulses arising in these cells then initiate nerve impulses which travel back along the **auditory nerve** to the brain.

The ear is a remarkably precise and versatile sense receptor. Many people, especially when young, can hear sounds with frequencies (pitches) from as low as 16 to as high as 20,000 cycles per second. Furthermore, the ear can detect sounds over a wide range of intensities. The loudest sound we can hear comfortably is over one trillion times as loud as the faintest we can detect. The faintest sound is so faint that if our ears were any more sensitive, we would probably detect the sound of random molecular collisions (Brownian movement) within the ear. The power of discrimination of frequencies is also great. A trained musician can distinguish about 15,000 pitches.

The way in which the organ of Corti discriminates among different pitches is now fairly well understood. At first glance, it might seem appropriate for the hair cells to send impulses back to the brain at the same frequency as the sound. Something of this sort may actually occur at very low frequencies. It could not occur at frequencies greater than about 1000 cycles per second because, as we will see in the next chapter, sensory neurons cannot conduct impulses any faster than that. Actually, even before this limit is reached, the basilar membrane and hair cells begin to respond selectively to the sound frequencies. Low frequencies stimulate the area of the organ of Corti nearest its tip. High frequencies are detected near its base. The intermediate frequencies are detected in an orderly, progressive fashion from one end of the organ of Corti to the other. Evidence to support this view has been obtained by exposing laboratory animals to very intense, pure tones. Eventually the animals become deaf to these frequencies although their ability to hear other pitches is not impaired. In every case, examination of the organ of Corti reveals destroyed hair cells in a single area whose location can easily be correlated with the pitch of the destructive sound.

The hearing ability of bats is extraordinary. The research of zoologist Donald Griffin has shown that bats can hear frequencies as high as 150,000 cycles per second. Sound at such ultrasonic frequencies travels in fairly straight lines. Bats, flying in complete darkness, are able to locate obstacles (Fig. 27-12) and even insect prey by emitting pulses of this ultrasonic sound and then adjusting their course of flight to the echo which returns to their ears. Such a system of echo-location works on the same principle as the underwater sonar devices developed for submarine detection during World War II.

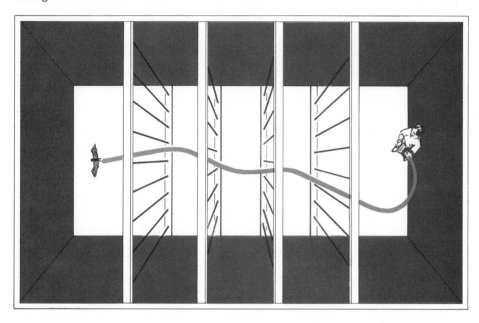

Echo location in the bat. A blindfolded bat can fly between the wires, touching them only rarely. A bat whose ears are plugged collides repeatedly with the wires.

Fig. 27-12

Hearing plays an important part in the lives of other animals, too. Avoidance of predators, the location and courtship of a mate, and the staking out of territorial "claims" may all involve the detection of sounds.

EQUILIBRIUM 27-8

The inner ear also detects: (1) the position of the body with respect to gravity and (2) the motion of the body. These two functions are quite distinct from its function in sound detection and rather distinct from each other. Just above the cochlea are two interconnecting, lymph-filled sacs (Fig. 27-11). These are lined with hair cells which, in turn, are connected to sensory neurons. Attached to the hairs of the hair cells are tiny spheres of calcium carbonate. These are acted upon by gravity and deflect the hairs downward. As the body (or at least the head) is oriented in different directions, the "ear stones" shift their position. The nerve impulses that are initiated by the hair cells are sent back to the brain and inform it of the change.

Analogous (but not homologous) structures, called **statocysts,** are found in many aquatic invertebrates. In the crayfish, these hair-lined sacs contain tiny grains of sand instead of ear stones. When the crayfish sheds its exoskeleton, it also sheds its statocysts. As soon as the new exoskeleton is hardened, however, the crayfish seeks out grains of sand to place within its new statocysts. If iron filings are offered to the crayfish instead of sand, it will use these. When the job is complete, a few minutes of experimentation with a strong magnet will vividly demonstrate the action of the statocysts in maintaining balance. Placing the magnet just above the crayfish draws the iron filings upwards. This, in turn, triggers receptors which would normally be affected only if the animal were upside down. Consequently, the crayfish does, in fact, turn itself upside down in response to the erroneous information received by its central nervous system.

Motion of the human body is detected in the three semicircular canals at the top of each inner ear (Fig. 27-11). These are three fluid-filled tubes, each one of which is oriented in one of the three planes of space. At one end of each canal is a small chamber containing sensory hair cells. Whenever the head is moved, the semicircular canals move, too. The fluid within lags in its motion, however, and consequently there is relative motion between the walls of the canals and the fluid. This motion stimulates the hair cells to send impulses back to the brain. The maintenance of proper balance during athletic activity would be practically impossible without this mechanism. When the hair cells are stimulated in unfamiliar ways, as may occur in a boat or aircraft during rough weather, motion sickness can occur.

CHEMORECEPTORS

Man's receptors of chemicals in the external environment are the taste buds, located principally on the tongue, and the olfactory epithelia, located high in the nasal cavity.

27-9   TASTE

In order for a substance to be tasted, it must be soluble in the moisture of the mouth. Only when in solution can it then stimulate the **taste buds.** Four types of these can be distinguished morphologically. Most of them are located on the surface of the tongue although a few are found on the soft palate, high in the back of the mouth.

Most experimenters agree that there are only four primary taste sensations: sweet, sour, salty, and bitter. By using dilute solutions of sucrose, hydrochloric acid, sodium chloride, and quinine sulfate, respectively, one finds that each of the four primary tastes is localized in a special area of the tongue (Fig. 27-13). However, mapping experiments of this sort also show considerable overlapping of taste areas and considerable variation from one person to the next.

The existence of four kinds of taste buds and four primary tastes suggests that each type of bud is responsible for one specific taste. With the possible exception of the bitter taste, however, there seems to be no correlation between bud type and the taste detected.

You may well argue that you can detect more than just four tastes. So you can, but this involves other factors. First of all, combinations of the four primary tastes produce new tastes. More important is the role which smell, temperature, and touch receptors play in the tasting process. As one chews food, vapors probably escape through the oral pharynx into the nasal cavity and are detected by our odor receptors. The marked loss of taste which we experience when our nasal cavities are plugged with mucus during a cold supports this point. You can demonstrate it vividly under more pleasant circumstances by applying water, in which two or three cloves have been boiled, to the tongue of a blindfolded subject. He will taste the mixture readily when his nasal passages are open. When holding his nose, however, he will have a very difficult time distinguishing the clove solution from plain water. The temperature and texture of food also play an important part in our sensations of taste.

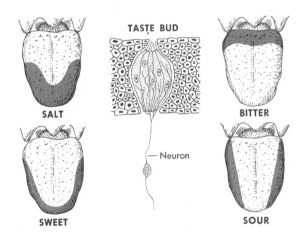

SALT **BITTER** **SWEET** **SOUR** **TASTE BUD** — Neuron

Fig. 27-13

The sense of taste is initiated in the taste buds of the tongue. When stimulated by dissolved chemicals, each initiates one of the four primary taste sensations. While the distribution of taste areas shown is typical, there is considerable variation from person to person.

Many insects have a well-developed sense of taste. The red admiral butterfly can taste a 0.000078-molar solution of sucrose, which is far too dilute for us to taste. Its taste receptors are located on its legs. Other insects have taste receptors on their antennae and mouth parts.

SMELL 27-10

Man detects odors by means of receptor cells located in the two **olfactory epithelia** high in the nasal cavity (Fig. 27-14). Each of these areas is about the size of a postage stamp, 250 mm². Air drawn in through the nostrils passes over them. Water- and fat-soluble molecules present in the air dissolve in the mucus layer covering the epithelia and give rise to sensations of smell. Vigorous sniffing improves the exposure of the olfactory epithelia to airborne substances.

It is customary to consider man's sense of smell one of his poorest senses. It is true that the sensitivity and the power of discrimination (the ability to disinguish between similar odors) of such animals as the dog and deer are somewhat better than that of man. Nevertheless, man is able to detect a virtually unlimited variety of odors (but just one at a time!) and in many cases at very low thresholds. He can, for example, detect as little as 0.0000000002 gm of vanillin (the active ingredient in vanilla flavoring) vaporized in 1000 liters of air.

The mechanism by which we are able to detect such a great variety of different odors has puzzled scientists for a long time. Only two kinds of receptor cells can be distinguished in the olfactory epithelium by their *structure*. It seems likely, though, that several (perhaps seven) can be distinguished by their *function*. According to one theory, each of these seven kinds of receptors responds to molecules of a particular class. In most cases, the shape of the molecule determines what class it is in and thus to which receptor it will become temporarily attached. Each class of molecules produces a *primary* odor such as musky, pepperminty, pungent, etc. Complex odors arise when the molecules have a shape that permits them to attach to more than one receptor. They can also arise when a variety of molecules are being given off by the odorous substance. Many odors do, in fact, represent the combined effect of a complex array of chemicals. For example, over 100 substances participate in the production of the odor of geraniums.

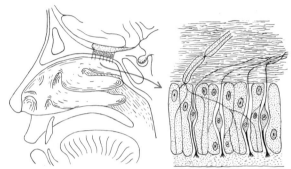

Fig. 27-14

Left: The sense of smell originates in the olfactory epithelium high in the nasal cavity. Right: Although only two kinds of receptor cells can be distinguished, we are capable of discriminating between a wide variety of odorous substances.

Part of the explanation for the low regard we have for our sense of smell is that it does not play a very important part in our lives. Other animals, however, depend greatly on smell to enable them to locate mates, locate food, and escape predators. The male silkworm moth can smell the pheromone released by a female moth two or three miles upwind. Its odor receptors, like those of most insects, are located on the antennae.

The remarkable ability of Pacific Coast salmon to return, after a span of four or five years in the sea, to the same fresh-water streams in which they were born probably involves the sense of smell (or taste—there really is not much of a distinction between the two for an animal that lives surrounded by water). Odor receptors in the salmon as well as in most bony fishes are located in two small chambers just in front of the eyes. Water enters and leaves each of these chambers through separate openings, the nostrils. It is interesting to realize that nostrils first served an odor-detecting function in our vertebrate ancestors. Only later, when vertebrates became air-breathing, did the nostrils come to be used to take air to and from the lungs.

Snakes and lizards have a well-developed odor (or taste?) receptor organ, Jacobson's organ, located in the roof of the mouth. They alternately stick their tongue out into the air and then into their Jacobson's organ. Thus they "taste" the air and detect the presence of odors (look back at Fig. 27-9).

27-11 **INTERNAL CHEMICAL RECEPTORS**

Man also has receptors that detect chemical changes in the *internal* environment. In the carotid arteries (in addition to the pressure receptors mentioned earlier) are cells which are sensitive to increased concentrations of carbon dioxide and other cells that detect decreased concentrations of oxygen. When stimulated, both types initiate nerve impulses that eventually increase the rate of breathing and the rate of heartbeat. Can you remember (see Sections 13-10 and 14-19) how these responses aid the body in preserving homeostasis?

Sensitive carbon-dioxide receptors are also found in the medulla oblongata. These initiate nerve impulses controlling rate and depth of breathing. They provide our most precise control over this function. (See Section 13-10.)

Our sensation of **thirst** arises as a result of stimulation of special cells in the hypothalamus of the brain. These cells are remarkably sensitive to changes in the osmotic pressure of the blood. If this increases (through loss of water or extra intake of salts), we quickly become conscious of thirst. In addition, vasopressin is released from the posterior lobe of the pituitary gland and acts on the tubules of the kidney to produce maximal reabsorption of water. You remember (see Section 26-8) that it is the hypothalamus itself which manufactures vasopressin for storage in the posterior lobe of the pituitary gland.

Experiments with laboratory rats indicate that they have still other areas in the hypothalamus concerned with sensation. Electrical stimulation of one area causes the rat to feed even though its stomach may be full. Electrical stimulation of another area seems to give the rat a feeling of satiety even though it is actually starving. An increase in the level of blood sugar (glucose) stimulates a similar satiety center in the hypothalamus of dogs.

It would be unwise to draw definite conclusions yet on the relevance of these experiments to man. Even assuming that man has similar hunger and satiety centers in his hypothalamus, these may not actually be the primary stimulus receptors. They may simply receive nerve impulses from receptors located elsewhere in the body. In either case, we have no knowledge of what the actual physical or chemical stimuli are which give rise to these sensations.

SUMMARY 27-12

It should now be clear that man possesses more than just the traditional five senses (touch, taste, smell, vision, and hearing). All of his senses depend upon the presence of specific stimulus receptors. These provide a constant flow of information as to the state of both the external and internal environment. In order to accomplish their functions, all stimulus receptors must possess three general features: (1) they must be so constructed as to have a lower threshold for one type of stimulus than for any other; (2) they must be connected to a sensory neuron; (3) they must be capable of initiating nerve impulses in that neuron.

Most of our stimulus receptors have a fourth characteristic which is their property of *adapting* quickly to the stimulus. When the stimulus is first applied, the receptor initiates a volley of impulses in the sensory neuron to which it is attached. With constant exposure to the stimulus, however, the rate of impulse propagation decreases and may eventually cease entirely. This phenomenon is readily apparent in the speed with which we cease to detect an odor to which we are exposed. Sensory adaptation is a useful function in that our nervous system is not continuously bombarded with information about such insignificant matters as the touch and pressure of our clothing. Remember that we defined a stimulus as a *change* in the environment, and it is change that our sense receptors detect. You might well question whether adaptation occurs in vision but, in fact, it does. However, through constant slight, involuntary movements of our eyes, we shift the position of the image on our retinas and thus continue to observe the scene even though no change may have occurred in it. Only stretch receptors such as our proprioceptors and the stretch receptors in the aorta and carotid arteries seem to adapt very little to continuous stimulation.

It should be stressed again that when conscious sensation occurs, it occurs solely in the brain. All types of stimulus receptors send the same message to the brain: electrochemical impulses in the sensory neurons. It is the brain that assigns meaning to these impulses. A hard blow to the head may exceed the threshold of neurons in the retina and thus trigger nerve impulses in the optic nerve. Although a mechanical force rather than light has given rise to them, the brain still interprets these in the usual way. Consequently, we "see stars."

This principle can be demonstrated more pleasantly with two clean dissecting needles, two lengths of insulated wire, and a dry cell. When the two needles are applied gently to the tongue, a sensation of touch only is felt. When each needle is wired to a terminal of the dry cell, however, a strong taste is detected (Fig. 27-15). The most likely explanation is that electrical stimulation of the taste buds has given rise to these sensations. Can you think of any other possibilities? How could you test them?

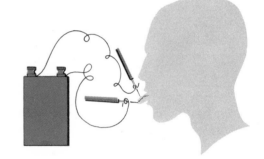

Fig. 27-15

A weak current is detected as a strong taste. When no current is flowing, the dissecting needles are tasteless. What explanation might there be for this?

The detection of changes in the external environment is just the first step by which nervous responsiveness and coordination are achieved. The next step involves the conduction of nerve impulses from one part of the body to another. The anatomical and physiological mechanisms by which nerve impulses are generated and circuited throughout the body is the topic of the next chapter.

EXERCISES AND PROBLEMS

1 When trying to see a faint star at night, it is helpful to look slightly away from the spot where the star is. Can you think of an explanation for this?

2 Which of our sense receptors detect events occurring outside of the body? Which detect events occurring within the body?

3 Why does a deficiency of Vitamin A cause night blindness?

4 Why does one's enjoyment of food diminish with a severe cold?

5 Review the different ways in which unit membranes are used in cells.

6 What is a stimulus?

7   Why are we not constantly aware of the touch and pressure of our clothing?

8   What function is common to all sense receptors?

9   In what ways are the compound eye and the human eye similar in function? In what ways are they different?

REFERENCES

1   Miller, W. H., F. Ratliff, and H. K. Hartline, "How Cells Receive Stimuli," *Scientific American*, Reprint No. 99, September, 1961. Describes the role of "generator currents" with special emphasis on the ommatidia of *Limulus*.

2   Wald, G., "Eye and Camera," *Scientific American*, Reprint No. 46, August, 1950. A comparison of the structure and function of these two image-forming devices.

3   Rushton, W. A. H., "Visual Pigments in Man," *Scientific American*, Reprint No. 139, November, 1962. Discusses how the presence of rhodopsin and two of the cone pigments can be detected by shining monochromatic (single wavelength) light on the retina. A third, blue-absorbing cone pigment has been detected by similar techniques since this article was written.

4   Benzinger, T. H., "The Human Thermostat," *Scientific American*, Reprint No. 129, January, 1961. Reports experiments that show the role of the hypothalamus in keeping the temperature of the blood from rising.

5   Loewenstein, W. R., "Biological Transducers," *Scientific American*, Reprint No. 70, August, 1960. Shows how sense receptors convert environmental stimuli into nerve impulses, with special emphasis on the Pacinian corpuscles.

6   Livingston, W. K., "What Is Pain?", *Scientific American*, Reprint No. 407, March, 1953. Examines pain from both the physiological and psychological points of view.

7   von Békésy, G., "The Ear," *Scientific American*, Reprint No. 44, August, 1957.

8   Griffin, D. R., "More About Bat Radar," *Scientific American*, July, 1958.

9   Amoore, J. E., J. W. Johnston, Jr., and M. Rubin, "The Stereochemical Theory of Odor," *Scientific American*, Reprint No. 297, February, 1964. Presents evidence to support the idea that there are seven primary odors, each triggered by molecules of a particular shape or electrical charge.

10 Hasler, A. D., and J. A. Larsen, "The Homing Salmon," *Scientific American*, Reprint No. 411, August, 1955. Discusses both laboratory and field experiments which indicate that salmon use their sense of smell to return to the stream where they were born.

11 Roeder, K. D., "Moths and Ultrasound," *Scientific American*, Reprint No. 1009, April, 1965. Describes how certain moths are able to detect and respond to the sonar signals of the bats that prey on them.

12 MacNichol, E. F., Jr., "Three-Pigment Color Vision," *Scientific American*, Reprint No. 197, December, 1964. Demonstrates that the 3 pigments used in color vision are located in separate cones.

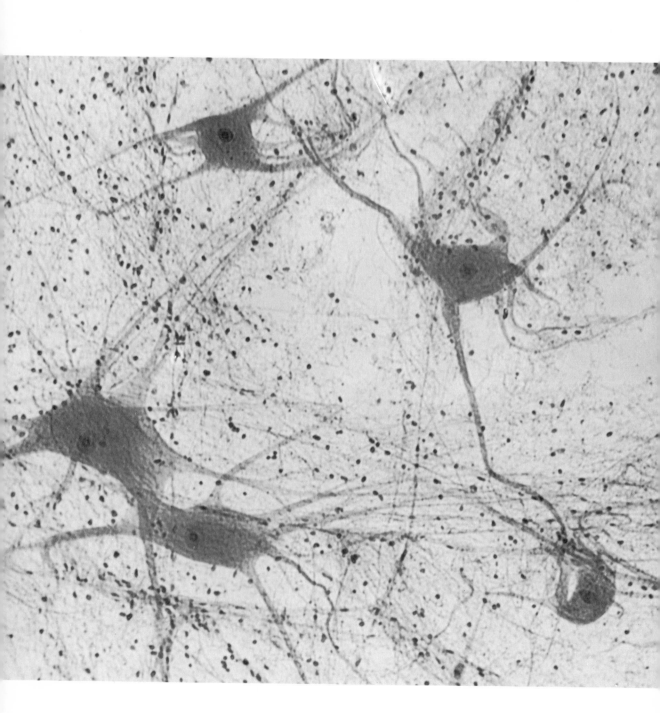

The ability of animals to respond quickly and in a well-coordinated way to changes in the environment requires more than the presence of stimulus receptors alone. There must also be a system of conductors to transmit information from the receptors to the structures, chiefly muscles and glands, that will take the appropriate action. This system of conductors constitutes the nervous system.

All stimulus receptors give rise to nerve impulses. As we will see, these are basically all alike despite the wide variety of stimuli that initiate them. They are then conducted along an elaborate system of neurons. The route taken by these impulses determines what action is produced. The over-all response of the organism, the coordination of the separate actions participating in this response, and the conscious perception of the stimulus itself all depend upon the circuits traveled by the nerve impulses.

Probably all living cells are capable of detecting stimuli. When an amoeba is pricked with a pin, the entire cell responds to the stimulus. In fact, electrical activity has been detected in the amoeba which resembles that of the nerve impulse in animals.

Animals, with the possible exception of the sponges, have cells that are specialized for conducting electrochemical impulses. The structure, function, and organization of nerve cells are surprisingly similar in the various animals. These cells are called neurons.

THE NEURON 28-1

A neuron is simply a cell that is specialized to conduct electrochemical impulses over a substantial distance. This function is accomplished by means of hairlike cytoplasmic extensions, the nerve fibers. In a large animal such as a horse, these may be as much as several feet in length although only a few micra in diameter. They grow out from the **cell body,** which houses the nucleus of the cell. Destruction of the cell body always results in the eventual death of these fibers.

The length of some nerve fibers is so great that it is hard to see how the cell body could exert any kind of metabolic control over them. Nevertheless, there is a steady transport of materials from the cell body along the entire length of the axon. This flow is probably facilitated by the many microtubules (see Section 8-13) present in the cytoplasm within the axon. There is also evidence that the axon receives materials from accessory cells, called Schwann cells. These cells are spaced regularly along the length of the nerve fibers and practically (but not completely) surround them (Fig. 28-1).

In most neurons the nerve impulses arise in short branched fibers, the **dendrites** (Fig. 28-1). The dendrites transmit the nerve impulse to a single long fiber, the **axon,** which may branch along its length, however. Each branch of an axon terminates in a cluster of strands, the **end brush.**

◄ Giant nerve cells from the spinal cord of an ox.

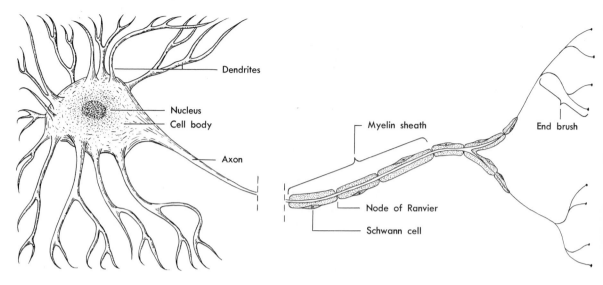

Fig. 28-1   Structure of a motor neuron. Most of the axon has been omitted.

Many axons are covered with a glistening fatty sheath, the **myelin sheath** which consists of the greatly expanded cell membrane of a surrounding Schwann cell. The membrane is folded around and around the axon to form the sheath. It is believed that the myelin sheath increases the speed with which the nerve impulse passes along the axon. Where the sheath of one Schwann cell meets that of the next, the axon is unprotected. This region, called the node of Ranvier, also seems to play a part in the propagation of the nerve impulse.

Structurally, as well as functionally, neurons can be placed in three distinct groups.

1) **Sensory** neurons. Sensory neurons run from the various types of stimulus receptors (discussed in the last chapter) to the central nervous system (brain and spinal cord). The receptors initiate nerve impulses which then travel the length of the sensory neuron. The cell bodies of the sensory neurons are located in clusters (**ganglia**) next to the spinal cord. The end brushes usually terminate at association neurons.

2) **Association** neurons. Association neurons are found exclusively within the spinal cord and brain. They are stimulated by impulses which reach them from sensory neurons or from other association neurons.

The association neurons form the intermediate link in the pathway of almost all nervous coordination. The vast number of association neurons in man's central nervous system (several billion at least) and the incredible number of cross connections between them provide us with a virtually limitless number of possible circuits for nerve conduction.

3) **Motor** neurons. Motor neurons transmit impulses from the central nervous system to the muscles and glands which will bring about the coordinated response of the body. They are usually stimulated by association neurons although, in a few cases, impulses may pass directly from a sensory neuron to a motor neuron.

Whatever their differences in appearance, we have no reason to believe that the three types of neurons differ in the nature of the impulses they transmit. However, most of our knowledge of the nerve impulse has come from the study of motor neurons.

With delicate electrodes and sensitive recorders (Fig. 28-2), it is possible to study the electrical properties of the nerve impulse. This equipment reveals that the cytoplasm of the resting neuron is negatively charged with respect to the ECF. The size of this charge across the cell membrane is about 0.07 volt. It exists only so long as the neuron carries on a slow, but unceasing, oxidation of glucose to produce ATP. The energy stored in ATP is used to actively transport Na^+ ions from the interior of the neuron to the ECF and potassium (K^+) ions from the ECF to the interior. This process of active transport leads to a concentration of Na^+ in the ECF ten times as large as that in the cytoplasm and a concentration of K^+ ions in the cytoplasm thirty times that in the ECF. These differences in concentration create a strong tendency for the K^+ ions to diffuse out of the neuron and the Na^+ ions to diffuse into it. The membrane of the resting neuron is virtually impermeable to the passage of Na^+ ions. The K^+ ions do diffuse out, however, and as they do so the interior of the neuron

Fig. 28-2

The nerve impulse. In the resting neuron the interior of the axon membrane is negatively charged with respect to the exterior (A). As the nerve impulse passes (B), the polarity is reversed. Then the outflow of K^+ ions quickly restores normal polarity (C). At the instant pictured in this diagram, the moving spot, which has traced these changes on the screen of the oscilloscope as the impulse swept past the intracellular electrode, is at position C.

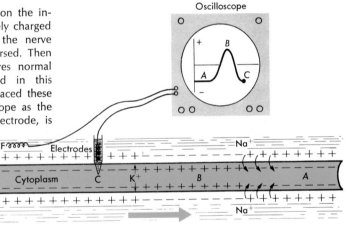

becomes negatively charged with respect to the exterior. When the charge reaches about 0.07 volt, the process reaches equilibrium. The tendency of the K^+ ions to diffuse out because of the concentration gradient is balanced by the electrical attraction of these positively charged ions for the negatively charged interior. There are a variety of stimuli such as a negatively charged electrode, heat, mechanical deformation, and certain chemicals that will increase the membrane's permeability to Na^+ ions and permit them to re-enter the neuron. This, in turn, reduces the voltage between the ECF and the cytoplasm. If the stimulus is a very weak one, the process does not go too far. The tiny current generated dies out quickly and the normal 0.07-volt polarity is re-established. In such a case, we say that the stimulus was subthreshold. However, if the stimulus is strong enough, the depolarization proceeds to the point where the voltage is reduced to about 0.05 volt. At this value (the **threshold**), the permeability of the membrane to the inflow of Na^+ ions suddenly increases sharply, and Na^+ ions flow in with a rush, eliminating the voltage entirely.

In fact, they create a momentary overshoot, with the interior of the membrane now becoming positively charged.

The sudden influx of Na^+ ions at the stimulated point of the membrane has the interesting property of increasing the permeability of adjacent portions of the membrane to Na^+ ions. Consequently, the process is repeated continuously along the length of the nerve fiber, each portion of the fiber triggering the depolarization of the portion adjacent to it (Fig. 28-2). The resulting wave of depolarization which sweeps down the fiber is the nerve impulse.

In myelinated fibers, depolarization seems to occur only at the nodes of Ranvier. However, the depolarization of one node creates at the next node an almost instantaneous *generator current* which leads to *its* depolarization. The nerve impulse thus jumps rapidly from node to node. It is not surprising that myelinated axons conduct nerve impulses more rapidly than nonmyelinated ones.

The strength of the nerve impulse is simply a property of the neuron itself. It has nothing to do with the strength of the stimulus. As long as a stimulus just exceeds the threshold of the neuron, the neuron will "fire." Stimuli of greater strength can do no more than this. We say that the response of the neuron is "all-or-none," but it should be noted that strong stimuli may give rise to a greater number of impulses in a given period of time than weak ones.

The nerve impulse should not be compared to the flow of current in a wire. The processes are not at all similar. In the latter case, an electrical impulse is conducted along the wire at the speed of light. In the neuron, an electro*chemical* reaction is simply moving down the length of the neuron.

Even in our fastest neurons, this wave of depolarization proceeds at less than 200 miles/hour. In one sense this is very rapid, but of course it does not begin to compare with the speed of light (186,000 mi/sec).

A better analogy for the nerve impulse is the fuse to a string of firecrackers. When a burning match is applied to the end of the fuse, its threshold is reached and a spark begins to pass along the fuse. The energy for this movement comes from the energy of the chemicals stored in the fuse itself, not from the energy of the burning match. There is no weakening of the spark with distance traveled. If the fuse branches, the spark travels with undiminished vigor along each branch. (Neither of these conditions occurs in electrical circuits.)

A second stimulus applied to a neuron less than 1/1000 sec after the first will not trigger any impulse. The membrane is depolarized and the neuron is said to be in its **refractory period.** In some of our neurons, the refractory period lasts for only 1/1000 to 2/1000 of a second. This means that the neuron can transmit 500–1000 impulses every second. Other neurons, especially those of cold-blooded animals, repolarize more slowly. When the 0.07 volt polarity is re-established, the neuron is ready to "fire" again. Repolarization is established by the rapid diffusion of K^+ ions from within the cell to the ECF. Only when the neuron is finally rested are the Na^+ ions that came in at each impulse actively transported out of the cell. For each one that leaves, a K^+ ion returns, thus maintaining normal polarization.

28-3   **THE SYNAPSE**

If a nerve fiber is stimulated in the middle of its length, the resulting impulse travels in both directions. In normal situations, as we have mentioned, the impulses in a single neuron always travel in just one direction: dendrites to axon. This one-way flow of impulses is maintained by the synapses.

Although the end brush of one neuron may seem to be in direct contact with the dendrites or cell body of another, the electron microscope shows us that a tiny gap exists between them. This gap is the synapse. While there is no evidence that the electrical activity passing into an end brush can itself jump this gap and continue along the next neuron, we do know that at synapses located outside the central nervous system, **acetylcholine** (ACh) is released by the end brush. As the ACh accumulates in the synaptic space, it reduces the polarization of the dendrites or cell body of the next neuron.

If enough ACh accumulates, the next neuron will "fire" and a nerve impulse will travel down it. Because dendrites do not release any chemical transmitter, any nerve impulse passing along a single neuron from axon to dendrites would die out at the synapse. Thus, the synapse acts as a valve permitting only one-way flow of nerve impulses.

Chemical transmission of the nerve impulse across the synapse occurs in the central nervous system, too. Positive identification of the substances used has been difficult, but ACh has been found in the central nervous system as have association neurons that are stimulated by it. Other chemical transmitters occur as well, although their chemical nature has not been positively established.

Impulses arriving at the end brush of some association neurons in the central nervous system *inhibit* depolarization of the neurons with which they synapse. The chemical transmitter used in these cases seems to exert its effect by increasing the permeability of the neuron membrane to K^+ ions. As additional K^+ ions diffuse out of the cell, the interior becomes even more negative with respect to the exterior. This *hyper*polarization may reach a value of 0.08 volt. A neuron that is hyperpolarized by the influence of an inhibitory transmitter substance appears to have an increased threshold, that is, the cell is less easily stimulated. Actually, the threshold *voltage* (about 0.05) has not changed. It is simply a matter of whether the depolarization produced by the excitatory synapses *minus* the hyperpolarizing effect of the inhibitory synapses can reach this value or not.

Of what use are inhibiting neurons? Inhibition of muscles is just as important as stimulation, if coordinated movements are to be made. Imagine trying to catch a ball if all your muscles contracted at once. While *failure to stimulate* does result in inhibition, specific inhibitory neurons in the central nervous system undoubtedly provide even more precise control.

The proper operation of the synapse requires that the chemical transmitter be removed from the synaptic gap as soon as it has done its job. If it is not, it will "fire" the neuron over and over again. The removal of ACh is accomplished by the enzyme acetylcholinesterase, which hydrolyzes the molecule into inactive fragments. Substances have been discovered which interfere with the action of acetylcholinesterase. These seriously upset normal nervous activity. Some of them are used as insecticides; others are manufactured for possible use as "nerve gases" in warfare.

The physiology of the synapses in the central nervous system can best be interpreted in terms of the release of a chemical transmitter. It is known, for example, that there is a definite delay (about 0.6 millisecond) in the transmission of a nerve impulse from one neuron to the next. This can be explained by the need for a sufficient amount of the "transmitter" substance to be released to trigger the next neuron. It is also known that synapses present substantial resistance to the continued movement of nerve impulses. A single impulse often dies out at a synapse, but several impulses reaching the synapse within a brief period of time will trigger an impulse in the next neuron. Probably the quantity of "transmitter" substance released by just a single impulse does not depolarize the neuron sufficiently to exceed its threshold.

28-3 / The Synapse

On the other hand, rapid, repeated use of a given synapse will soon cause it to become fatigued. It presents an increasingly steep barrier to the passage of nerve impulses. This can be interpreted on the basis of a temporary exhaustion of the reserves of "transmitter" substance stored in the end brush.

28-4   ### THE REFLEX ARC

In man, the simplest unit of nervous response is the reflex arc. The individual neuron is the unit of structure of the nervous system, but the reflex arc is the unit of function. We can illustrate the reflex arc by examining what goes on when you touch a hot stove and quickly pull your hand away. This response is called a withdrawal reflex. In order for it to be carried out, the following actions take place:

1) The stimulus is detected by receptors in the skin.

2) These initiate nerve impulses in the *sensory* neurons leading from them to the spinal cord.

3) These impulses enter the spinal cord and initiate impulses in one or more *association* neurons.

4) Association neurons initiate impulses in the appropriate *motor* neurons.

5) When these impulses reach the junction between the motor neurons and the muscles, the *muscles* (called *flexors*) are stimulated to contract. Your hand is withdrawn.

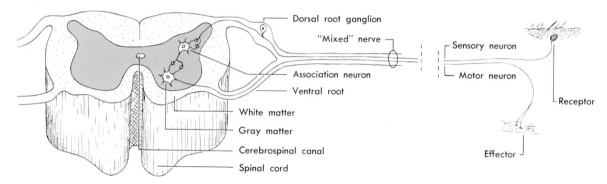

Fig. 28-3   The anatomical basis of the reflex arc. Response to stimuli requires a receptor of the stimulus, which initiates a nerve impulse in a sensory neuron. This impulse usually passes to one or more association neurons, then to a motor neuron which conducts it to the effector. The effector carries out the response. Incoming impulses also pass to *inhibitory* association neurons. These inhibit the motor neurons running to those effectors whose action would interfere with the response.

As mentioned earlier, efficient withdrawal of the hand also requires that some of the muscles in your arm (the *extensors*) be inhibited. This is accomplished by inhibitory association neurons in the spinal cord. When they are stimulated by the sensory neurons, they inhibit the motor neurons running to the extensor muscles.

The structural basis for these actions is shown in Fig. 28-3, although it is a vastly oversimplified representation of what actually takes place. The organization of sensory, association, and motor neurons is not a simple 1:1:1 pattern. The end brushes of a given sensory neuron form synapses with several association neurons. A given association neuron may, in turn, have hundreds of different end brushes (both of sensory neurons and other association neurons) converging upon it. A motor neuron may have as many as 5000 different association (and occasionally sensory) neurons converging upon it (Fig. 28-4). Furthermore, as we saw in the previous section, some association neurons may inhibit synaptic transmission from other association neurons. It is this multitude of interconnections which provide for complex responses and which also enable us to keep informed of what our body is doing. The withdrawal reflex does not require the participation of the brain at all. However, you are aware of what you have done. You can even learn to inhibit your response to the stimulus. These actions would be impossible were it not for other association neurons running up and down the spinal cord informing the brain what is happening and perhaps relaying modifying commands to the motor neurons.

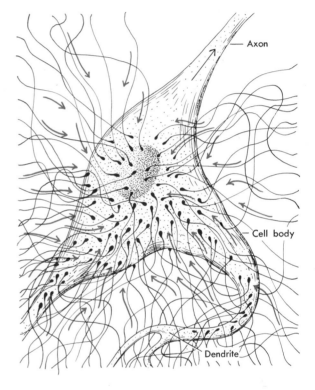

Fig. 28-4

The dendrites and cell body of a single motor neuron in the human may have as many as 5000 association neurons converging on them. Some of these release excitatory substances at the synapse. Others release inhibitory substances. Several excitatory impulses must reach the motor neuron at once in order to initiate a nerve impulse in it. The number must be increased if inhibitory impulses are reaching the motor neuron at the same time.

The multitude of interconnections in the central nervous system also provides the basis for variability of response. Many of our complex activities, for example those involved in an athletic maneuver, can be markedly improved with practice. There is improvement in the speed of the response as well as in its precision. This improvement suggests that the nerve impulses are finding ever-shorter, but already existing, routes through the brain and spinal cord. These alternative routes are made possible by the large number of interconnections between sensory, association, and motor neurons.

Dissection of most animals more complex than cnidarians leads one to distinguish two different parts of the nervous system. The **central nervous system** of such different forms as planarians, the earthworm, and the grasshopper consists of clusters of cell bodies, the ganglia. Generally the ganglia are located in parts of the body where a good deal of sensory information is being received (e.g. the head) or precise control of muscles (e.g. near the mouth parts) is needed. The ganglia are connected to one another by one or more nerve cords consisting chiefly of the fibers of association neurons (Fig. 28-5). Sensory and motor axons run to and from the ganglia. They are bundled together in cables (nerves) and make up the **peripheral nervous system.** Because most nerves contain both sensory and motor axons, they are called **mixed nerves.**

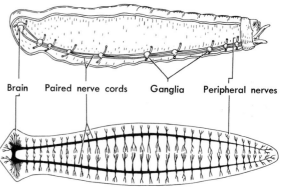

Brain Paired nerve cords Ganglia Peripheral nerves

Fig. 28-5

Nervous system of the grasshopper (above) and planarian (below).

The peripheral nervous system serves to inform the central nervous system of stimuli that have been detected and to cause the muscles and glands to carry out a response. The central nervous system serves as a coordinating center for the actions to be carried out. From what we have said, it should be clear that neither the central nor the peripheral nervous system can function independently of the other. However, with an organism as complex as man, we will better understand the special features of each system if we study them separately.

THE CENTRAL NERVOUS SYSTEM OF MAN

Our central nervous system consists of the spinal cord and the brain.

28-5 **THE SPINAL CORD**

The spinal cord is a glistening white cord which runs from the base of the brain down through the backbone. A cross section of the spinal cord reveals that only the outer portion, the "white matter" of the cord, is white. The inner portion is gray and is called the "gray matter." Running vertically through the gray matter is a central canal filled with cerebrospinal fluid; the canal connects with cavities (ventricles) in the brain which are also filled with this fluid.

The white matter consists chiefly of long, myelinated nerve fibers running up and down the cord. The gray matter is closely packed with the cell bodies of association and motor neurons.

At evenly spaced intervals along each side of the spinal cord are thirty-one pairs of projections, the nerve **roots.** These unite directly to form the mixed nerves of the peripheral nervous system. All the sensory neurons reaching the spinal cord in a mixed nerve pass into a dorsal root and then into the gray matter of the cord itself. The cell bodies of these sensory neurons are located in ganglia in the dorsal roots (Fig. 28-3). All our motor neurons originating in the spinal cord pass out ventral roots before uniting with the sensory axons to form the mixed nerves.

The separation of sensory and motor axons in the roots is easily demonstrated when they become accidentally cut or otherwise damaged. Destruction of dorsal roots causes a loss of sensation in that part of the body which supplied sensory impulses to the damaged roots. Destruction of ventral roots, on the other hand, causes a muscular paralysis of that part of the body supplied by the motor neurons running through those roots. To achieve substantial anesthesia or paralysis, several adjacent roots must be cut because there is considerable overlapping of function between the mixed nerves they form.

The spinal cord carries out two main functions in nervous coordination. First, it connects the peripheral nervous system to the brain. Information reaching the spinal cord through sensory neurons may be transmitted up the cord by means of association neurons. In the brain all this information can be compared and then appropriate action dictated. Impulses leaving the brain travel back down the cord by way of other association neurons and then leave the cord in the motor neurons.

The association neurons carrying impulses *from* specific receptors or *to* specific effectors are not organized randomly in the spinal cord but are, instead, grouped together in **tracts.** Impulses from the body's pain receptors, temperature receptors, proprioceptors, etc., each pass up the cord in their own special tracts. Impulses passing down the cord to the motor neurons are also localized in tracts. Curiously enough, impulses reaching the cord from the left side of the body eventually pass over to tracts running up to the right side of the brain, and vice versa. In some cases, this "crossing over" occurs as soon as the impulses enter the spinal cord. In other cases, it does not take place until the tracts actually enter the brain.

The second function of the spinal cord is to act as a minor coordinating center itself. Simple reflex responses, like the withdrawal reflex, can take place through the sole action of the spinal cord. The brain does not need to receive or initiate any nerve impulses for the action to be carried out successfully. Although only relatively simple coordination can be carried out by the spinal cord alone, its actions are a good deal more complex than we have suggested. Even for such a "simple" response as the withdrawal reflex, many motor neurons must be stimulated at the proper moment while other motor neurons are inhibited.

THE BRAIN   28-6

The activity of the brain is even less well understood than the activity of the spinal cord. Basically, the brain receives nerve impulses from the spinal cord and from cranial nerves leading directly to it from the eyes, inner ear, etc.; it then organizes these impulses. This organization process is the key to brain function: conscious sensation, memory, the association of one stimulus with another or with a memory, and the coordinated body action necessary for proper responsiveness all depend upon the circuits taken by nerve impulses within the brain. Furthermore, the initiation of impulses to be sent to the motor neurons of the body does not necessarily depend upon sensory impulses reaching the brain. It is quite clear that our brain can initiate body responses simply as a result of its own self-contained activity. An example of this would be action taken as a result of something suddenly remembered. The evidence suggests that man's brain is almost unique in this respect. The earthworm, grasshopper, and frog, for example, seem far more dependent

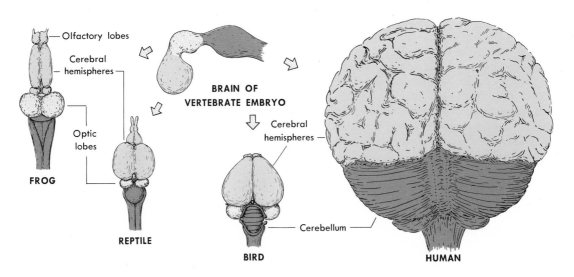

Fig. 28-6   The developing brain of the vertebrate embryo consists of three lobes. From these arise the structures of the forebrain (light color), midbrain (gray), and hindbrain (dark color). The human brain is shown from behind so that the cerebellum can be seen.

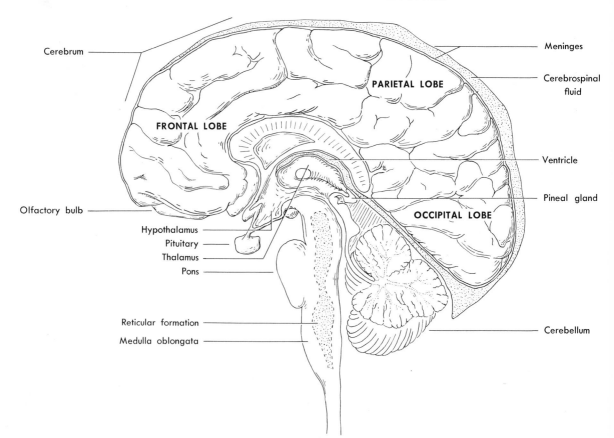

Fig. 28-7   The human brain cut lengthwise between the two cerebral hemispheres.

on specific stimuli for initiating responses. We say that these creatures are more sense dominated.

The human brain consists of two large hemispheres (Fig. 28-6). Because of the crossing over of the spinal tracts, the left hemisphere of the brain controls the right side of the body and vice versa. The brain, as well as the spinal cord, is covered with three protective membranes, the **meninges** (Fig. 28-7). Cerebrospinal fluid is found between the inner two membranes and probably helps to cushion the brain from blows to the skull. Within the brain are four chambers, the ventricles, also filled with cerebrospinal fluid. There are large capillary beds within two of these ventricles, permitting the exchange of materials between the blood and the cerebrospinal fluid. The cells lining the ventricles are ciliated and keep the cerebrospinal fluid circulating.

Extending from the brain are twelve pairs of cranial nerves. Not all of these are mixed nerves; the optic nerves and olfactory nerves, for example, contain sensory neurons only.

The brain is divided into three regions: forebrain, midbrain and hindbrain. These divisions are not immediately obvious in the adult human brain because each is, in itself, made up of several parts or lobes. However, the pattern is clearly visible during the development of the brain in the embryo. The brains of all vertebrates are constructed on this basic plan (Fig. 28-6).

The Hindbrain 28-7

The two main portions of the hindbrain are the **medulla oblongata** and the **cerebellum.** The medulla oblongata has the appearance of simply a swollen tip to the spinal cord. Though small in size, it is absolutely essential to life. The nerve impulses which stimulate the intercostal muscles and diaphragm, and thus permit breathing, originate in the medulla. Nerves regulating heartbeat, diameter of the arteries and other important functions also arise here. It is not surprising that destruction of the medulla brings about immediate death. We have no direct conscious control over the functions of the medulla although we can modify its action somewhat through the use of other brain centers.

The cerebellum consists of two deeply convoluted hemispheres. Its most important function seems to be coordinating muscular activity in the body. Such activity is initiated by impulses arising in the motor area of the forebrain. These impulses not only travel down the spinal cord to the motor neurons but also pass into the cerebellum. As the body action is carried out, sensory impulses from the proprioceptors, the eyes, the semicircular canals, etc., are also sent to the cerebellum. The cerebellum then compares the information on what the body is actually doing to what the forebrain had instructed it to do. If a discrepancy exists, the cerebellum sends modifying signals to the forebrain so that the appropriate corrective signals can be sent out to the muscles. It is not surprising that birds have relatively large cerebella (Fig. 28-6) when we consider that they must be capable of moving swiftly and accurately in three dimensions of space while we and other earthbound animals spend most of our lives moving about on fairly flat surfaces.

The Midbrain 28-8

The midbrain in man is quite small and inconspicuous. It relays nerve impulses between the forebrain and hindbrain and between the forebrain and the eyes. It also participates in the maintenance of balance. Some other vertebrates have relatively large midbrains. The prominent optic lobes of fishes, frogs, reptiles, and birds are part of their midbrains (Fig. 28-6).

Running up through the center of the medulla oblongata and the midbrain is a network of nerve fibers known as the **reticular formation.** It serves to activate or awaken the forebrain. Sensory tracts of the spinal cord lead both to the forebrain and to the reticular formation, but the forebrain cannot respond to impulses reaching it from the sensory tracts unless it is first awakened by the reticular formation. As you might guess from your own experience, the reticular formation is quite selective in its action. It may not arouse the forebrain when large, but familiar, stimuli (such as traffic sounds) are received. A creaking floorboard, on the other hand, may produce instant wakefulness. Destruction of the reticular formation results in a permanent coma followed eventually by death.

28-9   **The Forebrain**

The most prominent part of man's forebrain is the **cerebrum.** It is made up of two large, deeply convoluted hemispheres. Each of these is subdivided into four lobes: frontal, parietal, occipital, and temporal (Fig. 28-7). In most other vertebrates (e.g. the frog) there are large olfactory lobes which are present as outgrowths of the cerebrum (Fig. 28-6), but this portion of the brain is relatively small in man. The forebrain also includes the thalamus, hypothalamus, part of the pituitary gland, and the pineal gland.

Surely no other body structure sets man so far apart from the other vertebrates as his cerebrum. The volume of the two cerebral hemispheres averages approximately 1350 ml. While a few large mammals such as whales have still larger cerebrums, the ratio of the size of the cerebrum to that of the rest of the central nervous system is far greater in man than in any other vertebrate.

Man and the other mammals have still another important feature in the organization of the cerebrum. The exterior of the cerebrum, the cortex, is made up of gray matter, masses of cell bodies. The myelinated nerve fibers of which white matter is composed are located within the cerebral hemisphere. This, you will recall, is just the reverse of the arrangement in the spinal cord. It is also the reverse of the arrangement in other vertebrate brains. The surface of the frog's cerebrum is glistening and white like all the rest of the central nervous system.

The significance of this reversal of pattern probably lies in the greater surface area it provides for the cell bodies. Many biologists feel that the extraordinary properties of our brain are dependent upon the enormous (over 5 billion) number of cell bodies present in the cerebral cortex and the unimaginably large number of possible connections which can be made between them. The many deep convolutions of the cerebral cortex provide additional surface area for these cell bodies to occupy.

Less than 1% of the neurons in the cerebrum send nerve fibers out of the cerebrum to other parts of the brain. What then are these vast numbers of self-contained neurons accomplishing? To date, we can do little more than speculate. We do know that a great deal of electrical activity goes on in the cerebrum. Through use of the electroencephalograph, an instrument that detects and records brain "waves," we know that this electrical activity changes during sleep, wakefulness, excitement, etc. The instrument has even been used successfully to diagnose disorders of the brain such as a tendency toward epileptic seizures. Despite the limited success of this technique, we still know practically nothing of the internal activity of the cerebrum.

Many biologists think that the cerebrum functions in a way similar to a modern electronic computer. They compare the activity of the neurons to the actions of the vacuum tubes, transistors, relays, etc., of the computer. If this parallel has any worth, we should be awed by our endowment from the process of evolution. It has been estimated that a computer with the circuitry to compare with an inferior human brain would need a building the size of Rockefeller Center to house it. All the power produced at the Hoover Dam would be needed to run it, and the water flowing over Niagara Falls would be needed to keep it cool.

Although the detailed electrical activity of the cerebrum is only dimly understood, some general functions of the cerebrum have been discovered. These discoveries have been made as a result of two kinds of studies. One is simply to destroy a portion of the cerebrum and see what happens to the victim. While this has been used with success on laboratory animals (using all the surgical precautions a human patient would receive), it is obviously risky to apply such findings to man. However, many cases of brain damage as a result of injury or infection have been studied in man and related to the presence of specific symptoms. The second technique is to expose the brain and then stimulate tiny portions of it with electrodes. Although this is of only limited use in laboratory animals, many humans undergoing brain surgery have volunteered to let such experiments be carried out on them while their brains were exposed. No pain is involved and when not under general anesthesia, the patients can report their sensations to the experimenter. Experiments of this sort have given us great insight into the function of the cerebrum. For example, they have revealed the presence of a band of cortex running parallel to and just in front of the fissure of Rolando (Fig. 28-8), which controls the action of the body's skeletal muscles. Stimulation of discrete areas within this band results in the contraction of the muscles controlled by that area. The larger the area of cortex involved, the more abundant the supply of motor neurons to the part of the body controlled by it.

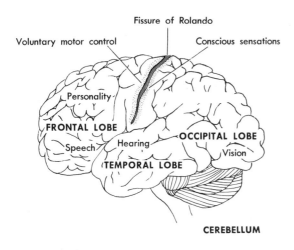

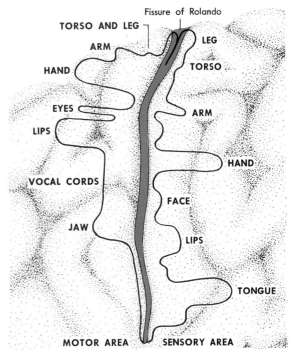

Fig. 28-8

Functions of the human cerebrum. The motor and sensory areas adjacent to the fissure of Rolando are shown in detail in the right-hand drawing. The left side of the brain (shown here) is concerned with the right side of the body, and vice versa.

A similar region has been discovered in a parallel band of cortex posterior to the fissure of Rolando. This region is concerned with *sensations* from the various parts of the body. When isolated spots are stimulated electrically, the patient reports sensation in some specific area of the body. A map can be prepared in accordance with such reports (Fig. 28-8).

When portions of the occipital lobe are stimulated electrically, the patient reports the sensation of light. Not only does this region seem to be necessary for the primary act of seeing, but certain regions within it are necessary for associations to be made with what is seen. Damage to these regions may result in the person's being perfectly capable of seeing objects but incapable of associating them with previous experiences — of recognizing them. Such a defect is known as aphasia. The centers of hearing and understanding what is heard are located in the temporal lobes.

Although a few other functions have been assigned to specific areas of the cortex, the function of large areas of the cortex still remains unknown. Manipulation of these "silent" areas fails to reveal any specific activity. This is especially true of the large frontal lobes. Perhaps these large areas are responsible for carrying out some of man's "higher" mental activities. Learning, memory, logical analysis, foresight, creativity, and some emotions may all depend upon the nervous activity of the frontal lobes and other silent areas. The dependency must be quite general, though, because no one has yet succeeded in relating any one of these mental activities with any specific spot in the cortex. Perhaps the vast number of neurons involved enables one portion of these silent areas to take over the function of some other portion that has become damaged.

Damage to the frontal lobes may produce changes in human behavior. Evidence of this was acquired in 1848 when a Vermont quarry worker, Phineas P. Gage, accidentally exploded some blasting powder with a crowbar. The explosion drove the crowbar right through the front portion of his head, severely damaging his frontal lobes. Miraculously, he survived the accident. Furthermore, he lost none of the clearly defined functions of the brain. His vision, hearing, other sensations, speech, and body coordination were unimpaired. Nevertheless, a marked change in personality was soon noted. Formerly a reasonable, sober, conscientious person, Phineas became thoughtless, irresponsible, fitful, obstinate and profane. In short, certain special, hard-to-measure, human qualities had been radically altered by his accident.

In 1935, 74 years after Phineas died (his skull now resides in the museum of the Harvard Medical School — with crowbar resting nearby), it was learned that destruction of the frontal lobes alleviates certain forms of mental illness. Presumably these mental derangements were brought on by excessive worry, feelings of guilt, etc., and were thus helped by destruction of the frontal lobes. Of course, the operation, called prefrontal lobotomy, was not carried out with a crowbar, nor were the lobes actually destroyed. Instead, the fibers connecting the frontal lobes to the thalamus were simply severed.

Today, the operation is performed only infrequently. For one thing, many desirable, human, attributes are irrevocably lost as a result of the operation. Furthermore, the development of potent tranquilizing drugs has permitted doctors to achieve the same type of improvement in a much less drastic way.

Our discussion of the forebrain would not be complete without mention of the thalamus and hypothalamus (Fig. 28-7). The thalamus is the "gatekeeper" of the cerebral cortex. All sensory messages reaching the brain must pass through the thalamus in order to be sensed consciously.

We have already discussed some of the important functions carried out by the hypothalamus. In addition to monitoring and regulating the temperature and water content of the blood, the hypothalamus is the coordinating center for many of the activities of our internal organs. In other animals, and perhaps in man, the hypothalamus is the center of such "feelings" as thirst, hunger, satiety, sex drive, and rage. The hypothalamus not only has nervous activity but also, as we have seen, produces hormones. Two of these (oxytocin and vasopressin) are stored in the posterior lobe of the pituitary before being released into the bloodstream. Others pass to the anterior lobe of the pituitary in veins draining the hypothalamus. There they stimulate the release of the anterior lobe's own hormones.

INHIBITION OF THE CENTRAL NERVOUS SYSTEM   28-10

Neurons are extremely sensitive to lack of oxygen. Deprivation for as little as 10 minutes can cause permanent damage to them. It is interesting that the sensitivity of our nervous system to oxygen lack seems to decrease from "top to bottom"; that is, the frontal lobes of the forebrain are most sensitive and the medulla oblongata of the hindbrain least sensitive.

The same pattern of sensitivity occurs in alcohol intoxication. Despite the common belief to the contrary, ethyl alcohol (beverage alcohol) is not a stimulant. It has a depressant effect on the neurons of the central nervous system. This seems to occur first in the frontal lobes, and the resulting removal of inhibitions may well give rise to the illusion of being stimulated. As the level of alcohol in the bloodstream increases, one can watch the progressive symptoms resulting from the depression of lower and lower brain centers. Loss of coordination and insensitivity to touch and pain occur as the motor and sensory regions of the cortex become inhibited. Depression of the visual area of the cortex produces faulty vision; depression of the reticular formation, unconsciousness. In rare cases, people have ingested enough alcohol to depress even the medulla oblongata. Death is the result.

THE PERIPHERAL NERVOUS SYSTEM OF MAN

The peripheral nervous system is made up of the sensory and motor nerve fibers which run to and from the central nervous system and the rest of the body. It can be subdivided into the sensory-somatic system and the autonomic system.

THE SENSORY-SOMATIC SYSTEM   28-11

The sensory-somatic system consists of 12 pairs of cranial nerves, not all of which are *mixed* nerves (see Section 28-6), and 31 pairs of spinal nerves, all of which are mixed. These nerves transmit impulses from our receptors (chiefly of external stimuli) to the central nervous system. They also transmit impulses from the central nervous system to all the skeletal muscles of the body.

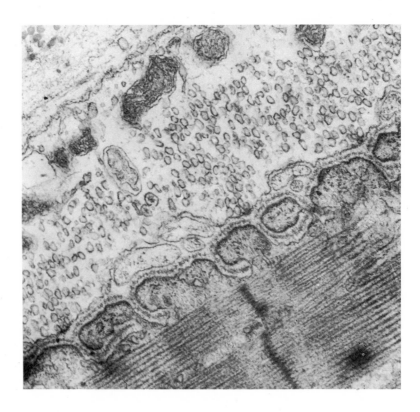

Fig. 28-9   The neuromuscular junction. Many vesicles can be seen in the portion of the motor end plate shown. These are thought to contain acetylcholine. Its release into the gap next to the folded membrane of the muscle fiber (running diagonally upward from the lower left) initiates the events leading to contraction. (Courtesy Prof. B. Katz.)

Impulses traveling down motor neurons of the sensory-somatic system cause the skeletal muscle fibers at which they terminate to contract. Body movement results. The junction between the terminal end of the motor neuron and the muscle fiber is called the **neuromuscular junction.** Its properties are quite like those of a synapse. The tips of the motor axons are called motor end plates (Fig. 28-9). They contain thousands of tiny vesicles, in or on which are molecules of ACh. When a nerve impulse reaches the motor end plate, hundreds of vesicles release their ACh onto the surface of the muscle fiber. As is the case in a synapse, this reduces the membrane potential of the muscle fiber and initiates a stimulating impulse along it. Muscle contraction follows. With the job completed, acetylcholinesterase destroys the liberated ACh and leaves the field cleared for another impulse.

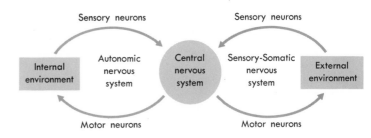

Fig. 28-10

Relationship between the three major divisions of the nervous system.

All our conscious awareness of the external environment and all our motor activity to cope with it operate through the sensory-somatic portion of the peripheral nervous system (Fig. 28-10).

THE AUTONOMIC NERVOUS SYSTEM   28-12

The autonomic nervous system consists of sensory and motor neurons running between the central nervous system (especially the hypothalamus) and the various internal organs: the heart, viscera, and many glands, both exocrine and endocrine. It is thus responsible for detecting certain conditions in the internal environment and bringing about appropriate changes in them.

The actions of the autonomic nervous system are almost entirely involuntary in contrast to those of the sensory-somatic system. Another difference between the two systems is that two groups of motor neurons are used to stimulate the effectors instead of just one. The first, or *preganglionic,* neurons arise in the central nervous system and run to a ganglion in the body. Here they synapse with the second, *postganglionic,* neurons which run to the effector. The autonomic nervous system has two subdivisions, the sympathetic and parasympathetic nervous systems, each with its special organization and functions.

The Sympathetic Nervous System   28-13

The preganglionic motor neurons of the sympathetic nervous system arise in the spinal cord. They leave by way of the ventral root of a spinal nerve and pass into a sympathetic ganglion (Fig. 28-11). These ganglia are organized into two chains running parallel to and on either side of the spinal cord (Fig. 28-12). The preganglionic neuron may do one of three things in the sympathetic ganglion. It may (1) synapse with postganglionic neurons which then re-enter the spinal nerve and ultimately pass out to the sweat glands and the walls of blood vessels near the surface of the body, (2) pass up or down the sympathetic chain and finally synapse with postganglionic neurons in a higher or lower ganglion, or (3) leave the ganglion by way of a cord leading to special ganglia (e.g. the solar plexus) in the viscera (Fig. 28-12). *Here* it may synapse with postganglionic neurons running to the muscular walls of the viscera. However, some of these preganglionic sympathetic neurons pass right on through this second ganglion and into the adrenal medulla. Here they synapse with the highly modified postganglionic cells which make up the secretory portion of the adrenal medulla.

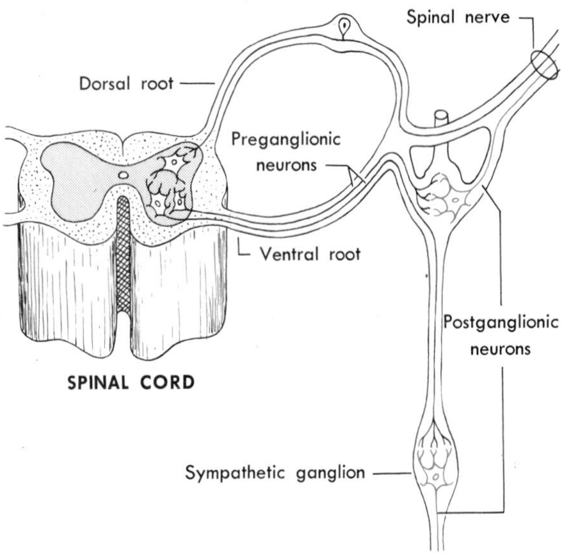

Fig. 28-11

Pathways of the sympathetic neurons. The preganglionic neurons are shown in black; the postganglionic neurons, in color.

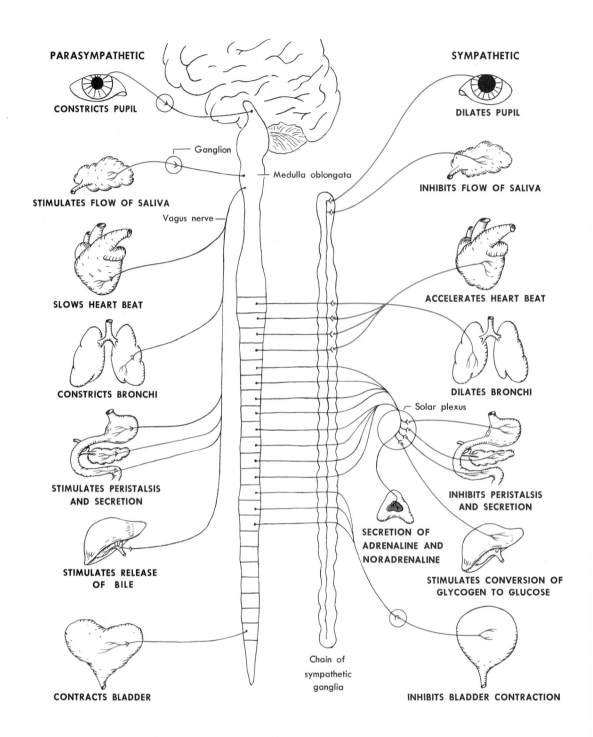

PARASYMPATHETIC

CONSTRICTS PUPIL

STIMULATES FLOW OF SALIVA

SLOWS HEART BEAT

CONSTRICTS BRONCHI

STIMULATES PERISTALSIS
AND SECRETION

STIMULATES RELEASE
OF BILE

CONTRACTS BLADDER

SYMPATHETIC

DILATES PUPIL

INHIBITS FLOW OF SALIVA

ACCELERATES HEART BEAT

DILATES BRONCHI

INHIBITS PERISTALSIS
AND SECRETION

SECRETION OF
ADRENALINE AND
NORADRENALINE

STIMULATES CONVERSION OF
GLYCOGEN TO GLUCOSE

INHIBITS BLADDER CONTRACTION

Ganglion

Medulla oblongata

Vagus nerve

Solar plexus

Chain of
sympathetic
ganglia

Fig. 28-12 The autonomic nervous system. The sympathetic nerves prepare the body for emergencies. The parasympathetic nerves reverse the effects of sympathetic stimulation. The preganglionic neurons are shown in black; the postganglionic neurons, in color.

The transmitter substance of the preganglionic sympathetic neurons is ACh. It serves to transmit impulses to the postganglionic neurons. A chemical stimulator is also released by the end plates of the postganglionic neurons. In most cases, this is noradrenaline, although in some other animals (for example the frog) the sympathetic fibers release adrenaline instead. The action of noradrenaline (or adrenaline) on a specific gland or muscle is excitatory in some cases, inhibitory in others. Its release by these end plates stimulates heartbeat, raises blood pressure, dilates the pupils, dilates the trachea and bronchi, and stimulates the conversion of liver glycogen into glucose. Sympathetic stimulation also shunts blood away from the skin and viscera to the skeletal muscles, brain, and heart. It inhibits peristalsis in the alimentary canal and contraction of the bladder and rectum. In short, stimulation of the sympathetic branch of the autonomic nervous system duplicates most, if not all, of those actions carried out by the adrenaline and noradrenaline released into the blood by the adrenal medulla. This should not be surprising when we remember that the adrenal medulla really is a part of the sympathetic nervous system, its secretory cells being modified postganglionic cells.

The actions produced by stimulation of the sympathetic nervous system are quite general. There are two reasons for this. One is that a single preganglionic neuron usually synapses with about three postganglionic neurons. What starts as a single impulse becomes magnified into three. Second, the release of adrenaline and noradrenaline into the bloodstream ensures that every cell of the body will be exposed to these substances when necessary, even if no postganglionic neurons reach them directly.

The Parasympathetic Nervous System 28-14

The main nerve of the parasympathetic system is the tenth cranial nerve, the **vagus** nerve, which arises in the medulla oblongata. Other preganglionic parasympathetic neurons also extend from the brain as well as the lower tip of the spinal cord (Fig. 28-12.)

Each preganglionic parasympathetic neuron synapses with only one postganglionic neuron, which is located near or in its effector organ, a muscle or gland. The end brushes of the preganglionic neurons and the end plates of the postganglionic neurons both release acetylcholine. Stimulation of the parasympathetic nerves causes a slowing down of heartbeat, lowering of blood pressure, constriction of the pupils, increased blood flow to the skin and viscera, and promotes peristalsis in the alimentary canal. In brief, the parasympathetic nervous system serves to return our body functions to normal after they have been altered by sympathetic stimulation. In times of danger, the sympathetic nervous system prepares us for violent physical activity such as fighting or fleeing. These changes would be harmful if prolonged unnecessarily, and the parasympathetic system reverses them when the danger is over. We must therefore include the antagonistic activity of these two branches of the autonomic nervous system among the most important body mechanisms for maintaining homeostasis.

The discovery that specific chemical substances are released when either branch of the autonomic nervous system is stimulated was made by the Nobel Prize-winning physiologist, Otto Loewi, in 1920. He carefully removed the living heart of a frog with its sympathetic (accelerator) and parasympathetic nerve supply intact. As was expected, electrical stimulation of the first speeded up the heart while stimulation of the second slowed it down.

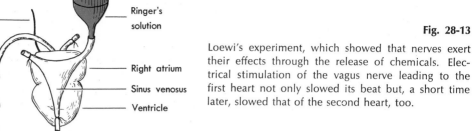

Fig. 28-13

Loewi's experiment, which showed that nerves exert their effects through the release of chemicals. Electrical stimulation of the vagus nerve leading to the first heart not only slowed its beat but, a short time later, slowed that of the second heart, too.

Loewi also found that these two responses would occur in a second frog heart if he simply bathed it with Ringer's solution taken from the stimulated heart (Fig. 28-13). This showed that chemical substances were produced by the first heart which duplicated the action of nervous stimulation. In the case of parasympathetic (vagus) stimulation, the substance was later identified as acetylcholine. During sympathetic stimulation, adrenaline (in the frog) is released.

28-15   **SUMMARY**

In these chapters we have distinguished between chemical coordination and nervous coordination of body functions. Now we see that all coordination is really chemical. The only thing which differs is the means used to distribute the chemical. Hormones are transported throughout the body by the bloodstream. Transmitter substances are deposited in specific, localized spots by the action of the end plates of motor neurons.

By its very organization, the latter system permits more rapid, more specific, more variable body activity than the former. There is still another advantage to it. Localized release of transmitter substances by motor neurons permits the build-up of a higher concentration of the substance than could safely be tolerated by the body as a whole. It has recently been shown that the concentration of noradrenaline necessary to stimulate cells in the fatty tissue of laboratory mice and rats would be very harmful if allowed to circulate freely in the bloodstream. Its localized production by sympathetic neurons leading to the fatty tissue avoids this danger.

The body cannot respond to changes in its environment without the third essential feature of nervous coordination: the effectors. These are the structures that take action. Their morphology and physiology is the topic of the next chapter.

EXERCISES AND PROBLEMS

1   Meningitis is an inflammatory disease of what body structures?

2   What parts of the nervous system participate in the maintenance of balance and coordinated body movements?

3   Trace the route taken by nerve impulses arising when a withdrawal reflex is initiated.

4 The drug mecholyl stimulates parasympathetic nervous activity. What is its effect on (a) the pupil, (b) the salivary glands?

5 The drug atropine inhibits parasympathetic activity. Why is it used by ophthalmologists who wish to examine the interior of a patient's eye?

6 Damage in the left hemisphere of the brain interferes with the proper functioning of which side of the body?

7 Distinguish between cranial nerves and spinal nerves.

8 Describe the changes that occur in the body in times of emergency. Tell how each change helps prepare the body to cope with the emergency.

9 Distinguish between a nerve and a neuron.

10 What are ganglia?

REFERENCES

Most of the following articles from *Scientific American* are available in inexpensive reprints distributed by W. H. Freeman and Company, San Francisco, California:

1 Katz, B., "How Cells Communicate," *Scientific American*, Reprint No. 98, September, 1961. An excellent summary of the structure and function of neurons.

2 Baker, P. F., "The Nerve Axon," *Scientific American*, Reprint No. 1038, March, 1966. Tells how experiments with the giant axon of the squid have helped reveal the nature of the nerve impulse.

3 Eccles, Sir John, "The Synapse," *Scientific American*, Reprint No. 1001, January, 1965. Describes how both excitatory and inhibitory synapses work.

4 Wilson, V. J., "Inhibition in the Central Nervous System," *Scientific American*, May, 1966. Discusses four ways in which inhibitory association neurons help to improve the precision of our muscular actions.

5 Snider, R. S., "The Cerebellum," *Scientific American*, Reprint No. 38, August, 1958.

6 French, J. D., "The Reticular Formation," *Scientific American*, Reprint No. 66, May, 1957.

7 Gray, G. W., "The Great Ravelled Knot," *Scientific American*, Reprint No. 13, October, 1948. Deals with the discoveries leading us to a better understanding of the functions of the cerebral cortex.

8 Funkenstein, D. H., "The Physiology of Fear and Anger," *Scientific American*, Reprint No. 428, May, 1955. Explores the hypothesis that whether one responds to a stress with fear or with anger is related to the relative amounts of adrenaline and noradrenaline secreted.

9 Guyton, A. C., *Textbook of Medical Physiology*, 2nd Edition, W. B. Saunders Company, Philadelphia, Penn., 1961. Chapters 46 through 47 and 56 through 60 treat most of the topics in this chapter in detail.

10 Loewi, O., "On the Humoral Transmission of the Action of Heart Nerves," *Great Experiments in Biology*, ed. by M. L. Gabriel and S. Fogel, Prentice-Hall, Inc., 1955. Loewi describes his discovery that nervous stimulation of the heart accomplishes its effects through the release of neurohumors.

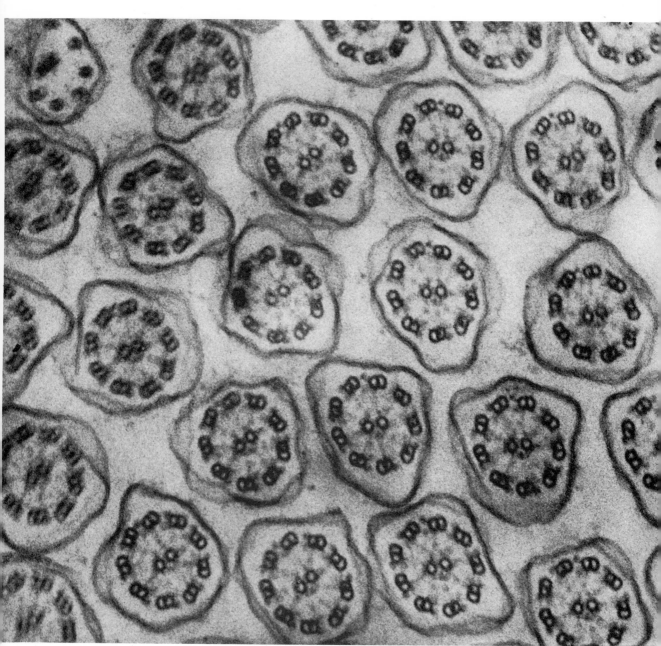

When we say that all living organisms respond to stimuli, we mean that they do things when the external or internal environment changes in a significant way. The cells, tissues, or organs with which animals carry out actions are called effectors. The most widespread and most important of the effectors are those which secrete substances and those which bring about motion.

Secretory effectors are glands. As we have noted previously, exocrine glands release the secreted material to the *external* environment through a duct. Endocrine glands release their secretions, hormones, into the *internal* environment. Glandular effectors are directly under either nervous control or chemical control or both.

CYTOPLASMIC STREAMING   29-1

Motion is a fundamental property of life. Plants, though they display no locomotion, do move in response to stimuli. These movements may be the result of unequal growth or of sudden changes in turgor (see Section 25-1). Even the contents of cells, especially plant cells, may be in motion. This phenomenon is known as cytoplasmic streaming. In plant cells, it usually occurs in a circular motion around the inner margin of the cell wall. Its function is probably the rapid distribution of materials throughout the cytoplasm. While the exact mechanism responsible for this motion is unknown, an abundance of microtubules (see Section 8-13) are found in streaming cytoplasm.

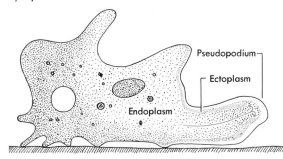

Pseudopodium

Ectoplasm

Endoplasm

Fig. 29-1

Amoeboid movement. The clear layer at the tip of the pseudopodium is water that is freed when the endoplasm is converted into ectoplasm.

In some animals and protists, the movements of cytoplasm within the cell may bring about locomotion of the cell. Both the amoeba and a white blood corpuscle move by the streaming of their cytoplasm into **pseudopodia.** Energy in the form of ATP is needed, and proteins which contract in the presence of ATP have been isolated from the amoeba. However, the exact mechanism by which the energy is converted into motion is not yet known. (Several theories are examined in references No. 1 and No. 3 cited at the end of the chapter.) It seems to depend on changes in the properties of the cytoplasm itself. The cytoplasm in the interior of the amoeba, the "endoplasm," is watery. This endoplasm flows into the growing pseudopod (Fig. 29-1). As it does so, it becomes converted into a clear, semisolid "ectoplasm." At the rear of the cell, the opposite change takes place and thus the balance of endoplasm and ectoplasm is maintained. Probably it is the contraction of cytoplasmic proteins that brings the endoplasm forward into the pseudopodium, but just where the force is exerted remains to be established.

◀ Cross sections of cilia on the gill of a fresh-water mussel, 98,000 X.
(Courtesy Dr. Peter Satir.)

Other protists move by means of many fine, hairlike cilia or one or more longer, whiplike flagella. Although cilia and flagella seem rather distinct in form, studies with the electron microscope reveal that they have the same basic structure and function in about the same way. Highly magnified cross sections of both cilia and flagella show that they are made up of a cylindrical array of long protein fibrils. Nine of these are evenly spaced around the periphery of the cylinder. Each appears to be a microtubule (see Section 8-13) with an accessory tubule attached to it. This gives them a "figure 8" appearance when viewed in cross section (Fig. 29-2). Running up through the center of the bundle are two fibrils, which are circular in cross section and identical to microtubules. The entire assembly of fibrils is sheathed in a membrane which is simply an extension of the cell membrane.

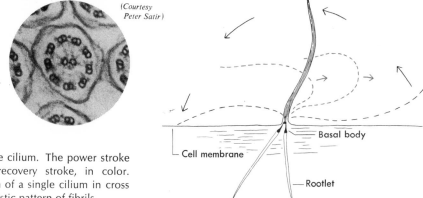

(Courtesy Peter Satir)

Fig. 29-2

At right, drawing of a single cilium. The power stroke is shown in black; the recovery stroke, in color. Above, electron micrograph of a single cilium in cross section. Note the characteristic pattern of fibrils.

Each cilium (and flagellum) is attached to a basal body embedded in the cytoplasm. Basal bodies are identical to centrioles (see Section 8-14) and are, in fact, produced by them. For example, one of the centrioles in developing sperm cells becomes a basal body and produces a flagellum after it has completed its role in the distribution of chromosomes during cell division (see Section 22-1).

No one yet knows just how cilia and flagella work. One theory that has been proposed is that an impulse starts in the basal body and passes up the central fibrils. This causes the outer fibrils on one side to contract rapidly, producing a "power stroke." Then a second impulse passes directly, but slowly, up the outer fibrils on the opposite side. This causes them to contract slowly, thus bringing the cilium back in a "recovery stroke" (Fig. 29-2). The motion of flagella is usually more complex, involving rippling and lashing movements. ATP is the source of energy for the motion of both cilia and flagella.

Cilia and flagella are not found just in the protists. The sperm cells of all animals and even of many plants (mosses, for example) move by means of flagella. Ferns produce ciliated sperm cells. Ciliated epithelial cells are found in almost all animals except arthropods and nematodes. These cells are not free to move, but the beating of their cilia moves the ECF past them.

In man, cilia are present in the epithelial cells lining his air passages. A flagellum propels his sperm cells. Even movement by pseudopodia is found in his wandering white blood corpuscles. However, the chief effectors in man for achieving motion are his muscles.

HUMAN MUSCLES AND HOW THEY WORK

Three distinct kinds of muscles are found in the human. **Skeletal** muscle is attached to the skeleton and permits locomotion. **Cardiac** muscle makes up the heart, and its contraction forces blood through the circulatory system. **Smooth** muscle lines the walls of all our other hollow organs and its contraction regulates the size of these organs.

Voluntary, directed body movements, such as those that occur when someone throws a ball or runs a race, would be impossible without the structural and functional coordination of both the skeletal muscles and the skeleton to which they are attached.

THE HUMAN SKELETON   **29-3**

The human skeleton is made up of cartilage and bone. The nature of both these types of supporting connective tissue was discussed in Section 8-20, 2. Two hundred and six bones are found in most humans. These range in size from the tiny ossicles of the middle ear to the thigh bone or femur (Fig. 29-4). The bones of the skeleton are attached to one another at **joints,** most of which are held together by **ligaments,** a type of binding connective tissue. Motion of the skeleton is brought about by exertion of a muscular force across the joint. The motion of the lower arm illustrates this principle nicely. The upper-arm bone, the *humerus,* forms a "hinge" joint with one of the two-lower-arm bones, the *ulna* (Fig. 29-3). The *biceps* muscle runs from the humerus to a second lower-arm bone, the *radius,* which is held parallel to the ulna. Thus, contraction of the muscle causes the arm joint to be bent. The biceps muscle is thus a *flexor*. Because muscles can exert force only when contracting, not when relaxing, a second muscle, an *extensor*, is needed to straighten the joint. The *triceps* muscle, which extends from humerus to ulna, accomplishes this. Similar pairs of muscles, working antagonistically across joints, enable us to carry out almost all our skeletal movements.

The two ends of a skeletal muscle are not attached to the skeleton in the same way. Referring again to the triceps muscle, we see that the upper end, or **origin,** is attached directly to a large area of the humerus. The lower end, or **insertion,** tapers into a glistening white **tendon** which is attached to the ulna. During contraction, the origin remains stationary while the insertion does the moving. This pattern is found throughout the body.

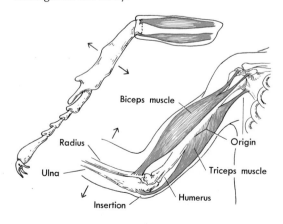

Biceps muscle

Radius

Ulna

Origin

Triceps muscle

Insertion

Humerus

Fig. 29-3

Mechanism of skeletal movement in the arthropod (above) and in the human (below). Antagonistic pairs of skeletal muscles accomplish movement of both exoskeletons and endoskeletons.

Fig. 29-4   The human skeleton.

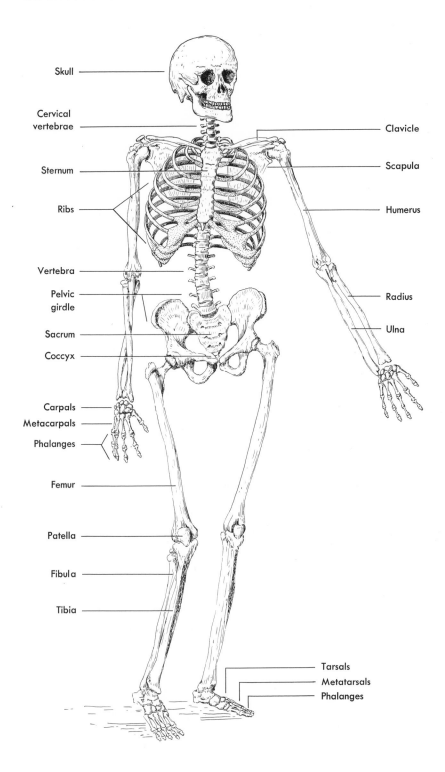

Skull

Cervical
vertebrae

Sternum

Ribs

Vertebra

Pelvic
girdle

Sacrum

Coccyx

Carpals

Metacarpals

Phalanges

Femur

Patella

Fibula

Tibia

Clavicle

Scapula

Humerus

Radius

Ulna

Tarsals

Metatarsals

Phalanges

Our skeleton has other functions besides motion. It provides a supporting framework for the soft organs of the body. For example, the bones of the pelvis support a large part of the weight of the viscera. The skeleton also provides protection against mechanical damage to delicate internal organs. Thus, the skull protects the brain, the spinal column of vertebrae protects the spinal cord, and the ribs and breastbone (sternum) protect the lungs and heart. Some of our bones (e.g., sternum, rib bones) possess a central, marrow-filled chamber. As we saw in Section 14-12, red and white blood corpuscles are manufactured here.

THE ARTHROPOD SKELETON — 29-4

Skeletal muscle is the only kind of muscle found in arthropods, and thus it carries out the movements of the digestive tract, heart, etc. as well as those of locomotion. The latter occurs by means of antagonistic pairs of muscles working against the joints of the exoskeleton. Note, however, that the muscles are attached *internally* (Fig. 29-3).

The arthropod exoskeleton also provides support and protection to the soft, delicate internal organs. In fact, an exoskeleton, like a suit of armor, provides more protection than an internal skeleton. However, an exoskeleton (also like a suit of armor) imposes severe weight limitations on its owner. The volume of any growing thing, whether it be a single cell (see Fig. 8-11) or an entire organism, increases more rapidly than its surface area. Other things being equal, a 2-ft long arthropod will have eight times the volume but only four times the surface area of a 1-ft long specimen. The weight of the animal increases in proportion to its volume but the size of the exoskeleton increases only in proportion to the surface area. In order to support its much greater weight, the 2-ft arthropod would have to have a thicker exoskeleton, and added thickness would reduce its maneuverability drastically. It is no wonder, then, that insects never become very large. In fact, our large arthropods, such as the lobster and the horseshoe crab, *Limulus,* are too encumbered to move quickly except when buoyed up by the watery medium in which they live.

A rigid exoskeleton presents problems to a growing arthropod. Growth can take place only by periodically shedding the old exoskeleton (molting) and forming a new one. During the time that the new exoskeleton is hardening, the arthropod is quite vulnerable to its enemies.

THE STRUCTURE OF SKELETAL MUSCLE — 29-5

A single skeletal muscle, such as the biceps muscle, consists of a thickened muscle *belly* attached at each end to bone. A cross section through the belly of the muscle reveals thousands of muscle **fibers** (Fig. 29-5). All these are arranged parallel to one another and probably extend uninterrupted from origin to insertion. The fibers are bound together by connective tissue through which blood vessels and nerves also run. The number of fibers in a muscle is probably fixed. Increased strength and size of the muscle is produced by an increase in the thickness of the individual fibers and an increase in the amount of other tissue, such as blood vessels and connective tissue, in the muscle.

Seen from the side, the muscle fibers show a pattern of cross-banding or striations. This banded appearance gives rise to another common name for skeletal muscle: striated muscle.

Although they may be many inches long, single muscle fibers range from only about 10μ to 100μ in diameter. A magnified cross section of a single muscle fiber reveals that it is packed with **myofibrils** in much the same way the muscle belly was packed with muscle fibers. The myofibrils are all stacked lengthwise and seem to run the entire length of the fiber. The myofibrils are embedded in a liquid cytoplasm which also contains many nuclei, mitochondria, and an extensive endoplasmic reticulum. The presence of many nuclei is a consequence of the fact that during embryonic development each muscle fiber is formed by the fusion of a number of individual cells. Strictly speaking, then, the muscle fiber is not really a cell but a syncytium (see Section 8-17). For this reason, its parts are often given special names (e.g. sarcolemma for cell membrane, sarcoplasmic reticulum for endoplasmic reticulum), although this tends to obscure the essential similarity in structure and function of these structures and those that are found in "true" cells.

The nuclei are located just beneath the cell membrane (Fig. 29-5). The mitochondria and the tubes of the endoplasmic reticulum are found between the myofibrils.

The pattern of striations in a muscle fiber arises from the striations present in the individual myofibrils. Normally, these are all in register with one another, although in specimens prepared for electron microscopy, the parallel registration is usually disrupted.

With the electron microscope, it is now possible to examine the structure of an individual myofibril. In cross section, these are seen to be made up of a neat geometrical array of **filaments.** These filaments are of two sizes, thick and thin, the former about 16 mμ and the latter about 6 mμ in diameter. Chemical analysis of the myofibrils indicates that the thick filaments are made up of a protein, **myosin,** while the thin filaments are made up of a second protein, **actin.**

Longitudinal examination of myofibrils shows that the filaments do not extend the entire length of the myofibril but are stacked in repeating arrays, called sarcomeres, that are arranged end-to-end throughout the length of the myofibril. The boundaries of the

Fig. 29-5

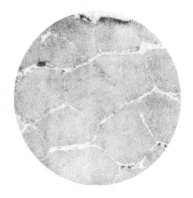

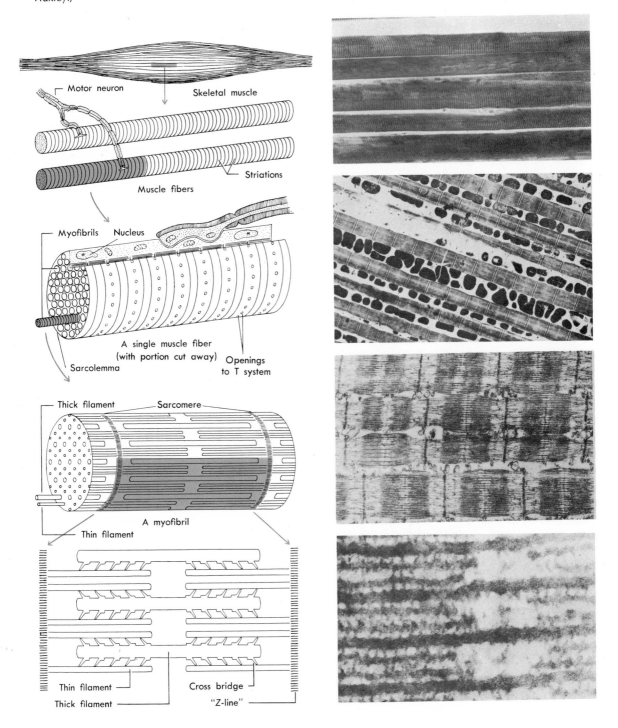

Organization of skeletal muscle at various levels of magnification. The pictures on the opposite page are cross sections corresponding roughly to the drawings on the left, below. The pictures on the right are corresponding longitudinal views. (All electron micrographs courtesy Dr. H. E. Huxley.)

Fig. 29-5
(cont.)

Motor neuron

Skeletal muscle

Striations

Muscle fibers

Myofibrils   Nucleus

A single muscle fiber
(with portion cut away)

Openings
to T system

Sarcolemma

Thick filament   Sarcomere

A myofibril

Thin filament

Thin filament

Thick filament

Cross bridge

"Z-line"

sarcomeres (called the "Z-lines") and the overlapping of the thick and thin filaments produce the pattern of striations characteristic of the myofibrils and, for that matter, of the whole fiber. It is easy to see that less light will pass through the portions where the thick and thin filaments overlap than where they do not.

29-6   THE PHYSIOLOGY OF THE MUSCLE FIBER

The exterior of the skeletal muscle fiber, like that of the neuron, is positively charged (about 0.1 volt) with respect to the interior. This polarization of the membrane is maintained by the active transport of Na^+ and K^+ ions just as in the neuron. Electric shocks and certain chemical substances are capable of reducing this polarity which, again like the neuron, increases the permeability of the membrane to Na^+ ions. If the stimulus has sufficient strength, the threshold of the fiber is reached and a wave of depolarization, the **action current,** sweeps down the length of the fiber. The response is "all-or-none" in that the fiber either fires or does not. A stimulus greater than threshold produces no greater response than a threshold stimulus.

No visible change takes place in the muscle fiber during the period in which the action current is sweeping down it. Hence, this period which may be from 3 to 10 msec long, depending on the particular fiber studied, is called the **latent period.** During this time, the action current also penetrates the interior of the fiber. This is important because the efficient contraction of the muscle fiber requires that all its myofibrils receive the signal to contract at approximately the same time. Spaced evenly along and around each fiber are inpocketings of its membrane which carry the action current into the interior. This is known as the T system (Fig. 29-5). The tubes of the T system terminate at the "Z-line" of the myofibrils, that is, at the boundaries of each sarcomere. The endoplasmic reticulum is particularly well developed in this region, and it is thought that the arrival of the action current triggers the release of calcium (Ca^{++}) ions by the endoplasmic reticulum. The Ca^{++} ions, in some way, cause contraction of the sarcomeres. Thus the entire fiber contracts. Over a period of about 50 msec, the fiber shortens, exerting a force if there is any resistance offered to its shortening. While the fiber is contracting, the pattern of light and dark striations is altered, indicating, presumably, that the thick and thin filaments in the myofibrils are sliding over one another. Chemical studies confirm that actin and myosin link together during contraction of the fiber, and the electron microscope shows cross bridges between the two kinds of filaments. The protein molecules of these cross bridges may actually contract, pulling the actin and myosin filaments past each other in a ratchetlike action (Fig. 29-5). In any case, we know that the individual *filaments* do not shorten, thicken, or fold during the process.

Contraction of the muscle fiber (which is also all-or-none) is automatically followed by relaxation if the fiber is not stimulated again. The fiber takes about 50 msec to resume its original length. However, the fiber will not relax if it is stimulated again before the relaxation period begins. There is only a 7-msec **refractory period** after the action current sweeps down the muscle fiber. Then the polarity of the membrane is restored by the passage of K^+ ions out of the cell, and the fiber is ready to be stimulated again. Note that the refractory period is much shorter than the time it actually takes the fiber to contract and relax. This means that the fiber can be maintained in the contracted state so long as it is stimulated frequently enough (50 stimuli/sec does very nicely). Such sustained maximal contraction is called **tetanus.** As we normally use our muscles, the individual fibers usually go into tetanus for brief periods rather than simply undergo single twitches.

The stimulus that depolarizes the skeletal muscle fiber is ACh released at the neuromuscular junction (see Section 28-11). This acts upon the muscle fiber membrane, causing its depolarization. If sufficient ACh is released, the depolarization exceeds the threshold value and an action current is generated.

Once the ACh has done its job, it must be removed in order to prevent permanent tetanus of the muscle fiber. This is accomplished by the enzyme acetylcholinesterase, which quickly breaks the ACh down into inactive products and clears the field of action.

Anything which interferes with the action of acetylcholinesterase causes a serious disturbance of muscular activity. A great many substances have been discovered which do just this and, in every case, they are quite poisonous. Powerful organophosphate insecticides, such as parathion and the closely related "nerve gases," function in this way. Exposures to toxic amounts of these substances leads to convulsions, paralysis, and perhaps death.

In man, motor neurons have only a stimulating effect on muscular contraction. Inhibition of muscles occurs as a result of preventing nerve impulses in the central nervous system from reaching specific motor neurons. In the crayfish, however, motor neurons have been found which release a hyperpolarizing substance at the neuromuscular junction, thus inhibiting contraction of the muscle fiber. It should be clear that the properties of the neuromuscular junction and the synapse are very much alike. Just as the synapse can become fatigued through repeated use, so can the neuromuscular junction, but fatigue at this site does not appear as quickly as it does at the synapse.

THE PHYSIOLOGY OF THE ENTIRE MUSCLE 29-7

Although the individual muscle fiber is the *structural* unit of skeletal muscle, it is not the *functional unit.* All motor neurons leading to skeletal muscles have branching axons, each of which terminates in a neuromuscular junction with a single muscle fiber. Nerve impulses passing down a single motor neuron will thus trigger contraction in all the muscle fibers at which the branches of that neuron terminate. This minimum unit of contraction is called the **motor unit.** For some muscles over which we have very precise control (for example, the muscles controlling eye movements) a single motor neuron may trigger only 2 to 6 muscle fibers. For other muscles (e.g. the biceps) over which our control is less precise, the motor units may include several hundred muscle fibers (scattered fairly uniformly through the muscle belly).

We have seen that the response of a single muscle fiber is all-or-none. Nevertheless, we know that an entire muscle does not behave in this fashion. It is possible to contract a muscle any desired degree from practically relaxed to maximally contracted. This can be demonstrated in the laboratory by stimulating the calf muscle (gastrocnemius) of a frog with an electrical stimulator and measuring, by means of a writing lever, the amount of contraction of the entire muscle. Too weak a shock will have no effect at all. When threshold is reached, the muscle twitches slightly. Then as the strength of the stimulus is increased, the amount of contraction increases up to a maximum. Still greater stimuli are no more effective (Fig. 29-6). How can we reconcile this graded response of the entire muscle with the all-or-none properties of the individual fibers which make it up? The answer is that the strength of contraction of an entire muscle increases as the number of individual contracting fibers increases. Thus, in the intact animal, the strength of the muscular response is controlled by the *number of motor units* activated by the central nervous system.

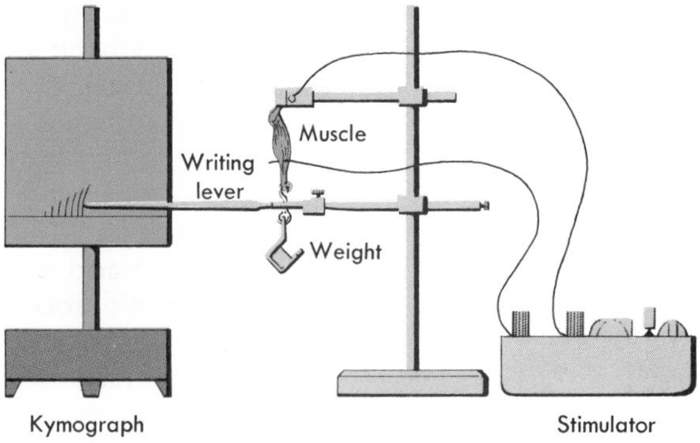

Fig. 29-6

Measuring the response of the calf muscle (gastrocnemius) of a frog to single shocks of increasing voltage. Contraction of the muscle lifts the writing lever, which makes a mark on the paper wrapped around the kymograph drum.

Even at rest, most of our skeletal muscles are in a state of partial contraction called **tonus.** If this were not so, we would have a very difficult time maintaining good posture. The action of the motor units provides us with a physical basis for tonus. A few motor units are activated at all times even in the resting muscle. As one set of motor units relaxes, another set takes over. This synchronous activation and de-activation of a small percentage of the total number of motor units maintains the tonus of our skeletal muscles.

29-8 **THE CHEMISTRY OF MUSCULAR CONTRACTION**

Muscular contraction produces heat and may perform work. It therefore cannot occur without a source of energy. The energy comes from the same source as the energy for all other types of cellular work: the high energy phosphate bonds of ATP.

Contraction of muscle fibers requires actin, myosin, ATP, Ca^{++}, and Mg^{++} ions. Even in the test tube, actin and myosin strands can be made to contract when supplied with ATP and traces of the necessary ions. The exact chemical mechanism is not fully understood, but the passage of the action current through the T system leads to the release of Ca^{++} ions by the endoplasmic reticulum and the union of actin and myosin to form actomyosin. Actomyosin is a powerful ATPase, that is, it is an enzyme that splits the third phosphate group from the ATP molecule. This leaves actomyosin and ADP and a phosphate group. In some way, the energy initially stored in the high-energy phosphate bond is used to provide the energy for contraction. Then the Ca^{++} ions are taken back into the endoplasmic reticulum, the actin and myosin become separated, and the ADP is resynthesized into ATP in the mitochondria. Figure 29-5 shows how the mitochondria are arranged in neat rows between the myofibrils of the flight muscles of a blowfly. The mitochondria manufacture ATP by the process of cellular respiration and this ATP is released just where it can be most efficiently used.

Very little ATP is stored in the muscle fiber. A burst of muscular activity quickly (after a few twitches) exhausts the supply. Additional ATP can be supplied by cellular respiration, but if violent, continued muscular activity is called for, the output from this source will be temporarily unable to meet the demand. This is because there is a definite delay in the increase of the rate and strength of heartbeat, the rate and depth of breathing, and hence in the transport of additional supplies of oxygen to the muscle. Fortunately, our muscles are equipped to carry on successfully during this lag period.

Each muscle fiber contains a supply of **creatine-phosphate.** This substance contains a phosphate group attached by a high-energy bond and thus can serve as a reservoir of $\sim P$. The creatine-phosphate serves to resynthesize ATP by giving up its high-energy phosphate to ADP. This mechanism enables muscles to work at the maximum rate for about 15 sec. During violent effort, however, even 15 sec is not enough time for the heart and lungs to adapt to the oxygen requirements of the muscles. To bridge the gap, the muscle fibers manufacture ATP by fermentation. Glycogen stored in the muscle is broken down into lactic acid by the mechanism we discussed in Chapter 11 (see Section 11-2). Although this process (which takes place in the endoplasmic reticulum) produces ATP and thus enables the muscle to keep functioning, it is only a temporary expedient. As we have noted, fermentation is an extremely inefficient method of energy production. Most of the potential energy of the glycogen remains trapped in the lactic acid. Furthermore, the accumulation of lactic acid lowers the pH of the muscle fluids. If the pH shift is too great, the muscle fiber loses its ability to contract, thus becoming *fatigued.* A general lowering of the pH of the ECF may produce serious consequences elsewhere in the body, too.

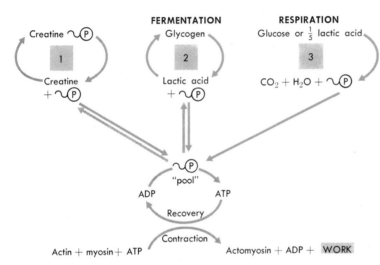

Fig. 29-7

The chemistry of muscular contraction. (Pathways in color function during payment of oxygen debt.)

Therefore, protracted muscular exertion, such as that which occurs in running or swimming a distance race, requires that the heart and lungs quickly supply sufficient oxygen to the muscles to enable ATP to be produced by cellular respiration. When the race is finally over, we all know that the rates of breathing and heartbeat do not drop back to normal levels immediately. First, the **oxygen debt** must be paid. This is the quantity of oxygen which was needed by the muscles for respiration during the early part of the race but was not supplied. In chemical terms, it is measured by the accumulation of lactic acid during that period. Lactic acid leaves the muscle cells (by way of the intracellular channels provided by the endoplasmic reticulum) and is carried in the blood to the liver. Here payment of the oxygen debt takes place. It is accomplished by the respiration of about 1/5 of the accumulated lactic acid to CO_2, H_2O, and ATP. The ATP is then used to resynthesize glycogen from the remaining 4/5 of the lactic acid. *Muscle* glycogen is restored by transport of glucose from the liver to the muscles. Note, too, that just as soon as a little excess ATP becomes available in the muscle fiber, it is used to resynthesize creatine-phosphate, thus refilling the reservoir of high-energy phosphate bonds (Fig. 29-7).

HEAT PRODUCTION

The conversion of the chemical energy of ATP into the mechanical energy of muscle contraction is, at best, no more than 40% efficient. The remaining energy is liberated as heat, which is, however, a valuable by-product. Birds and mammals are homeothermic; that is, they are able to maintain the temperature of their ECF practically constant despite wide fluctuations in the temperature of the external environment. Even with the insulation provided by feathers and fur, these creatures lose heat to the environment whenever its temperature falls below that of their body. The process can be and is slowed by shutting down the capillary beds of the skin, thus cutting down the radiation of heat from the blood. To replace lost heat, however, the homeothermic organism depends primarily on the heat produced during muscular contraction. In fact, shivering is an involuntary muscular response during which virtually all of the energy of ATP is being converted into heat. The goose flesh that may appear on our skin at the same time is simply a now-useless response which, in our hairy ancestors, served to thicken the layer of fur and thus improve its insulating qualities.

Too great a production of heat in warm surroundings brings about reactions that aid in cooling the body. The capillary beds of the skin become filled with blood which is thus able to radiate the heat transported from the internal organs. The sweat glands secrete sweat which, as it evaporates, absorbs heat from the body, thus cooling it. Man is unusual among the mammals in possessing so many sweat glands scattered over the surface of his body. These probably compensate for his lack of body hair which, after all, is just as effective at keeping heat out as keeping it in.

The various responses of the body to heat and cold are regulated by the autonomic nervous system. The controlling impulses originate in the hypothalamus where the temperature of the blood is monitored constantly. The heat and cold receptors of the skin may also play a minor role in initiating these responses.

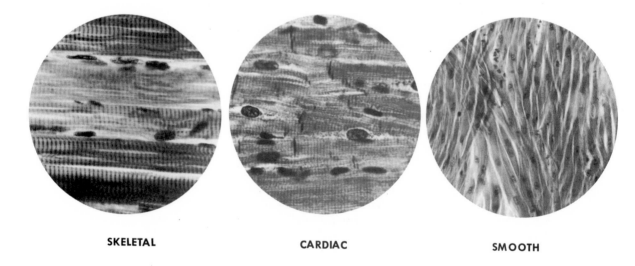

SKELETAL **CARDIAC** **SMOOTH**

Fig. 29-8 The three kinds of muscle as they appear under the light microscope. Skeletal and cardiac muscle are made up of long, multinucleate fibers. Smooth muscle is made up of single, spindle-shaped cells. (Skeletal muscle courtesy Ward's Natural Science Establishment, Inc. Others, courtesy General Biological Supply House, Inc.)

Cardiac muscle is made up of short, interlocking, striated fibers (Fig. 29-8). Each fiber is a single elongated cell. If you look back at Fig. 14-12, you will see that the myofibrils run roughly parallel to one another and that the organization of the sarcomeres is like that found in skeletal muscle. However, the myofibrils in cardiac muscle are often branched and mitochondria are more abundant than in our skeletal muscle fibers.

Cardiac muscle differs from skeletal muscle in its physiology as well. The impulse which causes cardiac muscle to contract is self-generated. It is true that sympathetic and parasympathetic nerves run to the heart, but their control is purely accessory. Even when they are destroyed, the heart continues to beat as long as glucose and oxygen are available.

The response of the entire heart muscle is all-or-none. Every beat is a maximal beat and uses all the energy available at that moment. Any deprivation of oxygen, such as that which occurs in a coronary occlusion (see Section 14-8), results in death of the portion of heart-muscle so deprived. Cardiac muscle, unlike skeletal muscle, has a longer refractory period than relaxation period. Hence, no tetanus is possible.

SMOOTH MUSCLE 29-11

Each smooth muscle fiber is a single spindle-shaped cell with a single nucleus (Fig. 29-8). The cells are arranged in sheets. Smooth muscle is also nonstriated muscle because no pattern of cross striations can be seen under the light microscope. However, the electron microscope has revealed that the cell is filled with very thin contractile filaments that are arranged parallel to the long axis of the cell. These filaments are made of actin. How they produce the force of contraction is not yet known.

Smooth muscle may sometimes contract spontaneously, but it is primarily controlled by the motor neurons of the sympathetic and parasympathetic nervous systems. It is not under voluntary control.

As we have seen, parasympathetic postganglionic neurons release ACh at their end plate just as the motor neurons of the sensory-somatic system do. Sympathetic postganglionic neurons usually release noradrenaline. The effect of these substances on a given piece of smooth muscle varies with the particular muscle but is always antagonistic. If ACh stimulates the muscle, noradrenaline inhibits it and vice versa. For example, ACh stimulates contraction of the muscular wall of the intestine while noradrenaline inhibits it. On the other hand, ACh inhibits the contraction of the muscular walls of the arteries supplying blood to the viscera while noradrenaline stimulates their contraction.

The action of smooth muscle is much slower than that of skeletal muscle. It may take anywhere from 3 seconds to 3 minutes for it to contract. Furthermore, smooth muscle differs from skeletal muscle in its ability to remain contracted at varying lengths. This state is also called tonus, but unlike tonus in skeletal muscle, it does not seem to require continual stimulation and energy production.

Smooth muscle lines the walls of all our hollow organs and vessels. Its contraction regulates the size of these structures and thus controls the passage of materials through them. Constriction of arteries and arterioles, emptying of the bladder, peristalsis in the alimentary canal, even childbirth all depend upon the special contractile properties of smooth muscle.

Smooth muscle is found exclusively in many invertebrates. The earthworm, for example, accomplishes all its body movements, including locomotion, with it alone.

OTHER EFFECTORS

Other effectors besides glands and locomotor structures are found here and there in the animal kingdom.

29-12 **ELECTRIC ORGANS**

Certain fishes (for example, the South American electric eel) possess electric organs. These are masses of flattened cells, called electroplates, which are stacked in neat rows along the sides of the animal. The posterior surface of each electroplate is supplied with a motor neuron; the anterior surface is not. At rest, the interior of each electroplate, like a muscle or nerve cell, is negatively charged with respect to the two exterior surfaces. The potential is about 0.08 volt but, because the charges alternate (Fig. 29-9), no current flows. When a nerve impulse reaches the posterior surface, however, its polarization reverses. It is believed that the liberation of ACh by the neuron increases the permeability of the posterior membrane to the inflow of Na$^+$ ions so that a momentary reversal of charge occurs as in the action current in nerves and muscles. (In most fishes, electroplates are, in fact, modified muscle cells.) The anterior surfaces remain positively charged but the posterior surfaces become negatively charged. The charges now reinforce each other and a current flows just as it does through an electric battery with cells wired in "series." Voltages as high as 650 volts are produced by the several hundreds of thousands of electroplates in the South American electric eel. The flow (amperage) of the current is sufficient (¼–½ ampere) to stun a man if not kill him. The pulse of current can be repeated several hundred times each second.

Electric organs are probably used both as offensive and defensive weapons. Prey can be stunned for leisurely consumption. There is evidence that some fishes with

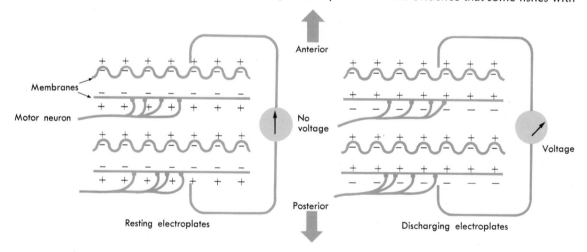

Fig. 29-9 Method of action of the electroplates in the South American electric eel. Nerve impulses reaching the posterior membranes reverse their potential and cause each electroplate to function like a cell in a battery. With several thousand of these cells arranged in "series," voltages as high as 650 volts are produced.

electric organs too weak to use as weapons use them instead to detect the presence of other objects, like predators or prey, in murky water. Such objects probably alter the conduction of electricity through the water, and this alteration is detected by special electric *receptors*. Not only do electric fishes have receptors for detecting electric currents in the water, but at least one species that has no electric *organs* does have electric receptors. Perhaps it uses these to detect the approach of electric fishes!

This winter flounder resting on a checkerboard pattern shows how versatile is its use of chromatophores for camouflage. (Courtesy Field Museum of Natural History.)   **Fig. 29-10**

CHROMATOPHORES   **29-13**

Chromatophores are purely defensive effectors. They are irregularly shaped, pigment-containing cells such as the melanophores of the frog (Fig. 26-8). By changing the distribution of pigments in these cells, the animal is able to alter its body color and blend into its surroundings. Figure 29-10 shows how remarkably effective this mechanism can be. Many experiments have shown that these protective changes in body coloration require the presence of eyes and nervous system. However, motor neurons do not activate the chromatophores directly in amphibians and crustaceans. Instead, hormones transmit the stimulus from the central nervous system to the chromatophores (see Section 26-8, 7).

Many marine protists, cnidarians, crustaceans, mollusks, fishes, and "worms" give off visible light. This is particularly common in those species which live in the dark depths of the ocean. In some cases, special luminescent organs emit the light. In others, the light is produced by luminescent bacteria which adhere to the animal's body.

Most of us are more familiar with the luminescence of the firefly. The periodic flashes of light which we see so frequently on warm summer evenings are produced by special luminescent organs in the abdomen of the insect. The mechanism by which the light is produced is now fairly well understood. It involves a chemical (**luciferin**), an enzyme (**luciferase**), oxygen, and ATP (Fig. 29-11). The more ATP available, the brighter the light. In fact, at least one manufacturer of biochemicals sells ground firefly "tails" to be used for determining the concentration of ATP in different biological materials. The ATP-containing material is added to a carefully prepared extract of the firefly tails, and the amount of light given off is measured with a sensitive light meter. The company itself is kept supplied with frozen fireflies by youngsters in the southern part of the United States who earn extra money by trapping the insects and selling them.

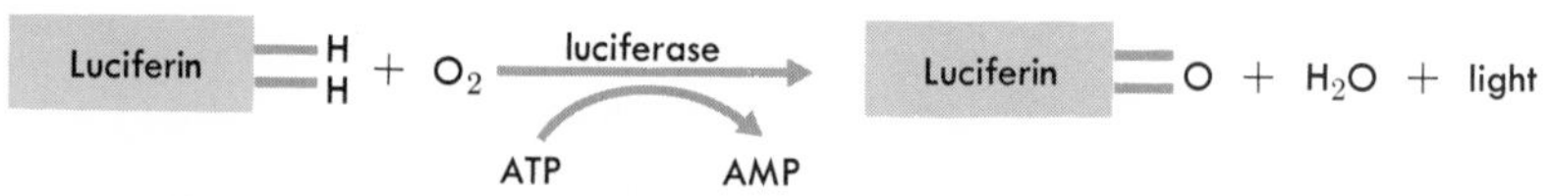

$$\boxed{\text{Luciferin}} \!\begin{array}{c} -H \\ -H \end{array} + O_2 \xrightarrow[\text{ATP} \quad \text{AMP}]{\text{luciferase}} \boxed{\text{Luciferin}} = O + H_2O + \text{light}$$

Fig. 29-11   Chemistry of luminescence in the firefly. (AMP = adenosine monophosphate. Subterminal $\sim$ bond is used.)

The widespread occurrence of luminescent organs among deep-sea animals reflects the perpetual darkness in which these creatures live. At least one fish has its luminescent organ located at the tip of a protruding stalk and uses it as bait to lure prey within reach of its jaws. When disturbed, one species of squid emits from its mantle cavity a cloud of luminous water instead of the protective smokescreen of ink that its shallow-water relatives employ. Some marine animals living nearer the surface have their luminescent organs on their underside. These probably make it more difficult for predators lurking beneath to see them against the light background of the surface. Luminescent organs also serve to attract mates and thus assure that eggs and sperm will be released close to one another. It has been well demonstrated that male and female fireflies attract each other with their flashing lights. The pattern of flashing differs from species to species. In one species, the females sometimes mimic the pattern used by the males and females of another species. When the males of the second species respond, they are eaten!

Receptors, conductors, effectors: these are the structures which enable animals to detect changes in their environment, both external and internal, and to respond in appropriate, coordinated ways to these changes.

When these responses are directed externally, as in motion or locomotion, we say that the organism is displaying behavior. Some of the varied ways in which organisms behave will be considered in the next chapter.

EXERCISES AND PROBLEMS

1 Outline the chemical changes that occur in the leg muscles of a mile runner from the time the starter's gun is fired until the runner is completely recovered.

2 Why is the dangerous disease "lockjaw" known scientifically as *tetanus?*

3 What kind of muscle lines the walls of arteries?

4 List the various functions carried out by the skeleton and give a specific example of bones that carry out each function.

5 What is the structural unit of the biceps muscle?

6 What is the functional unit of the biceps muscle?

7 How does fermentation in skeletal muscles differ from yeast fermentation?

8 In what ways does the physiology of a skeletal muscle fiber resemble that of a motor neuron? In what ways does it differ?

9 Although most birds are homeothermic, the body temperature of hummingbirds drops at night. Can you suggest an explanation for this?

10 Summarize the cell activities that are energized by ATP.

11 Distinguish between (a) skeletal muscle, (b) cardiac muscle, and (c) smooth muscle on the basis of both structure and function.

12 Distinguish between tetanus and tonus in skeletal muscles.

13 How can you reconcile the graded response of skeletal muscles with the all-or-none law?

14 In what ways does the physiology of the electroplates of electric organs resemble that of skeletal muscle?

REFERENCES

1 Allen, R. D., "Amoeboid Movement," *Scientific American,* Reprint No. 182, February, 1962.

2 Satir, P., "Cilia," *Scientific American,* Reprint No. 79, February, 1961.

3 Hayashi, T., "How Cells Move," *Scientific American,* Reprint No. 97, September, 1961. The author points out similarities in the molecular events associated with amoeboid movement, the beating of cilia, and the contraction of muscle.

4 Huxley, H. E., "The Mechanism of Muscular Contraction," *Scientific American,* Reprint No. 1026, December, 1965.

5 Porter, K. R., and Clara Franzini-Armstrong, "The Sarcoplasmic Reticulum," *Scientific American,* Reprint No. 1007, March, 1965. Describes the modified endoplasmic reticulum found in muscle fibers and the role it plays in muscle contraction and relaxation.

6 Grundfest, H., "Electric Fishes," *Scientific American,* October, 1960.

7 Lissmann, H. W., "Electric Location by Fishes," *Scientific American,* Reprint No. 152, March, 1963.

8 McElroy, W. D., and H. H. Seliger, "Biological Luminescence," *Scientific American,* Reprint No. 141, December, 1962.

9 Best, C. H., and N. B. Taylor, *The Human Body: Its Anatomy and Physiology,* Holt, Rinehart and Winston, New York, 1963. Includes a thorough description of the anatomy of the human skeleton and muscular system.

Behavior is action which alters the relationship between the organism and its environment. It is externally directed activity and does not include the many internal changes which are constantly taking place in living things.

Behavior may occur as a result of an external stimulus. Receptors are necessary to detect the stimulus, conductors are needed to coordinate the response, and the effectors actually carry out the action. Behavior may also occur as a result of an internal stimulus. A hungry animal searches for food. A thirsty animal behaves in a way which will lead to satisfying its thirst. More often than not, the behavior of an organism results from a combination of both external and internal stimuli. Internal stimuli, such as hunger, provide the *motivation* for the action taken when food is actually seen or smelled.

Some biologists feel that behavior is found only in animals and not in all of them at that. They would exclude sponges and certain parasites, like the tapeworm, from the list. Certainly these organisms, as well as plants and many protists, do not display elaborate or rapid forms of behavior. They do, however, respond to changes in their environment, and most of them are capable of at least some active movement. Hence, we will look for behavior in all organisms, plants as well as animals, that are capable of any type of self-generated, active movement.

In studying behavior, it is worthwhile to try to distinguish between innate and learned forms of behavior. The former are responses whose nature is determined by inherited receptor-conductor-effector patterns. They are quite inflexible, a given stimulus always giving rise to a given response. A salamander raised away from water until long after its cousins begin swimming successfully will swim every bit as well as they the very first time it is placed in water. Clearly this rather elaborate response is "built in" the species and not something that must be acquired by practice. Learned behavior, on the other hand, is behavior which has become more or less permanently altered as a result of the experience of the individual organism. Only by diligent practice can one learn to play baseball well.

INNATE BEHAVIOR

BEHAVIOR IN PLANTS   **30-2**

All behavior in plants seems to be innate. All the members of any one species respond in the same inflexible way to a given stimulus. There is nothing voluntary about any plant response.

◀ Konrad Lorenz with imprinted goslings.
Tom McAvoy—courtesy LIFE Magazine, © 1955, Time, Inc.

Plants do not possess a nervous system and, as we saw in Chapter 25, plant behavior is restricted to growth movements and turgor movements. Movements whose direction is determined by the direction from which the stimulus strikes the plant are called **tropisms.** The bending of the oat coleoptile toward a source of light is a positive phototropism (see Section 25-2). Generalized movements, that is, movements which are not oriented in a particular direction, are called nastic movements or nasties. The opening of tulip flowers on warm days is a thermonasty.

30-3 **BEHAVIOR IN PROTISTS**

Many protists exhibit distinct patterns of behavior. The feeding action in *Amoeba* (see Section 10-2) and the swimming of *Euglena* toward regions of moderate light intensity and away from regions of excessive brilliance are examples. In each case, the response is quite automatic and improves the chances for survival of the organism. Paramecia provide particularly good examples of behavior among the protists. When a swimming paramecium encounters an obstacle of some sort, e.g. a toxic substance or physical barrier in the water, it stops its forward motion, swims backward a few lengths, changes course about 30° and swims forward again. This response is called the **avoiding reaction.** If the obstacle is encountered again, the paramecium repeats the avoiding reaction until its way is clear. At first it seems remarkable that a single-celled creature can behave in such a coordinated, precise way. Remember, though, that the paramecium (as well as the other ciliates) is actually a very elaborate and highly specialized organism. Though not constructed on a cellular basis, it possesses *organelles* which accomplish the same functions as tissues and organs in multicellular animals. In this case, a neuromotor center and a system of conducting fibrils play an essential part in its behavior.

30-4 **KINESES**

By assembling the apparatus shown in Fig. 30-1, you can study other responses of paramecia. The little creatures will congregate within a drop of weakly acid water that is introduced into the culture chamber, but stay away from a drop of 0.5% NaCl solution. These responses are not a result of swimming toward or away from the chemical stimulus. Careful observation shows that in both cases the direction of the swimming is quite random. However, when the paramecia reach the acid water, they slow up and turn less often. If they start to leave the drop, they turn before proceeding forward. In this way, the paramecia gradually collect within the drop.

Such a response, which occurs even though the actual direction of the organism's movements is quite random, is called a **kinesis.** In this case, it is of definite survival value to the paramecia, since decay bacteria, upon which they feed, generally lower the pH of the surrounding water.

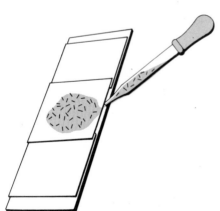

Fig. 30-1

Experimental chamber for observing behavior of paramecia.

As for their response to the drop of salt water, this occurs because of the avoiding reaction. When random movements bring them to the edge of the salt water, they back away and turn before proceeding onward. Because even this response does not depend upon the direction from which the stimulus strikes the organism, it is really a special case of a kinesis.

TAXES 30-5

Some organisms respond to a stimulus by automatically moving directly toward or away from or at some definite angle to it. These responses are called **taxes.** They are similar to the tropisms of plants except that actual locomotion of the entire organism is involved. When the grayling butterfly is threatened by a predator (e.g. a bird), it immediately flies up toward the sun. This maneuver makes pursuit more difficult. Honeybees, as well as certain ants and crustaceans, use the sun as a navigational aid in finding their way back home (see Section 30-13); they move at definite angles to the sun.

THE SIMPLE REFLEX 30-6

Probably the simplest innate response among animals having a nervous system is the simple reflex. This is an automatic response of part of the body to a specific stimulus. The response is inborn; that is, its nature is determined by the inheritance, not the experiences, of the organism. Two main types of simple reflexes occur in humans, and both seem to have a definite function in the body. The sudden withdrawal of one's hand from a painful stimulus, such as a hot object, involves a *flexion* reflex (see Section 28-4). Note that this response is definitely self-protective. The second category of simple reflexes is the *stretch* reflexes. The familar knee-jerk reflex is one of these. You have undoubtedly had your doctor tap you just below the knee cap with a rubber-headed hammer. Your response, a sudden kick with the lower leg, was an example of a stretch reflex. You may well wonder what value this reflex has under normal circumstances. Actually, it is important in maintaining balance and posture. If a standing person begins to lose his balance, proprioceptors in the tendons and muscles of the leg initiate nerve impulses which travel through the reflex arc and produce corrective muscular contraction in the legs. Remember that even simple reflexes such as this one involve the coordinated contraction of certain muscles and the inhibition of others.

It is not always easy to determine whether a particular response is a simple reflex or a response that has been learned. The blinking of our eyes when an object approaches them rapidly is a case in point. Newborn babies do not display this reflex. One might therefore assume that it is not inborn but is, rather, a response learned as a result of experiencing pain when an object touches the eyeball. This may not be the case at all. Every simple reflex depends upon the functional organization, the circuitry, of the neurons in the nervous system. This organization may not be fully established at the time of birth but only after a period of *maturation*.

INSTINCTS 30-7

Instincts are complex behavior patterns which, like simple reflexes, are inborn, rather inflexible, and of value in adapting the animal to its environment. They differ from simple reflexes in their degree of complexity. The entire body participates in instinctive

Fig. 30-2 The scratching behavior of a dog and a European bullfinch is part of their genetic heritage and is not changed by training. The widespread habit of scratching with a hindlimb crossed over a forelimb is common to most birds, reptiles, and mammals. (Courtesy Rudolf Freund and *Scientific American*.)

behavior, and an elaborate series of actions may be involved. Instinctive behavior is probably the most important type of behavior in insects. Fishes, reptiles, and birds also depend to a large degree on inborn, instinctive patterns of behavior.

The spider's building of a web is an example of instinctive behavior. A long series of complex actions are required to spin the web, but these, and thus the final shape of the web, are entirely dependent upon instinct. A spider spins a web which is characteristic of its species even though never before exposed to that particular pattern. Nest building in birds is also an example of instinctive behavior. Even when it has never been allowed to see another member of its species or any nest, the weaverbird builds a nest characteristic of the species. Instincts, then, are inherited just as the structure of tissues and organs is inherited.

This fact has been beautifully demonstrated by breeding experiments between closely related species with differing instinctive behavior patterns. The German psychologist Konrad Lorenz has succeeded in breeding two different species of ducks together. The offspring of these interspecific matings carry out courtship activities which differ from those of either parent. In some cases, the behavior is a combination of the traits found in the parents; in others, patterns of behavior in the offspring do not resemble those of either parent but are similar to behavior patterns in other species of ducks.

The African peach-faced lovebird carries nesting materials to the nesting site by tucking them in its feathers. The closely related Fischer's lovebird uses its bill to transport nesting materials. When these two species are mated, the offspring are successful at transporting materials in the bill only. Nevertheless, they invariably go through the motions of trying to tuck the materials in their feathers first.

The fact that instinctive patterns of behavior are so characteristic of a species has led several students of animal behavior to look for homologous behavioral traits which could be used to study evolutionary history just as homologous organs have been used in the past (Fig. 30-2). Their work makes it quite clear that the more closely animals seem to be related on the basis of morphology, the more closely their instinctive behavior patterns resemble one another.

The relative inflexibility of instinctive behavior has been demonstrated with many organisms. The tropical army ant (Genus *Eciton*) gets its name from the foraging marches that the entire colony makes over the jungle floor. While the motions of the colony suggest elaborate military maneuvers, in reality they arise from the simple interplay of three factors: (1) the stimulus to move, (2) the tendency of individual ants to remain close to one another following the pheromone laid down by those in front, and (3) the presence of obstacles or food in the line of march. On occasion, these factors become arranged in such a way that the behavior of the ants is truly revealed as blind and instinctive rather than the result of conscious, warlike motives. On a flat surface, such as a paved road, the lead ants begin to move away from the swarm, but their conflicting tendency to stay with the group results in their walking a circular path. The chemical trail laid down is followed by the others and soon the entire swarm is marching around and around in a circle (Fig. 30-3). Unless some obstacle interrupts the path established, the ants will march themselves to their own destruction.

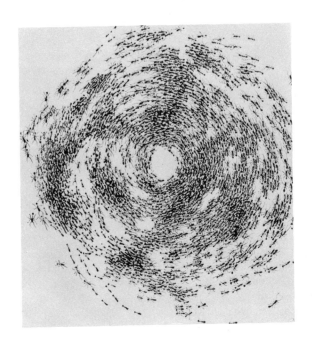

Fig. 30-3

The inflexibility of instinctive behavior. The circular column of army ants (*Eciton*) formed spontaneously and lasted for over 30 hrs. (Courtesy Dr. T. C. Schneirla, American Museum of Natural History, Nov. 1944.)

In most circumstances, instinctive behavior promotes the survival of the species. To the human observer, the complexity and usefulness of the behavior suggests the presence of reason and foresight in the animal. It is only when unusual circumstances arise that the true, inflexible, unthinking nature of instinctive behavior is revealed.

The carrying out of instincts often depends upon the conditions in the internal environment, the ECF, of the organism. In many vertebrates, courtship and mating behavior will not occur unless sex hormones are present in the bloodstream. The target organ, in at least some cases, appears to be a small region of the hypothalamus.

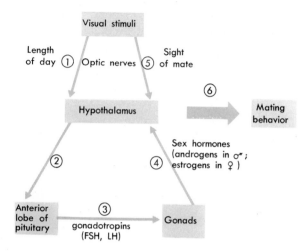

Fig. 30-4

Interaction of external and internal stimuli leading to mating behavior in the rabbit.

When stimulated by the presence of sex hormones in its blood supply, the hypothalamus initiates the activities leading to mating. The level of sex hormones in the blood is, in turn, regulated by the activity of the anterior lobe of the pituitary gland (see Section 26-8). Figure 30-4 outlines the interactions that lead an animal, such as the rabbit, to seek a sexual partner and mate with it.

30-8   RELEASERS OF INSTINCTIVE BEHAVIOR

Once the body is prepared internally for certain types of instinctive behavior, an external stimulus is needed to initiate the response. N. Tinbergen and his students at Oxford, England, have found that this external stimulus need not necessarily be appropriate to be effective. During the breeding season, the female three-spined stickleback (Fig. 30-5) normally follows the red-bellied male to the nest that he has prepared and lays eggs in it. She will, however, follow almost any small red object presented to her. Once within the nest, the presence of neither male nor red object is necessary any longer. Any object touching her near the base of the tail will cause her to liberate her eggs. It is as though the stickleback were primed internally for each item of behavior and needed only one specific signal to release the behavior pattern. For this reason, signals which trigger instinctive acts are called **releasers.** Once a given response has been released, it usually runs to completion even though the effective stimulus is immediately removed. One or two prods at the base of the tail will release the entire sequence of muscular actions involved in the liberation of the eggs.

Perhaps the most remarkable releasers of instinctive behavior yet discovered are the stars. The experiments of the German ornithologist E. G. F. Sauer indicate that European warblers, migrating at night, navigate by means of them. This is particularly remarkable in view of the fact that in the fall the young birds fly to their winter home in Africa independently of their parents. With the patient help of his wife, Sauer has even raised young warblers entirely apart from other members of their kind. (This is no small task. Warblers eat insects only and a young bird will consume dozens each day.) When fall comes, these young hand-reared birds become restless. Presented with a view of the "stars" inside a planetarium, they orient themselves toward the southeasterly course they would ordinarily follow. Although the constellations are in apparent motion throughout the night, the young birds are able to compensate for this and continue to maintain their proper orientation.

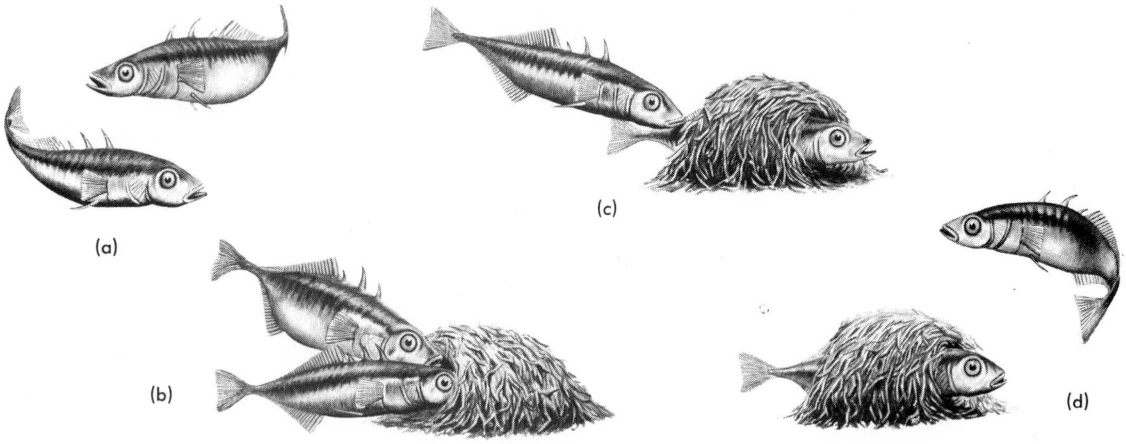

Fig. 30-5

Courtship behavior of sticklebacks. Male leads female toward nest (a), guides her into it (b), then prods the base of her tail (c). After the female lays her eggs, the male drives her from the nest, enters it himself (d), and fertilizes the eggs. (Biological Sciences Curriculum Study, *Biological Sciences: Molecules to Man,* Houghton Mifflin Co., 1963.)

RHYTHMIC BEHAVIOR AND BIOLOGICAL "CLOCKS" 30-9

The migratory "urge" of birds in the fall is one of many examples of behavior that is repeated at definite intervals. Such behavior is described as rhythmic or periodic. The cycles of rhythmic behavior may be as short as two hours or as long as a year. The common laboratory rat provides an example of a very short cycle. Even when food is available at all times, it generally feeds at two-hour intervals.

A great many animals alter their behavior on a daily basis. Nocturnal animals, for example, become active once every 24 hours. Fruit flies hatch in greatest numbers just at dawn. You might well claim that such periodic behavior is simply a response to the daily changes of light and darkness. This is not the complete answer, though. Even when the animals are kept under constant environmental conditions (e.g. under continuous illumination in the laboratory), many of these rhythms continue. They may, however, tend to drift one way or the other. In other words, the cycles may occur every 23 or every 25 hours instead of exactly at 24-hour intervals. For this reason, such rhythms are called *circadian,* from the Latin words *circa* (about) and *dies* (day). Under natural conditions of alternating night and day, most of these rhythms remain correctly adjusted to a 24-hour cycle.

Cycles of approximately two and four weeks are known. In Section 22-2, we discussed how the male and female California grunions (fishes) come on the beaches to spawn at the time of the full moon and new moon, that is, at intervals of about two weeks. This behavior clearly seems to be triggered by the phase of the moon and/or the height of the tides (which reach a maximum at full moon and new moon). On the other hand, you ought to be able to think of a 28–30 day cycle which is now, at least, independent of the phase of the moon (and now more physiological than behavioral).

The reproductory behavior of the California grunion does not occur throughout the year but only in the spring. Thus its two-week cycle is superimposed on an annual cycle. Other animal activities also occur on a yearly basis. A few examples are the preparations for hibernation carried out by many mammals, the migration of birds, and the onset and termination of diapause in insects. As we have seen in the case of insect diapause (see Section 26-2), these responses generally depend on the only reliable indicator of the time of year: the relative length of day and night. In other words, most of these activities are regulated by changes in the photoperiod.

The ability to respond to photoperiod requires that the organism have some mechanism for measuring the hours of daylight or the hours of darkness. (Some organisms seem to measure one, some the other.) In other words, these organisms must have some sort of biological "clock." Although the exact nature of the clock mechanism is still unknown, various physiological activities have been found to fluctuate on a daily basis within the organs, tissues, and even the individual cells of organisms with circadian rhythms. Perhaps it is these internal circadian rhythms, which can maintain their periodicity independent of fluctuations in the external environment, that provide the clockwork by which photoperiod can be measured.

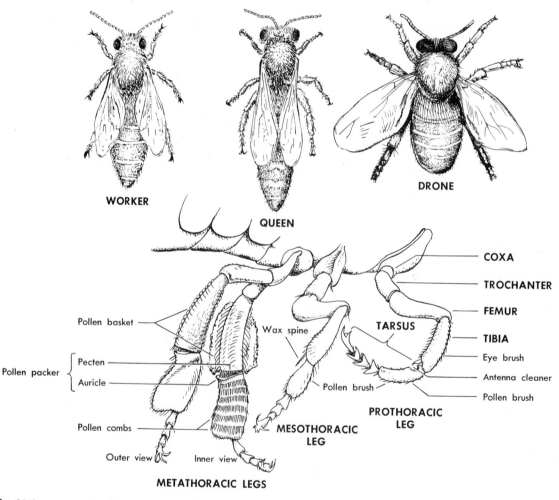

Fig. 30-6   Honeybee anatomy. The three body forms found in the colony are at the top. The legs of the worker bee are shown beneath.

Probably no group of animals has developed such a varied repertory of instinctive behavior as the colonial insects—the ants, termites, and honeybees. There is not space
in a book of this sort to describe the incredibly diverse and elaborate kinds of behavior
which all these animals exhibit, but we will examine some of the behavior displayed
by the domestic honeybee, *Apis mellifera*. (If you are interested in pursuing further
the behavior of other colonial insects, reading one or two of the pertinent references
listed at the end of this chapter will be well worth your effort.)

The life of the honeybee colony revolves around the activities of its single **queen**
(Fig. 30-6). During the spring and summer months, she spends most of her time laying
eggs in the wax cells of the honeycomb. The queen fertilizes most of these eggs, just
before they are deposited in the cells, by releasing sperm from storage sacs (sperm
receptacles), which were filled at the time of her mating flights. These eggs hatch
into larvae (the grubs) after three days. The larvae are carefully tended and fed by
worker bees for six days. At the end of this time, the workers cap the cells with wax,
and the larvae undergo metamorphosis. Three weeks after the egg is laid, a new
worker bee emerges. She is a female but does not have functional sex organs.

Early in the spring the queen bee deposits a fertilized egg in each of several special cells, the queen cells (Fig. 30-7). These develop into fertile females, one of which
will become the future queen of the hive. The different fate of these eggs is probably
accounted for by differences in the diet supplied to the larvae. Young larvae are fed
a protein-rich secretion from the salivary glands of adult bees. The composition of
the secretion fed to the larvae destined to become workers differs from that fed to
larvae in the queen cells. The latter material is called "royal jelly."

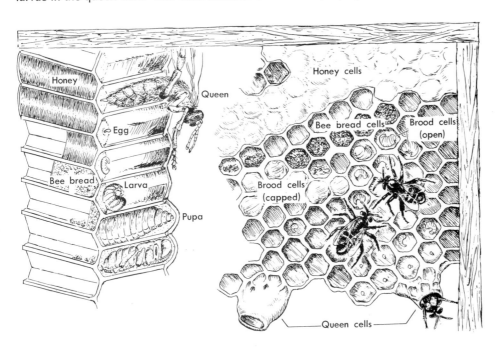

Honeybee comb as seen face on (right) and in section (left). The cells are constructed by the
workers out of wax secreted by glands in their abdomen.

Fig. 30-7

The queen bee can also lay unfertilized eggs. These hatch and develop into male bees, the **drones.** Development of unfertilized eggs is called *parthenogenesis* (see Section 23-2).

The active, normal beehive thus contains one queen, a few hundred drones and many thousands of workers. Before a new queen emerges, the old queen leaves the hive, taking a substantial proportion of the workers with her. This is the phenomenon of swarming. After a few days, the new queen leaves the hive, too, but just long enough to mate (while flying high in the air) with several drone bees. Then she returns to the hive to begin her egg-laying duties. Other developing queens are killed unless the hive is so crowded that additional swarms are appropriate.

The appearance of several distinct body types in a species is called **polymorphism.** In the case of the honeybees, the different forms (worker, drone and queen) are each adapted to carry out specific functions.

30-11   **THE WORK OF THE HIVE**

From the moment a worker bee emerges from her cell, her work for the colony begins. For the first three weeks of her life, she stays within or close to the hive. Her duties during this period are undertaken in a definite sequence:

Days 1–3. This period is spent in cleaning cells for re-use. The worker feeds upon a pollen-honey mixture, bee bread, and her salivary glands become greatly enlarged.

Days 4–9. This period is devoted to nursing the grubs. At first the worker feeds them the protein-rich secretion of her salivary glands. After her glands shrink to normal size, she feeds them bee bread instead.

Days 10–16. The wax glands on the ventral side of the last four abdominal segments begin to secrete beeswax. The worker uses her wax spine (Fig. 30-6) to remove the plates of wax and her mandibles to mold them into new cells for the comb.

Days 17–19. During this period, the workers receive the nectar which foraging bees bring back to the hive, convert it into honey, and store it in cells. Honey production involves evaporating water from the nectar and digesting the sucrose into glucose and fructose. If the hive gets too hot, the workers receive *water* from the foragers and spread it on the surface of the combs. By fanning the water with their wings, they hasten its evaporation, thus cooling the hive. During this period, the workers also remove any debris (e.g. dead workers) that may collect in the hive.

Day 20. This is spent patrolling in front of the hive and attacking and stinging any intruders. A worker can often sting another insect and survive, but her sting usually cannot be removed from the elastic skin of vertebrates. It is pulled from her body, inflicting fatal damage to her abdominal organs.

Two additional points should be noted about the work of the hive. The sequence just outlined is somewhat flexible. Worker bees spend a good deal of time simply patrolling the hive, and they will shift their activities to remedy special needs that they discover. Although bees are proverbially busy, they actually spend only about 40% of their time in the activities described. The remainder is spent simply standing around in the hive. They work hard enough, however, so that their life span as an adult rarely exceeds six weeks in the summer. Workers hatching in the fall have virtually nothing to do, and most of them remain alive throughout the entire winter.

After three weeks in or near the hive, the summer workers take to the field as **foragers.** They collect nectar and pollen from the flowers of angiosperms. The nectar is collected in a special chamber (the honey stomach—Fig. 10-6) of the digestive tract and brought back to the hive to be converted into honey. The pollen is moistened with nectar and brought back in the pollen baskets on the metathoracic legs (Fig. 30-6). This material is bee bread. The collection of nectar and pollen are vitally important to the plants as well as to the bees. By accidentally transferring some pollen from one flower to the next, the bees enable cross-pollination of the plants to take place with subsequent sexual reproduction and the development of seeds.

RECEPTORS, CONDUCTORS, AND EFFECTORS IN THE HONEYBEE   30-12

The intricate, well-coordinated activities of the bees would be impossible without good receptors, conductors, and effectors. The large, multifaceted compound eyes (see Section 27-2) provide a fair amount of pattern discrimination (Fig. 30-8) as well as four-color vision. The odor receptors, which are located on the antennae, enable the bee to discriminate among a wide variety of odors and to detect rather faint ones. Despite many claims to the contrary, though, the bee's ability to detect and discriminate among odors is probably no better developed than man's. The mouth parts of the bee contain taste receptors. The bee seems to distinguish the same four taste sensations that we do: sweet, sour, salty and bitter. The bee's threshold to sour and salty is lower than man's while its threshold to bitter and sweet is higher. The relatively high threshold to sweet is of value to the bee as it prevents her from collecting nectar too dilute to be converted efficiently into honey.

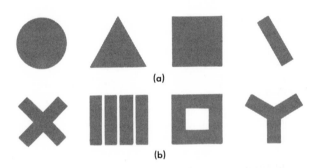

(a)

(b)

Fig. 30-8

Pattern discrimination in honeybees. Bees cannot distinguish between any of the figures in row (a) or row (b) but can distinguish any figure in row (a) from any in row (b).

The nervous system of the worker bee is well organized to receive information from the sense receptors and to coordinate the action of the muscles controlling legs, wings, and mouth parts.

The legs of the honeybee are far more than simply structures to walk on. They are highly specialized manipulative organs which enable the bee to carry out many of its tasks.

The anterior legs have soft hairs (the eye brush) on the tibia (Fig. 30-6). As the name implies, the eye brush is used for removing pollen and other debris from the eyes. The pollen brush on the first tarsal segment is made of rather stiff bristles. It is used to brush pollen off the body hairs. The first tarsal segment also contains a notch in which the bee can place its antenna. Then when the bee crooks the leg, a spur on the tibia holds the antenna in the notch while the bee cleans off pollen, etc., in a wiping motion. The entire apparatus is called the antenna cleaner.

The middle, or mesothoracic, legs also contain pollen brushes on the first tarsal segments. In addition, a wax spine sticks down from the tibia. This is used to dig plates of wax out of the wax glands.

Each hind or metathoracic leg contains pollen combs on the inner surface of the first tarsal segment, a pollen packer in the joint between the tibia and the first tarsal segment, and a pollen basket on the outer surface of the tibia. The pollen combs collect pollen from the pollen brushes of the other legs. Then with the stiff spines (the pecten) of the pollen packer of one leg, the bee removes the pollen from the pollen combs of the opposite leg. Straightening of the leg then forces the anvil-shaped auricle up against the pollen caught under the pecten. The pollen is squeezed through the joint and up into the pollen basket on the outside of the tibia.

All these manipulations are carried out in the brief interval it takes the bee to fly from one flower to another. When pollen is plentiful, the amount transported in the pollen baskets is truly impressive (Fig. 30-9).

Fig. 30-9   Worker honeybee foraging for pollen. Note the full pollen baskets on the metathoracic legs. (Courtesy W. T. Davidson, National Audubon Society.)

The mouth parts of the honeybee (look back at Fig. 10-6) are also highly specialized and enable the bee to manipulate the materials essential to the life of the colony. The mandibles are used for kneading wax to make more honeycomb. The maxillae, the labium, and the tongue are modified to form a long proboscis for sucking nectar from the nectaries of flowers (see Section 10-5).

The colonial way of life places great emphasis upon the home. The hive is the center of activity and, no matter how far afield the workers roam, they almost invariably return to their own hive. Considering that bees may forage several miles from the hive, they must be good navigators to find their way back successfully. Certainly bees have sufficiently good vision to be able to navigate by means of prominent landmarks, and evidence suggests that they often do. It has also been discovered, however, that most foragers do not leave the hive until food has actually been discovered by so-called **scout bees.** As soon as the scouts find food, they return to the hive. Shortly after their return, many foragers leave and fly directly to the food supply. The remarkable thing about this behavior is that the foragers do not follow the scouts back to their discovery. Instead, they fly to the food while the scouts are still within the hive. This implies two things. First, the foraging bees must have been told in some way how to locate the food source. Second, they must have some method of navigating over unfamiliar territory as they follow these instructions.

The discovery of how scout bees communicate with the foragers and how the foragers navigate over unfamiliar territory was made by the German zoologist Karl von Frisch. Throughout his entire professional career, he has patiently studied and experimented with honeybees. Many of the facts of bee life which we have discussed were discovered by him.

By marking scout bees with paint and watching them upon their return to an observation hive (Fig. 30-10), von Frisch discovered that the scouts perform a little dance on the vertical surface of the combs after depositing their load of nectar or pollen. This dance seems to stimulate the foragers and soon they begin to leave the hive and fly to the food source. Unless the food source is quite close (less than 75 yards) to the hive, the scout bees dance a so-called tailwagging dance (Fig. 30-11). It did not take von Frisch long to realize that the speed with which the scout bees perform this maneuver is related to the distance of the food from the hive (Fig. 30-12); the scouts even compensate for wind speed. However, the knowledge that food is present three miles from the hive is not very useful when you consider the long circumference included. But von Frisch also

Fig. 30-10

Applying paint to foraging bees so that they can be identified on their return to the observation hive. (Courtesy Dr. M. Renner.)

noted that the direction of the tailwagging portion of the dance varies with the direction of the food source from the hive and with the time of day. At a given time of day, the direction of the dance changes with varying locations of food. With a fixed source of food, the direction of the dance changes by the same angle as the

Fig. 30-11

Left: The round dance of the bee is used when food is found close to the hive. Right: The tail-wagging dance is used when food is found more than 100 yds from the hive. The speed of the dance indicates just how far away the food is, and the direction of the straight portion indicates in what direction.

sun during its passage through the sky. This suggests that the scout bees indicate the direction of the food source in relation to the direction of the sun. The sun is not visible in normal hives, however, and the bees dance on the vertical surface of the combs. How, then, do they translate flight angles in the darkened hive? When the food source is in the same direction as the sun, they orient the straight portion of the wagging dance up and down with their heads pointing up. It is as though they translate a positive phototaxis as a negative geotaxis. If the food source is at some angle to the right or left of the sun, the scouts dance at the same angle to the right or left of the vertical (Fig. 30-13).

The foraging bees cluster around the dancing scouts and presumably learn the direction and distance of the food in this way. If the food source is scented, the foragers also learn what odor to search for. Thus the language of the bees enables one bee to tell the others: (1) that food is available, (2) what direction it is in, (3) how far away it is, and (4) what its odor is.

If the dancing bees are confined to the hive for a long period of time, they shift the direction of their dance as the direction of the sun shifts. Remember, though, that they cannot observe the apparent motion of the sun while within the hive. This suggests that the bees are able to make the necessary corrections because they are "aware" of the passage of time. This fact has long been known to people who like to have tea, toast, and jam in their gardens at a fixed time every day. Within minutes of the appointed hour, foraging bees arrive in large numbers for their share of the jam. Here, then, is another example of a biological "clock." Its rate of ticking seems to be related to the bee's rate of metabolism. If a group of normally punctual bees are chilled (to lower their rate of metabolism) or exposed to anesthetizing concentrations of carbon dioxide, their next arrival at the tea table will be correspondingly delayed (Fig. 30-14).

Fig. 30-12

Graph showing relationship between distance of food source and rapidity of tail-wagging dance in the honeybee (3885 observations).

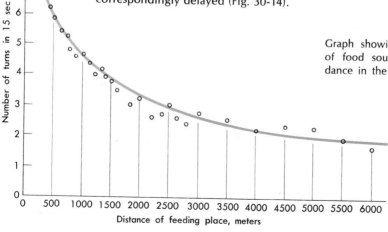

Number of turns in 15 sec

Distance of feeding place, meters

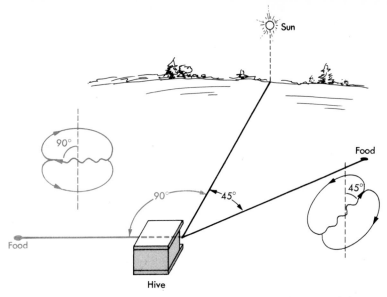

Relationship between the angle of the dance on the vertical comb and the bearing of the sun with respect to the location of food. When the food and the sun are in the same direction, the straight portion of the dance is directed upward. When the food is at some angle to the right (black) or left (color) of the sun, the bee orients the straight portion of its dance at the same angle to the right or left of the vertical.

Fig. 30-13

These discoveries made by von Frisch are deceptively easy to describe. Like most scientific discoveries, they are the fruit of years of patient work, cleverly designed experiments, and carefully interpreted results. For a better idea of the actual process of scientific discovery, you should read von Frisch's own account (listed at the end of this chapter) of the long series of experiments which led him to these, and many other, discoveries concerning the behavior of bees.

When one first learns about the elaborate behavior of honeybees, he is apt to credit these little creatures with a high degree of intelligence, foresight, etc. Actually, this would be a mistake, since most of their behavior is instinctive and thus relatively inflexible. Within certain narrow limits, however, they can alter their behavior. When behavior is more or less permanently modified as a result of the experiences of the organism, we say that learning has occurred. The bee's association of food with a certain location, odor, or time of day is certainly an example of learning.

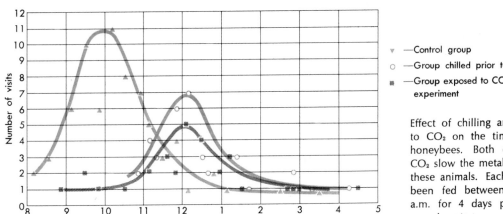

▽ —Control group

○ —Group chilled prior to experiment

■ —Group exposed to CO_2 prior to experiment

Fig. 30-14

Effect of chilling and exposure to CO_2 on the time sense of honeybees. Both chilling and CO_2 slow the metabolic rate of these animals. Each group had been fed between 9 and 11 a.m. for 4 days prior to the experiments.

LEARNED BEHAVIOR

Learned behavior, then, is behavior that is more or less permanently acquired or modified as a result of the experiences of the individual. Although many hours of patient experimentation have been spent in an effort to detect learning in protozoans and the radially symmetrical cnidarians and echinoderms, no definite proof that these organisms can learn has ever been found. Many of them do modify their responses to repeated stimuli, but the modification is only temporary. It probably represents some sort of receptor fatigue (see Section 27-12) rather than true learning.

30-14   HABITUATION

All the metazoa with bilaterally symmetrical nervous systems, on the other hand, have been shown to be capable of some degree of learning. For example, they are able to learn not to respond to repeated stimuli which have proven to be harmless. This phenomenon is known as habituation and is an example of true learning. If you make an unusual noise in the presence of the family dog, it will respond—usually by turning its head towards the source of the sound. If, however, the stimulus is given repeatedly and nothing either pleasant or unpleasant happens to the dog, it will finally cease to respond. That this is a case of true learning rather than simply the result of the adaptation of sense receptors is indicated by the fact that the response is long-lasting. When fully habituated, the animal will not respond to the stimulus even though weeks or months have elapsed since it was last presented.

30-15   IMPRINTING

One of the most narrowly specialized, clearcut examples of learning is imprinting. If newly hatched geese (goslings) are exposed to a moving object of reasonable size emitting reasonable sounds, they will begin following it just as they would normally follow their mother. This is called imprinting. The time of exposure is quite critical. A few days after birth imprinting does not take place. Prior to this time, though, the results are quite remarkable. The gosling imprinted to a moving box or clucking man will, forsaking all others, try to follow this object for the rest of its life. In fact, when the gosling reaches sexual maturity, it will make the imprinted object, rather than a member of its own species, the goal of its sexual drive. Much of our knowledge of imprinting has been gained from the patient research of Konrad Lorenz. (See the chapter opening illustration.)

30-16   THE CONDITIONED RESPONSE

Perhaps the simplest form of learned behavior is the *conditioned response*. Basically, this is a response which, as a result of experience, comes to be caused by a stimulus different from that which originally triggered it. We owe our understanding of the mechanism of the conditioned response to the research of the Russian physiologist Ivan Pavlov. Pavlov found that the placing of food in a dog's mouth causes it to salivate. This is probably a simple, inborn reflex involving taste buds, sensory neurons, association neurons in the brain, and motor neurons running to the salivary glands.

Pavlov found further that if he rang a bell every time he introduced meat into the dog's mouth, the dog eventually salivated upon hearing the bell alone. *This* is the conditioned response. The dog has learned to respond to a substitute stimulus, the *conditioned stimulus*.

We assume that the physiological basis of the conditioned response is the transfer, by association neurons, of nervous activity in the auditory area of the brain to the motor neurons controlling salivation. This process involves the use of new circuits which, we may also assume, is characteristic of all forms of learning.

In fact, some psychologists feel that all learned behavior arises from the development of conditioned responses. They feel that the conditioned response is the fundamental unit of even the most complex forms of human behavior. While our knowledge of our own higher mental processes is still far too poor to accept or reject this theory outright, there is no longer any question that humans can be conditioned to some degree. In the years since Pavlov's discoveries, his own countrymen have exploited this technique in an attempt to win loyal adherents to the political regime in Russia. In fact, whenever rigid political establishments have arisen in recent years, e.g. Nazi Germany, the techniques of conditioning have been used with some success to produce conformity of thought and action. Even in free societies, we find the basic techniques of conditioning used in such areas as advertising. It may well turn out that man's large cerebrum permits too great a complexity and flexibility of mental activity for conditioning normally to play a large part in his behavior. Whether it does or not, all of us should be careful not to allow others to use the scientific technique of conditioning in ways which are inconsistent with the kind of life we wish to live.

Although the exact part played by conditioning in our lives is open to debate, laboratory experiments on conditioning have taught us a good deal about the learning process in man. Conditioning occurs most rapidly when (1) the unconditioned stimulus and conditioned stimulus are presented together frequently, (2) when there are no distractions, and (3) when a reward of some sort is given for successful performance of the conditioned response. Similarly, as every student knows, learning in school and college proceeds most successfully with repetition, lack of distraction, and good motivation.

The conditioned response has proved to be an excellent tool for determining the sensory capabilities of other animals. As we have seen from Fig. 27-4, honeybees can be trained to seek food on a piece of blue cardboard. They learn to associate the color blue with the presence of food. This is a conditioned response. By offering other colors to the blue-conditioned bee, we can discover which she confuses with blue and which she does not. In this way, Karl von Frisch determined that honeybees can see only four distinct colors: yellow-green, blue-green, blue-violet, and ultraviolet. The ability of animals to discriminate between similar shapes and musical tones has also been studied by the technique of conditioning.

HABITS   30-17

A habit is a learned response which through repetition becomes automatic. It differs from the conditioned responses discussed above in two ways. First, it is usually more complex, a whole sequence of actions being involved. (Some psychologists feel that each item in the sequence is a conditioned response, with each response serving as the stimulus for the next.) Second, habits are not simply passively acquired as is the response of salivation at the sound of a bell. The animal participates actively in the development of the habit, frequently exploring various responses by trial and error and eventually making a consistent choice. We are all familiar with habits in our daily lives. Many of these are extremely valuable to us. The motor actions involved in tying one's shoelaces, performing one's morning ablutions, typewriting, etc., would be prohibitively time and energy consuming if we had to think through each action every time it was performed. Once a habit is learned, it permits us to accomplish routine chores with speed and little expenditure of effort. Of course, some habits are undesirable. Unfortunately, these usually involve an element of pleasure or reward and thus are especially difficult to break.

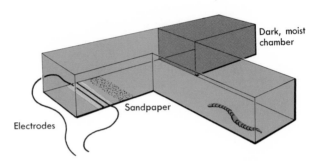

Fig. 30-15

A *T*-maze. Earthworms can learn to make the correct choice 90% of the time.

All animals with bilaterally symmetrical nervous systems can learn to make some simple, consistent choices when confronted with alternatives. In a *T*-maze (Fig. 30-15) an earthworm or a planarian can eventually learn to take the arm of the maze which leads to a reward (e.g. food, moisture) and/or away from punishment (e.g. sandpaper, electric shock). The development of this habit is a slow process, however, and never reaches the point of 100% correct choices. Interestingly enough, the earthworm learns to solve this maze even after its cerebral ganglia have been removed; but once new cerebral ganglia regenerate, the worm forgets its prior learning and must be retrained. Ants and mice are excellent solvers of mazes. It takes some ants as few as 28 trials to solve the maze shown in Fig. 30-16.

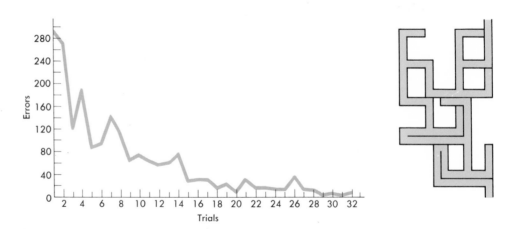

Fig. 30-16   Trial-and-error learning in the ant.

Receipt

No. 208496

Date June 13th 1999

FROM Robert cunning me million

$ 1,000,000

DOLLARS

○ FOR RENT
○ FOR air lines

FROM Robert TO AA

ACCT.		○ cash
PAID		○ check
DUE		○ money order

BY Robert

DC 2501

Anyone who has tried to train an animal in a procedure, such as running a maze, that requires the animal to participate actively and to make choices knows that it can be a very frustrating procedure. The student psychologist is apt to find that when rat and newly constructed maze are brought together, the rat simply curls up in a corner. The basic problem here, as in the development of all habits, is one of motivation. The animal must want to participate in the learning process. Among most animals, motivation (or "drive" as it is sometimes called) is connected with its physical needs. A thirsty animal will search for water and a hungry animal will search for food. A sexually aroused animal will search for a mate. The satisfaction of its drives is the motivating force behind the animal's behavior. At times, the internal drive can be very precise. A rat with sugar, or salt, or even thiamine missing from an otherwise adequate diet will seek out food containing the missing substance in preference to that which does not. Perhaps we can go so far as to say that most of the spontaneous behavior of these animals results from an attempt to maintain homeostasis. Many of these drives have their origin in the hypothalamus. In some cases (thirst, for example) the hypothalamus actually detects the deficiency in the ECF. In all cases, the hypothalamus seems to initiate the responses which lead to a reduction of the drive. It may also inhibit some of these responses when the point of satiation is reached.

While we can trace a good deal of man's behavior to the desire to satisfy physical needs, not all of it can be explained in such terms. Many of the things we do we seem to do for their own sake. Goats, monkeys, and chimpanzees, too, have been found to engage in problem-solving activity even when no external reward or punishment is involved (Fig. 30-17). The carrying out of the process itself seems to be its own reward.

Fig. 30-17

Curiosity in a monkey. The monkey repeatedly works the puzzle with no other motivation than that created by the task itself. (Courtesy Myron Davis and *Scientific American*.)

Chimpanzees and men are unusual also in that they will both work for distant goals. Both chimps and men can learn to work for coins even though the coins themselves satisfy no physical need. Of course, the coins can be converted into food, and this expectation provides sufficient motivation for brief periods of work in chimpanzees and a lifetime of work in men.

Most animals solve mazes and other problems by trial and error. As long as sufficient motivation is present, they try each alternative and gradually, through repeated successes and failures, learn to solve the problem (Fig. 30-18). Trial-and-error learning plays a negligible role in man, however. When presented with a problem, he may make one or two random attempts at solving it and then, all of a sudden, he "gets it" (Fig. 30-19). We call this response **insight**. (Sometimes it is referred to as the "aha!" reaction.)

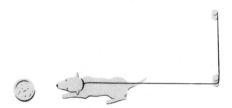

Fig. 30-18

A detour problem. A dog finally solves it by trial and error.

Responses that occur as a result of insight are quite different from anything we have considered up to now. While they depend upon previously learned material, they are an entirely new response for the individual. Insight involves putting familiar things together in new ways. It is thus a truly creative act. Insight also depends upon the development of concepts or principles. This can be illustrated by a hypothetical experiment (Fig. 30-20). A rat is placed in front of a semicircle of doors, three of which are opened at a time. No matter which particular doors are opened, if the rat enters either the left-hand or right-hand door, it receives a shock. If it

Fig. 30-19   Insight. After a brief period of trying to fit the pieces of the puzzle together by trial and error, the subject suddenly sees the solution. (Courtesy Mrs. Ruth M. Roehrig.)

enters the middle door, it finds a reward of food. If the rat ever should learn to go immediately to the middle door (even if that door led to a shock on the previous trial), the rat would have learned a **concept.** In this case, the concept would be the idea of *middleness.* The rat would not be responding to any concrete, specific stimulus but rather to an idea. From its experience with particular doors it would have developed an idea about doors in general.

Fig. 30-20

If the rat could learn always to go to the middle one of whichever three doors happen to be open, he would have learned a concept. Although a chimpanzee can solve such a problem with ease, the rat cannot.

Actually, a rat would fail this test. Rats and most other animals have little or no ability to make abstract generalizations about specific things. A man can solve this sort of problem, of course. Chimpanzees are also capable of developing abstract ideas. Monkeys, elephants, raccoons, and dogs show only rudiments of such behavior.

Problem solving of the type illustrated by our hypothetical rat in front of the semicircle of doors involves some form of reasoning. Chimpanzees, which can solve this problem, are probably reasoning without the aid of a language. Nevertheless, two different, but related, thought processes are involved. One, *inductive* reasoning, involves learning the general principle (middleness) from experience with the specific, concrete situation. The other, *deductive* reasoning, involves applying the general principle to some new specific situation. If the chimp had a language, it might say, "If food is always located behind the middle door, then this time it must be located behind *that* door."

LANGUAGE **30-20**

All humans, even in the most primitive societies, possess a highly developed language of some sort. This involves a second level of abstraction. The very idea of a chair or door, like the idea of middleness, is an abstraction. When these ideas are then represented by symbols, a second level of abstraction occurs. There is nothing chairlike about the letters *c h a i r.*

Of course, it would be perfectly possible to create a written language with a unique symbol, such as a sketch, for each concept. This occurred to some degree in the development of language among the Chinese, Japanese, and the Indians of North America. A more flexible arrangement is to use a relatively small number of symbols which can then be assembled in unique ways for each concept. Our written language is made up of twenty-six letters whose varied arrangement makes our written language possible. Contrast, if you will, the meanings associated with *r a t* and *t a r.* In a similar way, our spoken language is made up of some three to five dozen (depending on who is doing the counting) distinct sounds or **phonemes.**

Language is important because it enables individuals within a species to communicate with one another. From communication can arise cooperation. Tasks which individuals cannot carry out alone, such as building skyscrapers, become possible when teamwork is possible. Language is particularly important for those animals that live in societies. We have seen how communication among the honeybees insures the efficient running of the hive. Note, though, how much more limited the bees' language is than our own; we possess a system of interchangeable symbols which permits far greater flexibility than the tail-waggings of the bee.

Language has another important function besides making cooperation possible. It permits the knowledge acquired by one generation to be passed on to the next. Although this is often done verbally in primitive societies, we depend chiefly upon written language to do the job in ours. By reading this book, you are able to profit from the time-consuming experiments and observations of hundreds of biologists in years past. If so inclined, you will be ready, with just a few more years of study, to build upon the work of the past and extend our knowledge into new areas.

30-21   **MEMORY**

All learning depends upon memory. If the organism is to modify its behavior from experience, it must be able to remember what its experience has been. Once something is learned, memory is necessary for the learning to be retained.

As we have seen, learning (and thus memory) seems to be associated with bilaterally symmetrical nervous systems. Unfortunately, it has been very difficult to discover what activities in these nervous systems make memory possible. Two basic theories have been proposed. One is that memory is a dynamic process. According to this theory, sensations give rise to nerve impulses, which then circulate indefinitely through the network of neurons in the central nervous system. When one considers the vast network of association neurons in the human cerebrum, such a theory seems plausible. The delay circuits used to store information in some modern computers operate on the same principle. This dynamic theory of memory is supported by the startling fact that no specific area of the human brain has ever been found essential to the retention of old memories. Whatever defects may occur as the result of damage to one region of the brain or another, loss of memory does not seem to be involved. On the other hand, a dynamic memory must always be in action. If all nerve impulses in the brain ceased, even for an instant, then this type of memory would be lost. Experiments with hamsters indicate that such loss does not occur. Maze-trained hamsters have been carefully chilled to the point where no electrical activity in the brain can be detected; when rewarmed, they remember their prior training.

This fact supports the second theory of memory which is that each remembered sensation results in some permanent, physical alteration in the brain. Perhaps a change in the resistance of certain synapses occurs, although the fact that memory does not seem to be localized anywhere in the brain argues against this view. Recently, several biologists have suggested that our memories may be stored in a chemical code within the brain. Some look to the nucleic acid RNA, some to proteins, as the substances in which memories are coded. As you remember, these macromolecules can be built in an almost infinite number of ways.

It is a demonstrated fact that the RNA content of neurons increases with their activity so long as this activity is within normal ranges. Furthermore, it has been found that the RNA content of neurons in the human spinal cord increases from age 3 to age

40. After age 40 the RNA content of these cells remains quite constant until age 55 or 60, when it declines rapidly. Following this clue, psychiatrists in Canada have tried injecting RNA into elderly patients. They claim to have brought about improved memory in them by this technique.

Equally suggestive are some experiments which have been carried out on planarians. As we mentioned, these creatures can learn to solve a T-maze. They can also learn a conditioned response. The head of the worm dominates the tail in these responses. If the worm is cut into two pieces, both the head and the tail regenerate the missing parts. Both regenerated worms retain some memory of their prior training. However, if the pieces are allowed to regenerate in pond water to which some of the RNA-digesting enzyme, ribonuclease, has been added, only the dominant, trained head retains its memory. The head that is regenerated by the severed tail performs no better than a totally untrained worm. Another experimenter has claimed that when trained (conditioned) planarians are ground up and fed to untrained ones, the latter can be similarly trained in a much shorter time than normally fed individuals.

Such exciting reports as these have produced a flurry of related experimentation in many different laboratories. These experiments have been done not only with planarians but also with "higher" animals such as rats and mice. Some workers claim that learning can be transferred from one animal to another with RNA extracted from the trained animals and injected into untrained ones. Other investigators claim to have accomplished the same feat with proteins. Some workers have found drugs which, they claim, speed up RNA synthesis and also learning. Unfortunately, in every one of these cases, workers in other laboratories have often been unable to duplicate these results. Perhaps this should not really be too surprising when you consider the many subtle factors that could influence the behavior of an animal like a rat but be overlooked by the experimenter. Furthermore, the transfer of learning that is claimed really involves simply *faster learning* on the part of the recipients than in the controls. Perhaps these extracts and chemicals that are thought to transfer or speed up learning may simply be speeding up the *general* activity of the recipients.

It is still too soon to say just what the nature of memory is. Perhaps both dynamic processes as well as physical-chemical alterations are involved. This would certainly be consistent with the discovery that the acquisition of a memory seems to occur in at least two distinct steps. In man, for example, damage to the temporal lobes may result in the loss of ability to remember new learning for more than about one hour. Such damage has no effect on memories acquired in the years before the damage occurred. Mental patients undergoing electroshock therapy are unable to remember events that occurred just prior to the treatment, but the memory of earlier events is unimpaired. In goldfish, on the other hand, the application of chemicals that inhibit protein synthesis has been shown to prevent the acquisition of long-term memories but not of short-term ones.

It should be apparent from this chapter that we know a great deal more about the simple forms of behavior, such as the simple reflex and the conditioned response, than we do about the more elaborate processes involved in insight and reasoning. We can be reasonably certain that further study will gradually tell us more about the mechanisms of these more elaborate mental activities so characteristic of man. While we look forward to these discoveries, we must also be warned by the memory of the ways in which past scientific discoveries, such as nuclear fission, have sometimes been used. The knowledge of how men's minds function is knowledge that will have to be used with great wisdom.

EXERCISES AND PROBLEMS

1 Design an experiment to show *whether or not* scout bees can communicate to other foragers information about the direction of a food source 200 yds from the hive.

2 How could you prove that the odor receptors of the honeybee are located on the antennae? Describe your procedure in detail.

3 If a man is shocked through his foot, simple reflex withdrawal of the foot will occur. Describe how this reflex might be "conditioned." What changes in the functioning of the nervous system occur during this process?

4 On March 20th, the sun rises in the east at 6:00 a.m. and sets in the west approximately 12 hours later. At 9:00 a.m., a scout bee does the tail-wagging dance so that the straight portion of the dance is 135° to the right of the vertical. In which direction is the food that it is reporting?

5 How will a scout bee dance in the hive at noon on March 20th when it has discovered food 1000 m to the north of the hive?

6 How will it dance when food has been discovered 5000 m northeast of the hive?

7 Summarize the various methods of intraspecific communication found among animals.

8 Distinguish between a tropism and a taxis.

9 Design an experiment to show whether a dog can discriminate between two adjacent whole notes on the piano.

10 Design an experiment to show whether ants have any color vision.

REFERENCES

1 Dethier, V. G., and E. Stellar, *Animal Behavior,* 2nd ed., Foundations of Modern Biology Series, Prentice-Hall, Inc., 1964. A general survey.

2 Lorenz, K. Z., "The Evolution of Behavior," *Scientific American,* Reprint No. 412, December, 1958. Examines homologies in the instinctive behavior patterns of animals and attempts to relate these to their evolutionary history.

3 Dilger, W. C., "The Behavior of Lovebirds," *Scientific American,* Reprint No. 1049, January, 1962.

4 Schneirla, T. C., and G. Piel, "The Army Ant," *Scientific American,* Reprint No. 413, June, 1948.

5 Tinbergen, N., "The Curious Behavior of the Stickleback," *Scientific American,* Reprint No. 414, December, 1952.

6 Sauer, E. G. F., "Celestial Navigation by Birds," *Scientific American,* Reprint No. 133, August, 1958.

7 von Frisch, K., *Bees: Their Vision, Chemical Senses, and Language,* Cornell University Press, New York, 1950. In this small book (available in a paperback edition) von Frisch describes the experiments which led him to so many discoveries in the fascinating behavior of bees.

8 von Frisch, K., "Dialects in the Language of the Bees," *Scientific American,* Reprint No. 130, August, 1962. Different kinds of bees vary in the details of their dances. These variations provide clues to the evolution of this system of communication.

9 Lindauer, M., *Communication Among Social Bees,* Harvard University Press, Cambridge, Mass., 1961. A report by a former student of von Frisch's of further discoveries in the role that communication plays in the lives of bees.

10 Michener, C. D., and Mary H. Michener, *American Social Insects,* D. Van Nostrand Co., Inc., Princeton, N.J., 1951. Beautifully illustrated accounts of the lives of wasps, bees, ants, and termites.

11 Cheesman, Evelyn, *Insects: Their Secret World,* William Sloan Associates, New York, 1953. Includes many fascinating examples of insect behavior.

12. Hess, E. H., " 'Imprinting' in Animals," *Scientific American,* Reprint No. 416, March, 1958.

13 Liddell, H. S., "Conditioning and Emotions," *Scientific American,* Reprint No. 418, January, 1954. Points out some of the problems in studying animal behavior and shows how the conditioned response can be used as a tool to solve some of these.

14 Fisher, A. E., "Chemical Stimulation of the Brain," *Scientific American,* Reprint No. 485, June, 1964. Predictable behavior patterns in rats can be triggered by the application of certain chemicals to specific areas of the brain.

15 Butler, R. A., "Curiosity in Monkeys," *Scientific American* , Reprint No. 426, February, 1954. Examines the nature and importance of this form of motivation.

16 Rensch, B., "The Intelligence of Elephants," *Scientific American,* Reprint No. 421, February, 1957. Presents evidence that elephants can develop rudimentary concepts.

17 Hockett, C. F., "The Origin of Speech," *Scientific American,* Reprint No. 603, September, 1960. The characteristics of human language and how it compares with other forms of animal communication.

18 Gerard, R. W., "What is Memory?," *Scientific American,* Reprint No. 11, September, 1953.

19 Hyden, H., "Satellite Cells in the Nervous System," *Scientific American,* Reprint No. 134, December, 1961. Shows how the RNA content of nerve cells increases with their activity and how this may be related to the problem of memory.

20 Best, J. B., "Protopsychology," *Scientific American,* Reprint No. 149, February, 1963. The first part of this article reviews the experiments on learning in planarians which suggest that memory may be encoded in RNA molecules.

21 Lorenz, K. Z., *King Solomon's Ring,* Thomas Y. Crowell Company, New York, 1952. A lively account of behavior in the birds, mammals, and fishes that share the author's home with him.

22 Scott, J. P., *Animal Behavior,* The Natural History Library, Doubleday & Co., Inc., New York, 1963. A clearly written and thorough survey.

PART VII

EVOLUTION

Partially exposed dinosaur bones in Wyoming.
(Courtesy American Museum of Natural History.)

In 1859, the British naturalist Charles Darwin published his *Origin of Species*. It has been said that this book ranks second only to the *Holy Bible* in its impact on man's thinking. What did it say that made it so influential?

First, the *Origin of Species* said that all living things on earth are here as a result of descent, with modification, from a common ancestor. This is the theory of **evolution.** Expressed another way, it tells us that species are not fixed, unchanging things but, on the contrary, have, through a process of gradual change, evolved from preexisting, different species. The theory implies, too, that all species are cousins, that is, any two species on earth have shared a common ancestor at some point in their history. This theory of evolution directly contradicts the still widely accepted idea that species are unchangeable, each species having been placed on earth in its present form.

Second, Darwin's *Origin of Species* presented a large number of facts which Darwin felt could best be explained by a theory of evolution and could not be adequately explained by a theory of special creation. In this chapter, we will examine some of these facts along with additional evidence that has been discovered since Darwin's time.

Finally, Darwin proposed a mechanism to explain how evolutionary change takes place. This theory, the theory of **natural selection** is the cornerstone of the *Origin of Species*. The idea of evolutionary change is very old. Evidence to support it had been presented before Darwin's time. It was Darwin, however, who built a virtually airtight case for the idea and then proposed the theory of natural selection to explain how evolution works. This theory and the clarification and enlargement it has received at the hands of later workers will be discussed in Chapter 32.

The idea of evolution provides a plausible explanation for a host of otherwise hard-to-explain facts. Let us now turn our attention to these.

31-1   THE EVIDENCE FROM PALEONTOLOGY

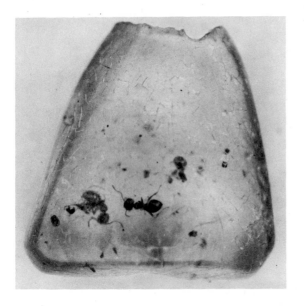

Paleontology is the study of **fossils.** We can define a fossil as any sort of remains of a once-living organism. A variety of kinds of fossils are found.

Under special circumstances, the **entire body** of an organism may be preserved after death. Insects, trapped in the sticky pitch of conifers growing along the Baltic Coast over 30 million years ago, can now be studied entombed in amber as easily as if they had just died (Fig. 31-1). Perhaps you have heard stories of the frozen woolly mammoths found in Siberia in the early years of this century. The meat of these animals was sufficiently well-preserved to be fed to dogs after thousands of years in nature's deep freeze.

Fig. 31-1

Ants fossilized in a piece of amber.

Such total preservation of dead organisms is very rare. Usually, the soft portions of the body are quickly destroyed after death by the action of scavengers or decomposed by decay bacteria. **Hard parts,** such as bones or shells, are more resistant to such destruction and hence more likely to be fossilized. If surrounded by sediments of clay or sand, they may yield easily recognizable fossils 500 million years later, long after the enclosing sediments have turned to rock such as shale or sandstone (see chapter opening illustration). These hard-part fossils may even retain traces of organic matter for surprisingly long periods. Amino acids and small peptides have been recovered from some that are over 300 million years old.

The hard parts of an organism may be destroyed even after entombment in sedimentary deposits. However, if the sediments turn to rock before this occurs, a **mold** of the organism remains. Such molds may often preserve details with remarkable accuracy. Sometimes a mold becomes filled with mineral deposits which then form a replica, or **cast,** of the original specimen.

Closely related to molds are the **imprints** left by plant and animal remains on the sediments upon which they rested. Tracks, trails, and tunnels made by long-vanished animals have been similarly preserved when the mud flats in which they occurred were quickly covered and protected from erosion. Figure 31-2 shows the footprints left by dinosaurs some 120 million years ago as they walked along the bed of a stream in the region that is now central Texas.

One other common fossil is the **petrifaction** or replacement fossil. This is a copy in stone of some plant or animal part. As the original remains disintegrated, they were replaced bit by bit with mineral deposits. This process can proceed so slowly that the original specimen is reproduced in all its detail. Figure 31-3 shows the clearly preserved annual rings in a piece of petrified wood. None of the original material is present in this specimen. It is not made of cellulose but of silica. Nevertheless, the faithfulness of the copy makes the fossil as useful as the actual specimen would be.

Fig. 31-2

Dinosaur footprints in limestone near the town of Glen Rose, Texas. The tracks on the right were made by a large dinosaur walking on all four legs. The tracks on the left were made by a smaller, bipedal dinosaur, perhaps a predacious species. The tracks were formed during the Cretaceous period some 120 million years ago. (Courtesy Roland T. Bird.)

We know that fossils have aroused the curiosity of man at least since the time of the ancient Greeks. With rare exceptions, fossils are not the remains of organisms still found living on the earth. How, then, can we explain their existence? A series of special creations followed by world-wide catastrophic extinctions has sometimes been given as the explanation. The theory of evolution provides a more satisfying answer, however. The idea that all organisms alive today share a common ancestry at some period in history implies that there were fewer kinds of living things in the past and that these were less complex. This decribes the fossil record very well. In descending into the Grand Canyon (Fig. 31-4), one passes layer after layer of sedimentary rock, the deeper layers being the older ones. As one proceeds downward, the number of different kinds of fossils decreases. Furthermore, the complexity of the organisms represented in the deeper layers is less than in the upper layers. Fossil reptiles appear late in the geological record while fossil annelid worms appear very early.

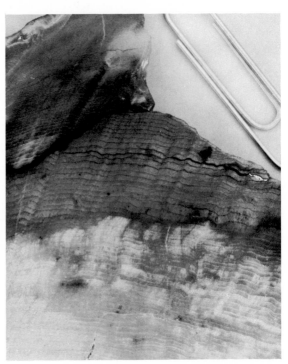

Fig. 31-3

A piece of petrified cypress wood. Although all organic matter has been replaced by silica, the pattern of annual rings stands out clearly.

It must be noted that one never finds an unbroken fossil history in one location. Geological upheavals of the land (which, after all, is the only way fossils of marine organisms could ever be exposed to our view) are always followed by erosion and hence erasure of part of the fossil record. Sometimes sedimentary rock of an earlier time may become thrust over younger rock. Fortunately, geologists can easily detect these "unconformities."

Many of Darwin's critics cited the failure of paleontologists to find "missing links" as a serious weakness of the idea that present forms have evolved from forms now known only as fossils. This argument has steadily lost effectiveness as more and more "missing links" have been found. If a biologist should try to describe an animal intermediate between the birds of today and the reptiles from which we believe they evolved, he would almost perfectly describe *Archeopteryx*, one of the many no-longer-missing links (see Section 34-15).

Gaps in the fossil record are still quite noticeable among the soft-bodied animals and among the prehumans. This is not surprising when you consider the remote chances of either type of organism's becoming fossilized in the first place. Soft-bodied animals are likely to decay too quickly and terrestrial ones (especially intelligent primates) are not likely to die where their remains will be quickly protected by enclosing sediments.

Then, too, we must remember that we can never expect to find more than fragments of the fossil record. Most of the fossils ever formed are still imprisoned within mountain ranges, under the earth and oceans, or have been destroyed by subsequent erosion and other geological disturbances.

Grand Canyon as seen from the south rim. The various layers of sedimentary rock, spanning much of the Paleozoic era, are clearly visible. (Courtesy Josef Muench.)

Fig. 31-4

Perhaps the greatest obstacle to finding missing links is that the evolution of new species of plants and animals seems, in general, to have occurred in small populations of poorly specialized forms. The fossil record is, however, filled chiefly with the remains of "climax" groups, large populations of highly specialized organisms which flourished for a period only to become extinct when conditions on earth changed.

Though we may never be able to trace the evolution of all living forms through the fossils of their ancestors, the presence and distribution of fossils already discovered provide us with some of the most direct evidence of the theory of evolution.

THE EVIDENCE FROM COMPARATIVE ANATOMY

In comparing the anatomy of one mammal with another, one cannot help being struck by the many cases in which certain parts of the body are built to the same basic plan in each specimen. This might not seem surprising if the similarly constructed parts were used in similar ways. One could argue that there was only one best way to construct the organ in question and that the Creator used it. However, these organs may actually be used in a variety of ways. Figure 2-2 illustrates the organization of bones in the forelimbs of the human, a whale, and a bat. Although these forelimbs are used for such diverse activities as lifting, swimming, and flying, the same basic structural plan is evident in all of them. Organs which have the same basic structure, the same relationship to other organs, and (as it turns out) the same type of embryonic development are said to be **homologous.**

It hardly seems reasonable that a single pattern of bones represents the best possible structure to accomplish the varied tasks to which these mammalian forelimbs are put. However, if we interpret the persistence of the basic pattern as evidence of inheritance from a common ancestor, we see that the various modifications are simply adaptations of the plan to the special needs of the organism.

The various mammalian forelimbs constitute just one example of homologous organs. Both the animal and plant kingdoms contain a large catalogue of such structures. This is hardly surprising in view of our belief that all organisms have shared a common ancestor at some time in their evolutionary history. Presumably, the more recently two species have shared an ancestor, the more homologous organs they will have in common. Homologies in more distantly related species may be harder to determine, although fossil evidence is often a great help in this.

You remember (see Section 2-2) that we classify organisms on the basis of the number of shared homologies. The greater the number of these, the smaller the taxonomic unit in which we place the organisms. The dog and the coyote share many more homologous features than the dog and man. Consequently, we place the dog and coyote in the same genus. They share only a common class (Mammalia) with man. Although Linnaeus did not believe in evolution, his recognition of the value of classifying on the basis of homologous organs has given us a scheme which we believe reflects the actual kinship of the organisms being classified.

One category of homologous organs deserves special mention for providing evidence of evolution. These are homologous organs which in some species have no apparent function. Dissection of a boa constrictor or a whale reveals bones that are thought to be homologous to the hip bones of other vertebrates. No function seems to be accomplished by these structures. If all species have been specially created, it seems like poor designing to include nonfunctional parts. If, on the other hand, we assume that both snakes and whales have evolved from four-legged ancestors, then we can understand why traces of their evolutionary heritage still remain.

Man, too, has similar **vestigial organs.** The fused vertebrae which make up the base of the human spine are interpreted as the vestigial remnants of the tail possessed by our ancestors. In fact, human babies occasionally are born with short tails. These are, however, quickly and easily removed.

THE EVIDENCE FROM EMBRYOLOGY

The embryonic development of all vertebrates shows striking uniformities. This is particularly true during cleavage, morphogenesis, and the early stages of differentiation (Fig. 31-5). These similarities are often cited as evidence of an evolutionary relation-

Comparison of vertebrate embryos. (G. J. Romanes, *Darwin and After Darwin*, Open Court Publishing Co.)

Fig. 31-5

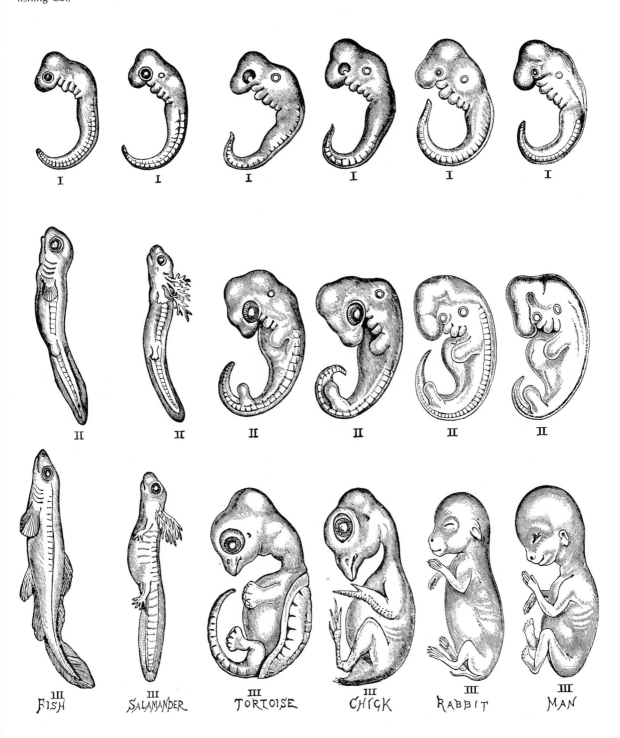

I I I I I I

II II II II II II

III III III III III III
FISH SALAMANDER TORTOISE CHICK RABBIT MAN

ship among the vertebrates. Of course, one might argue that there is only one effective way that a vertebrate can be constructed from a fertilized egg. There may well be considerable truth in this idea but, on the other hand, it does not adequately explain one aspect of these similarities. This is the fact that some structures appear during the development of the most advanced vertebrates just as they do in the more primitive species, only to disappear or become almost unrecognizably modified in the later stages of development. The month-old human embryo has a series of paired branchial grooves in the neck region (Fig. 31-5). These are matched on the interior by a series of paired gill pouches. This pattern appears not only in man but in the embryonic development of all vertebrates. In the fishes, the pouches and grooves eventually meet and form gill slits, the openings which allow water to pass from the pharynx over the gills and out of the body. In the "higher" vertebrates the grooves and pouches disappear. In man the chief trace of their existence is the Eustachian tube and auditory canal, which (interrupted only by the eardrum) connect the pharynx with the outside of the head. The temporary possession of a tail and a two-chambered heart are other examples of developmental stages through which the human embryo passes. Surely there must be more direct ways to achieve the final adult form. What explanation, then, can we give for these seemingly inefficient procedures? Again evolution provides the clue. We and the other vertebrates continue to pass through many (not all) of the embryonic stages that our ancestors passed through because we have all inherited developmental mechanisms from a common ancestor. We then go on to modify these in ways appropriate to our diverse ways of life. Therefore, it should be no surprise to find that the more distantly related two vertebrates are, the shorter the period during which they pass through similar embryonic stages (Fig. 31-5). Conversely, the more closely related two vertebrates are, the longer their embryonic development proceeds in a parallel fashion.

The idea that our embryonic development repeats that of our ancestors is called the theory of **recapitulation.** This theory is not restricted to the vertebrates. There is some evidence (which we shall examine in Chapter 34) that the ancestors of the insects had a pair of legs on each of their body segments. In this, they resembled today's millipedes. (In fact, the millipedes may well represent a second line of descent from these early forms.) In any case, during the embryonic development of insects, limb buds appear on the abdomen just as they must have in their multi-legged ancestors (Fig. 31-6). But by the time the larva hatches, only the six legs on the thorax remain.

Even in plant development we see recapitulation. Germinating moss and fern spores produce a short filament of green cells which resembles a filamentous green alga (Figs. 21-1 and 21-2). Soon these develop into the mature moss and fern gametophytes. For a brief period, though, mosses and ferns both pass through a stage reminiscent of the algae from which we think they evolved.

Fig. 31-6

Two stages in the embryonic development of an insect. Although limb buds appear in all segments, as they surely did in the ancestors of the insects, only those in the thorax (color) become legs. The ones in the head develop into mouth parts. The ones in the abdomen disappear.

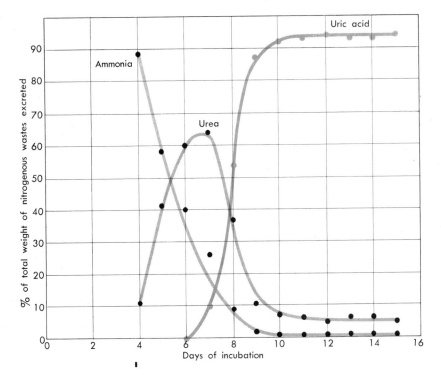

Biochemical recapitulation in the chick embryo.

Fig. 31-7

Biochemical as well as anatomical recapitulation occurs. As you learned in Chapter 16, fish excrete a large part of their waste nitrogen as ammonia, while amphibians have the less toxic urea as their chief nitrogenous waste. Actually, the fishlike *tadpole* excretes ammonia until it undergoes metamorphosis into the adult frog. Only then does its chief nitrogenous waste become urea.

Birds go one step further and convert their waste nitrogen compounds into the almost insoluble compound, uric acid. It is interesting to see (Fig. 31-7) that the developing chick embryo does not excrete uric acid from the very first but instead passes through an ammonia-excreting stage followed by a urea-excreting stage. This certainly suggests that the chick is repeating stages in the biochemical development of its ancestors.

THE EVIDENCE FROM COMPARATIVE BIOCHEMISTRY

Just as the study of comparative anatomy has shown the presence of anatomical homologies, so the study of the biochemistry of different organisms has revealed biochemical homologies. In fact, the biochemical similarity of living organisms is one of the most remarkable features of life.

Cytochrome enzymes are found in almost every living organism: plant, animal, and protist. One of these, cytochrome c, is a polypeptide chain of 104 to 112 amino acids (depending upon the organism in which it is present). In recent years the exact sequence of amino acids in these chains has been determined for the cytochrome c's of such diverse organisms as man, the rabbit, the king penguin, the rattlesnake, the tuna fish, a moth, the red bread mold *Neurospora* (Fig. 20-7), and many others. Although there is considerable variation in the sequences, especially between organisms that we assume are only distantly related, there is a surprising amount of similarity as well. The sequence in man differs from that in the monkey at only one place in the chain. Cytochrome c from the wheat plant differs from man's in 35 of the amino acids. However, another 35 of the amino acids in the chains have proved to be the same in every single species examined. This includes one section of 11 consecutive amino acids (Nos. 70–80) that are common to all organisms known. We have seen how the nucleotide sequence in DNA molecules codes for the amino acid sequence in proteins. The occurrence in such a wide variety of organisms of genes for cytochrome c—genes that contain much of the same genetic information—would be virtually inexplicable without a theory of evolution. Surely this phenomenon means that we have all inherited this gene, albeit with an accumulation of mutations, from a common ancestor.

The same argument can be applied to other biochemical similarities among organisms. Studies of the amino acid sequences in mammalian hemoglobins reveal close similarities, especially so among those species thought to be closely related. DNA and RNA are found in every living organism and, so far as we can determine, contain the same hereditary coding mechanism. As you learned in Chapter 26, most vertebrates share the same, or similar, hormones. For example, LTH is found in vertebrates as diverse as fishes, birds, and mammals, although its function differs in each of these classes (see Section 26-8, 2). Thus we have a parallel on the chemical level of the homologous forelimbs we discussed earlier in the chapter: a hormone inherited from a common ancestor but with its function modified in ways appropriate to the life of each animal.

The remarkable uniformity of biochemical organization that underlies the incredible diversity of living things is difficult to interpret in any other way but an evolutionary one. Presumably these molecules appeared very early in the history of life, and almost all modern forms have inherited the ability to manufacture and use them.

The study of antigen-antibody relationships has provided some especially interesting support to the theory of evolution. As you learned in Section 14-12, antigens are large molecules which, when introduced into the body of an animal to which they are foreign, induce the formation of antibodies. Antibodies are proteins which inactivate antigens. The inactivation of antigens by antibodies occurs as a result of an actual physical union between the two molecules.

When foreign proteins, e.g. those present in human serum, are injected into the bloodstream of a rabbit (simply a convenient animal to use; any other mammal would do), the rabbit manufactures appropriate antibodies. These are called precipitins because, in combining with the foreign molecules, they form an insoluble complex which settles out of solution as a precipitate. When rabbit-blood serum containing antihuman antibodies is mixed in a test tube with human serum, the amount of precipitate formed can be easily measured. What makes this reaction interesting so far as our present story is concerned is that these antihuman precipitins will also react with the blood serum of certain other mammals but to a lesser degree; that is, a smaller amount of precipitate is formed. Antihuman antibodies mixed with the serum of man, an ape, an Old World monkey, a New World monkey, and a pig (in each of 5 separate test tubes) produce a precipitate in each tube. The amount produced decreases, however, from man to pig (Fig. 31-8). As we will see in Chapter 34, this corresponds closely to the presently accepted degree of kinship between man and these other mammals.

Not only has this method (called comparative serology) corroborated some evolutionary relationships which had already been agreed upon, but it has been very helpful in establishing relationships for which anatomical evidence had failed to provide clear-cut answers. For many years, the exact position of the horseshoe crab, *Limulus* (Fig. 5-12), among the arthropods was unclear. Now, however, a strong reaction between anti-*Limulus* antibodies and arachnid antigen has caused *Limulus* to be placed in the class Arachnida. Similarly, rabbits, although they show some structural resemblances to rodents, are now placed in an order of their own, the Lagomorpha. Serological tests show that little affinity exists between rabbits and rodents; in fact, rabbits seem to be more closely related to even-toed ungulates like the pig! Whales, too, reveal by serological testing a closer relationship to the even-toed ungulates than any other mammalian order. Even plant proteins have been used as antigens and several evolutionary puzzles have been cleared up by this technique.

Reaction between antihuman precipitins (prepared in rabbit) and serum of various mammals, with human taken as 100%

Man	100%
Chimpanzee	97%
Gorilla	92%
Gibbon	79%
Baboon	75%
Spider monkey*	58%
Lemur	37%
Hedgehog (Insectivora)	17%
Pig	8%

*New World species

Fig. 31-8

THE EVIDENCE FROM PROTECTIVE RESEMBLANCE 31-5

Probably no more dramatic evidence of evolution exists than the spread of **industrial melanism.** Approximately 10% of the more than 700 species of larger moths that are found in the British Isles have been undergoing a dramatic darkening in coloration in regions of heavy industrial activity. This change is called industrial melanism. Perhaps the best-studied example is the peppered moth, *Biston betularia*. The wings and body of this moth used to be light in color with scattered dark markings (giving rise to its common name). In 1848 a coal-black mutant form of the moth was discovered near Manchester, England. Since that time, the black form (*Biston betularia* var. *carbonaria*) has gradually become more prevalent. Today over 90% of the moths in this region are black. Here certainly is an example of a change in a species taking place in nature and rapidly enough to be recorded by observant naturalists.

What accounts for this evolutionary change? *Biston betularia* flies at night and rests by day on tree trunks in the forest. In areas far from industrial activity, the trunks of forest trees are encrusted with lichen growth. As Fig. 31-9 shows so clearly, the light-colored form of the moth is practically invisible against such a background. In areas where air pollution is severe, the combination of toxic gases and soot has killed the lichen growth and darkened branches and trunks. Against such a background, the light-colored moth stands out sharply. *Biston betularia* is preyed upon by birds which pluck it from its resting place by day. In polluted woods, it is easy to see that the dark form would have a much better chance of surviving undetected. In fact, when the English geneticist H. B. D. Kettlewell released marked moths of both kinds in these woods, he was able to recapture twice as many of the dark forms as of the light. Careful observation showed that predatory birds did, indeed, eat a much higher proportion of the light moths released than of the dark. It is no wonder that the dark form is now dominant in these regions. In unpolluted areas (e.g. Scotland and southwestern England), the woods are still lichen-encrusted and the light form of *Biston betularia* is still dominant.

Fig. 31-9 Left: the peppered moth *Biston betularia* and the dark form *carbonaria* on a lichen-encrusted tree trunk. Right: Both forms of the moth are shown resting on a blackened tree trunk typical of those near industrial areas. (Courtesy Dr. H. B. D. Kettlewell.)

Industrial melanism is only one example of the development of protective resemblance. There are butterflies which, at rest, look like dead leaves. There are insects which look for all the world like twigs (Fig. 31-10). The robber fly mimics the bumblebee and presumably thereby gains protection from predators. (Note that the robber fly, despite its resemblance to the bumblebee, has not been able to dispense with its evolutionary heritage. Like all diptera, it has two wings instead of the four possessed by the bumblebees and other hymenoptera.) We have no reason to believe that these few additional examples of protective resemblance came about any differently from industrial melanism. Evolution explains their existence, too, but in the case of industrial melanism, we have actually been able to see the process of evolution taking place.

31-6 **THE EVIDENCE FROM GEOGRAPHICAL DISTRIBUTION**

It is perfectly obvious to anyone who has given a moment's thought to the question that each species of animal or plant is not found evenly distributed throughout the world. If inhabitants of North America wish to view a gorilla, they must visit a circus or zoo or travel to Africa. To a large extent, the discontinuous distribution of plant and animal species can be explained on the basis of the presence of a favorable environment. No one would look for tropical orchids in the arctic. However, still unexplained is the existence throughout the world of habitats which do not contain species that would presumably be well adapted there. If each kind of living thing had been specially created, we might expect it to be found in all habitats suitable for it.

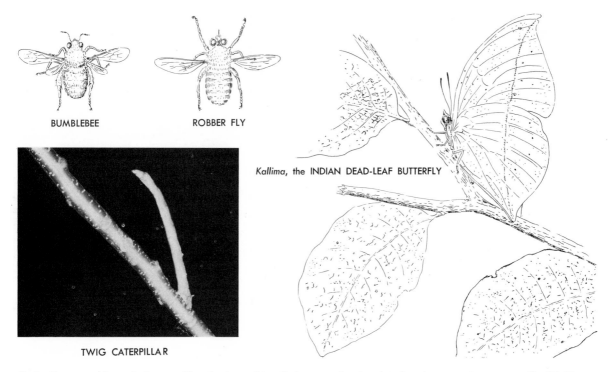

BUMBLEBEE

ROBBER FLY

Kallima, the INDIAN DEAD-LEAF BUTTERFLY

TWIG CATERPILLAR

Protective resemblance in insects. The stingless robber fly is more closely related to the mosquito than to the bumblebee. Although the true veins of a butterfly's wing radiate from the point of attachment, *Kallima's* resemblance to a leaf extends even to having a dark line crossing its veins that matches the midvein of a leaf. The motionless twig caterpillar, complete with "buds" and "lenticels," often escapes detection by birds but may occasionally have some other insect lay eggs on it by mistake. (Courtesy Muriel V. Williams.)

Fig. 31-10

Such is not the case. The Hawaiian Islands contain satisfactory habitats for frogs, toads, and salamanders, but none are to be found there. The deserts of Africa contain species not found in the deserts of North America and vice versa. Of course, we may sometimes fail to see that one habitat is not exactly equivalent to another. However, the history of accidental animal and plant introductions supports the general idea. Rabbits have overrun Australia, an area where they were not found before being introduced by man. The explosive spread of the mongoose in the West Indies, of the ascomycete causing the Dutch elm disease in this country, and many other examples prove that the presence or absence of an organism in a given location is often due to factors other than suitability.

What, then, can explain the discontinuous distribution of plants and animals? If we assume that all creatures are the product of evolution, then we can view the problem in a historical way. Each species must have evolved somewhere on the face of the earth. Its subsequent dispersal was regulated by the efficiency of its dispersal mechanism (locomotion in the case of animals, spores and seeds in the case of plants) and the presence or absence of barriers to its dispersal. Wherever amphibians first evolved, we feel quite sure that they were never able to reach the Hawaiian Islands because there has never been a land bridge which would enable the animals to get there. Amphibians, you remember, have no mechanism to protect themselves from the dehydrating effects of the hypertonic sea water. They are found on many islands,

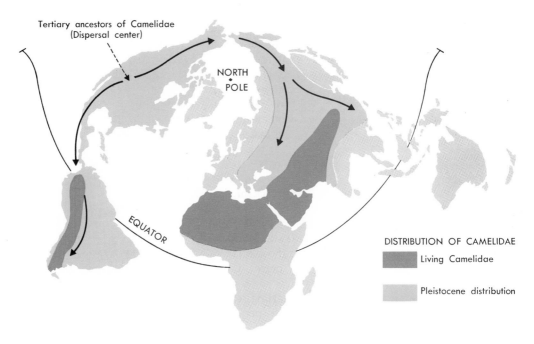

NORTH
POLE

Tertiary ancestors of Camelidae
(Dispersal center)

EQUATOR

DISTRIBUTION OF CAMELIDAE

Living Camelidae

Pleistocene distribution

Fig. 31-11   The present discontinuous distribution of the members of the camel family (Camelidae) is accounted for by the discovery of an unbroken distribution of fossil camels between the two regions. (Simpson, Pittendrigh and Tiffany, *Life,* Copyright 1957. Reproduced by permission from Harcourt, Brace & World, Inc. Based on a figure from Matthews, *Climate of Evolution,* 2nd ed., N.Y. Acad. of Sci., Vol. 1, 1939.)

such as those in the East Indies, but we are sure these islands were at one time connected to the continental land mass.

The distribution of camels provides another example which is hard to explain in any way except by evolution and gradual dispersal. Members of the camel *family* occur today in two widely separated areas of the world. True camels inhabit an area that includes parts of Africa, Asia, and the Near East. Their closest living relatives, the llamas, are found thousands of miles away in the Andes Mountains of South America. Again, this distribution can best be explained in terms of evolutionary history. Starting with a common ancestor, these two lines of camels diverged and, while so doing, migrated from their point of origin. A land bridge linking North America and Asia at the time permitted dispersal from one hemisphere to the other (Fig. 31-11). Today, the descendants of the early camels have reached the extreme ranges mentioned, while for some reason camels have become extinct in the intermediate regions. There are no missing links to this story, though. Fossil camels are known in a continuous band from one region to the other. Interestingly enough, the most primitive of these ancestral camels are found in North America suggesting that the family originated here.

In 1876 the British naturalist Alfred Wallace (who conceived the idea of evolution and natural selection independently of Darwin), proposed that the continental areas of the world could be divided into six main regions on the basis of their animal populations (Fig. 31-12). The greatest diversity of living things is found in the two great tropical areas, the Ethiopian (tropical Africa) and the Oriental (tropical Asia and the nearby offshore islands). Fossil evidence suggests that in these regions have evolved most of our dominant plants and vertebrates. Europe and northern Asia make up the Palearctic region, while North America is the Nearctic. Spread of plants and animals into and through these regions has often been seriously limited by the harshness of the climate. The two remaining continental regions are the Neotropical (South America) and the Australian (Australia, New Zealand and New Guinea). The unusual animal life (fauna) and plant life (flora) of these regions can be explained by their intermittent isolation from the nearby land masses. The Australian region is isolated right now, of course, while the Neotropical region has been enjoying a land bridge with the Nearctic for the last few million years.

The distribution of plants and animals in the oceanic islands provides particularly strong support for the theory of evolution. Oceanic islands (e.g. the Hawaiian Islands) are those that have never been connected to one of Wallace's continental regions. Nevertheless, they all support rich and varied fauna and flora. As a young man of 26, Darwin visited a group of such islands, the Galapagos Islands off the coast of Ecuador (Fig. 31-12). While the marine birds were those found elsewhere in the Pacific, Darwin found scattered over the islands thirteen species of land birds which were not known anywhere else in the world. At first glance, some of these birds seemed quite diverse (see Fig. 32-4). Some had stout beaks for eating seeds. Others had beaks adapted for eating insects of one size or another. One species had a beak like a woodpecker's and actually used it for drilling holes in wood. However, it lacked the long tongue which our woodpeckers use for removing insects from the wood. Instead, it used a cactus spine, held in its beak, to dig the insect out. Underlying this superficial variety of types was a basic similarity: all these birds were finches. Although one looked far more like a warbler than a finch, its internal anatomy showed its true kinship. Here, then, were a group of birds found nowhere else on earth and all showing definite similarities. This indeed would be a curious exercise in special creation. Far more plausible is Darwin's thought that each of these birds is the result of descent with modification (evolution) from a common finch ancestor which accidentally reached the islands from its original home in South America. Probably nothing else so

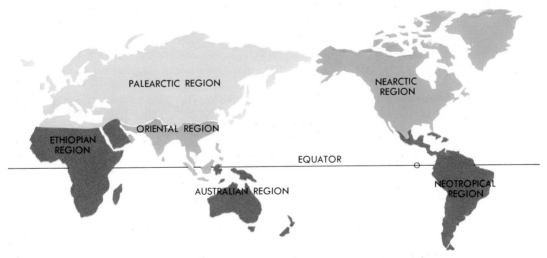

Wallace's faunal regions. The circle on the equator shows the location of the Galapagos Islands.

Fig. 31-12

strengthened Darwin's eventual conviction that species are changeable and are the product of evolution than the example of his finches.

The examples that we have cited as evidence of evolution all involve the discontinuous distribution of living things. However, even in cases in which a species is uniformly distributed through a large region, we find evidence of evolution at work. The common leopard frog (*Rana pipiens*) is found throughout the eastern portion of North America. At no place in its range can one sharply divide this population into northern forms and southern forms. Nonetheless, significant differences in physiology and behavior exist between northern and southern animals. In fact, if one breeds Vermont frogs with Texas ones, the offspring develop abnormally. This certainly suggests that genetic differences exist between the specimens so great as to prevent successful hybrid formation. With a Vermont frog in one hand and a Texas frog in the other, one would be quite justified in assigning them to separate species. But at every place from Vermont to Texas leopard frogs are breeding freely with one another and clearly constitute a single species. Such a continuous distribution of animals or plants which vary gradually from one end of their range to the other constitutes a **cline.** It provides irrefutable evidence that species are not necessarily uniform and unchangeable groups of organisms, hence lending strong support to the theory of evolution.

31-7   THE EVIDENCE FROM DOMESTICATION

The deliberate cultivation of plants and animals has occupied man for thousands of years. During all of this time, but especially in the last two centuries, he has developed varieties or breeds of plants and animals which yield more and better food or which, in other ways, better serve his purposes. While, with rare exceptions, he has not created new species in this process of domestication he has certainly created forms which differ greatly from the ancestral stock. The extraordinary diversity of the domestic dog, from Chihuahuas to Saint Bernards, provides dramatic evidence of man's ability to alter a species by selective breeding procedures. In fact, the corn plant (*Zea mays*) has been altered so greatly in the course of domestication that it can no longer survive without the aid of man. The many breeds of horses, cows, goats, sheep, chickens, and rabbits, which can be seen at any country fair, are dramatic testimony to the variability of species and man's ability to create evolutionary changes for his own benefit.

The standard by which a theory is judged is its ability to explain the *most* facts in the simplest manner and to make possible the prediction of new facts. The slowness with which most evolutionary change occurs has hampered the theory of evolution in the second respect. In its ability to provide a simple, comprehensive explanation for a vast array of facts, however, the theory of evolution justly stands as the most important theory in biology. Every aspect of the living world that man studies, from biochemistry and cytology to anthropology and history, has been nourished and broadened by it.

While the geographical distribution of animals may have provided Darwin with his most compelling evidence that evolution has occurred, it was his study of the process of domestication that gave him the clue as to how it occurs. It is his theory of the mechanism of evolutionary change which truly makes his *Origin of Species* such an epoch-making work. We shall turn our attention to this theory in the next chapter.

EXERCISES AND PROBLEMS

1 What has happened to most of the fossils that were formed during the history of life?

2 The theory of recapitulation is often stated: "ontogeny recapitulates phylogeny." Find out what these three words mean.

3 Does the statement of the theory of recapitulation in Question 2 accurately describe the facts? Explain.

4 Which two of the six animals whose embryonic stages are illustrated in Fig. 31-5 do you think have most recently shared a common ancestor? Explain.

5 How would you go about preparing antibovine (anticow) antibodies?

6 A far greater diversity of plant and animal species is found in the Ethiopian and Oriental regions than in the other four. Can you account for this?

7 Frogs (Eleutherodactylus) were not found in Bermuda before being introduced by man in 1880 but were prevalent in the islands of the West Indies. Can you explain why they were found in one location and not the other?

8 Would you predict on the basis of the data in Fig. 31-8 that we are more closely related to the Old World monkeys or the New World monkeys? Explain.

9 The evolutionary history of mollusks and reptiles is known much better than that of flatworms. Why?

REFERENCES

1 Brues, C. T., "Insects in Amber," *Scientific American*, Reprint No. 838, November, 1951.

2 Abelson, P. H., "Paleobiochemistry," *Scientific American*, Reprint No. 101, July, 1956. Describes how amino acids have been discovered in fossils as old as 300 million years.

3 Moody, P. A., *Introduction to Evolution*, 2nd Edition, Harper & Bros., New York, 1962. The first two-thirds of this clearly written text is devoted to the evidence of evolution.

4 Frieden, E., "The Chemistry of Amphibian Metamorphosis," *Scientific American*, Reprint No. 170, November, 1963. An example of biochemical recapitulation.

5 Zuckerkandl, E., "The Evolution of Hemoglobin," *Scientific American*, Reprint No. 1012, May, 1965. Demonstrates with mammalian hemoglobins how knowledge of the amino acid sequences of homologous proteins can be used to unravel evolutionary relationships.

6 Kettlewell, H. B. D., "Darwin's Missing Evidence," *Scientific American*, Reprint No. 842, March, 1959. A description of industrial melanism in *Biston betularia*.

7 Portmann, A., *Animal Camouflage*, University of Michigan Press, Ann Arbor, Michigan, 1959. This little book is filled with many fascinating examples of protective resemblance in animals.

8 Lack, D., "Darwin's Finches," *Scientific American*, Reprint No. 22, April, 1953.

Twenty-two years elapsed from the time that Darwin returned home convinced of the truth of evolution and the actual publication of the *Origin of Species*. During this long interval, Darwin accumulated still more data to bolster his case. Living in rural England, he had plenty of opportunity to watch local farmers practice the art of animal breeding. Art it was, because the science of genetics was still unborn. Nonetheless, improved varieties of all sorts of domestic animals were being created. Darwin, recognizing these as evolutionary changes, sought the mechanism by which they were produced. He found that animal breeders could only develop new breeds from variants that appeared naturally in their livestock. Only if some animals were born heavier or taller or darker-coated than others could the breeders develop heavier or taller or darker-coated breeds. Darwin also realized that these variants could not arise simply from exposure to a different environment. Individuals that are heavier simply as a result of better diet could never supply the raw materials for a heavier breed. Only **inheritable variations** could be used for this purpose.

The second vital ingredient in the formation of new varieties was **selective breeding.** Once individuals with desirable inherited traits were identified, they were mated together in hopes that (1) a higher proportion of their offspring would have the trait than in the population as a whole and (2) the expression of the trait would be intensified in the offspring. By repeating this process of selective breeding, it eventually was possible to develop pure-breeding lines displaying the new trait. The various breeds of horses, cattle, swine, dogs, and cats, to mention just a few, have been produced in this manner.

Man, then, can bring about evolutionary change. Does a similar mechanism exist in nature? The first thing we must look for in populations of wild organisms is inherited variations which can serve as the raw material for evolution. Anyone who has studied a large sample of individuals in a single species knows that variation does exist in nature. Such variation takes two forms.

1) **Continuous Variation.** Many traits found in a population of plants or animals vary in a smooth, continuous way from one extreme to the other. Body weight, body length, and coat color are just three traits in which we might expect to find a whole range of variations. Typically, most of the individuals fall near the middle of the range with fewer individuals at the extremes. You can demonstrate the existence of this type of variation right around you. Although your classmates may not qualify as a wild population, calculation of their heights or weights (of one sex) will reveal a wide, unbroken range of values with more individuals in the middle of the range than at the extremes. These data can be plotted on a graph (look back at Fig. 18-8) and the curve that results is typical of those obtained by studying continuous variation in wild populations.

2) **Discontinuous Variation.** With respect to certain traits, the individuals of some populations fall into two or more distinct categories with no intergrading between them. The various castes in a honeybee colony (see Section 30-10) are an example of such discontinuous variation. The fact that all humans have one of four possible ABO blood types is another. Such variation is called **polymorphism.**

◀ Charles Darwin (1809-1882). (Courtesy Culver Pictures, Inc.)

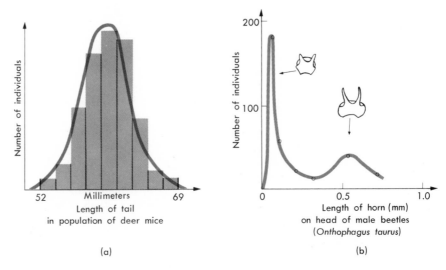

(a)

(b)

Fig. 32-1   Examples of (a) continuous variation and (b) discontinuous variation. (Redrawn by permission from D'Arcy W. Thompson, *On Growth and Form*, Vol. I, Cambridge University Press, 1959.)

The light and dark forms of *Biston betularia* (see Section 31-5) illustrate polymorphism, too. There are no gray individuals. Plotting the distribution of polymorphic traits, one gets not a single bell-shaped curve but discrete peaks for each form of the trait (Fig. 32-1).

Both continuous and discontinuous variation can provide the raw materials for evolution, but only if they arise from hereditary rather than just environmental factors. Perhaps the continuous variation in the height of your classmates is simply a reflection of variation in their diet as infants. We already have seen (see Section 26-15)

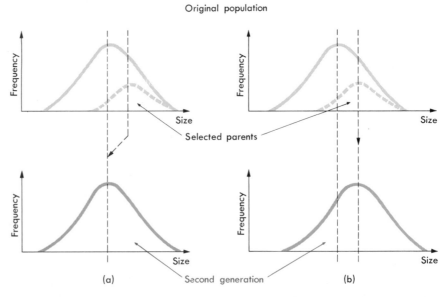

Fig. 32-2   Effect of selective breeding when variations are caused by (a) the environment and (b) heredity.

that the development of supplementary egg-laying females in a honeybee colony deprived of its queen is controlled by the withdrawal of a chemical substance. How, then, can we determine whether variation in a wild population is to some degree inherited? As a practical matter, this is often very difficult. It involves the mating of individuals both of whom are extreme examples of the trait under study. If, for example, the offspring of two extra-large mice are significantly larger than the average for the population, hereditary factors are undoubtedly at work (Fig. 32-2). On the other hand, if the offspring occupy the same range as the average for the population, environmental factors are working alone. A population of bean seeds of a pure strain varies over a range of several mm in length. If extra-small beans are crossed, however, the new crop will show no shift toward a smaller size. Variation in size, then, does not seem to be inherited in this particular case.

NATURAL SELECTION 32-2

Granted that inherited variability does occur in wild populations, is there a mechanism in nature to accomplish the selective breeding that Darwin saw was an indispensable part of the process of domestication? The answer to this question and the key to the whole theory of evolution came to Darwin as a result of reading the *Essay on Population* by the English clergyman Thomas Malthus. In this work, Malthus pointed out the remarkable reproductive potential of all organisms. We have already seen (see Section 22-4) that the American oyster may release 1,000,000 eggs in a season and a single puffball fungus (genus *Lycoperdon*) may release 700,000,000,000 spores in the same period. Obviously, the earth would quickly be overrun with oysters, puffballs, in fact even the slowest-breeding plants and animals, if their populations were not kept in check by some means. Darwin called this means **natural selection.**

His theory of natural selection is a conclusion based upon three observable facts of nature and one preliminary conclusion. We can summarize the theory as follows:

Fact No. 1. All species have a high reproductive potential. From oysters to elephants, they are capable of filling the earth with their kind.

Fact No. 2. Except for minor fluctuations, the population of any given species remains fairly constant from year to year.

Conclusion No. 1. Therefore, we must conclude that all creatures face a *continual struggle for existence.*

Fact No. 3. There is inherited variation among the individuals of any species.

Conclusion No. 2. Therefore, we may conclude that those individuals whose variations best fit them for their environment will be most likely to survive. This idea of the *survival of the fittest* is what we call Darwin's theory of natural selection. It is the mechanism Darwin thought accomplishes in nature what man's selective breeding accomplishes in domestication.

THE MEASURE OF "FITNESS" 32-3

Darwin's theory of natural selection has often been seriously misunderstood. To many people, it has implied that a "dog-eat-dog" existence is natural and hence justifies man's most ruthless exploitation of his fellow man and of the other resources of his environment. Actually, fitness measured in terms of aggressiveness applies to only a portion of the world of living things and even then is only one of many criteria involved. Fitness as a biological concept can be measured only in terms of the ability to produce mature offspring. The fittest organisms in any population are those that leave the largest number of mature offspring. A variety of mechanisms may play a role in this.

1) Survival. The most important is simply the ability to stay alive until one's reproductory age is over. (Many organisms, as we have seen, continue to reproduce as long as they live. These include the perennial plants, many invertebrates, fishes, amphibians, and reptiles.) Any trait which increases the organism's chances of surviving to and through this period makes that organism more "fit" than the others of its species. We call such traits **adaptations.** They may involve a change in body structure, a change in body physiology, a change in behavior, or all of these. While strength, long claws, fangs, etc., do promote survival in some cases, this kind of adaptation probably plays a minor role in the evolution of living things. For every adaptation associated with aggressive behavior, one can cite literally dozens of examples of adaptations which play a more inconspicuous, but every bit as important, role in promoting survival. The mimicry of the Indian dead-leaf butterfly, the twig caterpillar, and the robber fly (Fig. 31-10) are examples of morphological adaptations that make their owners more fit by reducing the likelihood of their being eaten by predators. The melanism of *B. betularia* var. *carbonaria* similarly promotes survival and hence makes the form more "fit." In fact, any change which merely improves the efficiency of an organ promotes survival. In a real sense, this entire book has been a catalogue of adaptations that confer fitness on the individuals having them.

Physiological and behavioral adaptations go hand in hand with morphological ones. The ability of reptiles to excrete their nitrogenous wastes as uric acid is dependent upon the development of a nephron in which glomerular filtration is reduced and tubular excretion increased (see Section 16-11). Similarly, the mimicry of the Indian dead-leaf butterfly would be of no avail if this creature did not make a practice of resting quietly on twigs with its wings closed. The remarkable morphology of the twig caterpillar would have no survival value if this creature spent its time moving about on the broad surfaces of leaves.

The fact that natural selection can operate only on traits that promote survival through the reproductive years has interesting consequences for those organisms, such as man, in whom reproduction usually ceases long before death. Any traits that appear for the first time after reproduction has ceased cannot be selected for, because no mechanism remains for their gradual increase in the population. Of course, traits that improve well-being late in life may improve fitness early in life, too. However, the absence of any specific selection of traits that improve physical and mental health late in life may well account for the sharp rise in degenerative changes that occur in old age (Fig. 24-7). It may also account for the fact that despite the dramatic increase in the *average* life span of Americans and Europeans during the last half century, our *maximum* life span remains virtually unchanged.

2) Sexual Selection. Another factor affecting "fitness" is sexual selection. Any inherited trait that makes some individuals more desirable to the opposite sex than others will thus make them more successful in mating. Consequently, a larger proportion of the next generation will have inherited this trait. Darwin was familiar with many examples of sexual selection. Brilliant plumage in male birds is a trait which may often be explained on this basis.

Sexual selection probably operates in a negative as well as a positive way. Certain structural variations may be less successful in "releasing" mating behavior in individuals of the opposite sex. In 1950, the husband-and-wife team of Sheldon and Elizabeth Reed set up a culture of fruit flies containing equal numbers of red-eyed males, red-eyed females, white-eyed males, and white-eyed females. Although previous experimentation had shown that white-eyed flies are just as healthy and live just as long as red-eyed flies, after 25 generations there was not a white-eyed fly to be found in the culture. These investigators had noted that not only did red-eyed females prefer red-eyed males but white-eyed females did, too. Such sexual selection was strong enough to eliminate the less "fit" variants in a remarkably short span of time.

3) Family Size. Any trait resulting in the production of larger mature families is also a measure of fitness. It is necessary to stress mature families because only mature offspring will be able to pass these traits on to still another generation. In animals, such as fish and oysters, which provide little or no care for their young, the way to larger mature families is through a larger number of newborn. In these species, fitness is measured by the number of fertilized eggs they can produce. On the other hand, in species where the young are cared for by their parents, selection acts to reduce family size. Assuredly, if humans had as many offspring as oysters, they could not begin to care for their young, and fewer, rather than more, adults would be produced. With respect to family size, then, the "fittest" individuals are those with the largest families at the end, not necessarily at the beginning.

One of the criticisms leveled at Darwin's theory of natural selection was that it failed to provide any explanation of how desirable traits are passed on from generation to generation. In other words, Darwin was not able to explain the mechanism of inheritance. Such a criticism was hardly fair. As you know, the science of inheritance (genetics) had to await the rediscovery of Mendel's work at the beginning of this century. Furthermore, so long as it is granted that natural selection can work only on inheritable variation, our not knowing what the mechanism of inheritance is does not weaken the theory of evolution. In any case, today we do understand many of the principles of genetics, and they have indeed greatly increased our appreciation and understanding of the mechanism of evolution. Evolution involves a gradual change in the traits of a species. But traits are the expression of the genotype, and thus evolution must also involve a change in the genotypes of the individuals in the species. Let us now analyze the theory of natural selection in the language of genetics.

THE GENETIC SOURCE OF VARIABILITY

Genetics gives us the means to understand the origin of inherited variability in populations. The process of **sexual reproduction** creates new gene combinations, new genotypes, and hence new phenotypes or variants in the population. You remember (see Section 17-7) that these new gene combinations originate in three ways: (1) At the time of gamete formation (spore formation in plants), **crossing over** of homologous chromosomes during meiosis produces new combinations of genes. (2) At metaphase of meiosis, **random assortment** of the homologous chromosomes on either side of the equatorial plate provides a further reshuffling of the genes inherited from the individual's parents. (3) The union of gametes from genetically dissimilar individuals, **outbreeding,** is also a source of variability as the maternal and paternal genes interact to produce a new phenotype, a new, unique individual.

Underlying these three processes is **mutation.** If all the individuals in a population were homozygous for the same genes at every gene locus, no amount of genetic "reshuffling" would create anything new. It is mutation that produces new alleles which can then be combined in various ways with existing genotypes.

Most mutations that geneticists have studied are harmful. This has led many people to question how the process of mutation can provide for progressive evolutionary change. The solution to this puzzle is probably historical. Species alive on the earth today are the products of two billion or more years of evolutionary change. With natural selection operating over such a vast span of time, it should not be surprising that the genes still present have proved to be of definite survival value. Any change in a gene now is far more likely to produce a harmful effect than a helpful one.

In comparing the animals and higher plants with the lower plants (e.g. mosses) and protists, we find that the diploid generation is dominant in the former while many of the latter are haploid during the major part of their lives. If we can assume that the higher plants and animals represent a more elaborate and more successful sequence of evolutionary changes, the occurrence of diploidy may well be a factor in this. Recessive genes, as you have learned, often remain "hidden" in heterozygous individuals, the dominant allele having full expression in the phenotype. This is, however, true of diploid organisms only. In haploid organisms there is only one gene present for each gene locus. Consequently, recessive genes express themselves in the phenotype. Natural selection operates only on genes which affect the phenotype. Hence, we can expect natural selection to work more vigorously on the genes of haploid organisms than of diploid. Hidden in the recessive condition, a moderately disadvantageous gene in a diploid organism gets a chance to spread in the population and to be reshuffled in various combinations with other genes. Thus it gets a chance to prove itself advantageous in some combinations or in some environments instead of being quickly weeded out of the population by natural selection.

Our study of genetics also provides us with an understanding of the basis of hereditarily controlled variation, both continuous and discontinuous. Continuous variation that is under hereditary control arises from **multiple factors** (see Section 18-9). The distribution of multiple factors in the offspring of heterozygous parents forms a bell-shaped curve similar to the one we found that describes continuous variation as it occurs in nature. Discontinuous variation (polymorphism), on the other hand, probably is controlled by a single gene locus (e.g. human ABO blood types) or, in the case of differences associated with sex (e.g. bright plumage in male birds), the presence or absence of a sex chromosome.

In applying the discoveries of genetics to the subject of evolution, we must consider the genotypes of entire populations rather than just individuals. This is known as **population genetics.** Students often experience some difficulty in applying the genetics of individuals to populations. For example, one common error is to assume that any phenotype (such as blood Type B) which is present in only a small portion of the population will ultimately disappear. Many students seem to feel intuitively that a gene, such as L^B, which is present in only a small percentage of the population will eventually be swamped by its more prevalent allele. But intuition is insufficient in this case. Let us see why.

32-5   **THE HARDY-WEINBERG LAW**

In mating two individuals heterozygous (hybrid) for a given trait, we found that the F_2-generation consists of 25% homozygous dominants, 50% hybrids, and 25% homozygous recessives. We determined this by setting up a Punnett's square (Fig. 32-3). On the left-hand side and across the top, we placed symbols representing the genotypes of the two kinds of gametes that can be formed by these individuals. Implicit in this was the fact that the two kinds of gametes were present in equal numbers, i.e. 50% of the sperm (or eggs) contained the dominant allele, 50% the recessive. But in an entire population of breeding organisms (homozygous dominants, homozygous recessives, as well as hybrids), the total number of gametes that contribute to the formation of the next generation will in most cases not be equally divided between those carrying the dominant allele and those carrying the recessive one. As a hypothetical case, let us examine a population of hamsters in which 80% of all the gametes formed carry the dominant allele for black coat color (B) and 20% carry the recessive allele for gray coat (b). What genotypes will be produced in the next generation? We can set up a Punnett's square for this problem, too, but in this case we must be explicit about the percent of each allele in the "pool" of gametes. Eighty percent of the sperm carry B and fertilize eggs at random. Eighty percent of these also carry B, so we predict that 64% (.80 × .80 = .64) of all the zygotes will be BB. Twenty percent of the sperm carry b and fertilize the eggs at random. Eighty percent of these, you remember, carry B and so we would expect 16% of the zygotes formed to result from this combination and to be heterozygous (Bb) for the trait. Another 16% of the zygotes would also be heterozygous as they would result from the 80% of B sperm fertilizing the 20% of b eggs. Only 4% of all zygotes produced would be homozygous for gray coat (bb) since the 20% of the sperm carrying allele b had only a 1-in-5 chance of fertilizing an egg carrying b (.20 × .20 = .04).

Fig. 32-3

(a) Results of random union of the gametes produced by two hybrids.
(b) Results of random union of the gametes produced by an entire population with a gene pool containing 80% B and 20% b.

(a)

(b)

The result, then, of random mating in such a population of hamsters would be a generation of offspring 96% of whom had black coats and only 4% gray coats. Here is a situation where intuition might suggest that gray-coated hamsters will gradually disappear. Let us see what happens, though, when this generation is mated. Sixty-four percent of all the hamsters, both male and female, will contribute only B-containing gametes as they are homozygous for B. Half of the gametes produced by the 32% heterozygous individuals, in other words 16% of the total, will also contain the B-allele. None of the gray hamsters will contribute B-containing gametes, of course. Therefore, of the entire pool of gametes available for creating the next generation, 80% will contain the B-allele (Fig. 32-3).

All of the gray hamsters (4% of the population) will contribute the b-allele to the pool of gametes. In addition, half of the gametes produced by the heterozygous individuals also contain the b-allele. Consequently, a total of 20% (4% + 16%) of all the gametes will contain this allele.

Bringing these gametes together at random, we find that we have duplicated our first situation exactly. Once again, a generation of 96% black hamsters and 4% gray hamsters will be formed. The proportion of allele b in the population has not diminished but has remained at the same level. The heterozygous individuals, although of black phenotype, help ensure that each generation will contain four gray hamsters out of a hundred.

Our modified Punnett's square is a little cumbersome for dealing with population genetics. The same results can be achieved by using the mathematical relationship $(p + q)^2 = p^2 + 2pq + q^2$. (Perhaps you remember from your study of algebra that $p^2 + 2pq + q^2$ is called the expansion of the binomial $(p + q)^2$.) The total number of genes in a population is its **gene pool.** If p represents the percent of one gene in the gene pool and q represents the percent of its *single* allele ($p + q$ must always equal 1 —why?), the genotypes of the next generation can be quickly computed: p^2 equals the percentage of the population homozygous for the dominant gene; q^2, the percentage homozygous for its recessive allele; and $2\ pq$ the proportion of heterozygous individuals in the population. In our example, $p = .80$, $q = .20$, and thus

$$(.80 + .20)^2 = (.80)^2 + 2(.80)(.20) + (.20)^2 = .64 + .32 + .04.$$

This is precisely the result that we obtained by using our modified Punnett's square.

Not the least advantage of the algebraic method, rather than the Punnett's square method, is that we can work backward as well as forward. In fact, we were really putting the cart before the horse when we selected a population with a gene pool containing 80% B and 20% b. The only way this value can be established is by determining the percentage of the recessive phenotype and computing from it the value for q. In the case of our hamsters, $q^2 = .04$, $q = \sqrt{.04} = .20 = 20\%$, the percentage of b-alleles in the gene pool of the population. Since $p + q = 1$, $p = 1 - q$ and allele B must constitute 80% of the gene pool. Because B is completely dominant over b, we cannot distinguish the hybrids from the homozygous dominants by their phenotype. However, substituting in the middle term ($2pq$) of our expansion, we can determine the percentage of hybrids in the population:

$$2pq = (2)(.80)(.20) = .32 = 32\%.$$

In cases of *incomplete dominance* in such a polymorphic species, the three genotypes will, of course, each give a distinct phenotype (see Section 20-7).

The results of our calculations show that recessive genes do not tend to be lost from a population no matter how small their representation in the gene pool. Stated more generally, we can say that so long as certain conditions (to be discussed below) are met, gene frequencies in a sexually breeding population remain constant from generation to generation. This is known as the *Hardy-Weinberg law* in honor of the two men who first realized the significance of the binomial expansion to population genetics and hence to evolution.

What are the implications of the Hardy-Weinberg law for evolution? Certainly the mechanism described by the law is not an evolutionary one. Evolution involves changes in the gene pool, and this is precisely what does not occur with the conditions under which the Hardy-Weinberg law operates. What the mechanism does provide is a **reservoir of variability** so that if future conditions require it, the genetic constitution of the population can change. If recessive alleles were continually tending to disappear from a population, the population would soon become homozygous. As we have seen, such a uniform genotype would provide no variability and hence no opportunity for evolutionary change. On the other hand, under the conditions of the Hardy-Weinberg law, genes which may be of no particular value to a population will nonetheless be retained. At some future time, these genes might hold the key to survival in a changed environment, and their presence then could enable the population to avoid extinction.

To see what forces lead to evolutionary change, we must examine the circumstances in which the Hardy-Weinberg law may fail to apply. There are four:

1) **Mutation.** In order for the Hardy-Weinberg law to apply, either there must be no mutations occurring in the population or the rate of forward and back mutation must be in equilibrium. The latter qualification is the only one that really interests us because mutations are continually occurring in all populations. Genes vary in their mutability but, on the average, a given gene locus undergoes a "spontaneous" mutation once in every 100,000 to 1,000,000 duplications. The number of mutations can be increased by appropriate mutagenic agents (see Section 20-3) but, even so, the mutation of any given gene locus is strictly governed by chance. We can increase the likelihood of a given gene's mutating by increasing the over-all mutation rate, but we cannot force a selected gene locus to mutate. A gene which mutates from, say, B to b may at a later time back-mutate from b to B. Just so long as one back-mutation occurs for every forward mutation, the processes are in equilibrium and the Hardy-Weinberg law still applies. Note that this is not the same as saying that at equilibrium the gene pool will contain 50% B and 50% b alleles. A banana placed in a box with 100 flies may soon have 89 flies walking on its surface while the remaining 11 fly about. If every time a fly leaves the banana, another takes its place, the forward and back processes are in equilibrium. Note, too, that the presence of multiple alleles (see Section 20-8) suggests that mutation may occur in more than one direction. But no matter how many alleles

$$B \rightleftharpoons b \rightleftharpoons b'$$
$$b''$$

are involved, equilibrium can be reached throughout the system and, at such time, the Hardy-Weinberg relationship will again hold true. Mutation, then, by itself seldom causes the gene pool to shift in one direction. Mutation is not evolution but it does provide the raw materials of evolution. A variety of alleles is made available in the gene pool.

2) **Random Genetic Drift.** Although many species of plants and animals have large, widespread populations, the number of individuals with which any one plant or animal may mate is usually limited to those in the immediate vicinity. Insect-pollinated angiosperms are apt to be fertilized by individuals growing relatively near to them. Despite their powers of locomotion, animals also tend to breed in a rather restricted area and hence have available a relatively small number of potential mates. Careful field studies show that most small mammals and insects stay close to the area in which they were born. Even birds, which may migrate over thousands of miles, usually return, season after season, to the same small area for breeding.

If geographical barriers also prevent the members of a small local population from breeding with individuals outside the locality, the local population becomes genetically isolated from the rest of its species. The gene pool of a population that combines small size and genetic isolation may not observe the Hardy-Weinberg equilibrium. Let us see why.

In discussing Mendel's experimental results (see Section 18-4), we noted the importance of a large sample in making a sound statistical analysis. A coin flipped ten times may very likely not show five heads and five tails. So it is with small breeding populations. The Hardy-Weinberg law is a statistical law and, in order to be valid, a sample size sufficiently large to minimize chance deviations must be taken. A hundred or fewer breeding pairs may very well not reassort their genes according to the laws of chance. Happenstance may simply eliminate certain individuals (e.g. homozygous recessives) out of proportion to their numbers in the population. In such a case, the frequencies of certain genes in the population may begin to drift toward higher or lower values. Ultimately they may represent 100% of the gene pool or, just as likely, disappear from the population entirely. This phenomenon is known as random genetic drift. Its significance to evolution was first made clear by the American geneticist Sewall Wright.

Random genetic drift produces alterations in the gene pool of the population, and hence it produces evolutionary change. However, unlike Darwin's idea of evolution, the new individuals in the population may very well be no more "fit" than their ancestors. Evolution by random genetic drift is aimless, not progressive.

Granted that many breeding populations of plants and animals are small enough for random genetic drift to occur, is there any evidence that it does? This is a difficult question to answer, for who can say whether an observed change in the gene pool came about because it conferred greater "fitness" on the individuals or simply as a result of random genetic drift? Although it may not invariably be true, geneticists generally feel that no combination of L^A, L^B, and I blood-group alleles in the human population confers any significantly greater degree of fitness than any other. Therefore, marked changes in the distribution of these alleles might indicate the operation of genetic drift. Some years ago, a study of genetic traits, including blood type, was made of a religious sect called the Dunkers, many of whose members live in Franklin County, Pennsylvania. These people (formally known as the Old Order German Baptist Brethren) have, since the establishment of their sect in West Germany in the early eighteenth century, tended to marry exclusively within the group. In the communities studied, the number of pairs of parents in each generation has been about ninety, a breeding population small enough for random genetic drift to occur. Sixty percent of the Pennsylvania Dunkers studied had blood Type A. In the United States population as a whole, the figure is 42%. In West Germany, the region from which the Dunkers emigrated, the figure is 45%. We can rule "fitness" out as a factor here because the non-Dunkers living in the same region show no such preponderance of A-type blood. Some marriages outside the group have occurred, but these would naturally tend to reduce the percentage of the L^A allele in the population. Despite this tendency, the Dunkers display a distribution of blood types found elsewhere only in such groups as Eskimos, Polynesians, and American Indians. We may confidently conclude then that random genetic drift has accounted for this unusual pattern.

Just how important a role random genetic drift plays in evolution is not yet known. It seems probable that where drift does occur in a small population, variability in that population diminishes. In other words, it is apt to lead to the complete loss of certain alleles from the gene pool. In this respect, then, random genetic drift works counter to the force of mutation. Mutation produces a new supply of alleles, a source of variability, while drift results in the elimination of all but one (*which* one cannot be predicted) at a given gene locus.

Although random genetic drift leads to loss of variability in a particular population, it may increase variability within the species as a whole. Small, isolated populations may develop traits quite different from those generally characteristic of the species. With a sudden environmental change, these new traits might enable the small group to survive while the members of the larger population succumbed.

3) Gene Migration. The total isolation of a local population represents an extreme that probably occurs rarely. On the other hand, there are species with large, wide-ranging populations in which distinctive, local subpopulations do not occur at all. Between these two extremes, we find many cases where local populations within a species do become established. The members of these populations generally breed only with one another, but from time to time they may breed with immigrants from adjacent populations of the same species. Although a given local population may have its own distinctive gene pool, when immigrants arrive from other populations with different gene pools, new genes are introduced. This phenomenon is called gene migration. It acts to maintain genetic variability in small populations that might otherwise lose it by random genetic drift or natural selection.

It is usually difficult to detect evidence of gene migration unless the adjacent subpopulations differ in some easily visible trait controlled by one or a few gene loci. Such a situation occurs with the dark and light forms of the peppered moth, *Biston betularia,* which differ from one another by a single gene. In general the proportion of dark forms in an area is related to the degree of industrial pollution in that area (see Section 31-5). However, the moth population in some polluted areas has a higher proportion of light forms than would be expected. Where this situation has been analyzed, geographical barriers (such as an intervening body of water) separating that particular population from adjacent dark populations have been more effective in preventing interbreeding than the barriers separating it from adjacent light populations. Gene migration from the light population has prevented the population in question from showing the proportion of dark forms that natural selection in its habitat would normally be expected to produce. (The light population may also be affected by migration of the gene for melanism into *it.*)

Just how important gene migration has been in the evolution of animals is debatable. In plants, it seems to have played a significant role. Here we find that it occurs not only between subpopulations of the same species but, even more important, between different (but still related) species. Breeding between species is called **hybridization** and it is quite commonly observed in plants. When the hybrid formed by the mating of individuals of two different species then breeds with one of the parental types (a backcross—see Section 18-6), new genes are passed into the gene pool of that parent. This phenomenon is often called introgression, but it is simply a case of gene migration *between* species rather than *within* them.

Many good examples of hybridization and introgression have been studied. It occurs most often in areas where the habitat has been so disturbed (usually by man's gardens, roads, pastures, etc.) that hybrid individuals can survive there as well as or better than either parental type. The many "weed" species, which are so characteristic of unsettled habitats, are particularly apt to show its effects. One species of wild lettuce, a weed common along our roadsides, often shows signs of genes acquired by hybridization with the domesticated species growing in nearby gardens. As a result of repeated backcrossing, these genes spread through the wild-lettuce population, giving rise to increased variability as they go. Gene migration, then, in contrast to random genetic drift, brings about increased rather than decreased variability in the gene pool.

4) Differential Reproduction. The fourth circumstance under which the Hardy-Weinberg law fails to apply occurs when differential reproduction takes place. If individuals having certain genes are better able to raise large mature families than those without them, the frequency with which those genes appear in the population will increase. This is simply a modern way of defining natural selection: the alteration of gene frequencies in the gene pool as a result of differential reproduction. In our discussion of random genetic drift, we mentioned that certain genes make individuals more "fit." This means that these genes give their owners a greater-than-average opportunity to pass them on to the next generation by (1) improving their chances of surviving through the reproductory period, (2) increasing their attractiveness to potential mates, or (3) improving their chances of raising their family to maturity (see Section 32-3). In any or all of these situations, the union of gametes is not the random process described by the Hardy-Weinberg law, but certain genotypes have a definite "edge" over others. Thus change in the gene pool does occur. This is evolution—evolution by Darwin's natural selection.

32-7 THE EFFECTS OF INCREASED SELECTION PRESSURE

The vigor with which the forces of natural selection operate varies from time to time and place to place. Man is not the only species that undergoes both "hard times" and "easy times." When times are hard, the forces of natural selection operate with greatest efficiency. We describe this as increased selection pressure. It arises from one or more of several causes. An increase in the number or efficiency of its predators challenges the existence of a species. More frequently, perhaps, its existence may be threatened by other species that compete with it for food, nesting areas, sunshine and water (in the case of plants), or some other essential aspect of its environment. If the population of the species is large, its members are also thrown into direct competition with each other for the necessities of life. Furthermore, a crowded population is more susceptible to parasitism by some other species, and a devastating epidemic may occur. An increase in the severity of any or all of these conditions constitutes an increase in selection pressure. The result of increased selection pressure is a reduction in the variability of the species. Predators and parasites will weed out the weak, the poorly camouflaged, or those who in any other respect are less well adapted to their environment. Only those genotypes in the population that confer the best camouflage, the most effective offensive or defensive weapons, the most efficient food-gathering structures, the greatest resistance to disease, etc., will perpetuate themselves successfully. The deviant, less efficient genotypes will be the first to suffer from increased selection pressure and will become less common.

Changes in the "standard" genotype may also occur, but they will be in the direction of increased efficiency at withstanding the increased selection pressure. This usually means that the species becomes more narrowly specialized in its requirements and hence more narrowly specialized in its structural, physiological, and behavioral adaptations. The species comes to occupy an ever-narrower portion of its habitat but exploits its diminished share more effectively. The moth with the 10-inch proboscis which pollinates the tropical orchid with the 10-inch nectary has certainly followed this evolutionary trend. Tapeworms, flukes, sporozoans, in fact parasites in general, also show an extreme degree of specialization in a very limited environment.

Such an evolutionary path may provide temporary success for the species and a resulting increase in the size of the population. If the trend to increased specialization continues, however, the species commits itself to a rather uncertain future. You can well imagine what would happen to the moth with the 10-inch proboscis if its orchid should succumb to environmental changes. What would happen to *Plasmodium vivax* if all the anopheline mosquitoes that transmit this sporozoan were eradicated from the face of the earth? The study of paleontology reveals a large number of extinct animals whose fossil remains suggest that they were extremely specialized. In most cases, we can only speculate as to what environmental change led to their downfall. The principle seems clear, though. Any species that becomes very uniform and increasingly efficient at exploiting an ever-narrower aspect of its environment runs the risk of extinction when its environment changes. Evolution in times of rigorous selection pressure is thus a conservative force. The optimum genotypes are selected for, and less efficient genotypes have a reduced chance of survival.

THE EFFECTS OF RELAXED SELECTION PRESSURE 32-8

The evolutionary picture changes when selection pressure is relaxed. When times are easy, a species can increase its population without at the same time becoming more specialized.

Reduction in the severity of predation or parasitism or an increase in available food enable deviant genotypes to compete on more nearly equal terms with their better-adapted cousins. A sudden population explosion may occur and with it a marked rise in the variability within the species. History tells us that human societies develop their most flourishing culture in times of prosperity. So, too, relaxed selection pressure enables other populations to experiment with new, perhaps inefficient, genotypes. Instead of being a conservative force, evolution now becomes a dynamic force and the genetic variability permitted by sexual reproduction now has a chance to express itself fully.

The evidence of both the past and the present suggests that the most frequent cause of relaxed selection pressure is entry into a new environment which is relatively free of (1) competing species, (2) predators, (3) parasites, or all three. When the ancestor of Darwin's finches (see Section 31-6) reached the Galapagos Islands, it found at most a handful of songbird species established there. With few reptiles or birds of prey and probably no mammals present, predation must have been practically nonexistent, too. Only under such unusual circumstances was a warblerlike and woodpecker-like finch able to evolve. If true warblers or woodpeckers had been present in the islands, we can be sure that their efficiency would have prevented the appearance of competing forms among Darwin's finches.

In more recent times, the introduction of rabbits into Australia and destructive crop insects into this country have provided just two of many dramatic examples of the explosive success a species can achieve when introduced into a new environment where selection pressure is reduced. Unfortunately, there have not been sufficient field studies to prove that reduced selection pressure goes hand in hand with increased intraspecific variability, but there is some evidence to support this.

THE ORIGIN OF SPECIES

The idea of evolution involves two processes. First is the gradual change in genotype and phenotype of a population of living organisms. Usually these changes are adaptive; that is, the organisms become increasingly efficient at exploiting their environment. Second is the formation of new species. Assuming that life has arisen only once on the earth, the 1.2 million known species of protists, plants, and animals living today (not to mention all the species that have become extinct) must have arisen from ancestors that they shared in common. So a theory of evolution must tell us not only how organisms become better adapted to their environment but also how new species are produced.

WHAT IS A SPECIES?

The zoologist Ernst Mayr defines species as groups of actually or potentially inter-breeding natural populations which do not interbreed with other such groups even when there is opportunity to do so. We must qualify this somewhat by adding that if on rare occasions breeding between species does take place, the offspring produced are not so fertile and/or efficient as either of the parents. Although a horse and donkey can breed together, the mule that results is sterile. (In plants, even this re-striction sometimes fails to hold true if conditions in the habitat have been altered. As we saw in Section 32-6 (3), plant hybrids *may* be more successful than either parent in such areas.)

It seems quite clear that the process of gradual evolutionary change in a popula-tion and the process of species formation are related. Over a period of time, the accumulation of changes in the gene pool of a population must reach a point where we may say that a new species has been formed. This involves a purely arbitrary judg-ment, however. Who is to say just when the transition was made from one species to the next? Even if we could resurrect some of the ancestral forms to see if they could breed successfully with their modern descendants, our question would remain unanswered. An unbroken line of forms stretches back in time from each living species, and the breaking up of this line into distinct species is an entirely arbitrary (although useful) operation.

Evolution has not, however, been just a matter of gradual change in a single genealogical line. The fossil record tells us that there has been a marked expansion in the number of species present on the earth. To put this another way, we believe that all our present species have diverged from common ancestors and initially from a single, first form of life. What can the theory of evolution tell us about **speciation,** that is, the formation of many species from few?

THE ROLE OF ISOLATION

The first requirement for speciation is reduced selection pressure and the intra-specific variability it promotes. But this is only the start of the story. Even with increased variability in a species, there is a continuous intergrading of traits from one extreme to the other. The formation of two or more species from one requires that gaps appear in the population where no intermediate forms exist. For this to occur, some form of geographical isolation of the various subpopulations seems essential. Only then can natural selection or perhaps random genetic drift produce a definite shift away from the gene frequencies of the parental type. It is no accident that the various races or subspecies of living organisms almost never occupy the same territory. The seven distinct phenotypes (and thus genotypes) associated with the seven American subspecies of the Yellowthroat *Geothlypis trichas* (Fig. 2-7) would quickly merge into one if these subspecies occupied the same territory and inter-bred with one another. Only in isolation can distinctive genetic differences become established.

Darwin's finches illustrate this point nicely. Not only did the absence of com-petitors and predators on the Galapagos Islands provide a greatly relaxed selection pressure for the ancestral bird that reached them, but the relative isolation of the vari-ous islands permitted the establishment of unique island races or subspecies. From these have arisen the thirteen species which inhabit the islands today (Fig. 32-4). Many of these species are now, in turn, made up of several distinct subspecies isolated on the various islands.

Darwin's finches. The finches numbered 1–7 are ground finches. They seek their food on the ground or in the low shrubs. The finches numbered 8–13 are tree finches. They live primarily on insects. 1. Larger cactus ground finch. 2. Large ground finch (*Geospiza magnirostris*). 3. Medium ground finch (*G. fortis*). 4. Cactus ground finch. 5. Sharp-beaked ground finch. 6. Small ground finch (*G. fuliginosa*). 7. Woodpecker finch. 8. Vegetarian tree finch. 9. Large insectivorous tree finch (*Camarhynchus pauper*). 10. Large insectivorous tree finch (*Camarhynchus psittacula*). 11. Small insectivorous tree finch. 12. Warbler finch. 13. Mangrove finch. (From Biological Sciences Curriculum Study, *Biological Science. Molecules to Man*, Houghton Mifflin Co., 1963.)

Fig. 32-4

The importance of geographical isolation in the formation of species is vividly illustrated by the single finch species that is found on Cocos Island, some 500 miles to the northeast of the Galapagos. The ancestral bird arriving there must also have found a very relaxed selection pressure with few predators or competitors. How different the outcome here than in the Galapagos, though! One species gave rise to thirteen in the various Galapagos Islands, but no such divergence has occurred on Cocos Island. One finch species is still all that exists there.

The distribution of cottontail rabbits in this country provides still another example of the role played by geographical isolation in the formation of species. In the eastern half of our country, only eight species are found, while in the mountainous western states there are 23. In this case, high mountains have provided geographical isolation as effective as the ocean water between the various Galapagos Islands.

32-11   **REUNION**

We have learned that consistent, distinctive differences in phenotype (and thus genotype) are found within subpopulations of a species that are somewhat isolated from one another. The island races of some of Darwin's finches and the races of *Geothlypis trichas* are cases in point. So long as these forms remain geographically separate, we prefer to consider them different subspecies of the same species. If brought together, they might not, in fact, breed together, but so long as we lack this information, we assume that they would. The question of their status, if they ever do come to occupy the same territory again, is soon answered. If successful interbreeding occurs, the differences will gradually disappear, and a single population with continuously intergrading traits will be formed again. Speciation will not have occurred. If, on the other hand, the two reunited subpopulations do not interbreed successfully, then speciation will have occurred.

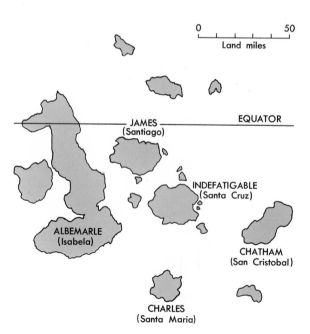

0   50
Land miles

JAMES
(Santiago)

EQUATOR

INDEFATIGABLE
(Santa Cruz)

ALBEMARLE
(Isabela)

CHATHAM
(San Cristobal)

CHARLES
(Santa Maria)

This is well illustrated by the large insect-eating, tree-dwelling finches on the Galapagos, *Camarhynchus pauper* and *Camarhynchus psittacula*. Of the two, *C. pauper* appears to be more primitive in its traits and thus the earlier form. Today it is found only on Charles Island (Fig. 32-5). The closely related *C. psittacula* is found on all the central islands, including Charles. Were it not for its presence on Charles, both forms would be considered subspecies of the same species. Because they do

Fig. 32-5

The Galapagos Islands. Now belonging to Ecuador, each island has been renamed. The modern names are shown in parentheses.

coexist and maintain their separate identity on Charles, we know that speciation has occurred. It looks as though *C. psittacula* evolved in isolation from *C. pauper* to the point where merging of the two groups did not occur when *C. psittacula* recolonized Charles Island.

What might keep two subpopulations from interbreeding when reunited geographically as *C. psittacula* and *C. pauper* have been on Charles Island? At first it may simply be a matter of one group's lacking the releasers to evoke mating behavior in the other. On Charles, *C. psittacula* has a longer beak than *C. pauper* and the evidence indicates that Darwin's finches choose their mates primarily on the basis of beak size. In other birds, plumage may be the big factor.

In the course of time, other factors that tend to prevent interbreeding may arise. The two groups may come to occupy different habitats in the same area and thus fail to meet at breeding time. The timing of reproductory activity in the two groups may not be the same. The northern and southern forms of *Rana pipiens* could not breed in nature because the females lay eggs at different times of the year. Differences in time of flowering may also prevent otherwise closely related species of angiosperms from interbreeding. Structural differences in the sex organs may also be an isolating mechanism. With continued separation, a final, irrevocable separation of the two groups takes place. This occurs when their genetic make-up becomes so different that no vigorous, fertile offspring can be produced even if mating should occur. At this point, all would agree that absolute speciation had occurred.

This evolutionary process may be hastened when two formerly isolated groups are reunited. Even if they no longer interbreed, they probably are still similar in many ways, including their requirements for the necessities of life. Thus the reuniting of two groups may create an intense selection pressure, so intense in fact, that one species is eliminated entirely. Perhaps this has happened to *C. pauper* on some of the central Galapagos Islands. On the other hand, increased selection pressure may, as we have seen, lead to increased specialization within each group and so lessen the competition between them.

The range in beak sizes of *C. pauper* on Charles and *C. psittacula* on Albermarle is roughly the same. This probably means that these two groups take the same type and size of insect. On Charles, however, *C. psittacula* has a substantially larger beak than *C. pauper* and thus presumably differs enough in its food requirements for the two species to coexist there (Fig. 32-6).

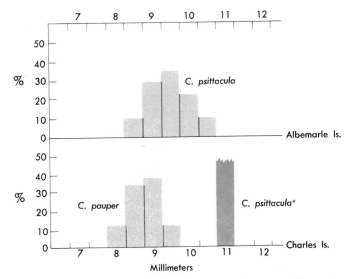

Fig. 32-6

Histograms of depth of beak in *C. pauper* and *C. psittacula*. (Redrawn by permission from David Lack, *Darwin's Finches*, Cambridge University Press, 1947.)

* The number of collected specimens—16— was too small to compute reliable percentages, but all fell within the size range indicated.

It would be rash to conclude from the study of Darwin's finches that speciation in all organisms has occurred in exactly the same way. But his finches do illustrate beautifully what are probably the absolute essentials for the process. They are:

1) Reduced selection pressure (in this case achieved by moving into a new, unoccupied territory).
2) Increased variability within the species (arising from the process of sexual reproduction, working with genes no longer being selected against).
3) Isolation of a subpopulation of the species so that interbreeding with the main stock is prevented. This produces geographic races or subspecies.
4) Reuniting of the isolated group with the parental stock but without the resumption of interbreeding. At this point, true speciation has occurred.
5) Competition between the two reunited forms may be so intense that further divergence in their various traits is hastened.

This process need not occur simply once. Indeed, in the case of Darwin's finches, we are sure that it has been repeated several times, giving rise to new species, which gradually have divided the available habitats between them. From the first arrival have come a variety of ground-feeding and tree-feeding finches including a warblerlike finch and the extraordinary, tool-using, woodpeckerlike species (Fig. 32-4). The production of a number of diverse species from a single ancestral one is often referred to as **adaptive radiation.** We will study several other well-illustrated examples in Chapter 34.

32-12   **SPECIATION BY POLYPLOIDY**

Speciation, as we have described it, is a gradual process. It begins with differences between individuals in a population, proceeds to the accumulation of consistent differences found at the subspecies level, and ends with the fixed differences associated with species formation. The entire procedure may take hundreds or thousands of years to be completed. There is one kind of species formation, however, which occurs much more rapidly. This arises from the chromosomal aberration of polyploidy (see Section 19-5).

Meiosis in polyploid (for example, $4n$) individuals produces gametes ($2n$) that are fertile with one another but often not with gametes of the parental type (n). Thus polyploid individuals are immediately isolated genetically from the parental type and a new species has been created almost overnight. In 1927, the Russian plant geneticist Karpechenko reported the artificial production of a plant containing a full ($2n$) set of radish chromosomes and a full ($2n$) set of cabbage chromosomes produced as a result of crossing these two species (which are from different genera). Ordinarily, hybrids of such different parents would be sterile since their gametes would contain only a partial assortment of the chromosomes from each of the two parents. However, Karpechenko's hybrid being polyploid, each gamete contained one of each of the chromosomes found in both the radish and the cabbage ancestors. Fertilization produced vigorous plants which combined traits of both cabbages and radishes (unfortunately, the roots of the cabbage and the leaves of the radish). These plants were capable of breeding successfully with one another but not with either ancestral type. Karpechenko had thus produced in a very brief period a new species of plant. There is abundant evidence that species production by polyploidy, with or without hybridization, has often occurred naturally in plants. The phenomenon is, however, very rare in animals.

Flying phalanger

Flying squirrel

Wombat

Woodchuck

Convergent evolution. The flying squirrel (top right) and woodchuck (bottom right) are more closely related to you than they are to the marsupials on the left. (This woodchuck, or ground-hog, is a rare albino form.) (Courtesy New York Zoological Society.)

Fig. 32-7

CONVERGENT EVOLUTION 32-13

We have noted that species (e.g. bird and bat, whale and fish, woodchuck and wombat) are sometimes found which resemble each other superficially but fail to reveal the homologies that would indicate close kinship. Evolution as a result of which two species of different genealogy come to resemble one another closely is termed *convergent evolution*. It can be explained on the basis of the same forces of natural selection working in a similar way on two originally different phenotypes. There are certain structural and physiological requirements that must be met before any organism, no matter what its ancestry, can fly or swim.

Convergent evolution is in no sense the opposite of speciation. While two unrelated species may come to resemble one another closely as similar selective forces work on them, each species is, at the same time, diverging from its own ancestral stock. The many Australian marsupials which resemble placental mammals in both appearance and habits (Fig. 32-7) illustrate convergent evolution with respect to the placental mammals. With respect to the ancestral marsupials, however, they represent a most dramatic example of adaptive radiation, in other words, the multiplication of species.

The theory of evolution is the most important generalization about living organisms that has been made. In the last chapter we examined some of the kinds of evidence that can best be explained by a theory of evolution. In this chapter we have examined the mechanism by which evolutionary change is thought to occur. Now let us round out the story by trying to piece together the actual evolutionary history of life on this earth.

EXERCISES AND PROBLEMS

1   The Kaibab squirrel has long ears and a white belly and lives on the north rim of the Grand Canyon. The Abert squirrel, which lives on the south rim, is quite similar in appearance although it has a black belly.
    (a) How can you account for the presence of these two similar, but distinguishable, populations?
    (b) What possible futures might await these squirrels if the canyon should be obliterated?

2   Fossil evidence indicates that evolutionary changes in honeybees have taken place unusually slowly. Can you think of a possible reason why natural selection might operate particularly slowly in this group?

3   A large proportion of the so-called "living fossils" is found in the sea. Can you think of a reason for this?

4   How can you account for the superficial resemblance of a porpoise and a fish?

5   Summarize Darwin's theory of evolution.

6   What term would Darwin have applied to nonrandom reproduction?

7   List 3 mechanisms by which variant genotypes are produced in nature.

8   Which of these is denied to a hermaphroditic organism that practices self-fertilization exclusively?

9   What phenomenon must occur for the mechanisms in Question 7 to be effective in producing variant genotypes?

10 The proportion of homozygous recessives of a certain trait in a large population is 0.09. Assuming that the gene pool is in equilibrium and all genotypes are equally successful in reproduction, what proportion of heterozygous individuals would you expect to find in the population?

11 Why are most mutations harmful?

12 Considering the strong selection pressure against the gene for hemophilia, what reasons can you give for the continuing presence of the gene in the human population?

13 What is the genetic effect of continued inbreeding in a population?

14 Why does continued inbreeding often lower the vigor of the individuals in a population?

15 Define a species.

16 How can the Darwinian theory of evolution account for the long neck of the giraffe? How does this differ from Lamarck's explanation?

17 Distinguish between interspecific and intraspecific competition.

REFERENCES

1 Eiseley, L. C., "Charles Darwin," *Scientific American,* Reprint No. 108, February, 1956. A brief biography.

2 Darwin, C., *The Origin of Species,* The New American Library, New York, 1958. One of three paperback editions of this classic.

3 Wallace, B., and A. Srb, *Adaptation,* 2nd Edition, Foundations of Modern Biology Series, Prentice-Hall, 1964. Examples of ways in which species are adapted to the conditions of their environment and the evolutionary mechanisms that have brought about these adaptations.

4 Crow, J. F., "Ionizing Radiation and Evolution," *Scientific American,* Reprint No. 55, September, 1959. Discusses the sources and significance of genetic variability.

5 Dobzhansky, Th., "The Genetic Basis of Evolution," *Scientific American,* Reprint No. 6, January, 1950.

6 Hardy, G. H., "Mendelian Proportions in a Mixed Population," *Great Experiments in Biology,* ed. by M. L. Gabriel and S. Fogel, Prentice-Hall, Inc., 1955. In this brief note Hardy outlines the principle that became known as the Hardy-Weinberg law.

7 Anderson, E., "The Role of Hybridization in Evolution," *This is Life,* ed. by W. H. Johnson and W. C. Steere, Holt, Rinehart and Winston, New York, 1962. Several well-illustrated examples are presented.

8 Lack, D., *Darwin's Finches,* Harper Torchbooks, New York, 1961. A detailed analysis of these remarkable birds as a case study of the process of speciation.

9 Savage, J. M., *Evolution,* Holt, Rinehart and Winston, New York, 1963. An excellent survey of the mechanisms at work in evolution.

10 Hardin, G., *Nature and Man's Fate,* Mentor, 1961. Discusses the impact of Darwin's theory on man's thinking, the genetic basis of evolution, and the significance of these discoveries to our society.

CHAPTER 33 THE ORIGIN AND EVOLUTION OF LIFE: PROTISTS AND PLANTS

The theory of evolution explains the diversity of life on earth today by the descent of each and every species from common ancestors. Certainly the fossil record tells us that in former times, there were fewer species on the earth and that these were not so complex as most of our modern species. In theory, then, the study of evolution should lead us back to a first form of life from which all others have been descended. What was this first form? We do not know, and the best we can do is to make intelligent guesses about its characteristics. Where did it come from? We do not know the answer to this question either, although every thoughtful person has probably wondered about it at one time or another. Even people who know nothing about or disbelieve in the theory of evolution ask themselves how life first appeared on the earth.

THEORIES OF THE ORIGIN OF LIFE   **33-1**

Among the first attempts at answering this question in our civilization were the stories of creation that are found in the Bible. Other cultures, too, have their stories of the creation of life. These stories share two features in common. First, they were created long before man had gained any knowledge of the physical, chemical, and biological principles that are the basis of life. Second, they invoke divine intervention in the creation of life and thus fall outside the scope of scientific inquiry. Scientists assume that the forces governing the world can be known, that these forces act uniformly at all times and in all places, and that their effects can be predicted, at least in a statistical way. While the scientist's faith may be ill-founded, it is the only basis upon which he can work. If his experiments are subject to unique, supernatural, or capricious intervention, there is no point in performing them. In fact, if some *unrepeatable* result is detected, the scientist assumes that an error in his equipment and/or observation has crept in.

The Cosmozoa Theory. This theory of the origin of life does fall within the scope of scientific inquiry. It explains the presence of life on our earth by assuming it was brought here from elsewhere in the universe, perhaps incorporated in a falling meteorite. The recent interest in space science has led to many meteorites being examined for the presence of living organisms or, at least, organic matter. While evidence of each has been discovered, the possibility that the meteorites were contaminated after reaching the earth cannot be excluded. Even if life could withstand the rigors of interplanetary space and the fiery trip through the atmosphere of the earth, the cosmozoa theory really does not answer our basic question. It simply removes it from this planet to some other location.

◀ Carboniferous forest. An artist's reconstruction of what the swamp forests of the Mississippian and Pennsylvanian periods looked like. The large trunks on the left and lying flat in the foreground are of tree-sized lycopsids. The trees on the right are sphenopsids. Ferns and seed ferns are also present. (Courtesy Field Museum of Natural History.)

The Theory of Spontaneous Generation. Until about one hundred years ago, it was commonly believed that life could arise spontaneously from nonliving matter. Van Helmont even gave a recipe — grains of wheat and a dirty shirt in a dark container — for producing mice spontaneously! As more was learned about biology, however, men began to doubt the possibility of spontaneous generation. In 1668 the Italian physician Francesco Redi performed an experiment to show that maggots do not arise spontaneously in decaying meat but are produced from the eggs of flies (Fig. 33-1). Although the spontaneous generation of large forms of life began to be doubted after this, van Leeuwenhoek's discovery of microorganisms reopened the question. Surely these tiny creatures, which appeared so suddenly in rotting food, etc., arose spontaneously! The Italian priest Lazzaro Spallanzani tried to show that even they did not do so. He boiled nutritious broth in glass flasks and then sealed them so that nothing could get into the broth from the outside. The broth remained clear and sterile. Skeptics argued, however, that heating the air within the flask had so altered it that spontaneous generation could not occur.

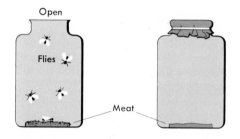

Fig. 33-1

Redi's experiment. Maggots (larval flies) appeared in the meat in the open jar but not in the covered jar.

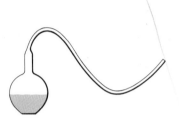

Fig. 33-2

Pasteur's flask. The swan neck permitted fresh air to re-enter the flask after boiling but trapped airborne bacteria before they reached the broth.

It was the immortal French biochemist and microbiologist Louis Pasteur who one hundred years ago finally silenced the skeptics. He, too, boiled flasks of broth, but instead of sealing the necks of the flasks, he drew them out into an S-shape, leaving the ends open (Fig. 33-2). Now fresh air could reach the interior of the flask but, Pasteur reasoned, any bacteria or other microorganisms floating in it would be trapped in the long neck. Sure enough, the broth usually stayed sterile until he tipped a little into the neck of the flask and then allowed it to run back. Only after doing this, did microorganisms begin to grow in it. Some of the flasks that Pasteur prepared are still in existence (resealed), their contents of broth clear and pure.

Two important points about Pasteur's work are often overlooked. First of all, he did not prove that spontaneous generation can never and has never occurred. It is virtually impossible to prove the negative of something. Pasteur, like Redi before him, simply showed that supposed examples of spontaneous generation failed to work if already living organisms were kept away. Actually, we have good reasons for thinking that life is not created spontaneously today but we certainly have no rigid proof of this.

The second point about Pasteur's work is that if it does really mean that the spontaneous generation of life is impossible, then the problem of the origin of life cannot be explained on scientific grounds. Fortunately, a way out of this dilemma was proposed in 1936 by the Russian biochemist A. I. Oparin.

Oparin's Theory. While conceding that life does not arise spontaneously now, Oparin felt that it might well have arisen spontaneously under the conditions that existed earlier in the history of the earth. According to his theory, the oceans of the early earth contained a rich supply of organic molecules. (They do not today. Can you guess why not?) Over an unimaginably vast span of time, these molecules became associated with one another in temporary complexes. Ultimately, one such complex developed: (1) some sort of membrane to separate it from the "soup" of organic molecules around it, (2) the ability to take in molecules from this soup and discharge other molecules into it, (3) the ability to incorporate the absorbed molecules into the characteristic pattern of the complex, and (4) the ability to split apart portions of itself that had all these features, too. Such a complex could have been the first living thing. Metabolism, growth, and reproduction, perhaps even responsiveness, would have been present and hence all the attributes of life. From this first form, surely far simpler than even the simplest protists alive today, could have evolved by natural selection the present diversity of life.

The plausibility of Oparin's theory depends greatly on the earth's being somewhat different then than it is now. In order for organic molecules characteristic of life to have accumulated in the oceans, there must have been substantial concentrations of the inorganic ingredients out of which they could be synthesized and a source of energy to accomplish these syntheses. Analysis of the atmosphere of the large, cold planets, Jupiter and Saturn, reveals the presence of methane (CH_4) and ammonia (NH_3). If these two gases, together with water vapor (H_2O) were present in the atmosphere of the early earth, all the elements would have been present (C, H, O, N) for the synthesis of most of the amino acids, the carbohydrates and fats, and the purines and pyrimidines. Radioactivity, ultraviolet radiation from the sun, heat from volcanos, and electrical discharge all might have provided energy for the synthesis of various organic molecules from these gases.

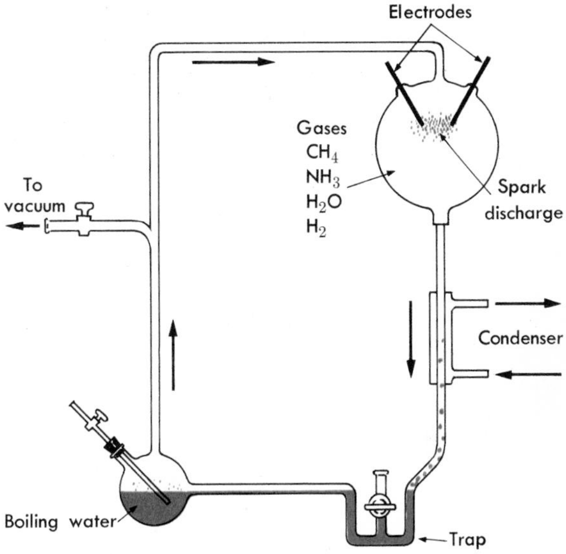

Could such a system really work? A student of biochemistry, Stanley Miller, sought to answer this question as part of his work toward a PhD degree. He built the apparatus

Fig. 33-3

Miller's apparatus. After running for one week, a variety of organic molecules had formed in it.

illustrated in Fig. 33-3 and filled it with water, methane, ammonia, and hydrogen. This mixture was kept circulating by continuously boiling and then condensing the water. The gases passed through a chamber containing two electrodes with a spark passing continuously between them. At the end of a week, chemical analysis of the contents of the flask revealed the presence of several amino acids (e.g. glycine, alanine) and other organic molecules including one, succinic acid, which is found in the citric acid cycle. Miller's results encouraged others to vary his procedure, using different mixtures of substances that might have been present on the primitive earth and other sources of energy. Polypeptides, purines and pyrimidines (see Section 7-4), and sugars have been produced in these later experiments.

None of these experimental re-creations of what might once have been the conditions on the earth has produced anything alive. Undeniably, though, they have produced some of the molecules uniquely associated with life. Could these have eventually associated themselves into a complex with the attributes of life? We may never know. Such an event would be extremely unlikely and a week, or even a million years, might not be long enough for the necessary chance association to occur. Furthermore, there must have been some way in which organic molecules, once formed, could be protected from degradation by the same forces that created them. In Miller's apparatus, the electric spark can break organic molecules back down as easily as it promotes their synthesis. Dissolved in the oceans of the primitive earth or adhering to the surface of minerals, complex associations of organic molecules might have been better protected against breakdown.

In any case, one sure requirement for an event such as the spontaneous creation of life must have been a vast span of time. On uncountable occasions, complexes must have almost reached the point where they would have been alive only to become degraded again. Was there enough time for chance to finally succeed?

33-2   THE AGE OF THE EARTH

Not until little more than a century ago did men begin to appreciate just how old the earth is. Without a knowledge of the facts of geology and geochemistry, they simply could not conceive of the great length of the history of the earth. One biblical scholar, Archbishop Ussher, calculated from his studies that the earth was created at 9:00 A.M. on October 12 in the year 4004 B.C. However, calculations based on geological studies produced quite a different picture of the antiquity of the earth. One of the first estimates was based on the increasing salinity of the oceans. Dividing the salt concentration of our present oceans by their annual increase in salinity, one arrives at a figure of about 50 million years for their age. Unfortunately, this method requires us to assume that the oceans have been getting saltier at a constant rate through the years, and we have no grounds for believing this. A similar attempt was made to establish the age of the earth by measuring the total thickness of sedimentary rock deposits and dividing this by the estimated annual increase in the thickness of ocean sediments. Although this method doubled previous estimates, it suffered from the same defect as the first. Perhaps sediments were deposited more or less rapidly at other periods in the history of the earth than they are today. An additional problem was the fact that a continuous record of sedimentary rock is not available, for erosion has erased entire chapters of this portion of the geological history of the earth.

Is there a geological process which we can be sure proceeds at a constant rate? The discovery of the radioactive elements has provided us with one. Radioactive elements contain unstable isotopes which, by emitting subatomic particles such as electrons and alpha particles (helium nuclei), become "transmuted" into other isotopes. Atoms of U-238, the most abundant isotope of uranium, undergo a series of transmutations as they "decay" radioactively. Each atom in the series is also unstable and itself decays. Finally, though, an isotope of lead (Pb-206) is formed that is stable, and the process stops. The important thing about these transformations from our point of view is that they take place at a definite, measurable rate. It takes 4.51 billion years for half the atoms in any sample of U-238 to decay. (We call this period the "half-life" of the isotope.) Neither high temperatures nor low, neither gravity, magnetism, electrical currents nor any other physical or chemical force can alter this inexorable rate. Here, then, is a geological clock which keeps perfect time and whose elapsed running time can be computed simply from the ratio of Pb-206 atoms to

U-238 atoms in a rock sample (Fig. 33-4). Fortunately, delicate chemical and physical methods exist for making these determinations. The oldest terrestrial rocks to be dated by this method are from Southern Rhodesia. They are 2.7 billion years old. However, they surely were not formed at the time the earth itself was formed. The study of other isotopes in other minerals (as well as in meteorites) indicates that the earth (and the solar system) was formed some 4.7 billion years ago.

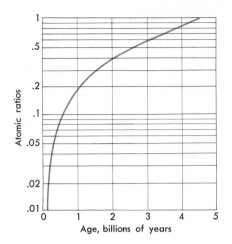

Fig. 33-4

Change in ratio of Pb-206 : U-238 over a period of 4.5 billion years.

THE DAWN OF LIFE 33-3

No one knows exactly when life first appeared on the earth. We would not expect the first forms of life to leave fossil remains for us. However, fossils that resemble algae have been found in rocks over three billion years old. This still leaves us with almost two billion years for life to have arisen on the earth. Even the most unlikely event will probably occur sometime. Two billion years provides plenty of time for false starts in the chance production of the first living organism.

Nourishment for the first form of life was no problem. Surrounded by the same soup of organic molecules from which it arose, it had only to use these molecules to supply its needs for energy and the materials for growth and reproduction. We assume that the first living organism secured its energy from these organic molecules by fermenting them. Life probably could not have arisen if oxygen had been present in the primitive atmosphere, and for several reasons we believe that there was none.

Fermentation could not continue indefinitely as the only way of life of the earliest organisms. No matter how large the primeval soup of molecules, someday it must have become exhausted. If this experiment in life was not to cease then, some organisms must have evolved a means of synthesizing new organic molecules from the inorganic substances found in the environment. Such synthesis requires energy and probably the energy came from the sun. The appearance of photosynthetic organisms not only provided an inexhaustible supply of organic molecules to meet the needs of life but ultimately provided oxygen as well. With the accumulation of oxygen in the atmosphere, the way was open for heterotrophic organisms to secure their energy needs by the vastly more efficient process of cellular respiration. With an inexhaustible supply of energy-rich molecules and an efficient method for extracting energy from them, the full potentialities of life could be realized.

If our theory of the spontaneous generation of life is correct, does it mean that Redi, Spallanzani, and Pasteur were wrong? Not at all. The theory Redi and the others tried to refute was that modern forms of life arise spontaneously. On the other hand, Oparin's theory is that an organism, far more primitive and simple than any that lives today, arose once in the history of the earth. (Our conviction that this event occurred just once is based on the remarkable similarities of biochemistry (see Section 31-4) and subcellular structure in all living things.) We believe that additional spontaneous generations could not occur today. For one thing, there are no longer appreciable quantities of organic molecules in the waters of the earth. Second, any complex of organic molecules that might form spontaneously would quickly be destroyed by (1) the oxygen which is now present in the atmosphere and acts as a powerful oxidizing agent and (2) the already existing forms of life (for example, bacteria) which would consume our hopeful complex long before it developed to the point where we could consider it to be alive.

33-4 THE GEOLOGICAL ERAS

Although we do not know just when life first appeared on the earth, we are quite sure that it was over three billion years ago because traces of algae in rocks of at least that age have been found. Fossils in such old rocks are very rare. It is not until we examine sedimentary rocks formed about 600 million years ago, at the start of the Paleozoic era, that we find a wide variety of fossil organisms. This means that through more than four-fifths of the unimaginable span of time that life has existed on this earth, it left little or no record of its presence. Since that time, the record of evolving life has been quite well preserved.

The geological and biological history of the earth since the first appearance of abundant fossils is divided into three major eras (Fig. 33-5). Each of these is further subdivided into periods. At first glance it might seem surprising that marked geological changes in the earth should coincide with marked changes in the species present. Consider, though, that changes in geology (e.g. mountain formation, lowering of the sea level) bring changes in climate, and both of these alter the habitats available for living organisms. The forces of natural selection must surely have changed when the geology of the earth changed. As you can see in Fig. 33-5, the dates of the various periods are not precisely known. Only a few of the rocks (e.g. those of the early Permian) contain enough uranium to be dated accurately. The others must be dated on the basis of their relative thickness, and we have already noted the uncertainties of this method.

As we discuss the history of evolutionary change in this chapter and the next, you will want to refer frequently to Fig. 33-5 to see how the details fit into the whole panorama of life.

THE EVOLUTION OF THE PROTISTS

Geology tells us very little about the evolution of the protists. Only those with hard parts (e.g. foraminifera, diatoms) leave satisfactory remains. The best we can do is to make intelligent guesses about their evolutionary relationships on the basis of the study of modern forms. Underlying this technique is our conviction that some present-day species have changed less during their evolutionary history than other species with which they share a common ancestor. The former species are properly called "primitive" and a comparison of their structure, biochemistry, and embryonic development with more "advanced" forms may help us trace the evolution of the latter. As we do this, though, remember that we are simply making educated guesses on the basis of the evidence available. Furthermore, not all biologists interpret this evidence in the same way. As new evidence comes to light, the evolutionary scheme to be presented in the rest of this chapter will surely have to be revised.

ERAS	PERIODS	EPOCHS with approximate starting dates in millions of years ago	AQUATIC LIFE		TERRESTRIAL LIFE
Cenozoic 63 ± 2	Quaternary 0.5-3	Recent		AGE OF MAMMALS	Man in the New World
		Pleistocene	Periodic glaciation		First men
	Tertiary 63 ± 2	Pliocene Miocene Oligocene Eocene Paleocene	All modern groups present		Hominids and Pongids Monkeys and ancestors of apes Adaptive radiation of birds Modern mammals and herbaceous angiosperms
Mesozoic 230 ± 10			Mountain building (e.g. Rockies, Andes) at end of period	AGE OF REPTILES	
	Cretaceous 135 ± 5		Modern bony fishes Extinction of ammonites, plesiosaurs, ichthyosaurs		Extinction of dinosaurs, pterosaurs Rise of woody angiosperms, snakes
	Jurassic 180 ± 5		Inland seas, warm climate		
			Plesiosaurs, ichthyosaurs abundant Ammonites again abundant Skates, rays, and bony fishes abundant		Dinosaurs dominant First lizards: Archeopteryx Insects abundant First angiosperms
	Triassic 230 ± 10		Warm climate, many deserts		
			First plesiosaurs, ichthyosaurs Ammonites abundant at first Rise of bony fishes		Adaptive radiation of reptiles (thecodonts, therapsids, turtles, crocodiles, first dinosaurs) First mammals
Paleozoic 600 ± 50	Permian 280 ± 10		Appalachian Mts. formed, periodic glaciation and arid climate		
			Extinction of trilobites, placoderms		Reptiles abundant (cotylosaurs, pelycosaurs). Cycads and conifers; ginkgos
	Pennsylvanian 310 ± 10	Carboniferous	Warm humid climate	AGE OF AMPHIBIANS	
			Ammonites, bony fishes		First reptiles. Coal swamps
	Mississippian 345 ± 10		Warm humid climate		
			Adaptive radiation of sharks		Forests of lycopsids, sphenopsids, and seed ferns. Amphibians abundant. Land snails
	Devonian 405 ± 10	AGE OF FISHES	Periodic aridity		
			Placoderms, cartilaginous and bony fishes. Ammonites, nautiloids		Ferns, lycopsids, and sphenopsids First gymnosperms and bryophytes First insects. First amphibians
	Silurian 425 ± 10		Extensive inland seas		
			Adaptive radiation of ostracoderms; eurypterids		First land plants (psilopsids, lycopsids) Arachnids (scorpions)
	Ordovician 500 ± 10		First vertebrates (ostracoderms) Nautiloids, Pilina, other mollusks Trilobites abundant	Mild climate, inland seas	none
	Cambrian 600 ± 50		Trilobites dominant First eurypterids, crustaceans Mollusks, echinoderms Sponges, cnidarians, annelids Tunicates	Mild climate, inland seas	none
Pre-Cambrian 3000			Fossils rare but many protistan and invertebrate phyla probably present	Periodic glaciation	none

The history of life as revealed by the fossil record.

Fig. 33-5

Probably no modern organism is the little-changed descendant of the first form of life which, you remember, fermented the organic compounds in the primeval soup around it. However, the photosynthesizing organisms which must have evolved from it may possibly be still represented today by the **green photosynthetic bacteria.** These organisms live on the surface of ocean mud and, like the purple sulfur bacteria (see Section 12-7), manufacture organic compounds from CO_2, H_2S, and the energy from sunlight:

$$CO_2 + 2H_2S \xrightarrow{\text{light}} (CH_2O) + H_2O + 2S.$$

Their light-absorbing pigment resembles, but is not identical to, the chlorophyll of plants. In the dark, they secure their energy by the fermentation of organic molecules. In fact, these organisms cannot grow in the presence of oxygen. They would therefore have been perfectly able to survive in the atmosphere of the primitive earth.

From such primitive, H_2S-using photosynthetic bacteria could have evolved forms capable of using water as the source of hydrogen with which to reduce carbon dioxide to carbohydrates:

$$CO_2 + 2H_2O \xrightarrow{\text{light}} (CH_2O) + H_2O + O_2.$$

Photosynthesis by these organisms would have liberated oxygen into the atmosphere and thus established the conditions for the evolution of aerobic, respiring organisms.

Perhaps the **blue-green algae** were the descendants of the green sulfur bacteria first to use water in photosynthesis. What evidence is there to link them with the bacteria? Neither the photosynthetic bacteria nor the blue-green algae have their photosynthetic pigments in plastids. Neither of them have a nuclear membrane around their single chromosome. Neither of them have mitochondria. Neither group shows any evidence of cytoplasmic streaming. *Each of these traits sets them apart from all* other organisms. Furthermore, the bacteria and the blue-green algae are the only organisms on earth to possess the amino acid diaminopimelic acid in their proteins (in place of lysine), and the structure of their ribosomes is different from that of all other organisms.

Red algae, too, may have been among the first photosynthesizers to release oxygen into the atmosphere. Although present members of the phylum are considerably more complex than the blue-green algae (they have nuclei and chloroplasts), the lack of any flagellated forms and the fact that they share with the blue-greens certain pigments not found in the other algae suggests that they are basically a primitive group.

The presence of oxygen in the atmosphere opened the way for the evolution of the aerobic, **heterotrophic bacteria.** Many of these move by means of a simple flagellum which resembles one of the central fibrils of the multistranded cilia and flagella of more advanced organisms (Fig. 29-2). The aerobic heterotrophs are able to secure energy from the respiration of food materials, a process far more efficient than fermentation. At the same time, **chemoautotrophic bacteria,** such as the colorless sulfur bacteria, may have made their appearance. As you learned in Section 12-8, they secure the energy for carbohydrate synthesis from the oxidation of inorganic materials (such as H_2S) in the environment. Only much later would have appeared the various parasitic descendants of the heterotrophic bacteria, the **spirochetes, rickettsias, mycoplasmas,** and (perhaps) **viruses.**

The next step in the evolution of life may have been the appearance of unicellular, chlorophyll-containing protists able to move about actively by means of flagella with the multistranded organization of 9 + 2 fibrils that we studied in Section 29-2. The development of efficient locomotion must have been of great selective advantage, especially for photosynthetic organisms. They could move to regions in the water where the light intensity and other factors were optimum. Flagellated cells would also have been far more successful in finding others of their kind in order to carry out sexual reproduction. As you know, sexual reproduction promotes variability and thus can hasten the rate of evolutionary change. In any case, the presence of flagella (or cilia, which are similar in structure) in so many plants and animals as well as protists encourages us to believe that flagellated protists were ancestral to all the "higher" groups.

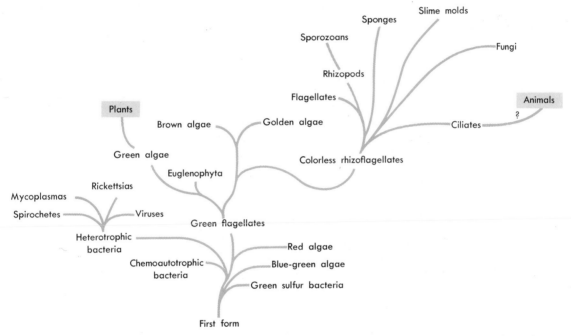

The suspected evolutionary relationships of the protists.

Fig. 33-6

   The evidence suggests that evolution in the earliest green flagellates took three directions (Fig. 33-6). One group of descendants includes today creatures like *Euglena* (Phylum Euglenophyta) and the green algae (Chlorophyta). A second group is made up of the remaining algal phyla, including the browns, the diatoms, and the other golden algae. We think that the third group of descendants lost their chlorophyll, thus forsaking an autotrophic existence for a heterotrophic one. With the waters of the earth becoming populated with autotrophs, there should have been ample food available to support heterotrophs. Furthermore, such an evolutionary loss should not seem surprising when we remember that even today there are colorless flagellates identical in every other way to chlorophyll-containing forms. Thus, *Astasia* seems to be a colorless twin of *Euglena* (see Section 3-3, 1).

The colorless flagellates probably developed a second, supplementary method of locomotion, amoeboid movement (see Section 29-1). Even today, there are several species of flagellates that are capable of locomotion by pseudopodia as well as flagella (Fig. 33-7).

As many as five separate groups could have diverged from the first colorless, amoeboid-flagellated forms.

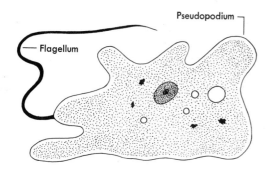

Fig. 33-7

Mastigamoeba moves by means of pseudopodia and a flagellum.

1)   The Rhizopods and Flagellates. Although usually placed in separate classes, the occurrence of such forms as *Mastigamoeba* suggests a close relationship between these groups. In fact, the name Rhizoflagellata has been proposed to encompass both the rhizopods and the flagellates.

The **sporozoans** are probably descended from early rhizoflagellates. Like all parasites, they must have evolved from free-living forms, and the fact that flagellated and amoeboid stages appear in the life cycles of some members supports the idea that their ancestors were rhizoflagellates. Evolution of the sporozoans has surely kept pace with evolution in the animal kingdom. There is hardly an animal known that is not parasitized by at least one sporozoan. In many cases (including *Plasmodium,* which causes malaria in humans), the adaptation of the parasite to the structure and physiology of its host is remarkably efficient.

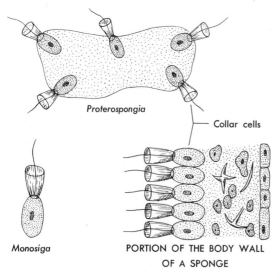

2)   The Sponges. Sponges are multicellular organisms which we classified as animals in Chapter 5. Except for their multicellularity, however, they do not resemble other kinds of animals. For this reason, the sponges are sometimes placed in a special subkingdom, the Parazoa, to separate them from the other animals, which are placed in the subkingdom Metazoa.

Fig. 33-8

The presence of collar cells in sponges suggests that these multicellular animals have evolved from colonial forms like *Proterospongia*. They, in turn, probably evolved from unicellular forms.

Sponges are aquatic, sessile organisms which filter food particles from the water and engulf them into food vacuoles (see Section 5-1). The movement of the water and the engulfing of food particles are both accomplished by flagellated **collar cells** found in the inner cell layer of the sponge (Fig. 33-8). The close resemblance between these collar cells and certain flagellated protozoans suggests that the sponges have evolved from colonies of rhizoflagellate ancestors. Even today, the sponge body is really little more than a colony of cells. There is not so much specialization of cell types as one finds in true tissues.

3) **The Slime Molds.** The slime molds are likely descendants of the rhizoflagellates. In some species, a stage that moves by both flagella and pseudopodia occurs in the life cycle (see Section 3-8).

4) **The Fungi.** These protists can also be linked to the rhizoflagellates. The aquatic forms appear to be the most primitive, and their possession of flagellated zoospores suggests their kinship with the rhizoflagellates. The terrestrial forms may have evolved from the aquatic ones. Such evolution probably did not gain much headway until after the earth had been colonized by the land plants, and their bodies, both living and dead, provided nourishment for so many of these fungi.

5) **The Ciliates.** The fundamental similarity of flagella and cilia gives us confidence that the ciliates have also evolved from colorless rhizoflagellates. As we learned in Chapter 3, there is nothing primitive or simple about these protists. Forms such as *Paramecium* are not only large for single cells, but have many intricate organelles which parallel in function the organs found in multicellular creatures. Indeed, the complexity of the ciliates has led some biologists to consider them acellular (not cellular) rather than unicellular organisms. What they wish to stress is that the *Paramecium* "body" is far more elaborate in its organization than any cell out of which multicellular organisms are made. Whether this is a sound approach or not, the fact remains that the ciliates are the most elaborate of all the protozoans.

The high degree of specialization of modern ciliates has suggested to some biologists that they represent an evolutionary dead-end. However, it is possible to make a case for the evolution of the metazoans from early ciliates. If this is true, the ciliates will have to be moved from their present obscure position to the very center of the stage of evolution. In the next chapter we will examine the grounds on which this theory is based.

THEIR CHLOROPHYLL-CONTAINING DESCENDANTS

The descendants of the earliest green flagellates that retained their chlorophyll seem to have evolved in at least two major directions. One group includes the diatoms and other golden algae (Chrysophyta) and the brown algae (Phaeophyta). Although seeming to differ greatly from one another, both these phyla include flagellated forms and share a number of biochemical similarities. One of the most notable of these is the possession of a modified form of chlorophyll, chlorophyll c, in addition to chlorophyll a.

The second major group is made up of the Euglenophyta and the green algae, the Chlorophyta. Both these phyla of algae have the same two chlorophylls that we found in plants, that is, chlorophyll a and b. All modern euglenophytes (e.g. *Euglena*) retain the flagella of their ancestors. Some of the green algae are flagellated, too, (e.g. *Chlamydomonas*), and even those that are not (e.g. *Ulva*) produce flagellated gametes and/or zoospores.

The manner in which colonial and multicellular algae may have evolved from unicellular ancestors is suggested by the series of flagellated forms (*Chlamydomonas, Gonium, Pandorina, Eudorina, Pleodorina,* and *Volvox*) that we examined in Section 8-18 (see Fig. 8-12). The story they tell us is that colonial forms arose when the daughter cells of unicellular forms remained attached to one another following mitosis. As colonies became larger and more elaborate, specialization among their constituent cells produced truly multicellular organisms, eventually even forms as large as *Ulva*.

Although direct fossil evidence is lacking for some, we believe that almost all of the groups of organisms discussed up to this point appeared in the waters of the earth in the Pre-Cambrian period, before the start of Paleozoic era (Fig. 33-5). During the Cambrian and Ordovician periods, the oceans and bodies of fresh water must have continued to support an elaborate array of protists and (as we will see in the next chapter) aquatic invertebrates. The picture was quite different on land. No carpet of green existed to soften the barren, desolate scene. Where sea met land, however, green algae may have been evolving features that would enable them to survive intermittent periods of dryness. By the Silurian, descendants capable of life on dry land had appeared and begun to colonize this new environment. These were the plants.

THE EVOLUTION OF THE PLANTS

33-9   **THE FIRST VASCULAR PLANTS**

Although the anatomy of the first plants is not entirely clear, we are confident that they belonged to the phylum Tracheophyta and were more or less adapted to life on land. By the Devonian period, four distinct groups had appeared (Fig. 33-9), each of which has left some descendants right up to the present time. These groups were the Psilopsida, Lycopsida, Sphenopsida, and Pteropsida (see Section 4-2). The psilopsids, like their modern descendant *Psilotum* (Fig. 4-2), had no roots or leaves. They did, however, have both underground stems (rhizomes) and erect stems, each containing xylem and phloem. Photosynthesis was accomplished in the erect stems and these also produced the sporangia. The photosynthetic pigments were surely chlorophyll *a* and *b*, the same pigments found in their algal ancestors. Although we cannot be sure that the psilopsids were the ancestors of the other three subphyla, they certainly were the most primitive of the vascular plants. From a study of *Psilotum*, we deduce that they produced only one kind of spore, and these developed into tiny gametophytes which, in turn, produced both antheridia and archegonia. Fertilization was by swimming sperm and hence these plants must have been restricted to habitats which were quite wet, at least some of the time.

Both the lycopsids and sphenopsids had roots and leaves, each containing xylem and phloem tissue connected with that of the stem. The leaves were simple and small, all their vascular tissue occurring in just a single, unbranched vein.

Some of the lycopsids produced not one but two kinds of spores: microspores (♂) and megaspores (♀). These developed into separate ♂ and ♀ gametophytes, respectively. In some cases, the megaspore was retained within the tissues of the parent sporophyte and, as in the gymnosperms and angiosperms of today, this provided a protected environment for fertilization to take place.

Although the club mosses (*Lycopodium, Selaginella*) and the horsetails (*Equisetum*) are practically the only modern representatives of these two subphyla, their ancestors were once many and varied and often of considerable size. Great forests of tree-sized lycopsids and sphenopsids existed during the Mississippian and Pennsylvanian periods (see chapter opening illustration), and much of the world's present coal was formed by them at that time. For this reason, these two periods are sometimes referred to collectively as the Carboniferous period. When we burn this coal today, we are releasing energy stored by these plants some 300 million years ago.

The first pteropsids, the ferns, also contributed a large array of species to the flora of the Devonian landscape. Unlike the members of the other subphyla, the ferns had large leaves with branching veins. Like most of our temperate-climate ferns of today, they were **homosporous;** that is, only one kind of spore was produced. Each fern spore, you remember, develops into a prothallus that bears both male and female sex organs. Fertilization requires moisture in which the ciliated sperm can swim to the egg. For this reason, the ferns are still restricted to habitats where surface water is present during part of the growing season.

Fossil remains from the Devonian indicate that some early fernlike plants were **heterosporous,** that is, they produced both microspores and megaspores. The megaspore was retained within the moist tissue of the parent sporophyte. Fertilization took place here, freed from dependence on a supply of surface water. On the other hand, the necessity for the microspores to be carried from one plant to another in order to reach the female gametophyte robbed them of their value as agents of dispersal. This function was probably taken over by seeds—dormant, protected, embryo sporophytes.

The seed ferns, as these plants are called, were among the earliest of the **gymnosperms,** another class in the subphylum Pteropsida. Although seed ferns are now extinct, some of their descendants, the cycads (which resemble them closely) and the ginkgo (see Fig. 4-6), survive to this day. These modern seed-bearing plants reveal their ancient lineage by the fact that after the microspore reaches the ovule, it liberates a ciliated sperm which, by swimming in moisture supplied by the parent sporophyte, reaches the egg.

Both ferns and the early gymnosperms flourished during the Mississippian and Pennsylvanian periods. Along with the lycopsids and sphenopsids, they contributed to the formation of coal deposits. Toward the end of these periods, the conifers arose. The microspores of these gymnosperms develop into a pollen tube, the sperm nucleus of which accomplishes fertilization. No motile sperm are produced. The conifers (e.g. pines, spruces, and firs) are the most abundant of the modern gymnosperms, but they dominate the landscape only in regions where the winters are very cold (see Section 35-4, 3).

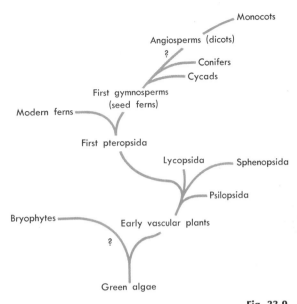

Fig. 33-9

The suspected evolutionary relationships of the plants.

THE MOSSES AND LIVERWORTS

The nonvascular plants have sometimes been considered the ancestors of the vascular plants. Their simplicity of structure, lack of vascular tissue, and restriction to damp locations do suggest that they are intermediate forms between the algae and the vascular plants. The fossil record indicates, however, that this interpretation is false. No bryophyte fossils are found in rocks formed before the Devonian period, but as we have seen, vascular plants were already present in the Silurian. We may conclude, then, that the mosses and liverworts either represent a second, rather unsuccessful, colonization of the land by aquatic ancestors or possibly (as some have suggested) are descendants of land plants that have lost many of the adaptations of their ancestors. In either case, the lack of a vascular system and woody tissue and the necessity for surface water in which the sperm can swim from antheridia to archegonia have limited the evolutionary potentialities of these organisms.

THE ANGIOSPERMS

Although the first angiosperms appear in the fossil record in Jurassic deposits, it was not until the end of the Mesozoic era that they became the dominant plants of the landscape. That they are the dominant plants on earth today is unquestionable. There are some 200,000 species of living angiosperms. The rest of the plant kingdom includes only about 34,000 living species. The angiosperms are found in practically every habitat. Although they incorporate a variety of features that enable them to live even in arid locations, some (e.g. *Anacharis*) have returned to an aquatic existence.

To what can we attribute the great success of the angiosperms? Probably the answer is that they incorporate the most efficient adaptations to dry-land living with the most varied and efficient methods of sexual reproduction and dispersal. Let us review the features which have permitted angiosperms (and, in varying degrees, other plants) to invade the dry land.

The possession of roots permits the extraction of moisture and minerals from beneath the surface of the land. Roots also serve to anchor the plant against the wind. The presence of a cambium capable of producing woody tissue provides for the support, high in the air if need be, of leaves and flowers. Xylem and phloem enable water, foods, hormones, etc., to be translocated long distances in the plant quickly and efficiently. A waxy cuticle on leaves and herbaceous stems and the cork on woody stems prevent rapid loss of water from the plant by evaporation. Such a waterproof covering is also gasproof, but the needs of gas exchange are taken care of by stomata and lenticels. The shedding of leaves in most temperate-climate angiosperms further reduces loss of water during the winter (when soil water may be frozen) and also helps reduce the likelihood of mechanical damage to the plant from the accumulation of ice and snow.

The angiosperms share with the gymnosperms the characteristic of retaining the female gametophyte within the megasporangium. As we have seen, this device puts an end to the need for surface water to effect the transfer of sperm from one plant to another. Instead, pollen grains can be transported by air to the megasporangium, thus bringing the gametes together. In the gymnosperms and some angiosperms, the pollen grains are simply blown from plant to plant by the wind. Many other angiosperms attract insects or other animals by their flowers and thus exploit the animal's power of locomotion to aid cross-pollination. The quantity of pollen produced by animal-pollinated angiosperms is usually far less than that produced by wind-pollinated species.

The embryo sporophyte plant, the seed, is also an effective adaptation to dry-land living. Protected by seed coats and supplied with food reserves, the seed can withstand harsh, dry conditions for long periods while still remaining ready to germinate when conditions finally become suitable. Seed production in the angiosperms is more efficient than in the gymnosperms in that food is translocated into the seed only if fertilization has taken place. In the gymnosperms, the food reserves of all the potential seeds are deposited before fertilization and thus wasted if pollination should fail to occur.

Most of the adaptations mentioned so far are not unique to the angiosperms. They have played a role in allowing the other plants to colonize the land, too. It is only in the production of flowers and fruits that the angiosperms stand alone. The efficient methods of pollination and seed dispersal which flowers and fruits make possible, added to all the other features which reach their fullest development in the angiosperms, have enabled these plants to invade nearly every conceivable habitat on this earth. In the angiosperms, we see the most adaptable group of plants yet produced by evolutionary change in organisms that were once restricted to an aquatic world.

The colonization of the land by vascular plants in the Silurian had far-reaching consequences. Plants are autotrophic and their presence on land provided there for the first time an abundance of food for heterotrophic organisms. The fungi and many animals were quick to exploit this and soon followed the plants in adapting to the special conditions of dry-land living. In the next chapter, we will examine how animals accomplished this transition. It will be an important part of our larger story of the evolution of the animals as a whole.

EXERCISES AND PROBLEMS

1 List 6 characteristics of angiosperms that make them better adapted than algae to life on land.

2 In what ways are the bacteria and blue-green algae similar?

3 Some biologists have maintained that virus-like particles were the first form of life on earth. What evidence supports this hypothesis? What evidence weakens it?

4 The cells of *Oscillatoria erythraea* are bright red in color. Why, then, is this species classified as a blue-green alga?

5 Did Pasteur prove that the spontaneous generation of life has never and does never occur? Explain.

6 How many items of evidence can you think of that suggest that all organisms on earth arose from a single first form of life?

7 Starting with 10 gm of U-238, how much would be left in 9 billion years?

8 How many protons are present in the nucleus of an atom of Pb-206? How many neutrons? (Hint: See Fig. 6-2.)

9 Distinguish between homospory and heterospory.

10 Distinguish between ferns and seed ferns.

REFERENCES

1 Gabriel, M. L., and S. Fogel, *Great Experiments in Biology,* Prentice-Hall, Inc., 1955. Includes papers by Redi, Spallanzani, and Pasteur on the theory of spontaneous generation.

In references 2 through 4, below, one can trace the development of scientists' current ideas on how life may have arisen on earth.

2 Oparin, A. I., *The Origin of Life,* Dover Publications, Inc., New York, 1953. First published in 1936.

3 Wald, G., "The Origin of Life," *Scientific American,* Reprint No. 47, August, 1954.

4 Miller, S. L., "The Origin of Life," *This is Life,* ed. by W. H. Johnson and W. C. Steere, Holt, Rinehart and Winston, New York, 1962.

5 Brown, H., "The Age of the Solar System," *Scientific American,* Reprint No. 102, April, 1957.

6 Hutner, S. H., "Nutrition of Protists," *This is Life,* ed. by W. H. Johnson and W. C. Steere, Holt, Rinehart and Winston, New York, 1962. The first part of this article relates the nutrition of modern protists to their possible evolutionary history.

7 Delevoryas, T., *Plant Diversification,* Holt, Rinehart and Winston, New York, 1966. A survey of the evolutionary changes that have taken place in the plant kingdom.

Remains of a eurypterid.
(Courtesy American Museum of Natural History.)

THE ORIGIN OF ANIMALS. TWO THEORIES.

There are at least two ways in which unicellular organisms could have evolved into multicellular animals. One is through the formation of colonies of cells. With the development of specialized cells within the colony, interdependence of parts follows, and the boundary between a colony and a multicellular individual has been crossed. In the sponges the presence of collar cells, which closely resemble certain unicellular flagellates (Fig. 33-8), suggests that sponges did evolve this way.

What about the other animals? Perhaps they, too, arose this way, but independently of the sponges. Some biologists think that colonial green algae were not only the ancestors of the plants but also the ancestors of the animals. This theory is supported by the existence of larval cnidarians whose structure—a ciliated, hollow ball of cells—is suggestive of the structure of *Volvox*. Inward migration of some of the surface cells of this larva produces two tissue layers, and later the gastrovascular cavity of the mature cnidarian develops within. The flatworms, which also have a gastrovascular cavity with a single opening, are considered descendants of the cnidarians. (One wonders, though, what happened to that most distinctive feature of the cnidarians, the cnidoblast. It is true that some flatworms have cnidoblasts, which they use as weapons, but they do not grow them. They simply incorporate them into their own epidermis after first securing them by eating hydras!) With the penetration of the gastrovascular cavity through the other end of the organism, the tube-within-a-tube body plan of the other animals could have been formed.

While it is thus plausible that the multicellular animals evolved from colonial ancestors, there is considerable evidence to suggest that the animals arose by a second method: the formation of cell membranes within a multinucleate (having several nuclei) protozoan. What is the nature of this evidence? Unfortunately, it does not include any fossils. The first animals were soft-bodied and hence not likely to leave any remains. Furthermore, the evolutionary story we wish to reconstruct took place in Pre-Cambrian times. Very few rocks from this period have distinct fossils within them. So our attempt to discover the origin and evolution of the animals must rest on the same kind of evidence we used in setting up a family tree of the protists. Homologous structures, homologies in patterns of development, even biochemical homologies—all in living forms—provide the basis for our speculations. Remember, too, that we are just developing a theory of the evolutionary relationships among the animals. The evidence we use is factual. The conclusions we draw are strictly tentative (as they must always be). We will simply attempt to establish one plausible family tree of the animals. You can be certain that as new evidence is accumulated in the future, revisions of this scheme will be required.

How can we relate the animals to multinucleate protozoans? An examination of two living forms may be helpful. *Dileptus* (Fig. 34-1) belongs to the class Ciliata. This unicellular organism is large by protozoan standards (over ½ mm), being easily visible to the naked eye. It moves actively by means of cilia, whose motion is coordinated by a system of neurofibrils. It has contractile fibrils within the cell which enable very flexible movements to be made. Food is ingested through a mouth and incorporated into food vacuoles. Many polyploid macronuclei are present, this probably being an adaptation necessitated by the large volume of cytoplasm to be controlled. Many micronuclei are also scattered through the cell.

Let us turn now to one of the simplest members of the Phylum Platyhelminthes, the marine, free-living turbellarian *Afronta*. This little worm is not much larger than *Dileptus*. It is covered with cilia which it uses in locomotion. Contractile fibrils are present within its body. They aid in locomotion and other body movements. A network of noncellular neurofibrils is present, providing for coordinated movements. Food is ingested through a simple mouth and incorporated into food vacuoles. Most interesting of all, almost the entire body of the worm is a syncytium, that is, it consists of continuous masses of cytoplasm in which many nuclei are embedded. There are no special circulatory or excretory systems.

It is perfectly clear that today's *Dileptus* is not the ancestor of today's *Afronta*. They are contemporaries and do not even share the same habitat. (Most *Dileptus* species live in fresh water, while *Afronta* is marine.) Our examination of these two forms does, however, suggest a plausible way in which the animals might have arisen from the protozoans. Then, from a syncytial turbellarian, it is not much of a jump to more specialized forms such as the planarians. In these worms, each nucleus is confined to a separate compartment (the cell), and definite nervous, muscular, and excretory systems are present. The parasitic flatworms (e.g. the tapeworm) represent a secondary loss of structure and not a primitive condition. Their vertebrate hosts did not even appear on earth until long after the events we have been considering would have occurred.

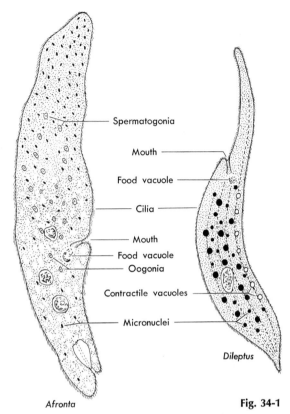

Spermatogonia

Mouth

Food vacuole

Cilia

Mouth

Food vacuole

Oogonia

Contractile vacuoles

Micronuclei

Dileptus

Afronta

Fig. 34-1

A syncytial flatworm (left) compared with a ciliated protozoan (right). The only true cells in *Afronta* are the oogonia and spermatogonia.

THE CNIDARIA   **34-2**

If we accept a primitive turbellarian as the first animal (excepting, of course, the unique sponges), we must be able to show how all the other animal phyla could have evolved from it. This is not easy to do for the Cnidaria. The flatworms are bilaterally symmetrical, while the cnidarians have radial symmetry (although the sea anemones possess aspects of both). It is possible that the radial symmetry of the cnidarians is simply a secondary acquisition in keeping with their sessile (or floating) mode of existence. On the other hand, some biologists feel that the Cnidaria, like the sponges, arose independently from the protists and hence do not share a close kinship with the other animals we will discuss in this chapter.

THE ASCHELMINTHES   **34-3**

The most important members of this phylum are the roundworms or nematodes. They show two evolutionary advances over the flatworms from which they may have evolved. They have a digestive tract with two openings, the mouth and anus. As we learned in Section 5-4, this arrangement greatly increases the efficiency with which food can be digested and absorbed. They also have a cavity between the digestive tract and the body wall. It develops from the blastocoel cavity during embryonic development and is not therefore related to the coelom which, as you remember, develops totally surrounded by mesoderm. For this reason it is often called a *pseudocoel*. In it are found various internal organs including those of reproduction. The presence of a definite body cavity rather than a solid mass of mesoderm allows for greater freedom of movement although the whiplike motion so characteristic of nematodes does not seem to exploit this.

Although the basic roundworm plan must have evolved in Pre-Cambrian times, evolutionary modifications in the group have continued right up to the present. In addition to the myriads of roundworms which live independently in water and damp soil, there are many parasitic representatives. Even our most recently evolved species of plants and animals are host to them.

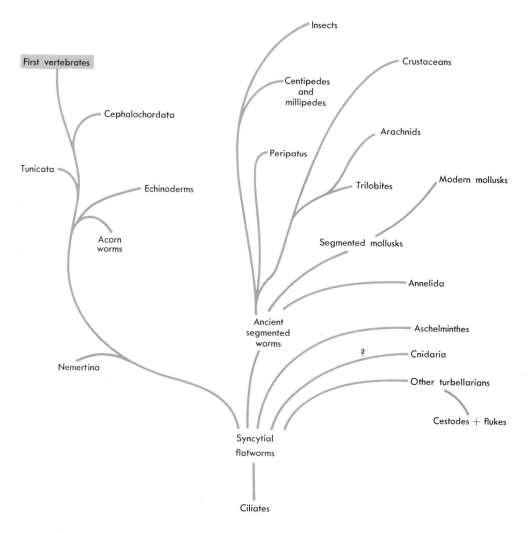

Fig. 34-2 Suspected evolutionary relationships among the invertebrates.

A careful study of such widely diverse animals as the annelid worms, mollusks, and arthropods indicates that they have all evolved from a common ancestor. This is thought to have been a segmented worm which, in turn, was descended from the primitive flatworms (Fig. 34-2).

The organization of the body into segments appears to have been a significant evolutionary advance. Segmentation is a way of achieving additional size without having to increase the size or efficiency of individual organs. It is necessary only to repeat them in segment after segment. Size, in turn, has advantages. Larger organisms can cope successfully with food too large to be eaten by their smaller competitors.

In addition to their segmentation, the ancient segmented worms probably had a true coelom, that is, a body cavity completely lined with mesoderm. Having the internal organs placed in a fluid-containing coelom permits them to slide easily against one another and thus makes extensive movements of the body easier to carry out.

The formation of the coelom in the ancient segmented worms, and their many descendants, is quite interesting. Early in cleavage, special mesodermal cells are formed within the embryo. Mitosis of these cells produces a mass of mesoderm tissue. Eventually a space appears within this mass and this enlarges to form the coelom.

Among the descendants of the ancient segmented worms, only the annelids have retained an extensive coelom. In the mollusks and arthropods, it is greatly reduced in size, the main body cavity being the **hemocoel** (derived from the embryonic blastocoel).

THE ANNELIDS 34-5

Although no modern representatives of the ancient segmented worms exist, the annelid worms seem to represent the least drastic departure from them. Although primarily a marine group, freshwater and terrestrial annelids also exist. The latter are really only semiterrestrial since they must remain in moist soil in order to carry on gas exchange through their skin.

THE MOLLUSKS 34-6

The members of this phylum make up one of the three dominant animal groups on the earth today. As adults, they bear no resemblance to segmented worms. Nevertheless, we think that they share a common ancestry with the annelids because each group produces similar larvae. The striking similarity of these larvae, called trochophores (Fig. 34-3), is hard to explain on any other grounds but kinship.

Although the vast majority of mollusks are unsegmented, the discovery of the "living fossil" Neopilina (see Section 5-6) confirms our suspicion that the mollusks have evolved from segmented worms. This little mollusk, whose nearest relatives are known only as Ordovician fossils, clearly shows segmentation of the body and probably represents the primitive molluscan type from which the other classes have evolved.

Fossils of snails, bivalves, and cephalopod mollusks are found in Cambrian rocks. Perhaps the earliest snails used their rasping, tonguelike radula to scrape unicellular algae from underwater objects. Some snails, however, capitalized on the presence of

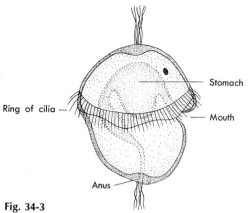

Fig. 34-3

A trochophore larva. These are produced by members of several animal phyla, including annelids and mollusks.

Stomach

Ring of cilia

Mouth

Anus

their slow-moving or sessile bivalve cousins as a food source. Even today, bivalve shells cast up on the beach often reveal the tiny hole which some predacious snail drilled with its radula, preparatory to eating the occupant. The appearance of plants on land opened up still another food source to snails and the Carboniferous period witnessed the appearance of land species. The protection of the shell, internal fertilization (sometimes embryonic development as well), and the modification of the mantle into a "lung" enabled them to shift from the aquatic to the terrestrial environment.

It is the evolutionary success of the snails and bivalves that makes the phylum one of the three that are dominant on the earth today. Of some 100,000 species, all but a few hundred belong to these two classes. It was not always so. The Ordovician and Silurian seas were well populated by the nautiloids, a group of shelled cephalopods whose only living descendants are three species of chambered nautilus (see the opening illustration of Chapter 5.) Some of these forms possessed shells 15 ft long. In the Mesozoic era, the ammonites, another group of cephalopods, were the dominant invertebrates in the sea. Although now sharply reduced in numbers, the surviving cephalopods are still impressive. The 50-ft squid ranks as the largest invertebrate that ever lived.

34-7   THE ARTHROPODS

Among the most abundant fossils of the Cambrian period are the **trilobites.** These early arthropods were segmented and had paired, jointed appendages and an exoskeleton just like those of their modern descendants. Although we suspect that the anterior appendages aided in food-getting while the posterior ones were used for locomotion, they were quite uniform in structure (Fig. 34-4). Aquatic **arachnids,** called eurypterids (Fig. 34-5), and primitive **crustaceans** also appear in the Cambrian. The eurypterids probably evolved from early trilobites, and the crustaceans must have been close relatives. Their chief structural advance over the trilobites was the development of a variety of modifications in their appendages. The modern crayfish with its flipper, swimmerettes, walking legs, pincer legs, maxillipeds, maxillae, mandibles, and antennae (Fig. 34-4) stands in sharp contrast to the trilobite. The structural diversity of these numerous crayfish appendages reflects the variety of functions carried out by them.

By Silurian times, terrestrial arachnids had evolved. The scorpions, mites, ticks, spiders, and daddy longlegs of today are their descendants. Although eurypterids as long as 9 ft existed in the Silurian, they and the trilobites became extinct by the end of the Paleozoic era. The horseshoe crab *Limulus* is the only aquatic arachnid to survive into modern times. It has done so with practically no evolutionary change since the genus first appeared in the Triassic period over 200 million years ago. Except for the pill (or sow) bugs, which have been able to use their gills for air-breathing, the crustaceans have remained an aquatic group.

Millipedes and centipedes probably arose in the Devonian period, although clear fossil remains are found only as far back as Carboniferous times. Insects, however, were definitely established by the Devonian. This versatile, fast-reproducing, fast-evolving group must have found abundant food in the lush forests that covered the earth by that time. Of the several classes of arthropods, no other solved the problems of dry-land living so successfully. The exoskeleton is quite impervious to water and thus prevents fatal dehydration of the body when the surrounding air is dry. Gas exchange is accomplished by a system of tracheal tubes (see Section 13-6), which penetrate to every portion of the body. The paired, jointed, clawed appendages provide not only for locomotion but also for ingestion of food. Mandibles, maxillae, and labia are fashioned in remarkably diverse ways to produce sucking, biting, chewing, and rasping mouth parts. The first insects must have depended directly on plants for their food, but soon their increasing numbers set the stage for the evolution of carnivorous predators.

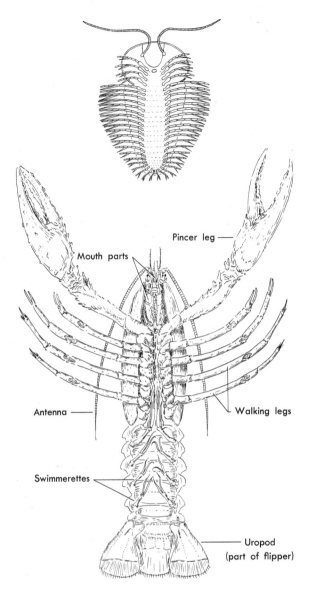

Mouth parts

Pincer leg

Antenna

Walking legs

Swimmerettes

Uropod (part of flipper)

Fig. 34-4

A trilobite (above) and crayfish compared. The paired, jointed appendages of the crayfish show far more structural and functional specialization than do those of the trilobite.

Fig. 34-5

An artist's reconstruction of aquatic life of the Silurian period. The segmented animals are eurypterids, a now-extinct group of aquatic arachnids. (Courtesy Field Museum of Natural History.)

Other adaptations to a terrestrial life included the development of wings for flying. (The insects were the first animals to use this medium for locomotion.) Internal fertilization and embryonic development within a waterproof egg solved the problem of bringing the gametes together and protecting the embryo without the aid of water. Finally, the ability to excrete their nitrogen-containing wastes as uric acid must be counted as one of the important evolutionary adaptations to a dry habitat. Not only does uric acid require very little water for its excretion (see Section 16-3), but the fact that what little is used is then reclaimed in the rectum enables these creatures to deposit wastes which are practically dry.

The efficiency of insect structure and function cannot be disputed. Both in terms of number of species (more than all the species of protists, plants, and other animals combined) and number of individuals, the insects earn a position as one of the most successful groups on earth. They are man's chief competitors for food. Except for the oceans, insects have adapted to practically every habitat available on the earth.

Fig. 34-6

Peripatus. This little animal has many features of both annelid worms and insects. It is found in a few tropical localities. (Courtesy Ward's Natural Science Establishment, Inc.)

The fossil record tells us little about the evolutionary relationships of the millipedes, centipedes, and insects. However, a living animal, *Peripatus*, supports our view that they, too, evolved from a primitive segmented worm. *Peripatus* (Fig. 34-6) has internal segmentation, pairs of nephridialike excretory organs in each segment, a cuticle, and a muscular body wall, all quite suggestive of the annelids. Furthermore, the excretory and sex organs are ciliated as they are in annelids, and the structure of the digestive tract, central nervous system, and legs is similar to that of annelids. On the other hand, the legs of *Peripatus* bear insectlike claws, and the circulatory system is open with the blood passing through an extensive hemocoel. Furthermore, these little creatures breathe air by means of tracheae, and the embryonic development of their eggs resembles that of arthropods.

Peripatus is certainly not the ancestor of the millipedes, centipedes, and insects. However, its curious anatomy suggests that it may be a relatively little-changed descendant of forms which also led to these arthropods. Fossil members of its phylum have been found side-by-side with fossil trilobites, crustaceans, and annelids. The fact that *Peripatus* occurs in small, isolated parts of the jungles of Central and South America, Africa, Asia, and Australia indicates that it may represent the last-surviving remnants of a once-flourishing group.

Up to this point, we have been discussing a group of animal phyla which show striking similarities to one another. Neither the echinoderms nor the chordates fit into this picture. In fact, echinoderms and chordates share many features between themselves which do not occur in the other animal phyla. This is particularly apparent in their embryonic development.

As we saw in Fig. 23-2, the cleavage furrows in chordate eggs occur in regular planes either perpendicular or parallel to one another. This is also true of echinoderm eggs. However, in all the other animals we have discussed [with the possible exception of the arthropods, whose method of cleavage is unusual (Fig. 23-2)], the planes of cleavage are progressively tipped with respect to one another so that a *spiral cleavage* results.

The cells produced by the first cleavage or two in echinoderm and chordate eggs are fully capable of developing into a complete embryo if isolated from each other. For this reason identical twins can and do occur in both groups. On the other hand, cleavage in the invertebrates which we have studied up to this point results in cells that have lost some of their potentiality. Identical twins do not occur.

In the echinoderms and chordates, gastrulation begins at that portion of the embryo which will become the anus of the adult (see Section 23-3). However, in the other phyla with a complete digestive tract, it begins at the end which ultimately becomes the mouth. Both groups possess a true coelom, but the mechanism of its formation is quite different. In annelids, arthropods, and mollusks, the coelom arises by a splitting of a mass of mesodermal cells which have their origin within the embryo. In echinoderms and chordates, the coelom develops within a sheet of cells which pushes in from the exterior during gastrulation. One other distinction between these two groups which deserves mention is a chemical one. As you learned in Section 29-8, the compound creatine phosphate serves as a reservoir of high-energy phosphate in the muscles of man. It also performs the same function in all other vertebrates and in many of the invertebrate chordates (e.g. *Amphioxus*—Cephalochordata) and in some echinoderms (e.g. brittle stars). Most of the other invertebrates that have been examined have a related substance, arginine phosphate, which we assume performs a similar function for them. The sea urchins, acorn worms (Hemichordata), and tunicates (Tunicata) have one or the other or both of these substances.

The occurrence of so many sharp contrasts between the echinoderms and chordates on the one hand and most of the remaining animals on the other has led some taxonomists to establish two superphyla: the echinoderm superphylum (to which we belong) and the annelid superphylum. It has also made it quite clear that we cannot expect to find clues to the evolutionary origins of man by examining such advanced and distantly related forms as mollusks and arthropods. How, then, can we account for the origin of vertebrates and, thus, of ourselves? Fossil echinoderms were present in the Cambrian so we know that the echinoderm superphylum was established before that time. We do not know from which more primitive group it evolved. One that has been suggested as possibly ancestral to the echinoderms and chordates is the Nemertina. This phylum, which has not been discussed before, contains a small group of flattened, ciliated worms that are generally thought to be closely related to the flatworms. But one important way in which they differ from the flatworms is that gastrulation produces a one-way digestive tract with both mouth and anus. In some nemertines, however, the site of gastrulation (the blastopore) becomes neither the mouth nor the anus. Instead it becomes sealed over in later embryonic development, and mouth and anus formation occur on opposite sides of it. Perhaps these worms are descendants of a group in which the site of gastrulation was in transition from the mouth end of the archenteron (annelid superphylum) to the anus end (echinoderm superphylum). This hypothesis is supported by the discovery of some two dozen structures in the nemertines which seem to be homologous to structures found in one of the most primitive vertebrates, the hagfish (Class Agnatha).

Assuming that the echinoderm superphylum is descended from nemertine ancestors, we must now attempt to unravel the evolutionary relationships within the superphylum. All of the chordates have at some stage of their life a **notochord,** a **dorsal tubular central nervous system, gill pouches,** and bilateral symmetry. On the other hand, the echinoderms are radially symmetrical and have none of the other features. The radial symmetry should not fool us, though, for the larvae of the echinoderms are bilaterally symmetrical. Adhering to our conviction that embryonic features are the more primitive ones, we conclude that the radial symmetry of adult echinoderms is a secondary adaptation to a sessile or, at most, sluggish way of life. (Remember the Cnidaria.) The fossil record tells us that the earliest echinoderms were sessile animals attached by means of a stalk. Some of the modern descendants of these early echinoderms (the sea lilies) are still sessile, and all of them at least pass through a stalked stage.

The echinoderms have been moderately successful in their rather limited habitat of the oceans. From the earliest stalked members of the phylum arose the other classes: the sea urchins, brittle stars, starfish, and sea cucumbers (see Section 5-8). The abundance of these organisms, their internal skeleton, and their marine habitat have resulted in a remarkably complete fossil record of their evolution.

The position of the acorn worms in this story is puzzling. A notochordlike structure, gill slits, and what has been claimed to be a dorsal central nervous system have led to their being classed as chordates by some biologists. Their affinity with the echinoderms is undisputed, however. The larva of the acorn worm is practically indistinguishable from the larva of the sea cucumber. Acorn worms have both creatine phosphate and arginine phosphate as do the sea urchins. Finally, comparative serology clinches the argument. Antibodies developed in response to acorn worm proteins (see Section 31-4) also react strongly with sea cucumber proteins. No wonder, then, that these animals with *both* chordate and echinoderm features have been placed in a phylum (Hemichordata) of their own.

Despite the superficial resemblance of *Amphioxus* (Cephalochordata) to fishes (Fig. 5-16), it is to the tunicates (Subphylum Tunicata) that we look for the origin of the vertebrates. Actually, examination of an adult tunicate such as the sea peach, *Halocynthia* (Fig. 34-7), could not reveal a more unlikely-looking candidate for vertebrate ancestry. This sessile, filter-feeding organism with its "tunic" containing cellulose has no notochord and only a rudimentary nervous system. However, the larvae produced by these organisms are strikingly different in form. They are free-swimming, bilaterally symmetrical "tadpoles" with gill slits, a dorsal, tubular central nervous system, and a tail through which runs a notochord (Fig. 34-7). In fact, if one tries to visualize what a primitive, idealized chordate should have looked like, he arrives at an organism not much different from a sea squirt larva.

One difficulty remains. The fossil evidence suggests that vertebrates arose in fresh water while the tunicates are exclusively marine. The tunicates do, however,

ADULT TUNICATE (*Halocynthia*)

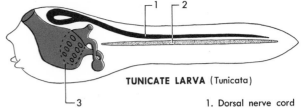

TUNICATE LARVA (Tunicata)

1. Dorsal nerve cord
2. Notochord
3. Gill slits

Left: an adult tunicate, *Halocynthia*. (Courtesy Ralph Buchsbaum.) Right: anatomy of a tunicate larva.

Fig. 34-7

live close to shore and their larvae could have entered the mouths of rivers. Furthermore, the steady one-way current of river water may well have altered selection pressure in favor of an active, bilaterally symmetrical form. Thus, the ancestral tunicate larva may have abandoned metamorphosis to the adult and provided the start of vertebrate evolution. The abandonment of metamorphosis is not unknown elsewhere. Remember the axolotl (Fig. 26-5), which reaches sexual maturity as a gill-breathing larva. Here, too, the environment (lack of iodine) has selected for the retention of juvenile traits.

THE EVOLUTION OF THE VERTEBRATES

THE JAWLESS FISHES (AGNATHA)

34-9

Turning from speculation to fact, the first vertebrates to appear in the fossil record are jawless fishes, the **ostracoderms.** Some appear in Ordovician rocks, although they become far more abundant in the Silurian. These creatures were relatively small (6 to 12 in.) flattened fishes (Fig. 34-8), which probably lived by sucking up organic debris from the bottom of the streams they inhabited. Gas exchange occurred at the pairs of internal gills, each gill supported by a bony arch. Water entered the mouth, passed over the gills and left through a series of gill pouches which opened out at the surface. There were no fins, the fish swimming by means of undulating movements.

The body was encased in an armor of bony plates. This may have provided some protection against the large eurypterids which shared the same habitat. It may also have reduced the inflow of water in the hypotonic environment. The gills had to be exposed to the water, however, so some continual inflow was unavoidable. The

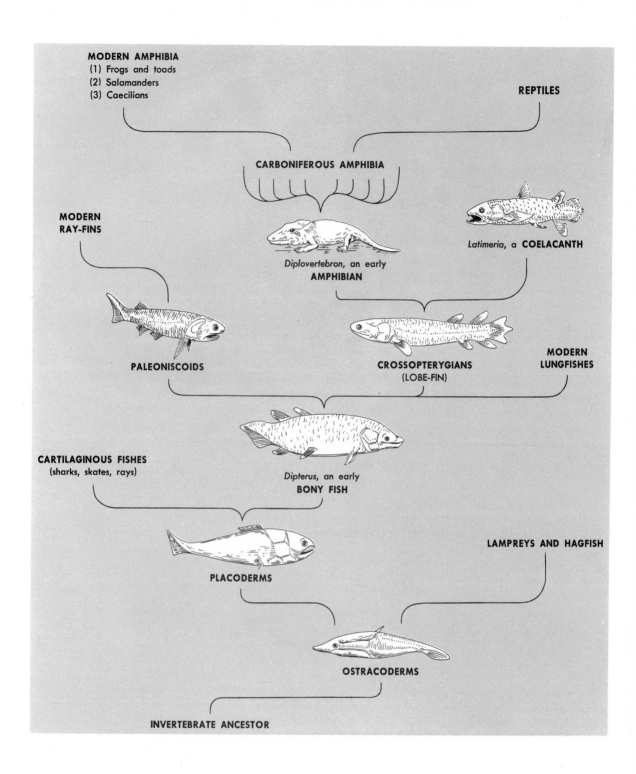

MODERN AMPHIBIA
(1) Frogs and toads
(2) Salamanders
(3) Caecilians

REPTILES

CARBONIFEROUS AMPHIBIA

Latimeria, a **COELACANTH**

MODERN RAY-FINS

Diplovertebron, an early
AMPHIBIAN

PALEONISCOIDS

CROSSOPTERYGIANS
(LOBE-FIN)

MODERN LUNGFISHES

Dipterus, an early
BONY FISH

CARTILAGINOUS FISHES
(sharks, skates, rays)

PLACODERMS

LAMPREYS AND HAGFISH

OSTRACODERMS

INVERTEBRATE ANCESTOR

Fig. 34-8   The evolution of the fishes and amphibians.

solution to the problem was to use the pressure created by the contraction of the heart to pump water back out of the body. The ostracoderm probably had inherited nephridialike excretory tubules from its invertebrate ancestors. The development of a glomerulus near the opening (the nephrostome) of each permitted the transfer of fluid (nephric filtrate) from the blood to the tubule and thence to the exterior. Of course, valuable materials (e.g. salts) would also be lost by such a mechanism so we must assume that reabsorption of such materials occurred in the tubules. The presence of a capillary network draining the glomeruli provided the increased blood supply necessary for increased tubular reabsorption. Thus evolved the first kidneys.

They were not primarily organs for excretion but for maintaining water balance in a hypotonic environment. Nitrogenous wastes (chiefly ammonia) were probably excreted at the gills. This is certainly true of the modern fresh-water fishes. This first kidney did, however, establish a pattern which was to be adapted to the excretory and water-balance needs of each of the later vertebrate classes.

THE PLACODERMS   34-10

A second group of armored fishes appeared early in the Devonian. These placoderms (Fig. 34-8) differed from their agnath ancestors in two fundamental respects. They had jaws and they had paired fins. The former enabled them to prey actively on smaller animals; the latter aided locomotion by stabilizing the fish in the water. The resulting shift away from bottom feeding was also reflected in the development of a cylindrical body in contrast to the flattened body of the agnaths.

The fossil record reveals an extensive adaptive radiation of these fishes during the Devonian. Most of them later became extinct, but some produced lines of descent which led to the two major classes of modern fishes, the cartilaginous and bony fishes, the Chondrichthyes and Osteichthyes respectively (see Section 5-10). (Actually *bony fish* is not a uniquely descriptive name for the latter because their placoderm and agnath ancestors also had skeletons of bone.)

The Devonian was marked by periods when many lakes and streams dried up or became much smaller and warmer. This environmental change must have imposed a rigorous selection pressure on the fresh-water Devonian fishes. Two solutions to the problem lay open to these animals, and both were taken. On the one hand, they could return to the ocean. On the other, the development of lungs for air-breathing would enable them to survive temporary periods of diminished water supply.

THE CARTILAGINOUS FISHES   34-11

Retreat to the oceans was the method of escape taken by the first cartilaginous fishes. These fishes (the earliest were sharks little different from our modern forms) get their name from the fact that their skeleton is made of cartilage, not bone. Like the placoderms, the sharks have jaws. The jaw "bones" developed from the first two pairs of gill arches (Fig. 34-9).

It is worth noting that in so doing, one pair of gill slits was no longer required. However, the opening still persists in some modern fishes. It is called the spiracle.

When the first cartilaginous fishes returned to the sea, they were exchanging a hypotonic environment (fresh water) for a hypertonic one. Instead of being faced with the problem of getting rid of excess water, they had to develop a method of conserving body water against the dehydrating effects of the sea. As you know, they

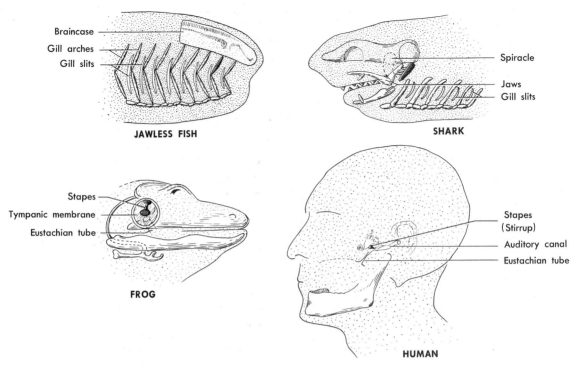

Fig. 34-9 Evolutionary transformation of the first gill slit and second (hyoid) gill arch of the jawless fishes. The bones homologous to the upper portion of the hyoid are shown in color.

accomplished this by converting their nitrogenous wastes into urea and allowing its concentration to build up in the blood until the blood was isotonic to the sea water. Today this requires a concentration of 2.5% which far exceeds that found in other vertebrates (0.02%). Because the ability to reach osmotic balance with the sea by this method develops late in the embryology of these animals, the eggs cannot simply be deposited unprotected in the water.

One solution to this problem is to deposit the egg, surrounded by a suitable fluid medium, in an impervious case in which embryonic development can occur. A second solution is simply to retain the eggs, and the embryos into which they develop, within the mother's body until they are capable of coping with the sea-water environment. Both these solutions require that internal fertilization take place, and the cartilaginous fishes were the first vertebrates to develop this. The pelvic fins of the male are specially modified for depositing sperm in the reproductive tract of the female.

34-12   THE BONY FISHES

The so-called bony fishes (Class Osteichthyes) employed the second solution to the problem of periodic droughts. They developed a pair of pouched outgrowths from the pharynx which served as primitive lungs. They were inflated by air taken in through the mouth. The bodies of these fishes were covered with scales, the only vestige of their ancestors' armor being the bones of the cranium.

These fishes quickly (still in the Devonian) diverged into three distinct groups, the paleoniscoids, the lungfishes, and the crossopterygians.

The **paleoniscoids** were distinguished by the presence of ray-fins (fins in which neither muscle nor bone was present) and the fact that ventilation of the lungs continued through the mouth. Many of them migrated to the sea during the late Paleozoic and the Mesozoic eras. In a stable aquatic environment, lungs were not necessary, and they were transformed into a swim bladder by means of which the fish could alter its buoyancy in the water. All of our modern commercial fish, both marine and fresh-water (e.g. salmon, tuna, mackerel, trout, and bass), are descendants of this group.

Fig. 34-10

The African lungfish surfaces from time to time to fill its lungs with air. Its gills are vestigial. (Courtesy American Museum of Natural History.)

The **lungfishes** developed a significant innovation not possessed by their ancestors. Their nostrils, which in the first Osteichthyes had opened only to the outside and were used for smelling (as in all modern paleoniscoid descendants), developed internal openings to the mouth cavity. This made it possible to breath air with the mouth closed. Once a rather successful group, the lungfishes of today are found in a few restricted localities of Africa, Australia, and South America, where their lungs still enable them to survive periodic droughts (Fig. 34-10). The widely scattered distribution of these fishes indicates that they are isolated remnants of a once-widespread group.

Judging from presentday lungfishes, two other significant adaptations evolved in this group. One was the development of two atria and a partial septum in the ventricle of the heart. This permitted at least a partial separation of oxygenated blood returning from the lung(s) and deoxygenated blood returning from the rest of the body and thus provided a marked improvement in circulatory efficiency (see Section 14-6). The second adaptation was the development of the enzyme system necessary to convert ammonia into the less toxic urea (see Section 16-9). This is particularly well developed in the African and South American species. While in the water, these fishes excrete their waste nitrogen as ammonia just as all the ray-fins do. In times of drought, however, these animals burrow into the mud and switch over to urea production.

The **crossopterygians** also had internal nostrils through which the lungs could be inflated. In addition, their pectoral and pelvic fins were lobed; that is, they were fleshy and were supported by bones. A glance at Fig. 34-11 shows that the pattern of bones (a bony girdle articulating with a single bone which, in turn, articulates with two others, etc.) is the one we find in all four-legged vertebrates. Each of our arm and leg bones is homologous to a bone in the crossopterygian pectoral and pelvic fins, respectively.

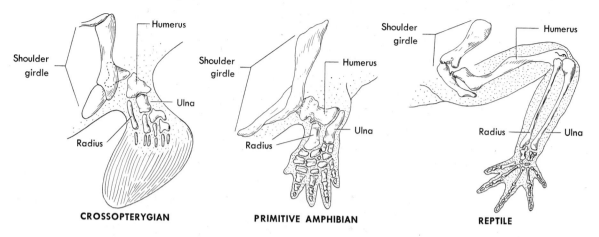

Fig. 34-11 Evolutionary development of the tetrapod forelimb from the pectoral fin of a crossopterygian.

Fossil remains tell us that the ancient lungfishes, like some of their modern descendants, burrowed in the mud and became dormant during periods of drought. The crossopterygians with their lobe-fins were able to attack the problem more aggressively. Their lobe-fins enabled them to waddle from one shrinking pool to another in search of better conditions. The combination of lungs and lobe-fins thus provided the necessary equipment to enter a new, uncrowded habitat, the land. One group of crossopterygian descendants did just that, although in a rather tentative manner. These were the amphibians. Another group turned instead, as so many other Devonian fishes had done, to the sea. These, the coelacanths, were quite successful for a time in their new habitat but became extinct by the end of the Mesozoic era, some 70 million years ago. Or so everyone believed until 1938. In that year a living coelacanth (*Latimeria*) was pulled up from the ocean depths off the East Coast of Africa. Since then more than two dozen specimens have been caught. These "living fossils" still have paired lungs like those of their ancestors, but they are no longer functional.

The Devonian has been called the "Age of Fishes." This is surely appropriate in view of the extraordinary adaptive radiation which took place in the group during that period. Both fresh water and salt water became well-populated by them. Toward the end of the Devonian, however, a new group of vertebrates appeared. These were the amphibians, the first of the four-legged vertebrates or **Tetrapods.**

34-13   **THE AMPHIBIANS**

The amphibians were the vertebrate pioneers of the land. Their lungs and bony limbs, inherited from their crossopterygian ancestors, provided a means of locomotion and a means of breathing air. A second atrium in the heart permitted oxygenated blood to be returned directly to it for pumping to the body under full pressure. While some mixing of oxygenated and deoxygenated blood occurred in the single ventricle, the three-chambered heart must have provided a substantial increase in circulatory efficiency and thus ability to cope with the more changeable, demanding land environment.

On land, the ability to detect sound is of great importance, and the amphibians developed simple ears out of structures inherited from their ancestors. The spiracle (Fig. 34-9) was covered with a membrane that served as an eardrum and a no-longer-used jawbone (itself originally derived from an agnath gill arch) served to transmit vibrations from this membrane to the inner ear. The innermost ossicle (the stirrup) of our middle ear is homologous to this bone.

As their name implies, the amphibians were only semiterrestrial. They had to return to water in order to lay eggs, and their modern descendants, at least, cannot withstand long exposure to dry air. The periodic shift from water to land and back again imposes additional problems in maintaining water balance and excreting nitrogenous wastes. In the water, the continual inflow must be pumped out of the glomeruli, as in the fresh-water fishes. On land, water must be conserved, and the amphibian accomplishes this by reducing the blood supply to the glomeruli and, hence, the filtration rate. Of course, this also diminishes the blood flow from the glomeruli to the tubules. Tubular function must be maintained, however, and increased activity of the auxiliary renal portal system (Fig. 16-9) permits this.

The earliest amphibians were large enough by modern standards (*Diplovertebron,* Fig. 34-8, reached a length of about 2 ft), but some of the later forms were truly of impressive size. Some fossil specimens are 8 ft long. These amphibians flourished during Carboniferous times. Vast swamps covered the earth, plant life was abundant, and there were plenty of insects on which the amphibians could feed. This period is often referred to as the Age of Amphibia.

It was followed by a period (the Permian) when the earth became colder and dryer. A decline in the fortunes of the amphibians set in that has continued to this day. Only three orders remain today: frogs and toads, salamanders, and the limbless, wormlike caecilians (see Section 5-11). Lacking a waterproof skin and waterproof eggs, these creatures have never fully adapted to the conditions of land life.

THE REPTILES   **34-14**

The first truly terrestrial animals were the reptiles. These evolved from amphibians during Carboniferous times. With the arrival of the Permian, they were able to cope with the new conditions better than the amphibians. The chief advance the earliest reptiles (the "stem" reptiles or **cotylosaurs**) showed over the amphibians was the development of a shelled, yolk-filled egg which could be deposited on land without danger of its drying out. A shell impervious to water is just as impervious to sperm and the development of the shelled egg coincided with the development of internal fertilization.

The embryo developing within the egg produced four extra-embryonic membranes (see Section 22-4). Protected by the fluid contained within the **amnion,** it secured food through the **yolk sac,** breathed through the **chorion** and **allantois,** and stored its metabolic wastes in the sac formed by the allantois.

Probably these earliest reptiles, whose short legs extended sideways from the body, still spent most of their time in the water and simply laid their eggs on land where they could be better hidden from predators. With the increasing dryness of the Permian, however, other modifications for dry-land living evolved. Development of a dry skin enabled them to leave the water safely. But dry skin could not be used for gas exchange. Improved lungs, inflated by expansion of the rib cage, solved this problem. A partial septum in the ventricle reduced the mixing of oxygenated with deoxygenated blood and thus improved the efficiency of circulation. The success of

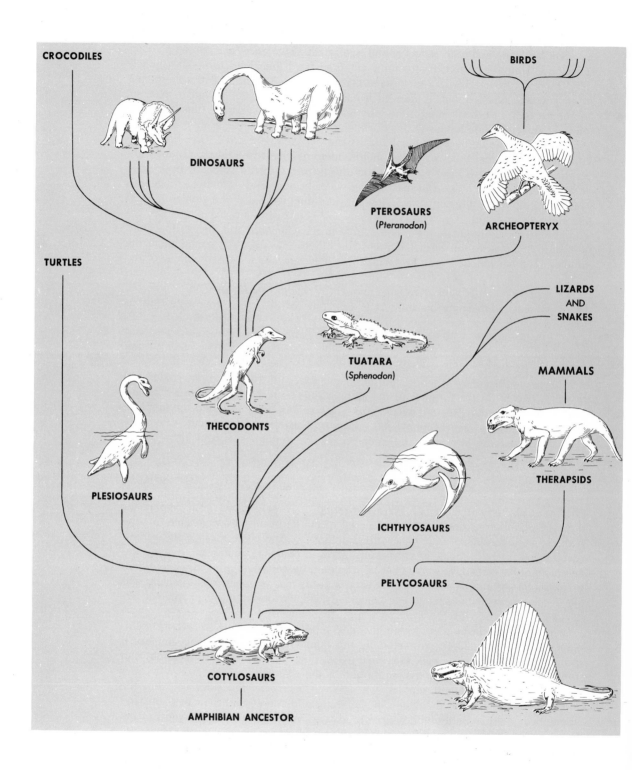

CROCODILES

BIRDS

DINOSAURS

PTEROSAURS
(*Pteranodon*)

ARCHEOPTERYX

TURTLES

LIZARDS
AND
SNAKES

TUATARA
(*Sphenodon*)

MAMMALS

THECODONTS

PLESIOSAURS

THERAPSIDS

ICHTHYOSAURS

PELYCOSAURS

COTYLOSAURS

AMPHIBIAN ANCESTOR

Fig. 34-12   The evolution of the reptiles.

these evolutionary developments was immediate. The stem reptiles underwent an adaptive radiation, producing five major lines of descent (Fig. 34-12).

1) Although the **pelycosaurs,** too, probably spent most of their time in the water, their legs were positioned under, rather than at the sides of, the body. This position allowed for more rapid and effortless running on land. From the pelycosaurs evolved a group of small, active, land-dwelling reptiles, the **therapsids.** At the start of the Mesozoic, these were the most abundant of the reptiles, but they soon were overshadowed in importance by other groups. But it was only a temporary (about 100 million years) eclipse, since the descendants of the therapsids, the mammals, ultimately inherited the earth.

2) The **turtles.** Although the evolution of the reptiles produced animals capable of living on dry land, many of them did not do so. From their origin early in the Mesozoic era right down to the present time, most turtles have lived in either fresh water or the ocean. Despite their habitat, they have not abandoned their heritage of land adaptations. They breathe air (although the ribs now form the bony box covering the animal and hence cannot help to ventilate the lungs) and lay shelled eggs on land. It is interesting to realize that while our terrestrial toads are returning to fresh water each spring to lay their eggs, the freshwater turtles are crawling up on land to scoop out a hole in sand or soil in which to lay theirs. Although never a prevalent group, the turtles deserve recognition for still being with us after over 200 million years on the earth, a span of time which has seen most of their early reptile contemporaries vanish.

3) and 4) Both the **plesiosaurs** and **ichthyosaurs** (Fig. 34-12) were marine reptiles which flourished during the Jurassic but became extinct by the end of the Mesozoic era. They were undoubtedly fisheaters and quite specialized for life in the sea. In fact, their finlike appendages were so unsuited for locomotion on land that the ichthyosaurs, at least, took to retaining their eggs within the mother's body rather than laying them on land. The young were born alive and active, as many shark young are born today.

5) The remaining line of descent from the stem reptiles had one further modification for land living. This was the ability to convert nitrogenous waste into the almost-insoluble compound, uric acid. As you learned in Chapter 16, this physiological modification allows potentially toxic nitrogenous wastes to be excreted safely and with almost no loss of water. Some uric acid is filtered at the glomeruli, but most of it is excreted directly into the tubules. In fact, in the interests of water conservation, the glomeruli are reduced to the point where they produce little more nephric filtrate than is needed to flush the uric acid into the cloaca. Here even this small amount of water is largely reabsorbed. The residue of uric acid is a whitish paste that passes out with the feces. The ability of this group of reptiles and their descendants to excrete their nitrogenous wastes in this manner has almost totally freed them from dependence on drinking water. The water in their food plus that produced by cellular respiration is usually sufficient for their needs.

Evolution in this group of reptiles soon diverged into two separate lines. One group of descendants were lizardlike in appearance. The rare tuatara of New Zealand (Fig. 5-20) is a living remnant of these animals. Our modern **lizards** (Fig. 34-13), which first appeared in the Jurassic, are also descendants although not quite in the same genealogical line. They are still important colonizers of the deserts and forests of warm parts of the world. One group of Cretaceous lizards became burrowing animals.

Fig. 34-13

The Komodo monitor lizard, a native of Malaya, is the largest of the lizards. This specimen weighed over 200 pounds. (Courtesy New York Zoological Society.)

Their legs eventually disappeared and thus the **snakes** were established. (Vestigial remnants of hind legs can still be detected in the boa and python.) Although they are able to survive in temperate regions by hibernating during the winter, the snakes also have been more successful in the subtropical and tropical regions of the world.

The second branch of the uric-acid-excreting, fully terrestrial reptiles were the **thecodonts** (Fig. 34-12). These animals were able to run quickly over the land by rising up on their hind legs and using their long tail for balance. The hind legs became larger and more powerful than the front. The great agility of these animals, combined with their tolerance of dry conditions, provided an enormously successful evolutionary plan. From them evolved five additional orders of reptiles. The members of this remarkable adaptive radiation are often referred to as the **ruling reptiles** because they completely dominated both land and air during the rest of the Mesozoic era.

a) The **crocodiles.** The crocodiles and alligators abandoned the bipedal locomotion of their thecodont ancestors but retained (and still have) the larger hind limbs. Although specimens in zoos do not often do so, these animals are capable of moving quickly with the entire torso lifted off the ground (Fig. 34-14). They are the only reptile descendants of the thecodonts that have not become extinct.

Fig. 34-14

The American alligator is *able* to move rapidly on land although it usually does not. (Courtesy American Museum of Natural History.)

b) and c) The **dinosaurs.** Late in the Triassic, two orders of dinosaurs appeared, each of which underwent an extraordinary adaptive radiation. Throughout the remainder of the Mesozoic era, the earth was populated by dinosaurs of every size, shape, and description. Many of the larger forms were so huge that they probably were restricted to wallowing about in marshes, letting the buoyancy of the water support some of their body weight. The abundance and habitat of these forms have given us a remarkably complete fossil record of them. The discovery and mounting of fossil dinosaurs was the most active branch of paleontology for many years and captured the imagination of people everywhere. When we look at the reconstructed skeletons of such forms as *Tyrannosaurus* (Fig. 34-15), which was 47 ft long and stood 19 ft high (note the greatly reduced forelimbs), and *Brachiosaurus,* which probably weighed close to 50 tons, we can well understand why. Although representing only two out of some 15 orders of reptiles in existence then, the dinosaurs alone fully justify our calling the Mesozoic era the "Age of Reptiles."

d) and e) Two groups of Mesozoic reptiles took to the air. The two-legged gait of the thecodonts had freed the forelimbs for use as wings. At first these probably were used only for gliding but later sustained flight became possible. One of these groups, the **pterosaurs,** ruled the air throughout most of the Mesozoic era. *Pteranodon* (Fig. 34-12), with its wingspread of 27 ft, was the largest member of the order.

Fig. 34-15

Fossil skeleton of *Tyrannosaurus rex,* one of the largest bipedal dinosaurs. Note the small forelimbs of this carnivore. (Courtesy American Museum of Natural History.)

THE BIRDS   **34-15**

The second group of reptiles that took to the air developed a modification not found in the pterosaurs: **feathers.** These scaly outgrowths provided a broad, light, but strong, surface for the wings. They also provided heat insulation for the body, making possible the development of a constant body temperature. These thecodont descendants were the first birds.

The discovery of *Archeopteryx* in Jurassic rock (Fig. 34-16) has provided us with one of the best examples of a "missing link." This creature possessed feathers, and thus we may arbitrarily call it a bird. But its relationship to the reptiles is obvious. The rather rudimentary wings had claws. There were teeth in the mouth, and it had a long tail. These are reptilian features no longer found in living birds.

Although they were well established by the end of the Mesozoic era, it was in the Cenozoic that the birds underwent such an extensive adaptive radiation. The large number of species and their wide distribution attest to their success.

The structure and physiology of birds is adapted in a variety of ways to efficient flight. Chief among these, of course, are the wings. Although wings now enable birds to travel long distances in search of suitable and abundant food, they probably first arose as an adaptation which helped them escape from predators. The presence of wingless birds in the Antarctic, New Zealand, and other regions where predators are rare gives indirect evidence of this.

An efficient bird, like an efficient airplane, needs to be light and powerful. Lightness has been achieved by feathers, hollow bones, and a single gonad (in the females) which enlarges and is active only during the breeding season. Loss of teeth has reduced the weight of the head. Their function has been taken over by the gizzard which is located near the center of gravity.

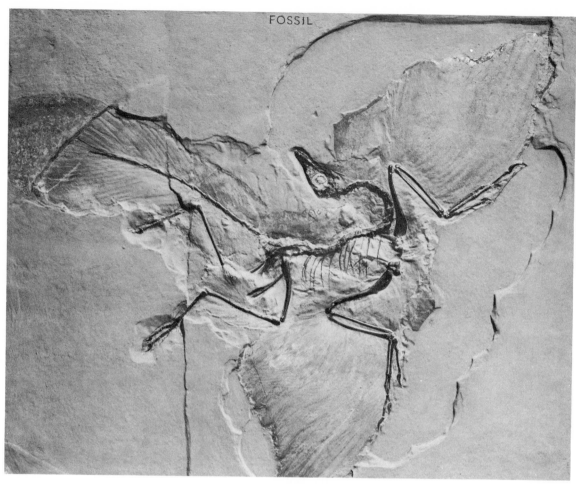

Fig. 34-16   Cast of fossil of *Archeopteryx*. The long tail, teeth, and claws on the wings are reptilian features. The feathers, clearly visible, cause it to be classified as a bird. (Courtesy American Museum of Natural History.)

Power is achieved by large breast muscles attached to a greatly enlarged sternum (Fig. 34-17). Birds also have a four-chambered heart, and its efficiency has permitted the development of a fixed body temperature (homeothermy). Homeothermy, in turn, permits a high metabolic rate under all environmental temperatures. Birds can remain active in cold weather, unlike their reptile cousins, which become sluggish as the temperature falls. The high metabolic rate reflects a rapid release of energy for flying. Birds secure their energy from concentrated foods, particularly those rich in fats such as seeds, insects, and other animals.

The end of the Mesozoic era was marked by great geological and biological changes on the earth. We are sure that the two were interrelated although as yet we can only speculate as to how. Geologically, this period was marked by an up-lifting of mountain ranges in several parts of the world. The Rockies, the Andes, and the Himalayas achieved their present eminence at this time. Biologically, it was marked by the extinction of most of the reptilian orders that had flourished during the Mesozoic. By the dawn of the Cenozoic, the plesiosaurs, the ichthyosaurs, the pterosaurs, and every single dinosaur had vanished from the face of the earth. While we do not yet understand just why these reptiles were unable to survive the geological changes of those times, we do know that the widespread extinction of the reptiles opened up habitats on land, in the air, and in the waters of the earth. Ready to move into these habitats were the birds and the mammals.

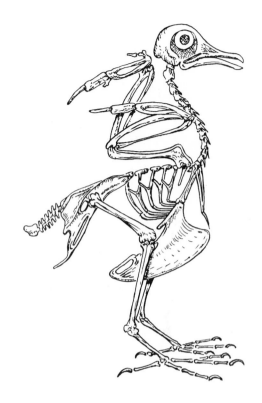

Fig. 34-17

Skeleton of a pigeon. Note the large sternum to which the flight muscles are attached. Compare the tail with that of *Archeopteryx* (Fig. 34-16).

THE EVOLUTION OF THE MAMMALS   34-16

We think that the first mammals arose late in the Triassic period from therapsid (Fig. 34-12) ancestors. They were small but very active animals whose diet probably consisted chiefly of insects. Associated with their active life was their ability to maintain a fixed body temperature (homeothermy). As in the birds (which did not appear until the Jurassic) this went hand in hand with the development of a four-chambered heart and completely separate oxygenating and systemic circuits. Conservation of body heat was made possible by the development of **hair.** While the earliest mammals laid eggs as did their reptile ancestors, the young, after hatching, were nourished with **milk** secreted by glands in the mother's skin.

In contrast to their reptile ancestors, the teeth of the mammals became specialized for cutting (incisors), tearing (canines), and grinding (molars) their food. The gray matter of the cerebrum, which is covered by white matter in the reptiles, grew out and over the surface of the brain. This modification was to have far-reaching consequences.

Evolution of the earliest mammals took several different routes. Of the groups that evolved, only three have survived to the present (Fig. 34-18). Each of these was distinguished by the way in which the young were cared for during embryonic development. One group, the **monotremes,** continued to lay eggs as the therapsids had. The duckbill platypus and the spiny anteaters (echidnas, Fig. 5-21), are the only descendants of this group still on the earth. In the second group, the **marsupials,** the young are retained for a short period within the reproductory tract of the mother. During this brief time, some nourishment is secured by means of the yolk sac which

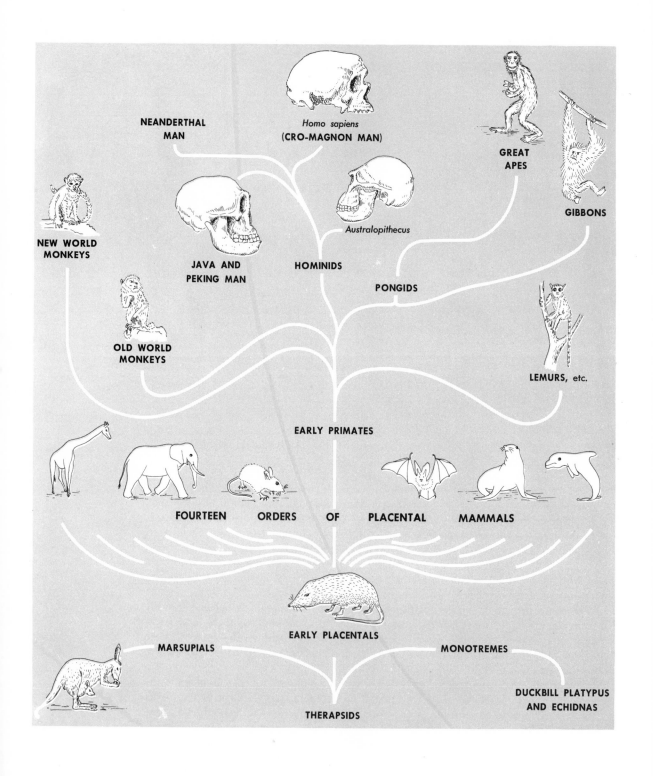

Fig. 34-18   The evolution of the mammals.

grows into the wall of the uterus. At a very early stage of development, though, the young are born. They then crawl into a pouch on the mother's abdomen and attach themselves to a milk-dispensing nipple. Development is completed here.

Probably the earliest marsupials resembled our opossum, but in the relative isolation of Australia and South America, the group underwent an elaborate adaptive radiation. The later reuniting of South America to North America brought the third and most advanced group of mammals, the **placental mammals,** into direct competition with the South American marsupials, all but 69 species of which have since become extinct. Only in Australia and New Zealand, areas where placental mammals have just recently gained entrance, does a rich diversity of marsupials survive today. The monotremes also survive only in these areas.

The placental mammals retain their young within the uterus of the mother until development is well advanced. There is little yolk in the egg but the extra-embryonic membranes form an umbilical cord and placenta through which the developing young are able to secure nourishment directly from the mother.

For some 70 million years in the Mesozoic era, the placental mammals were represented by just a single order. However, by the end of the second epoch, the Eocene, of the Cenozoic era, the placentals had radiated into at least fourteen different orders (see Fig. 5-23). What explains their long period of insignificance followed by such an explosive burst into prominence? The first requirement for speciation is relaxed selection pressure, and it was not until the extinction of the ruling reptiles that the mammals secured this. With most of the reptiles gone, a variety of habitats was available for occupancy by the mammals. Ungulates replaced the herbivorous dinosaurs. Carnivores preyed upon them. The cetaceans (whales, etc.) and some carnivores replaced the plesiosaurs in the oceans. The ancestors of the bats even found a new habitat. With the aid of echo location, they were able to prey upon night-flying insects. This ability and the lack of competition in this area have resulted in their order's becoming second only to the rodents in number of species.

THE EVOLUTION OF THE PRIMATES 34-17

One order of placental mammals, the Primates, is of particular interest to us because we are members of it. It had its origin some 60 million years ago at the very dawn of the Cenozoic. The first members were probably descended from the insect-eating placentals of the Mesozoic. During the Paleocene epoch, these evolved into a group of tree-living animals of which the lemurs and tarsier of today are the little-changed descendants. Grasping hands (with nails) and good vision are both of great value for life in the trees, and, as Fig. 34-19 makes clear, these animals are equipped with both. Not only is travel through the tree tops made easier and safer, but these features pay an extra dividend in permitting the animal to feed while keeping a constant watch for enemies.

By the Oligocene, these early primates had split into 3 separate stocks, the "New World" monkeys, the "Old World" monkeys and the ancestors of the apes. Their most significant evolutionary advance was the development of stereoscopic ("3D") vision as well as good color vision. The New World monkeys seem always to have been confined to tropical America. The other two groups spread over Africa, parts of Europe, and Asia.

The ancestors of the apes differed from the Old World monkeys in developing longer arms, a more erect posture and in losing their tails. These modifications reflected their method of locomotion: swinging from branch to branch in the trees.

Fig. 34-19

A tarsier. His large, forward-looking eyes and his grasping hands are typical of the primates. (Courtesy New York Zoological Society.)

In the Miocene, they subdivided again into the "hominids," who came down out of the trees and took to walking over the plains in search of food, and the true apes (pongids) who remained in the trees. From these latter forms have come the so-called "great apes," the gorilla, chimpanzee, and orangutan.

We look to the hominids for our ancestors. Unfortunately, the scarcity of fossil remains prevents us from tracing our genealogy exactly. Nevertheless, exciting discoveries in South Africa and Tanzania have revealed the presence of hominids who, no longer needing their hands for swinging through the trees, had taken to using and (later) making simple stone tools. These creatures, often called "man-apes," are generally classified in the genus *Australopithecus*. Their remains have been subjected to radioactive dating techniques, and some are as old as 2.5 million years, thus dating back to the early Pleistocene.

Now only one adaptation remained to complete the fabrication of man: the great enlargement of the cerebral cortex which enabled him to exploit fully his tool-making capabilities. By 500,000 years ago the first true men existed. These were the Java and Peking men of Asia and, somewhat later, Neanderthal man in Europe. Finally, about 35,000 years ago, *Homo sapiens* appeared in the form of the Cro-Magnon man of Europe, who seems to have co-existed for a time with Neanderthal man but eventually replaced him.

There is some evidence that *Homo sapiens* reached the Western Hemisphere not long after his spread through the Old World. He probably arrived via the land "bridge" which has periodically connected Asia and North America in the Bering Strait region. In any case, by 12,000 years ago men were well established in North, Central, and South America. These were the Indians whom Columbus found when, in 1492, the colonization of the New World began from Europe and Africa.

In tracing the evolutionary history of the animals, it is tempting to see in the story a guiding hand working out the destiny that ultimately produced man from the first flatworms. According to such a view, lungs, limbs, and the shelled egg evolved so that animals could colonize the land, and grasping hands arose so man could become a tool user. Such a view of evolution is called teleological. It interprets the process of evolution as one of working toward a predetermined goal. There is no evidence in the fossil record to support such a view. On the contrary, we see that the evolution of lungs and limbs was the result of selection pressure acting to enable the crossopterygians to remain in the water. The shelled egg probably evolved because the aquatic, early reptiles that produced it could hide it on land out of sight of hungry aquatic predators. The grasping hand evolved in response to the needs of life in the trees. But, note that each of these adaptations, which arose in response to certain selection pressures, then provided a plan that enabled a new environment to be colonized. The amphibians found the earth filled with plants and insects. So did the more efficient reptiles, and the amphibians began a decline which has continued to this day. Two-thirds of the history of the mammals was spent in obscurity. With the widespread extinction of reptiles, however, the land was left open for the mammals to begin their period of dominance which still continues. Could the reptiles ever take over again? Certainly not until or unless the now-dominant mammals disappear in large numbers from the face of the earth. The fossil record is filled with examples, both major and minor, of animal groups which arise, flourish for a time, finally become extinct and, in so doing, pave the way for an adaptive radiation of some other animal group. No pattern, no goal can be seen here. No, it is a story of adaptations, evolving to meet some immediate need, which by chance alone turn out to open new opportunities, new, less crowded ways of life to their owners.

Our story makes it clear that evolution in any group involves not only the members of that group but also the impact of the physical environment and other organisms in the environment on the group. The study of the interrelationships between organisms and all aspects of their environment is called **ecology.** It is the study to which we will turn in the next and final part of this book.

EXERCISES AND PROBLEMS

1   Summarize the major differences between the members of the annelid superphylum and those of the echinoderm superphylum.

2   If someone brought a radially symmetrical animal to you, what conclusions might you draw about (a) its habitat, (b) its power of locomotion, (c) its feeding habits?

3   In what ways does the evolutionary history of the amphibians parallel that of the mosses? In what ways does it differ from it?

4   *Brachiosaurus* probably lived in swamps. Why?

5   Summarize the specific structural and physiological modifications that make birds so successful in their way of life.

6   Summarize the adaptations which have made reptiles more successful at colonizing the land than the amphibians have been.

7   How does a shark differ from a trout?

8   What three features are characteristic of all chordates, at least at some time during their life?

9   For each of the following, tell whether it belongs to the annelid or echinoderm superphylum: (a) trochophore larva, (b) tunicate, (c) identical twins, (d) squid, (e) sea cucumber.

10   What adaptations in the crossopterygians enabled them to migrate from a water to a land environment?

11   In what ways does *Peripatus* resemble an earthworm? A millipede?

12   The largest vertebrate and the largest invertebrate live in the ocean. Can you think of an explanation for this?

13   The Java man was once classified as *Pithecanthropus erectus*. Now some anthropologists classify him as *Homo erectus*. What change in their thinking does this reflect?

14 Hemoglobins consist of a protein to which is attached the prosthetic group, heme. Hemoglobins are found in vertebrates, *certain* mollusks, nemertines, annelid worms, insects, crustaceans, nematodes, echinoderms, and even some plants. Does their presence in these forms indicate close kinship? If not, can you account for the repeated independent evolution of hemoglobins?

15 On the basis of the evidence presented in this chapter, would you say that adaptive radiations have had their origin in highly successful, specialized groups of animals? Defend your position.

16 What features of man are unique to him?

17 Would you consider man as the most specialized of the mammals? Defend your view.

18 Should caecilians be considered primitive amphibians? Defend your view.

REFERENCES

1 Buchsbaum, R., *Animals Without Backbones*, University of Chicago Press. Chicago, Ill., 1948. Chapters 27 and 28 examine the fossil record of the invertebrates and their possible evolutionary relationships.

2 Hanson, E. D., *Animal Diversity*, 2nd Edition, Foundations of Modern Biology Series, Prentice-Hall, Inc., 1964. Chapter 7 speculates on the evolutionary relationships of the various animal phyla.

3 Romer, A. S., *The Vertebrate Story*, University of Chicago Press, Chicago, Ill., 1959. Traces the evolution of the vertebrates from their suspected origins to the modern forms, including man, that inhabit the earth today. A wealth of information on the fossil links between the various groups is also included.

4 Smith, H. W., *From Fish to Philosopher*, Doubleday & Co., Inc., New York, 1961. Tells the story of vertebrate evolution with special emphasis on the structural and physiological changes in the kidneys.

5 Colbert, E. H., *Evolution of the Vertebrates*, Science Editions, New York, 1961. A history of vertebrate evolution in a paperback edition.

6 Howells, W., *Mankind in the Making*, 2nd ed., Doubleday & Co., Inc., New York, 1967. Emphasizes the evolution of the primates.

Each of the following articles from *Scientific American* is available in an inexpensive reprint distributed by W. H. Freeman and Company, San Francisco, Calif.

7 Glaessner, M. F., "Pre-Cambrian Animals," *Scientific American*, Reprint No. 837, March, 1961.

8 Millot, J., "The Coelacanth," *Scientific American*, Reprint No. 831, December, 1955.

9 Colbert, E. H., "The Ancestors of Mammals," *Scientific American*, Reprint No. 806, March, 1949.

10 Newell, N. D., "Crises in the History of Life," *Scientific American*, Reprint No. 867, February, 1963. Attempts to explain the repeated mass extinctions that have occurred in the evolution of animals.

11 Broom, R., "The Ape-Men," *Scientific American*, Reprint No. 832, November, 1949.

12 Clark, J. D., "Early Man in Africa," *Scientific American*, Reprint No. 820, July, 1958.

13 Napier, J., "The Evolution of the Hand," *Scientific American,* Reprint No. 140, December, 1962.

14 Washburn, S. L., "Tools and Human Evolution," *Scientific American,* Reprint No. 601, September, 1960.

15 Weckler, J. E., "Neanderthal Man," *Scientific American,* Reprint No. 844, December, 1957.

16 Howells, W., "The Distribution of Man," *Scientific American,* Reprint No. 604, September, 1960.

17 Dobzhansky, Th., "The Present Evolution of Man," *Scientific American,* Reprint No. 609, September, 1960.

PART VIII

ECOLOGY

Jeffrey pine, shaped by the force of the prevailing winds.
(Courtesy H. Armstrong Roberts.)

The life of every organism is inseparably connected with its surroundings, its external environment. *Metabolism* involves the taking in of materials from and the release of materials to the environment. *Reproduction* increases the amount of living matter in the environment. *Responsiveness* includes action taken with respect to changes in the environment. *Evolution* is the development of adaptations in response to forces in the environment and, when conditions in the environment permit, the production of new species.

Organisms are not passive things simply living at the mercy of their environment. Their own life activities may exert a profound influence on it. For example, we believe the oxygen that now represents one-fifth of our atmosphere has been placed there by photosynthesizing protists and plants.

The study of the interrelationships between organisms and their environment is known as **ecology.** The environment of every organism consists of both **physical factors,** such as climate, and **biotic factors,** that is, the presence of other organisms which directly or indirectly affect it. As we will see, these physical factors and biotic factors are related but, for the sake of convenience, we will discuss them separately. In this chapter we will examine some of the physical factors in the environment.

35-1   **THE MEDIUM**

Every living thing is surrounded by a "fluid" medium, either air or water. Even organisms that live in the soil exist either in air spaces between soil particles or in water adhering to or present between them. Some organisms live in both media. In the case of land plants, the root hairs are in contact with soil water while the stem and leaves extend up into the air. The amphibians alternate between one and the other. This is true also for those marine organisms that live on the coast in the region between the high-tide and low-tide marks. Four times a day their medium changes as they are alternately submerged and exposed by the tides.

As you learned in Chapter 33, water was the medium for all the earliest forms of life. This should not be surprising when you consider that water is the chief constituent of all living things. Only later in the course of evolution did plants and animals develop modifications which enabled them to leave the water and live on land while still preserving a watery medium within.

In considering the properties of water as a medium for life, we must distinguish between salt water and fresh water. Salt water occurs in the lowest parts of the earth, the ocean basins. The water can leave only by evaporation, with energy being supplied by the sun. In this process, it is distilled, that is, the salts are left behind. Eventually, the water vapor condenses to rain or snow. This is fresh water and, when it falls on land, it provides for the needs of all terrestrial and fresh-water organisms. As it flows downhill to the sea again, it picks up some minerals which are carried to the sea, increasing its salinity little by little (Fig. 35-1).

For today's marine invertebrates, salt water is virtually an extension of their internal environment. Their ECF is isotonic to sea water, and there is no problem in maintaining suitable amounts of water within the body.

The situation is not quite so simple for organisms that live in fresh water. Theirs is a hypotonic environment and they are constantly faced with the problem of having their internal environment diluted by an inflow of water from the exterior. Cell walls, contractile vacuoles, and kidneys are three adaptations to cope with this problem.

Water need not necessarily be "wet." Sea water is hypertonic to the ECF of vertebrates. For those, the fishes, which have membranes exposed to it, sea water represents as dry a medium as air is for the kangaroo rat living in the desert. We have studied (see Section 16-10) how both the cartilaginous and bony fishes cope with the dehydrating effects of their medium.

Most aquatic organisms are adapted to life either in sea water or in fresh water but not in both. Marked changes in the salt content of their medium is fatal. Such organisms are described as *stenohaline*. On the other hand, many aquatic organisms can tolerate wide fluctuations in the salt content of the water. Many such *euryhaline* creatures are found at the mouths of rivers. The salt content of their medium is influenced primarily by which direction the tide is flowing. Some organisms (the eel and salmon are well-known examples) pass completely from one medium to the other at certain stages in their life cycle. As yet we have little information on how euryhaline species adjust to such profound changes in their medium.

Water has several other advantages as a medium for life besides its role in supplying the chief ingredient of the internal environment. The slowness with which water changes temperature provides a far more stable environment in this respect than air does. Marine organisms are not exposed to rapid and wide changes of temperature. While freshwater organisms may be exposed to a somewhat wider range of temperatures, the thermal stability of the water ensures that the changes will occur slowly. Water also provides a suitable medium into which sperm and eggs can be released for fertilization.

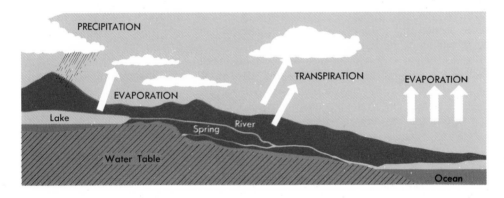

The distribution of water. Evaporated sea water as it falls on land replaces the fresh water that flows constantly into the sea.

Fig. 35-1

The vast numbers of tiny floating organisms, plankton, in the upper regions of the water make it practical for many aquatic animals to adopt a sessile life. Sponges, cnidarians, barnacles, many annelid worms, and many bivalves satisfy their food requirements simply by waiting for plankton to be brought to them in currents of water.

The buoyancy of water provides mechanical support for the organisms that live in it. Many marine cnidarians (e.g. jellyfish) float safely in the sea despite their delicate construction. Kelps reach lengths of over 100 ft without any woody tissues to support their bodies. The giant squid, which reaches a length of 50 ft, is the largest invertebrate on the earth. Despite its enormous size, it has virtually no supporting skeleton. Although the great blue whale has an internal skeleton, it could never support the animal's 170-ton weight on land. When whales accidentally become beached, they are totally helpless.

Water has certain disadvantages as a medium for life. Even cool, well-aerated water contains less than 1/25 the quantity of oxygen found in an equal volume of air. This means that a correspondingly greater volume of water must be moved over a given area of gills to provide the same amount of gas exchange that would occur in lungs of the same surface area. It is no accident that all homeothermic animals (birds and mammals) get their oxygen from the air even if they live in water, as whales do.

Even the clearest water quickly absorbs the light which strikes it. This means that photosynthetic protists and plants are restricted to relatively shallow layers of lakes and oceans. It is in just these layers that turbulence of the water is greatest. Consequently creatures living here must be able to withstand mechanical damage. The flexibility of rockweeds and kelps, and the hard outer coverings of barnacles, mussels, snails, etc., are modifications enabling these organisms to survive the particularly violent wave action of the intertidal zone (Fig. 35-13).

Plants, the first organisms to invade the land, really live in two mediums at once, their roots in soil water and their stems and leaves in air. Plants vary widely in the amount of soil water they need. Most of our common terrestrial plants are *mesophytes*. Their roots must be in moist, but not saturated, soil. Prevention of water loss from the exposed parts of the plant is important, and we have reviewed (see Section 33-11) the mechanisms by which this is achieved.

Some plants, the *xerophytes,* have become adapted to prolonged periods of unusual dryness. These plants (the cacti are examples) possess several modifications that enable them to withstand such dry conditions. Many of them are succulent, that is, they have thick leaves and/or stems which store water. One often finds, associated with these, spines or some other device which discourages thirsty animals. A thick cuticle and stomata recessed beneath the surface of the leaf or stem reduce water loss through transpiration. In the case of the cacti, the transpiring surface is further diminished by the absence of broad leaves. The leaves are reduced to protective spines and photosynthesis becomes a function of the stem. The root systems of xerophytes are very elaborate and, in sand dunes, are a major factor in reducing erosion.

At the other extreme are plants that live either totally immersed in water or with their root systems standing in water. These *hydrophytes* represent a return to water of what are basically terrestrial organisms. In so doing, the amount of woody tissue has been reduced (e.g. *Anacharis,* water lilies) and the root systems are small with few or no root hairs.

Currents occur in both water and air, and these have been exploited by many organisms for dispersal. Spores and seeds may be transported long distances by wind and water. Insects and spiders are often carried passively by the wind. Violent windstorms, such as tornadoes, have been known to carry fish for surprisingly long distances. The presence of the same fresh-water, stenohaline fishes in rivers whose only water connection is the sea may in some cases be explained by such transport. Sessile marine animals such as colonial cnidarians, barnacles, and tunicates disperse their species by means of larvae which, though capable of swimming only short distances, may be carried long distances in ocean currents.

35-2   THE SUBSTRATUM

With the exception of plankton and many fishes that spend their entire lives floating freely or swimming in the water, living things generally are attached to or move about on some surface. This surface is called the substratum. Rocks, soil, sand, and mud are the most widely used kinds of substrata. Sessile organisms must have some sort of attachment to the substratum so that they will not be carried away by wind or water currents. Examination of the rocks exposed at low tide along our seacoast reveals a rich variety of algae and animals clinging tenaciously to their substratum (Fig. 35-13). Holdfasts, suckers, and cement organs are some of the structural modifications that keep these creatures from being swept away in the waves. Those that live on mud or sand must rely on roots (e.g. various grasses) or the ability to burrow in order to escape that fate.

The only sessile land organisms are the plants and a limited number of protists such as lichens. Can you think of a reason why no land animals are sessile? Some lichens grow right on the surface of rocks. Many plants, especially in subtropical and tropical regions, live perched on the branches of other plants. "Spanish moss" is a common example in our southern states. These plants do not extract any nourishment from their host plants. In fact, Spanish moss grows quite well on clotheslines! They simply use the host plant to secure a place in the sun. A plant that grows on another for position only is called an **epiphyte.**

The dominant substratum of the terrestrial environment, though, is soil. Soil anchors plants, thus enabling them to extend their leaves up into the sun and, at the same time, supplying them with minerals and water. With these provisions, photosynthesis is possible and hence the production of organic molecules on which we and all other animal life depend.

Soil varies greatly in its chemical composition, its texture, its thickness, and its moisture content. This variability is always reflected in the type and richness of the plant life it can support. The nature of the plant life in turn affects the animal life of the region.

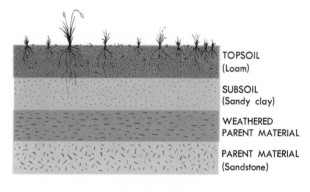

Fig. 35-2

A soil profile characteristic of the plains states. The rainfall is so light that soil minerals are seldom carried below the subsoil. As a result the fertility of this soil is easy to maintain.

TOPSOIL
(Loam)

SUBSOIL
(Sandy clay)

WEATHERED
PARENT MATERIAL

PARENT MATERIAL
(Sandstone)

The composition of the soil is not uniform from top to bottom. A vertical section through the soil reveals several distinct **horizons** (Fig. 35-2). Although the thickness and properties of each of these varies from region to region, a typical soil "profile" contains five of them. At the top is a thin layer of rotting organic matter such as leaves. Beneath this is the topsoil. This horizon is usually rather dark in color because of the organic matter, **humus,** which has been incorporated into it from above. Successful agriculture depends upon a thick layer of rich topsoil.

The next horizon is the subsoil. This is usually lighter in color. It may be rich in minerals but it lacks humus. Beneath the subsoil we find a layer of rocky debris in the process of physical and chemical breakdown. This is not considered soil although it represents a step in the formation of new subsoil. Finally we reach solid rock which, as it disintegrates through chemical action, adds to the layer above it.

The properties of any given soil depend on a number of factors. One of these is the nature of the underlying rocks. Limestone, shale, and granite all produce different types of soil as they disintegrate. A second factor is material that may be deposited from other areas. Both water and wind move soil from one spot to another. The thick, rich soil of river deltas is formed from soil particles brought downstream.

The kind of plants growing in the soil also affects its properties. Plants such as mosses and grasses add large quantities of humus to the soil. Pine needles and oak leaves lower the pH of the soil they fall on. Still another factor is the direction of water movement in the soil. In the eastern part of our country, the annual rainfall is sufficiently great that a regular movement of water from the topsoil down to the water table (Fig. 35-1) occurs. As this water passes downward, it dissolves valuable minerals from the soil and removes them. Calcium ions are among these, and their removal lowers the pH of the soil. Successful agriculture in these regions requires a regular program of liming (adding Ca^{++}) and fertilizing the soil in order to restore a proper pH and the mineral nutrients essential to plant growth.

A different situation occurs in the plains states. Here the annual rainfall is rather low so that little or no rainwater ever percolates down to the water table. Therefore, Ca^{++} and other minerals are not carried below the reach of plant roots and consequently remain available for use. The retention of Ca^{++} and other ions near the surface keeps the pH near neutrality and the general fertility high. This is one reason, then, why the plains states are the "breadbasket" of our nation.

Another factor affecting the composition of the soil is the action of burrowing animals and soil microorganisms. Ants, earthworms, moles, woodchucks, etc., alter the texture of the soil as they burrow through it and accomplish some mixing of the top three horizons. The microorganisms in the soil hasten the decay process and, as we will see in Section 35-6, play a vital role in establishing the fertility of the soil.

35-3   **TEMPERATURE**

The activities of all organisms are affected by their body temperature. With the exception of the birds and mammals, this, in turn, is affected by the temperature of the environment. The rate of metabolism and thus body activity, the necessity for a period of cold temperature to break bud and seed dormancy, and the varying sensitivity of organisms to freezing are just three examples of how temperature affects living things and even limits the regions in which they can survive. The temperature of the environment results from an interaction of three factors: latitude, altitude and terrain.

1)   **Latitude.** The axis of the earth is tipped 23½° with respect to the plane in which the earth moves around the sun. For this reason, the northern hemisphere receives more than 12 hours of sunlight during the six months (approximately March 21 to September 23) when the axis of the earth is tipped toward the sun and less than 12 hours during the remaining months when the axis is tipped away. The reverse situation occurs in the southern hemisphere (Fig. 35-3). This phenomenon results in a net gain of solar radiation during one half of the year, a net loss during the other half, and hence it is responsible for the seasons. The farther north one travels, the more pronounced the cooling of the earth in winter and the longer it takes for warm temperatures to return in the spring.

Not only is there great seasonal *variation* in the amount of sunlight received at high latitudes, but the *total* amount received during the course of the year is less than that in the tropics. This is true even though the total number of hours that the sun is above the horizon is the same. The long days of summer do not, however, compensate for the short days of winter. There are several reasons for this. The higher the latitude, the closer the sun is to the horizon even at mid-day. Its rays, entering the atmosphere at an angle, must traverse a longer path before they reach the surface of the earth, and increased losses by absorption thus occur. Furthermore, the intensity of the light is reduced because a given amount of light shines on a larger area in the higher latitudes than it does at the equator (Fig. 35-3). The low angle at which the rays strike the earth and the presence of ice and snow result in substantial losses by reflection, thus further reducing the amount of energy available for warming the region.

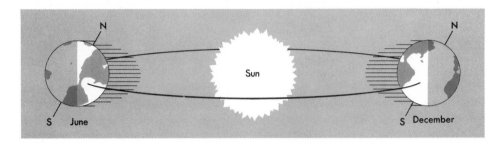

The origin of seasons. Not only are the days shorter during winter but the intensity of the sunlight at the surface of the earth is diminished.

Fig. 35-3

2) **Altitude.** The earth receives its energy in the form of ultraviolet, visible, and infrared radiation from the sun. The visible rays pass most easily through the atmosphere, are absorbed by the surface of the earth, and, in large measure, transformed into radiation of longer wavelength: heat. The moist air near the surface of the earth absorbs heat quite efficiently and is warmed in the process. Thus we find that the lower levels of the atmosphere are generally warmer than the upper. On the average, the temperature drops about 3°F for every 1000-ft increase in elevation. At a given latitude, then, higher locations in general have cooler temperatures than lower ones.

3) **Other Features of the Terrain.** Temperature may also be markedly affected by the topography of the land. In the northern hemisphere, a ridge running east and west will be substantially warmer on its southern exposure than on its northern one. The slopes of hills often do not have a killing frost so late in the spring or so early in the autumn as valleys do, even though their altitude is greater. The reason is that the dense layers of cold air, formed close to the ground as the earth cools at night, flow down into the valley and are replaced by warmer air.

The proximity of large bodies of water, lakes or the ocean, has a moderating effect upon temperature. Such regions have cooler temperatures in summer and warmer temperatures in winter because of the great heat capacity of water (see Section 7-7). Offshore ocean currents may alter the picture further. The northwest coast of Scotland is sufficiently warm throughout the year that such semitropical plants as palms, tree ferns, eucalyptus trees, camellias, and magnolias are able to grow there. Warm surface currents originating in the Gulf Stream make this possible even though the latitude is that of the northern part of the Canadian province of Alberta!

Fig. 35-4

Vegetation in the Everglades of Florida. The abundance of vines and epiphytes is characteristic of the tropical rain forest biome. (Courtesy William H. Amos.)

35-4   THE BIOMES

If you should take a trip from the southern tip of Florida to the northern part of Quebec, you would pass through four regions which are markedly different with respect to the type of vegetation and (less obvious) of animal life present. These distinctive plant and animal communities are called biomes. The sequence of these four biomes reflects a progressive lowering of average annual temperature as one moves farther north.

1)   **The Tropical Rain Forest.** The southern tip of Florida is the only part of continental United States where one can find a tropical rain forest biome. It is characterized by vegetation so dense that little light reaches the forest floor. The branches of the trees are festooned with epiphytes and vines (Fig. 35-4), adaptations that enable their owners to reach a place in the sun. Most of the plants are evergreen, not deciduous.

Fig. 35-5

Beeches and maples growing in the temperature deciduous forest of New Hampshire. (Courtesy Eliot Porter.)

In the Western hemisphere, the tropical rain forest reaches its fullest development in the jungles of Central and South America. The forest trees are very tall, very dense, and of a great variety of species. It is rare to find two trees of the same species growing close to one another. A large proportion of the animal species, mammals and reptiles as well as birds, live in the trees. Monkeys, sloths, and many lizards and snakes share the jungle trees with the birds.

2) **The Temperate Deciduous Forest.** The temperate deciduous forest biome of North America occupies the eastern half of the United States. It is characterized by hardwood trees (beech, maple, oak, hickory, etc.) which shed their leaves in the autumn. The number of different tree species here is far more limited than in the tropical rain forest biome, and large stands of a single species may often be found. As for animal life, deer, racoons, and salamanders are especially characteristic of this biome (Fig. 35-5.)

Fig. 35-6

The taiga, popularly known as the "spruce-moose" biome. (Courtesy Lee E. Yeager.)

Fig. 35-7

Caribou grazing in the tundra of northern Canada. (Courtesy Fritz Goro, *Life*.)

3) **The Taiga.** As one moves north into Canada, a new picture presents itself: a landscape dominated by conifers, especially spruces and firs (Fig. 35-6). This is the taiga, named after the similar biome found in the U.S.S.R. It is a land dotted with lakes and populated by bears, rodents (e.g. squirrels), birds, and moose. The latter is such a typical member that it has led some to call this the "spruce-moose" biome. During the cold winters, many of the mammals hibernate, while many of the birds migrate south.

4) **The Tundra.** Still farther north, the trees of the taiga become stunted by the harshness of the subarctic climate. Finally they disappear to reveal a land of bogs and lakes, a land so cold in winter that even the long days of the brief arctic summer are unable to thaw the permafrost beneath the surface layers of soil. Sphagnum moss, a wide variety of lichens, and some grasses and fast-growing annuals dominate the landscape during the short growing season (Fig. 35-7). Caribou feed upon this growth. So do vast numbers of insects. Swarms of migrating birds, especially waterfowl, invade the tundra in the summer to raise their young, feeding them with insects and a large variety of aquatic invertebrates and vertebrates. As the arctic summer draws to a close, the birds fly south, and all but a few of the permanent residents, in one way or another, prepare themselves to spend the winter in a dormant condition.

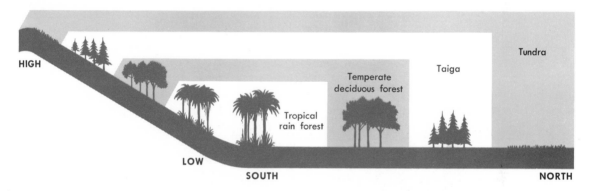

The biomes change not only with latitude (right) but also with altitude (left).   **Fig. 35-8**

There is another way to visit the different biomes which does not require traveling hundreds of miles. Temperature is the major influence in establishing the four biomes discussed and, as we have seen, temperature varies with altitude as well as latitude. A trip up New Hampshire's Mt. Washington on the famous cog railway will, in a short time, enable one to pass from a temperate, deciduous, hardwood forest in the valley, through a region dominated by spruces, up into an alpine, lichen- and moss-dominated region near the summit. While the physical and biotic features of these zones are not identical with the biomes established by latitude, there are many close parallels (Fig. 35-8). As a rule, a climb of 1000 ft is roughly equivalent, in changed flora and fauna, to a trip northward of some 600 miles.

Two other major biomes are found in North America: grassland (prairie or plains) and desert. The controlling factor in these two biomes is not so much temperature but limited moisture. The prevailing winds in the western half of our country blow in from the Pacific laden with moisture. Each time this air rises up the western slopes of, successively, the Coast Ranges, the Sierras and Cascades, and finally the Rockies, it

Fig. 35-9   The grasslands biome. This plains area in Weld County, Colorado, has been only lightly grazed by cattle. (Courtesy U.S. Forest Service.)

Fig. 35-10   The desert biome in southern Arizona. Xerophytic species such as saguaro cactus (right) and creosote bush dominate this arid land. (Courtesy Dr. Dale A. Zimmerman and Ward's Natural Science Establishment, Inc., Rochester, N.Y.)

expands and is cooled. Its moisture condenses to rain, which drenches the mountain slopes beneath. When the air reaches the eastern slopes, it is relatively dry, and much less rain falls. How much falls and how regularly determine whether the biome in these areas will be grasslands or desert.

5) **Grasslands.** The irregular and relatively low rainfall of the grasslands is incapable of supporting forest growth except along river valleys. It can, however, support a variety of grasses, and these dominate the landscape (Fig. 35-9). The abundance of grass for fodder coupled with the lack of shelter from predators produces a unique fauna in grasslands throughout the world. The dominant vertebrates are swiftly moving, herbivorous ungulates. In this country, bison and antelope were conspicuous occupants of the grasslands before the coming of the white settlers. Now the level grasslands supply our nation with an abundance of corn, wheat, and other grains, while the hillier areas support our domesticated ungulates, cattle and sheep.

6) **The Desert.** The extreme dryness of the desert permits colonization only by xerophytic plants such as cactus (Fig. 35-10), sagebrush, mesquite, and fast-growing annuals whose seeds can germinate, develop into mature plants, flower, and produce a new crop of seeds within a few weeks following a rare, soaking rain. Most of the animals of the desert (mammals, lizards and snakes, insects and arachnids, even some birds) are adapted for burrowing out of the scorching heat of the desert sun. Many of them limit their forays for food to the night hours.

LIGHT   35-5

Light plays a major role in the world of living things. A substantial portion of the energy of the sun reaches us as light and, after conversion into heat, helps to control the nature of the biome. Most animals have light receptors of some sort, often of vital importance to their success. The hawk searching the ground for prey, the female stickleback watching the courtship of the male, the worker bee navigating by the direction of the sun, the rabbit whose gonads begin to enlarge with the lengthening days of spring (Fig. 30-4) are just four examples of the importance of light to the welfare of animals.

Animals depend on light in another way, which is indirect but even more important. Light is necessary for photosynthesis, and all animals ultimately depend upon photosynthetic plants or protists for their nourishment.

On land, the chief photosynthesizers are the green plants. They carpet the earth except on bare rock, in the desert, and where man has plowed the soil, allowed it to erode, or covered it with pavement and buildings. Plants have met the competition for light in several ways. One is simply to grow tall, as the trees do. But this poses problems for the herbaceous, shrubby plants in their shade. Many plant species, by mechanisms not yet clear, are somewhat shade tolerant; that is, they can carry on photosynthesis in light far less intense than full sunlight. Others, in the temperate deciduous forest, solve the problem by making their maximum growth in the early spring before the trees have developed a new set of leaves. In the evergreen tropical rain forest, vines climbing on the forest trees and epiphytes perched on their branches are common solutions to the problem of exposure to light.

The organization of the leaf (see Section 12-4) and the geometrical arrangement of leaves on the plant are also adaptations resulting in the maximum exposure to light and thus a high rate of photosynthesis (Fig. 35-11). Leaves which become shaded, and hence a metabolic drain to the plant, are soon shed. Despite all these adaptations,

Fig. 35-11 Leaves of ivy growing on a wall. The orientation and spacing of the leaves provide optimum exposure to the light.

rarely does more than two percent of the energy of the sunlight reaching the earth become converted into chemical energy by photosynthesis (Fig. 35-12).

Although estimates are difficult to make, probably even more photosynthesis occurs in the oceans than on land. Because of the rapid absorption of light by water (see Section 35-1), virtually all photosynthesis occurs within 300 feet of the surface. In muddy bays and estuaries, a few angiosperms (e.g. eel grass) are important photosynthesizers. In deeper and more rocky locations, the sessile algae are dominant. They occur in fairly distinct zones. A thin film of blue-green algae adheres to the surface of rocks above the high-tide mark. Although moistened by spray, their medium is air rather than water and they receive ample amounts of light for photosynthesis. Green algae, such as sea lettuce (*Ulva*), are found close to the surface where the color of the light has been least altered by pas-

UTILIZATION OF VISIBLE SUNLIGHT IN A CATTAIL MARSH

Photosynthesis	2.2%
Reflection	3.0
Evaporation (incl. transpiration), and heating of surroundings	94.8
Total	100.0%

Fig. 35-12

sage through the water. In deeper water, rockweeds and kelps (brown algae) appear. Deeper still are species of red algae. It is thought that their red pigments absorb the weak blue light that reaches this depth and pass the energy on to chlorophyll molecules for photosynthesis. Along rocky coasts with a marked rise and fall of the tides, these various zones of algae, down to the layer of the kelps, can be easily observed when the tide is out (Fig. 35-13).

Photosynthesis is also carried on by floating (planktonic) algae. They support the animal life of the open sea. This includes the animals that live in the dark depths of the ocean and depend on the organic debris drifting down from the upper layers. Although no sunlight reaches these depths and hence no photosynthesis goes on, the region is not entirely without light. A large variety of its inhabitants employ bioluminescence (see Section 29-14) in the luring of prey and location of mates.

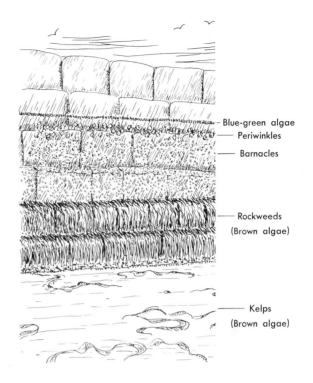

Blue-green algae
Periwinkles
Barnacles

Rockweeds
(Brown algae)

Kelps
(Brown algae)

Low tide reveals the characteristic zonation of sessile algae on a breakwater. Each zone also has its characteristic animals. Only organisms adapted to withstand violent wave action and periodic exposure to the air can survive here. Despite the harsh conditions, such a habitat is teeming with life.

Fig. 35-13

THE INORGANIC NUTRIENTS   35-6

All life depends on carbon, nitrogen, oxygen, hydrogen, and phosphorus atoms as well as small quantities of a variety of other mineral elements (see Section 9-2, 3). Animals satisfy these needs by feeding on organic matter initially produced by plants and absorbing oxygen (and, in many cases, water) from the environment. Plants and photosynthetic protists satisfy their needs, and indirectly those of heterotrophs, by extracting inorganic nutrients from both their medium and their substratum and incorporating them into a variety of organic molecules by using the energy of sunlight.

A review of Fig. 6-1 reminds us that many of the elements needed for life are in relatively short supply on the earth. Life has existed here for over 3 billion years. If during this span of time the inorganic nutrients had simply been extracted from the physical environment, the supply of many would have long since been exhausted. This has not occurred because living things, as they metabolize and as they decay after death, release these essential elements back into the environment. Thus life goes on, using and re-using inorganic nutrients as part of several never-ending cycles of materials.

The Carbon Cycle.   The source of carbon atoms for life is the CO_2 of the atmosphere (0.03%) and the variable concentration of CO_2 and HCO_3^- ions in water. These carbon atoms are reduced to organic compounds through the process of photosynthesis and (to a minor extent) chemosynthesis. The organic compounds in plant and protist bodies then supply the needs of all heterotrophic organisms. Cellular respiration returns CO_2 to the air and water. The carbon tied up in plant and animal wastes as well as in their dead bodies is released to the environment by the action of decay bacteria or, in some cases, by burning. Coal and oil are remains of once-living organisms which have escaped decay and, until burned, these fuels represent carbon taken out of the cycle.

With the atmosphere containing only 0.03% carbon dioxide, you might worry that the balance between its use and its return would be a precarious one. Fortunately, the oceans of the earth provide a huge reservoir of CO_2 in the form of limestone deposits (e.g. coral). Any shortage or excess in the atmosphere is probably quickly adjusted by the breakdown or build-up of these deposits as the reversible reactions involved are shifted first one way and then the other. The various interactions in the carbon cycle are summarized in Fig. 35-14.

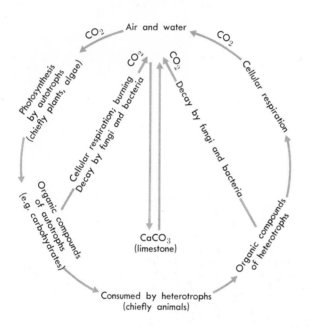

Fig. 35-14

The carbon cycle. The heterotrophic microorganisms of decay produce CO_2 by the respiration of organic molecules secured from the bodies of plants and the bodies and excreta of animals.

The Oxygen Cycle.   Although oxygen represents one-fifth of our air supply, respiring animals and plants would probably exhaust the supply in about 2000 years if it were not returned as a by-product of photosynthesis (Fig. 35-15). Oxygen in the air dissolves in the waters of the earth and supplements that produced by aquatic autotrophs. In respiration, oxygen is combined with hydrogen to form water. In photosynthesis, water is decomposed, releasing oxygen for re-use.

The Nitrogen Cycle.   An essential component of life is protein, and protein contains nitrogen. The enormous demand for nitrogen by living things poses quite a problem. It is not that there is not enough nitrogen available. The atmosphere is 79% nitrogen. The problem is to "fix" this relatively inert element into compounds which can be used in protein synthesis. Very few organisms are capable of turning this trick. Certain bacteria, when growing in nodules on the roots of legumes (e.g. peas and beans) and a few other angiosperms, can incorporate free, atmospheric nitrogen into organic molecules for their own use and for the use of the host plant. For this reason, they are known as **nitrogen-fixing** bacteria. Other bacteria which live free in the soil, as well as certain blue-green algae, are also capable of fixing atmospheric nitrogen into compound form. These latter organisms play a more important role in the tropics than in temperate regions. Nitrogen fixation by living organisms is supplemented by lightning, which, as it passes through the air, produces oxides of nitrogen. These are washed into the soil and form nitrates, which can then be absorbed by nonleguminous plants and incorporated into plant proteins. Animal protein is manufactured from the amino acids first synthesized by plants. The excretions of animals and the dead bodies of both plants and animals contain organic nitrogen compounds which are ultimately decomposed into ammonia (NH_3) by the action of **decay** bacteria. This ammonia can then be oxidized into nitrites (NO_2^-) and nitrates (NO_3^-) by the action of the chemoautotrophic **nitrifying** bacteria (see Section 12-8). Production of nitrates by these organisms thus replenishes the pool from which most nonleguminous plants must draw. Another group of bacteria, the **denitrifying** bacteria, undoes the hard metabolic work of the nitrogen-fixers. These microorganisms reduce nitrates and nitrites to free nitrogen, which then returns to the atmosphere. The complex and exceedingly important interactions of the nitrogen cycle are summarized in Fig. 35-16.

Other Inorganic Nutrients. Potassium, calcium, sodium (animals only), phosphate and, to a lesser extent, a variety of other ions (Fig. 9-1) are also necessary to life. Plants absorb these from soil water through their roots. Animals ingest inorganic ions in their food and water or, in the case of aquatic species, absorb them through their gills. In the case of phosphorus and sulfur, animals supply their needs by ingesting phospholipids, nucleic acids, and proteins in their diet. All of these elements are returned to the soil and water by the action of decay bacteria on animal wastes and plant and animal bodies.

Over large areas and long spans of time, the natural recycling of inorganic nutrients provides adequately for the welfare of succeeding generations of living organisms. Under some conditions, however, local shortages may occur. This is particularly apt to happen when man practices intensive agriculture. Minerals are removed from the soil with the crops, but little or no decaying matter is returned to the soil to replenish the supply. Under these conditions, it is necessary to add

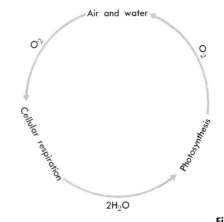

Fig. 35-15

The oxygen cycle.

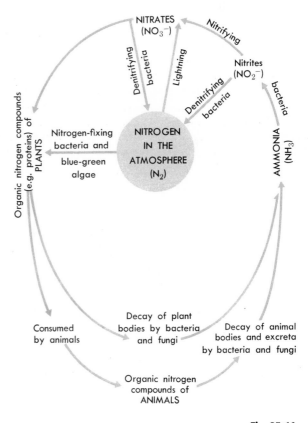

Fig. 35-16

The nitrogen cycle.

fertilizers to the soil in order to maintain productivity. Nitrates and phosphates are especially apt to be depleted quickly, and the loss can be offset by the addition of such materials as "nitrate of soda" ($NaNO_3$) and "superphosphate," largely $Ca(H_2PO_4)_2$. These minerals and others like them are mined or manufactured synthetically for this purpose. Some fertilizer is made from slaughterhouse waste, and in using this, man is simply hastening and making more uniform a natural step in the recycling of minerals. Fertilizers that contain a source of nitrogen, phosphorus, and potassium are called "complete." The concentration of each nutrient is indicated by a number on the package. The first gives the percent by weight of nitrogen which is, of course, in some compound form. The actual compounds incorporating phosphorus and potassium atoms vary from one sample to the next, but by convention the concentration of these elements is expressed as if they were present as oxides, P_2O_5 and K_2O, respectively.

Thus, 5-10-10 fertilizer, for example, contains 5% nitrogen (in compound form) and a weight of phosphorus and potassium atoms equivalent to 10% P_2O_5 and 10% K_2O. Limestone ($CaCO_3$) is frequently added to the soil, especially in the eastern part of our country, to counteract the natural tendency of the soil to become more acid. Fertilizers containing magnesium, manganese, copper, boron, zinc, and sulfate ions are also used in special circumstances.

In this chapter we have examined the ways in which the lives of plants and animals are affected by the conditions in their physical environment. It should also have become clear that living things by their own activities can profoundly modify certain aspects of the physical environment. This is particularly true of soil formation and the cycling of nutrients. We cannot, then, really consider the physical environment of an organism independently of its biotic environment, that is, all the other organisms whose activity affects its life. Certain important aspects of the biotic environment will be considered in the next chapter.

EXERCISES AND PROBLEMS

1 List the six major terrestrial biomes.

2 List four different kinds of bacteria that participate in the nitrogen cycle, and tell specifically what each does.

3 How does each of the following adapt to its hypotonic environment: (a) an amoeba, (b) *Anacharis*, (c) a trout?

4 In what ways is a cactus well adapted to life in the desert?

5 What is the percentage of nitrogen by weight in a sample of 8-6-4 fertilizer?

6 Why do plants need nitrates and phosphates?

7 In northern climates how does each of the following manage to survive the winter: (a) frog, (b) maple tree, (c) hummingbird, (d) an annual grass such as "crabgrass," (e) a tulip, (f) a cinnamon fern, (g) a bear, (h) a carrot plant, (i) a snake, (j) a pickerel, (k) a potato plant, (l) honeybees, (m) most other insects?

8 Describe the movement of soil minerals in (a) the tropical rain forest, (b) the temperate deciduous forest, (c) grassland, (d) deserts.

9 The layer of topsoil tends to be much thicker in grasslands than in the taiga. Can you think of a reason why this is so?

10 As sunlight passes through the water, first the red, orange, and yellow rays are absorbed, then the green, and last the blue. Does this *help* explain the vertical distribution of the various phyla of marine algae? How?

REFERENCES

1 Clarke, G. L., *Elements of Ecology,* John Wiley & Sons, Inc., New York, 1954. The first half of this textbook describes the various aspects of the physical environment.

2 Revelle, R., "Water," *Scientific American,* September, 1963.

3 Went, F. W., "The Ecology of Desert Plants," *Scientific American,* Reprint No. 114, April, 1955.

4 Kellogg, C. E., "Soil," *Scientific American,* Reprint No. 821, July, 1950.

5 Ellison, W. D., "Erosion by Raindrop," *Scientific American,* Reprint No. 817, November, 1948. Describes one of the major problems in conserving soil.

6 Plass, G. N., "Carbon Dioxide and Climate," *Scientific American,* Reprint No. 823, July, 1959. Examines the hypothesis (and its implications) that the carbon dioxide concentration of the atmosphere regulates the average temperature of the earth.

7 Llano, G. A., "The Terrestrial Life of the Antarctic," *Scientific American,* Reprint No. 865, September, 1962. The severity of the physical environment of the Antarctic is reflected in the small number of species found there.

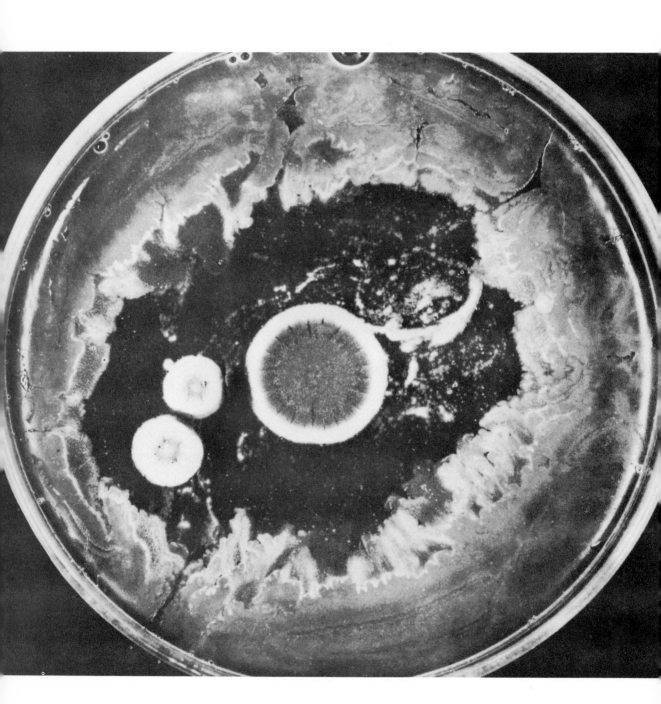

The life of every organism is affected by the lives of other organisms. Just as each organism must cope with the conditions in its physical environment, so it must cope with the problems and opportunities presented by other organisms, in other words, the conditions in its biotic environment. The influence of some parts of the biotic environment is quite direct. Without suitable plant species on which to feed, the cow dies. Without the flagellate *Trichonympha* within its digestive tract, the termite cannot secure nourishment from the cellulose it consumes (Section 7-1, 3).

Other influences of the biotic environment are less direct. An English naturalist of Darwin's time dramatized this point by saying that England's greatness was dependent upon her old maids. His reasoning went like this. England's power was dependent upon her navy, which in turn depended upon the physical well-being of her sailors. Good English roast beef took care of that and was supplied abundantly by cattle feeding on lush fields of clover (a legume and hence rich in protein). Reproduction of clover follows pollination by bumblebees. Bumblebee nests are preyed upon by field mice. Field mice are kept in check by cats and, of course, old maids keep cats! While this argument is somewhat fanciful, it does illustrate the point that any change in the biotic environment has not only direct effects (more cats = fewer field mice) but also indirect effects, which spread throughout the community of living organisms.

FEEDING RELATIONSHIPS WITHIN A COMMUNITY

FOOD CHAINS   36-1

Most of the interactions between species involve food. Competing for food, eating, and avoiding being eaten are the most common ways in which animals affect one another. In the case of green plants, the problem is chiefly one of securing adequate amounts of sun, water, and soil minerals. Many angiosperms are also directly dependent upon the activity of one or a few species of pollinating animals.

Let us consider one example of feeding relationships in a community of organisms. A hawk may dine on a snake which has eaten frogs. The frogs may have eaten grasshoppers and they, in turn, consumed grass. Perhaps no other animal will prey upon the hawk, but parasites may invade its tissues and get nourishment from it. Whatever the cause of death, scavenging organisms such as the bacteria of decay will finally decompose the remains of the hawk.

Such a pathway of food consumption is called a **food chain.** This one is more complicated than some, less complicated than others. It does, however, illustrate the basic ingredients of all food chains.

◀ The growth of bacteria on the agar in this culture dish has been inhibited near the three circular colonies of the fungus *Penicillium notatum.* The antibiotic penicillin, diffusing outward from the colonies, is responsible for this effect. (Courtesy Merck & Co., Inc.)

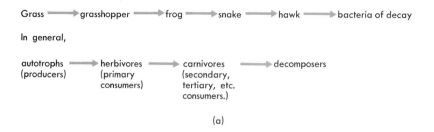

(a)

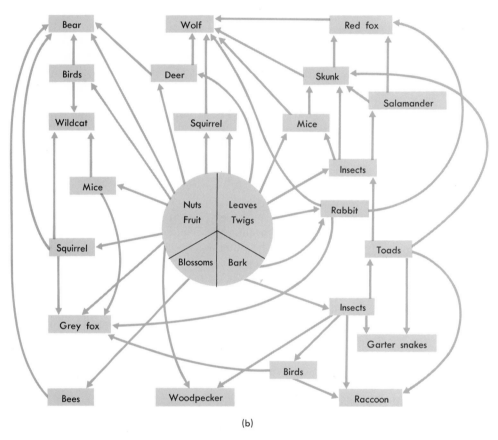

(b)

Fig. 36-1   (a) Food chains. (b) A food web in a temperate deciduous forest. (Courtesy Dr. V. E. Shelford.)

All food chains must start with an autotrophic organism, a green plant or protist. These are called **producers** because only they can manufacture food from inorganic raw materials. Any organism, such as a grasshopper, which feeds directly upon a plant is an herbivore or **primary consumer.** Carnivores like the frog that feed upon herbivores are **secondary consumers.** Carnivores like the snake that eat secondary consumers are **tertiary consumers,** and so on. Death at each stage in the food chain provides nourishment for **decomposers,** and they release materials for re-use by the producers.

Our example of a food chain represents simply an isolated strand in the network of feeding relationships that exist in this particular community. Other organisms feed upon grass, grasshoppers, frogs, and snakes. Each of these is a link in other food chains. Furthermore, the various food chains are interconnected. The hawk may eat a field mouse that has eaten beetles whose larvae consumed grass. A careful study of all the feeding relationships in a community thus presents us with **food webs** of some complexity (Fig. 36-1). No matter how complex, though, the path of food is always from autotroph to herbivore and then to carnivore and ultimately to decomposers such as the bacteria of decay.

THE ENVIRONMENTAL NICHE 36-2

Some animals consume a variety of foods in their diet. Our hawk may dine on mice, other birds, etc., in addition to snakes. Other animals are more selective in their food. The cotton boll weevil feeds exclusively on cotton plants. The term **niche** is often used to describe the particular role that an organism plays in the community, especially its role as a consumer of food. The niche of the hawk is a fairly broad one. It alters its diet in accordance with the relative abundance of the large variety of animals that can serve as prey. The niche of the cotton boll weevil is a narrow one. Where there is no cotton, there are no boll weevils. The occurrence of similar niches in different parts of the world helps explain the phenomenon of convergent evolution. The flying phalanger and wombat occupy in Australia the niches which are filled in this country by the flying squirrel and woodchuck (Fig. 32-7). While the niches of many animal species in a community overlap, it may well be that no two species ever occupy *exactly* the same niche in the same location. If they did, we would expect that one species would be more efficient than the other at exploiting the niche and would eventually replace the less well-adapted species completely. This principle of **competitive exclusion** may not always hold. For example, two species of insects might occupy the same niche but other factors (weather, parasitism, predation) could be so severe that neither population could become large enough to diminish the food supply seriously. Generally, however, a close study of the feeding habits of two species which seem to occupy the same niche reveals some differences. While three of Darwin's finches, *Geospiza magnirostris, G. fortis,* and *G. fuliginosa* (see Fig. 32-4), eat a certain amount of the same food, each includes in its diet seeds of sizes not usually consumed by the others.

We can thus conclude that the number of niches occupied by heterotrophs in any region is approximately equal to the number of species there. Despite the diversity of niches, they each fall within one of three general categories: **predation, scavenging,** and **symbiosis.**

PREDATION 36-3

The majority of heterotrophic species (both animals and protists) secure their food by preying on other organisms. Although exceptions exist, most predators are larger than the prey they consume. Their relationship with their prey is usually a temporary one, just long enough to consume it or at least part of it. Animals which prey upon other animals almost always kill their prey. On the other hand, herbivorous predators (e.g. deer, rabbits, insects) usually just browse on a portion of the prey's body. The regenerative ability of most green plants then ensures that additional food will be available at a later time.

When we consider the central role food plays in the lives of all animals, we should not be surprised at the many adaptations which increase the effectiveness of predation. Think of the eyes of the eagle, the sharp ears of the owl, the keen sense of smell of the wolf, the echo-location of the bat, and the value of wings and legs to predators. Strong jaws, cutting teeth, sharp claws, hooked beaks, the long tongue of the frog, the fangs of the rattlesnake, and the mandibles of insects are other examples of structural modifications which assist predation.

Fig. 36-2

Ptarmigan in summer plumage, incubating her eggs. In the winter these birds are white. (Courtesy American Museum of Natural History.)

On the opposite side of the coin, these devices are useful also to avoid being eaten. Eyes, ears, and a keen sense of smell are just as effective at discovering predators as prey. The ability to run, fly, or swim away from a predator when it is detected is naturally of great survival value. It is not the only solution to the problem, though. Camouflage is another way of minimizing attack by predators (Fig. 36-2). The inky smokescreen expelled by the startled squid hides its escape route. It has been shown that the robber fly is not so apt to be eaten by an animal previously exposed to the well-armed bumblebee (see Fig. 31-10). Weapons such as teeth and jaws, a sting, poison fangs, and the pincer legs of the crayfish can be used defensively as well as offensively. The quills of the porcupine, and the scent glands of the skunk are other familiar examples. Millipedes secrete poisonous hydrocyanic acid when disturbed. Many insects have special glands and aiming devices which enable them to squirt potential predators with such noxious substances as 85% acetic acid and 40% formic acid. Some animals are often able to escape from predators by sacrificing a portion of their body. Grasp a "glass snake" (really a legless lizard) by the tail, and in an instant you will be holding the tail only while the former owner goes off to regenerate a new one. Many a sea cucumber has escaped consumption by expelling its sticky, offensive-smelling viscera when molested.

Cooperation between members of the same species often reduces the severity of predation. A mother bobwhite fluttering away from her nest while feigning a broken wing, distracts the attention of a predator from her young. Grazing ungulates are usually organized so that the strong are on the outside of the herd, the weak within. The presence of many sets of eyes and ears in the herd makes the predator more easily detected and his approach more difficult. Smelt, a kind of fish, have been shown to release a pheromone into the water when alarmed. This serves to warn the other members of the school. When a honeybee stings an enemy, she releases a chemical, called isoamyl acetate, which excites other bees to join the attack.

The only plants that are predacious are the insectivorous plants. They have interesting modifications for trapping and digesting insects. Specialized leaves of the Venus's flytrap (see Fig. 4-12) close quickly (because of a sudden loss of turgor) when an insect alights on their inner surfaces. The animal is then digested by enzymes.

Is there any explanation for this curious reversal of behavior in which a plant eats an animal? All the insectivorous plants contain chlorophyll and thus, like other green plants, they are able to manufacture their carbohydrates by photosynthesis. To manufacture proteins, however, green plants require nitrates. The activity of the nitrifying bacteria provides one major source of these. As you learned in Section 35-6, these bacteria convert the ammonia produced when dead organisms decay into nitrates, which can then be absorbed by green plants for protein synthesis. But nitrifying bacteria cannot operate successfully in an environment that is very acid. Bog soils, with a pH of four or even less, are quite acid and it is in just such soil that the insectivorous plants are found. Insect eating is probably an adaptation to secure nitrogen compounds when the normal source is limited.

More common among plants are devices to avoid predation. Toxic chemicals (including hydrocyanic acid) and thorns or spines are defensive mechanisms frequently found. The ability of grasses to repeatedly send up new leaves from underground enables them to withstand a degree of browsing which would be fatal to most dicots.

Here, then, are just a few examples of the adaptations by means of which organisms prey and avoid being preyed upon. You can surely add many more to the list.

SCAVENGING 36-4

Many organisms "prey" upon the dead bodies of plants and animals. We call them scavengers. Among the larger animals, jackals and vultures secure their nourishment in this way. But the most important early scavengers by far are the insects. Literally hundreds of different species of insects and their larvae may participate in consuming and burrowing through the flesh of a corpse. Although we may think such a way of life rather unpleasant, scavengers play an important role in the economy of nature. It is more than a matter of the aesthetic value of not being surrounded by corpses. As our study of the materials cycles should have made clear, we depend upon scavengers to release for re-use the nutrients locked up in dead bodies.

The final scavengers are the decomposers, the fungi and bacteria of decay. These saprophytes (see Section 10-3) not only supply their own needs by digesting plant and animal bodies (and animal wastes) but ultimately provide a fresh supply of inorganic nutrients in the soil or water for use by the autotrophs. Their action thus terminates one food chain and sets the stage for the start of another.

SYMBIOSIS

Symbiosis means "living together." It refers to the situation in which the niche of one species happens to be more-or-less closely associated with the body of another organism. The organism whose niche it is always benefits from the relationship. The organism who supplies the niche may be relatively unaffected by the relationship (commensalism), may be injured by it (parasitism), or may also benefit from it (mutualism).

Commensalism

Commensalism means "at table together." It is used to describe the symbiotic relationship in which one organism consumes the unused food of another. The relationship between the remora and the shark is a classic example. The dorsal fin of the remora is modified into a sucker by means of which the remora can form a temporary attachment to the shark (see Fig. 5-18). The shark does not seem to be inconvenienced by this and makes no attempt to prey upon the remora. When the shark does feed, however, the remora is in a position to pick up scraps the shark fails to consume. There are certain species of barnacles that are found only as commensals on the jaws of whales. There are even species of barnacles found only as commensals on the barnacles that grow on whales!

Many of the bacteria living in our large intestine should be classed as commensals. They feed on undigested food materials and generally do not harm us. In fact, there is considerable evidence that some, at least, produce B-complex vitamins, which we then absorb. Thus they are of positive value to us in supplementing the vitamins in our diet. A relationship such as this, which is mutually beneficial, is referred to as mutualistic.

Mutualism

Mutualism is an interspecific relationship in which both partners benefit. You have already studied several examples. Nitrogen-fixing bacteria in the soil invade the roots of legumes. Once inside, they receive nourishment from the host plant. In return, they "fix" atmospheric nitrogen into organic nitrogen compounds which the legume can then use to synthesize proteins. Although each organism is able to survive independently (soil nitrates must then be available to the legume), growth together is clearly beneficial to them both.

Lichens are an example of mutualism between a fungus and an alga. Although the alga may be able to survive alone in nature, the fungal partner is never found to do so. The heterotrophic fungus receives carbohydrates from the alga, while the alga is protected from dehydration by the tough, gelatinous walls of the fungus. Acids secreted by the fungus may also aid the algal partner by liberating minerals from the substrate (e.g. rock).

Algae are often found living within the bodies of protists (e.g. the ciliate *Stentor*), aquatic animals (such as the green hydra *Chlorohydra*), and some marine, syncytial flatworms. Their presence provides an internal supply of food and oxygen. The former may be sufficient to enable the animal host to go without eating for long periods. The alga benefits by the availability of CO_2, the protected location, and the fact that it can be transported to a spot where ample light is present. The vitamin-producing bacteria in our large intestine, the cellulose-digesting bacteria in the cow's rumen, and *Trichonympha* in the termite's gut all provide valuable nutrients to their host in return for a protected, moist, food-filled environment.

Mutualistic relationships often involve intricate adaptations of structure, function, and even behavior on the part of the two species. Some species of ants secure their food by growing gardens of a particular fungus in their underground nests. The fungus is nourished by leaves the ants collect, bring underground, and chew into a nutritious pulp. The fact that the fungus is never found except in ant gardens indicates a close physiological adaptation to the conditions of its culture. The behavior of the ants is certainly adapted to the needs of the mutualistic relationship. Even a

Cleaning symbiosis. The Nile crocodile opens its mouth and permits the Egyptian plover to feed on any leeches attached to its gums. Cleaning symbiosis is more common in fishes.

Fig. 36-3

special structural adaptation exists: a pouch in the head of the queen into which she stuffs some of the fungus mycelium before going off to start a new colony! Figure 36-3 illustrates still another kind of mutualistic relationship that involves elaborate behavioral adaptations.

Parasitism 36-7

A parasite is an organism that lives on or in the body of another organism (the host) from whose tissues it derives its nourishment and to whom it does some degree of damage. The distinction between parasites and predators is not always clear. The tick or leech attaches itself to the body of its host for a short period while it sucks blood. In a sense, this is simply a form of predation in which the smaller and weaker organism is browsing on the larger and stronger one. In the case of blood-sucking hookworms, the relationship is of long duration and clearly one of parasitism.

The distinction between commensalism and parasitism may sometimes be indistinct also. The protozoan *Endamoeba histolytica* often lives harmlessly in the human intestine but can cause fatal illness if it invades the tissues of its host.

Although there are obvious exceptions, a parasite usually does not kill its host. To do so is to deprive itself of a meal-ticket. Instead, the well-adapted parasite consumes just enough host tissue to supply its own needs without destroying the host. It has been said that a parasite lives on the host's income while a predator lives off the host's capital.

Almost all parasites are relatively small invertebrates or protists. Mites (arachnids), fleas and lice (insects), hookworms (nematodes), flukes and tapeworms (flatworms) are representative parasites from each of three animal phyla. Each of the four groups of protozoans contains parasitic forms; in fact, the sporozoans are exclusively parasitic. The role these latter organisms play in disease as well as that played by the bacteria and fungi was unknown until the 19th century. Louis Pasteur is justly honored as the man who first showed that many diseases of man and other animals are caused by invading bacteria. The last major category of infectious agents to be discovered were the viruses. The first of these, the tobacco mosaic virus (TMV) was discovered in 1892 by the Russian scientist Iwanowsky.

There is probably not an organism on this earth that is not parasitized at some time during its life. Animals are attacked by representatives of every category of parasite. Plants are parasitized by nematodes, fungi, bacteria, viruses, and a few other plants. Even the protists have parasites. For example, bacteria are attacked by viruses (bacteriophages).

Almost all locations on the host's body may become occupied by parasites. Viruses, rickettsias, mycoplasmas, a few bacteria, and the malarial parasites invade and multiply right within the very cells of the host. Most parasitic bacteria and protozoans, as well as many roundworms and flukes, invade the tissues of their host. In the case of animal hosts, one finds tapeworms, roundworms, protozoans, and bacteria within the alimentary canal. Most arthropod parasites (e.g. the louse) are ectoparasites, that is, they live on the surface of the body.

One problem faced by all parasites is how to invade the host. For animals (including man), four routes are used. Many parasites (e.g. tapeworm cysts, typhoid bacilli) are ingested in food or water. Many bacteria and viruses gain entrance to the body by being inhaled. These may cause respiratory tract diseases (e.g. "colds"). During coughing or sneezing, parasite-laden droplets are discharged into the air and can readily be inhaled by others (Fig. 36-4). Copulation enables the micro-organisms causing venereal disease to gain entrance into the body of a new host. This occurs in other animals as well as man. Finally, arthropod bites often act as hypodermic needles, introducing protozoans, bacteria, rickettsias, and viruses into the body of the host. Plants are often inoculated with disease-causing viruses as a result of the bites of aphids and other sucking insects.

Fig. 36-4

A violent, unstifled sneeze. High-speed flash illumination reveals the cloud of droplets produced. These are a major factor in the spread of bacteria and viruses that enter the body by way of the respiratory tract. (Courtesy Dr. Marshall W. Jennison, *Scientific Monthly*, Vol. 52, pp. 24-33, Jan., 1941.)

Once the parasite has gained entrance into the body of the host, there are three possible outcomes. The host may be killed by the parasite, it may tolerate it for an indefinite period of time, or it may destroy the parasite completely. Which of these three possible outcomes actually happens is dependent upon four factors: (1) the number of invading parasites, (2) their nature, (3) the defenses of the host and, where man is involved, (4) the nature of any treatment given.

Ingestion of undercooked pork containing a few *Trichinella* cysts (see Fig. 5-6) usually causes such a mild case of trichinosis that it is not even diagnosed as such. Eating heavily-infected meat frequently results in death. Often the body copes successfully with small numbers of invading parasites but succumbs to heavier infestations. Of course the absolute number of parasites which will overwhelm the host varies with the severity of the damage caused by the particular parasite.

Parasites vary in the severity of the damage they do to the host. Man may harbor a tapeworm for years with little harm done. However, 80% of the infections by a certain strain of rickettsias causing Rocky Mountain spotted fever end in death if no treatment is given.

Parasites damage their host in two ways. One is by actually consuming its tissues. Hookworms, *Endamoeba histolytica,* and the malarial parasites all cause this sort of damage. Some parasites do not consume enough of the material of their host to be dangerous, but in the process of their metabolism they release toxins which poison the host. The bacteria that cause tetanus ("lockjaw"), diphtheria, and scarlet fever are dangerous for this reason. Tetanus toxin interferes with synaptic transmission in the central nervous system. Diphtheria toxin exerts its poisonous effect on the cytochrome enzyme system. A curious twist to this kind of damage has been discovered in certain fungi which parasitize insects. These fungi produce juvenile hormone (Section 26-2) and, in so doing, upset the normal pattern of metamorphosis. In this case, the damage is not produced by a poisonous toxin but by the secretion of a normal constituent of the host in abnormal amounts at abnormal times.

What happens when a parasite enters its host also depends on the defensive mechanisms that the host puts into operation to combat the invasion. For obvious reasons, we know more about man in this respect, so he will be our example.

MAN'S FIGHT AGAINST DISEASE

DEFENSES OF THE BODY   **36-8**

In Section 10-3 we noted that the cavities of such structures as the alimentary canal and lungs are really just a part of the outside of the body folded in. In order for a parasite to actually invade the interior of the body, it has to penetrate the epithelia that separate the exterior from the interior. The human **skin** provides an effective barrier to the entrance of bacteria. Certain species (e.g. the staphylococci that cause boils and carbuncles) can, however, get through as can some viruses. The ciliated **mucus membranes** lining the lungs and air passages provide some protection from parasites entering by this route, but certain bacteria, viruses, and fungi get through with ease. The mucus membranes of the alimentary canal also provide a barrier, although it, too, is frequently penetrated. Our acid **gastric juice** possesses some bacteriocidal (bacteria-killing) effect and probably helps reduce the number of bacteria that get into the small intestine.

What happens if and when our protective barriers are penetrated by parasites? Let us examine the subsequent lines of defense as they are brought into play when bacteria, carried on a splinter, are introduced beneath the skin.

Mechanical damage by the splinter will kill some skin cells and as these disintegrate, they provide nourishment for the bacteria which were introduced into the wound. These begin to grow and multiply. However, damaged cells also liberate substances which signal the body to begin taking action against the invader. One of these, histamine, causes precapillary sphincters in the area to relax, thus increasing the blood supply. The walls of the capillaries become "leakier." The result of these two actions is an accumulation of lymph in the tissue spaces. This increase is not drained away by the lymph capillaries as they become plugged with a mesh of fibrin. Histamine also stimulates the conversion of serum globulin into polypeptide *kinins* (not to be confused with the cytokinins of plants), which pass into the tissue spaces and accelerate these changes. Some substance, perhaps a kinin, is produced which attracts **phagocytes** from the blood stream. These, mostly neutrophils (see Section 14-12, 2), migrate through the capillary walls into the tissue spaces and begin ingesting the bacteria and damaged cells. After consuming a number of bacteria, they die, and their disintegrated bodies are one component of pus. Other phagocytes establish a living barrier between the region of tissue destruction and intact healthy tissue. In this way, they isolate the site of infection.

All of these localized responses constitute **acute inflammation.** The external symptoms are redness (caused by the increased blood supply), tenderness (caused by the kinins), and if the wound is open, the oozing of pus. If all goes well, the process of acute inflammation will prevent the infection from spreading, and after all the bacteria have been destroyed, healing can begin.

It should be noted, though, that an inflamed tissue cannot properly carry out its normal functions. If the inflammation becomes widespread, it may become more dangerous than the parasite itself.

Furthermore, even localized inflammation sometimes fails to contain the invading parasites. They may escape into the lymph and/or blood capillaries. A second line of defense comes into play at this time. The sinuses of the **lymph nodes** are lined with "fixed" phagocytes, which engulf bacteria passing through and thus prevent them from reaching the bloodstream. If the invasion is especially heavy, the lymph nodes may themselves become infected and swollen. Hidden infections are sometimes first detected by the appearance of these "swollen glands" in such areas as the neck, armpits, and groin.

Bacteria that reach the bloodstream are engulfed by fixed phagocytes which line the sinuses of the **spleen.** The blood sinuses in the **liver** are similarly equipped to screen out the steady stream of bacteria which penetrate the lining of the intestine and reach the liver by way of the hepatic portal veins. In this way, these organisms are kept from entering the general circulation.

One of the most characteristic responses of the body to infection of any sort is fever. Unknown substances, released by damaged cells, shift the body's "thermostat" in the hypothalamus to a higher setting. What role this plays in the body's fight against disease is still a hotly-debated question. Perhaps it is of no help. There is evidence that fever actually makes the body more susceptible to certain infections. Certainly, too high a fever for too long a period can have disastrous consequences. However, fever may be a weapon against parasites in some cases. All of the body's reactions proceed more quickly as the temperature increases, and this probably includes its defensive ones as well (e.g. the production of kinins). The spirochete that causes syphilis is especially sensitive to fever. At one time, victims of the disease were deliberately infected with malaria so that the resulting high fever would eliminate the spirochete. Electrical heating of the body with diathermy apparatus was also used successfully until the availability of the antibiotic penicillin made such drastic measures no longer necessary.

For many infections, the thing that finally tips the balance in favor of the host is the production of **antibodies.** These are proteins produced in the body which inactivate antigens. Antigens are large molecules (frequently proteins) which are foreign to the body, that is, they have been introduced into it from outside. Invading parasites of all kinds are antigenic. Their body surfaces are covered with foreign protein and their toxins, if any, are proteins.

Antibodies are quite specific in their action. Each strain of polio virus and each strain of pneumococcus (see Section 20-1) causes the body to produce antibodies effective against it but not against other strains. The evidence indicates that antibodies inactivate antigens by combining physically with them. Presumably, each antigen has a particular surface, and the antibody produced in response to that antigen has a complementary surface which just fits it. Once the two molecules combine, the antigen is inactivated. Just how this occurs varies from case to case. **Antitoxins,** the antibodies produced in response to toxins, render the toxin harmless. **Opsonins** are antibodies which alter the surface of the antigenic bacteria so that they can be more easily engulfed by phagocytes. Pneumococci are extremely resistant to phagocytosis unless conditioned by opsonins. In the days before the development of an effective treatment for pneumonia, the body's production of opsonins marked the turning point in the progress of the disease.

Antibodies are serum globulins. Where and how they are manufactured has been the subject of an enormous amount of research, but the question is not yet completely answered. Antigen-ingestion by fixed phagocytes in the spleen, or in lymph nodes draining the site of a localized infection, appears to be the first step in the process. Then lymphocytes, also present within the lymph nodes and spleen, become activated, probably by a "message" transferred to them from the phagocytes. Several experiments suggest that this message consists of RNA, perhaps complexed with the antigen itself. For example, when RNA is extracted from phagocytes exposed to a particular antigen, it can induce production of the appropriate antibody in "naive" lymph-node cells grown in tissue culture.

Having been activated by the message, the lymphocytes begin dividing rapidly. At this time their cytoplasm is rich in messenger RNA and polysomes, but there is very little endoplasmic reticulum present. These lymphocytes leave the lymph nodes and spleen and enter the general circulation. The blood carries them to the tissue spaces and lymph nodes throughout the entire body. Here they may develop into **plasma cells.** An elaborate endoplasmic reticulum forms, and the antibody is manufactured by it. There is also some evidence that the lymphocytes may instead pass their message (as messenger RNA?) to plasma cells already present in the lymph nodes. In either case, it is the plasma cells that have the cellular machinery for making proteins, and they have actually been shown to synthesize antibodies. Plasma cells are abundant in lymph nodes, in the lining of the intestine, and in fact, anywhere that antigens may be introduced into the body.

Not only does the production of antibodies often turn the tide of disease in favor of the host, but after recovery antibodies provide the host with an **immunity** against the particular parasite that has just been eliminated. In some cases, such as polio, the antibodies may protect the host from reinfection for his entire lifetime. In other cases, such as influenza, the immunity is effective for only a year or two. The actual concentration of a particular antibody in the blood drops as time goes on. However, re-entry of the original antigen provokes a dramatic, fast rise in concentration. There is not the delay of several days which occurred when the antigen was introduced into the body the first time. It is as though the antibody-producing cells "remembered" the antigen from previous exposure and were all prepared to begin manufacturing antibody immediately. We do not yet understand how this is accomplished. However, the long life span of some lymphocytes (up to five years) suggests that they may serve as "memory" cells. Furthermore, there is evidence that messenger RNA can pass from lymphocyte to lymphocyte, thus transferring the instructions for the production of a specific antibody.

The newborn child is very poor at manufacturing antibodies. For several months after birth it depends on those received earlier across the placenta from the mother's bloodstream. It is now thought that during this period, the thymus gland (see Fig. 26-4) is producing cells which, after transferal to the lymph nodes and spleen, establish the antibody-manufacturing machinery.

Antibodies are also manufactured by the body in response to such noninfective protein materials as snake venom and grafted skin. This tells us that the ability to produce antibodies is more than just a defense against parasitism. It is the body's mechanism for destroying anything foreign to it. So long as the antibody mechanism is intact, skin grafts can "take" only when the donated skin is either from some other place on the patient's body or from an identical twin. As we have just noted, this ability to distinguish "nonself" from "self" only develops sometime after birth. Foreign proteins injected into a mammal before that period will be considered "self" from that time on. Even after the body's immune mechanism is finally established, reintroduction of that particular protein will call forth no antibody production.

The fact that exposure to a parasite provides some immunity against later infection has led medical scientists to attempt to provide immunity against dangerous diseases without causing the disease itself. This can be accomplished in some cases by the use of **vaccines.** These are preparations of antigen which has been altered chemically so as not to cause the disease. However, the alteration is not so drastic that antibodies produced in response to the altered antigen will not protect against the unaltered, disease-producing antigen. By treating bacteria and viruses with formaldehyde, they can be altered sufficiently to produce safe vaccines. The Salk polio vaccine is prepared in this manner.

The first scientific vaccination was performed by the English physician, Edward Jenner, in 1796. He made medical history by inoculating a human subject with material squeezed from the sores of a girl afflicted with cowpox and then, a few months later, with material from the sores of people afflicted with the dread disease smallpox. His subject remained perfectly well. Jenner performed this daring experiment because he (and others) had long noted that milkmaids who had contracted cowpox from their charges were protected from the ravages of smallpox. Today, we realize that they gained this protection by developing antibodies which were effective not only against the cowpox virus but against the closely related smallpox virus as well.

You have surely been given smallpox vaccine, polio vaccine, and perhaps vaccines against tetanus, diphtheria, and whooping cough as well. In the case of tetanus and diphtheria, it is the toxins we must guard against. Their vaccines thus consist of chemically altered toxins, called **toxoids.** Vaccines against typhoid fever, typhus fever, bubonic plague, Asiatic cholera, and yellow fever are all available for people who live or travel in regions where these diseases are present.

It has been known for some time that people sick with one virus possess a temporary immunity against infection by other viruses. This protection occurs because cells attacked by the first virus produce an antivirus agent called **interferon.** Interferon is a protein molecule produced by mammalian cells shortly after infection and, in every case, faster than antibodies can be produced. Unlike antibodies, interferon is not specific; that is, it is a single substance which seems to be effective against all viruses. In some way it alters the ribosomes of the cell so that they do not read the virus messenger RNA properly, and therefore new virus particles cannot be manufactured. If interferon can be made commercially available, it should provide an excellent weapon against virus diseases (which are just the ones against which other drugs are so ineffective).

We have been discussing the ways in which the human body responds to invasion by parasites. Although man has been far more extensively studied in this respect than any other organism, there is mounting evidence that we are not unique in our responses. Interferon is produced by monkey cells. Antibody formation has been detected in many other vertebrates, and there is some evidence that even invertebrates possess a similar defensive mechanism. Phagocytosis is found throughout the animals; in fact, it was first observed in the transparent body of the microscopic water "flea" *Daphnia* (a crustacean). Plants, too, seem to possess mechanisms for defense against parasites, although very little is known as yet about them.

TREATMENT OF DISEASE 36-9

Man differs from the other animals in being able to take supplementary action to assist the natural processes of his body in combating disease. In fact, in the last half century, he has been so successful at this that infectious disease no longer plays a major role in deaths before old age, at least in the more prosperous parts of the world. When considering this miraculous achievement in applied biology, it is somewhat startling to realize with what a small number of weapons man is able to combat parasites directly. These weapons are: (1) a limited number of chemical compounds whose origin, in most cases, has been in the organic chemistry laboratory, (2) the antibiotics, and (3) the antisera. All the rest of the vast number of substances that fill the druggist's shelves make the patient feel better but have no direct action whatsoever on the parasite causing his ailment.

a) **Chemotherapy.** A moment's thought should make it clear why there are so few substances capable of combating man's parasites once they are within his body. Throughout this book, we have stressed the underlying similarity in cell structure and biochemistry of all organisms, including man and his parasites. There are many substances which, when administered to man, would kill his parasites, but unfortunately they would kill him, too. The problem is to find substances that act against the parasite without damaging the host seriously.

Histologists (biologists who study tissues) have known for years that some biological stains are quite selective in their action. They will stain certain types of cells and not others. Following this clue, the German bacteriologist Paul Ehrlich attempted to find a substance which would combine selectively with the spirochete that causes syphilis and, in so doing, kill it without killing the host. After a long patient search, he found, on his 606th attempt, a substance which did just this. Thus was born (in 1910) Salvarsan, the first chemotherapeutic agent synthesized by man.

Another German scientist Gerhard Domagk followed his lead and, in 1932, found that a red dye called prontosil was effective against the streptococci ravaging his daughter's body. Later, a French chemist discovered that all the activity of prontosil resides in just a portion of the molecule. This portion (which is not a dye at all) was **sulfanilamide**, the first of a large family of sulfa drugs, which were developed just in time to play a major role in reducing the number of casualties in World War II.

The action of the sulfa drugs is dependent upon molecular mimicry. All organisms require folic acid (one of our B-vitamins) in order to grow. Most bacteria are

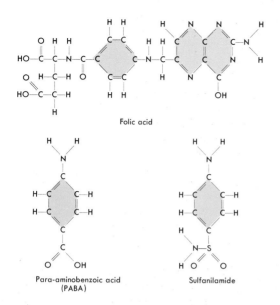

Folic acid

Para-aminobenzoic acid
(PABA)

Sulfanilamide

Fig. 36-5

Molecular mimicry accounts for the effectiveness of sulfa drugs.

able to synthesize it from simpler building blocks, one of which is para-aminobenzoic acid (PABA). A glance at Fig. 36-5 shows the similarity between the PABA and sulfanilamide molecules. When an excess of sulfanilamide is present in the medium, the bacteria use it instead of PABA but, in so doing, fail to produce the folic acid they must have. If we need folic acid, too, why isn't sulfanilamide lethal to us as it is to the bacteria? The answer is that the folic acid molecule is a vitamin for us; that is, we cannot synthesize it. Here, then, is a biochemical difference between host and parasite which can be exploited in killing one without killing the other.

Although the discovery and exploitation of such differences has been slow, some of man's metazoan and protozoan parasites can now be eliminated chemically. Hookworms and tapeworms are anesthetized and then expelled with the aid of a laxative. Atabrine and a few other drugs have proven of great value in curing malarial infections. One by one, effective chemical weapons are being developed against other parasitic protozoans such as trypanosomes (flagellates), ciliates, and amoeboid forms. With rare exceptions, though, virus infections must still be overcome by the body's own defenses. For direct attack against bacterial infections we are generally limited to the sulfas and the antibiotics.

b) **Antibiotics.** There is no fundamental difference between the antibiotics and the chemotherapeutic drugs discussed above. In both cases, specific molecules are involved, and laboratory synthesis of antibiotics is often possible, too. However, each antibiotic was discovered originally as the secretion of a fungus (usually an ascomycete) or a bacterium, which inhibited the growth of other bacteria. The first, and in many ways still the best, antibiotic was penicillin. Its discovery stemmed from the observation of Alexander Fleming that bacterial growth was inhibited in a culture dish which had accidentally become contaminated with a mold of the genus *Penicillium* (see chapter opening illustration). The significance of this discovery was appreciated in time to develop techniques of mass production of penicillin for use in World War II. Since then, laboratories throughout the world have tested hundreds of thousands of specimens of fungi and bacteria for antibiotic activity. When such has been found, the substance has been tested for safety. Very few antibiotics have passed all the hurdles, but chloramphenicol (sold as "chloromycetin"), streptomycin, the tetracyclines ("aureomycin" and "terramycin"), and a few others have now joined penicillin in the fight against bacterial infections.

c) **Antisera.** Antiserum is serum which contains antibodies against one or more specific antigens. If injected into the body of a person recently infected by or exposed to the antigen, it confers an immediate, but temporary, immunity on him. This immunity is described as passive because it is not produced by the patient's own immunological mechanism.

Antiserum is manufactured in live animals. For example, if sublethal quantities of tetanus toxin are injected into a horse or sheep, the animal develops antitoxin.

By bleeding the animal periodically and extracting its serum, the antitoxin can be harvested and used to treat human patients who may have been infected with tetanus bacilli from a splinter or other wound. Unfortunately, there is some danger to the use of antisera prepared in the bodies of other animals, because we can become allergic to other foreign proteins present in the mixture. Therefore, it is far wiser to use tetanus toxoid to develop one's own active immunity, although this must be done before infection actually occurs.

The gamma-globulin fraction of adult human blood is sure to contain many antibodies against common disease organisms. For this reason, it is often separated from donated blood and used as an antiserum. Temporary protection for children or adults exposed to polio or measles is commonly achieved by "shots" of gamma-globulin.

One special example of an antiserum is the "antivenin" used to treat victims of snakebite. Although no infectious organism is involved in this case, the antivenom antibodies (produced in the blood of a horse) provide a weapon which can go to work immediately on the poisonous antigen which has been introduced into the victim's body. The antigenic nature of snake venom varies somewhat from species to species, but serum containing a mixture of antibodies is available and will protect against bites by any of our poisonous snakes.

Man has greatly increased his life expectancy by learning how to aid his own body in ridding itself of parasites. If improperly administered, however, these techniques involve some dangers. For example, prolonged exposure to low doses of an antibiotic will alter the pressure of natural selection and actually select for those spontaneous mutants capable of withstanding the drug. Staphylococci that have developed resistance to penicillin are now a serious problem in many hospitals. It may seem ironical that this threat has arisen right within the hospital, center of man's fight against disease, but it should not surprise any student of the mechanism of evolution.

THE EVOLUTION OF PARASITISM 36-10

Parasitism is a two-way relationship. It is the product of evolutionary adaptations on the part of both host and parasite. The fact that each species of parasite is restricted to one or, at most, a few species of hosts suggests this. The extreme specialization of some parasites to conditions in their host and the host's ability to tolerate their presence is further evidence of a long history of mutual adaptations.

This raises the interesting question of how parasitism becomes established in the first place. The accidental entry of a small organism into a larger one may start the process. If the accidental visitor is able to survive at all in its new location, it will have found a new environmental niche to occupy. Perhaps the relationship will be commensalistic at first and only later will it evolve into parasitism as evolutionary change makes the visitor more efficient at exploiting his host. On the other hand, effective defenses on the part of the host may be able to restrict the potential parasite to a role of commensalism. Our throat, nasal passages, intestine, and other body cavities support a large population of microorganisms living commensalistically. In fact, we know that some of our intestinal bacteria live mutualistically with us (see Section 36-5). The balance is a precarious one, however. Tolerance is achieved only so long as our body defenses remain unimpaired. The rapid invasion of the body by these organisms following destruction of our phagocytes demonstrates this vividly (see Section 14-12, 2). The fact that most deaths from influenza are not caused by the virus itself but by secondary invaders in the weakened body is further evidence.

Prolonged exposure to stress may convert a tolerance of the tuberculosis bacteria walled off in lung nodules into a virulent infection.

The significance of mutual adaptations between host and parasite is often nicely demonstrated when a parasite gains accidental entrance into an abnormal host. Larval tapeworms, hookworms, and flukes, whose normal host is some vertebrate other than man, nonetheless may occasionally invade man. When they do so, they migrate widely through the body, causing extensive damage as they go. It is almost as though they were hunting for normal conditions. The rickettsia that causes Rocky Mountain spotted fever and the virus that causes yellow fever are two examples of parasites which exist in animal "reservoirs" (rodents and monkeys, respectively) and do little damage to these hosts. The outcome of their entry into man is often quite a different story.

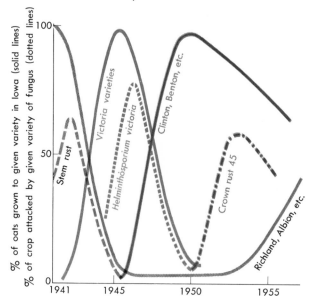

Fig. 36-6

Host-parasite relations between the domestic oat (*Avena sativa*) and some of its parasites.

There is no reason to think that mutual evolutionary change on the part of parasite and host ever ceases. As the host develops increased resistance, his parasites are apt to develop counterweapons. We see this process hastened through man's intervention. The use of antibiotics has been countered by the evolution of antibiotic-resistant bacteria. The development of rust-resistant grains by selective breeding is inevitably followed by the appearance of mutant rust strains capable of parasitizing them. One of the major and never-ending tasks of plant breeders in the U.S. Department of Agriculture is to keep one step ahead of the rusts and ensure that grain farmers will always be able to switch to a still-newer resistant variety as the older varieties begin to succumb. Figure 36-6 traces the changing tides of battle between our domestic oat and the fungi that parasitize it.

Parasites are often referred to as degenerate. In one sense, this is true. During the course of adapting to conditions in their particular niche, parasites have lost structures essential to the welfare of their free-living relatives. Looked at from the parasite's point of view, though, the loss of organs that are no longer appropriate represents a gain in efficiency and, thus, improved specialization. The tapeworm has no eyes, no digestive tract, and only vestiges of nervous, excretory, and muscular systems. But what good would these be anyway in the human intestine? On the other hand, the tapeworm has a scolex, a cuticle resistant to digestive enzymes, a highly efficient reproductive system, and a shape which practically ensures that it will not accidentally obstruct the intestine and endanger its host.

Loss of nonuseful structures and functions is characteristic of all parasites. *Rafflesia* is a parasitic angiosperm found in Malaya, which does not have roots, stems or leaves. It does, however, have tubes which penetrate the tissues of its host and one of the largest flowers (3 to 5 ft in diameter) known. This extreme emphasis on reproduction is also found in *Sacculina,* a crustacean which parasitizes crabs. The adult consists of no more than a sack (hence the name) containing reproductory organs, and not until the larvae were identified could it even be determined that the organism was a crustacean.

Viruses seem to represent an extreme of degeneration. The smaller viruses have none of the enzyme systems necessary for a free life. They consist simply of (1) DNA (sometimes RNA) capable of instructing the host cell how to manufacture more virus and (2) a coat of protein which helps the virus invade its host.

A serious problem facing all parasites is how to get from one host to another. Exit from the host body can be made by way of the lungs (during coughing and sneezing), by way of the anus (in the feces) and, in a few cases (e.g. the spirochete that causes syphilis), directly through the skin and mucus membranes. Bacteria and viruses that cause infection of the air passages and lungs are examples of the first case. They leave by the same route they entered. Intestinal parasites such as bacteria, viruses, and protozoans, leave in the feces or, in the case of tapeworms, hookworms, etc., deposit eggs which are expelled in the feces. Where personal and public sanitary conditions are poor, there is a good possibility that some of these organisms will be ingested by other hosts. Some of the worms which inhabit our alimentary canal produce larval stages which must develop in a second, intermediate, host before they are capable of infecting man again. The **intermediate host** of the pig tapeworm (*Taenia solium*) is the pig. It seems pretty clear that the intermediate host in this case is a device that improves the chances of the parasite's re-entering the **primary host,** man. Man is far more likely to ingest undercooked pork than human feces. This is not true for pigs raised under unsanitary conditions. The largest (33 feet or even more) tapeworm of man, the fish tapeworm, requires three hosts in order to complete its life cycle: a fresh-water crustacean (*Cyclops*), a fish, and man. When you consider that man's feces often reach bodies of water, that fresh-water fish eat *Cyclops* and man may eat improperly cooked fish, it is easy to see how this complicated life cycle actually improves the chances of this parasite's getting from one man to another.

The problem of transport is even more acute for those parasites that live in our blood or other tissues. The malarial parasite, the yellow fever virus, and the round-worm which causes elephantiasis can pass from man to man only with the help of an intermediate host, the mosquito, capable of withdrawing the parasite from the blood of one host and inoculating it into the blood of another. We use the term **vector** for any animal (most of them are insects) that transmits pathogenic micro-organisms in this way.

Even with elaborate life cycles that make reentry into the primary host easier, the chances of any one individual parasite's doing so are extremely small. It is there-fore not surprising that many of our parasites are amazingly fecund, that is, they produce enormous numbers of offspring. The fish tapeworm, mentioned above, dis-charges up to one million fertilized eggs into its host's feces each day. A female hookworm may lay 25 to 35 thousand eggs each day throughout her 5-year life span. Once we understand the problem a parasite faces in getting from host to host, we can appreciate why so many parasites (e.g. the tapeworms, *Sacculina,* and *Rafflesia*) are little more than efficient machines for sexual reproduction.

A knowledge of the life cycle of parasites also enables us to take effective measures to limit their activity and thus to reduce the amount of infectious disease. Any action which interferes with the transmission of a parasite from one host to another accomplishes this. The ultimate solution to the problem of malaria is eliminating the intermediate host, the anopheline mosquito. Eradication of gooseberry and wild currant bushes has saved untold thousands of white pines from fatal infection with white pine blister rust. The dusting of DDT on the clothes and bodies of the inhabitants of war-ravaged Naples, Italy, killed the lice which are vectors of the rickettsias of typhus fever and halted what otherwise would have been a devastating epidemic.

The sanitary disposal of human wastes, sanitary precautions in the raising and processing of food for human consumption, and chlorination of water supplies all interfere with the transmission of parasites and are important steps in the reduction of the amount of human disease. Quarantine is another valuable weapon. Many countries have kept smallpox, plague, and other diseases from becoming established by making sure that all people entering the country are disease-free. Quarantine of imported livestock and plants is also an important weapon in keeping their parasites out of the region.

Tests for persons harboring parasites but not showing symptoms are useful public health measures. The tuberculin test indicates the possibility of an unknown TB infection. Most states require a Wasserman or Kahn test for couples intending to marry. Both these tests indicate whether syphilis is present or not.

A second approach to the reduction of parasitism is to increase the resistance of the host. Proper diet, rest, cleanliness and exercise seem to increase the ease with which infections can be thrown off. The development of an active immunity against parasites apt to be encountered increases the specific resistance of the host. In many cases, this occurs as a result of exposure to the parasite in childhood when the body combats general infections most easily. In other cases (e.g. tetanus, polio, diphtheria, and smallpox), the appropriate vaccines should be taken to provide the necessary immunity. Probably the least desirable approach to the problem is to increase resistance by giving frequent doses of antibacterial drugs like the antibiotics and sulfas. This only increases the chance of developing a drug-resistant strain of the parasite.

In taking steps to reduce the amount of parasitism in any population, including ourselves, it is important that we understand clearly that we are altering the biotic environment. We are initiating ecological changes whose end results may sometimes be rather more than we bargained for. The man-sponsored development of drug-resistant parasites is just one example. The recent prevalence of polio in countries with high sanitary standards is another. It is not that polio virus is found only in these countries. On the contrary, most young children of underdeveloped countries are infected at an early age, but because of greater resistance in early childhood, few develop serious symptoms. But they do develop an active immunity. Where sanitation is more efficient, exposure to the virus may not occur until late in childhood or, increasingly, young adulthood. Then, the chance of serious illness and paralysis is much greater. Measles, mumps, and chicken pox, usually no more than a nuisance in childhood, can be quite serious in adulthood.

In reducing the amount of parasitism, man also reduces one of nature's checks on population growth. This, in turn, can lead to other problems. As the density of a population increases, the chances of parasites transferring from host to host also increases. A major epidemic may follow. This has been observed in many animal and plant populations, and man is no exception. It is no coincidence that epidemics are most common in cities and in other heavily populated regions. Furthermore, the growth of populations has other effects on the biotic environment. A shortage of food and other important resources may ultimately cause more drastic upheavals (e.g. war, famine, and a lowered standard of living, followed once again by epidemics) than the infectious diseases which we originally tried to avoid. These and other factors in man's influence on the balance of nature will be examined in the next chapter.

EXERCISES AND PROBLEMS

1 List, in the order in which they are brought into play, the natural defenses of the body against bacteria introduced into the dermis by a splinter.

2 Contrast tetanus toxoid and tetanus antitoxin with respect to (a) method of manufacture, (b) mechanism of action in the body, (c) appropriate medical use.

3 Why are the alga and fungus in a lichen considered to be living in a mutualistic relationship?

4 With respect to the pig tapeworm, why do we say that we are the final host and the pig is the intermediate host rather than the other way around?

5 In what ways is the pig tapeworm well adapted to its way of life?

6 What are the three problems that must be solved by all internal parasites? How have these been solved by the pig tapeworm?

7 Tender swellings in the left armpit are an indication of what?

8 What kind of organism ends every food chain?

9 What kind of organism starts every food chain?

10 Why are skin and organ grafts most successful when the donor and recipient are identical twins?

11 Distinguish between an antigen and an antibody.

12 Name a human parasite from each of the following groups: (a) rhizopods, (b) flatworms, (c) roundworms, (d) annelid worms, (e) sporozoans, (f) flagellates, (g) arachnids, (h) insects, (i) bacteria, (j) rickettsias.

13 Are any vertebrates parasitic?

14 Name the vector of each of the following parasites: (a) *Plasmodium vivax*, (b) bubonic plague bacillus, (c) rickettsia that causes Rocky Mountain spotted fever, (d) rickettsia that cases typhus fever, (e) the filarial worm, (f) the yellow fever virus.

15 To what taxonomic group do *all* the vectors in Question 14 belong?

REFERENCES

1 Limbaugh, C., "Cleaning Symbiosis," *Scientific American*, Reprint No. 135, August, 1961. Gives several examples of mutualism in which animals of one species secure food by cleaning animals of another species.

2 Burnet, Sir Macfarlane, *Natural History of Infectious Disease*, Cambridge University Press, Cambridge, England, 1953. Examines infectious disease from an ecological point of view.

3 Collier, H. O. J., "Kinins," *Scientific American,* Reprint No. 132, August, 1962. Describes their production and action in the body.

4 Wood, W. B., Jr., "White Blood Cells versus Bacteria," *Scientific American,* Reprint No. 51, February, 1951.

By reading the following five articles in chronological order, one can trace not only the development of our knowledge of the facts of immunity but also the changes these discoveries have made in our theories of immunity.

5 Burnet, Sir Macfarlane, "How Antibodies Are Made," *Scientific American,* Reprint No. 3, November, 1954.

6 Burnet, Sir Macfarlane, "The Mechanism of Immunity," *Scientific American,* Reprint No. 78, January, 1961.

7 Burnet, Sir Macfarlane, "The Thymus Gland," *Scientific American,* Reprint No. 138, November, 1962.

8 Speirs, R. S., "How Cells Attack Antigens," *Scientific American,* Reprint No. 176, February, 1964.

9 Nossal, G. J. V., "How Cells Make Antibodies," *Scientific American,* Reprint No. 199, December, 1964.

10 Billingham, R. E., and W. K. Silvers, "Skin Transplants and the Hamster," *Scientific American,* Reprint No. 148, January, 1963. Describes how this laboratory rodent is used to uncover the genetic basis of immunity.

11 Isaacs, A., "Interferon," *Scientific American,* Reprint No. 87, May 1961.

12 Brock, T. D., ed., *Milestones in Microbiology,* Prentice-Hall, Inc., 1961. A paperback that includes:
   a) Edward Jenner's paper on producing immunity against smallpox by inoculation with cowpox virus.
   b) Alexander Fleming's report on the antibacterial action of material from cultures of *Penicillium.*
   c) Gerhard Domagk's report on the antibacterial action of prontosil, a dye that is converted in the body into sulfanilamide.
   d) Donald D. Wood's analysis of the molecular mimicry by which sulfanilamide exerts its antibacterial effect.

13 Mudd, S., "The Staphylococcus Problem," *Scientific American,* January, 1959. Traces the development of resistant strains of this pathogen.

14 Rose, A. H., "New Penicillins," *Scientific American,* March, 1961. Describes how they are being used to attack "the staphylococcus problem."

15 Yoeli, M., "Animal Infections and Human Disease," *Scientific American,* May, 1960. Describes several diseases of humans, the parasites of which are transmitted to us from animal reservoirs by arthropod vectors.

16 Alvarado, C. A., and L. J. Bruce-Chwatt, "Malaria," *Scientific American,* May, 1962.

Rabbits in Australia.
(Courtesy Dunston, from *Black Star.*)

THE GROWTH OF POPULATIONS

There is not a species of living thing that could not completely fill its habitat with its kind if unlimited food were available to it, and if the other physical and biotic factors in its environment were favorable. Some would do it more rapidly than others. The ability of certain bacteria (e.g. *E. coli*) to double their weight and divide every twenty minutes would result in their blanketing the earth in a few days if nothing stopped them. Humans reproduce much more slowly but they, too, could theoretically cover the earth in a surprisingly short period of time. In fact, any species whose couples produce more than two offspring during their lifetime will expand in numbers unless the excess die before they themselves undertake parenthood. Under ideal conditions, then, populations grow logarithmically (see Figs. 24-1 and 37-1). As in the growth of individuals (see Section 24-1), this is simply a reflection of the fact that the product of growth itself grows. The time scale varies from species to species, but the potentiality for logarithmic growth is present in them all.

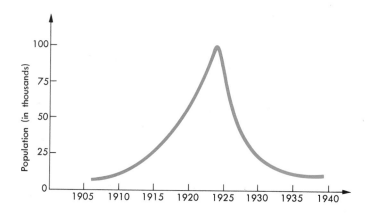

Fig. 37-1

Influence of predation and food supply on the deer population of the Grand Canyon National Game Preserve. Prior to 1907, the deer population was relatively stable. Predators kept the population size below that which the food supply could sustain. From 1907 to 1939, the following predators were killed: 30 wolves, 816 pumas, 863 bobcats, and 7388 coyotes. By 1918 the population had exceeded the capacity of the range to support it on an indefinite basis. By 1924, there was not enough food left to support the population through the winter, and during that winter and the next, 96,000 deer died of starvation. Although killing of predators continued until 1939, the deer population did not rebound. Overgrazing as a result of the earlier population explosion had seriously reduced the food supply. Food shortage had replaced predation as the limiting factor in population size. (By permission from the Wisconsin Conservation Department. From A. L. Leopold, *Wisconsin Conservation Bulletin*, August, 1943.)

The growth curve of individuals is S-shaped. After the logarithmic or exponential period, the rate of growth declines and, in many cases, growth finally ceases. Luckily, the same phenomenon also occurs in the growth of populations. Physical and biotic factors in the environment eventually check further population growth. This check arises from either or both of two factors. (1) The **capacity of the environment** to supply the needs of the species is limited. A point is always reached when the amount of food or, in the case of plants, sunlight, water, and minerals is insufficient to support any further increase in the population. This is not just a matter of an absolute limit to the resources available; it also involves the fact that other species are competing for these same necessities of life. (2) the efforts of **predators and parasites** to satisfy their need for food also provide definite checks on the size of populations. As a population increases, there are predators and parasites ready and willing to harvest it for their own use. These two factors, then, working to keep each species from realizing its potential to overwhelm the earth, serve to maintain the "balance of nature." Let us see just how each one operates.

THE CAPACITY OF THE ENVIRONMENT 37-2

The capacity of the environment to support life depends first on the amount of energy available. For green plants and protists, production of organic matter (and thus growth) is limited directly by the amount of the sun's energy they can trap. Heterotrophic organisms are limited by the amount of energy they can secure in the form

of energy-rich organic molecules. Their source of these molecules establishes their position in the food chain (see Section 36-1). Herbivores get them directly from plants. Carnivores get them from herbivores or other carnivores.

In Section 11-9 (6), we noted that the transformation of energy is never 100% efficient. Under normal growing conditions, plants transform only about 2% of the visible light that strikes them into the chemical energy of organic molecules. Whenever the rate of cellular respiration exceeds the rate of photosynthesis (e.g. at night), the amount available for the herbivores of the region is reduced. Far greater losses (usually 90% or more) occur in converting the organic matter (and hence energy) of plants into the organic matter of the herbivore. Some fails to be absorbed from its digestive tract. More is expended in cellular respiration to provide the energy for physical activity and for synthesizing the remainder into the molecules (e.g. proteins) characteristic of the species. Even under the best conditions, then, you cannot get 10 pounds of chicken from 10 pounds of chicken feed.

Fig. 37-2

A pyramid of energy. At each link in the food chain, energy that was originally stored by the autotrophic grass plants is dissipated. What other relationships exist in such a food chain?

Carnivores, getting their energy third-hand, are limited still further. Additional losses occur as they convert the molecules of herbivores into their own living substance. Of course, the situation is even worse for carnivores that prey upon other carnivores. At each link in a food chain, then, a portion of the sun's energy, originally trapped by the photosynthesizing autotroph, is dissipated back to the environment (ultimately as heat). Thus we can conclude that the total amount of energy stored in the bodies of a given population is dependent on its position in a food chain. The total amount of energy in a population of frogs must necessarily be less than that in the insects upon which they prey. The insects, in turn, must possess only a fraction of the energy stored in the plant population on which they feed. This decrease in available energy at each link in a food chain is sometimes described as a **pyramid of energy.** In the food chain we discussed in Section 36-1, the autotrophic grasses provide the base of the pyramid. The carnivorous hawk occupies the narrow apex (Fig. 37-2).

How does one measure the amount of energy in a population? One could incinerate the organisms and carefully measure the amount of heat given off. A less drastic method is simply to determine the mass of the population. Since all organisms are composed of roughly the same organic molecules, a measure of their dry weight is a rough measure of the amount of energy they contain. A census of the population, multiplied by the weight of an average individual in it, gives an estimate of the total weight of the population. This, too, diminishes with the distance along the food chain from the autotrophs, which make the organic molecules in the first place. The total weight of frogs in a given region must necessarily be less than the total weight of the insects upon which they feed. Figure 37-3 illustrates such a **pyramid of mass** as found in a marine community.

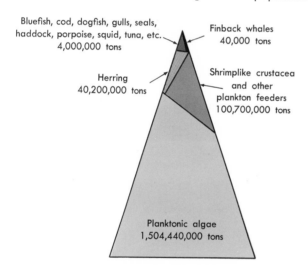

Bluefish, cod, dogfish, gulls, seals, haddock, porpoise, squid, tuna, etc.
4,000,000 tons

Finback whales
40,000 tons

Herring
40,200,000 tons

Shrimplike crustacea and other plankton feeders
100,700,000 tons

Planktonic algae
1,504,440,000 tons

Fig. 37-3

A pyramid of mass in the open sea. (Courtesy Lorus J. Milne and Margery Milne, *The Biotic World and Man,* 2nd Edition, Prentice-Hall, Inc., 1958.)

A third consequence of the ecological principles we have been discussing is that smaller animals are more numerous than larger ones. Figure 37-4 shows the **pyramid of numbers** resulting when a census of the populations of autotrophs, herbivores, and two levels of carnivores is taken in an acre of grassland. This pyramid arises principally from the fact that each species is limited in its total mass by its position in a food chain. If the size of the individuals is small, their numbers can be greater, and vice versa. Predators are usually larger than their prey, however, but being one step further along the food chain, the total mass of their population must be smaller. Consequently, the number of individuals in the predator population is distinctly smaller than in the prey population.

The limited capacity of the environment to provide usable energy establishes an absolute limit to population size. However, this limit is not apt to be reached under natural conditions. Every source of food is exploited by more than one species. Grasshoppers, rabbits, and cows all compete for the available grass. Thus, the population of each is kept in check by competition with the others. Under these conditions, we can appreciate that any inherited traits which diminish the severity of interspecific competition will, by natural selection, tend to become established in the population. The usual outcome is the evolution of adaptations which increase the feeding efficiency of the species. Increased efficiency goes hand in hand with increased specialization, however, and the result is a progressive narrowing of the niche of each species. The cotton boll weevil and the moth with the 10-in proboscis each represent an extreme of feeding specialization. Their niche is narrow but they exploit it more efficiently than their competitors can.

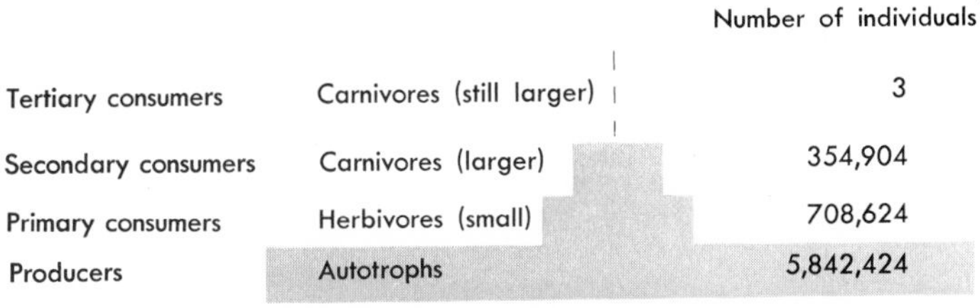

		Number of individuals
Tertiary consumers	Carnivores (still larger)	3
Secondary consumers	Carnivores (larger)	354,904
Primary consumers	Herbivores (small)	708,624
Producers	Autotrophs	5,842,424

Pyramid of numbers in an acre of bluegrass. (Redrawn by permission from E. P. Odum, *Fundamentals of Ecology*, 2nd ed., W. B. Saunders Co., Philadelphia, Pa., 1959. Based on data acquired by Evans, Cain, and Walcott.)

Fig. 37-4

Plants, too, are thrown into competition with other plant species for sunlight, soil, water, and minerals. Many are the specialized adaptations by which plants reduce interspecific competition for these necessities. Species with shallow root systems are able to coexist with deep-rooted species because each is tapping a different region in the soil. The seeds of shade-tolerant species fail to germinate in sunny locations where they would be at a competitive disadvantage and, similarly, the seeds of shade-intolerant species will not develop successfully in shady locations. In the desert, the leaves shed by the brittlebush leave a poison in the soil that keeps competing annuals at their distance. The evolution of epiphytism, vines, and (in the case of many woodland shrubs) growth before the forest trees reach full-leaf, represent adaptations to compete more effectively for sunlight.

PLANT SUCCESSION   37-3

The fact that plants differ markedly in their requirements for light sometimes leads to an interesting sequence, called succession, in the growth of plant populations. For example, the gray birch grows well only in sunny locations. The shade it casts prevents other gray birches from growing up beneath it but permits white pine seedlings to become established. When mature, white pines then cast so deep a shade that the gray birch is no longer able to survive in that area. By its growth, one population of plants alters the environment in a way unfavorable to it and favorable to some other plant population.

The process of plant succession begins just as soon as a land area capable of supporting plant life is formed. The exposure of rocks by a retreating glacier, the formation of beaches at the edge of oceans and lakes, and the gradual filling in of ponds all provide fresh terrain for plant colonization. Let us examine the plant succession which occurs on bare rock in the colder parts of the temperate deciduous forest biome.

The first colonizers are the lichens and certain mosses. Acids secreted by the lichens attack the rock substrate and provide bits of soil. Additional soil particles may be formed by weathering or be blown to the rock from elsewhere and lodge in its crevices. Damage and decay to the lichen growth supplies some humus. Soon sufficient soil is present in the cracks for other mosses to become established. They produce fresh growth each season, the old growth decaying and quickly providing additional amounts of humus. Soon there is enough soil for grasses and, later, low shrubby growth such as blueberries. These, in turn, provide excellent cultural conditions for the seeds of such sun-loving, fast-growing trees as gray birch and poplar (quaking aspen). As we noted above, white pine soon replaces these short-lived species. In the dense shade of white pines, only shade-tolerant maple and beech seedlings thrive. When these large trees finally take over, the succession comes to an end. Maple and beech seedlings are able to develop under the conditions imposed by their parents, and the population becomes self-sustaining. It is known as a **climax** forest.

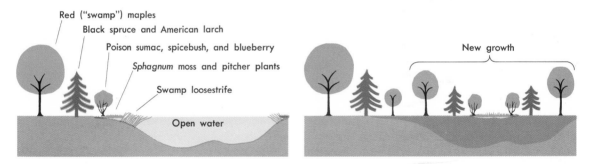

Red ("swamp") maples
Black spruce and American larch
Poison sumac, spicebush, and blueberry
Sphagnum moss and pitcher plants
Swamp loosestrife
Open water
New growth

Fig. 37-5   Plant succession in a bog. Starting with the stems of the swamp loosestrife, which grow right out of the water, an increasingly thick mat of vegetation is formed as the years go by and the area of open water diminishes. Where water is still present underneath, the bog "quakes" when walked on.

A similar process occurs as shallow ponds gradually fill in with soil washed in from the surrounding terrain and organic matter produced by underwater plants. As we walk from the edge of a poorly drained, boggy pond back into the forest, we pass through a series of zones that recreate in space the plant succession which has been occurring in time (Fig. 37-5). From the swamp loosestrife and arrowhead at the water's edge, past sphagnum moss and pitcher plants, then shrub-sized blueberries and poison sumac followed by black spruce and American larch and, finally, swamp maples and white pines, one passes concentric zones, each representing a later stage of plant succession as the soil has become firmer, dryer, and the shade denser.

Lumbering, grazing, farming, fires, and hurricanes interrupt the process of succession by removing the dominant plants in the community. Then the stage is set for a new succession to begin. The many abandoned farms in New England bear eloquent testimony to this. People often wonder why our pioneers built stone walls through the deep woods. The answer is they did not. The walls one sees in the woods today once marked the boundaries of fields and pastures, but when cultivation and grazing ceased, a **secondary succession** began. The grass of abandoned fields and pastures gave way to rank weeds and low shrubby growth. Soon gray birch, poplars, or cedars flourished. White pines, or, in sandy well-drained locations, oaks followed. If they are left alone, we will someday see once again a climax forest of maples and beeches.

The colonization of bare rock, the filling in of a pond, and the secondary succession following the abandonment of a field each involve different species in the early stages of succession. In any given region, though, the species in the final, self-sustaining climax forest are the same. The tendency for all plant successions to end in the same climax community is called **convergence.**

There are few parallels to plant succession in animal populations. An animal population may drastically alter the conditions of its environment so that it is no longer suitable for that population, but this is not inevitable. Nevertheless, succession in animal populations does occur simply as a consequence of succession in plant populations. As fields revert to woods, the kinds of birds, mammals, and invertebrates present change, too.

PREDATION AND PARASITISM 37-4

The second major check on the size of populations is predation and parasitism. To satisfy their need for food, predators kill and devour prey. In so doing, they reduce the size of the prey population. As we have seen, some parasites inflict heavy mortality on their host species. The combined efforts of predators and parasites usually keep the size of any given population well below the capacity of the environment to support that population.

The balance between prey and predator or host and parasite is a delicate one. If, for any reason, a population begins to increase, the greater density of individuals makes it easier for predators to find them and for parasites to be transferred between them. It is no accident that epidemic diseases are especially prevalent in densely populated regions. The same phenomenon forces the farmer who plants large areas to a single crop to wage a never-ending battle against destructive insects and plant diseases.

Usually the relationship between predator (or parasite) and prey is somewhat self-regulating. An increase in the population of the victim permits the predator population to increase. Increased predation then lowers the population density of the prey species and is followed by a reduction in the concentration of predators. Of course, that opens the way for another build-up in the prey population, and so it goes. There is apt to be some lag in these shifts with the result that the populations of predators and prey not only fluctuate, but the periods of maximum population of the two species do not always coincide. Figure 37-6 illustrates the cyclical relationship between the population estimates for the varying hare ("snowshoe rabbit") and for its chief predator, the lynx, in the region around Hudson Bay in Canada. Parasite-host populations are apt to follow the same cyclical relationship, although both species reach their points of maximum and minimum populations at about the same time. Even where mortality is low and no substantial reduction in the host population results, the size of some parasite populations waxes and wanes. This occurs when an epidemic leaves all survivors immune to the parasite. Not until that im-

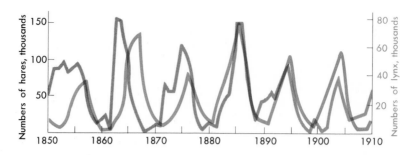

Fig. 37-6   Cyclical fluctuations of the varying hare and lynx populations in the Hudson Bay region from 1850 to 1910.

munity is reduced or a new crop of nonimmune youngsters comes along will the density of susceptible individuals reach the point where another epidemic can occur. Figure 37-7, which shows the annual incidence of measles in South Australia from 1916 through 1920, illustrates this nicely.

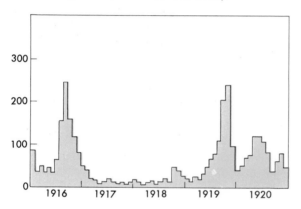

Fig. 37-7

Monthly notifications of measles in South Australia from 1916 to 1920. (Redrawn by permission from Sir Macfarlane Burnet, *Natural History of Infectious Disease*, 2nd ed., Cambridge University Press, 1953.)

It is obviously important to the balance of nature for the rise and fall of predator and prey populations not to be so extreme that the prey are completely exterminated. If this should occur, the predator (or parasite) population would soon follow suit unless an alternate source of food was available. This might be impossible for a predator occupying a narrow niche. In a restricted habitat such as a small fresh-water pond, mutual extinction could thus be a real threat. We know practically nothing as yet about how this danger is generally avoided in such situations, but at least one fascinating control mechanism has recently been discovered. In the eastern United States, fresh-water ponds are often populated by tiny mosquito fish (*Gambusia*), which feed on mosquito larvae (thus serving a useful function for us). *Gambusia* is, in turn, preyed upon by the pickerel, a fast-swimming, voracious predator. Mosquito fish do not hide in underwater vegetation and, after watching a hungry pickerel at work, it seems miraculous that any mosquito fish could escape being eaten by it. Escape they do, thanks to a nice, self-protective mechanism. Whenever mosquito fish detect the presence of a pickerel, they move up to the surface of the water and begin splashing about. So long as this goes on, the pickerel makes little effort to attack them and, when it does attack, often misses. Let one member drift beneath the surface, though, and he is devoured in an instant. The signal to the mosquito fish is a chemical one. When water where pickerel have been swimming is added to an aquarium containing mosquito fish, they immediately carry out their self-protective response. It is not yet fully understood just why the pickerel is so often unsuccessful while its prey is at the surface, but the value of this mechanism is perfectly clear. By failing to exterminate its prey, the pickerel avoids exterminating itself. By simply cropping the surplus *Gambusia* population, both populations are maintained at a stable level.

It is also easy to see how natural selection maintains this response in the *Gambusia*. Any individuals in the population whose genotype leads to a diminished response will be the first ones to disappear, genotype and all, down the throat of the pickerel.

ANOTHER SOLUTION?   **37-5**

Neglecting minor cyclical fluctuations, populations usually remain stable despite the enormous reproductory potential of all living organisms. The control measures are quite effective. Predators and parasites feed upon the surplus. If they fail, the limited quantity of essential materials in the environment, that is, its limited capacity, will prevent an unlimited population increase. On the one hand, there is early death at the hands of predators and parasites. On the other, there is early death from starvation. Early death, then, seems to be the chief mechanism by which population growth is held in check. It need not be the only mechanism. Remember that the growth of a population is dependent on birth rate as well as death rate. Are there mechanisms in nature for reducing the number of young produced in each generation to below the reproductive potential of the species? The answer is yes, three of them.

1) One way to achieve smaller populations is to reduce the number of offspring produced by each pair of adults. Exactly how this is accomplished among animals other than man is not yet clear. At least one species of turbellarian (free-living flatworms) has been shown to produce fewer young as the population of adults in its container increases. This phenomenon, which may be caused by an inhibitory chemical released in the water, occurs even when ample food, oxygen, and water are available. There is good evidence that hydras living in a crowded culture release into the water a substance (probably a protein) that inhibits asexual reproduction. Fruit flies living under crowded conditions lay fewer eggs. Laboratory rats living in a confined area soon reach a stable population size even though abundant food is available. This comes about through a sharp rise in infant mortality both before and after birth, a special case of early death. Reduced maternal care and even cannibalism take a heavy toll of the newborn.

2) Another mechanism which limits the number of individuals in the next generation is to limit the number of parents. Some mammals and birds achieve this by establishing breeding territories. Each mating pair occupies an area of a size sufficient to supply all its needs including those of its offspring. One or both members defend this area against intrusion from other members of the same species. Thus, they not only ensure that the capacity of their immediate environment will not be exceeded, but they may also keep the general population in check by preventing breeding among the surplus members of their species.

3) The formation of closely regulated societies is a third mechanism of population control which reduces the need for early death. Although there are many worker females in the beehive to accomplish the work of the hive (see Section 30-10), only the queen has functional reproductive organs. Her rate of egg-laying is adjusted to the over-all needs of the hive. Whenever bad weather or poor flowering reduces the amount of food being brought into the hive, she lays fewer eggs. In the late summer, she ceases her egg-laying entirely and thus avoids the necessity of using the hard-won winter stores of honey for the raising of young.

Although each of these devices reduces the number of offspring, each one actually promotes survival of the species as a whole. Competition within the species and with other species for the necessities of life is reduced, and the chances of exceeding the capacity of the environment to support life thereby lessened.

THE ECOLOGY OF MAN

37-6   THE HUMAN POPULATION

Is man, too, governed by the principles we have been discussing? He is a heterotrophic organism dependent ultimately upon the organic molecules produced by plants. He has a sufficiently high reproductive potential to live up to the capacity of the environment. Like all other organisms, he is subject to attack by many parasites. His predators are few but, in their stead, he has substituted a unique form of intraspecific predation, war. Famine, disease, and war have limited man's population growth in the same way that the populations of other species are kept in check.

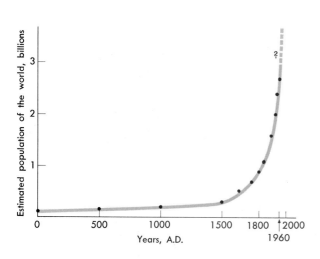

Fig. 37-8

Growth of the human population. The estimates since 1800 are based on more accurate data than those before.

Man does, however, differ from other organisms in significant ways. His large cerebrum, his ability to use tools, and his language (which permits the accumulation of knowledge) have enabled him to alter his physical and biotic environment far more drastically than any creature which has ever gone before. Over the past 100 years he has eliminated, at least in the more prosperous parts of the world, infectious disease as a major cause of early death. He has virtually eliminated all nonhuman predators. The removal of these checks on population has resulted in a dramatic increase in the number of humans inhabiting the earth (Fig. 37-8). As we have seen, in other animals the removal of these checks on population would quickly result in the species' expanding to the limit of the environment. Man has so far avoided this in North America, Europe, and a few other areas by improving his agricultural practices as fast as, or faster than, his numbers have increased.

Present crop yields are sufficient to (and do) support a human population many times greater than that which could be supported by foraging for food as other animals do.

Has man, then, freed himself from the ecological rules that govern other creatures? The answer is no. By his unique and powerful influences on the physical and biotic environment, he has achieved a population that otherwise would have been impossible. The inescapable fact remains, however, that even if he could eliminate all early deaths through parasitism and predation and even if he could exploit autotrophs on every square foot of the planet not occupied by himself, there would still be a limit to the number of humans that could exist. His reproductory potential is sufficient to reach that limit.

Malthus and Darwin knew that no population can ever grow indefinitely. Either an increase in the death rate or a decrease in the birth rate must follow any period of population growth. Some observers, alarmed by the present rapid rise in the world's human population, have advocated the former. War, the withholding of medical assistance, even the deliberate extermination of human populations, have been suggested, and, in some cases, carried out. On the other hand, there are those who prefer to see man deliberately limit the number of offspring produced in order to avoid the necessity for early death from famine, war, or disease. There are serious problems with this approach, too. The desire to reproduce is as strong in man as in other animals. The religious and social convictions of many are in conflict with any attempt to thwart this desire. There is no third alternative, however. The human population can only grow as large as the capacity of the environment to support it, and, although we have not reached them yet, this capacity has absolute limits.

Even as man's knowledge and skill achieve further increases in the capacity of the environment, every citizen must consider whether it is desirable to have the population increase accordingly. A population living close to the capacity of its environment faces a marginal existence at best. Although the necessities of life may be met one year, crop failure anywhere would, as it often has, lead to widespread famine the next. Furthermore, a population getting just enough food to stay alive and reproduce is not apt to have the interest or leisure to develop and maintain the cultural achievements which distinguish us from the other animals.

It must also be recognized that man's success at increasing the capacity of his environment has sometimes been a short-term affair. He has temporarily increased the productivity of some regions at the expense of their long-term capacity to support life. As with the person living off capital instead of income, a day of reckoning awaits.

MAN'S CHANGES TO THE PHYSICAL ENVIRONMENT   37-7

As the frontiers of this country moved westward, the early settlers were able to increase enormously the productivity of the land. Clearing forests enabled them to raise crops of domesticated plants which, in the rich virgin soil, provided a much larger return of digestible organic molecules than native vegetation could. But in drastically altering the biotic environment for their short-term benefit, the settlers altered the physical environment, too.

Plowed land, especially in hilly regions, was easily eroded by water and wind. In the South and Southwest, there are now regions from which most of the topsoil has gone. There, productivity is now less than it was before. In draining swamps to make them suitable for agriculture and in removing perennial vegetation everywhere to make room for crops, man simultaneously has removed natural basins and the spongy, root-held forest soil which formerly stored rain water. The water of melting snow and spring rains now has no place to go but down to the sea. It does, in floods. The total amount of precipitation does not change in compensation. The water which rushes off in floods in the spring is not available to maintain water supplies in rivers, streams, and the soil during the summer. Water shortage follows floods as night follows day.

The development of agriculture in our country was soon followed by the development of industry. Steel leads the list of metals on which efficient tools, transport, and a great amount of building construction depend. Copper provides the foundation for communications and the transport of electrical power. Coal and oil provide the major portion of the energy used to run our vast industrial machine. All of these materials, no less than our food, come out of the earth. However, unlike our food, the supply of these materials is strictly limited. With careful conservation of soil and water, the energy of sunlight can provide food crops year after year. When the world's stores of iron ore, copper ore, coal, and petroleum are gone, they are gone forever.

It is true that of the latter two, coal and probably petroleum are the products of living organisms and thus theoretically renewable. Perhaps some petroleum is being formed today. Nevertheless, the creation of our petroleum deposits has taken time measured in millions of years, not just decades or centuries. The first commercial oil well went into production in Pennsylvania in 1859. During the next 90 years (1859–1949), 64 billion barrels of petroleum were removed from the earth and consumed. By early 1961, just a little more than 11 years later, that figure had been doubled. Our consumption of petroleum continues to accelerate. Even with an estimated 277 billion barrels as yet untouched, it is obvious that present consumption cannot continue indefinitely. Already man is starting to turn to other sources of energy, such as atomic energy, and within your lifetime, you will see him do so *by necessity*.

Oil and coal, as well as the metal ores, are thus *nonrenewable resources,* and the rate at which man consumes them is a measure of the rate at which he is approaching the day when the capacity of his environment with respect to these materials will be sharply reduced. Substitutes for them will have to be found before that day if man is to continue to produce and transport food and other necessities for his growing population.

Mining and the industrial activities which stem from it have profoundly influenced man's physical and biotic environments in harmful as well as helpful ways. The dumping of industrial wastes (not to mention human wastes) into streams and rivers has drastically reduced their capacity to support fish and shellfish populations and thus, indirectly, man himself. As populations increase and water tables fall, an ever-larger number of people must look to the rivers for water to be used in the home. The presence of pollution increases greatly the cost of making this water safe for human consumption.

Industrial activities have altered still another part of our physical environment, the atmosphere. Aside from its unpleasantness, air pollution now stands implicated in many human deaths from respiratory (and perhaps other) causes. Man is not the only part of the biotic environment to be affected, either. Remember (see Section 31-5) how air pollution in industrial parts of the world has killed off lichen growth in surrounding forests and led to the evolutionary change of industrial melanism.

One of the most vivid examples of the effects of air pollution on both the physical and biotic environment can be observed in the southeastern corner of Tennessee. A traveler approaching the communities of Copperhill and Ducktown is suddenly struck by the eerie sensation of having arrived at some other, forbidding, planet. As far as the eye can see, not a green thing grows, no trees, no shrubs, no grass. Bare soil, eroded in deep gullies, meets the eye in every direction (Fig. 37-9). What has caused this desolation? Sulfur dioxide fumes, liberated into the air by a copper smelter, killed the surrounding vegetation. With no vegetation to hold the soil, wind and water began the work of erosion. The devastation has spread over some 23,000 acres. As fast as immigrant plants arrive on the scene, more wind and water rips at their substratum, loosening their temporary foothold and exposing still deeper layers of unprotected soil. Although attempts at reclamation are being made, it is an uphill battle with many setbacks.

Copper Basin, Tennessee. The vegetation in this region was killed by deliberate burning and air pollution from a copper smelter prior to 1907. Over half a century later, continued erosion still hampers attempts at reforestation. Average annual rainfall is less and temperatures are higher than in surrounding regions. (Courtesy U.S. Forest Service.)

Fig. 37-9

How long will it be before a carpet of green once more covers this land? No one knows for certain, but the release of SO_2 by the copper smelter has been stopped since 1907.

THE BALANCE OF NATURE 37-8

We have seen how our agricultural and industrial activities have brought about marked changes in the physical environment. Often these changes have reduced the long-term capacity of the environment to support us. Even where soil erosion and pollution of water and air have been avoided, these activities have caused changes in the *biotic* environment, many of which have also been harmful in the long run.

The very act of growing crops drastically alters the balance of nature. A variety of plant species, each with a low population density, is suddenly replaced by acres of a single plant. This manmade population explosion sets the stage for a major build-up in the populations of the insects and parasites which attack that crop. Acres of cotton fields increase enormously the capacity of the boll weevil's environment. Wheat fields stretching as far as the eye can see provide virtually unlimited nourishment for the wheat rust and easy transmission from host to host. The competitors of cultivated plants, the weeds, also flourish where the soil has been exposed and the natural vegetation replaced. Raising herds of domesticated animals, e.g. cattle and sheep, similarly alters the kinds and numbers of other species in the region.

Man is forced to alter the balance of nature in this way in order to feed himself. He must, however, expend heroic efforts to maintain this unbalanced state. Chemical poisons are one of man's most important weapons in his never-ending battle with the insects over food. Despite the enormous amount of money and effort expended, the insects take about one-tenth of all the food we grow. This represents some 4 billion dollars in crop losses each year. If it were not for the use of chemical insecticides, the figure would be far higher, so high, in fact, that we would be transformed from a nation that still enjoys the headache of food surplus to one facing widespread famine.

The use of chemical insecticides is not a cure-all. Nature is too adaptable for that. Within a few years of the first use of DDT, insects resistant to it appeared in several parts of the world. This should have been no surprise. Evolution works almost as rapidly in insect populations as it has in the bacterial populations that have developed resistance to penicillin. Fortunately, as in the case of antibiotic resistance, the work of chemists has provided a steady flow of new insecticides which, by affecting other links in the insect's metabolism, has enabled effective control to be maintained.

A second drawback to chemical control is that even the most carefully applied insecticides usually kill organisms in addition to the ones intended. Earthworms, fish, crustaceans, snails, and a wide variety of mammals and birds may succumb to poisons designed for certain harmful insects. Valuable insects are often killed, too. Once apple growers learned to control with chemicals the codling moth larva and apple maggot that attack their fruit, they soon found that scale insects and mites (arachnids) began to become a problem for the first time. The reason was simply that the poisons that killed the codling moth also killed the natural enemies of the scale insects and mites. Without this check on their population, their numbers increased alarmingly until new sprays, especially designed to control them, were applied.

The hazard of pesticides to "innocent" organisms is particularly acute for those species that live at the ends of food chains. DDT is not easily broken down or excreted by organisms that ingest it. Consequently, it accumulates in the body, especially in fat deposits. As a result of the spraying of a marsh to control mosquitoes, the microscopic aquatic organisms (the plankton) of the marsh will accumulate traces of DDT. In eating this plankton, small fishes and filter-feeders like clams are, in a real sense, harvesting DDT too. Concentrations of DDT ten times greater than those in the plankton have been measured in clams. Furthermore, the process of concentration continues right up to the end of the food chain. Gulls, which feed upon clams, may accumulate DDT to 40 or more times the concentration in their prey. This represents a 400-fold increase in concentration along the length of this short food chain. While gulls seem to be surviving despite such pesticide burdens, there is abundant evidence that other creatures at the ends of food chains (e.g. ospreys and eagles) are suffering serious declines in fertility and hence population because of this phenomenon.

An alternative to controlling one pest after another by chemicals is to encourage the natural enemies of the pests. Such biological control methods may be quite effective. Scale insects are preyed upon voraciously by ladybird beetles, and these have been cultured and released for this purpose. Although slower-acting than chemicals, they have provided effective control in some instances. Japanese beetle grubs are now controlled in some areas by treating the soil with the spores of a bacillus which causes a fatal illness in these insects. Another bacillus is being grown commercially so its spores can be used against tent caterpillars, the larvae of the gypsy moth, and other leaf-eating insects. Even weed pests have been attacked biologically. The Klamath weed, introduced into California in 1900, had overrun and ruined some 270,000 acres of valuable range land by 1945. In that year, two species of beetles which, after careful testing, had been shown to eat Klamath weed exclusively, were released in large numbers. Their activity has reduced the Klamath weed population to the point where it is no longer a threat.

One-crop agriculture upsets the balance of nature. Chemical insecticides, fungicides, and herbicides often upset it still further. Biological control measures may be able to replace chemical controls with far less disturbance to the over-all ecology of the region. However, it is crucially important that before such measures are taken, the complete ecology of the introduced organism be studied. Once a natural enemy has wiped out the intended prey, we do not want it to turn to other sources of food and become a nuisance itself. This has happened on occasion. When sugar cane was introduced into the West Indies as a major crop, rats began feeding on it, and the resulting increase in the rat population caused substantial crop losses. After several unsuccessful attempts at chemical and biological control, the mongoose of India was introduced in the hope that it would rid the islands of rats. It did this quite effectively but, when the job was done, then turned to native wildlife (including valuable predators of other pests) and even domestic animals. The mongoose now ranks as the most troublesome pest of all.

One of the most ingenious biological control methods yet attempted has resulted in the elimination of the screwworm fly from our southern states. This fly is a serious pest of livestock. The females lay their eggs in sores or other open wounds on the animals, and then the larvae eat the tissues of the host. As they do so, they expose a still larger area to egg-laying, and death of the host is the all-too-frequent outcome.

The eradication of this pest was actually accomplished by releasing some 2 billion *additional* flies into the natural population. But, before their release, these flies were exposed to just enough gamma radiation to make them sterile but not enough to injure them in any other way.

The success of the undertaking depended only on the sterile males. As their number was increased in an area, the chances of a fertile female in the natural population mating with one increased, too. Each time this occurred, the female would lay sterile eggs. Since the female mates only once, her reproductive career was thus ended without any offspring being produced. After 18 months of this, the pest was totally eliminated east of the Mississippi River. It has since been eradicated in the southwestern states as well.

Not only has the technique of swamping a pest population with sterile but otherwise healthy males been shown to be effective, but it has other advantages. In contrast to insecticides, it does not endanger any other animal population unless, of course, the sterile pests should be harmful. The development of resistant strains is not a problem. As the population of the pest grows smaller, the effectiveness of the method increases. Insecticides, in contrast, always miss some individuals, which can then rebuild the population.

The possibility of using sterile males to reduce the population of other pests is now being explored. The direct application of sterilizing chemicals to the natural population seems promising. It would eliminate the need to rear hordes of individuals in captivity but does raise once again the problem of endangering other species of animals.

Another approach that avoids this problem is to exploit the sexual incompatibility that sometimes exists between different strains of the same insect species. For example, mosquitoes from one region often cannot breed successfully with members of their species from another region. This incompatibility probably arises from differences in the cytoplasm of their eggs. In any case, the females who mate with "foreign" males lay infertile eggs just as the screwworm fly females did. Only two months after thousands of male mosquitoes from California were released in an isolated village in Burma, the species there was wiped out. Because the native mosquitoes were carriers of the filarial worm that so often causes elephantiasis (see Section 14-17), an important public health victory was thus achieved.

The discovery and synthesis of **pheromones** suggests still another way of killing insects more selectively than insecticide sprays can. Gyplure, the powerful sex-attractant of the gypsy moth, may well provide a mechanism by which the male moths in an area could be selectively drawn into poisoned traps. Without mates, the females would be unable to reproduce. Alternatively, the release of large amounts of sex attractant in an area might mask the presence of the females and thus prevent mating. The sex attractants of a number of harmful insects have been isolated or synthesized, and tests indicate that these substances may well provide effective — and selective — control measures against these species.

The shrinkage of our world, which began with the explorations of the fifteenth century and has yet to cease, has intensified the problem of maintaining a balance of nature. Geographical barriers to the spread of plants and animals are now easily overcome. Columbus probably brought smallpox and measles to the New World. He took syphilis as well as corn (maize) back. The forced migration of Negro slaves from Africa to the West Indian sugar plantations probably introduced malaria and yellow fever to this hemisphere. The transport of crop plants from one part of the world to another has often resulted in a simultaneous transport of their parasites and predators. All too often, the natural enemies of the latter were left at home or failed to become established in the new location.

Transport of raw materials and industrial products from one part of the world to another has also caused the transfer of pests from areas where they were held in natural check to areas where they were not. Elm wood, imported for cabinet making, brought the ascomycete causing Dutch elm disease and its beetle vectors to our shores in 1930. Since that time, our stately American elm has been dying in increasing numbers. Only vigilant removal of diseased trees and spraying of the insect vector (the elm bark beetle) has enabled many trees to survive. These measures only stem the tide of this fatal disease, however. Unless better control measures are discovered, the American elm may soon vanish as the American chestnut did.

A discussion of the temperate deciduous climax forest written in the early years of this century would have included the American chestnut along with the maple and beech (see Section 37-3); not so today. In 1904, an ascomycete causing a fatal illness in this species was introduced into this country and virtually wiped out all our chestnuts in a remarkably short period. Today only suckers from the old stumps can be found, and these become infected and die after a few years' growth.

Deliberate transferal of species from one part of the world to another has also frequently led to disaster. The example of the mongoose was mentioned earlier. The gypsy moth, which has caused such damage to trees in the northeastern states, was introduced into Massachusetts in 1869 in hopes that its larvae might be used to start a silk industry in this country. The European rabbit was introduced into Australia for sport in 1859. It multiplied explosively in a land where it had no important predators. The raising of sheep (another imported species) suffered severely as the rabbits competed with the sheep for forage. The situation became steadily worse until 1950, when rabbits infected with the myxoma virus were brought from Brazil and released. The epidemic which followed was fantastic. Millions of rabbits (perhaps as many as 99.5% of the population) died. Green grass returned. Sheep raising became easy once again. As extensive preliminary testing with the native marsupial population had indicated, only the European rabbit seems to be susceptible to the virus. Unfortunately, but predictably, resistant rabbits are now appearing.

The human population on the earth today could not be maintained if we did not deliberately upset the natural balance of other populations in our favor. Agriculture, industry, commerce, and speedy transportation have brought changes in our biotic environment which have been beneficial. They have also encouraged secondary changes in plant and animal populations (weeds, rabbits, predacious insects, etc.) which threaten us continually with a sudden reduction in the carrying capacity of the environment. Furthermore, as our influence has spread to every corner of the earth, we have sometimes threatened the very existence of species (e.g. the American chestnut, the bison) whose continued presence on earth, while perhaps not indispensable to our welfare, provides interest and variety to our lives.

WHAT DOES THE FUTURE HOLD?   37-9

With a fast-growing population in a fast-shrinking world, the margin for error in man's handling of his physical and biotic environment has been sharply reduced. If we are going to avoid future catastrophe, we must bring the *long-term* capacity of our environment into balance with our population. We must learn to conserve resources that cannot be renewed (e.g. metal ores, oil, and coal) at least until satisfactory substitutes can be found for them. We must direct our efforts, as much as possible, toward the use of renewable resources for this purpose, that is, materials which are the products of photosynthesis.

Our ever-increasing dependence on renewable resources requires that we do everything we can to avoid reducing the efficiency with which the energy of the sun can be converted into these materials. Soil must be conserved and its fertility carefully maintained. Water must be conserved and its purity guarded. We should also continue to breed plants and animals capable of transforming matter and energy with minimum losses, that is, capable of growing with maximum efficiency. We must exercise the greatest care in transporting species from one region of the earth to another and in applying chemical and biological controls to other populations. All these things will require biologists, in laboratories and in the field, who can unravel the complex ecological interactions which follow any change in the physical and/or biotic environment. It will also require men of affairs with the wisdom and foresight to put into practice the knowledge gained from ecology. Man must, and will, use his environment. He should not use it up. An ecological budget which is unbalanced for too long endangers the physical and spiritual well-being, in fact the very existence, of our future generations. It also endangers the future of the many other living things which share the planet with us and which have taught us so much about ourselves and about the nature of life itself.

EXERCISES AND PROBLEMS

1 Which of the following sources of energy depend ultimately on the energy of sunlight: (a) wood, (b) coal, (c) oil, (d) hydroelectric power, (e) atomic power?

2 After watching his neighbors harvest large oat crops for several years, a farmer decides to give up corn and plant oats, too. That year all the crops in the area suffer fungus damage. Can the farmer honestly blame "bad luck"?

3 How is the pyramid of numbers related to (a) the pyramid of mass, (b) food chains?

4 How is the problem of toxic accumulations of DDT in animal populations related to (a) food chains, (b) the pyramid of mass?

5 A bare rock succession usually begins with what organisms?

6 How do many birds reduce the pressure of intraspecific competition during the nesting season?

7 How exactly do populations of DDT-resistant flies arise?

8 One year a group of Maine farmers made a determined effort to kill as many hawks in the region as they could. The next spring an unusually large number of apple trees were found to have been girdled by field mice during the winter. What connection between these two events might there have been?

9 What parallels exist between the growth of multicellular organisms and the growth of populations?

10 What factors regulate the rate of growth of a population of animals started by a single breeding pair introduced into a new territory?

11 What factors limit the ultimate size of this population of animals?

12 Why do you think that Tennessee's Copper Basin has higher temperatures than the surrounding regions in summer?

REFERENCES

1 Odum, E. P., *Fundamentals of Ecology*, W. B. Saunders Co., Philadelphia, Pennsylvania, 1959. An excellent text with emphasis on populations and habitats.

2 Pequegnat, W. E., "Whales, Plankton and Man," *Scientific American*, Reprint No. 853, January, 1958. Examines a pyramid of mass in the Antarctic and its implications for solving human food needs.

3 Hickling, C. F., "The Cultivation of Tilapia," *Scientific American*, May, 1963. Tilapias are fresh-water fish grown for food in warm parts of the world. Their successful cultivation requires the practical application of the principles of population growth and the pyramids of mass and numbers.

4 Woodwell, G. M., "Toxic Substances and Ecological Cycles," *Scientific American*, March, 1967. Shows how toxic materials such as radioactive fallout and pesticides are concentrated — sometimes to harmful levels — as they pass from one link in a food chain to another.

5 Deevey, E. S., Jr., "Bogs," *Scientific American*, Reprint No. 840, October, 1958. Describes the historical development of bogs and the plant succession that occurs in them.

6 Wynne-Edwards, V. C., "Population Control in Animals," *Scientific American,* Reprint No. 192, August, 1964. The author cites several examples of animals whose populations seem to be controlled by forms of group behavior (such as territoriality) rather than by food supply, predation, or parasitism.

7 Deevey, E. S., Jr., "The Human Population," *Scientific American,* Reprint No. 608, September, 1960.

8 Lowdermilk, W. C., "The Reclamation of a Man-Made Desert," *Scientific American,* March, 1960. Describes the conservation measures being taken in Israel to make the land fertile and productive once again.

9 Watts, May T., *Reading the Landscape,* The Macmillan Co., New York, 1957. A popular account of how the landscape reveals to the alert eye the forces in the physical and biotic environment that have affected it.

10 Steinhaus, E. A., "Living Insecticides," *Scientific American,* August, 1956. Describes attempts being made to combat insect pests by deliberately infecting them with viral and bacterial diseases.

11 Knipling, E. F., "The Eradication of the Screw-Worm Fly," *Scientific American,* October, 1960.

12 Jacobson, M., and M. Beroza, "Insect Attractants," *Scientific American,* Reprint No. 189, August, 1964. How sex attractants are being used as a weapon against certain insects.

13 Williams, C. M., "Third-Generation Pesticides," *Scientific American,* July, 1967. Explores the potentialities of juvenile hormone as an insecticide.

14 Milne, L. J., and Margery Milne, *The Balance of Nature,* Alfred A. Knopf, New York, 1960. Includes many examples of changes brought about in the physical and biotic environments by man's actions.

15 Storer, J. H., *The Web of Life,* New American Library, New York, 1956. A popular and well-written introduction to ecology available in a paperback edition.

16 Bates, M., *Man in Nature,* 2nd Edition, Prentice-Hall, Inc., 1964. A brief history of man's physical and cultural evolution and the effects he has had on his environment.

17 Odum, E. P., *Ecology,* Holt, Rinehart and Winston, Inc., New York, 1963. A brief presentation with emphasis on the methods used in ecological research.

THE METRIC SYSTEM OF MEASUREMENT

LENGTH

Basic unit is the meter (m), which equals 39.37 in.

Common Multiples and Subdivisions

kilometer (km)	$= 10^3$ m	micron (μ)	$= 10^{-6}$ m
decimeter (dm)	$= 10^{-1}$ m	millimicron (mμ)	$= 10^{-9}$ m
centimeter (cm)	$= 10^{-2}$ m	angstrom (A)	$= 10^{-10}$ m
millimeter (mm)	$= 10^{-3}$ m		

VOLUME

Basic unit is the cubic decimeter (dm³), which equals 1.06 qt. This volume is more commonly called a liter (l). A liter of water at its maximum density weighs *almost* 1 kg. Therefore, 1 ml (1 ml $= 10^{-3}$ l) of water weighs, for all practical purposes, 1 gm. One cubic centimeter (cm³ or cc) is 10^{-3} dm³. Therefore, it is equal to 1 ml and the units ml and cc are used interchangeably.

MASS

Basic unit is the gram (gm).

Common Multiples and Subdivisions

kilogram (kg)	$= 10^3$ gm $= 2.2$ lb	milligram (mg)	$= 10^{-3}$ gm
centigram (cg)	$= 10^{-2}$ gm	microgram (μg)	$= 10^{-6}$ gm

TEMPERATURE

Basic unit is the Celsius (formerly known as centigrade) degree, °C. 0°C is the freezing point of water; 100°C is the boiling point of water. To convert from °C to °F (Fahrenheit) or vice versa: °F $- 32 = 9/5$ °C.

USEFUL EQUIVALENTS

1 in $= 2.54$ cm	1 U.S. fluid oz $= 29.57$ ml
1 oz $= 28.35$ gm	1 U.S. liquid qt $= 0.946$ l
1 lb $= 453.6$ gm	

Glossary

---

absorption spectrum Electromagnetic spectrum whose intensity at each wavelength is a measure of the amount of energy at the wavelength that has passed through a selectively absorbing substance.

acetylcholine \ə-,sēt-ᵊl-'kō-,lēn\ Organic compound secreted at the ends of many neurons. A neurohumor.

acid [L. *acidus,* sour] Molecule or ion that liberates protons, usually in water.

actinomycin D \,ak-ti-,nō-'mīs-ᵊn\ An antibiotic isolated from soil bacteria that blocks DNA-dependent RNA synthesis.

action spectrum Rate of physiological activity plotted against wavelength of light.

active transport Transfer of a substance across a cell membrane from a region of low to one of high concentration. Requires energy.

adaptation [L. *adaptare,* to fit]. Any characteristic of an organism that contributes to its survival in its environment.

adaptive radiation Evolution, from a single ancestral species, of a variety of descendent species adapted to different ways of life.

adenosine triphosphate (ATP) \ə-'den-ə-,sēn-,trī-'fäs-,fāt\ Organic compound that is the immediate source of energy for the activities of the cell.

adhesion Force of attraction between unlike molecules.

adventitious root Root that arises from a stem or leaf.

aerobic \,a-(ə-)'rō-bik\ [Gk. *aeros,* air; *bios,* life] Requiring the presence of free oxygen (O_2).

allantois \ə-'lant-ə-was\ [Gk. *allas,* sausage] Extraembryonic membrane of reptiles, birds, and mammals that forms a pouch growing out of the posterior part of the alimentary canal.

allele \ə-'lē-(ə)l\ Alternative form of a gene that may occur at a given gene locus.

amnion \'am-nē-,än\ Extraembryonic membrane of reptiles, birds, and mammals that encloses the embryo in a fluid-filled sac.

amylase \'am-ə-,lās\ [L. *amylum,* starch] An enzyme that digests (hydrolyzes) starch.

anabolism \ə-'nab-ə-,liz-əm\ Constructive metabolism in which complex substances are synthesized from simpler ones.

anaerobic \,an-ə-'rō-bik\ [Gk. *an,* not + aerobic] Not requiring the presence of free oxygen.

analogous \ə-'nal-a-gəs\ [Gk. *analogos,* proportionate] (Of organs in different species), having a similar function but a different structure and embryonic development.

androgen \'an-drə-jən\ One of a group of sex hormones of male vertebrates which promotes the development of the secondary sex characteristics.

anemia [Gk. *anaimia,* bloodlessness] Deficiency of red blood corpuscles or hemoglobin in the blood.

antibody A protein, produced within an animal, that can unite with a specfic antigen, rendering it inactive.

antigen \\'ant-i-jən\\ Macromolecule (usually a protein or polysaccharide) which, when introduced into the body of an animal it is foreign to, stimulates the formation of an antibody.

antitoxin Antibody formed in response to a toxin.

archenteron \\är-'kent-ə-,rän\\ Central cavity of the gastrula of an embryo, ultimately becoming the alimentary canal.

ascus \\'as-kəs\\ [Gk. *askos*, wineskin, bladder] Tubular spore sac of ascomycetes in which (usually) 8 ascospores are produced.

asexual \\(')ā-'seksh-(ə-)wel\\ **reproduction** Reproduction without the union of gametes (or any nuclear material).

assimilation [L. *assimulare*, to make similar] Conversion of the end-products of digestion of food into the structural materials of the organism.

atom \\'at-əm\\ [Gk. *atomos*, indivisible] Smallest particle of an element that can enter into combination with other elements.

atomic weight unit One-twelfth the weight of an atom of carbon-12.

auto-immune disease Disease caused by an individual's producing antibodies against constituents of his own tissues.

autosome \\'ot-ə-,sōm\\ Any chromosome that is not a sex chromosome.

autotrophic \\,ȯt-ə-'träf-ik\\ Capable of synthesizing organic compounds from inorganic raw materials.

auxin \\'ȯk-sən\\ [Gk. *auxein*, to increase] Plant hormone that, among other effects, promotes cell elongation.

axon \\'ak-,sän\\ Single extension of a neuron (usually long and often branched), which conducts nerve impulses away from the dendrites.

bacteriophage \\bak-'tir-ē-ə-,fāj\\ [bacterium + Gk. *phagein*, to eat] Virus that infects bacteria, usually fatally.

base Molecule or ion that can take a proton from an acid.

basidium \\bə-'sid-ē-əm\\ Club-shaped spore-producing structure of basidiomycetes on which four basidiospores are formed.

beta-galactosidase \\'bāt-ə ,gə-,lak-tə-'sī-,dās\\ An enzyme ("lactase") that hydrolyzes the disaccharide lactose.

bioassay \\,bī-(,)ō-'as-,ā\\ Quantitative determination of the strength of a biologically active substance from its effect on a living organism.

biome \\'bī-ōm\\ A region whose climate produces a characteristic climax community of plants and associated animals. The coniferous forest region of North America constitutes a single biome (the taiga).

blastula \\'blas-chə-lə\\ Early stage of animal development in which a single (usually) layer of cells surrounds a fluid-filled cavity (the blastocoel), thus forming a hollow ball.

botany \\'bät-°n-ē\\ [Gk. *botanē*, pasture, herb] The study of plants.

branchial grooves \\'braŋ-kē-əl\\ Series of external, paired grooves in the neck region of vertebrate embryos that correspond in position to the outpocketings of the pharynx (the gill pouches).

budding Asexual reproduction in which a new organism develops from an outgrowth of the parent.

calorie [L. *calor*, heat] The amount of heat required to raise the temperature of 1 gm of water 1°C. When capitalized, a unit of heat 1000 times larger than the above.

cambium \\'kam-bē-əm\\ Layer of meristematic cells in the roots and stems of many tracheophytes that produces secondary xylem and phloem.

carbohydrate \\,kär-bō-'hī-,drāt\\ Organic compound of carbon, hydrogen, and oxygen, generally with 2:1 ratio of hydrogen atoms to oxygen atoms. Sugars, starches, and cellulose are carbohydrates.

catabolism \\kə-'tab-ə-,liz-əm\\ Destructive metabolism in which complex molecules are broken down into simpler ones, with the liberation of energy.

catalyst \\'kat-°l-əst\\ Substance that accelerates the rate of chemical reaction without being used up in the process.

cephalization \\,sef-ə-lə-'zā-shən\\ Evolutionary tendency toward the concentration of sense receptors and central nervous system at the anterior end of an animal.

cephalothorax \\,sef-ə-lō-'thō(ə)r-,aks\\ Fused head and thorax found in arachnids and many crustaceans.

chemoautotrophic \\,kem-ō-,ȯt-ə-'träf-ik\\ Autotrophic, using energy secured by oxidizing some inorganic substance. Characteristic of certain bacteria.

chitin \\'kīt-ᵊn\\ Nitrogen-containing polysaccharide that forms the exoskeleton of arthropods and the cell walls of many fungi.

chlorenchyma \\klōr-'eŋ-kə-mə\\ Chlorophyll-containing parenchyma found chiefly in leaves and herbaceous stems.

chlorophyll [Gk. *chloros*, green] Green pigment that absorbs the light used in photosynthesis.

chloroplast \\'klōr-ə-‚plast\\ Plastid containing chlorophyll.

cholesterol \\kə-'les-tə-‚rȯl\\ The most abundant steroid in the human body. It probably serves as the starting material for the synthesis of the other steroids found in the body.

cholinesterase \\‚kō-lə-'nes-tə-‚rās\\ Enzyme that hydrolyzes and thus inactivates acetylcholine.

chorion \\'kor-ē-‚än\\ Extraembryonic membrane of reptiles, birds, and mammals that covers the embryo and, in mammals, contributes to the formation of the placenta.

chromosome \\'krō-mə-‚sōm\\ Elongated structures in the cell nucleus, containing DNA and protein and bearing the genes. The number in the nucleus is usually constant for each species.

circadian \\‚sər-'kā-‚dē-ən\\ [L. *circum*, round about + *dies*, day] Occurring approximately once a day.

cleavage Repeated mitotic division of the zygote which forms the many-celled blastula.

cline \\'klīn\\ Continuous gradation of structural or physiological differences exhibited by the members of a species along a line extending from one part of their range to another.

cloaca \\klō-'ā-kə\\ Posterior part of the alimentary canal into which the urinary and reproductive ducts empty in birds, reptiles, amphibians, and many fishes.

cnidaria \\nī-'da-rēə\\ [Gk. *knidē*, nettle] The phylum of animals that includes the hydra, jellyfishes, sea anemones, and corals. Formerly called Coelenterata.

codon The three adjacent bases in a molecule of DNA or messenger RNA that code for a particular amino acid.

coelom \\'sē-ləm\\ [Gk. *koilōma*, cavity] Main body cavity of many animals. It is lined with an epithelium derived from mesoderm.

coenocyte \\'sē-nə-‚sīt\\ Mass of cytoplasm, containing many nuclei formed by the repeated division of the nucleus of a single cell with no division of its cytoplasm.

coenyzme \\(')kō-'en-‚zīm\\ Organic compound that by combining temporarily with an enzyme makes it active.

cohesion Force of attraction between like molecules.

coleoptile \\‚kō-lē-'äp-tᵊl\\ [Gk. *koleos*, sheath] Protective sheath surrounding the plumule of monocot seedlings.

collenchyma \\kə-'leŋ-kə-mə\\ Supporting plant tissue consisting of living cells whose walls are thickened at the corners. Often found in young, growing stems and petioles.

colloid \\'käl-‚ȯid\\ [Gk. *kolla*, glue] Substance whose particles (macromolecules or aggregates of smaller molecules) range from 1 mμ to 100 mμ in size.

commensalism \\kə-'men(t)-sə-‚liz-əm\\ [L. *com*, together + *mensa*, table] A close living relationship between two species, in which one benefits from the other without harming or benefiting it.

compound Substance that can be decomposed into simpler substances. The elements of a compound are present in definite proportions by weight.

conjugation Form of sexual reproduction in which genetic material is exchanged during the temporary union of two cells. Occurs in many ciliates (e.g. *Paramecium*) and some bacteria.

convergence [L. *convergere*, to turn together] Evolution of superficially similar traits in unrelated organisms that live in a similar environment.

copulation \\‚käp-yə-'lā-shən\\ Physical union of two animals during which sperm cells are transferred from one to the other.

corepressor A small molecule that joins with a repressor molecule to block gene action.

cortex \\'kȯr-‚teks\\ [L. *cortex*, bark] The outer part of an organ.

covalent bond \\(')kō-'va-lənt\\ Chemical bond formed by one or more shared pairs of electrons.

cutin \\'kyüt-ᵊn\\ Waxy material secreted by the exposed epidermal cells of plants.

cyclosis \\sī-'klō-səs\\ [Gk. *kyklōsis*, encirclement] Circular streaming of cytoplasm within a cell.

cytochrome \\'sīt-ə-‚krōm\\ One of several iron-containing proteins, found in mitochondria, that transfer electrons in the process of cellular respiration.

cytokinin \\'sī-tō-ˌkī-nin\\ One of a group of adenine-containing compounds that stimulate mitosis in plants.

cytoplasm \\'sit-ə-ˌplaz-əm\\ General term for all the contents of a cell outside of the nucleus and within the cell membrane.

deamination \\(ˌ)dē-ˌam-ə-'nā-shən\\ Removal of an amino ($-NH_2$) group from a compound.

dedifferentiaton \\(')dē-ˌdif-ə-ˌren-chē-'ā-shən\\ Reversion of a specialized cell to a more generalized, embryonic type.

denaturation \\(ˌ)dē-ˌnā-chə-'rā-shən\\ Alteration of the physical properties and three-dimensional structure of a protein by agents too mild to break the peptide bonds.

dendrite \\'den-ˌdrīt\\ Branching, usually short, extension of a neuron in which the nerve impulse is generated.

deoxyribonucleic acid (DNA) \\dē-ˌäk-sē-'rī-bō-n(y)ü-ˌklē-ik\\ Nucleic acid found in chromosomes that stores the hereditary information of the organism.

diastole \\dī-'as-tə-lē\\ Phase of relaxation of the heart.

differentiation \\ˌdif-ə-ˌren-chē-'ā-shən\\ Structural and functional modification of an unspecialized cell into a specialized one.

diffusion Migration of molecules or ions, as a result of their own random movements, from a region of higher to a region of lower concentration.

digestion \\dī-'jes(h)-chən\\ Breakdown of insoluble macromolecules of food by hydrolysis.

dihybrid \\(')dī-'hī-brəd\\ Being heterozygous at two different gene loci.

dioecious \\(')dī-'ē-shəs\\ Having male sex organs on one plant, female on another of the same species. The holly is dioecious.

diploid \\'dip-ˌlȯid\\ Having twice as many chromosomes (*2n*) as are present in gametes.

disaccharide \\(')di-'sak-ə-ˌrīd\\ A sugar (e.g. sucrose) that can be hydrolyzed into two monosaccharide molecules.

dissociation \\(ˌ)dis-ˌō-s(h)ē-'ā-shən\\ Separation of ions from a molecule or crystal lattice in a solvent.

distal \\'dist-ᵊl\\ Situated away from the place of origin or attachment.

ecology \\ˌi-'käl-ə-jē\\ Study of the interrelationships of organisms and their environment.

ectoderm \\'ek-tə-ˌdərm\\ [Gk. *ektos,* outside + *derma,* skin] Outermost layer of cells of an animal embryo.

edema \\i-'dē-mə\\ [Gk. *oidema,* swelling] Abnormal accumulation of lymph in the tissue spaces.

effector \\i-'fek-tər\\ Body structure by which an organism acts. In man the chief effectors are the muscles and glands.

egestion \\i-'jes(h)-chən\\ [L. *egerere* to carry outside, discharge] Elimination of undigested materials from the alimentary canal.

electron \\i-'lek-ˌträn\\ Negatively charged particle present outside the nucleus of an atom.

electronegative Having an affinity for electrons.

electropositive Having a tendency to release electrons.

element Any of about 100 substances that consist of only one kind of atom and cannot be decomposed into simpler substances.

embryo An animal or plant in an early stage of development from a zygote.

emphysema \\ˌem(p)-fə-'sē-mə\\ [Gk. *emphysēma,* bodily inflation] A condition of the lungs characterized by a reduction in the surface available for gas exchange.

emulsion \\i-'məl-shən\\ [L. *emulgere,* to milk out] Mixture consisting of droplets of one liquid suspended in a second.

endoderm \\'en-də-ˌdərm\\ [Gk. *endon,* within + *derma,* skin] Innermost layer of cells of an animal embryo.

endosperm \\'en-də-ˌsperm\\ [Gk. *sperma,* seed] Nutritive tissue that surrounds and nourishes the developing embryo of seed plants.

energy [Gk. *energos,* active] Capacity for doing work.

enzyme \\'en- zīm\\ [Gk. *enzymos,* leavened] Protein catalyst produced by a living organism.

epicotyl \\'ep-ə-ˌkät-ᵊl\\ That portion of the shoot of a plant embryo or seedling above the node at which the cotyledons are attached.

epiphyte \\'ep-ə-ˌfīt\\ [Gk. *epi,* on + *phyton,* plant] Plant that grows entirely on another plant but for position and support only.

equilibrium State of balance between opposing actions.

estrogen \'es-trə-jən\ One of a group of female sex hormones which, among other effects, promotes the development of the secondary sex characteristics.

etiolation \'ēt-ē-ə-,lā-shən\ A phenomenon exhibited by plants grown in darkness, characterized by pale color, long internodes, and small leaves.

euryhaline \,yür-i-'hā-,līn\ Term describing an aquatic organism that is able to tolerate wide fluctuations in the salt content of the surrounding water.

excretion [L. *excretus,* sifted out] Elimination of metabolic wastes by an organism.

extensor \ek-'sten-sər\ A muscle that extends a limb.

extracellular fluid (ECF) The fluid, usually lymph, which bathes cells.

fauna \'fon-ə\ Animal life in a certain environment.

fermentation Anaerobic decomposition of an organic compound (e.g. glucose) by a living organism.

fetus \'fēt-əs\ [L. offspring] Unborn mammal after it has largely completed its embryonic morphogenesis and differentiation (in humans, after three months of development).

fission \'fish-ən\ [L. *fissus,* split] Asexual reproduction by division of the body into two or more equal parts.

flavin \'flā-vən\ [L. *flavus,* yellow] Yellow pigment that, when combined with a protein, transports electrons to the cytochromes.

flexor \'flek-sər\ A muscle that bends a limb.

flora Plant life in a certain environment.

fluorescence \(,)flů(-ə)r-'es-ᵊn(t)s\ Emission of light by a substance following the absorption of radiation of a different wavelength.

food chain Sequence of organisms in which each uses the next lower member of the sequence as a food source and is eaten by the one above.

fossil [L. *fossilis,* dug up] Any remains of an organism or evidence of its presence that has been preserved in the earth.

fovea \'fō-vē-ə\ [L., pit] Shallow depression in the retina, containing no rods or blood vessels but richly supplied with cones and providing the most acute vision.

fruit [L. *fructus,* fruit] Ripened ovary (and sometimes accessory parts) of a flower.

gamete \gə-'mēt\ [Gk. *gametes,* husband] Haploid reproductive cell which, after fusion with another gamete, initiates the development of a new individual.

gametophyte \gə-'mēt-ə-,fīt\ Haploid, gamete-producing stage in the life cycle of a plant.

ganglion \'gaŋ-glē-ən\ Small mass of nerve tissue containing the cell bodies of neurons.

gastrula \'gas-trə-lə\ Stage in the embryonic development of animals during which endoderm, mesoderm, and the archenteron are formed.

gel \'jel\ Jellylike mixture containing droplets of liquid of colloidal size dispersed within the meshes of a solid.

gene locus Location of a particular gene (or one of its alleles) on a chromosome.

gene pool All the genes in a given population of a species.

generator current Tiny current created across the membrane of a stimulated receptor cell. Its strength increases with the strength of the stimulus, and at a certain level (the threshold) it initiates one or more nerve impulses in an adjacent neuron.

genetic mosaic \mō-'zā-ik\ An individual containing cells of more than one genotype.

genotype \'jē-nə-,tīp\ Genetic constitution of an individual.

genus A taxonomic category that includes (usually) several closely related species. Similar genera are grouped in a family.

germination [L. *germinatus,* sprouted] Resumption of growth of the embryo within a seed, or of a spore.

gill slits Paired openings from the pharynx to the exterior that occur in many aquatic chordates when the gill pouches open out at the branchial grooves.

gonad \'gō-,nad\ Gamete-producing organ.

growth Increase in the size of an organism, resulting from an increase in its number of cells, their size, the amount of intercellular matrix or all of these. In each case, the amount of living material increases.

habituation \hə-ˌbich-ə-'wā-shən\ [L. *habitus*, habit] The process of becoming accustomed to anything.

haploid \'hap-ˌloid\ [Gk. *haploeidēs*, single] Having only a single set of chromosomes (*n*) as is present in gametes. Also called monoploid.

hemoglobin \'hē-mə-ˌglō-bən\ A red, iron-containing protein that transports O_2 and CO_2 in the blood of vertebrates and some invertebrates.

herbaceous \ˌ(h)ər-'bā-shəs\ [L. *herbaceus*, grassy] Nonwoody.

heterogamy \ˌhet-ə-'räg-ə-mē\ Condition in which the two gametes are unlike in structure, e.g. sperm and eggs.

heterotrophic \ˌhet-ə-rə-'träf-ik\ Requiring a supply of organic compounds (food) from the environment.

heterozygous \ˌhet-ə-rō-'zī-gəs\ Having two different alleles (e.g. A, a) at the corresponding gene loci on homologous chromosomes.

histone \'his-ˌtōn\ A basic protein usually found combined with DNA.

homeostasis \ˌhō-mē-ō-'stā-səs\ Maintenance of constancy of the internal environment (ECF).

homeothermic \'hōmēō-ˌthərmik\ Having a constant body temperature above that of the usual surroundings; therefore, "warm-blooded."

hominid \'häm-ə-ˌnid\ [L. *homo*, man] A manlike —as opposed to apelike—creature.

homologous \hō-'mäl-ə-gəs\ [Gk. *homologos*, agreeing] (Of organs in different species), showing a fundamental similarity of structure, embryonic development, and relationship.

homozygous \hō-mō-'zī-gəs\ Having identical alleles (e.g. AA or aa) at the corresponding gene loci on homologous chromosomes.

hormone \'hȯr-ˌmōn\ [Gk. *hormōn*, stirring up] Organic compound produced by cells in one part of a body, which, after being transported by body fluids, exerts an effect on the activities of cells elsewhere in the body.

humus \'hyü-məs\ Organic matter in the soil.

hybrid \'hī-brəd\ Organism produced by genetically dissimilar parents. It is heterozygous for one or (more often) many pairs of genes.

hydrolysis \hī-'dräl-ə-səs\ [Gk. *hydor*, water + *lysis*, loosening] Decomposition of a substance by the insertion of water molecules between certain of

its bonds. Extracellular digestion is accomplished by hydrolysis.

hydrophyte \'hī-drō-ˌfīt\ Plant growing in water or in very wet soil.

hypertonic \hī-pər-'tän-ik\ Having a lower water concentration than the solution under comparison.

hypocotyl \'hī-pə-ˌkät-ʼl\ That portion of the shoot of a plant embryo or seedling below the node at which the cotyledons are attached.

hypotonic \ˌhī-pə-'tän-ik\ Having a greater water concentration than the solution under comparison.

immunity Ability of an organism to resist infection by a pathogen.

inducer A molecule that activates genes, perhaps by blocking the action of a repressor.

induction Process in the embryo whereby one tissue directs the differentiation of another.

inflammation [L. *in*, into + *flamma*, flame] Response of a tissue to injury, characterized by increased blood flow, increased temperature, redness, accumulation of leucocytes, and pain.

ingestion [L. *ingerere*, to carry in] Taking of solid food or water into the body.

inorganic Term describing all compounds that do not contain carbon as well as a few simple carbon-containing substances such as carbon dioxide and the carbonates.

intermediate host Host normally used by a parasite just during an immature, or larval, stage of the parasite's life cycle.

introgression \ˌin-trə-'gresh-ən\ Introduction of the genes of one species into the gene pool of another species.

ion \'ī-ən\ Atom or group of atoms that has an electrical charge arising from the gain or loss of electrons.

ionic bond \ī-'än-ik\ Chemical bond formed between ions of opposite charge.

isogamy \ī-'säg-ə-mē\ [Gk. *isos*, equal + *gamos*, marriage] Condition in which the two gametes are alike in structure, as in *Chlamydomonas*.

isomer \'ī-sə-mər\ [Gk. *isomeres*, equally divided] Molecule with the same molecular formula as another but with a different structural formula, e.g. glucose and fructose.

isotonic \ˌī-sə-ˈtän-ik\ Having the same water concentration as the solution under comparison.

isotope \ˈī-sə-ˌtōp\ Atom that differs in weight from other atoms of the same element because of a different number of neutrons in its nucleus.

kinesis \kə-ˈnē-səs\ [Gk. *kinēsis,* motion] Automatic locomotion of a motile organism in response to a stimulus. The speed of the response is usually related to the strength of the stimulus, but its direction is not controlled by the direction from which the stimulus strikes the organism (in contrast to a taxis).

kinin \ˈkī-nin\ One of a group of polypeptides produced in the blood or tissues which dilate blood vessels and produce the pain associated with inflammation.

lactose \ˈlak-ˌtōs\ A disaccharide (milk sugar) that hydrolyzes to give one molecule of glucose and one of galactose.

larva \ˈlär-və\ [L., specter] Immature stage of many animals that must undergo metamorphosis to become an adult.

latent period \ˈlāt-ᵊnt\ Interval between the application of a stimulus and the first detectable response.

leukemia \lü-ˈkē-mē-ə\ Disease characterized by an abnormal increase in the number of leucocytes in the body.

lichen \ˈlī-kən\ Mutualistic association of a fungus and an alga.

lignin \ˈlig-nən\ [L. *lignum,* wood] Complex substance found in the cell walls of sclerenchyma and xylem tissue, which are strengthened by it.

linkage Tendency of two genes to be inherited together because they are located on the same chromosome.

lipase \ˈlīp-ˌpas\ Enzyme that digests fats.

lymph [L. *lympha,* water goddess] Fluid filtered from the blood into the tissue spaces. It is virtually plasma with a sharply reduced concentration of protein.

matrix \ˈmā-triks\ [L. womb] Intercellular material in which animal cells are imbedded, especially those of connective tissue.

medulla \mə-ˈdəl-ə\ Inner part of an organ.

medusa \mi-ˈd(y)ü-sə\ Jellyfish form occurring in the life cycle of some cnidarians.

meiosis \mī-ˈō-səs\ [Gk. *meiōsis,* diminution] The two successive cell divisions, with only one duplication of the chromosomes, which produce four cells, each containing one-half the number of chromosomes in the original cell.

meristem \ˈmer-ə-ˌstem\ [Gk. *meristos,* divided] Embryonic plant tissue which produces new cells by repeated mitosis.

mesoderm \ˈmez-ə-ˌdərm\ [Gk. *mesos,* middle + *derma,* skin] Layer of cells in an animal embryo, located between the ectoderm and endoderm.

mesoglea \ˌmez-ə-ˈglē-ə\ [Gk. *glia,* glue] Gelatinous layer located between the two cell layers of sponges and cnidarians.

mesophyte \ˈmez-ə-fīt\ Plant that grows under average conditions of moisture.

metabolism \mə-ˈtab-ə-ˌliz-əm\ [Gk. *metabolē,* change] Exchange of matter and energy between an organism and its environment and the transformation of this matter and energy within the organism.

metamorphosis \ˌmet-ə-ˈmȯr-fə-səs\ [Gk. *metamorphoun,* to transform] Process of change (usually abrupt) from larval to adult form.

mitosis \mī-ˈtō-səs\ [Gk. *mitos,* thread] Cell (or simply nuclear) division following duplication of the chromosomes, whereby each daughter cell (or nucleus) has exactly the same chromosome content as the parent.

mixture Material containing two or more substances, each of which retains its characteristic properties. The composition of a mixture is variable. A solution is a mixture.

mole Quantity of a substance whose weight in grams is numerically equal to the molecular weight of the substance, e.g. 18 gm of water is 1 mole.

molecular weight \mə-ˈlek-yə-lər\ Sum of the atomic weights of the atoms in a molecule.

molecule \ˈmäl-i-ˌkyü(ə)l\ [L. *moles,* mass] Smallest particle of a covalently bonded element or compound that retains the properties of that substance, e.g. O_2, H_2O.

molt To shed the outer covering.

monoecious \mə-ˈnē-shəs\ Having both male and female cones or flowers on the same plant.

monomer \\'män-ə-mər\\ Simple molecular unit which can be linked with others to form a polymer. The glucose molecule is the monomer of starch.

monosaccharide \\,män-ə-'sak-ə-,rīd\\ [Gk. *monos*, single + *sakcharon*, sugar] A simple sugar, e.g. glucose ($C_6H_{12}O_6$).

morphogenesis \\,mȯr-fə-'jen-ə-səs\\ Development of body form.

morphology \\mȯr-'fäl-ə-jē\\ [Gk. *morphē*, form + *logos*, study] Study of the structure of organisms.

motor unit All the skeletal muscle fibers stimulated by a single motor neuron.

mutation \\myü-'tā-shən\\ [L. *mutare*, to change] Stable, inheritable change in a gene.

mutualism Close, mutually beneficial association between two organisms of different species.

mycelium \\mī-'sē-lē-əm\\ Mass of interwoven hyphae of a fungus.

myelin sheath \\'mi-ə-lən 'shēth\\ Fatty covering found around many axons.

myoneural junction \\,mī-ō-'n(y)ùr-əl\\ Junction between a motor neuron and a muscle fiber. Also called a neuromuscular junction.

nectar \\'nek-tər\\ Sugar solution, secreted by plants, from which bees make honey.

nephron \\'nef-rän\\ [Gk. *nephros*, kidney] Functional unit of vertebrate kidneys.

nerve Bundle of axons.

neurohumor \\,n(y)ùr-ō-'hyü-mər\\ Substance released at the end brush or end plate of a neuron that either stimulates or inhibits the next neuron or muscle fiber. Acetylcholine and noradrenaline are important neurohumors.

neuromuscular junction\\,n(y)ùr-ō-'məs-kyə-lər\\ Junction between a motor neuron and a muscle fiber. Also called a myoneural junction.

neuron \\'n(y)ü-,rän\\ Nerve cell.

neutron \\'n(y)ü-,trän\\ Electrically neutral particle found in the nuclei of all atoms except hydrogen-1.

niche \\'nich\\ [L. *nidus*, nest] Way in which an organism uses the factors of its environment.

nicotinamide adenine dinucleotide (NAD) \\,nik-ə-'tē-nə-,mīd 'ad-ᵊn-,ēn 'dī-'n(y)üklēə,tīd\\ Coenzyme that transfers electrons within the cell. Also called

diphosphopyridine nucleotide (DPN) and Coenzyme I.

node [L. *nodus*, knot] In plants, the point on a stem at which one or more leaves develop.

nondisjunction Failure of two homologous chromosomes to separate during meiosis.

notochord \\'nōt-ə-,kȯ(ə)rd\\ [Gk. *nōton*, back + *chorda*, cord] Longitudinal, flexible rod located between the central nervous system and the alimentary canal at some stage in the development of all chordates. In vertebrates it is generally replaced by a column of vertebrae.

nucleic acid \\n(y)ü-'klē-ik\\ Compound consisting of nucleotides linked in a chain. DNA and RNA are the chief examples.

nucleotide \\'n(y)ü-klē-ə-,tīd\\ Molecule consisting of (1) a purine or pyrimidine, (2) a 5-carbon sugar, and (3) a phosphate group—all linked together.

ontogeny \\än-'täj-ə-nē\\ Process of development of an individual organism.

operator gene A gene that turns the structural genes adjacent to it "on" and "off."

operon A set of adjacent structural genes and the operator gene that controls them.

opsin \\'äp-sən\\ The protein part of the visual pigments of the eye.

opsonin \\'äp-sə-nən\\ Antibody that makes foreign cells, e.g. invading bacteria, more easily engulfed by phagocytes.

organ Group of tissues that perform a specific function for an animal or plant, e.g. stomach, leaf.

organelle \\,ȯr-gə-'nel\\ Specialized part of a cell, e.g. contractile vacuole, analogous to an organ.

organic \\ȯr-'gan-ik\\ Term describing all compounds whose molecules contain carbon, with a few exceptions such as carbon dioxide and the carbonates.

organism Individual living being.

osmosis \\ä-'smō-səs\\ Diffusion of a solvent (usually water) through a semipermeable membrane.

ossicle \\'äs-i-kəl\\ [L. *ossiculum*, a little bone] Small bone such as those that transmit vibrations through the middle ear.

outbreeding Mating of genetically dissimilar, relatively unrelated, individuals.

ovoviviparous \\,ō-(,)vō-,vī-'vip-(ə-)res\\ Having embryos that develop to adult form within the mother's body while securing nourishment from the egg rather than directly from the mother's tissues. Many insects, snails, fishes, lizards, and snakes are ovoviviparous.

ovulation \ˌō-vyə-'lā-shən\ Release of one or more eggs from the ovary.

ovule \'ō-(ˌ)vyü(ə)l\ [L. *ovum*, egg] Megasporangium found within the ovary of a seed plant. After fertilization of the egg inside, it develops into a seed.

oxidation Process of removing electrons from a substance.

parasite Organism living on or in another organism from which it derives its food and which it harms to some extent.

parenchyma \pə-'reŋ-kə-mə\ Plant tissue consisting of thin-walled cells, often loosely packed, that function in photosynthesis and/or food storage.

parthenogenesis \ˌpär-thə-nō-'jen-ə-səs\ [Gk. *parthenos*, virgin + *genēs*, born] Development of an unfertilized egg into a new individual. Often occurs naturally in certain plants and animals, e.g. aphids.

pathogen \'path-ə-jən\ Disease-causing organism or virus.

peristalsis \ˌper-ə-'stȯl-səs\ Successive waves of contraction passing along the walls of tubular organs, such as the intestine, thus forcing their contents along.

pH Negative logarithm of the hydrogen-ion concentration (in moles/liter) of a solution, which thus provides a measure of acidity and alkalinity.

phagocytosis \ˌfag-ə-(ˌ)sī-'tō-səs\ [Gk. *phagein*, to eat] Engulfing of solid particles by a cell.

phenotype \'fē-nə-ˌtīp\ [Gk. *phainein*, to show + *typos* type] Appearance of an organism, resulting from the interaction of its genotype and its environment.

pheromone \'fer-ə-ˌmōn\ [Gk. *pherein*, to carry] Compound secreted externally by an animal which influences other members of the same species.

phloem \'flō-ˌem\ [Gk. *phloios*, bark] Complex vascular tissue of plants that translocates food throughout the plant.

phoneme \'fō-ˌnēm\ [Gk. *phōnēma*, utterance] One of the basic sounds of which speech is made up.

phospholipid \ˌfäs-fō-'lip-ˌid\ A fat derivative in which one fatty acid has been replaced by a phosphate group and one of several nitrogen-containing molecules.

photoperiodism \ˌfōt-ə-'pir-ē-ə-ˌdiz-əm\ Developmental or behavioral response of an organism to the duration of daylight or darkness.

phylogeny \fī-'läj-ə-nē\ Evolutionary history of a species.

phylum \'fī-ləm\ [Gk. *phylon*, tribe] Major taxonomic category comprising one or more classes. In plant classification, the term *division* is often used instead.

physiology \ˌfiz-ē-'äl-ə-jē\ Study of the processes occurring in living organisms.

pigment [L. *pingere*, to paint] Substance that absorbs light, often selectively.

pinocytosis \'pīnō,sī'tōsəs\ [Gk. *pinein*, to drink] Engulfing of droplets of liquid by a cell.

plankton \'plaŋ(k)-tən\ [Gk. *planktos*, drifting] Floating, generally microscopic, protistan and animal life in a body of water.

plasma Fluid matrix of the blood.

plasmodium \plaz-'mōd-ē-əm\ Multinucleate, motile mass of protoplasm.

plasmolysis \plaz-'mäl-ə-səs\ Shrinkage of the cytoplasm away from the wall of a plant cell, placed in a hypertonic medium, because of the loss of water by osmosis.

plumule \'plü-(ˌ)myü(ə)l\ Terminal bud of a plant embryo, usually consisting of embryonic leaves and the epicotyl.

poikilothermic \'pȯikəlō,thərmik\ Having a body temperature that fluctuates with that of the surroundings. Commonly, "cold-blooded."

polarity \pō-'lar-ət-ē\ Intrinsic anterior-posterior orientation in an organism that seems to account, for example, for the regeneration of missing body parts (as in a planarian) in proper relationship to the rest of the body.

polymer \'päl-ə-mər\ [Gk. *polymerēs*, having many parts] Compound whose molecule consists of many repeating units linked together.

polymorphism \ˌpäl-i-'mȯr-ˌfiz-əm\ Occurrence of several distinct phenotypes in a population, e.g. queen, drone, and worker bees.

polyp \'päl-əp\ Anchored, tubular, body form characteristic of most cnidarians, at least during one stage of their lives. The hydra and corals are polyps.

polypeptide \ˌpäl-i-'pep-ˌtīd\ Molecule consisting of fewer than 100 amino acids linked together in a single chain.

polyploidy \'päl-i-ˌploid-ē\ Having 3 or more complete (=haploid number) sets of chromosomes.

polysaccharide \ˌpäl-i-'sak-ə-ˌrīd\ Carbohydrate, e.g. starch, cellulose, that is made up of 3 or more monosaccharides linked together.

precursor \pri-'kər-sər\ [L. *praecurrere*, to run before] Substance from which another substance is formed.

predation \pri-'dā-shən\ Living by devouring other organisms.

primary host Host normally used by a parasite during the adult stage of its life cycle.

proboscis \prə-'bäs-əs\ [Gk. *pro*, before + *boskein*, to feed] Tubular extension at the anterior end of an animal, usually used in feeding.

proglottid \(')prō-'glät-əd\ One of the segments of a tapeworm.

protease \'prōt-ē-ˌās\ Enzyme that digests proteins.

proton \'prō-ˌtän\ [Gk. *prōtos*, first] Positively charged particle found in the nuclei of all atoms. The hydrogen ion (H⁺) is a proton.

proximal \'präk-sə-məl\ Situated near the place of origin or attachment.

pupa \'pyü-pə\ [L. *pupa*, doll] Stage (usually dormant) between the larva and the adult of insects having complete metamorphosis.

purine \'pyu̇(ə)r-ˌēn\ Double-ring, nitrogen-containing base that is a component of nucleic acids and several other biologically active substances.

pseudocoel \'südō-ˌsēl\ Body cavity found in some animals, e.g. roundworms, between the body wall (mesoderm) and the alimentary canal (endoderm). It is not lined with a sheet of mesodermal cells as is a true coelom.

pyrimidine \pī-'rim-ə-ˌdēn\ Single-ring, nitrogen-containing base that is a component of nucleic acids.

radicle \'rad-i-kəl\ Root portion of the embryo of seed plants.

reactant \rē-'ak-tənt\ Substance that enters into a chemical reaction.

recapitulation Occurrence, in the embryonic devel-

opment of an individual, of stages thought to have occurred in the embryonic development of its ancestors.

reduction Process of adding electrons to a substance.

refractory period \ri-'frak-t(ə-)rē'pir-ē-əd\ Brief interval following the response of a neuron or muscle fiber during which it is incapable of a second response.

regeneration Regrowth of lost or injured parts of an organism.

regulator gene A gene that produces a repressor.

releaser Stimulus that initiates instinctive behavior.

repressor A substance that blocks gene action, perhaps by combining with operator genes. Repressors appear to be proteins or, possibly, ribonucleoproteins.

rhizoid \'rī-ˌzȯid\ Hairlike structure that serves as a root for bryophytes, fern prothallia, and certain fungi and lichens.

rhizome \'rī-ˌzōm\ Underground stem.

ribonucleic acid (RNA) \'rī-bō-n(y)ü-ˌklē-ik\ Nucleic acid found in both the nucleus and the cytoplasm that functions in the synthesis of protein.

ribonucleoprotein \'rī-bō-ˌn(y)ü-klē-ō-'prō-ˌtēn\ A complex of RNA and protein.

saprophyte \'sap-rə-ˌfīt\ [Gk. *sapros*, rotten + *phyton*, plant] Heterotrophic plant (or fungus) that secures its food by the extracellular digestion of nonliving organic matter.

sarcomere \'sär-kə-ˌmi(ə)r\ The repeating, contractile unit of the myofibril. It is bounded at each end by a "Z-line."

scavenger Organism that feeds on dead organisms or the wastes of organisms.

scion \'sī-ən\ Detached part of a plant, e.g. a piece of stem, that is grafted on to another plant.

sclerenchyma \sklə-'reŋ-kə-mə\ Supporting plant tissue consisting of cells whose walls are uniformly thickened and often lignified.

seed Embryo plant, supplied with food and protected by seed coats, that serves as the agent of dispersal of gymnosperms and angiosperms. It develops from the fertilized ovule.

sessile \'ses-əl\ [L. *sessilis*, fit for sitting] (1) In plants: lacking a stalk, e.g. a petiole-less leaf. (2) In animals: attached to the substratum; anchored.

sexual reproduction The production of new individuals by the union of the genetic material (DNA) of two different cells, usually gametes and usually from different parents.

sol \\'säl\\ Mixture containing solid particles of colloidal size dispersed in a liquid.

solute \\'säl-,yüt\\ Dissolved substance in a solution.

solution [L. *solutus*, loosened] Mixture consisting of molecules or ions less than 1 mμ in diameter, suspended in a fluid medium (water in most biological systems).

solvent Dissolving medium in a solution.

somite \\'sō-,mīt\\ [Gk. *sōma*, body] One of the blocks of mesoderm that develop in a longitudinal series on either side of the notochord in vertebrate embryos.

speciation \\spē-s(h)ē-'ā-shən\\ Formation of species.

species \\'spē(,)shēz\\ [L., kind] Taxonomic category consisting of a group of actually or potentially interbreeding natural populations which ordinarily do not interbreed with other such groups even when there is opportunity to do so. (The singular and plural are spelled alike.)

spiracle \\'spī-ri-kəl\\ [L. *spirare*, to breathe] (1) In insects, the external opening of a trachea. (2) In many fishes, the vestigial remnant of the first gill slit of their agnath ancestors.

sporangium \\spə-'ran-jē-əm\\ Structure within which asexual spores are produced.

spore [Gk. *spora*, seed] Asexual reproductive structure, usually unicellular, which serves to disperse the species and/or enable it to survive unfavorable conditions and which can develop into a new individual.

sporophyte \\'spōr-ə-,fīt\\ Diploid, spore-producing stage in the life cycle of a plant.

statocyst \\'stat-ə-,sist\\ Organ of balance, found in some aquatic invertebrates.

stenohaline \\,sten-ō-'hā-,līn\\ Term describing an aquatic organism that is unable to tolerate wide fluctuations in the salt content of the surrounding water.

steroid \\'sti(ə)r-,óid\\ One of many fat-soluble, biologically active compounds whose molecules contain a system of four rings made up of seventeen carbon atoms. (See Fig. 7–9.)

stimulus [L. *stimulus*, goad] Change in the environment of an organism that initiates a response.

stock Part of a plant (usually including roots) to which a scion is grafted.

stolon \\'stō-lən\\ [L. *stolon*, branch, sucker] Horizontal stem that produces new plants at its nodes.

strobilus \\'strä-bə-ləs\\ Aggregation of modified leaves bearing sporangia; a cone.

suberin \\'sü-bə-rən\\ Waxy material present in the walls of cork cells that makes them waterproof.

substrate \\'səb-,strāt\\ [L. *substratus*, spread under] (1) Substance that is acted upon by an enzyme. (2) Base (e.g. soil, rock) upon which an organism lives. Also called the substratum.

succession Progressive change in the nature of the plant population of an area.

suspension Mixture containing solid particles larger than 100μ distributed throughout a fluid. The particles will ultimately settle out under the force of gravity.

symbiosis \\,sim-,bī-'ō-səs\\ [Gk. *symbioun*, to live together] The living together in close association of organisms of different species. Mutualism, commensalism, and parasitism are forms of symbiosis.

synapse \\'sin-,aps\\ [Gk. *synapsis*, juncture] Gap between two neurons across which the nerve impulse is transmitted.

synapsis \\sə-'nap-səs\\ Union, side by side, of homologous chromosomes early in meiosis.

syncytium \\sin-'sish-(ē)-əm\\ Mass of cytoplasm, containing many nuclei, formed by the fusion of cells.

syngamy \\'sin-gə-mē\\ Union of gametes in sexual reproduction.

synthesis \\'sin(t)-thə-səs\\ [Gk. *syntithenai*, to put together] Formation of a compound from other, usually simpler, substances.

system Group of organs that perform one or more functions as a unit, e.g. the organs of the digestive system.

systole \\'sis-tə-lē\\ Phase of contraction of the heart.

taiga \\tī-'gä\\ [Russian] The northern coniferous forest.

taxis \\'tak-səs\\ Automatic locomotion of a motile organism in a direction determined by the direction from which the stimulus strikes it.

taxonomy \\tak-'sän-ə-mē\\ [Gk. *taxis*, arrangement + *nomos*, law] Classification of living organisms.

tetanus \\'tet-'n-əs\\ [Gk. *tetanus*, stretched, rigid] Sustained, maximal contraction of a muscle.

threshold \'thresh-,(h)ōld\ Minimum intensity of a stimulus to which a given structure responds.

thrombin \'thräm-bən\ [Gk. *thrombos*, clot] Enzyme that converts fibrinogen to fibrin.

tissue [L. *texere*, to weave] Association of cells, usually of one kind, bound together by cell walls (plants) or intercellular matrix (animals) that perform a particular function.

tonus \'tō-nəs\ [L. *tonus*, tension] Sustained, partial contraction of a muscle.

toxin Metabolic product (usually a protein) of an organism that is poisonous to another organism and, when introduced within the body, may stimulate the formation of antibodies.

toxoid Toxin treated to destroy its poisonous quality but leave it capable of stimulating the production of antibodies.

translocation (1) Transport of materials from one part of a plant to another. (2) Transfer of a piece of one chromosome to another, nonhomologous, chromosome.

transpiration [L. *trans*, across + *spirare*, to breathe] Evaporation of water from plants.

tropism \'trō-,piz-əm\ Automatic response of growth or orientation in a direction determined by the direction from which the stimulus strikes the organism.

tundra \'tən-drə\ [Russ.] Relatively flat, treeless plain north of the taiga and south of the polar region.

turgor \'tər-gər\ [L. *turgere*, to swell] Distention of the wall of a plant cell by the accumulation of water within the cell.

unit membrane Membrane (consisting of two layers of protein molecules within which are sandwiched layers of lipid and/or other molecules) that seems to be incorporated in the structure of many cell organelles, e.g. the endoplasmic reticulum, mitochondria.

vaccine \vak-'sēn\ [L. *vaccinus*, of cows] Preparation of dead or weakened pathogens which, when introduced into the body, stimulates the production of antibodies without causing the symptoms of the disease.

valence \'vā-lən(t)s\ [L. *valens*, being strong] Number of electrons gained, lost, or shared by an atom in bonding with one or more other atoms.

vascular \'vas-kyə-lər\ [L. *vasculum*, small vessel] Containing vessels that conduct fluid.

vector [L. *vectus*, carried] An animal, e.g. an insect, that transmits parasites.

vestigial \ve-'stij-(ē)əl\ Term applied to a degenerate or incompletely developed structure which was more fully developed at an earlier stage of the organism and/or in its ancestors.

viscera \'vis-(ə)rə\ Organs in the body cavity.

vitamin [L. *vita*, life] Organic compound which is needed in small quantities by an organism in its metabolism and which it cannot synthesize from the carbohydrates, fats, and proteins in its diet.

viviparous \vī-'vip-(ə)res\ Having embryos that develop to adult form within the mother's body while securing most of their nourishment from the mother's tissues rather than from the yolk of the egg.

xerophyte \'zir-ə-,fīt\ [Gk. *xēros*, dry] Plant adapted to live under dry conditions, as in the desert.

xylem \'zī-ləm\ Vascular tissue of plants that conducts water and dissolved minerals from the roots upward and often provides mechanical support to the plant. Wood is composed of xylem.

zoology \zō-'äl-ə-jē\ [Gk. *zōion*, animal] Study of animals.

zoospore \'zō-ə-,spō(ə)r\ Flagellated, swimming spore produced asexually.

zygote \'zī-,gōt\ [Gk. *zygōtos*, yoked] Cell formed by the union of two gametes.

Index